COLLEGE TRIGONOMETRY

William L. Hart *Professor of Mathematics*
University of Minnesota

COLLEGE

TRIGONOMETRY

 D. C. HEATH AND COMPANY BOSTON

THIS TEXT offers a substantial treatment of plane and spherical trigonometry incorporating current collegiate viewpoints in the content, arrangement, and emphasis. The book is designed for a college freshman who is likely to use trigonometry in more advanced mathematics and/or college courses in other fields. The principal parts of the text are couched at a level which can be attained by a student who has a satisfactory foundation in intermediate algebra. Supplementary material is available to test the abilities of interested students with more substantial previous mathematics. The book commences with an introductory chapter on the trigonometry of the general angle. The sections on analytic trigonometry are definitely emphasized, and are oriented with respect to needs in later mathematics. The treatment of computation, logarithms, and numerical trigonometry is well rounded, but is not overemphasized. Applications of plane triangles are suitably numerous, with a modern flavor. If desired, a relatively brief course in plane trigonometry can be organized conveniently on the basis of this text by merely omitting various whole chapters, or their final sections. The content includes a foundation in spherical trigonometry, with a chapter on its elementary applications. The text is bound with the author's extensive Logarithmic and Trigonometric Tables, augmented by a new six-page table of haversines and their logarithms.

★　　★　　★　　★　　★　　★　　★　　★　　★

The following features of the text may be noted.

Considerable care about terminology and definitions.

Specific measures to attain simplicity, clarity, and a high mathematical standard in the proofs and explanations.

Large numbers of illustrative examples.

Abundant problem material, with the examples carefully graded.

Numerous miscellaneous review exercises, including a very large comprehensive review list at the end of the Plane Trigonometry.

Special attention to questions about the accuracy of computation.

An expansive treatment of trigonometric equations and identities, arranged to allow various stages in the emphasis on this content.

Interpolation to *tenths of a minute* with five-place logarithms of the trigonometric functions.

A flexible organization of the Spherical Trigonometry which permits a very brief treatment, including the main applications, if a complete discussion of the content is not desired.

Arrangements which allow emphasis on either four-place or five-place logarithmic computation.

Division of the treatment of graphs between two chapters, to gain the advantage of a double exposure as well as to delay introduction of the more advanced aspects.

Answers for the odd-numbered problems bound with the text, and answers for the even-numbered problems in a separate pamphlet, when requested by the teacher.

Considerable use of haversines in the Spherical Trigonometry, with an associated five-place table of haversines and their logarithms.

Inclusion of a five-place table of the natural values of secants and co-secants.

Ample provision for supplementary work, where the material is earmarked with a black star or occurs at the ends of chapters or exercises.

★　★　★　★　★　★　★　★　★

The author takes pleasure in acknowledging the cooperation which he received from D. C. Heath and Company in efforts to obtain a legible format, an uncrowded page, and an efficient arrangement of the content and diagrams on the pages.

WILLIAM L. HART
University of Minnesota

CONTENTS

LIST OF TABLES

PLANE TRIGONOMETRY

ONE

FUNCTIONS OF THE GENERAL ANGLE

1. Introduction

In the history of mathematics, we find that the subject called *trigonometry* was first developed because of its usefulness in the indirect measurement of angles and distances, particularly in surveying and astronomy. Trigonometry is an essential tool in engineering and the physical sciences. The theoretical aspects of trigonometry are indispensable in pure mathematics and also in many fields of application.

2. Real numbers

The numbers met in arithmetic and the most elementary parts of later mathematics are called *real* numbers. They are classed as positive, negative, or zero. All numbers to be met in this text will be real numbers, except in Chapter Eleven. Any single letter which we introduce without a qualifying description will represent a *number*. For contrast with explicit numbers like 3, − 5, etc., we may call number symbols such as a, b, x, and y *literal* numbers.

The **reciprocal** of a number N is defined as $1/N$. Thus, the reciprocal of a fraction a/b is b/a because

$$1 \div \frac{a}{b} = 1 \cdot \frac{b}{a} = \frac{b}{a}.$$

ILLUSTRATION 1. The reciprocal of 5 is 1/5; of 5/7 is 7/5.

3. Absolute value

The *absolute value*, or *numerical value*, of a positive number or zero is defined as the number *itself*. The absolute value of a negative number is the *negative* of the given number. The absolute value of a number N is frequently represented by the symbol $|\,N\,|$. We say that two numbers b and c are **numerically equal** if b and c have the same absolute value. Then, b and c differ at most in sign.

ILLUSTRATION 1. The absolute value of + 5 is + 5. The absolute value of − 5 also is + 5. We read $|-3|$ as "*the absolute value of − 3*"; $|-3| = 3$.

3

4. Directed line segments

On a given line,* as in Figure 1, let it be agreed that distance will be considered positive if measured in one direction, and negative in the other direction. Then, the line is called a *directed line*. In referring to a segment AB of the line, the order of the letters indicates the direction of the segment, *from A to B*, and the *value* of AB is defined as the *directed distance from A to B*. The absolute value of AB is the *length†* of the segment, and AB is positive or negative depending on its direction. To reverse the letters in AB changes its direction, and the sign of its value. That is, we obtain

$$AB = -BA \quad or \quad AB + BA = 0.$$

ILLUSTRATION 1. In Figure 1, the arrowhead shows the positive direction. With the indicated unit, $AB = 3$; $BA = -3$; $BC = -2$; $CA = -1$.

5. A real number scale

In Figure 2, let OX be a directed line, with the positive direction to the right. On OX, select a unit of length for measuring distance and choose a point O to represent the number zero. Then, let each point P

FIG. 2

of OX represent the corresponding number x which equals the *directed distance OP*, where OP is *positive* if P is to the *right* of O and *negative* if P is to the *left* of O. Thus, all positive numbers x are represented in order by the points on OX to the right of O, and all negative numbers x by the points to the left of O. Finally, we refer to OX as a *real number scale*.

6. Inequality

One number M is said to be *less than* a second number N, or N is *greater than M*, in case M is to the *left* of N on the number scale, as in Figure 2. We use the inequality signs $<$ and $>$ to represent *less than* and *greater than*, respectively. On considering various relative positions for M and N, we verify that the statement "$M < N$" is equivalent to saying that $(N - M)$ *is positive*.

---

* The unqualified word *line* will always refer to a *straight line*.
† The word *length* will refer to the measure of a line segment in terms of some unit, and thus "*length*" is always *positive or zero*.

ILLUSTRATION 1. $-6 < -2$ because -6 is to the left of -2 on the number scale; also, we note that $-2 - (-6) = -2 + 6 = 4$, which is positive. Similarly, $-4 < 2$; $0 < 8$; $-3 < 0$. To state that M *is positive* is equivalent to saying $M > 0$. To state that M *is negative* is equivalent to saying $M < 0$.

We say that one number b is **numerically less** than a second number c in case *the absolute value of b is less than the absolute value of c*, or $|b| < |c|$. For contrast with numerical inequality, we sometimes place the word *algebraically* before *greater than* or *less than* as used in the ordinary sense.

ILLUSTRATION 2. -3 is *algebraically greater* than -7, or $-3 > -7$, but -3 is *numerically less* than -7 because

$$|-3| = 3, \quad |-7| = 7, \quad and \quad 3 < 7.$$

7. Rectangular coordinates

On each of the perpendicular lines OX and OY in Figure 3, we lay off a scale with O as the zero point. In the plane of OX and OY, we shall measure distances *vertically* in terms of the unit on OY, and *horizontally* in terms of the unit on OX. Also, we agree that all horizontal and vertical distances or line segments will be *directed*, with the positive direction *upward* on *vertical* lines and to the *right* on *horizontal* lines.

Let P be any point in the plane of OX and OY. Then, by definition, the *horizontal coordinate*, or the **abscissa** of P, is the directed perpendicular distance x from OY to P, where x is *positive* if P is to the *right* of OY and *negative* if P is to the *left* of OY. The *vertical coordinate*, or the **ordinate** of P, is the directed perpendicular dis-
tance y from OX to P, where y is *positive* if P is *above* OX and *negative* if P is *below* OX. Each of the lines OX and OY is called a **coordinate axis,** and their intersection O is called the **origin** of coordinates. The abscissa and ordinate of P together are called the **rectangular coordinates** of P. We shall use "$P:(x, y)$" to abbreviate "*point P with coordinates x, y.*" With axes labeled OX and OY, we may refer to the abscissa as the *x-coordinate*, and to the ordinate as the *y-coordinate*. The plane of OX and OY is called the *coordinate plane*.

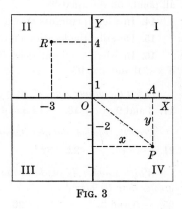

FIG. 3

ILLUSTRATION 1. In Figure 3, R has the coordinates ($x = -3, y = 4$), or R is the point $(-3, 4)$. We read $R:(-3, 4)$ as "$R, -3, 4$."

ILLUSTRATION 2. In the coordinate plane, the locus of all points with the abscissa 4 is the line perpendicular to OX where $x = 4$. We say that *the equation of this line is* $x = 4$.

Unless otherwise specified, in any coordinate plane, the *same unit* of length will be used on *both axes* and in measuring *all lengths* in the plane. Then, the distance of a point P from the origin is called the **radius vector** of P, and is always considered positive when it is not zero. In Figure 3, let r represent the radius vector OP. When the **Pythagorean theorem*** is applied to triangle AOP, we obtain

$$r^2 = \overline{OA}^2 + \overline{AP}^2,$$

where $\overline{OA}$ and $\overline{AP}$ are the lengths of OA and AP. Regardless of the signs of x and y, $\overline{OA}^2 = x^2$ and $\overline{AP}^2 = y^2$. Hence,

$$r^2 = x^2 + y^2; \quad r = \sqrt{x^2 + y^2}. \tag{1}$$

ILLUSTRATION 3. The radius vector of $R:(-3, 4)$ is $r = \sqrt{9 + 16} = 5$.

The coordinate axes divide the plane into four parts, called **quadrants,** numbered counter-clockwise, I, II, III, and IV as in Figure 3. Points on the axes are not said to lie in any quadrant.

EXERCISE 1

Plot each point and find its radius vector. Use Table I for roots.

1. $(3, 4)$.   **2.** $(-5, 0)$.   **3.** $(0, -4)$.   **4.** $(-8, 15)$.

5. $(-5, 6)$.   **6.** $(7, -24)$.   **7.** $(-6, -8)$.   **8.** $(-12, -6)$.

9. $(-1, 1)$.   **10.** $(1, \sqrt{3})$.   **11.** $(\sqrt{3}, -1)$.   **12.** $(-\sqrt{2}, \sqrt{2})$.

13. What is the abscissa of all points on the y-axis? What is the ordinate of all points on the x-axis?

14. In what quadrants may a point lie if its abscissa is 5; -3; 0?

15. Describe the location of all points whose ordinate is 7; -2; 0.

16. In what quadrant does $P:(x, y)$ lie if x is positive and y is negative; if $x < 0$ and $y < 0$?

Insert the proper sign, $<$ or $>$, between the numbers.

17. 3 and 9.   **18.** -12 and 4.   **19.** -4 and 0.   **20.** -3 and -8.

Read the symbol and give its value.

21. $|-81|$.   **22.** $|32|$.   **23.** $|-\frac{5}{3}|$.   **24.** $|6|$.

Which number is algebraically less than the other, and which is numerically greater than the other?

25. -5 and 3.   **26.** -16 and -4.   **27.** -14 and 18.

28. Find the reciprocal of

$$18; \quad -3; \quad \frac{2}{3}; \quad -\frac{3}{7}; \quad \frac{a}{d}; \quad \frac{b}{2c}; \quad \frac{a-b}{4}.$$

* In a right triangle with legs of lengths a and b and hypotenuse of length c, the theorem states that $c^2 = a^2 + b^2$.

8. Directed angles

In elementary geometry, an angle was thought of merely as a *ready-made figure* consisting of two half-lines radiating from a common point, and the measure of an angle was always a positive number or zero. For many reasons, it proves convenient to generalize our previous notion of an angle as follows.

Suppose that a half-line or ray, issuing from a fixed point O, rotates about O either clockwise or counter-clockwise from an initial position OA to a terminal position OB, as in Figure 4. Then, this rotation is said to *generate an angle AOB* whose **initial side** is OA and **terminal side** is OB. As a unit for measuring the amount of rotation, we define $1°$ as $1/360$ of a complete revolution. Then, the *value* of $\angle AOB$ is defined as the amount of rotation used in generating the angle, where we agree to **consider counter-clockwise rotation as positive,** and **clockwise rotation as negative.** The description of an angle is incomplete until we are told the *direction* and *amount of rotation* used in forming the angle. In a figure, we may show the amount of rotation by a curved arrow.

ILLUSTRATION 1. In Figure 4, the configuration AOB is the same in each diagram. In (1), $\angle AOB = 45°$. In (2), a complete revolution is indicated besides $45°$: $\angle AOB = 360° + 45° = 405°$. In (3), the rotation is $45°$ less than $360°$, clockwise: $\angle AOB = -315°$. In (4), $\angle BOA = -45°$.

FIG. 4

Note 1. The angular unit $1°$ is subdivided as in elementary geometry. Thus, we define one *minute*, $1'$, as $1/60$ of $1°$, and one *second*, $1''$, as $1/60$ of $1'$. The resulting system involving degrees, minutes, and seconds is called the *sexagesimal system* of angular measurement. The name *sexagesimal* is related to the Latin word *sexagesimus*, meaning sixtieth. Other systems of angular measurement will be introduced later.

ILLUSTRATION 2. Any positive angle whose value lies between $0°$ and $90°$ is called an **acute angle.** Any positive angle between $90°$ and $180°$ is called an **obtuse angle.**

Any number of complete revolutions, clockwise or counter-clockwise, may be added to any of the rotations in Figure 4 without altering the initial and terminal sides of the angles. Thus, we see that infinitely many positive and negative angles of unlimited numerical values correspond to any given pair of sides for the angles.

9. Standard position of an angle

We shall say that an angle* θ is in its *standard position* on a coordinate system if the vertex of θ is at the origin and the initial side of θ lies on the positive part of the horizontal axis.

ILLUSTRATION 1. To place 240° in standard position in Figure 5, imagine rotating OX about O through 240° counter-clockwise to find the terminal side: $\gamma = 240°$. Similarly, we construct $\alpha = -60°$ and $\theta = 30°$ in standard positions.

We shall say that an angle θ is *in a certain quadrant* if the terminal side of θ falls *inside* that quadrant when θ is in its standard position. If the terminal side of θ falls *on a coordinate axis*, then θ is not said to lie in any quadrant, but is called a **quadrantal angle.**

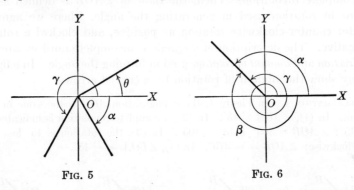

FIG. 5   FIG. 6

ILLUSTRATION 2. In Figure 5, θ is in quadrant I and γ is in quadrant III. Angles between $-180°$ and $-270°$ are in quadrant II. Obtuse angles lie in quadrant II. Examples of quadrantal angles are 0°, 90°, 360°, $-90°$, $-180°$.

Two or more angles are said to be **coterminal** if their terminal sides coincide after the angles are placed in their standard positions.

ILLUSTRATION 3. In Figure 6, α, β, and γ are coterminal, where $\alpha = 135°$, $\beta = -225°$, and $\gamma = 360° + 135° = 495°$.

EXERCISE 2

Sketch the angle in standard position and indicate the angle by an arrow. Give two coterminal angles, one positive and one negative, and indicate them by arrows.

1. 45°.	**2.** 90°.	**3.** 120°.	**4.** $-210°$.	**5.** $-60°$.
6. 150°.	**7.** $-270°$.	**8.** $-315°$.	**9.** $-180°$.	**10.** $-90°$.
11. 270°.	**12.** 420°.	**13.** 495°.	**14.** $-390°$.	**15.** 0°.
16. 135°.	**17.** $-225°$.	**18.** 870°.	**19.** 1050°.	**20.** $-1200°$.

* Usually we shall employ Greek letters to represent angles. The letters α, β, γ, θ, and ϕ are called *alpha, beta, gamma, theta,* and *phi,* respectively. Except where ambiguity might occur, the same symbol may be used to represent any *angle* as a *geometric entity,* and its *value* in angular units.

10. The function concept

In a given problem, a **constant** is a number symbol whose value does not change during the discussion. A **variable** is a number symbol which may take on different values, called the **range** of the variable. When desirable, we may think of a constant as a variable which may assume just one value. Related variables arise frequently, and thus we meet the following basic terminology.

DEFINITION I. *If a first variable u and a second variable v are so related that, whenever a value is assigned to u, a corresponding value or corresponding values of v can be determined, it is said that v is a* **function** *of u. In such a case, u is called the* **independent variable** *and v the* **dependent variable.**

ILLUSTRATION 1. The area A of a circle is given by $A = \pi r^2$, where r is the radius. In considering different circles, π is a constant while r and A are variables, and A is a function of r.

If y is described as a function of x by a formula involving only operations of algebra applied to x, we say that y is an *algebraic function** of x.

ILLUSTRATION 2. If $y = 3x^2 + \dfrac{18}{x} - x$, then y is an algebraic function of x.

11. Trigonometric functions of any angle θ

Let θ represent any angle, positive, negative, or zero. Place θ in its standard position on a coordinate system and let $P:(x, y)$ be any point other than the origin O on the terminal side of θ, as in Figure 7. With AP perpendicular to OX, we have a right triangle OAP, called a **reference triangle** for θ, in which $OA = x$, $AP = y$, and $OP = r$, the radius vector (positive) of P. Then, we form the ratios

$$\frac{AP}{OP} \quad or \quad \frac{y}{r}; \qquad \frac{OA}{OP} \quad or \quad \frac{x}{r}; \qquad \frac{y}{x}; \qquad \frac{x}{y}; \qquad \frac{r}{x}; \qquad \frac{r}{y}. \qquad (1)$$

On the terminal side of θ, select any second point† $P_1:(x_1, y_1)$, not O, with radius vector r_1. Then, new ratios (1) formed with x_1, y_1, r_1 equal the ratios formed with x, y, r. For instance, since the directed distances OA and OA_1 have the same sign, by properties of the similar triangles OAP and OA_1P_1 we obtain

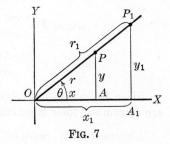

FIG. 7

$$\frac{x}{r} = \frac{OA}{OP} = \frac{OA_1}{OP_1} = \frac{x_1}{r_1}; \quad \frac{y}{x} = \frac{y_1}{x_1}; \quad etc.$$

---

* In more advanced mathematics, algebraic functions are defined so as to include those just mentioned and also more complicated functions.

† We read "P_1" as "P *sub* 1," or "P, 1" for short.

Hence, the values of the ratios in (1) depend *only on the terminal side of* θ and not on the particular point P used in obtaining x, y, r. Therefore, *corresponding to each value of θ* (with certain exceptions to be noted later) *there exists a unique value for each of the six ratios in* (1). Thus, each ratio is a *single-valued function of the angle* θ, called a *trigonometric function of θ*. We summarize the introduction of these functions as follows, where x, y, r are illustrated in Figure 8. We *name* and *read* the functions as at the left in (2), and *abbreviate the names* in writing as at the right in (2).

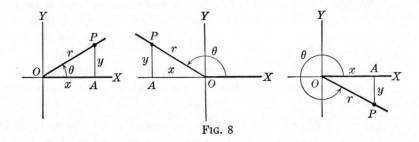

FIG. 8

DEFINITION I. *Place the angle θ in standard position on a coordinate system. Choose any point P, not the origin, on the terminal side of θ; let the coordinates and radius vector of P be (x, y) and r, respectively. Then,*

$$sine\ \theta = \frac{ordinate\ of\ P}{radius\ vector\ of\ P}, \quad or \quad \sin\theta = \frac{y}{r};$$

$$cosine\ \theta = \frac{abscissa\ of\ P}{radius\ vector\ of\ P}, \quad or \quad \cos\theta = \frac{x}{r};$$

$$tangent\ \theta = \frac{ordinate\ of\ P}{abscissa\ of\ P}, \quad or \quad \tan\theta = \frac{y}{x};$$

$$cotangent\ \theta = \frac{abscissa\ of\ P}{ordinate\ of\ P}, \quad or \quad \cot\theta = \frac{x}{y}; \qquad (2)$$

$$secant\ \theta = \frac{radius\ vector\ of\ P}{abscissa\ of\ P}, \quad or \quad \sec\theta = \frac{r}{x};$$

$$cosecant\ \theta = \frac{radius\ vector\ of\ P}{ordinate\ of\ P}, \quad or \quad \csc\theta = \frac{r}{y}.$$

Since Definition I involves only the terminal side of θ, **if two angles are coterminal their trigonometric functions are equal.**

ILLUSTRATION 1. Since 30° and 390° are coterminal, the functions of 390° are respectively equal to the functions of 30°.

Note 1. In order to find r when x and y are given, we recall

$$r^2 = x^2 + y^2; \qquad r = \sqrt{x^2 + y^2}. \qquad (3)$$

EXAMPLE 1. Find the functions* of θ if its terminal side passes through $P:(3, -4)$.

SOLUTION. A reference triangle for θ is shown in Figure 9. We have $x = 3$; $y = -4$. From (3), $r = \sqrt{3^2 + (-4)^2} = 5$. Hence, from (2),

FIG. 9

$$\sin \theta = -\frac{4}{5}; \quad \cos \theta = \frac{3}{5}; \quad \tan \theta = -\frac{4}{3};$$

$$\csc \theta = -\frac{5}{4}; \quad \sec \theta = \frac{5}{3}; \quad \cot \theta = -\frac{3}{4}.$$

ILLUSTRATION 2. If the terminal side of θ in its standard position passes through $P:(-\sqrt{3}, 1)$, then

$$r = \sqrt{(-\sqrt{3})^2 + 1} = 2 \quad and$$

$$\sec \theta = \frac{2}{-\sqrt{3}} = -\frac{2}{\sqrt{3}} \cdot \frac{\sqrt{3}}{\sqrt{3}} = -\frac{2}{3}\sqrt{3} = -1.155. \quad \text{(Table I)}$$

In the preceding line, we *rationalized* the denominator.

12. Simple properties of the trigonometric functions

From Definition I, page 10, we observe that the following reciprocal relations are satisfied by the functions:

$$\sin \theta = \frac{1}{\csc \theta}, \quad or \quad \csc \theta = \frac{1}{\sin \theta};$$

$$\cos \theta = \frac{1}{\sec \theta}, \quad or \quad \sec \theta = \frac{1}{\cos \theta}; \qquad (1)$$

$$\tan \theta = \frac{1}{\cot \theta}, \quad or \quad \cot \theta = \frac{1}{\tan \theta}.$$

ILLUSTRATION 1. $\dfrac{1}{\sin \theta} = \dfrac{1}{\dfrac{y}{r}} = \dfrac{r}{y}, \quad or \quad \dfrac{1}{\sin \theta} = \csc \theta.$

ILLUSTRATION 2. If $\tan \theta = \dfrac{5}{7}$ then $\cot \theta = \dfrac{7}{5}.$

In Figure 8 for any angle θ, neither $\overline{OA}$ nor $\overline{AP}$ is greater than $\overline{OP}$. Hence, the absolute value of x or of y *cannot exceed* r, and the absolute value of x/r or of y/r *cannot exceed* 1. Similarly, the absolute value of r/x or of r/y *cannot be smaller than* 1. That is,

$\begin{cases} \sin \theta \text{ and } \cos \theta \text{ are } \textit{numerically less than or equal to } 1; \\ \sec \theta \text{ and } \csc \theta \text{ are } \textit{numerically greater than or equal to } 1. \end{cases}$

---

* Until otherwise indicated, in any reference to a *function* or to a *trigonometric function* of an angle, we shall mean one of the *fundamental* functions of Definition I.

We verify the signs of the functions as indicated in Figure 10. In any quadrant, sin θ and csc θ have the same sign because sin $\theta = 1/\csc \theta$; tan θ and cot θ have the same sign; cos θ and sec θ have the same sign. Thus, if we remember the signs of sin θ, cos θ, and tan θ in any quadrant, the signs of the other functions can be specified immediately.

EXAMPLE 1. Determine the signs of the functions in quadrant II.

SOLUTION. If θ is in quadrant II, then $x < 0, y > 0, r > 0$ in Definition I, page 10. Hence, regarding only signs,

$$\sin \theta = \frac{y}{r} = \frac{+}{+} = +;$$

$$\cos \theta = \frac{x}{r} = \frac{-}{+} = -;$$

$$\tan \theta = \frac{y}{x} = \frac{+}{-} = -.$$

FIG. 10

EXAMPLE 2. If sin $\theta > 0$ and cot $\theta < 0$, in what quadrant does θ lie?

SOLUTION. Since sin $\theta > 0$, θ is in either quadrant I or quadrant II. Since cot $\theta < 0$, θ is in either quadrant II or quadrant IV. Hence, θ must lie in quadrant II.

EXERCISE 3

Find the functions of θ if the terminal side of θ, in its standard position, passes through the given point on a coordinate system. Draw a figure and find decimal values where radicals arise.

1. $(4, 3)$.
2. $(5, 12)$.
3. $(7, 24)$.
4. $(12, -5)$.
5. $(-3, -2)$.
6. $(-24, 7)$.
7. $(-15, 8)$.
8. $(-8, -15)$.
9. $(6, -8)$.
10. $(-1, 1)$.
11. $(1, -\sqrt{3})$.
12. $(\sqrt{3}, 1)$.
13. $(0, 4)$.
14. $(4, -5)$.
15. $(0, -2)$.
16. $(2, -3)$.
17. $(-1, -1)$.
18. $(5, 0)$.
19. $(-3, 5)$.
20. $(-2, 0)$.

21. Determine the signs of the functions to verify Figure 10 for quadrant I; quadrant III; quadrant IV.

By mere inspection, without a figure, give the value of another function of the angle whose function is given.

22. $\tan \theta = \frac{3}{7}$.
23. $\cos \alpha = \frac{4}{9}$.
24. $\cot \beta = \frac{5}{2}$.
25. $\sec \gamma = \frac{7}{3}$.

Under the given condition, in which quadrants may θ lie?

26. $\sin \theta < 0$.
27. $\tan \theta < 0$.
28. $\sec \theta > 0$.
29. $\cot \theta > 0$.

30. What are the signs of the trigonometric functions (*a*) of an acute angle; (*b*) of an obtuse angle?

Under the given conditions, in which quadrant must θ lie?

31. $\sin \theta < 0$ and $\tan \theta > 0$.

32. $\cos \theta < 0$ and $\sin \theta > 0$.

33. $\tan \theta < 0$ and $\sin \theta < 0$.

34. $\sec \theta < 0$ and $\tan \theta > 0$.

35. $\cos \theta < 0$ and $\cot \theta < 0$.

36. $\csc \theta > 0$ and $\cot \theta < 0$.

37. $\cos \theta < 0$ and $\tan \theta > 0$.

38. $\sin \theta < 0$ and $\cos \theta < 0$.

13. Quadrantal angles

EXAMPLE 1. Find the functions of 180°.

SOLUTION. **1.** Draw 180° in standard position, in Figure 11. The ordinate of any point on the terminal side is zero.

2. Choose P as $(-3, 0)$. Then $r = OP = 3$. On substituting $x = -3$, $y = 0$, $r = 3$ in (2) on page 10, we obtain

$$\tan 180° = \frac{0}{-3} = 0; \quad \sec 180° = \frac{3}{-3} = -1;$$

$$\sin 180° = \frac{0}{3} = 0; \quad \cos 180° = \frac{-3}{3} = -1.$$

Since $y = 0$, r/y and x/y are meaningless because *division by zero has no meaning*. Therefore, **180° has no cosecant and no cotangent.**

FIG. 11

If θ is any quadrantal angle, so that its terminal side falls on a coordinate axis, either cot θ and csc θ, or tan θ and sec θ, are *undefined* for the reason just met in discussing cot 180° and csc 180°. From Example 1 and later problems, a complete list of the undefined functions of angles from 0° to 360°, inclusive, is as follows:

$$\text{UNDEFINED FUNCTIONS} \begin{cases} \cot 0°; & \tan 90°; & \cot 180°; & \tan 270°; & \cot 360°; \\ \csc 0°; & \sec 90°; & \csc 180°; & \sec 270°; & \csc 360°. \end{cases} \quad (1)$$

We reserve this matter of undefined functions for later discussion.

14. Functions of 30°, 45°, 60°

EXAMPLE 1. Find the functions of 45°.

SOLUTION. Figure 12 shows the angle 45° in its standard position. The reference triangle AOP is *isosceles* with $\overline{OA} = \overline{AP}$. Hence, we may choose P with $x = 1$ and $y = 1$; then $r = \sqrt{2}$ and, from page 10,

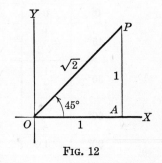

$$\sin 45° = \frac{1}{\sqrt{2}} = \frac{1}{\sqrt{2}} \cdot \frac{\sqrt{2}}{\sqrt{2}} = \frac{1}{2}\sqrt{2};$$

$$\sec 45° = \frac{\sqrt{2}}{1} = \sqrt{2}; \text{ etc.}$$

FIG. 12

Note 1. In the equilateral triangle ABD of Figure 13, drop a perpendicular BC to AD, obtaining two right triangles with the acute angles 30° and 60°. If we let $AB = BD = AD = 2$, then $AC = 1$ and

$$\overline{BC}^2 + \overline{AC}^2 = \overline{AB}^2 \quad or$$
$$\overline{BC}^2 = \overline{AB}^2 - \overline{AC}^2 = 4 - 1 = 3.$$

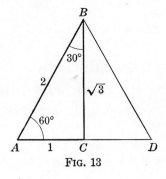

Thus, $BC = \sqrt{3}$. Hence, as a *standard right triangle with the acute angles* 30° *and* 60°, we may use triangle ABC with sides 1, 2, $\sqrt{3}$.

FIG. 13

ILLUSTRATION 1. To obtain the functions of 30°, after placing the angle in its standard position in Figure 14, we choose P on the terminal side so that $OP = 2$. Then, the reference triangle OAP has the acute angles 30°, 60°, and the standard sides 1, 2, $\sqrt{3}$; we find

$$\sin 30° = \frac{1}{2}; \quad \tan 30° = \frac{1}{\sqrt{3}} = \frac{1}{\sqrt{3}} \cdot \frac{\sqrt{3}}{\sqrt{3}} = \frac{1}{3}\sqrt{3}; \ etc.$$

To obtain the functions of 60° by use of Figure 15, we choose P so that $OP = 2$ and again the reference triangle has the acute angles 30°, 60° and sides 1, 2, $\sqrt{3}$. The student should now verify all entries in the following table by use of previous figures or new diagrams.

FIG. 14

FIG. 15

ANGLE	SIN	COS	TAN	COT	SEC	CSC
0°	0	1	0	*none*	1	*none*
45°	$\frac{1}{\sqrt{2}}$	$\frac{1}{\sqrt{2}}$	1	1	$\sqrt{2}$	$\sqrt{2}$
30°	$\frac{1}{2}$	$\frac{\sqrt{3}}{2}$	$\frac{1}{\sqrt{3}}$	$\sqrt{3}$	$\frac{2}{\sqrt{3}}$	2
60°	$\frac{\sqrt{3}}{2}$	$\frac{1}{2}$	$\sqrt{3}$	$\frac{1}{\sqrt{3}}$	2	$\frac{2}{\sqrt{3}}$
90°	1	0	*none*	0	*none*	1

15. The reference angle for a given angle

Let θ be an angle in any quadrant. Then, we define the *reference angle* for θ as *the acute angle α between the terminal side of θ and the x-axis,* after θ is in its standard position on a coordinate system.

ILLUSTRATION 1. The reference angle α for $120°$ in Figure 16 is $\alpha = 60°$; for $\theta = -150°$ in Figure 17, $\alpha = 30°$.

If the reference angle for θ is $30°, 45°,$ or $60°,$ the reference triangle for defining the functions of θ can be given the dimensions used in obtaining the functions of $30°, 45°,$ or $60°,$ respectively.

FIG. 16

ILLUSTRATION 2. If $\theta = 225°$, the reference angle is $45°$, in Figure 18, and triangle AOP has the sides $1, 1, \sqrt{2}$. The coordinates of P are $(-1, -1)$. Then,

$$\sin 225° = \frac{-1}{\sqrt{2}} = -\frac{1}{2}\sqrt{2}; \qquad \tan 225° = \frac{-1}{-1} = 1; \ etc.$$

For $\theta = 120°$ in Figure 16, and $\theta = -150°$ in Figure 17, $OP = 2$ and the reference triangles have the sides $1, 2, \sqrt{3}$; then

$$\tan 120° = \frac{\sqrt{3}}{-1} = -\sqrt{3}; \qquad \cos(-150°) = \frac{-\sqrt{3}}{2} = -\frac{1}{2}\sqrt{3}; \ etc.$$

On account of the similarity of the reference triangles for $45°$ and $225°$, any function of $225°$ differs *at most in sign* from the same function of $45°$. Likewise the functions of $120°$ and of $-150°$ *differ at most in signs* from the functions of their reference angles $60°$ and $30°$, respectively.

FIG. 17   FIG. 18

In Illustration 2 we met special cases of the theorem that *any function of an angle θ differs at most in sign from the same function of the reference angle for θ.* We shall prove this theorem later.

ILLUSTRATION 3. The angles between $90°$ and $360°$ with $30°$ as the reference angle, and hence with functions differing at most in signs from the functions of $30°$, are $150°, 210°, 330°$.

We have seen that we may compute the *exact* values of the trigonometric functions of quadrantal angles, and of any angle having 30°, 45°, or 60° as the reference angle. The functions of *any* angle may be computed by methods discussed in advanced mathematics. The functions of selected acute angles are collected in tables, to be considered later. The functions of any angle θ will then be found by attaching the proper signs to the functions of a corresponding reference angle α, whose functions will be obtained from tables.

EXERCISE 4

Place the angle in its standard position on a coordinate system and find the functions of the angle. Rationalize any radical denominator and compute by use of Table I, if necessary.

1. 0°.	**2.** 90°.	**3.** 30°.	**4.** 60°.	**5.** 135°.
6. 120°.	**7.** 150°.	**8.** 270°.	**9.** 360°.	**10.** 315°.
11. 330°.	**12.** 240°.	**13.** − 90°.	**14.** − 180°.	**15.** − 45°.
16. − 60°.	**17.** − 135°.	**18.** 225°.	**19.** 390°.	**20.** 405°.
21. 585°.	**22.** 495°.	**23.** 540°.	**24.** 480°.	**25.** − 495°.

26. Give all values of θ between − 360° and 360° such that the functions of θ are numerically equal to the corresponding functions of 45°; 30°; 60°.

27. Give all values of θ between − 720° and 720° for which (*a*) tan θ is not defined; (*b*) sec θ is not defined; (*c*) csc θ is not defined; (*d*) cot θ is not defined.

16. Functions of an angle for which one function is given

EXAMPLE 1. Find the functions of θ if sin $\theta = \frac{3}{5}$ and θ is an angle in quadrant II.

SOLUTION. 1. Since $\sin \theta = \dfrac{y}{r} = \dfrac{3}{5}$, the terminal side of θ in standard position passes through P in quadrant II where $y = 3$ and $r = 5$. We sketch OP *roughly* to scale in Figure 19, and indicate any corresponding angle θ.

2. From $r^2 = x^2 + y^2$, $\quad x^2 = r^2 - y^2 = 25 - 9 = 16$; $\quad x = \pm 4$.

3. Since P is in quadrant II, the abscissa of P is $x = -4$. From page 10 with $x = -4$, $y = 3$, $r = 5$, we have $\cos \theta = -\frac{4}{5}$, $\tan \theta = -\frac{3}{4}$, etc.

FIG. 19

FIG. 20

Comment. In Example 1, an accurate figure was unnecessary. However, to construct OP accurately, draw a circle of radius 5 with center at O in Figure 20; construct the line $y = 3$ which is 3 units above OX and intersects the circle at P in quadrant II and at Q in quadrant I. Then, $\sin \theta = \frac{3}{5}$ if θ is any angle in standard position with OP *or* OQ as the terminal side. In Example 3 we use OP.

Suppose that only angles which are *not* quadrantal are involved for the moment. Then, in Example 1 we illustrated the fact that, if the value of *one function* of an unknown angle θ and *its quadrant* are given, there exists just *one location* for the terminal side of θ; we can construct this side and thus find all functions of θ. Hence, just *one value of θ between* 0° *and* 360° corresponds to the given data. However, if *merely one function* of θ is given, there exist *two corresponding locations* for the terminal side of θ, and thus *two corresponding values* for θ between 0° and 360°.

ILLUSTRATION 1. Given $\sin \theta = \frac{3}{5}$, without knowing the quadrant for θ, in Figure 20 we observe two values for θ less than 360°, approximately $\theta_1 = 40°$ and $\theta_2 = 140°$.

EXAMPLE 2. If $\tan \theta = \frac{2}{3}$ and $\sin \theta < 0$, find all functions of θ.

INCOMPLETE SOLUTION. Angle θ is in quadrant III because $\tan \theta > 0$ and $\sin \theta < 0$. From page 10, $\tan \theta = \dfrac{y}{x} = \dfrac{2}{3}$. Hence, in quadrant III, point $P : (x = -3, y = -2)$ is on the terminal side of θ.

EXERCISE 5

The Roman numeral specifies the quadrant for θ. Construct θ in standard position and find the unknown functions of θ.

1. $\tan \theta = \frac{5}{12}$; θ in (I).
2. $\cot \theta = -\frac{4}{3}$; θ in (II).

3. $\sin \theta = \frac{4}{5}$; θ in (II).
4. $\cos \theta = \frac{5}{13}$; θ in (IV).

5. $\csc \theta = \frac{5}{3}$; θ in (I).
6. $\sec \theta = \frac{13}{12}$; θ in (I).

7. $\cot \theta = \frac{12}{5}$; θ in (III).
8. $\sin \theta = -\frac{15}{17}$; θ in (IV).

9. $\cos \theta = -\frac{15}{17}$; θ in (II).
10. $\tan \theta = -\frac{7}{24}$; θ in (II).

11. $\tan \theta = 1$; θ in (III).
12. $\sin \theta = \frac{2}{3}$; θ in (I).

13. $\sec \theta = \frac{4}{3}$; θ in (IV).
14. $\csc \theta = -\frac{5}{2}$; θ in (III).

15. θ is an acute angle and $\cos \theta = \frac{4}{5}$.

16. θ is an acute angle and $\sec \theta = \frac{25}{7}$.

17. θ is an obtuse angle and $\cot \theta = -\frac{8}{15}$.

18. θ is an obtuse angle and $\tan \theta = -\frac{24}{7}$.

Construct all angles θ between 0° *and* 360° *in standard positions corresponding to the data. Estimate the values of θ with a protractor.*

19. $\tan \theta = \frac{2}{3}$.
20. $\sin \theta = \frac{2}{5}$.
21. $\cos \theta = -\frac{2}{3}$.
22. $\cot \theta = -\frac{5}{2}$.

TWO

FUNCTIONS OF ACUTE ANGLES

17. Functions of acute angles

Let triangle ABC in Figure 21 be a right triangle with the 90° angle at C, and with α and β as the acute angles at A and B, respectively. Let a, b, c be the sides (or *lengths* of the sides) of triangle ABC opposite A, B, C, respectively. Hereafter, in any typical right triangle, we shall assume that the preceding notation is in use. By the Pythagorean theorem,

$$c^2 = a^2 + b^2. \tag{1}$$

Fig. 21

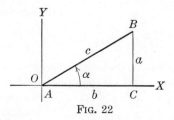

Fig. 22

Any acute angle α can be taken as the angle at A in a right triangle ABC. Then, to place α in standard position on a coordinate system, as in Figure 22, we locate triangle ABC with A at the origin, C on the positive half of the x-axis, and B above OX. Triangle ABC is now a *reference triangle* for α; B is a point on the terminal side of α with coordinates $(x = b, y = a)$ and radius vector $r = \overline{AB} = c$. We shall refer to a as the *side opposite* α, b as the *side adjacent* to α, and c as the *hypotenuse*. Then, with $x = b$, $y = a$, $r = c$ in the definitions of page 10, we obtain

$$\left.\begin{array}{ll}
\sin \alpha = \dfrac{a}{c} = \dfrac{\text{opposite side}}{\text{hypotenuse}}; & \csc \alpha = \dfrac{c}{a} = \dfrac{\text{hypotenuse}}{\text{opposite side}}; \\[3mm]
\cos \alpha = \dfrac{b}{c} = \dfrac{\text{adjacent side}}{\text{hypotenuse}}; & \sec \alpha = \dfrac{c}{b} = \dfrac{\text{hypotenuse}}{\text{adjacent side}}; \\[3mm]
\tan \alpha = \dfrac{a}{b} = \dfrac{\text{opposite side}}{\text{adjacent side}}; & \cot \alpha = \dfrac{b}{a} = \dfrac{\text{adjacent side}}{\text{opposite side}}.
\end{array}\right\} \tag{2}$$

We can read off the functions of an acute angle α from (2) as soon as we have located α in a right triangle, without using a coordinate system. Relations (2) are *not new definitions*. The relations are convenient consequences of the definitions on page 10. In (2), the verbal form has meaning only when α is acute, and is in a right triangle.

ILLUSTRATION 1. From Figure 23,

$$\sin \alpha = \tfrac{3}{5}; \qquad \cos \alpha = \tfrac{4}{5}; \qquad \tan \alpha = \tfrac{3}{4};$$

$$\csc \alpha = \tfrac{5}{3}; \qquad \sec \alpha = \tfrac{5}{4}; \qquad \cot \alpha = \tfrac{4}{3};$$

$$\sin \beta = \tfrac{4}{5}; \qquad \cos \beta = \tfrac{3}{5}; \qquad \tan \beta = \tfrac{4}{3};$$

$$\csc \beta = \tfrac{5}{4}; \qquad \sec \beta = \tfrac{5}{3}; \qquad \cot \beta = \tfrac{3}{4}.$$

FIG. 23

Note 1. In this chapter, unless otherwise specified, all angles referred to will be acute.

EXAMPLE 1. Construct α and find $\cos \alpha$ and $\tan \alpha$, if $\sin \alpha = \tfrac{3}{4}$.

SOLUTION. In equations (2), $\sin \alpha = a/c$. The student should construct a right triangle with $a = 3$ and $c = 4$. Then, $b = \sqrt{7}$ and

$$\cos \alpha = \frac{\sqrt{7}}{4}; \qquad \tan \alpha = \frac{3}{\sqrt{7}} = \frac{3}{7}\sqrt{7}.$$

ILLUSTRATION 2. In Figure 24, we may read off the functions of 30°, 45°, 60°.

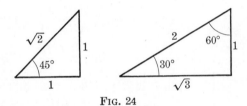

FIG. 24

18. Functions of complementary angles

If α and β are acute and $\alpha + \beta = 90°$, then α and β are said to be *complementary;* either is called the *complement* of the other angle.

ILLUSTRATION 1. The complement of 35° is (90° − 35°) or 55°.

If α and β are the acute angles of a right triangle ABC, then α and β are complementary, and $\beta = 90° - \alpha$. From Figure 25, side a is *opposite* α and *adjacent* to β. Hence, from relations (2) on page 18,

$$\sin \alpha = \frac{a}{c} = \cos \beta; \qquad \cos \alpha = \frac{b}{c} = \sin \beta;$$

$$\tan \alpha = \cot \beta; \qquad \cot \alpha = \tan \beta;$$

$$\sec \alpha = \csc \beta; \qquad \csc \alpha = \sec \beta.$$

FIG. 25

On using $\beta = 90° - \alpha$, the preceding results become

$$\left.\begin{array}{ll} \sin \alpha = \cos (90° - \alpha); & \sec \alpha = \csc (90° - \alpha); \\ \cos \alpha = \sin (90° - \alpha); & \csc \alpha = \sec (90° - \alpha); \\ \tan \alpha = \cot (90° - \alpha); & \cot \alpha = \tan (90° - \alpha). \end{array}\right\} \quad (1)$$

The trigonometric functions may be grouped as follows: *sine* and *cosine; tangent* and *cotangent; secant* and *cosecant.* In each pair, either function may be referred to as the *cofunction* of the other one. Then, (1) states that *any function of an acute angle α equals the cofunction of the complement of α.* We call (1) the *cofunction relations.*

ILLUSTRATION 2. $\sin 33° = \cos 57°$. $\tan 29° = \cot 61°$. $\csc 15° = \sec 75°$.

EXAMPLE 1.   Express $\tan 37° 38'$ as a function of another acute angle.

SOLUTION.   Since $90° - 37° 38' = 52° 22'$, $\tan 37° 38' = \cot 52° 22'$.

Note 1. In the Middle Ages, it was customary at first to refer to the *cosine,* in Latin, as *complementi sinus,* meaning the sine of the complement. Eventually, *complementi sinus* was abbreviated to *cosinus.*

19. Numerical properties of the functions

Let α and γ be acute angles where $\alpha < \gamma$. Then, in Figure 26, suppose that $AB = AB' = 1$.* We have

FIG. 26

$$\sin \alpha = \frac{CB}{AB} = \frac{CB}{1} = CB \quad and$$

$$\sin \gamma = \frac{C'B'}{1} = C'B'.$$

Since $\alpha < \gamma$, $CB < C'B'$ and $\sin \alpha < \sin \gamma$. Similarly, $\cos \alpha = AC$, $\cos \gamma = AC'$,   and $\cos \alpha > \cos \gamma$. Also,

$$\tan \alpha = \frac{CB}{AC} \quad and \quad \tan \gamma = \frac{C'B'}{AC'}. \quad (1)$$

Since $AC' < AC$ and $C'B' > CB$, we have $\tan \gamma > \tan \alpha$ because the numerator *increases* and the denominator *decreases* as we pass from $\tan \alpha$ to $\tan \gamma$ in (1). If we think of α as a variable angle and of γ as any angle obtained by increasing α, we have arrived at the following conclusions:

If the acute angle α increases, then $\sin \alpha$ and $\tan \alpha$ increase while $\cos \alpha$ and $\cot \alpha$ decrease.

Since $\sec \alpha = 1/\cos \alpha$ and $\csc \alpha = 1/\sin \alpha$, the preceding statement shows that $\sec \alpha$ *increases* and $\csc \alpha$ *decreases* if α increases.

* We read "AB'" as "A, B prime."

EXERCISE 6

Construct the acute angle α and find its functions.

1. $\tan \alpha = \frac{3}{4}$.
2. $\sin \alpha = \frac{4}{5}$.
3. $\cos \alpha = \frac{7}{25}$.
4. $\sec \alpha = \frac{17}{8}$.
5. $\cos \alpha = \frac{15}{17}$.
6. $\cot \alpha = \frac{12}{5}$.
7. $\csc \alpha = \frac{3}{2}$.
8. $\cos \alpha = \frac{1}{3}$.

9. By use of Figure 24, page 19, find the functions of 30°, 45°, 60°.

Express each function as a function of the complementary angle.

10. $\sin 20°$.
11. $\cos 15°$.
12. $\tan 49°$.
13. $\cot 38° 10'$.
14. $\sec 41°$.
15. $\csc 12°$.
16. $\sec 81°$.
17. $\tan 39° 5'$.
18. $\sec 85°$.
19. $\sin 67°$.
20. $\cot 67°$.
21. $\sin 82° 23'$.

22. By use of a protractor, construct on cross section paper a right triangle of generous dimensions with 35° as one acute angle. Then, by finding quotients of the measured lengths of the sides of the triangle, find the functions of 35° and 55° approximately to one decimal place.

23. In a standard right triangle ABC with sides a, b, c and acute angles α, β, observe that $a < c$ and $b < c$. What facts does this recall about $\sin \alpha$, $\cos \alpha$, $\sec \alpha$, and $\csc \alpha$?

24. In the triangle ABC of Problem 23, what is true about sides a and b if (1) $\alpha = 45°$; (2) $\alpha < 45°$; (3) $\alpha > 45°$? In each case, also state corresponding facts about $\tan \alpha$ and $\cot \alpha$.

20. Significant digits

Unless otherwise indicated, let us assume hereafter that any number referred to is written in decimal form. Then, in any number, we may visualize an endless sequence of zeros at the right of the last digit which is not zero, if there is such a last digit. A *terminating decimal* is one in which all digits to the right of a certain place are zeros. An *endless decimal* is one in which, no matter how far we proceed to the right, we never reach a place beyond which each digit is zero.

ILLUSTRATION 1. $1\frac{3}{4} = 1.75000 \cdots$, a terminating decimal. $\frac{1}{3} = .333 \cdots$, an endless repeating decimal. $\pi = 3.14159 \cdots$, an endless but not a repeating decimal.

In any number N, let us read its digits *from left to right*. Then, by definition, the *significant digits*, or *significant figures*, of N are its digits, in sequence, commencing with the first digit *not zero* and ending with the last one definitely specified. Notice that this definition does not involve any reference to the position of the decimal point in N. Usually, we mention any *final zeros* at the right in referring to the significant digits of N only when N is an approximate value of some quantity.

ILLUSTRATION 2. The significant digits of 410.58 or of .0041058 are 4, 1, 0, 5, 8. Since $21\frac{4}{5}$ is exactly 21.8, we would say that it has three significant digits, even though we could add zeros.

If T is the *true value* and A is an *approximate value* of a quantity, we agree to call the *absolute value* of $T - A$ the *error* of A. Any approximate value A should be written so that its error is *at most one half unit* in the last significant place used in A. If A has just k significant digits, A is called a **k-place approximation** to T; then, the error of A is at most one half unit in the kth significant place in A, or not more than 5 units in the next place to the right.

ILLUSTRATION 3. If a surveyor specifies that a measured distance is 256.8 yards, he should mean that the error is at most .05 yard and, thus, that the true result lies between 256.75 and 256.85, inclusive.

ILLUSTRATION 4. It is essential to specify any *final zeros* in an *approximate value A*. Thus, to say that a measured weight is 35.60 (pounds) means that the true weight lies between 35.595 and 35.605. To say that the measured weight is 35.6 means that the true weight lies between 35.55 and 35.65. Thus, there is a distinction between 35.60 and 35.6 as approximate values.

Note 1. In referring to a *place* in a number, we shall mean any place *where a significant digit stands*. In referring to a *decimal place*, the word *decimal* will be explicitly used.

To round off a number N to k figures, as the student has done in arithmetic,* means to write a k-place approximation A for N.

ILLUSTRATION 5. To round off $\pi = 3.141593$ to five places, we write 3.1416; we increased the 5th significant digit of π from 5 to 6 because the discarded part .000093 is greater than 5 in the 5th decimal place. The three-place approximation to π is 3.14, where we kept 4 unaltered because the discarded part is less than 5 in the third decimal place.

ILLUSTRATION 6. In rounding off 315.475 to five places, with equal justification we could give either 315.48 or 315.47. Arbitrarily, in such an ambiguous case, in this book **we agree to write the result with the last digit even,** and hence choose 315.48.

Until otherwise stated in this text, we shall assume that the data in any problem are *exact*, and we shall compute our results as accurately as is justified by the means at our disposal. Later, we shall introduce agreements about approximate data.

21. Four-place trigonometric table

In general, any value of a trigonometric function is an endless decimal. By advanced methods, the functions of any angle can be computed to as many decimal places as desired. We shall learn later how the functions of any angle θ can be expressed in terms of the functions of a reference angle α for θ, where $0° \leqq \alpha \leqq 90°$. Hence, if a table is available for

---

* For a review of some rules of arithmetic for computation with approximation values, see page 164 in the Appendix.

finding functions of angles from 0° to 90°, inclusive, the table will serve indirectly for corresponding angles of any size.

Table VII is a *four-place* table of the functions of acute angles at intervals of 10′. For angles at most equal to 45°, read angles at the *left* and titles of columns at the *top* in the main part of each page of the table. For angles greater than 45°, read titles at the *bottom* and angles at the *right*.

ILLUSTRATION 1. To find cot 5° 30′, look in the left-hand angle columns for 5° 30′: cot 5° 30′ = 10.39. To find sin 77° 20′, look for 77° 20′ in the right-hand angle columns: sin 77° 20′ = .9757.

Each entry in the function columns of Table VII is a function of some angle and, also, is the *cofunction of the complementary angle*, on account of the relations of Section 18 on page 20.

ILLUSTRATION 2. We read in Table VII that
$$.9757 = \sin 77° 20′ = \cos 12° 40′.$$

EXAMPLE 1. From Table VII, find α if $\cos \alpha = .4173$.

SOLUTION. We look for .4173 in the cosine columns in Table VII. We find .4173 on page 15 in the column with cosine at the bottom; hence we read
$$.4173 = \cos 65° 20′, \quad or \quad \alpha = 65° 20′.$$

Note 1. One of the most famous of the early printed tables of the trigonometric functions is the *Opus Palatinum*, compiled by the German mathematician RHAETICUS and published in 1596. This table gives the values of trigonometric functions to ten decimal places for angles spaced at intervals of 10″. It is often said that the work of Rhaeticus has never been surpassed.

EXERCISE 7

Find each function by use of Table VII.

1. sin 12°.	**2.** tan 33°.	**3.** cot 58°.	**4.** sec 64°.
5. csc 73°.	**6.** cos 9° 20′.	**7.** sin 13° 30′.	**8.** tan 53° 40′.
9. cot 85° 20′.	**10.** csc 73° 50′.	**11.** sec 18° 10′.	**12.** sin 42° 40′.
13. tan 68° 50′.	**14.** cot 79° 20′.	**15.** sec 88° 10′.	**16.** cot 32° 50′.
17. tan 5° 30′.	**18.** cos 43° 10′.	**19.** csc 62° 0′.	**20.** sec 81° 10′.

Find the unknown acute angle α by use of Table VII.

21. tan α = .4074.	**22.** sin α = .1016.	**23.** sec α = 1.167.
24. cot α = 1.621.	**25.** cos α = .9261.	**26.** csc α = 4.134.
27. csc α = 1.033.	**28.** tan α = 1.437.	**29.** cos α = .3035.
30. sec α = 1.932.	**31.** cot α = .4841.	**32.** cos α = .3584.
33. sin α = .6180.	**34.** tan α = 1.744.	**35.** cos α = .3502.
36. tan α = 21.47.	**37.** sec α = 1.184.	**38.** csc α = 1.081.

22. Interpolation in a four-place table

With the assistance of a method called *interpolation* by proportional parts, we shall use Table VII for angles not tabulated there. In this method, it is assumed that, *for small changes in an angle α, the corresponding changes in the value of any one of the functions of α are proportional to the changes in α.* This assumption, which is only approximately true, is called the **principle of proportional parts.** The principle leads to results which are sufficiently accurate for practical purposes.

EXAMPLE 1. By use of Table VII, find sin 27° 43′.

SOLUTION. 1. Notice that 27° 43′ is 3/10 of the way from 27° 40′ to 27° 50′.

2. By the principle of proportional parts, an increase of 3′ in the angle 27° 40′ causes 3/10 as much change in its sine as is caused by an increase of 10′ in the angle. *Since 27° 43′ is 3/10 of the way from 27° 40′ to 27° 50′, sin 27° 43′ is 3/10 of the way from sin 27° 40′ to sin 27° 50′.* Therefore,

$$\sin 27° \, 43′ = \sin 27° \, 40′ + .3(\sin 27° \, 50′ - \sin 27° \, 40′).$$

From table: sin 27° 40′ = .4643⎤	**Tabular difference** is
sin 27° 43′ = ? ⎬26	.4669 − .4643 = .0026.
From table: sin 27° 50′ = .4669⎦	.3(.0026) = .00078, or .0008.

3. Hence, sin 27° 43′ = .4643 + .0008 = .4651.

Comment. 1. We call .0008 the *proportional part* of the *tabular difference.* In passing from .4643 to .4669 there is an *increase* of .0026; hence we *added* .0008.

2. We changed from .00078 to .0008 in accordance with Rule I on page 164, because the table entries are accurate only to four decimal places.

EXAMPLE 2. Find csc 19° 27′ from Table VII.

SOLUTION. 1. 19° 27′ is 7/10 of the way from 19° 20′ to 19° 30′.

From table: csc 19° 20′ = 3.021⎤	**Tabular difference** is
csc 19° 27′ = ? ⎬.025	3.021 − 2.996 = .025.
From table: csc 19° 30′ = 2.996⎦	.7(25) = 17.5, or 17.

2. Hence, csc 19° 27′ = 3.021 − .017 = 3.004.

Comment. 1. We *subtracted* .017 because 3.021 > 2.996.

2. We found .7(25) = 17.5 under the *tenths of 25* in the column of *Proportional Parts* in the table. We could use 17.5 as either 17 or 18 with equal justification. In interpolation, whenever such an ambiguity is met, we agree to choose the last digit so as to **make the final result even in the last place.**

3. For a different solution, we could observe that 19° 27′ is 3/10 of the way from 19° 30′ to 19° 20′. Then, since csc 19° 20′ is *greater* than csc 19° 30′, we would *add* 3/10 of the tabular difference to obtain csc 19° 27′:

$$\text{csc } 19° \, 27′ = 2.996 + .3(.025) = 2.996 + .0075 = 3.004.$$

EXAMPLE 3.   Find α if sin α = .9254.

SOLUTION.   1. .9254 is not an entry in the sine columns of Table VII. Hence, we search for the consecutive entries between which .9254 lies:

$$.9250 = \sin 67° \ 40'; \qquad .9261 = \sin 67° \ 50'. \tag{1}$$

We say that the entries in (1) **bracket** .9254, or that .9250 and .9261 are the **bracketing entries.** Hence, α is **bracketed** by 67° 40′ and 67° 50′.

2. Let x represent the unknown difference in minutes between α and 67° 40′. Then, by the principle of proportional parts, we assume that

$$\frac{x}{10'} = \frac{4}{11} \quad or \quad x = \frac{4}{11} \cdot 10'. \tag{2}$$

That is, since .9254 is 4/11 of the way from .9250 to .9261, then α is 4/11 of the way from 67° 40′ to 67° 50′, or $x = \frac{4}{11}(10') = 4'$, to the nearest minute:

$$\alpha = 67° \ 40' + x = 67° \ 40' + 4' = 67° \ 44'. \tag{3}$$

The following summary gives the complete work devoid of explanation.

$$11\left[4\left[\begin{array}{l}.9250 = \sin 67° \ 40' \\ .9254 = \sin \alpha \\ .9261 = \sin 67° \ 50'\end{array}\right]x\right]10' \qquad \begin{array}{c}\frac{4}{11} = .36 = .4, \textit{ to the nearest tenth.} \\ x = .4(10') = 4'. \\ \alpha = 67° \ 40' + .4(10') = 67° \ 44'.\end{array}$$

Comment.   1. When using Table VII to find an unknown angle, we agree to state the result to the *nearest minute*, because such a stage of accuracy but no greater refinement is justified. Hence, in Example 3, we computed 4/11 to the *nearest tenth* because we were to multiply by 10′.

2. To gain speed, we could obtain $\frac{4}{11} = .4$ by merely inspecting the tenths of 11 in the column of proportional parts in Table VII. We read

$$.3(11) = 3.3, \quad or \quad .3 = \frac{3.3}{11}; \quad .4(11) = 4.4 \quad or \quad \frac{4.4}{11} = .4.$$

Since 4 is nearer to 4.4 than to 3.3, hence 4/11 is nearer to .4 than to .3.

EXAMPLE 4.   Find α if cot α = 1.387.

SOLUTION.   Since cot $\alpha > 1$, we have $\alpha < 45°$. Hence, we look in the columns of Table VII labeled cotangent at the *top*, and find the entries 1.393 and 1.385 which *bracket* 1.387. Since 1.387 is 6/8 of the way from 1.393 to 1.385, we assume that α is 6/8 of the way from 35° 40′ to 35° 50′.

$$8\left[6\left[\begin{array}{l}1.393 = \cot 35° \ 40' \\ 1.387 = \cot \alpha \\ 1.385 = \cot 35° \ 50'\end{array}\right]x\right]10' \qquad \begin{array}{c}\frac{6}{8} = .75 = .8 \textit{ approximately,} \\ x = .8(10') = 8'. \\ \alpha = 35° \ 40' + .8(10') = 35° \ 48'.\end{array}$$

23. Introduction to inverse trigonometric functions

The expression **"arcsin h,"** which we read *"arcsine h,"* means

$$\textit{"an angle whose sine is h."} \tag{1}$$

It is sometimes instructive to read arcsin *h without abbreviation*, as indicated in (1). By definition, the following equations are equivalent:

$$h = \sin \alpha \quad and \quad \alpha = \arcsin h. \tag{2}$$

If we think of α as a variable, the equation $h = \sin \alpha$ describes *h as a function of* α; the equation $\alpha = \arcsin h$ serves the *inverse* purpose of describing α *as a function of h*. Hence, we refer to arcsin *h* as an *inverse trigonometric function of h*. Similarly, we introduce the other inverse functions with meanings corresponding to (1):

arccos *h*;   arctan *h*;   arccot *h*;   arcsec *h*;   arccsc *h*.

ILLUSTRATION 1. Since tan 45° = 1, then arctan 1 = 45°, which we read "arctangent 1 equals 45°."

EXAMPLE 1. Find arccos .3287.

SOLUTION. We could read the problem as follows: "*find an angle whose cosine is .3287*," or "*find arccosine .3287.*" Let α = arccos .3287. Then cos α = .3287. By interpolation in Table VII, we find α = 70° 49'. That is,

arccos .3287 = 70° 49'.

At present, any inverse trigonometric function is taken to represent an acute angle. Later, we shall observe that an inverse function, such as arcsin *h*, where $|h| \leq 1$, has *infinitely many values*.

EXERCISE 8

Find each function by use of Table VII.

1. tan 4° 43'.	**2.** tan 5° 17'.	**3.** sin 46° 52'.	**4.** sin 47° 46'.
5. cot 27° 4'.	**6.** cos 33° 15'.	**7.** cos 24° 44'.	**8.** cot 32° 38'.
9. sin 14° 24'.	**10.** tan 32° 36'.	**11.** sec 45° 27'.	**12.** csc 56° 46'.
13. sin 80° 17'.	**14.** sin 28° 5'.	**15.** csc 65° 39'.	**16.** sec 53° 13'.
17. cot 77° 16'.	**18.** cos 28° 19'.	**19.** sin 1° 11'.	**20.** tan 6° 23'.
21. sec 83° 15'.	**22.** csc 76° 44'.	**23.** cos 35° 2'.	**24.** cot 67° 32'.
25. csc 87° 23'.	**26.** csc 4° 29'.	**27.** tan 81° 53'.	**28.** tan 81° 54'

Find the acute angle α *by use of Table* VII.

29. tan α = .0831.	**30.** sin α = .4955.	**31.** sin α = .3812.
32. sec α = 1.128.	**33.** cos α = .9381.	**34.** cot α = 1.558.
35. sec α = 1.506.	**36.** tan α = 1.031.	**37.** csc α = 1.265.
38. sin α = .7967.	**39.** cos α = .7037.	**40.** tan α = 1.322.
41. sec α = 1.183.	**42.** cos α = .9987.	**43.** sec α = 1.568.
44. cot α = .6720.	**45.** tan α = 1.026.	**46.** sec α = 1.817.

Find α, *without interpolation, to the nearest* 10' *by use of Table* VII.

47. sin α = .2231.	**48.** tan α = 7.703.	**49.** cot α = 4.671.

HINT for Problem 47. In Table VII, .2221 is the nearest entry.

50. cos α = .3437.   **51.** sin α = .6773.   **52.** csc α = 1.230.

53. sec α = 2.018.   **54.** tan α = .6258.   **55.** cot α = .7601.

Find the value of each inverse function from Table VII.

56. arccos .4423.   **57.** arccsc 3.462.   **58.** arccot 2.612.

59. arcsin .7354.   **60.** arctan .2978.   **61.** arcsec 2.314.

24. Five-place values of the functions

By means of Table XI, without interpolation we can find the functions of an acute angle α to five-decimal places if α is expressed to the nearest minute. And, if a function of α is given, without interpolation we can find α to the nearest minute by use of Table XI. By interpolation in Table XI, we can find the functions of angles expressed to the nearest tenth of a minute. And, if the five-place value of a function of α is given, we can find α to tenths of a minute.

ILLUSTRATION 1. From page 96 in Table XI, sin 67° 27' = .92355. If sin α = .57071, from Table XI we find α = 34° 48'.

ILLUSTRATION 2. If sin α = .03915, in the sine column for 2° in Table XI, the nearest entry is .03926. Hence, α = 2° 15', to the nearest minute.

EXAMPLE 1. Find cos 57° 33.6' by interpolation in Table XI.

SOLUTION. We observe that 33.6' is 6/10 of the way from 33' to 34'.

From table: cos 57° 33' = .53656 ⎤ x ⎤	x = .6(24) = 14.4.
cos 57° 33.6' = ? ⎦ ⎟24	cos 57° 33.6' = .53656 − .00014;
From table: cos 57° 34' = .53632 ⎦	cos 57° 33.6' = .53642.

EXAMPLE 2. Find α by interpolation if sin α = .03914.

SOLUTION. In the sine-cosine columns of Table XI, we find that .03914 is bracketed by .03897 and .03926, in the column for 2°.

29 ⎡ 17 ⎡ .03897 = sin 2° 14' ⎤ x ⎤	$\frac{17}{29}$ = .59 = .6, *approximately.*
.03914 = sin α ⎦ ⎟1'	*Hence,* x = .6(1') = .6'.
.03926 = sin 2° 15' ⎦	α = 2° 14' + .6' = 2° 14.6'.

EXERCISE 9

Find each function, or the unknown angle α, by use of Table XI.

1. cos 5° 27'.   **2.** csc 72° 18'.   **3.** sec 15° 8'.   **4.** tan 28° 17'.

5. sec 83° 12'.   **6.** sin 43° 5'.   **7.** csc 41° 51'.   **8.** sec 73° 19'.

9. sin α = .53263.   **10.** sin α = .30431.   **11.** tan α = .20557.

12. cos α = .57238.   **13.** tan α = 2.8344.   **14.** cot α = 2.8057.

By inspection of Table XI, find the angle α to the nearest minute.

15. sin α = .29245.   **16.** cot α = 6.9592.   **17.** cos α = .68125.

18. cos α = .34103.   **19.** cos α = .83824.   **20.** sin α = .03786.

Find each function by interpolation in Table XI.

21. sin 32° 13.6′.   **22.** cos 81° 28.6′.   **23.** cot 43° 36.2′.

24. tan 34° 32.3′.   **25.** sec 15° 8.2′.   **26.** tan 20° 18.7′.

27. cot 76° 35.4′.   **28.** sin 57° 39.9′.   **29.** cos 71° 11.5′.

30. sin 31° 51.7′.   **31.** cos 17° 42′ 38″.   **32.** sin 52° 47′ 23″.

HINT for Problem 31. Since $\frac{38}{60}$ = .63, 38″ = .6′ approximately.

33–38. In Problems 15–20, respectively, find α by interpolation.

Find the angle correct to the nearest minute by inspection of Table XI.

39. arcsin .51563.   **40.** arctan 1.5356.   **41.** arcsec 6.1803.

42. arccos .87340.   **43.** arccot .57190.   **44.** arccsc 1.1373.

25. Solution of a right triangle

A right triangle has six *parts*, consisting of *three sides* and *three angles*, one of which is 90°. By means of trigonometry, if *two sides* or *an acute angle and a side* of a right triangle are given,* we can compute its unknown parts. This computation is called the *solution* of the triangle.

FIG. 27

Recall the following formulas for the right triangle in Figure 27.

(1) $a^2 + b^2 = c^2$.   (2) $\alpha + \beta = 90°$.

(3) $\sin \alpha = \dfrac{a}{c} = \cos \beta$.   (4) $\cos \alpha = \dfrac{b}{c} = \sin \beta$.

(5) $\tan \alpha = \dfrac{a}{b} = \cot \beta$.   (6) $\cot \alpha = \dfrac{b}{a} = \tan \beta$.

(7) $\sec \alpha = \dfrac{c}{b} = \csc \beta$.   (8) $\csc \alpha = \dfrac{c}{a} = \sec \beta$.

From (3) and (4) we obtain the following useful formulas:

$$a = c \sin \alpha; \quad b = c \cos \alpha; \tag{9}$$

or, *the leg opposite α equals the hypotenuse times* sin α, *and the leg adjacent to α equals the hypotenuse times* cos α. We shall avoid (1) until we meet logarithms. As an aid to accuracy, we usually employ (3) or (4) in preference to (7) or (8) in finding angles. Formulas (7) and (8) are useful in avoiding division when finding *c*.

---

* Recall that it is then possible to construct the triangle by plane geometry.

SUMMARY. *Suggestions for solving a triangle.*

1. *By use of the data, sketch the triangle roughly to scale.*

2. *To find any unknown part, use a formula involving it but no other unknown. If possible, select a formula avoiding division.*

3. *As a rough check, compare results with the preliminary sketch. For a more refined check, substitute values in any one of formulas (3) to (8) which was not used in solving but which involves as many as possible of the computed parts; after substituting, compare the two sides of the check formula.*

4. *In the arithmetic, round off all lengths, quotients, and products to four or to five significant digits, and all angles to minutes or to tenths of a minute, according as four-place or five-place tables are used.*

EXAMPLE 1. Solve right $\triangle ABC$ if $b = 250$ and $c = 718$.

SOLUTION. 1. *Outline of formulas:*

To obtain β, $\qquad\qquad$ $\sin \beta = \dfrac{b}{c}.$ $\qquad\qquad$ (10)

From $\alpha + \beta = 90°$, $\qquad\qquad$ $\alpha = 90° - \beta.$ $\qquad\qquad$ (11)

From $\cot \beta = \dfrac{a}{b}$, $\qquad\qquad$ $a = b \cot \beta.$ $\qquad\qquad$ (12)

Check formula: $\qquad\qquad$ $a = c \sin \alpha.$ $\qquad\qquad$ (13)

2. *Computation.* $\qquad$ $\sin \beta = \dfrac{250}{718} = .3483.$

By interpolation in Table VII, $\qquad$ $\beta = 20° \, 23'.$

Hence,
$$\alpha = 90° - 20° \, 23' = 69° \, 37'.$$

From (12), and Table VII,
$$a = 250 \cot 20° \, 23' = 250(2.692) = 673.0.$$

Figure 28 is seen to check roughly with these results.

3. *Check.* $c \sin \alpha = 718 \sin 69° \, 37' = 718(.9374) = 673.1.$ Since $a = 673.0$, the check is satisfactory; the difference between 673.1 and 673.0 could be due to errors introduced by rounding off in computation.

FIG. 28

EXAMPLE 2. Solve right $\triangle ABC$ if $a = 30.5$ and $\beta = 32° \, 10'$.

OUTLINE OF SOLUTION. $\qquad$ Since $\alpha + \beta = 90°,$ $\qquad$ $\alpha = 90° - \beta.$

From $\dfrac{b}{a} = \tan \beta,$ $\qquad\qquad$ $b = a \tan \beta.$

From $\dfrac{c}{a} = \sec \beta,$ $\qquad\qquad$ $c = a \sec \beta.$

Check formula: $\qquad\qquad$ $b = c \cos \alpha.$

To solve, we would use Table VII.

EXAMPLE 3. Solve right $\triangle ABC$ if $c = 48$ and $\alpha = 22°$.

OUTLINE OF SOLUTION.   From (9), $a = c \sin \alpha.$
From (9), $b = c \cos \alpha.$
Since $\alpha + \beta = 90°$, $\beta = 90° - \alpha.$
Check formula: $b = a \tan \beta.$

EXERCISE 10

With the given data, solve right $\triangle ABC$ by use of Table VII.

1. $\alpha = 23° 30'$; $a = 50.$ **2.** $b = 75$; $\alpha = 68° 40'.$

3. $c = 125$; $\beta = 13° 20'.$ **4.** $c = 15$; $\alpha = 56° 30'.$

5. $a = 400$; $b = 446.$ **6.** $c = 7.5$; $b = 5.083.$

7. $a = 85.22$; $b = 65.$ **8.** $c = 1.4$; $\alpha = 16° 13'.$

9. $a = .518$; $c = 1.16.$ **10.** $b = .48$; $c = .97.$

11. $a = 2.3$; $b = 1.25.$ **12.** $a = .262$; $c = .43.$

13. $b = .425$; $c = .73.$ **14.** $a = 25.4$; $b = 89.6.$

15. $b = .013$; $\alpha = 52° 11'.$ **16.** $b = .38$; $\beta = 48° 1'.$

17. $c = 1.6$, $\alpha = 80° 12'.$ **18.** $a = 1625$; $b = 2950.$

19. $b = 4500$; $c = 8600.$ **20.** $b = .135$; $\beta = 79° 28'.$

21–30. Solve Problems 11–20, respectively, by use of Table XI without interpolation, rounding off angles to the nearest minute and sides to four significant digits. Use of Table XI as specified gives about the same accuracy as is obtainable by interpolation in Table VII.

★*Solve by use of Table XI, obtaining angles to tenths of a minute and sides to five significant digits.*

31. $a = 35$; $\beta = 68° 43.3'.$ **32.** $b = 14$; $\beta = 47° 28.7'.$

33. $c = 13.6$; $\alpha = 74° 14.3'.$ **34.** $c = .88$; $\beta = 26° 41.6'.$

35. Solve Problem 9.   **36.** Solve Problem 11.

26. Applications of right triangles

In any geometrical application of trigonometry, it is advisable to perform the following actions before computing.

1. *Construct a figure roughly to scale for the data.*

2. *Introduce single letters to represent unknown angles or lengths.*

3. *Outline the solution by specifying triangles or formulas to use; solve each formula for the quantity to be obtained from it.*

In either diagram in Figure 29, O is a point from which we sight an object at C, and OH is a horizontal line in the same vertical plane as C. Then, the acute angle COH between the line of sight to C and the horizontal line is called the *angle of elevation* of C or the *angle of depression* of C, as seen from O, according as C is *above* O or *below* O.

$D = Angle\ of\ depression$ $E = Angle\ of\ elevation$

FIG. 29

EXAMPLE 1.   From a cliff, 700 feet above a horizontal plane, the angle of depression of a church in the plane is 38° 27′.   Find the distance from the cliff to the church.

OUTLINE OF SOLUTION.   1. In Figure 30, C represents the church.   The angle of depression is $\angle CAH$, or θ.   We desire to find $x = KC$.

2. In right $\triangle AKC$ in Figure 30, $y = 700$ and $\theta = 38°\ 27′$.

3. Since

FIG. 30

$$\cot \theta = \frac{x}{y},$$

we would obtain x from $x = y \cot \theta$.

EXERCISE 11

Solve by use of four-place tables unless otherwise directed.

1. Find the length of the horizontal shadow of a man 6 feet tall when the angle of elevation of the sun is 75° 36′.

2. How tall is a chimney whose horizontal shadow is 90 feet long when the angle of elevation of the sun is 67° 42′?

3. A guy wire 35 feet long is stretched from level ground to the top of a pole 25 feet high.   Find the angle between the pole and the wire.

4. From a mountaintop 4000 feet above a fort, its angle of depression is 16° 45′.   Find the air-line distance from the mountaintop to the fort.

5. How high does an airplane rise in flying 4000 feet upward along a straight path inclined 28° 47′ from the horizontal?

6. From an airplane, flying 7000 feet above the ground, the angle of depression of a landing field is 19° 32′.   Find the air-line distance from the plane to the field.   Use Table XI.

7. Find the height of the Empire State Building in New York City if the angle of elevation of its top is 61° 37′ when seen from a point on the street level 675.4 feet from the building.

8. An inclined ramp into a garage is 260 feet long and rises 76 feet.   Find the inclination of the ramp from the horizontal.

9. The largest tree in California is the General Sherman tree in the Sequoia National Park. At a point 185 feet from the tree, at the same elevation as its foot, the angle of elevation of the top of the tree is 55° 49′. How tall is the tree?

10. In flying upward for 1260 yards along a straight inclined path, an airplane rises 156 yards. Find the climbing angle.

11. A spy arranges to show a light at an oil tank 250 feet above water level near an ocean beach. An observer 10 feet above water level on an enemy submarine finds that the angle of elevation of the light is 3° 27′. Find the line-of-sight distance from the submarine's guns to the tank.

12. A painter desires to reach a window 40 feet above the ground. Find the length of the shortest ladder he can use if it must not incline more than 78° from the horizontal.

13. On a 3% railroad grade, at what angle are the rails inclined to the horizontal, and how far does one rise in traveling upward 9000 feet measured along the rails? Use Table XI. (The tracks rise 3 feet for each 100 feet of horizontal distance gained.)

14. If the grade of a railroad is 6.75%, how far must one travel along the rails to rise 500 feet? Use Table XI.

15. From a cliff 150 feet above a lake, we see a boat sailing directly toward us. The angle of depression of the boat is seen to be 5° 7′, and then later is 11° 18′. Find the distance the boat sailed between these observations. Use Table XI.

16. From a mountaintop 5000 feet above a horizontal plane, we observe two villages in the plane due east of us, whose angles of depression are 8° 38′ and 5° 46′. How far apart are the villages? Use Table XI.

17. A gun G shoots at T at a range of 5400 yards, and the shot hits at S so that $\angle TGS = 3°$. Assume that $\angle GTS = 90°$. How far from T is S? Use Table XI.

THREE

LOGARITHMS

27. Simplification of computation

We shall define certain auxiliary numbers called *logarithms*. These will permit us to change the operations of *multiplication, division, raising to a power,* and *extraction of a root* to the easier operations of *addition, subtraction, multiplication,* and *division,* respectively, applied to the proper logarithms.

28. Rational and irrational numbers

A *rational number* is a number which can be expressed as a fraction u/v, where u and v are integers. A real number which is not a rational number is called an *irrational number*.

ILLUSTRATION 1. 4, $-$ 5, 0, and $\frac{16}{3}$ are rational numbers. π, $\sqrt{3}$, and $\sqrt[3]{5}$ are irrational numbers.

29. Exponents

We call a^m the mth *power* of the *base* a, and m the *exponent* of the power. We recall the following relations, where m and n represent positive integers and p is any rational number.

$$a^m = a \cdot a \cdot a \cdots a. \qquad (m \text{ factors}) \tag{1}$$

$$a^0 = 1. \tag{2}$$

$$a^{\frac{m}{n}} = \sqrt[n]{a^m} = (\sqrt[n]{a})^m. \qquad (n \text{ not even if } a < 0) \tag{3}$$

$$a^{-p} = \frac{1}{a^p}. \tag{4}$$

In elementary algebra, it is proved that the following theorems, called *index laws*, are true if the exponents are rational numbers.

I. *Law of exponents for multiplication:* $\qquad a^x a^y = a^{x+y}.$

II. *Law of exponents for division:* $\qquad \dfrac{a^x}{a^y} = a^{x-y}.$

III. *Law for finding a power of a power:* $\qquad (a^x)^k = a^{kx}.$

ILLUSTRATION 1. $a^4 = a \cdot a \cdot a \cdot a.$ $16^0 = 1.$ $8^{\frac{1}{3}} = \sqrt[3]{8} = 2.$

$a^{\frac{3}{2}} = \sqrt{a^3}.$ $16^{\frac{3}{4}} = (\sqrt[4]{16})^3 = 2^3 = 8.$ $\dfrac{a^{16}}{a^5} = a^{11}.$ $\dfrac{1}{5^3} = 5^{-3}.$

$\sqrt[6]{N} = N^{\frac{1}{6}}.$ $a^3 a^5 = a^8.$ $(x^3)^2 = x^6.$

We shall use irrational numbers as exponents, but a logical foundation for their use is beyond the scope of this text. Hence, without discussion, we shall assume that irrational powers have meaning, and that the preceding index laws hold if the exponents are any real numbers, when the base is positive.

30. Logarithms

Let b represent a fixed positive number, not 1. Then, if N is any *positive* number, there exists a corresponding real number x such that $N = b^x$. This leads to the following definition.

DEFINITION I. *The logarithm of a number N with respect to the base b is the exponent of the power to which b must be raised to obtain N.*

In other words, if $N = b^x$ then x is the logarithm of N to the base b. To abbreviate "*the logarithm of N to the base b*," we write "$\log_b N$." Then, by Definition I, the following equations state the same fact, the first equation in exponential form and the second in logarithmic form:

$$N = b^x \quad and \quad x = \log_b N. \tag{1}$$

ILLUSTRATION 1. If $N = 4^5$, then 5 is the logarithm of N to the base 4. We read "$\log_2 64$" as "*the logarithm of 64 to the base 2.*"

$$Since \ 64 = 2^6, \qquad \log_2 64 = 6.$$

$$Since \ \sqrt[3]{5} = 5^{\frac{1}{3}}, \qquad \log_5 \sqrt[3]{5} = \tfrac{1}{3}.$$

In order to find $\log_2 \tfrac{1}{8}$, we express $\tfrac{1}{8}$ as a power of 2:

$$Since \ \frac{1}{8} = \frac{1}{2^3} = 2^{-3}, \qquad \log_2 \frac{1}{8} = -3.$$

ILLUSTRATION 2. If $\log_b 16 = 4$, then $b^4 = 16$. Hence, $b = \sqrt[4]{16} = 2$.

ILLUSTRATION 3. If $\log_a 2 = -\tfrac{1}{3}$, then $a^{-\frac{1}{3}} = 2$. Hence,

$$\frac{1}{a^{\frac{1}{3}}} = 2; \qquad \frac{1}{2} = a^{\frac{1}{3}}; \qquad a = \left(\frac{1}{2}\right)^3 = \frac{1}{8}.$$

ILLUSTRATION 4. For any base b, we have $b^0 = 1$ and $b^1 = b$.

$$\log_b 1 = 0; \qquad \log_b b = 1.$$

If $b > 0$ and x is real, then b^x is positive in (1). This shows why we restrict Definition I to the case where N is *positive*. Thus, *we shall not define or use logarithms of negative numbers.* In very advanced mathematics, if $N < 0$ or $b < 0$, then $\log_b N$ is defined as a complex number.

EXERCISE 12

Express as a fraction or by use of a fractional exponent.

1. a^{-5}.   **2.** b^{-3}.   **3.** 2^{-4}.   **4.** 10^{-6}.   **5.** 3^{-2}.

6. $\sqrt{b}$.   **7.** $\sqrt[4]{b}$.   **8.** $\sqrt[3]{6}$.   **9.** $\sqrt[4]{8}$.   **10.** $\sqrt[6]{10}$.

Write an equivalent logarithmic equation.

11. $N = 3^5$.   **12.** $N = 5^{\frac{1}{4}}$.   **13.** $64 = 4^3$.   **14.** $\frac{1}{25} = 5^{-2}$.

Find the number N whose logarithm is given.

15. $\log_5 N = 2$.   **16.** $\log_8 N = 2$.   **17.** $\log_6 N = 3$.

18. $\log_4 N = \frac{1}{2}$.   **19.** $\log_{10} N = 0$.   **20.** $\log_9 N = 1$.

21. $\log_4 N = -2$.   **22.** $\log_{10} N = -2$.   **23.** $\log_8 N = \frac{1}{3}$.

24. $\log_{64} N = \frac{1}{3}$.   **25.** $\log_{81} N = \frac{1}{2}$.   **26.** $\log_{125} N = \frac{1}{3}$.

Find the logarithm.

27. $\log_6 36$.   **28.** $\log_2 32$.   **29.** $\log_4 2$.   **30.** $\log_{10} 100$.

31. $\log_3 27$.   **32.** $\log_6 216$.   **33.** $\log_{10} 1000$.   **34.** $\log_9 3$.

35. $\log_{100} 10$.   **36.** $\log_8 \frac{1}{8}$.   **37.** $\log_3 \frac{1}{81}$.   **38.** $\log_{10} .0001$.

Find b, N, or x, whichever is not given.

39. $\log_b 16 = 2$.   **40.** $\log_b 125 = 3$.   **41.** $\log_b 1000 = 3$.

42. $\log_b 9 = \frac{1}{2}$.   **43.** $\log_b 3 = \frac{1}{3}$.   **44.** $\log_b 10 = \frac{1}{4}$.

45. $\log_b 6 = -1$.   **46.** $\log_{81} N = \frac{3}{2}$.   **47.** $\log_{125} N = \frac{2}{3}$.

48. $\log_{100} N = \frac{5}{2}$.   **49.** $\log_{10} .1 = x$.   **50.** $\log_b 8 = -\frac{3}{2}$.

51. We do not use $b = 1$ as a base for logarithms because then no number except 1 would have a logarithm. Also, any number x would be the logarithm of 1 to the base 1. Why are these facts true?

31. Properties of logarithms useful in computation

I. *The logarithm of a product equals the sum of the logarithms of its factors. For instance,*

$$\log_b MN = \log_b M + \log_b N. \tag{1}$$

ILLUSTRATION 1. $\log_{10} 897(596) = \log_{10} 897 + \log_{10} 596$.

Proof of (1). Let $x = \log_b M$ and $y = \log_b N$. Then,

$M = b^x \quad and \quad N = b^y$.   (Definition of a logarithm)

$MN = b^x b^y = b^{x+y}$.   (A law of exponents)

Hence, by the definition of a logarithm,

$$\log_b MN = x + y = \log_b M + \log_b N.$$

Note 1. By use of (1), we may prove Property I for a product of any number of factors. Thus, since $MNP = (MN)(P)$,

$$\log_b MNP = \log_b MN + \log_b P = \log_b M + \log_b N + \log_b P.$$

II. *The logarithm of a quotient equals the logarithm of the dividend minus the logarithm of the divisor:*

$$\log_b \frac{M}{N} = \log_b M - \log_b N. \tag{2}$$

ILLUSTRATION 2. $\log_{10} \frac{89}{57} = \log_{10} 89 - \log_{10} 57.$

Proof of (2). Let $x = \log_b M$ and $y = \log_b N$. Then,

$$M = b^x \quad and \quad N = b^y.$$

Hence, $\dfrac{M}{N} = \dfrac{b^x}{b^y} = b^{x-y}.$ (A law of exponents)

Therefore, by the definition of a logarithm,

$$\log_b \frac{M}{N} = x - y = \log_b M - \log_b N.$$

III. *The logarithm of the kth power of a number N equals k times the logarithm of N:*

$$\cdot \log_b N^k = k \log_b N. \tag{3}$$

Proof. Let $x = \log_b N$. Then, $N = b^x$ and $N^k = (b^x)^k = b^{kx}$. Hence, by the definition of a logarithm,

$$\log_b N^k = kx = k \log_b N.$$

ILLUSTRATION 3. $\log_a 7^5 = 5 \log_a 7.$ $\log_a \sqrt[4]{3} = \log_a 3^{\frac{1}{4}} = \frac{1}{4} \log_a 3.$

Since $\sqrt[h]{N} = N^{\frac{1}{h}}$, by use of (3) with $k = 1/h$, we obtain

$$\log_b \sqrt[h]{N} = \frac{1}{h} \log_b N. \tag{4}$$

32. Common logarithms

Logarithms to the base 10 are called *common logarithms*, and are the most useful variety for computational purposes. Hereafter, unless otherwise stated, a *logarithm* will mean a *common logarithm*. For abbreviation, we use merely $\log N$ instead of $\log_{10} N$ for the common logarithm of N. We verify the following table by use of the definition of a logarithm.

$N =$	.0001	.001	.01	.1	1	10	100	1000	10,000	100,000
$\log N =$	-4	-3	-2	-1	0	1	2	3	4	5

ILLUSTRATION 1.   If we are given $\log 3 = .4771$ and $\log 7 = .8451$, the properties of Section 31 lead to the following results:

$$\log 21 = \log (3 \cdot 7) = \log 3 + \log 7 = .4771 + .8451 = 1.3222.$$

$$\log .07 = \log \frac{7}{100} = \log 7 - \log 100 = .8451 - 2 = -1.1549.$$

EXERCISE 13

Find the logarithm of each number by use of the properties of Section 31, the logarithms of integral powers of 10, and the following logarithms:

$\log 2 = .3010;$ $\log 3 = .4771;$ $\log 7 = .8451;$ $\log 17 = 1.2304.$

1. 6.
2. 34.
3. 30.
4. 70.
5. $\frac{7}{3}$.
6. $\frac{17}{7}$.

7. $\frac{7}{2}$.
8. $\frac{10}{7}$.
9. .7.
10. .17.
11. $\frac{51}{2}$.
12. $\frac{3}{14}$.

13. 9.
14. 49.
15. 27.
16. $\sqrt{8}$.
17. $\sqrt[3]{7}$.
18. $\sqrt{51}$.

19. $\frac{1}{3}$.
20. $\frac{1}{7}$.
21. $\sqrt[3]{14}$.
22. $\sqrt[3]{21}$.
23. $\sqrt{\frac{2}{7}}$.
24. $\sqrt[3]{\frac{3}{17}}$.

33. Characteristic and mantissa

Every real number, and hence every logarithm, can be written as the sum of *an integer and a decimal fraction*, which is *positive or zero* and *less than* 1. After log N is written in this way, we call the integer the *characteristic* and the fraction the *mantissa* of log N:

$$\log N = \text{(integer)} + \text{(positive or zero fraction, } < 1\text{);}$$
$$\log N = \text{characteristic} + \text{mantissa.} \tag{1}$$

Since the characteristic is an integer and the mantissa is less than 1, the characteristic is *negative* if and only if log N is *negative*.

ILLUSTRATION 1. Log N is an integer if and only if N is an integral power of 10. Thus, log $1000 = 3$; in this case the mantissa is zero and the characteristic is 3.

ILLUSTRATION 2. If log $N = 4.6832 = 4 + .6832$, the characteristic is 4 and the mantissa is .6832.

ILLUSTRATION 3. If log $N = -3.75$, log N lies between -4 and -3. Hence, log $N = -4 + (a\ fraction)$. To find this fraction we obtain $4 - 3.75$, or .25. Hence, log $N = -3.75 = -4 + .25$, and the characteristic is -4 while the mantissa is .25.

ILLUSTRATION 4. The following logarithms were obtained by later methods. The student should verify the three columns at the right.

LOGARITHM			CHARACTERISTIC	MANTISSA
$\log 300$	$=$	$2.47712 = 2 + .47712$	2	.47712
$\log .0385$	$=$	$-1.41454 = -2 + .58546$	-2	.58546
$\log 50$	$=$	$1.69897 = 1 + .69897$	1	.69897
$\log .001$	$=$	$-3.00000 = -3 + .00000$	-3	.00000
$\log 6.5$	$=$	$0.81291 = 0 + .81291$	0	.81291

Note 1. Let $x = \log M$ and $y = \log N$. Then $M = 10^x$ and $N = 10^y$. For integral values of x and y, the student has observed that $10^x < 10^y$ if and only if $x < y$. This relation holds for all values of x and y. That is,

$$M < N \quad \textit{if and only if} \quad \log M < \log N.$$

ILLUSTRATION 5. If $100 < N < 1000$, then

$$\log 100 < \log N < \log 1000, \quad or \quad 2 < \log N < 3.$$

Then, $\log N = 2 + (positive\ fraction)$; the characteristic of $\log N$ is 2.

34. Properties of the characteristic and the mantissa

ILLUSTRATION 1. All numbers whose logarithms are given below have the same significant digits, (3, 8, 0, 4). To obtain the logarithms, log 3.804 was first found from a table to be discussed later; the other logarithms were then obtained by use of Properties I and II of Section 31.

$$\log 380.4 \ = \log 100(3.804) = \log 100 + \log 3.804 = \quad 2 + .5802;$$
$$\log 38.04 \ = \log 10(3.804) \ = \log 10 + \log 3.804 \ = \quad 1 + .5802;$$
$$\log 3.804 \ = .5802 \qquad\qquad\qquad\qquad = \quad 0 + .5802;$$
$$\log .3804 \ = \log \frac{3.804}{10} \quad = \log 3.804 - \log 10 \ = \ -1 + .5802;$$
$$\log .03804 = \log \frac{3.804}{100} \quad = \log 3.804 - \log 100 = \ -2 + .5802.$$

Similarly, if N is any number whose significant digits are (3, 8, 0, 4), then N is equal to 3.804 multiplied, or else divided, by an integral power of 10; hence, it follows as above that .5802 is the mantissa of $\log N$.

In Illustration 1 we met special cases of the following theorems.

I. *The mantissa of* $\log N$ *depends only on the sequence of significant digits in* N. *That is, if two numbers differ only in the position of the decimal point, their logarithms have the* **same mantissa.**

II. *When* $N > 1$, *the characteristic of* $\log N$ *is an integer, positive or zero, which is* **one less than the number of digits in** N **to the left of the decimal point.**

III. *If* $N < 1$, *the characteristic of* $\log N$ *is a* **negative integer;** *if the first significant digit of* N *is in the* **kth decimal place,** *then* $-k$ **is the characteristic of** $\log N$.

ILLUSTRATION 2. We find the characteristic of $\log N$ by merely inspecting N. Thus, by Theorem III, the characteristic of log .00039 is −4 because 3 is in the 4th decimal place. By Theorem II, the characteristic of log 15,786 is 4, because there are five digits to the left of the decimal point (understood after 6).

Note 1. Besides common logarithms, the only other variety used appreciably is the system of **natural logarithms,** for which the base is a certain irrational number denoted by e where $e = 2.71828\cdots$.

Note 2. Logarithms were invented by a Scotchman, JOHN NAPIER, Baron of Merchiston (1550–1617). His original logarithms were not defined as exponents of powers of a base. Common logarithms were invented by an Englishman, HENRY BRIGGS (1556–1631), who was aided by Napier. Common logarithms are sometimes called *Briggs* logarithms.

ORAL EXERCISE 14

State the characteristic and mantissa of log N.

1. log N = 3.95.   **2.** log N = 4.86.   **3.** log N = 0.312.

4. log N = − 1.60.   **5.** log N = − .1561.   **6.** log N = − 3.23.

Find the characteristic of the logarithm of the number by mere inspection.

7. 2950.   **8.** 654.   **9.** .0036.   **10.** 6.27.   **11.** 1.47.

12. .0139.   **13.** 63,567.   **14.** .00062.   **15.** .00009.   **16.** 580,000.

Find the characteristic of log N *under the given condition.*

17. 100 $\leqq N <$ 1000.   **18.** 1000 $\leqq N <$ 10,000.   **19.** .001 $\leqq N <$ .01.

35. Standard form for a negative logarithm

Hereafter, for convenience in computation, *if the characteristic of* log N *is negative,* − k, *change it to the equivalent value*

$$[(10 - k) - 10], \quad or \quad [(20 - k) - 20], \ etc.$$

ILLUSTRATION 1. Given that log .000843 = − 4 + .9258,

$$\log .000843 = - 4 + .9258 = (6 - 10) + .9258 = 6.9258 - 10.$$

The characteristics in the following table are obtained by Theorem **III** of Section 34; the mantissas are identical.

1ST SIGNIF. DIGIT IN	ILLUSTRATION	LOG N	STANDARD FORM
1st decimal place	N = .843	− 1 + .9258 =	9.9258 − 10
2d decimal place	N = .0843	− 2 + .9258 =	8.9258 − 10
3d decimal place	N = .00843	− 3 + .9258 =	7.9258 − 10
6th decimal place	N = .00000843	− 6 + .9258 =	4.9258 − 10

36. Tables of logarithms

Mantissas can be computed by advanced methods and, except in special cases, are endless decimal fractions. Computed mantissas are found in *tables of logarithms*, also called *tables of mantissas*.

ILLUSTRATION 1. The mantissa for log 10705 is .029586671630457, to fifteen decimal places.

Table VIII gives the mantissa of log N correct to five decimal places if N is any number with at most four significant digits aside from additional zeros at the right. If N lies between 1 and 10, the characteristic of log N is *zero* so that log N *is the same as its mantissa.* Hence, a five-place table of mantissas is also a table of the *actual logarithms* of all numbers with at most four significant digits, from N = 1.000 to N = 9.999. In case N is less than 1 or greater than 10, we must supply the characteristic of log N by use of Theorems II and III of Section 34, besides obtaining the mantissa of log N from Table VIII.

EXAMPLE 1. Find log .03162 from Table VIII.

SOLUTION. 1. *To find the mantissa.* On page 22 we find the *first three digits*, 316, in the *column* headed "N." In the *row* of 316, in the *column* headed by 2 (the *fourth* digit of 3162) we find 996, the last three digits of the mantissa; its *first two* digits are 49, which appear in the column headed by 0. The complete mantissa is .49996. (A decimal point is understood at the left of each mantissa in Table VIII.)

2. By Theorem III of Section 34, the characteristic is − 2. Hence,

$$\log .03162 = -\ 2 + .49996 = 8.49996 - 10.$$

EXAMPLE 2. Find log 31,680 from Table VIII.

SOLUTION. 1. In the *row* of 316, in the *column* headed by 8 on page 22, we find *079; the asterisk (*) means that the first two digits are 50, instead of 49 as at the beginning of the row. The mantissa is .50079.

2. The characteristic is 4. Hence, log 31,680 = 4.50079.

EXAMPLE 3. Find N from Table VIII if log N = 2.88468.

SOLUTION. 1. *To obtain the significant digits of N.* The mantissa is .88468; its first two digits, 88, are in the column headed by 0 on page 31. Among the table entries belonging to this 88 we find 468 in the row with 766 at the left-hand margin, and in the column headed by 8. Hence, the significant digits of N are 7668.

2. The characteristic of log N is 2; by Theorem II of Section 34, N has *one more than two digits*, or *three digits*, to the left of the decimal point: N = 766.8.

DEFINITION I. *A number N is called the* **antilogarithm** *of L in case* log $N = L$. *We write $N =$* **antilog L**.

ILLUSTRATION 2. Antilog 5 = 100,000 because 10^5 = 100,000.

ILLUSTRATION 3. In Example 3, antilog 2.88468 = 766.8.

EXAMPLE 4. Find antilog (6.40209 − 10) from Table VIII.

SOLUTION. 1. We desire N so that log N = 6.40209 − 10.

2. The mantissa is .40209. We find the first two digits 40 in the column headed by 0 on page 21, and then find 209 in the row with 252 in the left-hand margin, and column headed by 4. Hence, the significant part of N is 2524.

3. The characteristic of log N is (6 − 10) or − 4. Hence, by Theorem III of Section 34, the first significant digit of N is in the 4th decimal place: N = .0002524, or antilog (6.40209 − 10) = .0002524.

The **four-place Table V** gives the mantissa of log N correct to *four* decimal places if N has at most *three* significant digits aside from final zeros.

ILLUSTRATION 4. By use of Table V, we verify

$$\log .0316 = -\ 2 + .4997 = 8.4997 - 10; \qquad \text{antilog } 3.6064 = 4040.$$

EXERCISE 15*

Find the five-place logarithm of each number by use of Table VIII.

1. 198.7.   **2.** 18.56.   **3.** 1.389.   **4.** 2.633.   **5.** .01118.

6. .2866.   **7.** .2563.   **8.** .0146.   **9.** 59,600.   **10.** 69,990.

11. .00018.   **12.** .00009.   **13.** .801.   **14.** 3.075.   **15.** 4168.

16. 10,070.   **17.** 1,000,000.   **18.** .000607.   **19.** $10^{.69897}$.   **20.** $10^{2.41326}$.

Find the antilogarithm of each number by use of Table VIII.

21. 1.25115.   **22.** 0.66058.   **23.** 9.42716 − 10.   **24.** 6.55630 − 10.

25. 2.47305.   **26.** 5.83052.   **27.** 8.58726 − 10.   **28.** 5.68124 − 10.

29. 4.68538.   **30.** 3.61899.   **31.** 7.49094 − 10.   **32.** 0.11361.

33. 3.77663.   **34.** 0.48001.   **35.** 9.09237 − 10.   **36.** − 2.69919.

Find the four-place logarithm of each number by use of Table V.

37. 53.2.   **38.** 6.97.   **39.** .0163.   **40.** .0279.   **41.** .00726.

42. .0578.   **43.** 8.45.   **44.** .000358.   **45.** .00005.   **46.** .0089.

Find the antilogarithm of each number by use of Table V.

47. 2.3838.   **48.** 3.1553.   **49.** 9.9232 − 10.   **50.** 6.7774 − 10.

51. 0.6684.   **52.** 3.7938.   **53.** 5.9004 − 10.   **54.** − 2.3979.

55. By use of Table VIII, find antilog (− 3.29835); antilog (− 1.87877).

37. Interpolation in a table of logarithms

Interpolation in a table of mantissas is based on the assumption that, *for small changes in N, the corresponding changes in* log *N are proportional to the changes in N.* This principle of proportional parts is merely an approximation to the truth but is sufficiently accurate for our purposes.

We agree that, when a mantissa is found by interpolation from a table, we shall express the result *only to the number of decimal places given in table entries.* Also, in finding N by interpolation in a table of mantissas when log N is given, we agree to specify just **four** or just **five** significant digits according as we are using a **four-place** or a **five-place** table. No greater refinement is justified.

In using a five-place table of logarithms, it is convenient to act as if each number N whose logarithm is to be mentioned has *just five significant digits*, perhaps including one or more zeros at the right. Thus, we attach one or more final zeros to the significant part of N if it has *less* than five significant digits. Or, we *round off N* to five significant digits if N initially has more than five-place accuracy. We then think of each entry in Table VIII as the mantissa for the logarithm of a number N with *five* significant digits, obtained by attaching a final zero to the significant part arising in the table.

* No interpolation is called for in this exercise.

ILLUSTRATION 1.   From Table VIII, log 26.380 = 1.42127.

EXAMPLE 1.   Find log 25.637 by use of Table VIII.

SOLUTION.   1. Since 25.637 has five significant digits, with the fifth not zero, the mantissa for its logarithm cannot be read directly from the table. By the principle of proportional parts, since 25.637 is 7/10 of the way from 25.630 to 25.640,

$$\log 25.637 \text{ is } \frac{7}{10} \text{ of the way from } \log 25.630 \text{ to } \log 25.640.$$

2. Each logarithm below has the characteristic 1, by Section 34.   Table VIII is used for mantissas.

> *From table:* log 25.630 = 1.40875 ⎤
>   log 25.637 =   ?   ⎟ 17   **Tabular difference** *is*
> *From table:* log 25.640 = 1.40892 ⎦   .40892 − .40875 = .00017.
>   .7(17) = 11.9, or 12.
>
>   log 25.637 = 1.40875 + .7(.00017) = 1.40875 + .00012;
>   log 25.637 = 1.40887.

EXAMPLE 2.   Find log .0012397.

SOLUTION.   For convenience, we shall disregard the decimal point temporarily and speak of *the mantissa for* 12397.   Since 12397 is 7/10 of the way from 12390 to 12400, the mantissa for 12397 is 7/10 of the way from the mantissa for 12390 to the mantissa for 12400.   We read these last two mantissas from Table VIII.

> 10 ⎡ 7 ⎡ 12390: *mantissa is* .09307 ⎤ ⎤ x   **Tabular difference** *is*
>   ⎢ ⎢ 12397: *mantissa is*   ?   ⎥ ⎥ 35 .09342 − .09307 = .00035.
>   ⎣ ⎣ 12400: *mantissa is* .09342 ⎦   x = .7(35) = 24.5.
>
>   *Mantissa for* log .0012397 *is* .09307 + .00025 = .09332.
>   *Characteristic for* log .0012397 *is* − 3; *hence,*
>   log .0012397 = 7.09332 − 10.

Comment.   We found .7(35) = 24.5 in the column of proportional parts. We used .00025 instead of .00024 to make the *final result even in the last place*, in agreement with our usual rule of choice.

EXAMPLE 3.   Find N if log N = 8.33094 − 10.

SOLUTION.   1. The mantissa, .33094, is not found as an entry on page 20 of Table VIII but is *bracketed* by the entries .33082 and .33102, which are the mantissas for 21420 and 21430.

2. Since .33094 is 12/20 of the way from .33082 to .33102, the significant part of N is 12/20 of the way from 21420 to 21430.   Thus, in the following summary, we find

$$\frac{x}{10} = \frac{12}{20} \quad or \quad x = \frac{12}{20}(10) = .6(10) = 6.$$

$$20\left[12\left[\begin{array}{l}.33082, \textit{ mantissa for } 21420\\.33094, \textit{ mantissa for } N\\.33102, \textit{ mantissa for } 21430\end{array}\right]x\right]10 \qquad \begin{array}{l}\tfrac{12}{20} = .6. \quad \textit{Hence,}\\ x = .6(10) = 6.\\ 21420 + 6 = 21426.\end{array}$$

Hence, .33094 is the mantissa for 21426.

3. Therefore the significant part of N is 21426. Since the characteristic of $\log N$ is $(8 - 10)$, or $- 2$, the first significant digit of N is in the second decimal place: $N = .021426$.

EXAMPLE 4. Find antilog 2.40971 by use of Table VIII.

SOLUTION. 1. Let $N = $ antilog 2.40971. Then, $\log N = 2.40971$. The mantissa is .40971, which is bracketed by the mantissas .40960 and .40976 in Table VIII, corresponding to 25680 and 25690.

$$16\left[11\left[\begin{array}{l}.40960, \textit{ mantissa for } 25680.\\.40971, \textit{ mantissa for } \quad ?\\.40976, \textit{ mantissa for } 25690.\end{array}\right]x\right]10 \qquad \begin{array}{l}\tfrac{11}{16} = .7, \textit{ to nearest tenth;}\\ x = .7(10) = 7.\\ 25680 + 7 = 25687.\end{array}$$

2. Since the characteristic of $\log N$ is 2, antilog $2.40971 = 256.87$.

Comment. We obtained $\tfrac{11}{16} = .7$, approximately, by inspection of the tenths of 16 in the column of proportional parts.

The methods introduced with Table VIII extend to the four-place Table V with simpler details. In using Table V, we act as if each number whose logarithm is involved has just four significant digits, if necessary including additional zeros at the right.

38. The scientific notation for numbers

We sometimes write a number N as the product of an integral power of 10 and a number P equal to or greater than 1 but less than 10, where P has *the same significant digits as* N. The resulting expression, $N = P(10^k)$, is called the *scientific notation* for N, and is convenient in abbreviating very large or very small numbers, and in indicating how many digits are significant in approximate values.

ILLUSTRATION 1. $.000'000'368 = 3.68(.000'000'1) = 3.68(10^{-7})$.

$.000368 = 3.68(.0001) = 3.68(10^{-4})$.

$132{,}560{,}000 = 1.3256(100{,}000{,}000) = 1.3256(10^8)$.

ILLUSTRATION 2. If 5,630,000 is an approximate value in which five digits are significant, we write $5.6300(10^6)$ for the number.

If $N = P(10^k)$ where $1 \leqq P < 10$, then $0 \leqq \log P < 1$ and

$$\log N = \log P + \log 10^k = k + \log P,$$

or k is the *characteristic* and $\log P$ is the *mantissa* of $\log N$.

ILLUSTRATION 3. If $N = 1.352(10^8)$, then

$$\log N = \log 1.352 + \log 10^8 = 8.1309. \qquad \text{(Table V)}$$

If $N = 1.352(10^{-4})$, then $\log N = .1309 - 4 = 6.1309 - 10$.

ILLUSTRATION 4. If $\log N = 9.7419$ and if we write N in the form $P(10^k)$ where $1 \leq P < 10$, then $k = 9$ and $\log P = 0.7419$; from Table V,

$$P = 5.520 \quad and \quad N = 5.520(10^9).$$

This form shows explicitly that only four digits are significant in N.

EXERCISE 16

Find the five-place logarithm of each number from Table VIII.

1. 18,563. **2.** 21.285. **3.** 4.7178. **4.** .89316. **5.** 61.597.

6. 25,632. **7.** .30129. **8.** 31.648. **9.** .75362. **10.** .071384.

11. 5.3217. **12.** .042087. **13.** .073563. **14.** 53.193. **15.** 896,910.

16. .0040063. **17.** .00078651. **18.** 966,910. **19.** $6.1324(10^{-12})$.

20. .0062873. **21.** $1.3006(10^6)$. **22.** .00041569. **23.** $5.0006(10^8)$.

Find the antilogarithm of each five-place logarithm by use of Table VIII.

24. 2.21388. **25.** $9.65328 - 10$. **26.** $9.00858 - 10$. **27.** 6.03271.

28. 3.21631. **29.** $8.12277 - 10$ **30.** $3.33412 - 10$. **31.** 5.45698.

32. 1.33740. **33.** $7.94014 - 10$. **34.** $6.24049 - 20$. **35.** 0.97035.

36. 2.05297. **37.** $9.77817 - 10$. **38.** $8.73168 - 20$. **39.** 0.28779.

Find the four-place logarithm of each number from Table V.

40. 2623. **41.** .001757. **42.** 529.3. **43.** 5322. **44.** 43,190.

45. 6.968. **46.** .3073. **47.** .02555. **48.** 1.298. **49.** .000061.

Find the antilogarithm of each logarithm from Table V.

50. 3.2367. **51.** $7.1247 - 10$. **52.** $9.6270 - 10$. **53.** 2.9276.

54. 5.5511. **55.** $4.1436 - 10$. **56.** $8.9935 - 10$. **57.** 4.5783.

58. Find antilog $(- 3.78789)$ from Table VIII.

39. Computation of products and quotients

Unless otherwise specified, we continue to assume that the data of any problem are *exact*. Then, the accuracy of a product, quotient, or power computed by use of logarithms depends on the number of places in the table being used. The result is frequently subject to an unavoidable error which, as a rule, is at most a few units in the last significant place given by interpolation. Hence, we compute with at least *five-place* logarithms to obtain *four-place accuracy*, and with at least *four-place* logarithms to obtain *three-place accuracy*. As a general custom, in any result we shall give *all digits obtainable by interpolation* in the specified table.

EXAMPLE 1. Compute $P = 787.97(.0033238)(14.431)$ by use of Table VIII.

SOLUTION. Log P is the *sum of the logarithms of the factors*. The computing form given in heavy black type was made up as a first step.

$$\left\{ \begin{array}{l} \log 787.97 = 2.89651 \\ \log .0033238 = 7.52163 - 10 \\ \log 14.431 = 1.15930 \end{array} \right. \qquad \begin{array}{l} \text{(Table VIII)} \\ \text{(Table VIII)} \\ \text{(Table VIII)} \end{array}$$

(add) log $P = 11.57744 - 10 = 1.57744.$

Hence, $P = 37.795.$ $\qquad$ (= antilog 1.57744, from Table VIII)

EXAMPLE 2. Compute $q = \dfrac{432.9132}{15.68278}$ by use of Table VIII.

SOLUTION. 1. Log q equals *the logarithm of the numerator minus the logarithm of the denominator.*

2. Before computing, we round off each given number to *five* significant digits because we are using a *five*-place table. Thus, $432.9132 \to 432.91$.

$$\begin{array}{ll} \log 432.91 = 2.63640 & \text{(Table VIII)} \\ (-) \log 15.683 = 1.19543 & \text{(Table VIII)} \\ \hline \log q = 1.44097. \quad \textbf{Hence,} \quad q = 27.604. & \text{(Table VIII)} \end{array}$$

EXAMPLE 3. Compute $q = \dfrac{257}{8956}$ by use of Table VIII.

SOLUTION.
$$\begin{array}{l} \log 257 = 2.40993 = 12.40993 - 10 \\ (-) \log 8956 = 3.95211 = \quad 3.95211 \\ \hline \log q = \quad ??? \quad = \quad 8.45782 - 10. \end{array}$$

Hence, $q = .028696.$

Comment. When we first tried to subtract log 8956 from log 257, we saw that the result would be *negative*. In order that log q should appear in the *standard form for a negative logarithm*, we changed log 257 by adding 10 and then subtracting 10 to compensate for the first change. Actually,

$$\log q = 2.40993 - 3.95211 = -1.54218 = 8.45782 - 10.$$

Whenever it is necessary to subtract a larger logarithm from a smaller one in computing a quotient, add 10 to the characteristic of the smaller logarithm and then subtract 10 to compensate for the change.

EXAMPLE 4. Compute $q = \dfrac{4.803(269.9)(1.636)}{7880(253.6)}$ by use of Table VIII.

INCOMPLETE SOLUTION. First make a computing form.

$$(+) \left\{ \begin{array}{l} \log 4.803 = \\ \log 269.9 = \\ \log 1.636 = \end{array} \right. \qquad\qquad (+) \left\{ \begin{array}{l} \log 7880 = \\ \log 253.6 = \end{array} \right.$$

$$\begin{array}{l} \hline \log \text{ numer.} = \\ (-) \log \text{ denom.} = \\ \hline \log q = \end{array} \qquad\qquad \begin{array}{l} \hline \log \text{ denom.} = \\ \\ \textbf{Hence, } q = \end{array}$$

EXAMPLE 5. Compute the reciprocal of 189 by use of Table VIII.

SOLUTION. Let $R = \dfrac{1}{189}$.

$$\log 1 = 0.00000 = 10.00000 - 10$$
$$(-)\ \log 189 = 2.27646 = 2.27646$$

Hence, $R = .0052910$. $\longleftarrow$ $\log R = ?? = 7.72354 - 10.$

★40. Cologarithms*

The logarithm of the *reciprocal* of N is called the *cologarithm* of N and is written **colog** N. Since $\log 1 = 0$,

$$\text{colog } N = \log \frac{1}{N} = 0 - \log N. \tag{1}$$

ILLUSTRATION 1. Colog $.031 = \log \dfrac{1}{.031}$:

$$\log 1 = 10.0000 - 10$$
$$(-)\ \log .031 = 8.4914 - 10$$
$$\text{colog } .031 = 1.5086.$$

The positive part of colog N can be quickly obtained by inspection of log N: *subtract each digit (except the last) in the positive part of log N from 9, and subtract the last digit from 10.*

EXAMPLE 1. Compute $q = \dfrac{16.083 \times 256}{47 \times .0158}$ by use of cologarithms.

SOLUTION. To *divide* by N is the same as to *multiply* by $1/N$. Hence, instead of *subtracting the logarithm* of each factor of the denominator, we *add the cologarithm* of the factor. We use Table V.

$$q = \frac{16.083 \times 256}{47 \times .0158} = (16.083 \times 256)\left(\frac{1}{47}\right)\left(\frac{1}{.0158}\right).$$

$$\log 16.08 = 1.2063$$
$$\log 256 = 2.4082$$
log 47 $= 1.6721$; hence, $\quad$ colog 47 $= 8.3279 - 10$
log .0158 $= 8.1987 - 10$; $\quad$ hence, colog .0158 $= 1.8013$
$q = 5542.$ $\longleftarrow$ (*add*) log $q = 13.7437 - 10 = 3.7437.$

EXERCISE 17

Compute by use of four-place or five-place logarithms, as directed by the instructor.

1. $31.57 \times .789$. $\qquad$ **2.** $925.6 \times .137$. $\qquad$ **3.** $.8475 \times .0937$.

4. $.0179 \times .356413$.† $\quad$ **5.** $925.618 \times .000217$.† $\quad$ **6.** $3.41379 \times .0142$.

7. $(-84.75)(.00368)(.02458)$. $\qquad$ **8.** $(-16.8)(-136.943)(-.00038)$.

HINT. Only *positive* numbers have *real* logarithms. First compute as if all factors were positive; then determine the sign by inspection.

* The instructor may desire to specify the use of cologarithms occasionally. It is not necessary to use them.

† Before finding the logarithm of a number N, we *round off N to four or to five significant digits* according as we are using *four*-place or *five*-place logarithms.

9. $\dfrac{675}{13.21}$.   10. $\dfrac{568.5}{23.14}$.   11. $\dfrac{728.72}{895}$.   12. $\dfrac{753.166}{9273.8}$.

13. $\dfrac{.0894}{.6358}$.   14. $\dfrac{.0421}{.53908}$.   15. $\dfrac{1}{325.932}$.   16. $\dfrac{1}{100,935}$.

17. $\dfrac{16.083 \times 256}{47 \times .0158}$.   18. $\dfrac{.42173 \times .217}{.3852 \times .956}$.   19. $\dfrac{9.32 \times 531}{.8319 \times .5685}$.

20. $\dfrac{5.4171 \times .429}{18.1167 \times 37}$.   21. $\dfrac{1}{.53819 \times .0673}$.   22. $\dfrac{1}{.00073 \times .965}$.

23. $\dfrac{(-.29)(.038)(-.0065)}{(-1006.332)(2.71)}$.   24. $\dfrac{5.6(-3.9078)(-.00031)}{(132)(-1.93)}$.

Compute the reciprocal of the number.

25. 63283.   26. .00382.   27. .02567.   28. .0683(.52831).

29. (*a*) Compute 652(735); (*b*) compute (log 652)(log 735).

30. (*a*) Compute .063(.952); (*b*) compute (log .063)(log .952).

31. (*a*) Compute .351 ÷ 625; (*b*) compute (log .351) ÷ (log 625).

32. Find the logarithms of 3.1570, 3.1569, 3.1568, 3.1567, 3.1566 from Table VIII and round off each result to four decimal places. Then, obtain log 3.157 from Table V. The similarity of the results shows the sense involved in the footnote for Problem 4.

33. By use of Table VIII, compute $10^{3.61738}$; $10^{-2.31462}$.

41. Computation of powers and roots

From page 36, we recall the following properties of logarithms.

$$\log N^k = k \log N. \tag{1}$$

$$\log \sqrt[h]{N} = \frac{1}{h} \log N. \tag{2}$$

ILLUSTRATION 1. From (1), $\log N^3 = 3 \log N$. From (2),

$$\log \sqrt{N} = \tfrac{1}{2} \log N; \qquad \log \sqrt[3]{N} = \tfrac{1}{3} \log N.$$

EXAMPLE 1. Compute $(.3156)^4$.

SOLUTION. From (1), $\log (.3156)^4 = 4 \log .3156$.

$$\log .3156 = \ 9.49914 - 10 \qquad \text{(Table VIII)}$$
$$4 \log .3156 = 37.99656 - 40 = 7.99656 - 10$$

Hence, $(.3156)^4 = .0099210$. [= antilog (7.99656 − 10), from Table VIII]

EXAMPLE 2. Compute $\sqrt[3]{856.31}$.

SOLUTION. From (2), $\log \sqrt[3]{856.31} = \tfrac{1}{3} \log 856.31$.

$$\log 856.31 = 2.93264 \qquad \text{(Table VIII)}$$
$$\tfrac{1}{3} \log 856.31 = 0.97755 = \log \sqrt[3]{856.31}$$

Hence, $\sqrt[3]{856.31} = 9.4962$.   (= antilog 0.97755, from Table VIII)

EXAMPLE 3.   Find $\sqrt[6]{.08351}$.

SOLUTION.   From (2), $\log \sqrt[6]{.08351} = \frac{1}{6} \log .08351$.

log .08351 =   8.92174 − 10   (Table VIII)
log .08351 = 58.92174 − 60   (Add 50 and subtract 50 above)
$\frac{1}{6}$ **log .08351** =   9.82029 − 10 = $\log \sqrt[6]{.08351}$

Hence, $\sqrt[6]{.08351}$ =   .66113.   [= antilog (9.82029 − 10), from Table VIII]

Comment. In the solution, if we had made no change in log .08351, we would have obtained the following inconvenient result:

$$\frac{1}{6} \log .08351 = \frac{8.92174 - 10}{6} = 1.48696 - 1.66667 = -.17971.$$

Remember the device in Example 3: *before dividing a negative logarithm by a positive integer, write the logarithm so that the negative part, when divided by the integer, will give* − 10 *as the quotient.*

EXAMPLE 4.   Compute $(34.625)^{-\frac{3}{2}}$.

SOLUTION.   We recall that $a^{-n} = 1/a^n$. Let

$$q = (34.625)^{-\frac{3}{2}} = \frac{1}{(34.625)^{\frac{3}{2}}}.$$

We use (2) in obtaining the logarithm of the quotient q. To keep control of last place accuracy, we *first multiply* by 3 and *then divide* by 2, in obtaining 3/2 of log 34.625.

log 34.625 = 1.53939	**3 log 34.625** = 4.61817
log 1 = 0.00000	= 10.00000 − 10
$\frac{1}{2}$(**3 log 34.625**) = 2.30908	= 2.30908 (−)
log q = ———	= 7.69092 − 10
q = .0049082.	

EXERCISE 18

Compute by use of four-place or five-place logarithms.

1. $(17.5)^3$.	**2.** $(.837)^5$.	**3.** $(.0315)^3$.	**4.** $(3.1279)^4$.
5. $(1.9572)^6$.	**6.** $(.0715)^3$.	**7.** $\sqrt{531.2}$.	**8.** $\sqrt[3]{2795}$.
9. $\sqrt[4]{861}$.	**10.** $\sqrt[5]{34168}$.	**11.** $\sqrt[3]{.857}$.	**12.** $\sqrt[5]{.0797}$.
13. $\sqrt[4]{.03107}$.	**14.** $\sqrt[6]{.0001}$.	**15.** $(.0138273)^{\frac{1}{2}}$.	**16.** $(143.54)^{\frac{3}{4}}$.
17. $(.0057)^{\frac{2}{5}}$.	**18.** $(.821)^{\frac{5}{3}}$.	**19.** $(139)^{-2}$.	**20.** $(26.812)^{-3}$.
21. $(.925)^{-2}$.	**22.** $(1.06)^{-1}$.	**23.** $(1.03)^{-5}$.	**24.** $(.003156)^{-\frac{2}{3}}$.

42. Problems in computation

It is important to realize that the properties of logarithms offer no assistance in the computation of a sum or difference, except perhaps in the auxiliary computation of individual terms.

ILLUSTRATION 1. To compute $q = \dfrac{\sqrt{896} + 5.672}{532 - (15.31)^2}$, we would first compute

$\sqrt{896}$ and $(15.31)^2$ by logarithms, then insert the results in the fraction, and finally compute it by logarithms.

ILLUSTRATION 2. A form for computing $q = \dfrac{(153.2)^2(257.3)}{1893.18(35830)}$ is as follows:

log 153.2 =

2 log 153.2 = ———   log 1893.2 = ———

log 257.3 = ——— (+)   log 35830 = ——— (+)

log numerator = ———   log denominator = ———

log denominator = ——— (−)

log q = ———

Hence, q = ———.

EXERCISE 19

Compute by use of four-place or five-place logarithms.

1. $5.713(2.56)^3$.

2. $.165\sqrt{9.13497}$.

3. $.0956(13.217)^2$.

4. $73.14\sqrt{.981358}$.

5. $(14.6)^2\sqrt[3]{.085}$.

6. $(3.456)^{-3}\sqrt[3]{.7316}$.

7. $\dfrac{758.32}{(46.3)^3}$.

8. $\dfrac{.0198}{(3.8262)^2}$.

9. $\dfrac{.03156(75.31)}{221.38(.3561)^2}$.

10. $\sqrt{\dfrac{89.1}{163(.62)}}$.

11. $\sqrt[3]{\dfrac{47.5317}{.031(.964)}}$.

12. $\dfrac{\sqrt[3]{-463.192}}{\sqrt{16.3144}}$.

13. $10^{.723}(8.52)$.

14. $\dfrac{10^{-1.42}\sqrt{.387}}{57(8.64)^2}$.

15. $\left(\dfrac{16.7(.58)^2}{65.1314}\right)^{\frac{2}{3}}$.

16. $\dfrac{\sqrt{956.314}}{10^{3.65}(.0138)}$.

17. $\dfrac{\sqrt{23} - \sqrt{134.91}}{453(.110173)}$.

18. $\dfrac{567.89 + \sqrt[3]{89}}{57 + \sqrt{.19538}}$.

19. $(3.57)^{1.6}$.

20. $(71.38)^{.85}$.

21. $(57.2)^{-.32}$.

22. $(.0895)^{.36}$.

HINT for Problem 21. $-.32 \log 57.2 = -.5624 = 9.4376 - 10$.

23. $\dfrac{3 + \log 75}{\log 63.6}$.

24. $\dfrac{\log .95 - 20}{658}$.

25. $\dfrac{753 \log 8}{\log .189}$.

26. If n is a positive integer, *the* **geometric mean** *of n numbers* is defined as the nth *root of their product.* Thus the geometric mean of M, N, R is $\sqrt[3]{MNR}$. Find the geometric mean of (a) 138, 395, 426, 537, 612; (b) .00138, .19276, .08356, .0131.

27. Compute $(1.03)^{100}$ entirely by use of five-place logarithms. Then, compute by using log 1.03 from Table XVI, and Table VIII to finish.

Compute the amount A in the formula of compound interest $A = P(1 + r)^k$ for the given data, with Table XVI used to obtain $\log(1 + r)$, and five-place logarithms used otherwise.

28. $F = \$265$; $k = 30$; $r = .02$.

29. $P = \$2358$; $k = 47$; $r = .04$.

30. If B is the height of a mercury barometer in inches, and $t°$ is the temperature (Fahrenheit), the weight w in pounds of a cubic foot of air is given approximately by $w = \dfrac{1.3253B}{459.6 + t}$. Find the weight of a cubic foot of air at 83.5° temperature if the barometer stands at 29.92 inches. Use Table VIII.

31. If a body has fallen s feet from rest in a vacuum near the earth's surface, the speed v of the body in feet per second is given by $v^2 = 2gs$ where $g = 32.16$, approximately. (a) Find the distance through which a body has fallen if $v = 488$. (b) Find the speed of a body which has fallen 1740 feet.

32. If a volume v_1 of air at a pressure p_1 is compressed to a volume v_2 at a pressure p_2, without losing any of the heat generated by the compression, then $p_2 = p_1\left(\dfrac{v_1}{v_2}\right)^{1.41}$. Find the pressure necessary to compress 117 cubic feet of air at a pressure of 25.8 pounds per square inch to 26 cubic feet.

33. The time t in seconds for one oscillation of a simple pendulum, whose length is l centimeters, is given by $t = \pi\sqrt{\dfrac{l}{g}}$, where $g = 980$. Find t for a pendulum where $l = 95.8$ centimeters.

34. Let d be the diameter in inches of a short solid circular steel shaft which is designed to transmit safely H horsepower when revolving at R revolutions per minute. A safe value for d is $d = \sqrt[3]{\dfrac{38H}{R}}$. Find the horsepower which can be transmitted safely at 1150 revolutions per minute if $d = 1.9834$.

35. Compute   (a) (antilog 2.6731)²;   (b) [antilog (− 1.4973)]³.

⋆43. Logarithmic and exponential equations

A *logarithmic equation* is one where the logarithm of some expression involving an unknown is present.

EXAMPLE 1. Solve for x: $\log x + \log \dfrac{2x}{5} = 6$.

SOLUTION. By use of Properties I and II of Section 31,

$$\log x + (\log 2 + \log x - \log 5) = 6.$$
$$2 \log x = 6 + \log 5 - \log 2 = 6.3980. \qquad \text{(Table V)}$$
$$\log x = 3.1990; \quad x = \text{antilog } 3.1990 = 1581. \qquad \text{(Table V)}$$

An equation where an unknown appears in an exponent is called an *exponential equation*. Sometimes, such an equation can be solved by taking the logarithm of each member to eliminate exponents.

EXAMPLE 2. Solve $16^x = 74$ by use of Table V.

SOLUTION. Equate the logarithms of the two sides: $x \log 16 = \log 74$;

$$x = \frac{\log 74}{\log 16} = \frac{1.8692}{1.2041}.$$

$$\begin{aligned}\log 1.869 &= 0.2716 \\ (-) \log 1.204 &= 0.0806 \\ \hline \log x &= 0.1910;\end{aligned}$$

hence, $x = 1.552$.

★EXERCISE 20

Solve for x by use of five-place logarithms.

1. $12^x = 31$.   2. $46^x = 975$.   3. $.69^x = 85$.   4. $5^{2x} = 64$.

5. $4^{3x} = 17$.   6. $.09^x = .15$.   7. $.85^x = .45$.   8. $3^x = 28(4^x)$.

9. $2^x = 3^x(17)$.   10. $27^{x^2} = 67$.   11. $(1.03)^{-x} = .475$.   12. $(1.02)^{-x} = .642$.

13. $\log x^2 - \log (2x/5) = 7.58$.   14. $\log 3x^2 + \log (5/x) = 4.725$.

15. The vapor pressure p of liquid arsenic trioxide is given approximately by the equation $T \log P = -2722 + 6.513\,T$, where $T°$ Centigrade is the absolute temperature (absolute zero is $-273°$ Centigrade) and p is measured in millimeters of mercury. (*a*) What is the pressure when $T = 300°$; $T = 400°$? (*b*) At what temperature is the pressure 140 millimeters?

16. A given radioactive substance decomposes at such a rate that, if B is the initial number of atoms of the substance and N is the number remaining at the end of t hours, then $N = Be^{-kt}$, where k is a constant and $e = 2.71828\cdots$. Given that, out of 21,000 atoms, 14,500 remain at the end of $\frac{1}{2}$ hour, (*a*) find k; (*b*) find when only $\frac{1}{2}$ of the atoms will remain.

17. The intensity, I, of a beam of light after passing through t centimeters of a liquid which absorbs light, is given by $I = Ae^{-kt}$, where A is the intensity of the light when it enters the liquid, $e = 2.71828\cdots$, and k is a constant for any given liquid. If $k = .12526$, find how many centimeters of the liquid are sufficient to reduce the intensity of a beam (*a*) by 75%; (*b*) by 10%.

★44. Logarithms to bases different from 10

If N and b are given and if $x = \log_b N$, we can find x by solving $N = b^x$ for x by use of *common* logarithms.

Note 1. Recall that the base of the natural system of logarithms is $e = 2.71828$, approximately.

ILLUSTRATION 1. To find $\log_e 35$, let $x = \log_e 35$; then $e^x = 35$. On solving by the method of Section 43, we find

$$x \log_{10} e = \log_{10} 35; \qquad x = \frac{\log_{10} 35}{\log_{10} e} = \frac{1.5441}{.4343} = 3.555. \qquad \text{(Table V)}$$

THEOREM I.   *If a and b are any two bases, then*

$$\log_a N = (\log_a b)(\log_b N). \qquad (1)$$

Proof. Let $y = \log_b N$; then $N = b^y$. Hence,

$$\log_a N = \log_a b^y = y \log_a b = (\log_a b)(\log_b N).$$

The number $\log_a b$ is called the **modulus** of the system of base a with respect to the system of base b. Given a table of logarithms to the base b, we could form a table of logarithms to the base a by multiplying each entry of the given table by the modulus, $\log_a b$.*

---

* For a related property of a logarithmic scale, see Note 2 in the Appendix.

★45. Graphs of exponential and logarithmic functions

Since the equations $y = \log_b x$ and $x = b^y$ are equivalent, they have the same graph.

FIG. 31 $y = \log_e x$

ILLUSTRATION 1. Figure 31 is a graph of $y = \log_b x$ when $b = 2.71828 \cdots$, but the general characteristics of the graph would not be changed if b had any other value greater than 1. This graph emphasizes the following facts:

1. *If $0 < x < 1$, $\log_b x < 0$, and $\log_b x > 0$ if $x > 1$.*

2. *For any $b > 0$, $\log_b 1 = 0$.*

3. *If x increases without bound, $\log_b x$ increases without bound.*

4. *If x approaches zero as a limit, $\log_b x$ decreases without bound, or becomes negatively infinite.*

★EXERCISE 21

Find each logarithm by use of four-place or five-place common logarithms.

1. $\log_e 75$.   2. $\log_e 1360$.   3. $\log_{15} 33$.   4. $\log_{12} 100$.   5. $\log_e 10$.

6. $\log_6 1.05$.   7. $\log_5 .097$.   8. $\log_e .001$.   9. $\log_{.8} 23.8$.   10. $\log_{.5} 185$.

11. Find the natural logarithm of (*a*) 4368.1; (*b*) 4.3681.

Note 1. We see that, if two numbers differ only in the position of the decimal point, their natural logarithms do *not* differ by an *integer*. This fact, as compared to Theorem I, page 38, causes us to prefer common logarithms for computation.

12. Find the modulus of each system with respect to the other: the Briggs system and the natural system of logarithms.

13. Prove that $\log_a b = 1/\log_b a$. State this result in words.

14. Graph $y = \log_{10} x$ for $0 < x \leq 30$.

15. (*a*) Graph $y = 2^x$ from $x = -5$ to $x = 5$. (*b*) From the graph, read the value of $\log_2 5$; $\log_2 10$; $\log_2 .5$.

FOUR

LOGARITHMIC SOLUTION OF RIGHT TRIANGLES AND APPLICATIONS

46. Logarithms of trigonometric functions

EXAMPLE 1. Compute 156 sin 21° 10′ by four-place logarithms.

SOLUTION. In Table VI we find **log sin** 21° 10′, *the logarithm of* sin 21° 10′. We read "log sin 21° 10′" briefly *as it is written*: "*log, sine,* 21° 10′."

log 156 = 2.1931	(Table V)
(+) log sin 21° 10′ = 9.5576 − 10	(Table VI)

log 156 sin 21° 10′ = 1.7507. Hence, 156 sin 21° 10′ = 56.32,

where we found antilog 1.7507 from Table V.

Comment. 1. The sine or cosine of any angle between 0° and 90°, or the tangent of any angle between 0° and 45°, or the cotangent of any angle between 45° and 90° is *not zero* and is *less than* 1. Therefore the logarithms of these functions have *negative* characteristics. For abbreviation, Tables VI and IX omit " − 10" belonging with each of these logarithms which is tabulated. Hence, **in using the columns labeled log sin, log cos, and log tan for 0° to 45°, we subtract 10 from each given entry.**

2. Table VI made it *unnecessary to use Table* VII in Example 1.

To abbreviate the tables, we omit the logarithms of secants and cosecants. Hence, before computing a trigonometric expression by use of logarithms, if a *secant* or *cosecant* occurs as a factor, we change this function to the *reciprocal* of the *cosine* or *sine*, respectively.

Note 1. Recall that tan α = 1/cot α and hence

log tan α = log 1 − log cot α = 0 − log cot α = − log cot α.

Therefore, **any** change in log tan α corresponds to a change of *equal numerical value, but opposite sign,* in log cot α. Hence, in Table IX, the single column headed "c d" gives the *common differences* for the columns headed *log tan* and *log cot.*

Sometimes the values of trigonometric functions are referred to as **natural functions,** to emphasize the distinction between them and *their logarithms.* We call Tables VII and XI *tables of the natural trigonometric functions.*

Note 2. In this chapter, we shall limit our consideration of angles to those lying between 0° and 90°, when trigonometric functions are mentioned.

EXAMPLE 2.   Find the five-place log cot 69° 32.3′ by use of Table IX.

SOLUTION.   69° 32.3′ is 3/10 of the way from 69° 32′ to 69° 33′. The entries for 69° 32′ and 69° 33′ are found on page 58 in Table IX. We find .3(39) = 11.7 in the column of proportional parts.

log cot 69° 32′ → 9.57197 ⎤ ⎤	$x = .3(39) = 11.7.$
log cot 69° 32.3′ → ? ⎥x ⎥39	$9.57197 - .00012 = 9.57185.$
log cot 69° 33′ → 9.57158 ⎦	log cot 69° 32.3′ = $9.57185 - 10.$

Comment.   We *subtracted* .00012 because 9.57197 *decreases* to 9.57158.

EXAMPLE 3.   Find the acute angle α if log cos $\alpha = 9.43254 - 10$.

SOLUTION.   The positive part, 9.43254, is *bracketed* by 9.43278 and 9.43233 in the *log cos*-column for 74° in Table IX. Hence, as below, we find that

α is 24/45 *of the way from* 74° 17′ *to* 74° 18′.

⎡ 24 ⎡9.43278 → 74° 17′ ⎤ ⎤	$\frac{24}{45} = .5,$ *to nearest tenth.*
45⎢ ⎢9.43254 → α ⎥x⎥1′	$x = .5(1′) = .5′.$
⎣ ⎣9.43233 → 74° 18′ ⎦	$\alpha = 74° 17′ + .5′ = 74° 17.5′.$

47. Accuracy of certain results

If the logarithm of some function of an unknown angle α is given, we find α by use of the *four*-place Table VI or *five*-place Table IX according as the given logarithm is specified to *four* or to *five* decimal places, respectively. Then, we agree to state the resulting value of α as follows:

To the nearest minute if four-place Table VI is used.

To the nearest tenth of a minute if five-place Table IX is used.

In finding a logarithm from a table, we state the result to the number of decimal places used in the table. No greater refinement is justified.

EXERCISE 22

1. (*a*) Find sin 12° 20′ from Table VII.   (*b*) Find the logarithm of the result of Part (*a*) from Table V.   (*c*) Find log sin 12° 20′ from Table VI.

Find the five-place logarithm of each function from Table IX.

2. sin 23° 17′.	**3.** sin 68° 19.8′.	**4.** cos 20° 4.1′.
5. cos 48° 19′.	**6.** cos 80° 39.6′.	**7.** sin 80° 0.3′.
8. sin 17° 23.6′.	**9.** cot 56° 8.1′.	**10.** tan 46° 0.7′.
11. tan 27° 39.7′.	**12.** sin 38° 23.7′.	**13.** cot 38° 19′ 26″.
14. cot 22° 33.3′.	**15.** cos 62° 33.7′.	**16.** sin 54° 31′ 29″.

Find the acute angle α by use of the five-place Table IX.

17. log tan α = 9.49474 − 10. **18.** log sin α = 9.39573 − 10.

19. log sin α = 9.04149 − 10. **20.** log tan α = 0.44796.

21. log cot α = 9.06445 − 10. **22.** log cot α = 0.97621.

23. log tan α = 0.86333. **24.** log cos α = 9.52714 − 10.

25. log tan α = 9.48750 − 10. **26.** log tan α = 9.59743 − 10.

27. log sin α = 9.38941 − 10. **28.** log sin α = 9.19516 − 10.

Find the four-place logarithm of the function from Table VI.

29. cot 55° 40′.   **30.** sin 78° 37′.   **31.** cos 45° 18′.   **32.** sin 53° 24′.

Find α by use of Table VI.

33. log cot α = 9.9595 − 10. **34.** log tan α = 0.3141.

35. log cos α = 9.4113 − 10. **36.** log sin α = 95470 − 10.

48. Logarithmic solution of right triangles

We recall the following formulas for the right triangle in Figure 32.

FIG. 32

(1) $a^2 + b^2 = c^2$.   (2) $\alpha + \beta = 90°$.

(3) $\tan \alpha = \dfrac{a}{b} = \cot \beta$.   (4) $\cot \alpha = \dfrac{b}{a} = \tan \beta$.

(5) $\sin \alpha = \dfrac{a}{c} = \cos \beta$.   (6) $\cos \alpha = \dfrac{b}{c} = \sin \beta$.

We may alter (1) by writing $a^2 = c^2 - b^2$ and $b^2 = c^2 - a^2$. Then, we obtain $a^2 = (c - b)(c + b)$ and $b^2 = (c - a)(c + a)$, or

$$a = \sqrt{(c - b)(c + b)}; \qquad (7)$$

$$b = \sqrt{(c - a)(c + a)}. \qquad (8)$$

Sometimes it is desirable to use (1), or (7) or (8), to find an unknown side when two sides are given. In such a case, logarithms or Table XII should be employed to compute squares or square roots. However, it is suggested that (1), (7), (8) may usually be reserved for use as *check formulas*. In employing (7) or (8) in checking, we use the equations obtained on taking logarithms in (7) and (8):

$$\log a = \frac{1}{2}\Big[\log (c - b) + \log (c + b)\Big]; \qquad (9)$$

$$\log b = \frac{1}{2}\Big[\log (c - a) + \log (c + a)\Big]. \qquad (10)$$

Different methods of solution may yield slightly different results, because of interpolation and rounding off in tables. This should be remembered in referring to the Answer Book.

EXAMPLE 1. By use of four-place logarithms, solve right $\triangle ABC$ if $a = 135.1$ and $c = 367.2$.

SOLUTION. We arrange the computing form, which is given in heavy type, *before looking up any logarithms*.

Formulas	Computation
	Data: $a = 135.1$, $c = 367.2$.
$\sin \alpha = \dfrac{a}{c}$.	$\log a = 2.1306$ (Table V) $(-) \log c = 2.5649$ (Table V) $\log \sin \alpha = 9.5657 - 10$ $\alpha = 21° 35'$. (Table VI)
$\cos \alpha = \dfrac{b}{c}$, *or* $b = c \cos \alpha$.	$\log c = 2.5649$ (Above) $(+) \log \cos \alpha = 9.9684 - 10$ (Table VI) $\log b = 2.5333$; $b = 341.4$. (Table V)
$\beta = 90° - \alpha$.	$\beta = 90° - 21° 35' = 68° 25'$.
Summary:	$\alpha = 21° 35'$, $\beta = 68° 25'$, $b = 341.4$.

Check. $a = \sqrt{(c - b)(c + b)}$,   *or* $\log a = \frac{1}{2} \log [(c - b)(c + b)]$.

$c - b = 25.8$ $\log (c - b) = 1.4116$

$c + b = 708.6$ $(+) \log (c + b) = 2.8504$

                               $\log [(c - b)(c + b)] = 4.2620$.

$\log a = 2.1306 \longrightarrow$ $\longleftarrow \frac{1}{2} \log [(c - b)(c + b)] = 2.1310$.

Comment. The check is satisfactory. The difference $(2.1310 - 2.1306)$, or .0004, could result from an error of less than one unit in the *fourth* significant digit of b, because this would affect the *third* digit of $(c - b)$.

EXAMPLE 2. Solve right $\triangle ABC$ if $a = .8421$ and $\alpha = 27° 40'$.

SOLUTION. The student should check the following solution by use of formula (7):

Formulas	Computation
	Data: $a = .8421$; $\alpha = 27° 40'$.
$\beta = 90° - \alpha$.	$\beta = 90° - 27° 40' = 62° 20'$.
$\dfrac{b}{a} = \cot \alpha$, *or* $b = a \cot \alpha$.	$\log a = 9.9254 - 10$ (Table V) $(+) \log \cot \alpha = 0.2804$ (Table VI) $\log b = 0.2058$; $b = 1.606$.
$\dfrac{a}{c} = \sin \alpha$, *or* $c = \dfrac{a}{\sin \alpha}$.	$\log a = 9.9254 - 10$ $(-) \log \sin \alpha = 9.6668 - 10$ $\log c = 0.2586$; $c = 1.814$.
Summary:	$\beta = 62° 20'$, $b = 1.606$, $c = 1.814$.

EXERCISE 23

Solve right $\triangle ABC$ *by use of five-place* logarithms and check.*

1. $a = 15.7;\ \alpha = 36°\ 20'.$

2. $c = .943;\ \beta = 62°\ 40'.$

3. $a = .3590;\ b = .6611.$

4. $a = 23.18;\ \beta = 47°\ 17'.$

5. $c = .685;\ \alpha = 29°\ 43'.$

6. $c = .3675;\ a = .1943.$

7. $a = .5731;\ b = .6298.$

8. $\alpha = 25°\ 8';\ c = 37.857.$

9. $\alpha = 31°\ 24.7';\ a = 1.6315.$

10. $a = 2.1523;\ b = 4.1392.$

11. $c = 915.62;\ b = 411.37.$

12. $\alpha = 68°\ 39'\ 14'';\ c = 1000.3.$

13. $\beta = 43°\ 17'\ 34'';\ a = 42.930.$

14. $\alpha = 53°\ 22.6';\ b = 93.142.$

Note 1. In Figure 33, $\triangle ABK$ is isosceles. The perpendicular KD to the base divides $\triangle ABK$ into two congruent right ⚼. In $\triangle ADK$, $x = \frac{1}{2}k$ and $\angle AKD = \frac{1}{2}\gamma$.

★*Find the unknown sides or angles of* $\triangle ABK$ *of Figure 33 under the given conditions. Use four-place or five-place logarithms.*

15. $\gamma = 68°\ 20';\ y = 456.$

16. $\gamma = 46°\ 56';\ h = 250.$

17. $k = 32.68;\ y = 23.48.$

18. $k = .63284;\ y = .83172.$

Fig. 33

Note 2. In any oblique $\triangle ABC$, let α, β, and γ be the angles at A, B, and C, and let a, b, and c be the lengths of the sides opposite vertices A, B, and C, respectively. If we are given *two sides and one angle* or *two angles and one side* of the triangle, we can find its unknown parts by solving two right triangles. To obtain them, we drop a perpendicular from an end of a known side to the opposite side, with our choice made so as to obtain a right triangle with a known side and angle.

★*Solve oblique* $\triangle ABC$ *by use of four-place or five-place logarithms.*

19. $\begin{cases} b = 275, \\ \alpha = 46°\ 26', \\ \gamma = 103°\ 54'. \end{cases}$

Fig. 34

HINT. See Figure 34, where $CD \perp AB$. In $\triangle ADC$, compute x and only log h because h itself will not be needed. In $\triangle CDB$,

$$\beta = 180° - (\alpha + \gamma).$$

Hence, we may compute y and a in $\triangle CDB$.

20. $\begin{cases} c = .9438, \\ \alpha = 43°\ 18', \\ \gamma = 61°\ 44'. \end{cases}$
21. $\begin{cases} c = 68.452, \\ b = 31.267, \\ \alpha = 28°\ 15.6'. \end{cases}$
22. $\begin{cases} a = 14.56, \\ b = 19.37, \\ \beta = 110°\ 50'. \end{cases}$

* In Problems 1–7, answers are given also for computation with four-place logarithms.

49. Problems with approximate data

In computation in this book up to the present time, the emphasis has been placed on computing with *all the accuracy obtainable from our tables*, under the assumption that *the data are exact*. Now, we consider computation where the given numbers are only *approximate values* of corresponding quantities. Then, we ask the following questions: (a) *With what refinement should computation be performed when the data are known to have only a specified degree of accuracy?* (b) *To what stage of accuracy should the final results be specified?* No hard and fast rules should be followed in answering (a) and (b) in any problem. Experience and sound judgment are involved in making any final decisions. However, the following working rules are satisfactory for problems of the types met in this text.

1. *In data concerning triangles, it is roughly true that three-place, four-place, and five-place accuracy in the lengths of sides correspond to accuracy to the nearest 10', 1', and .1', respectively, in the angles.*

2. *In computing, use four-place or five-place tables according as the data are accurate to three or to four places.*

3. *Round off final results to the same number of places as were specified in the data.*

In stating that certain data have *four-place accuracy*, for instance, we shall mean that the angular data are accurate to the nearest *minute*, and the lengths to *four significant digits*.

Note 1. Rule 2 is a suggestion to carry *one protective place* beyond the stage to which final results will be rounded off. Naturally, there is no objection to carrying *two* protective places, if convenient.

Hereafter in this book, assume that the data in any applied problem *stated in words* are *not exact* but are the result of measurement, with accuracy limited to the significant places in the given numbers. Answers to exercises will be listed as they appear after being rounded off to a number of places which appear reasonably justified by the data. It is admitted that, at times, different and equally valid decisions might be made about the number of significant places in the answers.

EXERCISE 24

Solve by use of logarithms except as directed.

1. From the top row in a football stadium, 85 feet above the ground, the angle of depression of the center of the field is 32° 10'. Find the air-line distance from the top row to the center of the field.

2. Find the area of a parallelogram whose sides are 150.6 feet and 235.3 feet long, if one angle is 127° 46'.

3. The *pitch* of a gable roof is defined as the *height* of its peak above the eaves *divided by* the roof's *width*. Find the pitch of a roof 45.7 wide whose peak is 17.6 above the lowest point (the eaves). Also, find the angle at which a side of the gable is inclined from the horizontal.

4. A porch, whose roof is 10.6 feet above the ground, projects 15.3 feet from the wall of a house. Find the length of the shortest ladder which would reach over the porch to a window 55.6 feet above the ground.

5. A regular octagon is inscribed in a circle whose radius is 36.8 feet. Find the length of a side of the octagon and the radius of its inscribed circle.

HINT. The radii to the ends of any side create an isosceles triangle with one angle equal to $\frac{1}{8}(360°)$.

6. Each side of a regular hexagon (six sides) is 50.8 inches long. Find the radii of its inscribed and circumscribed circles.

7. A tower stands on a cliff 653 feet above a horizontal plane. From a point A in the plane, the angles of elevation of the top and the bottom of the tower are 47° 28′ and 43° 36′. How high is the tower?

8. From two points 835.7 yards apart on a horizontal road running due east from a mountain, the angles of elevation of its top are, respectively, 43° 27′ and 30° 18′. How high above the road is the mountaintop?

HINT. 1. In Figure 35, we desire h; a, α, and β are given.

2. From $\triangle BCT$,
$$x = h \cot \beta. \tag{1}$$

3. From $\triangle ACT$, $\cot \alpha = AC/h$, or
$$a + x = h \cot \alpha. \tag{2}$$

4. Solve (1) and (2) simultaneously for h:

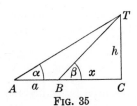

FIG. 35

$$h = \frac{a}{\cot \alpha - \cot \beta}. \tag{3}$$

To increase accuracy, Table XI should be used in (3).

9. An airplane is flying horizontally due east from us at a speed of 135 miles per hour. We observe the angle of elevation of the airplane to be 23° 17′; twelve seconds later its angle of elevation is 21° 39′. How high above us is the airplane flying?

10. In Figure 36, suppose that side a and angles β and γ are given. If h is the length of the altitude from A to BC, prove that

$$h = \frac{a}{\cot \beta + \cot \gamma}.$$

FIG. 36

11. A tower 20.7 feet high stands at the edge of the water on a riverbank. From a point directly opposite on the other bank, above water level, the angle of elevation of the top of the tower is 27° 17′ and the angle of depression of the image of its top in the water is 38° 12′. How wide is the river?

50. Projections

In a given plane, let OL be a given line and let CD be any line segment. Then, if A and B are the feet of the perpendiculars from C and D to OL, we call AB the *projection* of CD on OL. If OL and CD (possibly extended) form an acute angle α, as in Figure 37, we construct ECH parallel to OL and obtain triangle CHD. Then, $CH = AB$ and

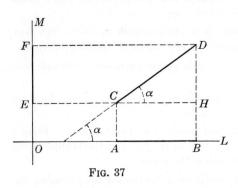

FIG. 37

$$\frac{CH}{CD} = \frac{AB}{CD} = \cos \alpha, \quad or$$

$$AB = CD \cdot \cos \alpha. \quad (1)$$

If OM is perpendicular to OL, in Figure 37, the projection of CD on OM is EF. Then, in triangle CHD, $HD = EF$ and

$$EF = CD \cdot \sin \alpha. \quad (2)$$

Thus, *the projection of CD on OL equals $CD \cdot \cos \alpha$, and the projection of CD on a line perpendicular to OL equals $CD \cdot \sin \alpha$,* where α is the acute angle formed by OL and CD.

ILLUSTRATION 1. If a train travels 3000 feet along a straight grade inclined $2° 37'$ from the horizontal, the horizontal and vertical projections of the path of the train are $3000 \cos 2° 37'$ and $3000 \sin 2° 37'$, respectively.

51. Bearing angle for a direction

In a horizontal plane, let any direction be represented by a directed line segment or arrow radiating from some fixed point O, as in Figure 38. Frequently, a direction is called a **bearing,** and it may be described by stating the acute angle made by it with the *north* or *south* direction. This angle will be called the **acute bearing angle** for the given direction.

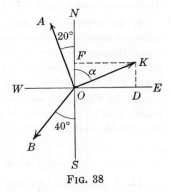

FIG. 38

ILLUSTRATION 1. In Figure 38, the bearing of OA is 20° west of north, abbreviated $N\ 20°\ W$. The bearing of OB is $S\ 40°\ W$. To describe the bearing of a line, we first write the letter N (or S), then the acute angle between the given line and ON (or OS), and finally write E or W to show on which side the given direction falls.

EXAMPLE 1. Find the bearing and distance of K as seen from O, if K is 30.6 miles north and 78.3 miles east of O.

SOLUTION. 1. In Figure 38, $FK \perp ON$; $OF = 30.6$; $FK = 78.3$.

2. In $\triangle OFK$, $\quad \tan \alpha = \dfrac{78.3}{30.6}$; $\quad \dfrac{OF}{OK} = \cos \alpha \quad$ or $\quad OK = \dfrac{OF}{\cos \alpha}$.

By use of four-place logarithms, $\alpha = 68° 39'$ and $OK = 84.0$. Hence, K is 84.0 miles from O in the direction $N\ 68° 39'\ E$. OD and OF are, respectively, the *east* and *north projections*, or *components*, of OK.

52. Azimuth

In the navigation of an airplane or a ship, in astronomy, and in the artillery service, the direction from a point G to a point B in the horizontal plane frequently is described by telling the angle through which a line GN pointing *north* must be *rotated* (clockwise) *toward the east* in order to coincide with GB. This angle is called the *azimuth* of B from G, or the azimuth of GB, and is an angle α such that $0° \leqq \alpha < 360°$. Frequently, to find the azimuth of a direction, we first find its acute bearing angle.

FIG. 39

ILLUSTRATION 1. In Figure 39, the azimuth of GB is $220°$. The bearing of GB is $S\ 40°\ W$.

In any problem which refers to the flight of an airplane, or the sailing of a ship, we shall assume that the motion is in a *horizontal plane*, unless otherwise specified. Essentially, then, we shall be dealing with a navigation problem in *plane sailing*. Other examples will be of the types met in the field of *plane surveying*, where the surveyor is assumed to work in a horizontal plane, except as points may be elevated above or below it. Plane sailing and plane surveying involve similar mathematical details. Problems in the exercises will be based on the minimum of technical language already introduced.* All paths involved in problems will be along one or more straight line segments.

EXERCISE 25

Find the horizontal and vertical projections of line segment AB with the given length and inclination from the horizontal.

1. 137.5 ft.; inclination $17° 18'$.   2. .1638 ft.; inclination $49° 7'$.

3. An airplane makes a straight ascent from A to B. Find the inclination of the path AB from the horizontal if its horizontal and vertical projections are 1780 ft. and 2360 ft., respectively.

* See Note 4 in the Appendix for an introduction to the vocabulary of plane surveying and associated problems. For a discussion of plane sailing, see any text on navigation, or *Plane and Spherical Trigonometry with Applications*, by William L. Hart; D. C. Heath and Company.

Find the azimuth of a direction having the given bearing.

4. $S\ 20°\ E$.   **5.** $N\ 39°\ W$.   **6.** $N\ 53°\ E$.   **7.** $S\ 72°\ 13'\ W$.

8. In planning a straight railroad grade to rise 75 feet, it is decided to incline the tracks $4°\ 32'$ from the horizontal. Find the horizontal projection of the grade, and its length.

How far north or south and how far east or west is M from P?

9. M is 385 miles from P in the direction $N\ 43°\ 20'\ W$.

10. P is 896 miles from M in the direction $N\ 73°\ 40'\ W$.

Find the distance MP, and the bearing and azimuth of MP.

11. M is 58.9 miles north and 32.7 miles east of P.

12. P is 138 miles north and 289 miles east of M.

13. A battery of artillery emplaced at B is ordered to fire at a target T which is 6480 yards west and 5720 yards north of B. Find the range, bearing, and azimuth of T from B.

An airplane travels from A to C on the path AB, BC. Find the distance bearing, and azimuth of C as seen from A.

14.

PATH	LENGTH	DIREC.
AB	130 mi.	$S\ 23°\ 40'\ E$
BC	250 mi.	$S\ 48°\ 32'\ W$

15.

PATH	LENGTH	DIREC.
AB	75 mi.	$N\ 18°\ 25'\ W$
BC	135 mi.	$N\ 67°\ 38'\ W$

Hint. Draw a figure. Add to the table a *row* labeled AC, and two *columns* labeled *E–W component* and *N–S component*. By use of Section 50, compute the components for AB, BC and *combine* to get the components for AC. Then, find the distance and bearing of AC.

An airplane flies or a ship sails from A to B and the navigator then heads for C. Find the distance and azimuth of C from B for the given data.

16. $AB = 120$ mi., $N\ 27°\ 16'\ E$; C is 257 mi. east and 55 mi. north of A.

17. $AB = 250$ mi., $S\ 57°\ 40'\ W$; C is 350 mi. west and 30 mi. north of A.

53. Vectors

A directed line segment or *stroke*, such as $\overrightarrow{OP}$ in Figure 40, is called a *vector*. The measure of the length of OP in terms of some linear unit is called the **magnitude** of $\overrightarrow{OP}$. Thus, the defining characteristics of a vector are its *direction* and *magnitude*. In this book, any vectors which are considered simultaneously will be *coplanar* (all in some given plane). We shall assume that a vector can be moved as we please in the plane, as long as the vector's length and direction are unaltered.

FIG. 40

Let two vectors $\overrightarrow{OF}$ and $\overrightarrow{OP}$ be given, and let them be drawn with a common initial point O, as in Figure 40. Then, we define the *sum*, or the **resultant**, of $\overrightarrow{OP}$ and $\overrightarrow{OF}$ as the vector $\overrightarrow{OR}$ which is the diagonal of the parallelogram having $\overrightarrow{OP}$ and $\overrightarrow{OF}$ as adjacent sides. This definition is referred to as the *parallelogram law for the addition of vectors*. We call $\overrightarrow{OP}$ and $\overrightarrow{OF}$ the *components* of $\overrightarrow{OR}$ along the lines of the corresponding sides of the parallelogram.

The resultant of $\overrightarrow{OP}$ and $\overrightarrow{OF}$, in Figure 40, may also be found as follows: draw $\overrightarrow{OP}$; then *place the initial point of $\overrightarrow{OF}$ on the terminal point of $\overrightarrow{OP}$, giving $\overrightarrow{PR}$*, which locates R and determines $\overrightarrow{OR}$.

ILLUSTRATION 1. Any *force* or *velocity** possesses a *direction* and a *magnitude*, and hence can be represented geometrically by a properly directed vector, with the measure of its length in some linear unit equal to the measure of the force or velocity in some physical unit. In Figure 40, let $\overrightarrow{OF}$ and $\overrightarrow{OP}$ represent any two forces pulling (or *acting*) simultaneously on an object at O. Then, in physics it is proved that the combined effect of forces $\overrightarrow{OF}$ and $\overrightarrow{OP}$ is the same as the effect of the single **resultant force** represented by the *resultant vector $\overrightarrow{OR}$*. This fact is referred to as the *parallelogram law for the composition of forces*. If $\overrightarrow{OF}$ and $\overrightarrow{OP}$ represent velocities simultaneously imposed on an object at O, the resultant velocity is represented by $\overrightarrow{OR}$. Thus, velocities also obey the parallelogram law in composition.

The components of a vector $\overrightarrow{OR}$ along two perpendicular lines ON and OE are the vectors obtained by projecting $\overrightarrow{OR}$ on ON and OE. In Figure 41, the magnitudes of the components are

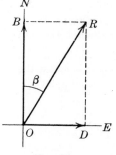

$$OB = OR \cos \beta;$$

$$OD = OR \sin \beta.$$

The given vector $\overrightarrow{OR}$ is the resultant of its components $\overrightarrow{OB}$ and $\overrightarrow{OD}$. In finding $\overrightarrow{OB}$ and $\overrightarrow{OD}$ in Figure 41, we say that we have *resolved* the given vector into *components*.

FIG. 41

ILLUSTRATION 2. In Figure 41, $\overrightarrow{OR}$ represents a force of 150 pounds acting in the direction N 31° E; the acute bearing angle is $\beta = 31°$.

$$OB = 150 \cos 31° = 129; \qquad OD = 150 \sin 31° = 77.$$

The north component is 129 pounds; the east component is 77 pounds.

* And other physical quantities, such as *accelerations*. In this text, vector applications of a physical nature will involve only forces and velocities.

Any physical quantity possessing a *magnitude* and a *direction* can be represented as a vector. If a given class of such quantities has the *further property* that composition of simultaneously acting quantities obeys the parallelogram law, we refer to the quantities as **vector quantities.** Thus, forces and velocities are vector quantities.

Note 1. If the *weight* of an object is w pounds, the attraction of gravity on it is a vertical *force* of w pounds acting at the object's center of gravity.

Note 2. The direction in which the nose of an airplane or the prow of a ship is pointed in its motion is called the *heading.* The direction of the motion relative to the ground is called the *course* of the airplane or ship.

EXAMPLE 1. An airplane is headed east with an airspeed of 240 miles per hour. A north wind is blowing with a speed of 40 miles per hour. Find the airplane's groundspeed and course.

SOLUTION. 1. In Figure 42, $\overrightarrow{OH}$ represents the wind velocity, with which the air moves. The airplane's velocity *in the moving air* is represented by $\overrightarrow{OP}$, called the *airspeed vector,* whose magnitude* is the *airspeed.* The airplane's ground velocity (relative to the ground) is represented by $\overrightarrow{OG}$, the resultant of $\overrightarrow{OH}$ and $\overrightarrow{OP}$. We call $\overrightarrow{OG}$ the *groundspeed vector;* its magnitude is the groundspeed; the *azimuth* of $\overrightarrow{OG}$ is called the *course* of the airplane.

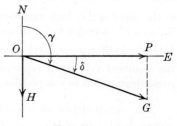

FIG. 42

2. In $\triangle OPG$, we have $OP = 240$ and $PG = 40$; on solving, we find $\delta = 9° 28'$ and $OG = 243$. The groundspeed is 243 miles and the course is azimuth $99° 28'$.

Comment. The smallest angle between the *heading* and *course* of an airplane is called the *drift angle.* It is $9° 28'$ in Example 2; the wind blows the airplane $9° 28'$ *off its heading.*

EXERCISE 26

Find the horizontal and vertical components of the force.

1. 153.8 lb. acting downward at inclination of $56° 34'$ from horizontal.

2. 2183 lb. acting downward at inclination of $36° 33'$ from horizontal.

Find the north or south and east or west components of the given force, or given ground velocity of an airplane.

3. 42.65 lb. force acting $S 31° 10' W$. **4.** 1329 lb. force acting $N 31° 37' W$.

5. Groundspeed of 300 miles per hour with azimuth $160°$.

6. Groundspeed of 150 miles per hour with azimuth $250°$.

* The *magnitude* of any *velocity* is called *speed.*

A body is acted upon by the given forces simultaneously. Find the magnitude of the resultant force and its direction, or inclination.

7. 17.8 lb. vertically upward; 32.6 lb. horizontally.

8. 162 lb. north; 53.7 lb. east.   **9.** 638 lb. south; 217 lb. west.

For the given wind velocity, find the groundspeed, course, and drift angle for the airplane. All speeds are "per hour."

10. Wind blowing 30 miles from west; airspeed 200 miles north.

11. Wind blowing 25 miles from east; airspeed 220 miles south.

12. A ship is headed east at the rate of 18 miles per hour relative to the water. An ocean current is carrying the water south at the rate of 3 miles per hour. Find the course of the ship and its speed with respect to the ocean floor.

13. A river flows at the rate of 7.8 miles per hour. A man, who can row 4 miles per hour in still water, heads directly across the river. Find the speed and direction of his resulting motion.

14. At what speed with respect to the water should a ship head south in order to sail in the direction with azimuth 168° 26', if the ship is in a current flowing east at the rate of 5 miles per hour?

15. At what airspeed should an airplane head west in order to fly in the direction with azimuth 289° 30', if a wind is blowing from the south at the rate of 40 miles per hour?

★54. Problems involving forces and velocities

EXAMPLE 1. Find the force which is just sufficient to keep a 1000-pound weight from sliding down a plane inclined 47° to the horizontal, under the assumption that there is no friction.

SOLUTION. 1. The attraction of gravity on the weight A, in Figure 43, is a vertical force $\overrightarrow{AW}$, of 1000 pounds. We resolve $\overrightarrow{AW}$ into two perpendicular components, $\overrightarrow{AK}$ acting along the plane and $\overrightarrow{AH}$ perpendicular to the plane. Force $\overrightarrow{AH}$ creates pressure on the plane and is counteracted by its supports. Force $\overrightarrow{AK}$ acts to move the weight A downward. Hence, we must apply force AF equal in magnitude to $\overrightarrow{AK}$ and opposite in direction.

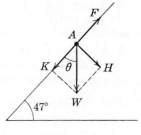

FIG. 43

2. In $\triangle KAW$, $\theta = 43°$ and $AW = 1000$. Thus we obtain

$$AK = 1000 \cos 43° = 731.4.$$

Hence, a force of 731.4 lb. would hold the weight steady. Any greater force would move the weight upward. The favorable difference between 1000 and 731.4 shows the advantage of the inclined ramp. A force slightly greater than 1000 lb. is necessary to raise the weight vertically.

★EXERCISE 27

1. A 150-pound shell for a battery of artillery is dragged up a runway inclined 42° to the horizontal. Find the pressure of the shell against the runway and the force required to drag the shell.

2. A truck weighing 6875 pounds moves up a bridge inclined 7° 32′ from the horizontal. Find the pressure of the truck against the bridge.

3. An automobile weighing 2600 pounds stands on a hill inclined 25° 36′ from the horizontal. How large a force must be counteracted by the brakes of the automobile to prevent it from rolling downhill?

4. Cables running due north from a telegraph pole AP, in Figure 44, create a horizontal pull of 580 pounds at the top of the pole. A supporting cable PC is run due south to the ground. Find the *tension* in CP if it is inclined 49° 50′ from the horizontal. (The tension is a *force*, pulling in the direction PC, whose horizontal component counteracts the pull on the pole and whose vertical component adds to the pressure of the pole against the ground.)

FIG. 44

5. A guy wire 78 feet long runs from the top of a telegraph pole 56 feet high to the ground and pulls on the pole with a force of 290 pounds. (*a*) What is the horizontal pull of the wire on the top of the pole? (*b*) What vertical force does the wire exert as an addition to the pressure of the pole against the ground?

6. What force must be exerted to drag a 150-pound weight up a slope which inclines 25° from the horizontal?

7. Find the largest weight which a man can drag up a slope inclined 35° from the horizontal, if he is able to pull with a force of 125 pounds.

8. A man finds that his strength is just sufficient to drag a 200-pound weight up a certain slope. Find the angle at which the slope is inclined to the horizontal, if the man is able to exert a pull of 140 pounds.

9. A man wishes to raise a 300-pound weight to the top of a wall 15 feet high by dragging the weight up an incline. Find the length of the shortest inclined plane which he can use, if his pulling strength is 135 pounds.

Find the magnitude and direction of the resultant of the given forces acting simultaneously on an object.

10. 50 lb. acting N 21° 16′ E; 150 lb. acting N 49° 28′ W.

HINT. Recall the method of Problem 14, page 62.

11. 57.3 lb. acting N 21° 10′ E; 158 lb. acting N 49° 20′ E.

12. 47 lb. acting N 23° 10′ W; 163 lb. acting S 84° 30′ W.

FIVE

FUNDAMENTAL CHARACTERISTICS OF THE FUNCTIONS

55. Graphical reduction to acute angles

Let θ be an angle in standard position, in any quadrant. Let α be the acute angle between the terminal side of θ and the x-axis. Then, we have agreed to call α the *reference angle* for θ. Various reference angles are exhibited in Figure 45.

$\theta = 140°$
$\alpha = 40°$

$\theta = 250°$
$\alpha = 70°$

$\theta = -130°$
$\alpha = 50°$

Fig. 45

Note 1. We verify the following facts:

θ *between* $90°$ *and* $180°$; *reference angle is* $\alpha = 180° - \theta$.   (1)

θ *between* $180°$ *and* $270°$; *reference angle is* $\alpha = \theta - 180°$.   (2)

θ *between* $270°$ *and* $360°$; *reference angle is* $\alpha = 360° - \theta$.   (3)

THEOREM I. *Any function of an angle θ, in any quadrant, is numerically equal to the same function of the reference angle for θ. That is,*

(any function of θ) = ± (same function of reference angle α),   (4)

where "$+$" or "$-$" is used according as the function of θ is positive or negative.

ILLUSTRATION 1. To find $\tan 140°$, we notice from Figure 45 that the reference angle for $140°$ is $180° - 140°$, or $40°$. Also, $\tan 140°$ is negative. Hence, by Theorem I and Table IV, $\tan 140° = -\tan 40° = -.839$.

ILLUSTRATION 2. The reference angle for $315°$ is $45°$. From (4),

$$\tan 315° = -\tan 45° = -1; \qquad \cos 315° = +\cos 45° = \tfrac{1}{2}\sqrt{2}.$$

Proof of Theorem I.   1. In Figure 46, the reference angle for θ is the acute angle α of the reference triangle AOP.

2. Let the positive numbers $\overline{OA}$ and $\overline{AP}$ be the *lengths* of OA and AP. Then, $x = \pm\ \overline{OA}$ and $y = \pm\ \overline{AP}$, where the sign "$+$" or "$-$" in each case depends on the signs of x and y in the quadrant where P is located.

3. In triangle AOP, $\overline{AP}$ and $\overline{OA}$ are the *lengths* of the sides opposite and adjacent to α, and $r = \overline{OP}$. Then, we obtain the functions of α by use of page 18, and the functions of θ from definitions on page 10:

FIG. 46

$$\sin\ \alpha = \frac{\overline{AP}}{r}; \qquad \sin\ \theta = \frac{y}{r} = \pm\ \frac{\overline{AP}}{r} = \pm\ \sin\ \alpha.$$

$$\tan\ \alpha = \frac{\overline{AP}}{\overline{OA}}; \qquad \tan\ \theta = \frac{y}{x} = \frac{\pm\ \overline{AP}}{\pm\ \overline{OA}} = \pm\ \frac{\overline{AP}}{\overline{OA}} = \pm\ \tan\ \alpha.$$

Similarly, each function of θ differs from the same function of α at most in sign. Since all functions of an acute angle are positive, the sign, $+$ or $-$, to use in (4) is the same as the sign of the function of θ which is involved.

ILLUSTRATION 3.   The reference angle for $-130°$ is $50°$, in Figure 45, page 67; $\tan\ \theta$ is positive if θ is in quadrant III. Hence, $\tan\ (-130°) = +\tan\ 50°$.

If θ and ϕ are on the range $0°$ to $180°$, inclusive, and $\theta + \phi = 180°$, then θ and ϕ are said to be *supplementary;* either is called *the supplement* of the other angle. If θ is an obtuse angle, its supplement $(180° - \theta)$ is *acute* and is the *reference angle* for θ. Hence, from (4),

(any function of obtuse angle θ) = $\pm$ [same function of $(180° - \theta)$].   (5)

ILLUSTRATION 4.   The supplement of $130°$ is $50°$, the reference angle for $130°$. Hence, from Table IV,

$$\cos\ 130° = -\cos\ 50° = -.643.$$

EXAMPLE 1.   Find $\tan\ 283°\ 27'$ by use of Table VII.

SOLUTION.   The reference angle is $360° - 283°\ 27'$, or $76°\ 33'$. By interpolation in Table VII,

$$\tan\ 283°\ 27' = -\tan\ 76°\ 33' = -4.181.$$

If the absolute value of θ is greater than $360°$, before finding a function of θ we may alter the angle by adding or subtracting an integral multiple of $360°$, because the new angle obtained is *coterminal* with θ.

ILLUSTRATION 5. $\sin\ 398° = \sin\ (398° - 360°) = \sin\ 38°.$

Note 2. For a quadrantal angle θ, we may call 0° or 90° the reference angle for θ according as its terminal side, in standard position, falls on the *horizontal* or *vertical* coordinate axis. Then, equation (4) holds for quadrantal angles as well as all other angles. However, this fact is seldom used because it is easy to memorize the functions of quadrantal angles.

EXAMPLE 2.   Compute 2753 sin 293° 27.6′.

SOLUTION.   1. The reference angle for 293° 27.6′ is 66° 32.4′ and the sine is negative in quadrant IV. Hence,

$$2753 \sin 293° 27.6′ = -2753 \sin 66° 32.4′.$$

2. Let $p = 2753 \sin 66° 32.4′$ and compute by use of Tables VIII and IX:

$$\begin{aligned} \log 2753 &= 3.43981 \\ \log \sin 66° 32.4′ &= 9.96253 - 10 \ (+) \\ \hline \log p = 13.40234 &- 10 = 3.40234; \qquad p = 252.55; \end{aligned}$$

$$2753 \sin 293° 27.6′ = -252.55.$$

EXERCISE 28

Sketch the angle in standard position and find the reference angle.

1. 121°. **2.** 203°. **3.** 267°. **4.** − 210°. **5.** 470°.

By use of a reference angle, find each function and its cofunction.. Give the result in exact form if the reference angle is 30°, 45°, or 60°, and otherwise obtain the answer by use of Table IV.

6. tan 115°. **7.** cot 142°. **8.** sin 208°. **9.** cos 225°.

10. sec 330°. **11.** csc 340°. **12.** sin 394°. **13.** cot 326°.

14. cos 117°. **15.** cot 153°. **16.** cot 210°. **17.** sin 120°.

18. sin (− 25°). **19.** tan (− 52°). **20.** cos (− 75°). **21.** sec (− 80°).

22. cot (− 130°). **23.** sec (− 120°). **24.** sin (− 210°). **25.** csc (− 230°).

26. sin 250°. **27.** sec 305°. **28.** tan 216°. **29.** cos 93°.

30. sin (− 200°). **31.** tan (− 302°). **32.** sec 420°. **33.** cos 495°.

34. sin 530°. **35.** cot 844°. **36.** sec (− 403°). **37.** cos 907°.

Find the value of the function by interpolation in Table VII. Also, read the value from Table XI.

38. sec 143° 17′. **39.** sin 133° 26′. **40.** cos 156° 12′.

41. tan 285° 42′. **42.** cot 216° 13′. **43.** cot (− 156° 8′).

Obtain the value of the function by interpolation in Table XI.

44. sin 216° 13.5′. **45.** cos 162° 23.4′. **46.** sin 128° 14.9′.

Compute by use of five-place logarithms.

47. .4314/tan 303° 36′. **48.** 31.47 cos 313° 10′.

49. .0937 cos 158° 10′. **50.** 1.630/cot 112° 50′.

51. .1342 tan 118° 20′. **52.** 152.3 cos 426° 15′.

56. Functional notation

If a variable y is a function (not necessarily a *trigonometric* function) of a variable x, we have agreed to call y the *dependent* variable and x the *independent* variable. Sometimes we represent a function of a specified independent variable by a symbol such as $f(x)$, $H(x)$, or $K(\theta)$. The letter in parentheses is the independent variable. The letter at the left of the parentheses is merely a convenient *name* letter or abbreviation for the function. We read "$f(x)$" as "*the f-function of x*," or simply "*f of x*." If $f(x)$ is a function of x and h is a particular value for x, then

$$f(h) \text{ represents the value of } f(x) \text{ when } x = h. \tag{1}$$

ILLUSTRATION 1. If $f(x) = 3x^2 + 2x - 7$, then

$$f(2) = 3(2^2) + 2(2) - 7 = 9;$$
$$f(-3) = 3(9) + 2(-3) - 7 = 14.$$

ILLUSTRATION 2. If $f(x) = \sin x°$, then $f(90) = \sin 90° = 1$.

Similarly, a function of two independent variables x and y may be represented by $F(x, y)$, $G(x, y)$, etc.

ILLUSTRATION 3. If $F(x, y) = x - 3xy^2$, then

$$F(2, -3) = 2 - 3(2)(-3)^2 = 2 - 54 = -52.$$

57. Review concerning equations and identities

An equation whose sides are equal for all permissible values of any variables involved is called an *identical equation*, or simply an *identity*. An equation whose members are not equal for all permissible values of the variables is called a *conditional equation*.

ILLUSTRATION 1. The equation $(x + y)^2 = x^2 + 2xy + y^2$ is an identity, because it is true for all values of x and y. The equation $x - 2 = 0$ is a conditional equation which is true only when $x = 2$.

ILLUSTRATION 2. The trigonometric equation $\sin \theta = 1/\csc \theta$ is an identity because it is true for all values of the angle θ for which $\csc \theta$ is defined. The equation $\sin \theta = 1$ is a conditional equation because it is true only when $\theta = 90°$, or when θ is an angle coterminal with $90°$.

The word *equation* by itself may be used in referring to both identities and conditional equations. However, the unqualified word *equation* usually applies to a conditional equation.

ILLUSTRATION 3. The reciprocal relations of page 11 are identities, for all values of θ for which the expressions are defined.

ILLUSTRATION 4. Certain relations exist between the functions of any two angles whose sum or difference is an *integral multiple of* $90°$. The resulting identities will be called *reduction formulas*.

58. Periodicity of the trigonometric functions

If an angle θ varies from one value to another, the terminal side of θ in standard position revolves about the origin of the coordinate system. The positions of the terminal side of θ, and hence the values of its trigonometric functions, repeat themselves periodically at intervals of 360° in the values of θ. Thus, for every value of θ, the angles θ and $(\theta + 360°)$, or $(\theta - 360°)$, are *coterminal* and their functions have identical values. Hence, we obtain the following reduction formulas:

$$[\text{any function of } (\theta + 360°)] = (\text{same function of } \theta); \qquad (1)$$

$$[\text{any function of } (\theta - 360°)] = (\text{same function of } \theta). \qquad (2)$$

On account of (1), we say that each trigonometric function of the variable angle θ is a **periodic function** of θ with 360° as a **period**. Equation (1) abbreviates six identities:

$$\sin(\theta + 360°) = \sin\theta; \quad \cos(\theta + 360°) = \cos\theta; \quad \cdots; \quad \csc(\theta + 360°) = \csc\theta.$$

ILLUSTRATION 1. From (1) and (2), the values of $\sin\theta$ repeat at intervals of 360° in the values of θ, if we *increase* or *decrease* θ. Thus, $\sin\theta$ repeats the value $\sin 30° = \frac{1}{2}$ at intervals of 360°:

$$\frac{1}{2} = \sin 30° = \sin(30° + 360°) = \sin(30° + 720°) = etc.;$$

$$= \sin(30° - 360°) = \sin(30° - 720°) = etc.$$

Identities (1) and (2) are equivalent, although in different notation. Thus, either (1) or (2) states that, *if two angles differ by* 360°, *corresponding functions of the two angles are equal.*

★*Note 1.* If $f(x)$ is a function of x, and p is a constant such that $f(x+p) = f(x)$ for all values of x, we say that $f(x)$ is *periodic* and has p as a *period.* Then, also,

$$f(x + 2p) = f[(x + p) + p] = f(x + p) = f(x),$$

so that $2p$ is seen to be a period. Similarly, $3p$, $4p$, or, in general, np is a period where n is any positive integer.

59. Functions of $(-\theta)$

Let us prove that, for all angles θ,*

$$\left. \begin{array}{ll} \sin(-\theta) = -\sin\theta; & \csc(-\theta) = -\csc\theta; \\ \cos(-\theta) = \cos\theta; & \sec(-\theta) = \sec\theta; \\ \tan(-\theta) = -\tan\theta; & \cot(-\theta) = -\cot\theta. \end{array} \right\} \qquad (1)$$

ILLUSTRATION 1. $\sin(-27°) = -\sin 27° = -.4540.$ (Table VII)

Proof of (1).   1. Let $\beta = -\theta$.   Then,† for a case where $\theta > 0$

---

* We add, *for which the functions involved will exist.* This proviso is understood in all future cases where trigonometric identities are described.

† The statements of the proof hold for any angle θ although a special figure is drawn. The student should draw other figures.

Figure 47 shows β and θ in their standard positions on a coordinate system. For any value of θ, its terminal side OP and the terminal side OP_1 for β will be *symmetrically located on opposite sides of the x-axis.* Choose P and P_1 so that $OP_1 = OP$. Then, line segment PP_1 is perpendicular to the x-axis and is bisected by it.

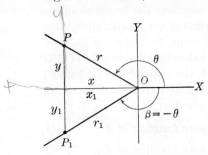

FIG. 47

2. Let the coordinates of P be (x, y), with $OP = r$. Then, the coordinates of P_1 are (x_1, y_1) and $OP_1 = r_1$, where

$$x_1 = x; \quad y_1 = -y; \quad r_1 = r. \quad (2)$$

3. From the definitions of page 10,

$$\sin (-\theta) = \frac{y_1}{r_1} = \frac{-y}{r} = -\sin \theta; \quad (3)$$

$$\cos (-\theta) = \frac{x_1}{r_1} = \frac{x}{r} = \cos \theta; \quad (4)$$

$$\tan (-\theta) = \frac{y_1}{x_1} = \frac{-y}{x} = -\tan \theta. \quad (5)$$

On taking the reciprocal of each side of $\sin (-\theta) = -\sin \theta$, we obtain

$$\csc (-\theta) = \frac{1}{\sin (-\theta)} = -\frac{1}{\sin \theta} = -\csc \theta. \quad (6)$$

Similarly, we verify $\sec (-\theta) = \sec \theta$ and $\cot (-\theta) = -\cot (\theta)$.

Note 1. The proof for (6) emphasizes the fact that, if the expressions for $\sin (-\theta)$, $\cos (-\theta)$, $\tan (-\theta)$ in (1) are remembered, the other identities in (1) can be quickly recalled.

EXERCISE 29

Express the function in terms of a function of a positive angle less than 360°.

1. $\sin (-25°)$.   2. $\cos (-95°)$.   3. $\tan (-12°)$.   4. $\sin (-85°)$.

5. $\cos (-128°)$.   6. $\cot (-350°)$.   7. $\sec (-35°)$.   8. $\csc (-35°)$.

9. $\csc (-148°)$.   10. $\sec (-250°)$.   11. $\tan (-130°)$.   12. $\cot (-175°)$.

13. $\cos (-\alpha)$.   14. $\sin (-\gamma)$.   15. $\sec (-H)$.   16. $\tan (-K)$.

17. $\sin 439°$.   18. $\tan 900°$.   19. $\cos (-465°)$.   20. $\cot (-575°)$.

21. Repeat the proof of identities (1), Section 59, by use of a figure in which θ is taken as an angle between 180° and 270°.

If $f(x) = 3x^2 - x - 5$, find the value of each symbol.

22. $f(3)$.   23. $f(-1)$.   24. $f(\frac{1}{2})$.   25. $f(\frac{2}{3})$.

If $G(y) = 2y - 3y^2$, find an expression for each symbol.

26. $G(a)$. **27.** $G(2b)$. **28.** $G(y + 4)$. **29.** $G(\tfrac{1}{2}x)$.

30. If $F(x, y) = 4x - y^2$, find $F(3, 2)$; $F(-1, 4)$.

60. Identities for functions of $(\theta + 180°)$ and $(\theta - 180°)$

$$\sin (\theta + 180°) = -\sin \theta; \qquad \csc (\theta + 180°) = -\csc \theta; \qquad (1)$$

$$\cos (\theta + 180°) = -\cos \theta; \qquad \sec (\theta + 180°) = -\sec \theta; \qquad (2)$$

$$\tan (\theta + 180°) = \tan \theta; \qquad \cot (\theta + 180°) = \cot \theta. \qquad (3)$$

Proof of (1), (2), (3). 1. For any angle θ, as illustrated in Figure 48, the terminal sides OP for θ and OP_1 for $(\theta + 180°)$ form a line through O. We select P and P_1 so that $OP = OP_1$; then, triangles OAP and OA_1P_1 are congruent. Hence, the corresponding directed line segments OA and OA_1 have *equal lengths* but *opposite directions;* that is, $|x| = |x_1|$ but $x_1 = -x$. Similarly, $y_1 = -y$. Also, $r_1 = r$.

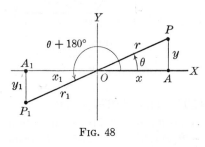

Fig. 48

2. From the definitions of page 10,

$$\sin (\theta + 180°) = \frac{y_1}{r_1} = -\frac{y}{r} = -\sin \theta;$$

$$\tan (\theta + 180°) = \frac{y_1}{x_1} = \frac{-y}{-x} = \frac{y}{x} = \tan \theta.$$

Similarly, we obtain all of identities (1), (2), (3).

We have seen that all the trigonometric functions of θ are periodic with 360° as a period. However, identities (3) show that $\tan \theta$ and $\cot \theta$ also have the *smaller period* 180°. Identities (1) and (2), where minus signs are met on the right-hand sides, show that $\sin \theta$, $\cos \theta$, $\sec \theta$, and $\csc \theta$ do *not* possess the period 180°.

ILLUSTRATION 1. Since $230° = 180° + 50°$,

$$\sin 230° = -\sin 50°; \qquad \sec 230° = -\sec 50°; \qquad \tan 230° = \tan 50°.$$

The student will be asked to prove later that

$$[\text{any function of } (\theta - 180°)] = \pm (\text{same function of } \theta). \qquad (4)$$

61. Identities for functions of $(90° + \theta)$ and $(270° + \theta)$

$$\sin (90° + \theta) = \cos \theta; \qquad \csc (90° + \theta) = \sec \theta;$$

$$\cos (90° + \theta) = -\sin \theta; \qquad \sec (90° + \theta) = -\csc \theta; \qquad (1)$$

$$\tan (90° + \theta) = -\cot \theta; \qquad \cot (90° + \theta) = -\tan \theta.$$

Proof of (1).   1. For any angle θ, as illustrated in Figure 49, the terminal sides OP for θ and OP_1 for $(\theta + 90°)$ are *perpendicular*.   With P and P_1 selected so that $OP = OP_1$, triangles AOP and A_1P_1O are congruent, with the equal angles A_1P_1O and AOP, and equal lengths for sides A_1O and AP, and A_1P_1 and OA.   Hence $|x| = |y_1|$ and $|x_1| = |y|$; since x_1 and y differ in signs, we obtain

$$x_1 = -y; \qquad y_1 = x; \qquad r_1 = r.$$

2. From the definitions of page 10,

$$\cos (90° + \theta) = \frac{x_1}{r_1} = -\frac{y}{r} = -\sin \theta;$$

$$\tan (90° + \theta) = \frac{y_1}{x_1} = \frac{x}{-y} = -\cot \theta; \text{ etc.}$$

FIG. 49

Similarly, we may show that

[any function of $(270° + \theta)$] $= \pm$ (cofunction of θ).   (2)

62. Reduction formulas for $(90° - \theta)$, $(180° - \theta)$, and $(270° - \theta)$

By use of the formulas for functions of $(-\theta)$ on page 71, we can obtain the following identities involving $(90° - \theta)$, $(180° - \theta)$, $(270° - \theta)$ from those for $(90° + \theta)$, $(180° + \theta)$, $(270° + \theta)$, respectively.

$$\sin (90° - \theta) = \cos \theta; \qquad \csc (90° - \theta) = \sec \theta; \qquad (1)$$

$$\cos (90° - \theta) = \sin \theta; \qquad \sec (90° - \theta) = \csc \theta; \qquad (2)$$

$$\tan (90° - \theta) = \cot \theta; \qquad \cot (90° - \theta) = \tan \theta. \qquad (3)$$

[Any function of $(180° - \theta)$] $= \pm$ (same function of θ).   (4)

[Any function of $(270° - \theta)$] $= \pm$ (cofunction of θ).   (5)

EXAMPLE 1.   Prove identities (2).

SOLUTION.   From (1) of Section 61, with $-\theta$ in place of θ, we obtain

$$\cos (90° - \theta) = \cos [90° + (-\theta)] = -\sin (-\theta). \qquad (6)$$

From Section 59, $\sin (-\theta) = -\sin \theta$.   Hence, $\cos (90° - \theta) = \sin \theta$.   If we take the reciprocal of each side of this equation, we obtain the identity $\sec (90° - \theta) = \csc \theta$.   This proves both of identities (2).

If θ is acute in (1), (2), (3), they become the *cofunction relations* for complementary angles.   However, (1), (2), (3) are now available for *all* angles θ.   If θ is not acute, we do not refer to $(90° - \theta)$ as the complement of θ.

Note 1.   If θ is on the range 0° to 180°, inclusive, $(180° - \theta)$ is the *supplement* of θ and (4) relates the functions of θ and its supplement.   In particular, for any value of θ, (4) gives

$$\sin (180° - \theta) = \sin \theta; \qquad \cos (180° - \theta) = -\cos \theta. \qquad (7)$$

63. General reduction formulas

We have proved special cases of the following identities, in which "*multiple of* $90°$" means an "*integral multiple, $n \cdot 90°$,*" where n is an integer.

$$\left\{ \begin{array}{c} \textbf{Any function of an} \\ \textbf{[(even multiple of 90°)} \pm \boldsymbol{\theta}\textbf{]} \end{array} \right\} = \pm \textbf{ (same function of } \boldsymbol{\theta}\textbf{).} \qquad (1)$$

$$\left\{ \begin{array}{c} \textbf{Any function of an} \\ \textbf{[(odd multiple of 90°)} \pm \boldsymbol{\theta}\textbf{]} \end{array} \right\} = \pm \textbf{ (cofunction of } \boldsymbol{\theta}\textbf{).} \qquad (2)$$

In (1) or (2), for any given function of θ and any given multiple of $90°$, just one sign, $+$ or $-$, applies on the right-hand side *regardless of the value of θ*. Any particular case of (1) or (2) can be proved geometrically, as in Sections 60 and 61, or may be established by use of other reduction formulas previously proved.* We shall use (1) and (2) without further proof.

Note 1. The student should memorize (1) and (2) and the most useful special cases, such as: *the periodicity relations for* $(360° + \theta)$; *the periodicity relations* $\tan (180° + \theta) = \tan \theta$ *and* $\cot (180° + \theta) = \cot \theta$; *the expressions for* $\sin (-\theta)$, $\cos (-\theta)$, *and* $\tan (-\theta)$ *from page 71; the cofunction relations for* $(90° - \theta)$.

EXAMPLE 1. Express $\cot (\theta + 270°)$ in terms of a function of θ.

SOLUTION. 1. From (2), since $270° = 3(90°)$, and since 3 is *odd*,

$$\cot (\theta + 270°) = \pm \tan \theta. \qquad (3)$$

2. To determine the sign $+$ or $-$ in (3), think of the case where θ is acute. Then, $(\theta + 270°)$ is in quadrant IV where the cotangent is *negative*. Since $\tan \theta$ is *positive* if θ is acute, we use the minus sign in (3) to give a negative right-hand side. Hence, $\cot (\theta + 270°) = - \tan \theta$. The special case, with θ acute, was convenient in determining the sign.

SUMMARY. *To obtain any particular reduction formula, use (1) or (2) to write the formula with an ambiguous sign. Then, determine the proper sign by checking signs on the two sides for the case where θ is acute.*

If desired, reduction formulas can be used to accomplish the aims of Section 55 where reference angles were employed. That is, if γ is a given angle in any quadrant, we may express any function of γ in terms of some function of a corresponding acute angle θ as follows:

1. *Express γ as a sum or difference of the nearest integral multiple of $90°$ and an acute angle θ (which may be taken at most equal to $45°$).*

2. *Use (1) or (2) to write a formula for the desired function of γ in terms of a function of θ, with "$+$" or "$-$" used on the right-hand side according as the function of γ is positive or negative.*

* See Note 5 in the Appendix for a general proof.

ILLUSTRATION 1.   From formula (2), $\sin 253° = \sin (270° - 17°) = \pm \cos 17°$. Since 253° is in quadrant III where the sine is negative and since cos 17° is positive, we choose the minus sign: $\sin 253° = - \cos 17°$.

ILLUSTRATION 2. $\tan (- 165°) = \tan (- 180° + 15°) = + \tan 15°$.

EXERCISE 30

Sketch the angle in standard position and express all functions of the angle in terms of functions of an acute angle less than 45°.

1. 47°.	**2.** 63°.	**3.** 129°.	**4.** 147°.	**5.** 218°.
6. 176°.	**7.** 243°.	**8.** 284°.	**9.** 304°.	**10.** 352°.
11. $- 37°$.	**12.** $- 56°$.	**13.** $- 124°$.	**14.** $- 256°$.	**15.** $- 310°$.
16. 305°.	**17.** 487°.	**18.** 638°.	**19.** $- 247°$.	**20.** 537°.
21. $- 112°$.	**22.** 131°.	**23.** 168°.	**24.** $- 283°$.	**25.** 849°.

Express in terms of a function of θ by use of Section 63, or from memory of formulas and periodicity properties.

26. $\cot (180° + \theta)$. **27.** $\sin (270° + \theta)$. **28.** $\cos (270° - \theta)$.

29. $\sec (180° - \theta)$. **30.** $\sec (270° + \theta)$. **31.** $\sec (90° - \theta)$.

32. $\tan (270° - \theta)$. **33.** $\csc (180° + \theta)$. **34.** $\csc (360° - \theta)$.

35. $\sec (360° + \theta)$. **36.** $\tan (180° + \theta)$. **37.** $\sin (540° + \theta)$.

38. $\cos (270° + \theta)$. **39.** $\csc (\theta - 360°)$. **40.** $\tan (450° - \theta)$.

41. $\sec (450° + \theta)$. **42.** $\sin (- 270° + \theta)$. **43.** $\cot (- 180° + \theta)$.

44. $\sin (360° + \theta)$. **45.** $\tan (630° - \theta)$. **46.** $\cos (- 360° + \theta)$.

47. $\tan (540° + \theta)$. **48.** $\sin (720° + \theta)$. **49.** $\csc (\theta - 720°)$.

★*By use of the method of Sections* 60 *and* 61, *give a proof of the reduction formulas for functions of the specified angle.   Use a figure where θ is an acute angle.*

50. $180° - \theta$.   **51.** $270° + \theta$.   **52.** $\theta - 90°$.   **53.** $\theta - 180°$.

★**54–55.** Repeat Problems 50 and 51 with θ in quadrant III.

★**56.** Write the reduction formulas for $(270° + \theta)$, and then prove formulas for $(270° - \theta)$ by use of page 71.

64. Variation of sin θ and cos θ

Let θ be an angle in standard position in Figure 50, where the circle has radius 1. Let $P:(x, y)$ be the intersection of the terminal side of θ and the circle; then, $r = OP = 1$;

$$\sin \theta = \frac{y}{r} = \frac{y}{1} = y; \quad \cos \theta = \frac{x}{1} = x.$$

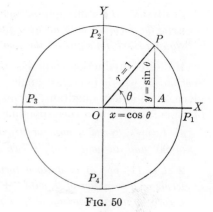

FIG. 50

That is, the *ordinate* of P is sin θ and the *abscissa* is cos θ. If we let θ be a variable which increases continuously from $\theta = 0°$ to $\theta = 360°$, the corresponding variation in sin θ and cos θ is shown by the changes in the coordinates of P.

ILLUSTRATION 1. If θ increases from $0°$ to $90°$, P moves on the circle from P_1 to P_2, and the ordinate sin θ of P increases from 0 to 1. If θ increases from $90°$ to $270°$, sin θ decreases from 1 to -1. If θ increases from $0°$ to $180°$, the abscissa cos θ of P decreases from 1 to -1.

65. Variation of tan θ

Let θ be an angle in standard position in Figure 51, where $P:(x, y)$ is chosen on the terminal side of θ so that $x = 1$. Then,*

FIG. 51

$$\tan \theta = \frac{y}{x} = \frac{y}{1} = y, \qquad (1)$$

or, the *ordinate* of P is equal to tan θ.

Suppose, now, that θ increases steadily from $0°$ and approaches $90°$ as a limit. Then, the corresponding point P in Figure 51 moves upward beyond all bounds on the vertical line through A; the ordinate tan θ of P increases from 0 *through all positive values*. Hence, tan θ becomes greater than any specified number, however large, for all values of θ sufficiently near $90°$. We summarize this by saying that tan θ *becomes positively infinite*, or *approaches* $+\infty$ (read *plus infinity*) as the acute angle θ approaches $90°$ as a limit. Figure 51 does not apply when $\theta = 90°$, and we recall from page 10 that tan $90°$ does not exist, because y/x is not defined if $x = 0$.

In Figure 52 for $\theta > 90°$, we choose $P:(x, y)$ so that $x = -1$ and, as in (1), find $y = -\tan \theta$. If θ decreases steadily from $180°$ and approaches $90°$ as a limit, tan θ decreases from 0 *without bound* through all negative values. We summarize this by saying that tan θ *becomes negatively infinite*, or *approaches* $-\infty$ (read *minus infinity*) as the obtuse angle θ approaches $90°$ as a limit. All the facts just mentioned about tan θ for θ near $90°$ are implied as the meaning of the symbolic equation

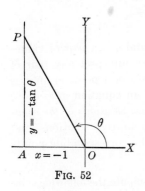

FIG. 52

$$\tan 90° = \infty, \qquad (2)$$

which is read "*tangent* $90°$ *is infinite.*" The symbol ∞, which we read *infinite* or *infinity*,

* See Note 6 in the Appendix for a detailed introduction of directed line segments to represent the values of the trigonometric functions.

is *not a number* and (2) is not an ordinary equation. It abbreviates the following facts:

I. *There is no tangent for* 90°.

II. *The absolute value of* tan θ *becomes greater than any specified number, however large, for all angles* θ *sufficiently near* 90°.

Similarly, tan $\theta = \infty$ (*tangent* θ *is infinite*) if θ is any angle whose terminal side in standard position falls on OY. Thus,

$$\text{tan } 270° = \infty.$$

ILLUSTRATION 1.   From trigonometric tables it is found that

$$\text{tan } 89° = 57; \qquad \text{tan } 89° \, 59' = 3438; \qquad \text{tan } 89° \, 59' \, 59'' = 206,265.$$

66. Variation of cot θ, sec θ, csc θ

Since cot $\theta = 1/\text{tan } \theta$, the angle θ has no cotangent when tan $\theta = 0$, because $1/0$ has no meaning. However, if θ varies so that tan θ *approaches the limit zero*, which occurs if θ approaches 0°, 180°, etc., the absolute value of $1/\text{tan } \theta$ grows large without bound, or cot θ *becomes infinite*. Thus, we obtain cot $\theta = \infty$ (*cotangent* θ *is infinite*) if θ is any angle whose terminal side in standard position falls on OX. That is,

$$\text{cot } 0° = \infty, \quad \text{cot } 180° = \infty, \quad \text{cot } 360 = \infty °, \text{ } etc.$$

ILLUSTRATION 1.   We recall sec $\theta = 1/\cos \theta$ and csc $\theta = 1/\sin \theta$. If θ is any angle whose terminal side in standard position falls on OY, then cos $\theta = 0$ and sec $\theta = \infty$; thus, sec 90° $= \infty$, sec 270° $= \infty$, etc. If θ is any angle whose terminal side falls on OX, then sin $\theta = 0$ and we obtain csc $\theta = \infty$; that is, we have

$$\text{csc } 0° = \infty, \quad \text{csc } 180° = \infty, \quad \text{csc } 360° = \infty, \text{ } etc.$$

Note 1.   The complete facts about the variation of the functions of a variable angle θ are best remembered in connection with later graphs.

67. General terminology of graphing

A *solution* of an equation in two variables x and y is a *pair* of values of x and y which satisfy the equation. We may interpret any pair of corresponding values of x and y as the coordinates of a point in an x, y coordinate plane. Then, we define the **graph of an equation** in x and y as the set of *all points whose coordinates* (x, y) *form solutions of the equation*. To graph an equation, we compute representative solutions, and then draw a smooth curve (or curves) through the corresponding points (x, y).

ILLUSTRATION 1.   To graph $3x - 5y = 15$, we compute the following solutions. We substitute $x = 0$ and obtain $y = -3$; thus, $(x = 0, \ y = -3)$ is a solution. If $y = 0$ then $x = 5$; if $x = -2$ then $y = -4\frac{1}{5}$; etc. The points (x, y) from the table are plotted in Figure 53, and lie on the line l, which is the graph of $3x - 5y = 15$. This illustrates the fact that the graph of any linear equation in x and y is a *line*.

FIG. 53

$x =$	-2	0	3	5	6
$y =$	$-4\frac{1}{5}$	-3	$-1\frac{1}{5}$	0	$\frac{3}{5}$

Let $f(x)$ represent any function (not necessarily a trigonometric function) of a variable x, and let $y = f(x)$. Then, we define the **graph of the function** $f(x)$ as the graph of the corresponding equation $y = f(x)$. That is, the graph of $f(x)$ is the set of all points in the x, y plane whose coordinates (x, y) form pairs of corresponding values of x and the function $f(x)$.

ILLUSTRATION 2. To graph the function of x defined by the formula $(\frac{3}{5}x - 3)$, we let $y = \frac{3}{5}x - 3$ and graph this equation. On multiplying both sides of it by 5, we obtain $3x - 5y = 15$. Hence, the equations

$$y = \tfrac{3}{5}x - 3 \quad and \quad 3x - 5y = 15 \tag{1}$$

have the same solutions; thus, the graph of $(\frac{3}{5}x - 3)$ is the line l in Figure 53, which is the graph of $3x - 5y = 15$.

68. Graphs of sin x and cos x

Let* x represent the measure of a variable angle in degrees.† Then, we shall obtain graphs of the trigonometric functions of x.

ILLUSTRATION 1. To graph $y = \sin x$, we first make up the entries in the following table from $x = 0°$ to $x = 90°$, from Table IV or memory. Then, we choose angles on the range 90° to 360° whose reference angles are those just used. Thus, with the reference angle 75°,

$$\sin 105° = \sin 75° = .97; \quad \sin 255° = -\sin 75° = -.97; \quad \sin 285° = -.97.$$

The points (x, y) from the table were used to obtain the graph in Figure 54 on page 80 from 0° to 360°. The complete graph consists of this wave and its endless repetitions on both sides, because $\sin x$ is a periodic function with 360° as a period, or $\sin (x \pm 360°) = \sin x$ for all values of x. Thus, to plot the point (x, y) on the graph where $x = -330°$, we use the ordinate for $x = 30°$

x	0°	30°	45°	60°	75°	90°	105°	120°	135°	150°	180°
$y = \sin x$	0	.50	.71	.87	.97	1.00	.97	.87	.71	.50	0

x	180°	210°	225°	240°	255°	270°	285°	300°	315°	330°	360°
$y = \sin x$	0	$-.50$	$-.71$	$-.87$	$-.97$	-1.00	$-.97$	$-.87$	$-.71$	$-.50$	0

* Notice this change in notation. In the future, only rarely will we use (x, y) for the coordinates of a point on the terminal side of an angle.

† Graphs with angular measure in a different unit will be met later.

because $30° - 360° = -330°$. The graph of $y = \cos x$ in Figure 55 is obtained similarly.

FIG. 54 $y = \sin x$

The identity $\sin (x + 90°) = \cos x$ states that *the cosine of any angle is the same as the sine of an angle which is* $90°$ *greater*. Therefore, if we shift the graph of $\sin x$ to the left, through a distance equal to $90°$ on the horizontal scale, we obtain the graph of $\cos x$.

FIG. 55 $y = \cos x$

ILLUSTRATION 2. In Figure 54, the values of $y = \sin x$ are seen to lie between -1 and $+1$, inclusive. If x varies from $x = 0°$ to $x = 90°$, the graph *rises*, or $\sin x$ *increases* from 0 to 1. If x varies from $90°$ to $270°$, the graph *falls*, or $\sin x$ *decreases* from 1 to -1; etc.

EXERCISE 31

Graph each equation.

1. $2x - 5y = 10$.   **2.** $3y - 4x = 12$.   **3.** $x = 5$.   **4.** $y = -7$.

Graph the function over the indicated range. In arranging x and y scales, make the distance for $180°$ on the x-axis approximately three times the unit distance on the y-axis. Use the periodicity property in restricting the table of values of (x, y) which are employed in plotting points.

5. $y = \sin x$ from $x = -180°$ to $y = 450°$.

6. $y = \cos x$ from $x = -270°$ to $x = 450°$.

7. By inspecting a graph, describe the variation of $\sin x$ and of $\cos x$, mentioning each range of $90°$, as x increases continuously from $x = -180°$ to $x = 360°$.

69. Graphs of tan x, cot x, sec x, csc x

Since tan x is a periodic function with 180° as a period, the complete graph of $y = \tan x$ consists of endless repetitions, to the left and the right, of the branch shown from $x = 90°$ to $x = 270°$, in Figure 56.

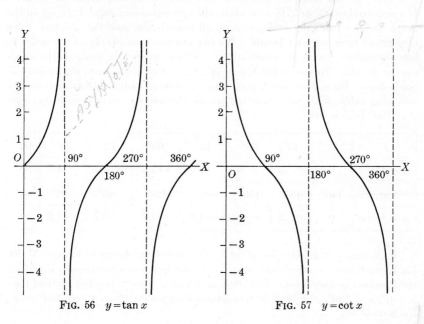

FIG. 56 $y = \tan x$ FIG. 57 $y = \cot x$

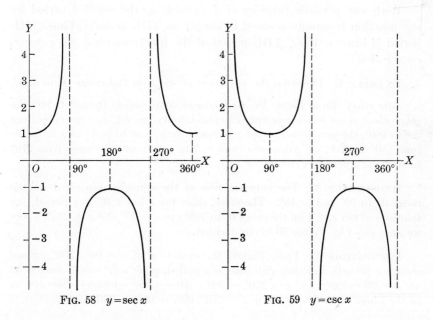

FIG. 58 $y = \sec x$ FIG. 59 $y = \csc x$

ILLUSTRATION 1. The graph of $y = \tan x$ in Figure 56 was constructed by use of the following table. In forming a similar table from $x = 180°$ to $x = 360°$, we would use the identity $\tan (x + 180°) = \tan x$. In Figure 56, the vertical broken lines, called **asymptotes,** with the equations $x = 90°$ and $x = 270°$, do not meet the graph because there is *no tangent for* 90° *or* 270°. If x approaches 90° or 270° as a limit, the corresponding point $P:(x, y)$ on the graph recedes from the x-axis beyond all bounds, because the absolute value of y grows large without bound. We can approach as closely as we desire to any asymptote, but never reach it, by receding sufficiently far from the x-axis on the graph. To construct Figure 56, the asymptotes were drawn first as guide lines; then, the curves were drawn through points obtained from the following table, with corresponding points plotted, by use of periodicity, from $x = 180°$ to $x = 360°$.

x	0°	15°	30°	45°	60°	75°	78°	90°
$y = \tan x$	0	.3	.6	1.0	1.7	3.7	4.7	∞
x	180°	165°	150°	135°	120°	105°	102°	90°
$y = \tan x$	0	− .3	− .6	− 1.0	− 1.7	− 3.7	− 4.7	∞

ILLUSTRATION 2. Graphs of $\cot x$, $\sec x$, $\csc x$ are shown in Figures 57–59. Each graph has a vertical asymptote corresponding to each value of x for which the function is undefined. Thus, the graph of $y = \csc x$ has the vertical lines $x = 0°$, $x = 180°$, $x = 360°$ as asymptotes because $\csc 0° = ∞$, $\csc 180° = ∞$, $\csc 360° = ∞$.

With any periodic function of a variable x, the *smallest* period for the function is usually referred to simply as THE period. Thus, THE period of $\tan x$ is 180°; THE period of the functions $\sin x$, $\cos x$, $\sec x$, $\csc x$ is 360°.

EXAMPLE 1. Describe the variation of $\sec x$ on the range 0° to 360°.

SOLUTION. From Figure 58, if x increases continuously from 0° to 90°, the graph *rises*, or $\sec x$ *increases* from 1 to plus infinity ($+ ∞$); as x increases from 90° to 180°, the graph *rises*, or $\sec x$ *increases* from $− ∞$ to $− 1$; as x increases from 180° to 270°, $\sec x$ *decreases* from $− 1$ to $− ∞$; as x increases from 270° to 360°, $\sec x$ *decreases* from $+ ∞$ to 1.

ILLUSTRATION 3. The only solution of the equation $\tan x = 1$ on the range 0° to 90° is $x = 45°$. Therefore, since $\tan x$ has 180° as a period, the solutions of $\tan x = 1$ on the range 0° to 360° are $x = 45°$ and $x = 225°$, where we were aided by Figure 56 in our decision.

ILLUSTRATION 4. From Figure 58, $\sec x = ∞$ if $x = 90°$, 270°. Since $\sec x$ is a periodic function with 360° as a period, other solutions of $\sec x = ∞$ are $x = 90° − 360°$ and $x = 270° − 360°$. Hence, the solutions of $\sec x = ∞$ on the range $− 360°$ to 360° are $x = 270°, 90°, − 90°, − 270°$.

ILLUSTRATION 5. To find all values of arccsc (-1) on the range $-360°$ to $360°$, we first let $x = $ arccsc (-1). Then, csc $x = -1$ and hence $x = 270°$. By periodicity, we also find $x = 270° - 360° = -90°$. Thus, on the range $-360°$ to $360°$, arccsc (-1) has the values $-90°$ and $270°$.

Note 1. A function of x (not necessarily a trigonometric function) is said to be *continuous* at a value of x where the graph of the function is continuous in the geometrical sense, and is said to be *discontinuous* at a value of x where there is a break in the graph. Thus, sin x and cos x are continuous at all values of x. Tan x, sec x, cot x, csc x are continuous except where the functions are undefined.

EXERCISE 32

Graph the function on the indicated range. Adjust the scales as suggested in Exercise 31. Draw any asymptotes which the graph possesses.

1. $y = $ cot x from $x = -180°$ to $x = 360°$.

2. $y = $ tan x from $x = -90°$ to $x = 450°$.

3. $y = $ sec x from $x = -90°$ to $x = 450°$.

4. $y = $ csc x from $x = -180°$ to $x = 360°$.

5. By inspection of graphs, describe the variation of each of the functions tan x, cot x, sec x, csc x as x varies from $x = 0°$ to $x = 360°$.

Find all solutions of the equation between $-360°$ and $360°$.

6. tan $x = 0$.   **7.** sin $x = 1$.   **8.** cos $x = -1$.   **9.** cot $x = 0$.

10. csc $x = 1$.   **11.** tan $x = -1$.   **12.** cot $x = -1$.   **13.** tan $x = \infty$.

14. cos $x = 0$.   **15.** sin $x = 0$.   **16.** csc $x = \infty$.   **17.** sec $x = 1$.

18. sec $x = -1$.   **19.** cot $x = \infty$.   **20.** cos $x = 1$.   **21.** sin $x = -1$.

22. On *one coordinate system*, over the range $x = -90°$ to $x = 270°$, draw smooth graphs rapidly by use of very few points, and any asymptotes, for $y = $ cos x and $y = $ sec x. Repeat the problem for $y = $ sin x and $y = $ csc x, from $x = 0°$ to $x = 360°$.

23. Obtain the values of the inverse function on the range $-360°$ to $360°$: arcsin (-1);   arctan 1;   arccsc 1;   arccos 0;   arccot (-1).

24. Add rows to the following table for $\theta = 90°, 180°, 270°, 360°$.

θ	SIN θ	CSC θ	COS θ	SEC θ	TAN θ	COT θ
0°	0	∞	1	1	0	∞

SIX

RADIAN MEASURE

70. Radian measure

Previously in this book, angles have been measured in degrees and their fractional parts. Hereafter, we shall frequently use an angular unit called a *radian*,* which is of fundamental importance in advanced mathematics and in its applications.

DEFINITION I. *One* **radian** *is the measure of an angle which, if its vertex is placed at the center of a circle, subtends on the circumference an arc equal to the radius of the circle.*

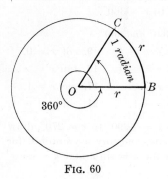

FIG. 60

ILLUSTRATION 1. In Figure 60, the measure of $\angle BOC$ is one radian. Hence, the length of the subtended arc BC is r.

Since an arc of length r subtends an angle of *one radian* at the center of a circle, the *whole circumference*, with length $2\pi r$, subtends an angle of $2\pi \times$ (*one radian*) or 2π *radians*.† In degrees, the whole circumference subtends $360°$. Hence,

$$360° = 2\pi \text{ radians};\qquad(1)$$

$$180° = \pi \text{ radians};\qquad(2)$$

$$1° = \frac{\pi}{180} \text{ radians} = .0174533 \text{ radians, } approximately;\qquad(3)$$

$$1 \text{ radian} = \frac{180°}{\pi} = 57.2958°, \text{ } approximately.\qquad(4)$$

Thus, from (3), to change degree measure to radian measure, multiply the number of degrees, in decimal form, by $\pi/180$. To change from radians to degrees, multiply the number of radians by $180/\pi$. Since $180° = \pi$ radians, any angle which is a convenient multiple of $180°$ is the same multiple of π radians.

* See Note 7 in the Appendix for a description of another somewhat related unit call a **mil,** which has military uses.

† Angles at the center of a circle are proportional to their subtended arcs.

ILLUSTRATION 2. $\frac{5}{6}\pi$ radians $= \frac{5}{6}(180°) = 150°$.

$$90° = \frac{1}{2}(180°) = \frac{1}{2}\pi \text{ radians} = \frac{\pi}{2} \text{ radians} = 1.5708 \text{ radians.}$$

$$3.2 \text{ rad.} = 3.2\frac{180°}{\pi} = \frac{(3.2)(180°)}{3.1416} = 183.35°, \text{ by logarithms.}$$

ILLUSTRATION 3. To change $143°\ 27'$ to radians, first express $27'$ as a decimal part of $1°$ and multiply by $\pi/180$ with the aid of logarithms. Thus,

$$27' = \tfrac{27}{60}(1°) = .45°;$$

$$143.45° = \frac{(143.45)(\pi)}{180} \text{ rad.} = \frac{(143.45)(3.1416)}{180} \text{ rad.} = 2.5037 \text{ rad.}$$

Hereafter, when *no unit is indicated* in giving the value of an angle, assume that the unit of measurement is a *radian*.

ILLUSTRATION 4. $\cos \pi$ means "*cosine of π radians*," or $\cos 180°$. Hence, $\cos \pi = -1$. From Table XIII, $\sin 1.18 = .92461$.

ILLUSTRATION 5. By use of Section 63, page 75, we find

$$\sin(\pi - \theta) = \cos \theta; \qquad \tan\left(\frac{3\pi}{2} + \theta\right) = -\cot \theta.$$

ILLUSTRATION 6. Since Table XIII extends only through an angle of 1.60 radians, for larger angles we must use reduction formulas before referring to Table XIII. To obtain $\cos 3.59$, we recall $\pi = 3.14$, and $3.59 - 3.14 = .45$:

$$\cos 3.59 = \cos(\pi + .45) = -\cos .45 = -.90045. \qquad \text{(Table XIII)}$$

Note 1. If considerable use in refined computation is to be made of functions of angles given in radian measure, a more extensive table like Table XIII would be employed. Without such aid, if an angle θ is given with high accuracy in radian measure, for example, to six decimal places, we can find the functions of θ to five decimal places by changing θ to degree measure, and using Table XI.

EXERCISE 33

Express the angle as a multiple of π radians.

1. 30°.	**2.** 45°.	**3.** 60°.	**4.** 36°.	**5.** 120°.
6. 135°.	**7.** 150°.	**8.** 720°.	**9.** $-90°$.	**10.** $-180°$.
11. 240°.	**12.** 270°.	**13.** 300°.	**14.** $-315°$.	**15.** 450°.

Given the radian measure of an angle, change to degree measure.

16. $\frac{\pi}{6}$.	**17.** $\frac{\pi}{3}$.	**18.** $\frac{3\pi}{4}$.	**19.** $\frac{\pi}{9}$.	**20.** $\frac{5\pi}{6}$.
21. $\frac{7\pi}{6}$.	**22.** $\frac{7\pi}{4}$.	**23.** $\frac{4\pi}{3}$.	**24.** $\frac{5\pi}{12}$.	**25.** $\frac{7\pi}{15}$.
26. 3π.	**27.** 2.	**28.** 4.	**29.** 2.5.	**30.** 3.6.

Construct the angle approximately to scale.

31. 3 rad.	**32.** 2 rad.	**33.** .1 rad.	**34.** 1.5 rad.

35. In a triangle, one angle is 36° and another is $\frac{2}{3}\pi$ radians. Find the third angle in radians.

36. Through how many radians does the hour hand of a clock revolve in 40 minutes?

37. Through how many radians does the minute hand of a clock revolve in 25 minutes?

38. Without using a table, write all functions of $\frac{\pi}{6}$; $\frac{\pi}{4}$; $\frac{\pi}{3}$.

Give the value of each function without using a table. As quickly as possible, learn to think in radians instead of changing to degrees.

39. $\sin \frac{1}{2}\pi$.   **40.** $\cos \pi$.   **41.** $\cos \frac{2}{3}\pi$.   **42.** $\sec 2\pi$.

43. $\sec 0$.   **44.** $\cos 0$.   **45.** $\sin \pi$.   **46.** $\tan \frac{2}{3}\pi$.

47. $\cot \frac{3}{4}\pi$.   **48.** $\csc \frac{3}{2}\pi$.   **49.** $\sec \frac{3}{4}\pi$.   **50.** $\sin \frac{5}{6}\pi$.

51. $\tan \frac{7}{6}\pi$.   **52.** $\cos \frac{11}{6}\pi$.   **53.** $\sin \frac{7}{4}\pi$.   **54.** $\cot \frac{5}{3}\pi$.

Find the value of the function by use of Table XIII.

55. $\sin 1.35$.   **56.** $\cos .84$.   **57.** $\tan 1.02$.   **58.** $\sin 1.47$.

Express in radians, using Table V.

59. 38° 21′.   **60.** 123° 50′.   **61.** 273° 45′.   **62.** 183° 18′.

Express each function in terms of a function of θ.

63. $\sin (\pi + \theta)$.   **64.** $\tan (2\pi - \theta)$.   **65.** $\sin (2\pi + \theta)$.

66. $\cos (\pi - \theta)$.   **67.** $\cos (2\pi - \theta)$.   **68.** $\cot (2\pi + \theta)$.

69. $\tan \left(\frac{\pi}{2} + \theta\right)$.   **70.** $\sin \left(\frac{3\pi}{2} + \theta\right)$.   **71.** $\csc \left(\frac{3\pi}{2} - \theta\right)$.

72. $\cot \left(\frac{3\pi}{2} - \theta\right)$.   **73.** $\sin \left(\frac{\pi}{2} - \theta\right)$.   **74.** $\sec \left(\frac{3\pi}{2} + \theta\right)$.

75. $\tan (\pi + \theta)$.   **76.** $\cot (\pi + \theta)$.   **77.** $\sin (\theta - \pi)$.

71. Relation between arc, angle, and radius

In a circle of radius r, in Figure 61, let s represent the length of the arc subtended on the circumference by a central angle of θ radians. Since 1 radian at the center subtends an arc whose length is r, then θ radians subtend an arc whose length is $\theta \cdot r$. That is,

$$s = r\theta; \tag{1}$$

arc = (radius) × (angle, in radians). (2)

FIG. 61

ILLUSTRATION 1. If $r = 25$ feet and $s = 75$ feet, then, from (1),

$$\theta = \frac{s}{r} = \frac{75}{25} = 3 \text{ radians.}$$

EXAMPLE 1. Find the length of the arc subtended by a central angle of 35° in a circle whose radius is 20 feet.

SOLUTION. 1. Find the radian measure of 35°:

$$\theta = 35 \cdot \frac{\pi}{180} = \frac{7\pi}{36} \text{ radians.}$$

2. Since $r = 20$, $\qquad s = r\theta = 20\frac{7\pi}{36} = \frac{35\pi}{9}, \text{ or } s = 12.2 \text{ ft.}$

Note 1. Example 1 can also be solved by use of a simple proportion, without use of radian measure. Thus, $s : 2\pi r = \theta : 360°$, or *the arc subtended by θ bears the same ratio to the circumference as θ bears to 360°.*

72. Linear and angular speed

Consider an object P which is moving with uniform speed on the circumference of a circle with center O and radius r. Let v represent the length of arc traversed by P in one unit of time. Then v is the **linear speed** of P. In Figure 62, let ω be the measure (positive) of the angle through which the line OP turns about O in one unit of time.

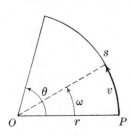

FIG. 62

Then, we call ω the **angular speed** of P with respect to O. If ω is expressed in radian measure, from (1) of Section 71 we obtain

$$v = r\omega. \tag{1}$$

If, in t units of time, P moves over an arc of length s and OP revolves through an angle θ, then

$$s = vt; \qquad \theta = \omega t. \tag{2}$$

Any circular motion which we shall consider will be at uniform speed.

EXAMPLE 1. If P moves 38 feet in 4 seconds on the circumference of a circle whose radius is 6 feet, find the angular speed of P.

SOLUTION. 1. From $s = vt$, $\qquad 38 = 4v$; $\qquad v = \frac{19}{2} \text{ ft. per sec.}$

2. From (1), $\qquad \frac{19}{2} = 6\omega$; $\qquad \omega = \frac{19}{12} \text{ radians per sec.}$

EXAMPLE 2. A belt passes over the rim of a flywheel, 30 inches in diameter. Find the speed of the belt if it drives the wheel at the rate of 5 revolutions per second.

SOLUTION. 1. The belt moves with the same speed as a point on the rim.

2. One revolution equals 2π radians; hence, $\omega = 5 \times 2\pi = 10\pi$ radians.

3. From (1), $v = 15(10\pi) = 150\pi = 471.2 \text{ in. per sec., the belt speed.}$

EXERCISE 34

Obtain each result correct to three significant digits.

By use of $s = r\theta$, find whichever of (r, s, θ) is not given; α represents the degree measure corresponding to θ radians.

1. $r = 10$ ft.; $\theta = 2.3$.   **2.** $r = 450$ ft.; $\theta = 5.7$.

3. $r = 25$ ft.; $\theta = 1.6$.   **4.** $\theta = \frac{5}{4}\pi$; $s = 150$ ft.

5. $\theta = \frac{7}{6}\pi$; $s = 125$ in.   **6.** $\theta = 6.8$; $s = 50.6$ in.

7. $\alpha = 120°$; $s = 375$ in.   **8.** $\alpha = 240°$; $s = 30.5$ in.

9. $s = 175$ in.; $r = 4$ ft.   **10.** $s = 2500$ ft.; $r = .75$ mi.

11. $\alpha = 135°$; $r = 16$ in.   **12.** $\alpha = 340°$; $r = 50$ ft.

13. On a circle, if an arc 30 feet long subtends an angle of 2 radians at the center, find the radius of the circle.

14. In a circle 16 inches in diameter, how long an arc is subtended on the circumference by an angle of 2.4 radians at the center?

15. Through what angle in radians would a runner turn in going 100 yards on a circular track 140 yards in diameter?

16. A railroad curve, in the form of an arc of a circle, is 850 yards long. If the radius of the circle is 950 yards, find the angle in degrees through which a train turns in going around the curve.

17. In going around a circular curve which is 645 yards long, a railroad train turns through an angle of 57° 35′. Find the radius of the curve.

18. At the intersection of two streets, a street-car track accomplishes a change of direction of 36° 25′ by following the arc of a circle for 185 feet. Find the radius of this arc.

19. If a flywheel is 4 feet in diameter, find the speed of a belt which drives the wheel at 400 revolutions per minute.

20. If a flywheel is 3 feet in diameter and if a belt over the wheel is traveling at the rate of 3000 feet per minute, find the number of revolutions of the wheel per minute.

21. Find the radius of a flywheel if it is turned at 1250 revolutions per minute by a belt over the rim with a speed of 60 feet per second.

22. A flywheel, 48 inches in diameter, is driven by a belt moving over the rim with a speed of 3600 feet per minute. Find the angular speed of the wheel (*a*) in radians per minute; (*b*) in revolutions per minute.

23. A moving belt drives two flywheels whose diameters are 30 inches and 50 inches. If the smaller wheel turns through 280 revolutions per minute, find the speed of the belt in feet per second and the angular speed of the larger wheel in revolutions per minute.

24. Find the angular speed in radians per minute of the end of (*a*) the minute hand of a watch; (*b*) the hour hand.

25. Assume that the earth is a sphere with a radius of 4000 miles which revolves on its axis once in 24 hours. Disregarding the other motions of the earth, find the linear speed per second of a point on the equator.

73. Trigonometric graphs, with angles measured in radians

Suppose that y is a trigonometric function of x, which is the measure of a variable angle in terms of a certain angular unit. Then, in drawing the graph of the function, if there is *no specified relation between the scales* on the coordinate axes, *no standard shape for the graph is associated with the angular unit.*

In most of the applications of trigonometric graphs in calculus and in many parts of applied mathematics, the graphs are made subject to the following agreements, which we adopt in the remainder of this chapter. The graphs obtained will be called *standard graphs.*

I. *If an expression is given for the value of an angle, this value is the measure of the angle* **in radians.**

II. *If y is a trigonometric function* of a variable x, in graphing the function we shall use the same unit of distance for the number scales on the x-axis and y-axis of the coordinate system.*

EXAMPLE 1. Graph $y = \sin x$ on the range $x = 0$ to $x = \pi$, inclusive.

SOLUTION. 1. Let γ be the degree measure corresponding to x radians. We select values of γ and find $\sin x$ from knowledge of $\sin \gamma$. We list values of x first as multiples of π and then as decimals, from Table XIII.

γ	0°	30°	45°	60°	75°	90°	105°	120°	135°	150°	180°
$x =$	0	$\frac{1}{6}\pi$	$\frac{1}{4}\pi$	$\frac{1}{3}\pi$	$\frac{5}{12}\pi$	$\frac{1}{2}\pi$	$\frac{7}{12}\pi$	$\frac{2}{3}\pi$	$\frac{3}{4}\pi$	$\frac{5}{6}\pi$	π
$x =$	0	.52	.79	1.05	1.31	1.57	1.83	2.09	2.36	2.62	3.14
$y = \sin x$	0	.50	.71	.87	.97	1.00	.97	.87	.71	.50	0

2. To form Figure 63, select a unit for distance and lay off a scale with this unit on both OX and OY. Then, plot (x, y) from the table as usual.

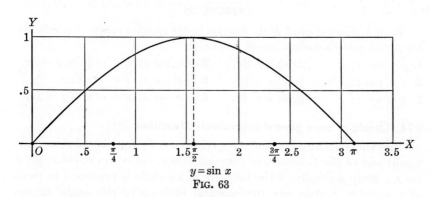

$y = \sin x$
FIG. 63

---

* Agreement II also applies when complicated trigonometric functions, or mixed algebraic and trigonometric functions are met.

EXAMPLE 2.   Obtain a standard graph of $y = \cos x$ on the range from $x = 0$ to $x = 2\pi$, inclusive.

SOLUTION.   1. Form the following table of values:

$x =$	0	$\frac{1}{6}\pi$	$\frac{1}{3}\pi$	$\frac{1}{2}\pi$	π	$\frac{3}{2}\pi$	2π
$y = \cos x$	1	$\frac{1}{2}\sqrt{3} = .87$	$\frac{1}{2}$	0	-1	0	1

2. In drawing a graph which does not have to be extremely accurate, we proceed as follows in order to avoid recalling many decimal values for x. *First*, choose a unit for distance in Figure 64 and mark the corresponding scales on OX and OY, in units.   Locate π and 2π accurately on OX as 3.14 and 6.28.   By use of compasses or dividers, or by visual estimation, without using decimal values, mark on OX the points $\frac{1}{2}\pi$, $\frac{1}{3}\pi$, $\frac{1}{6}\pi$, and corresponding points between $x = \frac{1}{2}\pi$ and $x = 2\pi$.   Then, plot the points (x, y) from the table, and add points between $x = \frac{1}{2}\pi$ and $x = 2\pi$ from knowledge of the symmetry of the wave for $y = \cos x$.

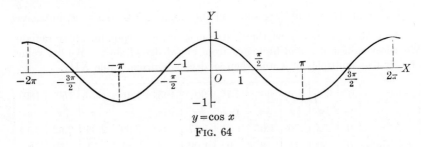

$$y = \cos x$$
FIG. 64

Note 1.   With the scales arranged in Figures 54–59 on pages 80–81, those graphs have essentially the standard shapes which result from agreements (I) and (II).

EXERCISE 35

Draw a standard graph of the function on the specified range.   Use relatively few plotted points but obtain smooth graphs.

1. $y = \sin x$; $x = -2\pi$ to $x = 2\pi$.   **2.** $y = \cos x$; $x = -\frac{3}{2}\pi$ to $x = \frac{5}{2}\pi$.

3. $y = \tan x$; $x = -\frac{1}{2}\pi$ to $x = \frac{5}{2}\pi$.   **4.** $y = \cot x$; $x = -\pi$ to $x = 2\pi$.

5. $y = \sec x$; $x = -\frac{1}{2}\pi$ to $x = \frac{5}{2}\pi$.   **6.** $y = \csc x$; $x = -\pi$ to $x = 2\pi$.

★74. Graphs of more general trigonometric functions

Previously, in any reference to a trigonometric function of x, we have meant one of the *fundamental* functions $\sin x$, $\cos x$, $\tan x$, $\cot x$, $\sec x$, $\csc x$.   More generally, if the measure of an angle is expressed in terms of a variable x, then any fundamental function of this angle, or any algebraic combination of such functions, is called a *trigonometric function of x.*

EXAMPLE 1. Graph the function $y = \sin 3x$ from $x = 0$ to $x = 2\pi$.

SOLUTION. 1. If x increases from 0 to 2π, then $3x$ increases from 0 to 6π, and $\sin 3x$ passes through the values obtained from $\sin \theta$ if θ varies from 0 to 6π. Thus, on the range $x = 0$ to $x = 2\pi$, the graph of $y = \sin 3x$ will consist of *three waves*, whereas the graph of $y = \sin x$ consists of just *one wave*. The waves for $\sin x$ and $\sin 3x$ have the same amplitude.

2. Since zero values of $\sin \theta$ occur at intervals of π in the values of θ, zero values of $\sin 3x$ occur at intervals of π in the values of $3x$, or $\pi/3$ in the values of x. Hence, integral multiples of $\pi/6$ are used for x to obtain the crests, troughs, and nodes of the waves, giving the full line graph in Figure 65.

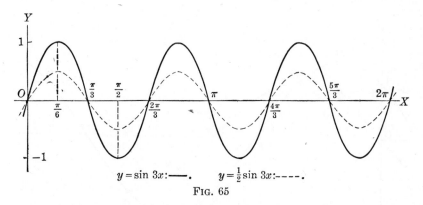

$y = \sin 3x$:——. $y = \frac{1}{2}\sin 3x$:----.

FIG. 65

Comment. Since $\sin \theta$ has the period 2π,

$$\sin 3x = \sin (3x + 2\pi) = \sin 3(x + \tfrac{2}{3}\pi).$$

Or, $\sin 3x$ is a periodic function with the period $2\pi/3$. This corresponds to the fact that there are three complete waves in Figure 65. Similarly, if n is a positive number,* $\sin nx$, $\cos nx$, $\sec nx$, $\csc nx$ are periodic functions of x with the period $2\pi/n$. The functions $\tan nx$ and $\cot nx$ are periodic functions of x with the period π/n because $\tan \theta$ and $\cot \theta$ have the period π.

ILLUSTRATION 1. The graph of $y = \frac{1}{2}\sin 3x$ is the broken-line curve in Figure 65, where each wave has one half the amplitude of the wave for $y = \sin 3x$. Values of y for graphing $y = \frac{1}{2}\sin 3x$ would be one half times those for $y = \sin 3x$ in Example 1.

75. Composition of ordinates

Let x be a variable and suppose that a function $F(x)$ is expressed as the sum of two functions, $F(x) = g(x) + h(x)$. In certain cases it may be desirable to obtain the graph of $F(x)$ by first graphing $g(x)$ and $h(x)$ on one coordinate system, and then adding, geometrically, corresponding ordinates of the graphs of $g(x)$ and $h(x)$. If this is done, we say that $F(x)$ is graphed by *composition* (or *addition*) *of ordinates*.

* Usually an integer in applications in this text.

EXAMPLE 1. Graph $y = \sin x + \cos x$ by composition of ordinates.

SOLUTION. 1. The graphs of $y_1 = \sin x$ and $y_2 = \cos x$ are shown in Figure 66.

2. To graph $y = \sin x + \cos x$, we note that $y = y_1 + y_2$. Hence, for any value of x, we obtain the ordinate y by geometrically adding y_1 and y_2, by use of dividers, with attention paid to the algebraic signs of y_1 and y_2.

3. If $y_1 = 0$, then $y = y_2$; this gives points A, B, C on the desired graph; D and E are obtained where $y_2 = 0$. If $y_1 = -y_2$, then $y = 0$; this gives F and G. Various other ordinates were added. The graph is the full-line curve in Figure 66.

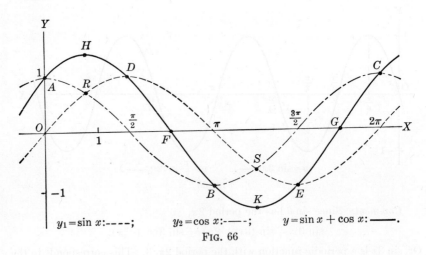

$y_1 = \sin x$:----; $y_2 = \cos x$:-----; $y = \sin x + \cos x$:———.

FIG. 66

★EXERCISE 36★

Graph each function, with x interpreted as radian measure, on the range from $x = 0$ to $x = 2\pi$.

1. $y = 3 \sin x$.   **2.** $y = -2 \cos x$.   **3.** $y = \sin 2x$.   **4.** $y = \cos 3x$.

5. $y = \cot 3x$.   **6.** $y = \tan 2x$.   **7.** $y = \sec 2x$.   **8.** $y = \csc 3x$.

9. $y = -3 \sin x$.   **10.** $y = -\sin 3x$.   **11.** $y = \sin \frac{1}{2}x$.

12. $y = \cos \frac{1}{3}x$.   **13.** $y = \cos x + \sin 2x$.   **14.** $y = \sin x - \cos x$.

15. $y = \cos 2x + \sin x$.   **16.** $y = \sin 2x + \cos 2x$.   **17.** $y = \cot x + \cos x$.

18. $y = x + \sin x$.   **19.** $y = x + \cos x$.   **20.** $y = 2x - \sin x$.

* The instructor may wish to permit this exercise (except for Problems 18, 19, 20) to be done with x interpreted as the *degree* measure of an angle, and with omission of agreement (II) of page 89.

SEVEN

APPLICATIONS OF FUNDAMENTAL IDENTITIES

76. The fundamental identities

By use of the definitions of the functions of θ on page 10, we proved that the reciprocal relations (1) below are true for all values of θ for which the expressions are defined. Similarly, we shall prove the quotient relations (2), and the relations (3) involving squares.

$$\csc \theta = \frac{1}{\sin \theta}; \qquad \sec \theta = \frac{1}{\cos \theta}; \qquad \cot \theta = \frac{1}{\tan \theta}. \qquad (1)$$

$$\tan \theta = \frac{\sin \theta}{\cos \theta}; \qquad \cot \theta = \frac{\cos \theta}{\sin \theta}. \qquad (2)$$

$$\sin^2 \theta + \cos^2 \theta = 1; \quad \tan^2 \theta + 1 = \sec^2 \theta; \quad 1 + \cot^2 \theta = \csc^2 \theta. \quad (3)$$

Note 1. To indicate a power of a trigonometric function, we place the exponent between the function's name and the angle. An exception is made in case the exponent is -1; thus, we write $(\sin \theta)^{-1}$, and not $\sin^{-1} \theta$, to mean $1/\sin \theta$.

Proof of (2). By use of Definition I, page 10,

$$\frac{\sin \theta}{\cos \theta} = \frac{\dfrac{y}{r}}{\dfrac{x}{r}} = \frac{y}{r} \cdot \frac{r}{x} = \frac{y}{x} = \tan \theta.$$

Similarly, the student will prove that $\cot \theta = \cos \theta / \sin \theta$.

Proof of (3). From page 10,

$$y^2 + x^2 = r^2. \qquad (4)$$

On dividing both sides of (4) by r^2, we obtain

$$\frac{y^2}{r^2} + \frac{x^2}{r^2} = 1 \quad or \quad \sin^2 \theta + \cos^2 \theta = 1.$$

Similarly, on dividing in (4) by x^2, and then by y^2, in turn, we obtain the other identities in (3).

Identities (1), (2), (3) should be memorized. Also, slight modifications of the identities should be recognized.

ILLUSTRATION 1. From (1), $\sin \theta = \dfrac{1}{\csc \theta}.$

From (2), $\sin \theta = \cos \theta \tan \theta;$ $\cos \theta = \sin \theta \cot \theta.$

From (3), $\sin^2 \theta = 1 - \cos^2 \theta;$ $\cos \theta = \pm \sqrt{1 - \sin^2 \theta}.$

From (1) and (2), all functions of θ are expressible in terms of $\sin \theta$ and $\cos \theta$ *without introducing radicals.*

ILLUSTRATION 2. On using (1) and (2) below, we obtain

$$\frac{\tan \theta + \cot \theta}{\tan \theta - \cot \theta} = \frac{\dfrac{\sin \theta}{\cos \theta} + \dfrac{\cos \theta}{\sin \theta}}{\dfrac{\sin \theta}{\cos \theta} - \dfrac{\cos \theta}{\sin \theta}} = \frac{\dfrac{\sin^2 \theta + \cos^2 \theta}{\sin \theta \cos \theta}}{\dfrac{\sin^2 \theta - \cos^2 \theta}{\sin \theta \cos \theta}}$$

$$= \frac{1}{\sin \theta \cos \theta} \cdot \frac{\sin \theta \cos \theta}{\sin^2 \theta - \cos^2 \theta} = \frac{1}{\sin^2 \theta - \cos^2 \theta}.$$

EXAMPLE 1.   If $\sin \theta = \frac{3}{5}$ and θ is in quadrant II, find all other functions of θ algebraically.

SOLUTION. 1. From (1),· $\csc \theta = \frac{5}{3}.$

2. From (3), $\cos^2 \theta = 1 - \sin^2 \theta = 1 - \frac{9}{25} = \frac{16}{25};$

$$\cos \theta = \pm \sqrt{\tfrac{16}{25}} = \pm \tfrac{4}{5}.$$

Since θ is in quadrant II, $\cos \theta$ is negative; hence, $\cos \theta = -\frac{4}{5}.$

3. From (1), $\sec \theta = -\frac{5}{4}.$

4. From (2), $\tan \theta = \dfrac{\frac{3}{5}}{-\frac{4}{5}} = -\frac{3}{4};$ from (1), $\cot \theta = -\frac{4}{3}.$

EXAMPLE 2.   If $\cot \theta = \frac{8}{15}$ and θ is in quadrant III, find all other functions of θ algebraically.

SOLUTION. 1. From (1), $\tan \theta = \frac{15}{8}.$

2. From (3), $\csc^2 \theta = 1 + \frac{64}{225};$ $\csc \theta = -\sqrt{\tfrac{289}{225}} = -\frac{17}{15}.$

3. From (1), $\sin \theta = -\frac{15}{17}.$

4. From (2),

$\cos \theta = \sin \theta \cot \theta = -\frac{15}{17} \cdot \frac{8}{15} = -\frac{8}{17};$ *then* $\sec \theta = -\frac{17}{8}.$

Note 2. Problems like Examples 1 and 2 were solved geometrically before.

EXERCISE 37

Prove each identity by direct use of Definition I, *page* 10.

1. $\dfrac{\cos \theta}{\sin \theta} = \cot \theta.$ **2.** $\cos \theta = \dfrac{\sin \theta}{\tan \theta}.$ **3.** $\sin \theta = \dfrac{\cos \theta}{\cot \theta}.$

4. $\sin \theta \csc \theta = 1.$ **5.** $1 + \tan^2 \theta = \sec^2 \theta.$ **6.** $1 + \cot^2 \theta = \csc^2 \theta.$

By recalling a fundamental identity, write a proper right-hand member involving only one function or one number.

7. $\dfrac{1}{\cot \theta} = ?$ **8.** $\dfrac{1}{\sec \theta} = ?$ **9.** $\dfrac{1}{\csc \theta} = ?$

10. $\cos \theta \sec \theta = ?$ **11.** $\tan \theta \cot \theta = ?$ **12.** $\sin \theta \csc \theta = ?$

13. $1 - \sin^2 \theta = ?$ **14.** $\sec^2 \theta - 1 = ?$ **15.** $\csc^2 \theta - 1 = ?$

16. $1 - \cos^2 \theta = ?$ **17.** $1 + \cot^2 \theta = ?$ **18.** $\sec^2 \theta - \tan^2 \theta = ?$

By use of fundamental identities, find all other functions of θ if θ is in the quadrant shown by the roman numeral. Do not introduce decimals.

19. $\sin \theta = \frac{4}{5}$; (I).   **20.** $\cos \theta = \frac{12}{13}$; (I).   **21.** $\tan \theta = \frac{5}{12}$; (III).

22. $\sin \theta = -\frac{8}{17}$; (IV).   **23.** $\sec \theta = \frac{5}{4}$; (IV).   **24.** $\cot \theta = -\frac{4}{3}$; (II).

25. $\tan \theta = -\frac{24}{7}$; (IV).   **26.** $\csc \theta = -\frac{17}{15}$; (III).   **27.** $\cos \theta = -\frac{12}{13}$; (II).

28. $\tan \theta = 2$; (III).   **29.** $\sin \theta = \frac{2}{3}$; (II).   **30.** $\sec \theta = -2$; (III).

31. Compute $3 \tan \theta (2 \cot \theta + 1 - \sec^2 \theta)$ if $\tan \theta = 2$.

32. Compute $3 \cot^2 \theta (\sin \theta + \csc \theta)$ if $\sin \theta = \frac{1}{4}$.

33. Compute $\tan \theta (\sin \theta - 1)$ if $\cos \theta = \frac{2}{3}$ and θ is in quadrant (IV).

Change the expression into a form involving no functions except $\sin x$ and (or) $\cos x$; combine into a simple fraction and simplify.

34. $\sec x \cot x$.   **35.** $\cos x/\sec x$.   **36.** $\cot x/\sec x$.

37. $\cot x + \tan x$.   **38.** $\tan x - \sec x$.   **39.** $\sin x/\csc x$.

40. $\dfrac{\cos x + \sin x}{\sec x + \csc x}$.   **41.** $\dfrac{\cot^2 x}{1 + \cot^2 x}$.   **42.** $\dfrac{\csc x}{\cot x + \tan x}$.

43. $\dfrac{\tan x - \cot x}{\tan x + \cot x}$.   **44.** $\dfrac{\sec^2 x + \csc^2 x}{\sec x \csc x}$.   **45.** $\dfrac{\cot x + \cos x}{1 + \sin x}$.

46. $\dfrac{1}{\sec x - \tan x} - \dfrac{1}{\sec x + \tan x}$.

Express each function of x in terms of the given function by use of fundamental identities.

47. $\tan x$.   **48.** $\sin x$.   **49.** $\cos x$.   **50.** $\sec x$.   **51.** $\csc x$.

HINT for Problem 47. $\cot x = 1/\tan x$; $\sec x = \pm \sqrt{1 + \tan^2 x}$; etc.

77. Proofs of identities

In applications of trigonometry, particularly in calculus, it is sometimes necessary to prove that one trigonometric expression is equal to another for all values of the angles involved. Or, it may be necessary to prove that one trigonometric expression can be transformed into some other expression. Thus, applications of trigonometry frequently make it necessary to prove *trigonometric identities*. The fundamental identities can sometimes be used to establish other identities. On account of the nature of the applications of identities, the following method should be emphasized, although other logically satisfactory procedures will be illustrated.

I. To prove an identity, leave one side unaltered, and change the other side until it has the same form as the first side.

EXAMPLE 1. Prove the identity:

$$\tan \theta + 2 \cot \theta = \frac{\sin^2 \theta + 2 \cos^2 \theta}{\sin \theta \cos \theta}.$$

SOLUTION. We decide to leave the right-hand side unaltered. Since it involves only $\sin \theta$ and $\cos \theta$, we express the left-hand side in terms of $\sin \theta$ and $\cos \theta$, by use of page 93:

$$\tan \theta + 2 \cot \theta = \frac{\sin \theta}{\cos \theta} + \frac{2 \cos \theta}{\sin \theta} = \frac{\sin^2 \theta + 2 \cos^2 \theta}{\sin \theta \cos \theta}. \qquad \text{Q.E.D.}$$

EXAMPLE 2. Prove the identity: $\tan x + \cot x = \dfrac{\csc x}{\cos x}.$

SOLUTION. We leave the right-hand side unaltered:

$$\tan x + \cot x = \frac{\sin x}{\cos x} + \frac{\cos x}{\sin x} = \frac{\sin^2 x + \cos^2 x}{\sin x \cos x}$$

$$= \frac{1}{\sin x} \cdot \frac{1}{\cos x} = \csc x \cdot \frac{1}{\cos x} = \frac{\csc x}{\cos x}. \qquad \text{Q.E.D.}$$

To prove an identity, we may *alter both sides independently until we finally exhibit them in identical form.**

ILLUSTRATION 1. To prove the identity of Example 2 by the method of the preceding paragraph, we operate on each side separately. A line is drawn below to separate the sides and thus emphasize the fact that their equality is not being assumed while we are trying to prove it.

$$\tan x + \cot x = \frac{\sin x}{\cos x} + \frac{\cos x}{\sin x} \ \bigg\| \ \frac{\csc x}{\cos x} = \csc x \cdot \frac{1}{\cos x}$$

$$= \frac{\sin^2 x + \cos^2 x}{\sin x \cos x} = \frac{1}{\sin x \cos x}. \ \bigg\| = \frac{1}{\sin x} \cdot \frac{1}{\cos x} = \frac{1}{\sin x \cos x}. \quad \text{Q.E.D.}$$

EXAMPLE 3. Prove the identity: $\dfrac{1 + \cos x}{\sin x} = \dfrac{\sin x}{1 - \cos x}.$

SOLUTION. On the right, multiply numerator and denominator by $(1 + \cos x)$:

$$\frac{\sin x}{1 - \cos x} \cdot \frac{1 + \cos x}{1 + \cos x} = \frac{\sin x (1 + \cos x)}{1 - \cos^2 x}$$

$$= \frac{\sin x (1 + \cos x)}{\sin^2 x} = \frac{1 + \cos x}{\sin x}. \qquad \text{Q.E.D.}$$

* See Note 8 of the Appendix for another method of proof.

EXAMPLE 4. Prove the identity:

$$\sqrt{\frac{\sec x - \tan x}{\sec x + \tan x}} = \frac{1}{\sec x + \tan x}. \tag{1}$$

SOLUTION. We leave the right-hand side unaltered, and rationalize the denominator on the left by multiplying both numerator and denominator by $\sec x + \tan x$ under the radical:

$$\sqrt{\frac{\sec x - \tan x}{\sec x + \tan x}} = \sqrt{\frac{\sec x - \tan x}{\sec x + \tan x} \cdot \frac{\sec x + \tan x}{\sec x + \tan x}} = \sqrt{\frac{\sec^2 x - \tan^2 x}{(\sec x + \tan x)^2}}$$

[Using (3), page 93] $\qquad = \dfrac{1}{\sec x + \tan x}.$ Q.E.D.

Comment. As a rule, in any identity involving a radical, as in Example 4, we shall assume that values of the variables are restricted to a range where any factor removed from under the radical is *positive*.* This will avoid the ambiguous sign $\pm$ on many occasions. Thus, in Example 4, we restrict x so that $\sec x + \tan x > 0$. If $\sec x + \tan x < 0$, a minus sign should precede the right-hand side in (1).

The following suggestions are useful in proving identities.

a. If possible, avoid using formulas involving radicals.

b. Perhaps express all functions in terms of sines and cosines.

c. If one side of the identity involves just one function, perhaps express everything on the other side in terms of this function.

EXERCISE 38

Prove the identity by use of the fundamental identities.

1. $\cos \alpha \csc \alpha = \cot \alpha.$

2. $\sin \theta \sec \theta = \tan \theta.$

3. $\cos^2 \theta - \sin^2 \theta = 2 \cos^2 \theta - 1.$

4. $\cos^2 \theta - \sin^2 \theta = 1 - 2 \sin^2 \theta.$

5. $\cot x + \tan x = \sec x \csc x.$

6. $\csc^2 x \tan^2 x = \tan^2 x + 1.$

7. $(\sin \theta + \cos \theta)^2 = 1 + 2 \sin \theta \cos \theta.$

8. $(\cot x + 1)^2 = \csc^2 x + 2 \cot x.$

9. $\tan \theta = \dfrac{\sec \theta}{\csc \theta}.$

10. $\sin \theta = \dfrac{\cos \theta}{\cot \theta}.$

11. $\dfrac{1 - \sin^2 x}{\sin x} = \dfrac{\cos x}{\tan x}.$

12. $\dfrac{1 - \cos^2 \beta}{\cos \beta} = \sin \beta \tan \beta.$

13. $\dfrac{\cos^2 \theta}{1 - \sin \theta} = 1 + \sin \theta.$

14. $\dfrac{\tan^2 \beta}{\sec^2 \beta} + \dfrac{\cot^2 \beta}{\csc^2 \beta} = 1.$

15. $\dfrac{1 - \tan^2 x}{1 + \tan^2 x} = 1 - 2 \sin^2 x.$

16. $\dfrac{\tan^2 \theta + 1}{\cot^2 \theta + 1} = \tan^2 \theta.$

17. $\dfrac{1 + \csc x}{\sec x} = \cos x + \cot x.$

18. $\dfrac{\tan \theta - 1}{\tan \theta + 1} = \dfrac{1 - \cot \theta}{1 + \cot \theta}.$

19. $\dfrac{\sin y - \cos y}{\sin y + \cos y} = \dfrac{\tan y - 1}{\tan y + 1}.$

* If $H > 0$, then $\sqrt{H}$ represents the *positive* square root of H. Hence, if $a > 0$, then $\sqrt{a^2} = a$. If $a < 0$, then $\sqrt{a^2} = -a$.

20. $\dfrac{\sin x - \cos y}{\sin x + \cos y} = \dfrac{\sec y - \csc x}{\sec y + \csc x}.$ **21.** $\dfrac{\sec x}{\cot x + \tan x} = \sin x.$

22. $\sec x + \tan x = \dfrac{\sin^2 x + \sin x + \cos^2 x}{\cos x}.$

23. $\dfrac{\tan x - \cos x \cot x}{\csc x} = \dfrac{\sin x}{\cot x} - \dfrac{\cos x}{\sec x}.$

24. $\cot x - \tan x = 2 \cos x \csc x - \sec x \csc x.$

25. $\dfrac{\tan x - \tan y}{1 + \tan x \tan y} = \dfrac{\cot y - \cot x}{\cot x \cot y + 1}.$ **26.** $\dfrac{\sec^2 x}{\sec^2 x - 1} = \csc^2 x.$

27. $\dfrac{\sin x - \cos x}{\tan x \csc x - \sec x \cot x} = \sin x \cos x.$

28. $\dfrac{\sec^2 x + 2 \tan x}{1 + \tan x} = 1 + \tan x.$ **29.** $1 + \sin x = \dfrac{\cos x}{\sec x - \tan x}.$

30. $(\csc x + \sec x)^2 = \dfrac{\sec^2 x + 2 \tan x}{\sin^2 x}.$

31. $\dfrac{1}{\csc x - \cot x} - \dfrac{1}{\csc x + \cot x} = \dfrac{2}{\tan x}.$

32. $\cos^4 x - \sin^4 x = 1 - 2 \sin^2 x.$ **33.** $\sec^4 x - \tan^4 x = \dfrac{1 + \sin^2 x}{\cos^2 x}.$

34. $\dfrac{\cos x \cos y - \sin x \sin y}{\cos x \sin y + \sin x \cos y} = \dfrac{\cot x \cot y - 1}{\cot x + \cot y}.$

35. $\dfrac{\sin x \cos y + \cos x \sin y}{\cos x \cos y - \sin x \sin y} = \dfrac{\tan x + \tan y}{1 - \tan x \tan y}.$

Prove the identity without altering the right-hand side.

36. $\dfrac{1 + \sin x}{\cos x} = \dfrac{\cos x}{1 - \sin x}.$ **37.** $\sqrt{\dfrac{1 - \sin x}{1 + \sin x}} = \sec x - \tan x.$

38. $\dfrac{1}{\sec x + \tan x} = \dfrac{1 - \sin x}{\cos x}.$ **39.** $\sqrt{\dfrac{\csc x - \cot x}{\csc x + \cot x}} = \dfrac{1 - \cos x}{\sin x}.$

40. $\sqrt{\dfrac{\sec x - 1}{\sec x + 1}} = \dfrac{\sin x}{1 + \cos x}.$ **41.** $\sqrt{\dfrac{\sec x - \tan x}{\sec x + \tan x}} = \dfrac{\cos x}{1 + \sin x}.$

78. Trigonometric equations in one unknown

The simplest type of trigonometric equation is one which is *linear* in one function of one unknown angle θ, and thus gives the value of this function immediately. Then, there are usually *two* corresponding values for θ on the range $0° \leq \theta < 360°$, as we observed geometrically in problems in Section 16, page 16. On account of the periodicity of the trigonometric functions, any trigonometric equation usually has infinitely many solutions, with unbounded absolute values. In this book, unless otherwise directed, *to solve a trigonometric equation in θ* will mean to obtain only those solutions which are on the range $0° \leq \theta < 360°$.

SUMMARY. *To find θ when one function of θ is given:*

I. *From a trigonometric table, or from memory,* * *find an angle α between* $0°$ *and* $90°$, *inclusive, whose corresponding function is the absolute value of the given function of θ.*

II. *From knowledge of the signs of the functions in the various quadrants, locate the values of θ on the range* $0° \leqq θ < 360°$ *having α as the reference angle.*

EXAMPLE 1. Solve: $2 \cos θ - 1 = 0$.

SOLUTION. 1. This equation is linear (of the *first degree*) in $\cos θ$. We find $2 \cos θ = 1$ or $\cos θ = \frac{1}{2}$.

2. Recall that $\cos 60° = \frac{1}{2}$ and that the cosine is positive in quadrants I and IV. Hence, in quadrant IV, θ has that value for which the reference angle is 60°. The solutions are $θ = 60°$ and $θ = 300°$.

Comment. Other solutions are $-60°$, $420°$, $660°$, etc., which are obtained by adding integral multiples of 360° to 60° or 300°. For every integral value of n, each of the following expressions is a solution, or these expressions give the complete set of solutions of the equation:

$$θ = 60° + n(360°); \qquad θ = 300° + n(360°).$$

EXAMPLE 2. Solve: $\cos θ = -.9872$.

SOLUTION. 1. Let α be the acute angle such that $\cos α = .9872$. From Table VII, $α = 9° 10'$.

2. The cosine is negative in quadrants II and III. The values for θ are the angles in these quadrants having 9° 10′ as the reference angle. Hence, $θ = 180° \pm 9° 10'$, or the solutions are $θ = 189° 10'$, $170° 50'$.

A trigonometric equation in one angle θ, which is in the *quadratic form* in one function of θ, can be solved by use of methods met in dealing with quadratic equations in algebra. In particular, solution by factoring may apply.

EXAMPLE 3. Solve: $2 \sin^2 x - \sin x - 1 = 0$.

SOLUTION. 1. We say that this equation is in the *quadratic form* in $\sin x$ because, if we should let $v = \sin x$ (*which is unnecessary*) the equation would become $2v^2 - v - 1 = 0$. To solve the given equation we first factor:

$$(2 \sin x + 1)(\sin x - 1) = 0. \tag{1}$$

2. The equation is satisfied if:

$2 \sin x + 1 = 0$; then $\sin x = -\frac{1}{2}$ and $x = 210°$ and $x = 330°$;

$\sin x - 1 = 0$; then $\sin x = 1$ and $x = 90°$.

To solve an equation by use of factoring, *the equation must first be written with one member* **zero**.

---

* Functions of 0°, 30°, 45°, 60°, 90° should be thoroughly reviewed at this point.

EXAMPLE 4. Solve: $\sin x \cos x = \cos x$.

SOLUTION. 1. Subtract $\cos x$ from both sides; then factor:

$$\sin x \cos x - \cos x = 0; \qquad \cos x(\sin x - 1) = 0.$$

2. If $\cos x = 0$, then $x = 90°$ or $270°$. If $\sin x - 1 = 0$, then $x = 90°$.

INCORRECT SOLUTION. Divide both sides by $\cos x$: $\sin x = 1$; $x = 90°$.

Comment. **If both sides of an equation are divided by an expression involving the unknowns, solutions may be lost.** Thus, the division by $\cos x$ caused the loss of the solution $270°$ for which $\cos x = 0$.

EXAMPLE 5. Find all values of arctan $\sqrt{3}$ on the range $0°$ to $360°$.

SOLUTION. Let $x = \arctan \sqrt{3}$. Then, $\tan x = \sqrt{3}$. The solutions are $x = 60°$ and $x = 240°$. That is, $\arctan \sqrt{3} = 60°$ and $\arctan \sqrt{3} = 240°$.

ILLUSTRATION 1. To solve $\sin^2 x = \frac{1}{2}$, we extract square roots, obtaining $\sin x = \pm \sqrt{\frac{1}{2}} = \pm \sqrt{2}/2$. If $\sin x = \sqrt{2}/2$, then $x = 45°$ or $x = 135°$. If $\sin x = - \sqrt{2}/2$, then $x = 225°$ or $x = 315°$. Thus, we have four solutions.

EXERCISE 39

Solve each equation. Use Table VII if necessary.

1. $\tan x = 1$.　　**2.** $\cos x = \frac{1}{2}$.　　**3.** $\sec x = -1$.　　**4.** $\cos x = 0$.

5. $\tan x = \infty$.　　**6.** $\sec x = \infty$.　　**7.** $\sin x = 3$.　　**8.** $\sec x = \frac{1}{3}$.

9. $2 \sin x - 1 = 0$.　　**10.** $2 \cos x + 1 = 0$.　　**11.** $\tan x - \sqrt{3} = 0$.

12. $3 \cot x - \sqrt{3} = 0$.　　**13.** $2 \sin x + \sqrt{3} = 0$.　　**14.** $\sec x - 2 = 0$.

15. $\sin^2 x = 1$.　　**16.** $3 \tan x + \sqrt{3} = 0$.　　**17.** $\cos x = -2$.

18. $\tan^2 x = 1$.　　**19.** $2 \cos^2 x = 1$.　　**20.** $\sec^2 x = 2$.

21. $4 \sin^2 x - 3 = 0$.　　**22.** $\tan x = 1.621$.　　**23.** $\tan x = 4.449$.

24. $\cos x = -.8225$.　　**25.** $\sin x = .4823$.　　**26.** $\sin x = -.8526$.

27. $\cot x = -7.770$.　　**28.** $\cos x = .9224$.　　**29.** $\sin x = .4318$.

30. $3 \tan^2 x - 1 = 0$.　　**31.** $(\sin x + 1)(2 \sin x - 1) = 0$.

32. $\cos x (2 \cos x - 1) = 0$.　　**33.** $(\tan x - \sqrt{3})(\tan x + 1) = 0$.

34. $2 \cos^2 x - \cos x - 1 = 0$.　　**35.** $\sin^2 x - 2 \sin x + 1 = 0$.

36. $\csc^2 x - 4 \csc x + 4 = 0$.　　**37.** $2 \cos^2 x + 3 \cos x + 1 = 0$.

38. $4 \cos^2 x - 1 = 0$.　　**39.** $\sin^2 x = \sin x$.　　**40.** $2 \cos^2 x = - \cos x$.

41. $\sec^2 x - 3 \sec x + 2 = 0$.　　**42.** $\csc^2 x - \csc x - 2 = 0$.

43. $2 \sin^2 x + \sqrt{2} \sin x = 0$.　　**44.** $3 \tan^2 x - \sqrt{3} \tan x = 0$.

45. $\sin x \sec^2 x - 2 \sin x = 0$.　　**46.** $\cos x \cot^2 x - 3 \cos x = 0$.

★*Solve by factoring or by use of the quadratic formula on page 173.*

47. $2 \sin^4 x - 3 \sin^2 x + 1 = 0$.　　**48.** $3 \tan^3 x - \tan x = 0$.

49. $3 \cot^4 x + 2 \cot^2 x - 1 = 0$.　　**50.** $2 \sin^2 x - 3 \sin x - 1 = 0$.

HINT for Problem 50. Let $v = \sin x$. Then, $2v^2 - 3v - 1 = 0$.

51. $3 \cot^2 x - 5 \cot x - 1 = 0$.　　**52.** $\sin^2 x - 8 \sin x + 15 = 0$.

79. Equations solved by the aid of identities

In solving a trigonometric equation, our aim is to find one or more equations, each involving just one function of one unknown angle, which are equivalent to the given equation. To accomplish this aim, it may be useful to modify given expressions by use of known identities. The following actions should be thought of as possibilities.

I. *Express each function of x in terms of one function.*

II. *Express each function of x in terms of* $\sin x$ *and* $\cos x$.

EXAMPLE 1. Solve: $\sin \theta - \cos \theta = 0.$

SOLUTION. 1. Divide by $\cos \theta$: $\dfrac{\sin \theta}{\cos \theta} - 1 = 0,$ or $\tan \theta - 1 = 0.$

2. Hence, $\tan \theta = 1$; the solutions are $\theta = 45°$ and $\theta = 225°.$

Comment. If $\cos \theta = 0$, then $\theta = 90°$ or $\theta = 270°$. By substitution, we see that neither value is a solution of the given equation. Hence, no solutions were lost on dividing both sides by $\cos \theta$.

EXAMPLE 2. Solve: $\tan^2 x + 3 \sec x + 3 = 0.$

SOLUTION. 1. Use $\tan^2 x = \sec^2 x - 1$: $\sec^2 x + 3 \sec x + 2 = 0.$

2. Factor: $(\sec x + 2)(\sec x + 1) = 0.$

3. If $\sec x + 2 = 0$, then $\sec x = -2$; $x = 120°$ and $x = 240°.$

4. If $\sec x + 1 = 0$, then $\sec x = -1$; $x = 180°$. The solutions are $120°, 180°, 240°.$

80. Extraneous solutions

In solving an equation, it is sometimes useful to employ one or both of the following operations.

I. *Square both sides, or raise both to any specified power.*

II. *Multiply both sides by an expression involving the unknowns.*

EXAMPLE 1. Solve: $\cos x + 1 = \sin x.$ $\qquad\qquad$ (1)

SOLUTION. 1. Use $\sin x = \pm \sqrt{1 - \cos^2 x}$:

$$\cos x + 1 = \pm \sqrt{1 - \cos^2 x}.$$

2. Square both sides: $(1 + \cos x)^2 = 1 - \cos^2 x;$

$$1 + 2\cos x + \cos^2 x = 1 - \cos^2 x; \quad 2\cos x + 2\cos^2 x = 0;$$

$$2\cos x(1 + \cos x) = 0. \qquad\qquad (2)$$

From (2), $x = 90°$, $x = 180°$, or $x = 270°$; **these may be solutions.**

3. **Test all values of x by substituting in (1).** *Test* $x = 270°.$

Does $\cos 270° + 1 = \sin 270°$? $\qquad$ *Does* $0 + 1 = -1$? *No.*

Hence, $270°$ is *not* a solution. Similarly, we find that $90°$ and $180°$ *are* solutions.

The new equation obtained by use of (I) or (II) may have solutions *not possessed by the given equation*. Such solutions are called *extraneous solutions*. Hence, if (I) or (II) is used, all values obtained for the unknowns must be *tested in the original equation* to reject extraneous solutions, if any. This procedure was used in Example 1.

EXAMPLE 2. Solve: $\sec \theta - 2 \cos \theta - \tan \theta = 0.$ (3)

SOLUTION. 1. Express each function in terms of $\sin \theta$ and $\cos \theta$:

$$\frac{1}{\cos \theta} - 2 \cos \theta - \frac{\sin \theta}{\cos \theta} = 0.$$

2. Multiply both sides by $\cos \theta$: $1 - 2 \cos^2 \theta - \sin \theta = 0.$
Use $\cos^2 \theta = 1 - \sin^2 \theta$: $1 - 2(1 - \sin^2 \theta) - \sin \theta = 0.$
Hence, $2 \sin^2 \theta - \sin \theta - 1 = 0.$

3. Factor: $(2 \sin \theta + 1)(\sin \theta - 1) = 0$; $\sin \theta = 1$ or $\sin \theta = -\frac{1}{2}.$

4. From Step 3, $\theta = 90°$, $\theta = 210°$, and $\theta = 330°$.

5. **Test.** By substitution in (3), we find that 210° and 330° *are* solutions. If $\theta = 90°$, the original equation has no meaning because $\sec 90° = \infty$ and $\tan 90° = \infty$. Hence, 90° is *not* a solution.

EXERCISE 40

Solve each equation. Use Table VII if necessary. Try to avoid radicals.

1. $2 \cos^2 x + \sin x - 1 = 0.$ **2.** $3 + 3 \cos x = 2 \sin^2 x.$

3. $\cos^2 x + \sin x + 1 = 0.$ **4.** $3 \sin^2 x - \cos^2 x - 1 = 0.$

5. $2 \sin^2 x - 2 \cos^2 x = 3.$ **6.** $\sqrt{3} \cot x + 1 = \csc^2 x.$

7. $\sec^2 x - 1 = \tan x.$ **8.** $2 \sec x + 3 = 2 \cos x.$

9. $3 \csc x + 2 = \sin x.$ **10.** $\csc^2 x - \cot x - 1 = 0.$

11. $\tan^2 x + \sec^2 x = 9.$ **12.** $\cot^2 x + \csc^2 x = 19.$

13. $\tan x = 3 \cot x.$ **14.** $\cos x = \sin x.$ **15.** $3 \sin \theta = \sqrt{3} \cos \theta.$

16. $3 \tan \theta - \cot \theta = 0.$ **17.** $\tan^2 x - \sec x = 1.$ **18.** $3 \cos \theta = -\sqrt{3} \sin \theta.$

19. $\cot^2 x + 3 \csc x + 3 = 0.$ **20.** $\csc x - 2 \sin x = \cot x.$

21. $\sec x = \cos x - \tan x.$ **22.** $3 \sec x + 3 \tan x = 2 \cos x.$

23. $\csc x + \cot x = 2 \sin x.$ **24.** $\csc x = \sin x - \cot x.$

25. $\sin x + 1 = \cos x.$ **26.** $\sin x = 1 + \cos x.$

27. $\cos x = 1 - \sin x.$ **28.** $\cot x + 1 = \csc x.$

29. $\tan x = \sec x + 1.$ **30.** $\sec x + \tan x = 1.$

31. $\sin^2 x \sec x + 2 \sec x - \cos x = 3 \tan x.$

32. $3 \cot x - \cos^2 x \csc x - 2 \csc x + \sin x = 0.$

33. $9 \csc^2 x = 4 \tan^2 x.$ **34.** $2 \cot^2 x = \sec^2 x.$ **35.** $\sec^2 x - 1 = \cot^2 x.$

36. $\sec^2 x + 3 \cot^2 x = 5.$ **37.** $3 \csc^2 x - \tan^2 x = 1.$

38. $\sec x + 3 = \tan x.$ **39.** $\cot x = \csc x + 2.$

REVIEW EXERCISE 41

Prove each identity by direct use of equations (2), page 10.

1. $\cot \theta = \dfrac{\csc \theta}{\sec \theta}$.

2. $\cos \alpha = \dfrac{\cot \alpha}{\csc \alpha}$.

3. $\dfrac{\tan^2 \beta}{\sec^2 \beta} + \dfrac{\cot^2 \beta}{\csc^2 \beta} = 1$.

4. By use of identities, find all functions of θ if (a) θ is in quadrant II and $\cos \theta = -\frac{7}{25}$; ($b$) θ is in quadrant III and $\tan \theta = \frac{24}{7}$.

5. Express $\sin \theta$ in terms of $\cot \theta$.

Solve each equation. Use Table VII if necessary.

6. $\sin \theta = -\frac{1}{2}$.

7. $\sec \theta = 2$.

8. $\tan \theta = -\frac{1}{3}\sqrt{3}$.

9. $\cos \theta = -.9580$.

10. $\sin \theta = .5519$.

11. $\tan \theta = .7173$.

12. $1 + \sin x - 2 \sin^2 x = 0$.

13. $\sec^2 x + 4 \sec x + 4 = 0$.

14. $2 \cot x \sin x - \cot x = 0$.

15. $\sin^2 x + \cos x + 1 = 0$.

16. $\cot x = 3 \tan x$.

17. $3 \tan x - 1 = 0$.

18. $2 \sin x - \cos x = 0$.

19. $3 \cot^2 x - \sqrt{3} \cot x = 0$.

20. $5 \sin x + 2 = 0$.

21. $3 \cos x + 4 = 0$.

Find all positive values of the inverse function less than $360°$.

22. arcsin $.3800$.

23. arccos $(-.2812)$.

24. arccot 2.714.

Prove the identity by use of the fundamental identities.

25. $\dfrac{\sin x}{\sin x + \cos x} = \dfrac{\sec x}{\sec x + \csc x}$.

26. $\dfrac{\sin x}{\sin x - \tan x} = \dfrac{\cos x}{\cos x - 1}$.

27. $\dfrac{\sin x}{\sin x + \sec x} = \dfrac{\cos x}{\cos x + \csc x}$.

28. $\dfrac{\cos x}{\cos x - \sin x} = \dfrac{1}{1 - \tan x}$.

29. $\dfrac{\sin x - \sec y}{\sin x + \sec y} = \dfrac{\cos y - \csc x}{\cos y + \csc x}$.

30. $\dfrac{\tan \theta - \csc \theta}{\tan \theta + \csc \theta} = \dfrac{\sin^2 \theta - \cos \theta}{\sin^2 \theta + \cos \theta}$.

31. $\cos^2 \alpha \tan \alpha = \dfrac{2 \sin \alpha}{\sec \alpha + \cos \alpha + \sin^2 \alpha \sec \alpha}$.

32. $\sec^4 \alpha + \tan^4 \alpha = 1 + 2 \sec^2 \alpha \tan^2 \alpha$.

33. $\dfrac{\sin \alpha \cos \beta + \cos \alpha \sin \beta}{\cos \alpha \cos \beta - \sin \alpha \sin \beta} = \dfrac{\tan \alpha \cot \beta + 1}{\cot \beta - \tan \alpha}$.

★*Determine whether the equality is an identity or a conditional equation. If not an identity, solve for the unknown.*

34. $8 \sin^4 x + 10 \cos^2 x - 7 = 0$.

HINT. Proceed as if the equality were a conditional equation. If this is not true, one or more obvious identities will be obtained eventually. These remarks are related to Note 8 in the Appendix.

35. $(\sin x - \cos x)^2 = 1 - 2 \cot x \sin^2 x$.

36 $(1 + \sec x)(1 - \cos x) = \tan x \sin x$.

37. $3 - \cos^2 x \csc x - 3 \sin^2 x = 2 \cos^2 x$.

38. $(\tan x + \cot x)^3 = \tan x \sec^2 x + \cot x \csc^2 x + 2 \tan x + 2 \cot x$.

39. $\sin \alpha \tan \alpha - 2 \sin^2 \alpha \cos \alpha + \tan \alpha - 2 \tan \alpha \cos^2 \alpha = 0$.

EIGHT

ADDITION FORMULAS AND
RELATED TOPICS

81. Sine and cosine of the sum of two angles

Let α and β represent any two angles; then, we shall prove that

$$\sin (\alpha + \beta) = \sin \alpha \cos \beta + \cos \alpha \sin \beta; \qquad \text{(I)}$$

$$\cos (\alpha + \beta) = \cos \alpha \cos \beta - \sin \alpha \sin \beta. \qquad \text{(II)}$$

Proof of (I) *and* (II) *when* α, β, *and* $\alpha + \beta$ *are positive and acute.*

1. Place α in its standard position on a coordinate system. Place β with its vertex at the origin and its initial side OP on the terminal side of α. Then, in Figure 67, angle MOQ is $(\alpha + \beta)$ and this angle is in its *standard position*.

2. From any point Q on the terminal side of β, drop a perpendicular to the terminal side of α. Draw QL and PM perpendicular to OX, and PH parallel to OX.

3. From a theorem of geometry, angle HQP equals α because HQ and QP are respectively perpendicular to OM and OP.

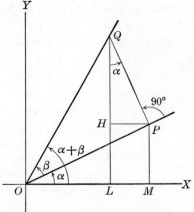

Fig. 67

4. Triangles QHP, OMP, and OPQ are right triangles. Hence,

from $\triangle OMP$,	$MP = OP \sin \alpha;$	$OM = OP \cos \alpha;$	(1)
from $\triangle QHP$,	$HQ = PQ \cos \alpha;$	$HP = PQ \sin \alpha;$	(2)
from $\triangle OPQ$,	$\dfrac{OP}{OQ} = \cos \beta;$	$\dfrac{PQ}{OQ} = \sin \beta.$	(3)

5. The coordinates and radius vector of Q are $x = OL$, $y = LQ$, and $r = OQ$. Therefore, from Definition I, page 10,

$$\sin(\alpha+\beta) = \frac{LQ}{OQ} = \frac{LH + HQ}{OQ} = \frac{MP}{OQ} + \frac{HQ}{OQ};$$ (Since $MP = LH$)

$$\sin(\alpha+\beta) = \frac{OP \sin \alpha}{OQ} + \frac{PQ \cos \alpha}{OQ}.$$ [From (1), (2)]

Hence, $\sin(\alpha+\beta) = \sin\alpha\cos\beta + \cos\alpha\sin\beta.$ [From (3)]

6. From Definition I, page 10,

$$\cos(\alpha+\beta) = \frac{OL}{OQ} = \frac{OM - LM}{OQ};$$

$$\cos(\alpha+\beta) = \frac{OM}{OQ} - \frac{HP}{OQ} = \frac{OP \cos \alpha}{OQ} - \frac{PQ \sin \alpha}{OQ};$$ [From (1), (2)]

$$\cos(\alpha+\beta) = \cos\alpha\cos\beta - \sin\alpha\sin\beta.$$ [From (3)]

Note 1. If α and β are acute and $\alpha + \beta > 90°$, the preceding proof applies without a single change in wording if the same construction and letters are used in the corresponding Figure 68. In this proof, it would be understood that the value of any line segment parallel to a coordinate axis is *positive* or *negative* according as the segment's direction is the *same as* or *opposite to* the positive direction on the axis. An analytical proof that (I) and (II) hold for all angles α and β is given in Note 10 of the Appendix, on the basis of the geometrical proof for the case where α and β are acute.

FIG. 68

Formula (I) states that *the sine of the sum of two angles equals the sine of one of the angles times the cosine of the other angle plus the cosine of the first times the sine of the second.* We call (I) and (II) the **addition formulas** for the sine and cosine. Without further discussion, we shall proceed under the assumption that (I) and (II) are true for all values of α and β.

EXAMPLE 1. Find $\sin 105°$ by expressing $105°$ as a sum.

SOLUTION. $\sin 105° = \sin(60° + 45°) = \sin 60° \cos 45° + \cos 60° \sin 45°;$

$$\sin 105° = \frac{\sqrt{3}}{2} \cdot \frac{\sqrt{2}}{2} + \frac{1}{2} \cdot \frac{\sqrt{2}}{2} = \frac{\sqrt{6} + \sqrt{2}}{4} = \frac{2.449 + 1.414}{4} = .966.$$

82. Addition formula for the tangent

We shall establish the *addition formula for the tangent:*

$$\tan(\alpha+\beta) = \frac{\tan \alpha + \tan \beta}{1 - \tan \alpha \tan \beta}.$$ (III)

Proof. 1. By use of (I) and (II),

$$\tan (\alpha + \beta) = \frac{\sin (\alpha + \beta)}{\cos (\alpha + \beta)} = \frac{\sin \alpha \cos \beta + \cos \alpha \sin \beta}{\cos \alpha \cos \beta - \sin \alpha \sin \beta}. \tag{1}$$

2. In (1), divide numerator and denominator by $\cos \alpha \cos \beta$:

$$\tan (\alpha + \beta) = \frac{\dfrac{\sin \alpha \cos \beta}{\cos \alpha \cos \beta} + \dfrac{\cos \alpha \sin \beta}{\cos \alpha \cos \beta}}{\dfrac{\cos \alpha \cos \beta}{\cos \alpha \cos \beta} - \dfrac{\sin \alpha \sin \beta}{\cos \alpha \cos \beta}} = \frac{\dfrac{\sin \alpha}{\cos \alpha} + \dfrac{\sin \beta}{\cos \beta}}{1 - \dfrac{\sin \alpha}{\cos \alpha} \cdot \dfrac{\sin \beta}{\cos \beta}}.$$

The final fraction is identical with the right-hand side in (III).

EXAMPLE 1. Find the sine, cosine, and tangent of $(\alpha + \beta)$ if α and β are acute, $\sin \alpha = \frac{3}{5}$, and $\cos \beta = \frac{5}{13}$.

SOLUTION. From a right triangle, in Figure 69, we find $\cos \alpha = \frac{4}{5}$. Similarly, $\sin \beta = \frac{12}{13}$. Hence,

$$\sin (\alpha + \beta) = \sin \alpha \cos \beta + \cos \alpha \sin \beta$$
$$= \frac{3}{5} \cdot \frac{5}{13} + \frac{4}{5} \cdot \frac{12}{13} = \frac{63}{65}.$$

Fig. 69

Similarly, by use of (II), $\cos (\alpha + \beta) = -\frac{16}{65}$. Therefore,

$$\tan (\alpha + \beta) = \frac{63}{65} \div \left(-\frac{16}{65} \right) = -\frac{63}{16}.$$

83. Functions of the difference of two angles

$$\sin (\alpha - \beta) = \sin \alpha \cos \beta - \cos \alpha \sin \beta; \tag{IV}$$

$$\cos (\alpha - \beta) = \cos \alpha \cos \beta + \sin \alpha \sin \beta; \tag{V}$$

$$\tan (\alpha - \beta) = \frac{\tan \alpha - \tan \beta}{1 + \tan \alpha \tan \beta}. \tag{VI}$$

Note 1. In proving (IV), (V), (VI), we shall use

$$\sin (- \theta) = - \sin \theta; \quad \cos (- \theta) = \cos \theta; \quad \tan (- \theta) = - \tan \theta. \tag{1}$$

Proof of (IV). 1. Since $\alpha - \beta = \alpha + (- \beta)$, we obtain $\sin (\alpha - \beta)$ from (I) of page 104 on replacing β by $- \beta$:

$$\sin (\alpha - \beta) = \sin [\alpha + (- \beta)] = \sin \alpha \cos (- \beta) + \cos \alpha \sin (- \beta). \tag{2}$$

2. From (1), $\cos (- \beta) = \cos \beta$; $\sin (- \beta) = - \sin \beta$. Hence, from (2),

$$\sin (\alpha - \beta) = \sin \alpha \cos \beta - \cos \alpha \sin \beta.$$

Similarly, on replacing β by $- \beta$ in (II) and (III), we obtain (V) and (VI), respectively.

ILLUSTRATION 1. On expressing 75° as a difference, we obtain

$$\sin 75° = \sin (135° - 60°) = \sin 135° \cos 60° - \cos 135° \sin 60°$$
$$= \frac{\sqrt{2}}{2} \cdot \frac{1}{2} - \left(-\frac{\sqrt{2}}{2} \cdot \frac{\sqrt{3}}{2} \right) = \frac{\sqrt{2} + \sqrt{6}}{4}.$$

EXERCISE 42

Express the angle as a sum or difference and solve by use of formulas (I)–(VI).

1. Find $\cos 135°$ and $\sin 135°$ by using functions of $90°$ and $45°$.

2. Find $\sin 225°$ and $\tan 225°$ by using functions of $180°$ and $45°$.

3. Find $\tan 210°$ and $\sin 210°$ by using functions of $180°$ and $30°$.

4. Find $\cos 330°$ by using functions of $270°$ and $60°$.

5. Find $\sin 315°$ and $\tan 315°$ by using functions of $360°$ and $45°$.

6. Find $\cos 150°$ and $\tan 150°$ by using functions of $180°$ and $30°$.

7. Find $\sin 180°$, $\cos 180°$, $\tan 180°$ by using functions of $240°$ and $60°$.

8. Find $\cos 45°$ and $\tan 45°$ by using functions of $180°$ and $135°$.

Find the sine, cosine, and tangent of the angle without using tables; the result may be left in radical form. Solve by first expressing the angle as a sum or difference of convenient angles.

9. $75°$. **10.** $105°$. **11.** $165°$. **12.** $195°$. **13.** $285°$. **14.** $255°$.

Expand by use of formulas (I)–(VI) *and insert known values.*

15. $\sin (30° + \alpha)$. **16.** $\cos (45° - \alpha)$. **17.** $\tan (\beta + 45°)$.

18. $\tan (45° - x)$. **19.** $\cos (A - 45°)$. **20.** $\sin (60° - x)$.

21. $\tan (\alpha - \frac{1}{3}\pi)$. **22.** $\tan (\alpha + \frac{3}{4}\pi)$. **23.** $\sin (\alpha - \pi)$.

24. $\sin (\frac{3}{2}\pi + x)$. **25.** $\cos (\frac{3}{2}\pi - x)$. **26.** $\cos (x + \pi)$.

Note 1. In Problems 23–26, notice special cases of the fact that (I)–(VI) become reduction formulas, from Chapter Five, when α or β is quadrantal.

27. Compute (*a*) $\sin 30° + \sin 45°$; (*b*) $\sin (30° + 45°)$.

28. Compute (*a*) $\tan 60° - \tan 45°$; (*b*) $\tan (60° - 45°)$.

Do not expand or substitute values of functions on the left-hand side; complete each equality with a right-hand member which is an explicit number or a single function of some angle.

29. $\sin 25° \cos 65° + \cos 25° \sin 65° = ?$

30. $\cos 125° \cos 55° - \sin 125° \sin 55° = ?$

31. $\dfrac{\tan 15° + \tan 30°}{1 - \tan 15° \tan 30°} = ?$ **32.** $\dfrac{\tan 240° - \tan 15°}{1 + \tan 240° \tan 15°} = ?$

33. $\sin A \cos 10° - \cos A \sin 10° = ?$

34. $\cos A \cos 40° + \sin A \sin 40° = ?$

35. $\cos 15° \cos 60° - \sin 15° \sin 60° = ?$

36. $\sin 2A \cos A + \cos 2A \sin A = ?$

37. $\dfrac{\tan 2x + \tan x}{1 - \tan 2x \tan x} = ?$ **38.** $\dfrac{\tan 3x - \tan x}{1 + \tan 3x \tan x} = ?$

Without tables, find all functions of $\alpha + \beta$ and $\alpha - \beta$, if α and β are acute.

39. $\sin \alpha = \frac{3}{5}$; $\cos \beta = \frac{12}{13}$.   **40.** $\tan \alpha = \frac{4}{3}$; $\cot \beta = \frac{12}{5}$.

41. $\tan \alpha = \frac{8}{15}$; $\sin \beta = \frac{12}{13}$.   **42.** $\sin \alpha = \frac{5}{13}$; $\cos \beta = \frac{24}{25}$.

43. Prove formulas (V) and (VI).

44. By the method of Sections 82 and 83, prove the addition formula for the cotangent, and the related formula for $\cot (\alpha - \beta)$:

$$\cot(\alpha + \beta) = \frac{\cot \alpha \cot \beta - 1}{\cot \alpha + \cot \beta}; \qquad \cot (\alpha - \beta) = \frac{\cot \alpha \cot \beta + 1}{\cot \beta - \cot \alpha}.$$

45. Without tables, find the quadrant in which the angle $(\alpha - \beta)$ lies in case α and β are acute, $\sin \alpha = \frac{5}{13}$, and $\cos \beta = \frac{7}{25}$.

Prove the identity.

46. $\sin (45° + x) - \sin (45° - x) = \sqrt{2} \sin x$.

47. $\cos (30° + x) \cos (30° - x) - \sin (30° + x) \sin (30° - x) = \frac{1}{2}$.

48. $\cos (\pi + x) \cos (\pi - x) + \sin (\pi + x) \sin (\pi - x) = \cos 2x$.

49. $\cot (45° + x) = \dfrac{1 - \tan x}{\tan x + 1}$.   **50.** $\tan (45° - x) = \dfrac{\cot x - 1}{\cot x + 1}$.

51. $\dfrac{\tan x + \tan (y + z)}{1 - \tan x \tan (y + z)} = \dfrac{\tan y + \tan (x + z)}{1 - \tan y \tan (x + z)}$.

Express in terms of $\tan A$ *and* $\tan B$, *without using radicals:*

52. $\dfrac{3 \sin A \cos B - \cos A \sin B}{3 \sin A \sin B + \cos A \cos B}$.   **53.** $\dfrac{\cos A \sin B + 3 \cos A \cos B}{\sin A \sin B + 3 \cos A \sin B}$.

84. Double-angle formulas

On substituting $\beta = \alpha$ in (I) and (II), we find

$$\sin (\alpha + \alpha) = \sin 2\alpha = \sin \alpha \cos \alpha + \cos \alpha \sin \alpha = 2 \sin \alpha \cos \alpha;$$

$$\cos (\alpha + \alpha) = \cos 2\alpha = \cos \alpha \cos \alpha - \sin \alpha \sin \alpha = \cos^2 \alpha - \sin^2 \alpha.$$

Thus, we obtain (VII) and (VIII$_a$) below. In (VIII$_a$), we substitute $\sin^2 \alpha = 1 - \cos^2 \alpha$ to prove (VIII$_b$). To obtain (VIII$_c$), we substitute $\cos^2 \alpha = 1 - \sin^2 \alpha$ in (VIII$_a$). To derive (IX), we let $\beta = \alpha$ in (III).

$$\sin 2\alpha = 2 \sin \alpha \cos \alpha. \tag{VII}$$

$$\cos 2\alpha = \cos^2 \alpha - \sin^2 \alpha. \tag{VIII$_a$}$$

$$\cos 2\alpha = 2 \cos^2 \alpha - 1. \tag{VIII$_b$}$$

$$\cos 2\alpha = 1 - 2 \sin^2 \alpha. \tag{VIII$_c$}$$

$$\tan 2\alpha = \frac{2 \tan \alpha}{1 - \tan^2 \alpha}. \tag{IX}$$

These results are called *double-angle formulas*. They express functions of *twice an angle* in terms of functions of *the angle*. From (VIII$_b$) and (VIII$_c$) we obtain

$$1 + \cos 2\alpha = 2 \cos^2 \alpha; \qquad 1 - \cos 2\alpha = 2 \sin^2 \alpha. \tag{X}$$

ILLUSTRATION 1. From (VIII$_b$) with $\alpha = 60°$,

$$\cos 120° = \cos 2(60°) = 2 \cos^2 60° - 1 = 2(\tfrac{1}{2})^2 - 1 = -\tfrac{1}{2}.$$

85. Half-angle formulas

In (X), α is *one half* of 2α. Hence, (X) expresses *twice the square of the cosine, and of the sine, of half of an angle* in terms of *the cosine of the angle*. To exhibit this otherwise, we substitute $\theta = 2\alpha$, or $\alpha = \frac{1}{2}\theta$, in (X):

$$2 \cos^2 \frac{\theta}{2} = 1 + \cos \theta; \qquad 2 \sin^2 \frac{\theta}{2} = 1 - \cos \theta. \qquad \text{(XI)}$$

Or,
$$\cos^2 \frac{\theta}{2} = \frac{1 + \cos \theta}{2}; \qquad \sin^2 \frac{\theta}{2} = \frac{1 - \cos \theta}{2}. \qquad (1)$$

Hence,
$$\tan^2 \frac{\theta}{2} = \frac{\sin^2 \frac{1}{2}\theta}{\cos^2 \frac{1}{2}\theta} = \frac{1 - \cos \theta}{1 + \cos \theta}. \qquad (2)$$

On taking square roots in (1) and (2), we obtain the *half-angle formulas*:

$$\sin \frac{\theta}{2} = \pm \sqrt{\frac{1 - \cos \theta}{2}}; \qquad \cos \frac{\theta}{2} = \pm \sqrt{\frac{1 + \cos \theta}{2}}. \qquad \text{(XII)}$$

$$\tan \frac{\theta}{2} = \pm \sqrt{\frac{1 - \cos \theta}{1 + \cos \theta}}. \qquad \text{(XIII)}$$

ILLUSTRATION 1. By use of (XIII) with $\theta = 120°$,

$$\tan 60° = \sqrt{\frac{1 - \cos 120°}{1 + \cos 120°}} = \sqrt{\frac{1 - (-\frac{1}{2})}{1 - \frac{1}{2}}} = \sqrt{\frac{\frac{3}{2}}{\frac{1}{2}}} = \sqrt{3}.$$

The " $+$ " sign in (XIII) was used because $60°$ is in quadrant I.

EXAMPLE 1. Prove the identity: $\quad \dfrac{\cot \theta - 1}{\cot \theta + 1} = \dfrac{1 - \sin 2\theta}{\cos 2\theta}.$

SOLUTION. $\quad \dfrac{1 - \sin 2\theta}{\cos 2\theta} = \dfrac{1 - 2 \sin \theta \cos \theta}{\cos^2 \theta - \sin^2 \theta}$

$(1 = \sin^2 \theta + \cos^2 \theta) \qquad = \dfrac{\sin^2 \theta + \cos^2 \theta - 2 \sin \theta \cos \theta}{\cos^2 \theta - \sin^2 \theta}$

$= \dfrac{(\cos \theta - \sin \theta)^2}{(\cos \theta - \sin \theta)(\cos \theta + \sin \theta)} = \dfrac{\cos \theta - \sin \theta}{\cos \theta + \sin \theta}$

(divide by $\sin \theta$) $\qquad = \dfrac{\dfrac{\cos \theta}{\sin \theta} - \dfrac{\sin \theta}{\sin \theta}}{\dfrac{\cos \theta}{\sin \theta} + \dfrac{\sin \theta}{\sin \theta}} = \dfrac{\cot \theta - 1}{\cot \theta + 1}.$ Q.E.D.

EXAMPLE 2. Express $\sin 3\alpha$ in terms of functions of 6α; of $\frac{3}{2}\alpha$.

SOLUTION. 1. Since $3\alpha = \frac{1}{2}(6\alpha)$, use (XII) with $\theta = 6\alpha$:

$$\sin 3\alpha = \pm \sqrt{\frac{1 - \cos 6\alpha}{2}}.$$

2. From (VII) with α replaced by $\frac{3}{2}\alpha$, $\quad \sin 3\alpha = 2 \sin \frac{3}{2}\alpha \cos \frac{3}{2}\alpha.$

The student is advised to concentrate on memorizing (XI) instead of (XII) and (XIII), because these can be recalled by use of (XI).

EXERCISE 43

By use of (VII)–(XIII), *find the sine, cosine, tangent of the first angle.*

1. 60°, by use of 30°.

2. 60°, by use of 120°.

3. 120°, by use of 240°.

4. 120°, by use of 60°.

5. 30°, by use of 60°.

6. 300°, by use of 150°.

7.* 90°, by use of 45°.

8.* 90°, by use of 180°.

9. − 135°, by use of − 270°.

10. − 270°, by use of − 135°.

By use of (VII)–(XIII), *give a right-hand member without radicals which involves only one function of some angle.*

11. $2 \sin 65° \cos 65° = ?$

12. $\cos^2 40° - \sin^2 40° = ?$

13. $1 - 2 \sin^2 80° = ?$

14. $2 \cos^2 125° - 1 = ?$

15. $2 \cos^2 20° = ?$

16. $2 \sin^2 20° = ?$

17. $1 + \cos B = ?$

18. $1 - \cos B = ?$

19. $2 \cos^2 40° = ?$

20. $1 + \cos 2B = ?$

21. $1 - \cos 2B = ?$

22. $2 \sin^2 80° = ?$

23. $1 + \cos 50° = ?$

24. $1 - \cos 70° = ?$

25. $\dfrac{2 \tan 38°}{1 - \tan^2 38°} = ?$

26. $\dfrac{1 - \cos x}{1 + \cos x} = ?$

27. $\dfrac{1 + \cos 40°}{1 - \cos 40°} = ?$

Prove the identity.

28. $\tan x = \dfrac{\sin 2x}{1 + \cos 2x}.$

29. $\cot x = \dfrac{1 + \cos 2x}{\sin 2x}.$

30. $\sec 2x = \dfrac{1}{1 - 2 \sin^2 x}.$

31. $\sec^2 x = \dfrac{2}{1 + \cos 2x}.$

32. $\csc^2 x = \dfrac{2}{1 - \cos 2x}.$

33. $\cot 2\theta = \dfrac{\csc \theta - 2 \sin \theta}{2 \cos \theta}.$

34. $(\sin \alpha + \cos \alpha)^2 = 1 + \sin 2\alpha.$

35. $\sec^2 \theta \cos 2\theta = \sec^2 \theta - 2 \tan^2 \theta.$

36. $2 \cos \theta - \cos 2\theta \sec \theta = \sec \theta.$

37. $\dfrac{\sec^2 x}{4 \sin^2 x} = \dfrac{1}{\sin^2 2x}.$

38. $\sec 2\alpha = \dfrac{\sec^2 \alpha}{1 - \tan^2 \alpha}.$

39. $\sec^2 2\alpha = \dfrac{\csc^2 \alpha}{\cot^2 \alpha - 1}.$

40. $\dfrac{\tan 2\alpha}{2 \tan \alpha} = \dfrac{\cot^2 \alpha}{\cot^2 \alpha - 1}.$

41. $\dfrac{1 - \tan x}{1 + \tan x} = \dfrac{1 - \sin 2x}{\cos 2x}.$

42. $\tan 2x = \dfrac{2}{\cot x - \tan x}.$

Express the sine, cosine, tangent of the given angle in terms of functions of the second angle.

43. 4α, in terms of 2α.

44. $2A$, in terms of $4A$.

45. $4x$, in terms of $8x$.

46. $8x$, in terms of $4x$.

47. $\tfrac{1}{2}x$, in terms of x.

48. α, in terms of $\tfrac{1}{2}\alpha$.

49. 3θ, in terms of $\tfrac{3}{2}\theta$.

50. $\tfrac{3}{2}x$, in terms of $3x$.

* A zero denominator occurs when the function involved does not exist.

Express the first function in terms of the second.

51. $\sin 3x$ in terms of $\sin x$. **52.** $\cos 3x$ in terms of $\cos x$.

HINT. $\sin 3x = \sin (x + 2x) = \sin x \cos 2x + \cos x \sin 2x =$ etc.

53. $\sin 4x$ in terms of $\sin x$. **54.** $\tan 3x$ in terms of $\tan x$.

86. Product formulas

We recall the following identities:

$$\sin (\alpha + \beta) = \sin \alpha \cos \beta + \cos \alpha \sin \beta; \tag{1}$$

$$\sin (\alpha - \beta) = \sin \alpha \cos \beta - \cos \alpha \sin \beta; \tag{2}$$

$$\cos (\alpha + \beta) = \cos \alpha \cos \beta - \sin \alpha \sin \beta; \tag{3}$$

$$\cos (\alpha - \beta) = \cos \alpha \cos \beta + \sin \alpha \sin \beta. \tag{4}$$

On adding corresponding sides in (1) and (2), we obtain the following formula (XIV). On adding (3) and (4) we obtain (XV). On subtracting (3) from (4) we obtain (XVI). On subtracting (2) from (1) we obtain (XVII).

$$2 \sin \alpha \cos \beta = \sin (\alpha + \beta) + \sin (\alpha - \beta). \tag{XIV}$$

$$2 \cos \alpha \cos \beta = \cos (\alpha + \beta) + \cos (\alpha - \beta). \tag{XV}$$

$$2 \sin \alpha \sin \beta = \cos (\alpha - \beta) - \cos (\alpha + \beta). \tag{XVI}$$

$$2 \cos \alpha \sin \beta = \sin (\alpha + \beta) - \sin (\alpha - \beta). \tag{XVII}$$

ILLUSTRATION 1. From (XIV),

$$2 \sin 150° \cos 30° = \sin (150° + 30°) + \sin (150° - 30°)$$
$$= \sin 180° + \sin 120° = 0 + \tfrac{1}{2}\sqrt{3} = \tfrac{1}{2}\sqrt{3}.$$

ILLUSTRATION 2. From (XV), with $\alpha = 8\theta$ and $\beta = 2\theta$,

$$2 \cos 8\theta \cos 2\theta = \cos 10\theta + \cos 6\theta.$$

Note 1. Although (XIV)–(XVII) are occasionally useful in applications, their main importance in this text is that they give a means for proving formulas in the next section.

★*Note 2.* Since $\sin (\alpha - \beta) = \sin [- (\beta - \alpha)] = - \sin (\beta - \alpha)$, we observe that (XVII) is the same as (XIV) with a mere interchange of α and β.

87. Sums and differences of sines or cosines

In formulas (XIV) to (XVII), let

$$x = \alpha + \beta; \qquad y = \alpha - \beta. \tag{1}$$

Then, $x + y = 2\alpha; \qquad x - y = 2\beta.$

Hence, $\alpha = \tfrac{1}{2}(x + y); \qquad \beta = \tfrac{1}{2}(x - y). \tag{2}$

On substituting (1) and (2) in (XIV), (XVII), (XV), and (XVI), respectively, we obtain

$$\sin x + \sin y = 2 \sin \frac{x+y}{2} \cos \frac{x-y}{2}; \qquad \text{(XVIII)}$$

$$\sin x - \sin y = 2 \cos \frac{x+y}{2} \sin \frac{x-y}{2}; \qquad \text{(XIX)}$$

$$\cos x + \cos y = 2 \cos \frac{x+y}{2} \cos \frac{x-y}{2}; \qquad \text{(XX)}$$

$$\cos x - \cos y = - 2 \sin \frac{x+y}{2} \sin \frac{x-y}{2}. \qquad \text{(XXI)}$$

These formulas express *sums and differences as products*.

ILLUSTRATION 1. By use of (XVIII),

$$\sin 50° + \sin 10° = 2 \sin \tfrac{1}{2}(60°) \cos \tfrac{1}{2}(40°) = 2 \sin 30° \cos 20°;$$

$$\sin 20° + \sin 80° = 2 \sin \tfrac{1}{2}(100°) \cos \tfrac{1}{2}(- 60°) = 2 \sin 50° \cos (- 30°)$$

[Since $\cos (- \theta) = \cos \theta$] $= 2 \sin 50° \cos 30°.$

Comment. Whenever a function of the *negative of an angle* is met in a result, change it to a function of the *corresponding angle*, by use of the formulas of Section 59 on page 71.

ILLUSTRATION 2. By use of (XX), with $x = 4A$ and $y = 2A$,

$$\cos 4A + \cos 2A = 2 \cos \tfrac{1}{2}(6A) \cos \tfrac{1}{2}(2A) = 2 \cos 3A \cos A.$$

EXAMPLE 1. Prove the identity:

$$\frac{\cos 5\alpha + \cos 3\alpha}{\sin 5\alpha - \sin 3\alpha} = \cot \alpha.$$

SOLUTION. We apply (XX) in the numerator and (XIX) in the denominator, to obtain

$$\frac{\cos 5\alpha + \cos 3\alpha}{\sin 5\alpha - \sin 3\alpha} = \frac{2 \cos 4\alpha \cos \alpha}{2 \cos 4\alpha \sin \alpha} = \frac{\cos \alpha}{\sin \alpha} = \cot \alpha. \quad \text{Q.E.D.}$$

EXERCISE 44

Check (XIV)–(XVII) *for the given values of* α *and* β.

1. $\alpha = 60°, \beta = 30°.$ **2.** $\alpha = 30°, \beta = 60°.$ **3.** $\alpha = 60°, \beta = 300°.$

Express as a sum or difference of functions of multiples of θ.

4. $2 \sin 3\theta \cos 5\theta.$ **5.** $2 \sin 2\theta \cos 5\theta.$ **6.** $2 \sin 3\theta \cos \theta.$

7. $2 \sin 3\theta \sin 5\theta.$ **8.** $2 \cos 3\theta \cos 5\theta.$ **9.** $2 \sin \theta \sin 9\theta.$

10. $2 \cos 5\theta \cos 7\theta.$ **11.** $2 \sin \theta \sin 7\theta.$ **12.** $2 \cos 3\theta \sin 2\theta.$

Express each sum or difference as a product.

13. $\sin 60° - \sin 20°.$ **14.** $\cos 40° - \cos 80°.$

15. $\cos 80° - \cos 30°.$ **16.** $\sin 30° - \sin 110°.$

17. $\sin 40° + \sin 30°.$ **18.** $\cos 40° + \cos 140°.$

19. $\cos 4x + \cos 2x$.   **20.** $\sin 3x + \sin 5x$.   **21.** $\cos 5y - \cos 2y$.

22. $\sin 4x - \sin 2x$.   **23.** $\cos 2x - \cos 4x$.   **24.** $\sin 7y + \sin 9y$.

25. $\cos 3x - \cos x$.   **26.** $\sin x - \sin 3x$.   **27.** $\cos 3y + \cos 8y$.

Prove each identity.

28. $\dfrac{\sin 5x + \sin 3x}{\sin 5x - \sin 3x} = \dfrac{\tan 4x}{\tan x}$.

29. $\dfrac{\cos x + \cos 9x}{\sin x + \sin 9x} = \cot 5x$.

30. $\dfrac{\sin 4x - \sin 2x}{\sin 4x + \sin 2x} = \dfrac{\tan x}{\tan 3x}$.

31. $\dfrac{\sin 3x + \sin 7x}{\cos 7x + \cos 3x} = \tan 5x$.

32. $\dfrac{\cos 3x + \cos x}{\cos 3x - \cos x} = -\dfrac{\cot 2x}{\tan x}$.

33. $\dfrac{\sin 3x - \sin 5x}{\cos 5x - \cos 3x} = \cot 4x$.

34. $\dfrac{\cos 4x - \cos 2x}{\cos 4x + \cos 2x} = -\dfrac{\tan 3x}{\cot x}$.

35. $\dfrac{\cos 2x - \cos 6x}{\sin 6x - \sin 2x} = \tan 4x$.

36. $\dfrac{\sin 5x + \sin 3x}{\cos 5x - \cos 3x} = -\cot x$.

37. $\dfrac{\sin 2x - \sin x}{\cos 2x + \cos x} = \tan \dfrac{x}{2}$.

38. $\dfrac{\cos 5x + \cos 2x}{\sin 5x + \sin 2x} = \cot \dfrac{7x}{2}$.

39. $\dfrac{\sin 4x - \sin 2x}{\cos 4x + \cos 2x} = \tan x$.

Express as a product involving only tangents or cotangents.

40. $\dfrac{\sin 75° + \sin 15°}{\sin 75° - \sin 15°}$.

41. $\dfrac{\sin 6A + \sin 7A}{\cos 6A + \cos 7A}$.

42. $\dfrac{\cos \alpha + \cos \beta}{\sin \alpha + \sin \beta}$.

43. $\dfrac{\cos 75° + \cos 15°}{\cos 75° - \cos 15°}$.

44. $\dfrac{\sin 5B - \sin 4B}{\sin 5B + \sin 4B}$.

45. $\dfrac{\sin \alpha + \sin \beta}{\cos \alpha - \cos \beta}$.

88. Miscellaneous identities*

In proving identities, the following suggestions may be useful.

I. *If possible, avoid introducing radicals.*

II. *Usually, it is best to express any cotangent, secant, or cosecant of a complicated angle in terms of the tangent, cosine, or sine, because of the nature of the formulas we have derived.*

III. *It may be convenient to express all functions in terms of functions of a single angle.*

EXAMPLE 1.   Prove the identity:

$$\cos 3x = \cos x - 4 \sin^2 x \cos x.$$

SOLUTION.   By use of (II),

$$\cos 3x = \cos (x + 2x) = \cos x \cos 2x - \sin x \sin 2x$$

$$= \cos x \,(1 - 2 \sin^2 x) - \sin x(2 \sin x \cos x)$$

$$= \cos x - 4 \sin^2 x \cos x. \quad \text{Q.E.D.}$$

---

* In a brief course, the remainder of this chapter could be omitted without eliminating later content.

EXAMPLE 2. Prove the identity: $\dfrac{\cos x}{\sec 3x} + \dfrac{\sin x}{\csc 3x} = \cos 2x.$

SOLUTION. Since $\sec 3x = \dfrac{1}{\cos 3x}$ and $\csc 3x = \dfrac{1}{\sin 3x},$

$$\dfrac{\cos x}{\sec 3x} + \dfrac{\sin x}{\csc 3x} = \cos x \cos 3x + \sin x \sin 3x = \cos (3x - x) = \cos 2x.$$

EXAMPLE 3. Prove the identity:

$$\sin 3\theta - \sin \theta = 2 \cos^2 \theta \sin \theta - 2 \sin^3 \theta.$$

SOLUTION. By use of (XIX) and (VIII$_a$),

$$\sin 3\theta - \sin \theta = 2 \cos 2\theta \sin \theta$$

$$= 2 (\cos^2 \theta - \sin^2 \theta) \sin \theta = 2 \cos^2 \theta \sin \theta - \sin^3 \theta. \quad \text{Q.E.D.}$$

EXAMPLE 4. Prove the identity: $\cot \dfrac{\theta}{2} = \dfrac{\sin \theta}{1 - \cos \theta}.$

SOLUTION. By use of (VII) with $\alpha = \frac{1}{2}\theta$, and (XI),

$$\dfrac{\sin \theta}{1 - \cos \theta} = \dfrac{2 \sin \dfrac{\theta}{2} \cos \dfrac{\theta}{2}}{2 \sin^2 \dfrac{\theta}{2}} = \dfrac{\cos \dfrac{\theta}{2}}{\sin \dfrac{\theta}{2}} = \cot \dfrac{\theta}{2}. \quad \text{Q.E.D.}$$

Comment. A more complicated solution would result from use of (XIII). Notice that a function of any angle is more conveniently expressible in terms of functions of *half of the angle* than in terms of functions of *twice the angle*.

EXERCISE 45

Prove the identity.

1. $\tan \alpha \sin 2\alpha = 2 \sin^2 \alpha.$

2. $2 \cos \alpha = \csc \alpha \sin 2\alpha.$

3. $\cot \alpha \sin 2\alpha = 1 + \cos 2\alpha.$

4. $(\sin x + \cos x)^2 = 1 + \sin 2x.$

5. $\cos 3x + \cos x = 4 \cos^3 x - 2 \cos x.$

6. $\sin 3x = 3 \cos^2 x \sin x - \sin^3 x.$

7. $\sin 4x = 4 \sin x \cos x \cos 2x.$

8. $\cos (x + \frac{1}{6}\pi) \cos (x - \frac{1}{6}\pi) + \sin (x + \frac{1}{6}\pi) \sin (x - \frac{1}{6}\pi) = \frac{1}{2}.$

9. $\dfrac{\sin x}{\sec 2x} + \dfrac{\cos x}{\csc 2x} = \sin 3x.$

10. $\csc 2\alpha = \dfrac{\tan \alpha}{2 \sin^2 \alpha}.$

11. $\dfrac{\cos 2x}{\sec x} - \dfrac{\sin x}{\csc 2x} = \cos 3x.$

12. $\dfrac{2 \tan \alpha}{\tan 2\alpha} = 1 - \tan^2 \alpha.$

13. $\cot 3\alpha = \dfrac{1 - 3 \tan^2 \alpha}{3 \tan \alpha - \tan^3 \alpha}.$

14. $\sec 2\alpha = \dfrac{\sec \alpha}{2 \cos \alpha - \sec \alpha}.$

15. $\sec 2\alpha = \dfrac{\sec \alpha}{\cos \alpha - \sin \alpha \tan \alpha}.$

16. $2 \tan \alpha = \dfrac{1 - \tan^2 \alpha}{\cot 2\alpha}.$

17. $\tan^2 \theta + \cos 2\theta = 1 - \cos 2\theta \tan^2 \theta.$

18. $\dfrac{\cos 3x}{\sec x} - \dfrac{\sin x}{\csc 3x} = \cos^2 2x - \sin^2 2x.$

19. $\cot 2\alpha = \dfrac{\cos \alpha - \sin \alpha \tan \alpha}{2 \sin \alpha}.$

20. $\dfrac{1 + \cot x}{\cot x - 1} = \dfrac{1 + \sin 2x}{\cos 2x}.$

21. $\dfrac{\csc x - \sec x}{\sec x + \csc x} = \dfrac{\cos 2x}{1 + \sin 2x}.$

22. $\dfrac{\sin x + \sin 3x}{\cos x + \cos 3x} = \dfrac{2 \cot x}{\cot^2 x - 1}.$

23. $\cos (\alpha + \beta) \cos (\alpha - \beta) = \cos^2 \beta - \sin^2 \alpha.$

24. $\sin 3x \cot x + \cos 3x = \sin 4x \csc x.$

25. $\cos \theta - \sin \theta \tan 2\theta = \cos 3\theta \sec 2\theta.$

26. $\dfrac{\tan 2x}{1 + \tan 2x} = \dfrac{2 \tan x}{1 + 2 \tan x - \tan^2 x}.$

27. $\sec (\alpha + \beta) = \dfrac{\sec \alpha \sec \beta}{1 - \tan \alpha \tan \beta}.$

28. $\sec 3x \sin 6x = 2 \tan 3x \cos 3x.$

29. $2 \cos 2\alpha = \csc 2\alpha \sin 4\alpha.$

30. $2 \cot 4x = \cot 2x - \tan 2x.$

31. $\sin 6\alpha \tan 3\alpha = 2 \sin^2 3\alpha.$

32. $\sec^2 2x - 1 = \dfrac{1 - \cos 4x}{1 + \cos 4x}.$

33. $\dfrac{1 + \cos 6x}{1 - \cos 6x} = \csc^2 3x - 1.$

34. $\dfrac{\cos x}{\cos \frac{1}{2}x + \sin \frac{1}{2}x} = \cos \frac{1}{2}x - \sin \frac{1}{2}x.$

35. $\dfrac{\sin x}{1 + \cos x} = \tan \dfrac{x}{2}.$

36. $\dfrac{\cos^3 x + \sin^3 x}{2 - \sin 2x} = \frac{1}{2} \sin x + \frac{1}{2} \cos x.$

37. $2 \cot x = \cot \dfrac{x}{2} - \tan \dfrac{x}{2}.$

38. $\dfrac{1 + \cos x}{1 - \cos x} = \csc^2 \dfrac{x}{2} - 1.$

39. $\cot^2 \dfrac{x}{2} - 1 = \csc^2 \dfrac{x}{2} \cos x.$

40. $\dfrac{1 + \sin x}{\cos x} = \dfrac{\tan \frac{1}{2}x + 1}{1 - \tan \frac{1}{2}x}.$

★*Prove the identity.*

41. $\dfrac{\cos x}{1 + \sin x} = \dfrac{\cot \frac{1}{2}x - 1}{\cot \frac{1}{2}x + 1}.$

42. $\sec 2x = \dfrac{1}{\cos^4 x - \sin^4 x}.$

43. $2 \sin 3\alpha \cos 2\alpha - \sin \alpha = \sin 5\alpha.$

44. $\cos 4\alpha = \cos 2\alpha - 2 \sin 3\alpha \sin \alpha.$

45. $1 + \cot \alpha \cot 3\alpha = \dfrac{2 \cos 2\alpha}{\cos 2\alpha - \cos 4\alpha}.$

46. $4 \cos 6x \sin 2x \cos 4x = \sin 4x - \sin 8x + \sin 12x.$

HINT. Alter the right-hand side by use of (XIX).

47. $4 \cos 3x \sin 2x \sin 5x - 1 = \cos 6x - \cos 4x - \cos 10x.$

48. $\sin 5x - \sin 3x + \sin 2x = 4 \sin x \cos \frac{5}{2}x \cos \frac{3}{2}x.$

49. $\cos 4\alpha = 8 \cos^4 \alpha + 8 \sin^2 \alpha - 7.$

50. $\sin 5\alpha = 16 \sin^5 \alpha - 15 \sin \alpha + 20 \sin \alpha \cos^2 \alpha.$

51. $\sin x - \sin (x + y) + \sin (x + 2y) = \sin (x + y) \cos \frac{3}{2}y \sec \frac{1}{2}y.$

52. $4 \sin^3 \theta = 3 \sin \theta - \sin 3\theta.$

53. $4 \cos^3 \theta = 3 \cos \theta + \cos 3\theta.$

89. Miscellaneous equations

An equation in x which explicitly states the value of *one* function of some multiple of x should be solved without alteration, by inspection or perhaps with the aid of a trigonometric table.

EXAMPLE 1. Solve: $\sin 3x = \frac{1}{2}$.

SOLUTION. 1. Recall that $\sin 30° = \frac{1}{2} = \sin 150°$. Either of these angles, plus any integral multiple of $360°$, is a value of "$3x$" which satisfies the equation. Hence, as values for $3x$, we obtain $30°$, $390°$, $750°$, $150°$, $510°$, $870°$, etc.

2. If $3x = 30°$, then $x = 10°$; if $3x = 390°$, then $x = 130°$; etc. The solutions for x between $0°$ and $360°$ are $10°$, $50°$, $130°$, $170°$, $250°$, $290°$.

Comment. We needed all values of $3x$ between $0°$ and **3(360°)** so that, *after dividing by 3,* we would have all values of x between $0°$ and $360°$.

To solve a trigonometric equation, we aim to find one or more equations, **each involving only one function of one angle,** whose solutions include all solutions of the given equation.

EXAMPLE 2. Solve: $\cos 2x - \cos x = 0$.

SOLUTION. 1. Use (VIII$_b$) so that *only functions of x* will remain:

$$2 \cos^2 x - 1 - \cos x = 0, \quad or \quad (2 \cos x + 1)(\cos x - 1) = 0.$$

2. We solve $2 \cos x + 1 = 0$ and $\cos x - 1 = 0$ and obtain

$$x = 0°, \quad x = 120°, \quad x = 240°.$$

EXAMPLE 3. Solve: $\sin \dfrac{\theta}{2} = \dfrac{\sqrt{3}}{2}$.

SOLUTION. 1. Recall that $\sin 60° = \frac{1}{2}\sqrt{3} = \sin 120°$.

2. Hence, $\frac{1}{2}\theta = 60°$ or $\frac{1}{2}\theta = 120°$. Therefore, $\theta = 120°$ or $\theta = 240°$.

EXAMPLE 4. Solve: $\sin 5x - \sin x = \cos 3x$.

SOLUTION. 1. Use (XIX): $2 \cos 3x \sin 2x = \cos 3x$.

$$2 \cos 3x \sin 2x - \cos 3x = 0; \quad \cos 3x (2 \sin 2x - 1) = 0.$$

2. Hence, $\cos 3x = 0 \quad or \quad 2 \sin 2x - 1 = 0$.

The student should complete the solution of these equations as in Example 1.

EXAMPLE 5. Solve: $\tan 3x - \cot x = 0$.

SOLUTION. 1.

$$\frac{\sin 3x}{\cos 3x} - \frac{\cos x}{\sin x} = 0;$$

$$\sin 3x \sin x - \cos x \cos 3x = 0;$$

$$\cos x \cos 3x - \sin 3x \sin x = 0;$$

from (II), $\cos(3x + x) = 0$.

2. From $\cos 4x = 0$, we find $x = 22\frac{1}{2}°$, $67\frac{1}{2}°$, $112\frac{1}{2}°$, $157\frac{1}{2}°$, $\cdots$, $337\frac{1}{2}°$.

Note 1. Suggestions (I) and (II) of Section 79 on page 101, for simple equations, and remarks (I), (II), and (III) of page 113 should be kept in mind when solving an equation.

EXERCISE 46

Find all positive or zero solutions less than 360°. If none exist less than 360°, then find one positive solution, if there are any solutions. Find the values on the corresponding range for any inverse function.

1. $\sin 2x = 0$.

2. $\sin 2x = -\frac{1}{2}$.

3. $\cos 2x = -1$.

4. $\tan 4x = \sqrt{3}$.

5. $\cos 2x = \frac{1}{2}\sqrt{3}$.

6. $\sin 3x = -1$.

7. $\csc 2x = -1$.

8. $\sin 3x = \frac{1}{2}\sqrt{3}$.

9. $\cos 3x = -\frac{1}{2}\sqrt{2}$.

10. $\cot 4x = 1$.

11. $\tan 3x = -1$.

12. $\sec 2x = \infty$.

13. $\sin \frac{1}{2}x = \frac{1}{2}$.

14. $\tan \frac{1}{2}x = -1$.

15. $\tan \frac{1}{3}x = -\sqrt{3}$.

16. $\cot \frac{1}{2}x = 1$.

17. $\cos \frac{1}{2}x = -\frac{1}{2}\sqrt{3}$.

18. $\sin \frac{1}{3}x = \frac{1}{2}\sqrt{2}$.

19. $\arccos 1 = 2x$.

20. $\arcsin \frac{1}{2} = 3x$.

21. $\arctan \frac{1}{3}\sqrt{3} = 2x$.

22. $\sin 2x = 2 \sin x$.

23. $\cos x = \sin 2x$.

24. $\cos 2x = \sin x$.

25. $\cos 2x = -\cos x$.

26. $\sin 2x = -\sin x$.

27. $\tan 2x = -\tan x$.

28. $\cos 2x = \cos^2 x$.

29. $\cos 2x = -\sin^2 x$.

30. $\sin 2x = 2 \cos^2 x$.

31. $\sin 2x = .2137$.

32. $\cos 3x = -.1572$.

33. $\tan 2x = .1874$.

34. $\sin x + \cos 2x - 1 = 0$.

35. $\cos 2x - \cos x + 1 = 0$.

36. $\cos 2x = 2 \sin^2 x - 2$.

37. $\cos 2x - 3 \cos x + 2 = 0$.

38. $4 \cos^2 3x = 3$.

39. $2 - \sec^2 2x = 0$.

40. $3 - \tan^2 2x = 0$.

41. $\cos 4x = \cos 2x$.

42. $\cos 4x = \cos^2 2x$.

43. $\sin 4x = 3 \cos 2x$.

44. $\tan 4x = \tan 2x$.

45. $\sin 4x = 5 \sin 2x$.

46. $\cot 4x + \cot 2x = 0$.

47. $\cos 2x \cos x + \sin 2x \sin x = 1$.

48. $\sin \frac{1}{2}x = \sin x$.

49. $\sin x = 2 \cos \frac{1}{2}x$.

50. $\cos x = \sin \frac{1}{2}x$.

HINT. Use a double-angle formula.

51. $\sin 3x + \sin x = 0$.

52. $\cos 3x - \cos x = 0$.

HINT. Change the sum or difference to a product.

53. $\cos 2x - \cos 6x = 0$.

54. $\cos 2x + \cos 3x = 0$.

55. $\sin 2x + \sin 4x = \sin 3x$.

56. $\sin x + \sin 5x = -\sin 3x$.

57. $\cos x - \cos 5x + 2 \sin 3x = 0$.

58. $\sin 3x = \sin 5x$.

59. $\csc \frac{1}{2}x + \cot \frac{1}{2}x = 2 \sin \frac{1}{2}x$.

60. $\cot^2 \frac{1}{2}x + 3 \csc \frac{1}{2}x + 3 = 0$.

61. $6 \sin^2 2x + 5 \sin 2x = 6$.

62. $\cot 3x + \cot x = 0$.

63. $\tan 3x \cos x - \sin x = 0$.

64. $\tan 5x - \tan 3x = 0$.

65. $\sin 3x + \sin 5x + \cos 2x - \cos 6x = 0$.

66. $\tan 2x - 2 \sin x = 0$.

67. $\tan 4x + 2 \sin 2x = 0$.

68. $\sin 2x - \sin 6x = 0$.

69. $\cos 5x - \cos x = 2 \sin 2x$.

70. $\cot 2x - \tan x = 1 + \cot 2x \tan x$.

REVIEW EXERCISE 47

Find the sine, cosine, and tangent of the given angle by the specified method, without using a table. Rationalize denominators.

1. 75°, by use of functions of the sum of two angles.

2. 105°, by use of functions of the difference of two angles.

3. 60°; use double-angle formulas.   **4.** $22\frac{1}{2}$°; use half-angle formulas.

5. If α and β are acute angles, with $\sin \alpha = \frac{3}{5}$ and $\cos \beta = \frac{8}{17}$, find the sine, cosine, tangent of (*a*) $\alpha + \beta$; (*b*) 2α; (*c*) $\frac{1}{2}\alpha$.

6. Express as a sum:

$$2 \cos 6° \sin 4°; \qquad 2 \sin 10° \cos 8°; \qquad 2 \cos 2\theta \cos 4\theta.$$

7. Express as a product:

$$\cos 4\alpha + \cos 5\alpha; \qquad \sin 35° + \sin 45°; \qquad \cos 3\alpha - \cos 5\alpha.$$

Prove the identity.

8. $\cos 2\alpha \sec \alpha = 2 \cos \alpha - \sec \alpha$.   **9.** $\cos^4 2x - \sin^4 2x = \cos 4x$.

10. $\sin 2\alpha + \cos 2\alpha \tan 3\alpha = \sin 5\alpha \sec 3\alpha$.

11. $\dfrac{\cos 2x + \sin 2x}{\cos 2x - \sin 2x} = \dfrac{\cot 2x + 1}{\cot 2x - 1}$.   **12.** $\cot \dfrac{\theta}{2} = \dfrac{1 + \cos \theta}{\sin \theta}$.

13. $\dfrac{\cos x - \cos 3x}{\cos 3x + \cos x} = \dfrac{\tan x}{\cot 2x}$.   **14.** $\dfrac{\sin x - \cos 2x}{\sin x + 1} = 2 \sin x - 1$.

15. $\left(\dfrac{1 + \tan x}{1 - \tan x}\right)^2 = \dfrac{1 + \sin 2x}{1 - \sin 2x}$.   **16.** $\sec \alpha = \dfrac{\sec \frac{1}{2}\alpha}{2 \cos \frac{1}{2}\alpha - \sec \frac{1}{2}\alpha}$.

17. $\dfrac{\sin x}{\sec 2x} + \dfrac{\cos x}{\csc 2x} = \dfrac{1}{\csc 3x}$.   **18.** $\dfrac{\sin 2x}{\cot x} = \dfrac{1 - \sin 2x - \cos 2x}{1 - \cot x}$.

Solve the equation.

19. $\sin 2x = \frac{1}{2}\sqrt{3}$.   **20.** $\tan^2 3x = 1$.   **21.** $\tan 2x = \infty$.

22. $\sin \frac{1}{2}x = -\frac{1}{2}\sqrt{2}$.   **23.** $\cos 2x = \cos^2 x$.   **24.** $\sin 3x = 3 \sin x$.

25. $\tan^2 2x + \sec^2 2x = 7$.   **26.** $\cos 3x = 1 - \sin 3x$.

27. $\cos 4x + 2 \cos^2 2x = 2$.   **28.** $\cos x + 2 \cos^2 \frac{1}{2}x = 2$.

★*Express each function in terms of the specified functions.*

29. $\sin (\alpha + \beta - \gamma)$; in terms of the sines and cosines of α, β, and γ.

30. $\tan (\alpha - \beta - \gamma)$; in terms of the tangents of α, β, and γ.

31. $\cos 4x$; in terms of $\cos x$.   **32.** $\sin 3\beta$; in terms of $\sin \beta$.

If $\alpha + \beta + \gamma = 180°$, prove the identity.

33. $\sin \alpha + \sin \beta - \sin \gamma = 4 \sin \frac{1}{2}\alpha \sin \frac{1}{2}\beta \cos \frac{1}{2}\gamma$.

Hint. Finally use $\frac{1}{2}\gamma = 90° - \frac{1}{2}(\alpha + \beta)$.

34. $\sin \alpha + \sin \beta + \sin \gamma = 4 \cos \frac{1}{2}\alpha \cos \frac{1}{2}\beta \cos \frac{1}{2}\gamma$.

35. $\cos \alpha + \cos \beta + \cos \gamma = 1 + 4 \sin \frac{1}{2}\alpha \sin \frac{1}{2}\beta \sin \frac{1}{2}\gamma$.

36. $\tan \alpha + \tan \beta + \tan \gamma = \tan \alpha \tan \beta \tan \gamma$.

37. $\sin^2 \alpha + \sin^2 \beta + \sin^2 \gamma = 2 + 2 \cos \alpha \cos \beta \cos \gamma$.

NINE

OBLIQUE TRIANGLES

90. Introduction

In any triangle ABC, as in Figure 70, let α, β, γ be the angles at A, B, C, and let a, b, c be the lengths of the corresponding opposite sides. The angles α, β, γ and sides a, b, c are called the *parts* of the triangle. We can construct a triangle if we are given any three of its parts, of which at least one is a side. Such data fall into four classes.

FIG. 70

I. *Given two angles and a side.*

II. *Given two sides and an angle opposite one of them.*

III. *Given two sides and the included angle.*

IV. *Given three sides.*

In this chapter, we shall develop methods for computing the unknown parts of a triangle under each of Cases I to IV. The computation of the unknown parts is called the *solution* of the triangle.

91. Law of cosines

In any triangle, the square of any side is equal to the sum of the squares of the other sides minus twice their product times the cosine of their included angle. That is,

$$a^2 = b^2 + c^2 - 2bc \cos \alpha; \tag{1}$$

$$b^2 = a^2 + c^2 - 2ac \cos \beta; \tag{2}$$

$$c^2 = a^2 + b^2 - 2ab \cos \gamma. \tag{3}$$

On solving (1), (2), and (3) for the cosines, we obtain

$$\cos \alpha = \frac{b^2 + c^2 - a^2}{2bc}; \quad \cos \beta = \frac{a^2 + c^2 - b^2}{2ac}; \quad \cos \gamma = \frac{a^2 + b^2 - c^2}{2ab}. \tag{4}$$

Note 1. Suppose that triangle ABC is a *right* triangle with $\gamma = 90°$. Then, $\cos \gamma = 0$, $\cos \alpha = \dfrac{b}{c}$, and $\cos \beta = \dfrac{a}{c}$. Hence, from (1), (2), and (3),

$$a^2 = b^2 + c^2 - 2b^2, \quad or \quad a^2 = c^2 - b^2; \quad b^2 = c^2 - a^2; \quad c^2 = a^2 + b^2.$$

Thus, *for a right triangle, the law of cosines is equivalent to the Pythagorean theorem.*

Proof of the law of cosines. 1. Let a, α be any side and the opposite angle in $\triangle ABC$. One of the other angles must be acute because we have $\alpha + \beta + \gamma = 180°$; hence, suppose that β is acute. In $\triangle ABC$, drop a perpendicular CD from C to AB, or AB extended. We obtain Figure 71 if α is acute, and Figure 72 if α is obtuse. In either figure, let

$$\overline{AD} = m; \qquad \overline{DC} = h.$$

Fig. 71

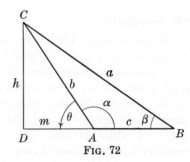

Fig. 72

2. In $\triangle ADC$, we find $b^2 = h^2 + m^2$, or

$$h^2 = b^2 - m^2. \tag{5}$$

In $\triangle DBC$, $\qquad\qquad a^2 = h^2 + (\overline{DB})^2$, or $\qquad\qquad\qquad$ (6)

$$a^2 = b^2 - m^2 + (\overline{DB})^2. \tag{7}$$

3. **If α is acute,** as in Figure 71, then $\overline{DB} = \overline{AB} - \overline{AD}$, or

$$\overline{DB} = c - m. \tag{8}$$

From $\triangle ADC$, $\cos \alpha = m/b$, or

$$m = b \cos \alpha. \tag{9}$$

On substituting (8) in (7) and using (9), we find

$$a^2 = b^2 - m^2 + (c - m)^2 = b^2 + c^2 - 2cm;$$
$$a^2 = b^2 + c^2 - 2bc \cos \alpha. \tag{10}$$

4. **If α is obtuse,** as in Figure 72, then $\overline{DB} = \overline{AB} + \overline{AD}$, or

$$\overline{DB} = c + m. \tag{11}$$

From $\triangle ADC$, $\cos \theta = m/b$ and $\alpha = 180° - \theta$. Hence, by use of equations (7) on page 74, $\cos \alpha = -\cos \theta$ or $\cos \alpha = -m/b$, and

$$m = -b \cos \alpha. \tag{12}$$

On using (11) and (12) in (7), we obtain

$$a^2 = b^2 + c^2 + 2cm = b^2 + c^2 - 2bc \cos \alpha. \tag{13}$$

Thus, (1) is true for *any* triangle. Since *a* represented *any* side, we obtain (2) by merely rewriting (1) with the roles of *a*, *α* and *b*, *β* interchanged, and derive (3) similarly.

Note 2. In Figure 71, $c = \overline{DB} + m$ or

$$c = a \cos \beta + b \cos \alpha. \tag{14}$$

In Figure 72, we use $c = \overline{DB} - m$ and (12) to obtain (14) again. Thus, for any triangle *ABC*, we obtain the *projection relations*

$$c = a \cos \beta + b \cos \alpha; \quad a = b \cos \gamma + c \cos \beta; \quad b = a \cos \gamma + c \cos \alpha. \tag{15}$$

These formulas are sometimes useful in checking the solution of a triangle.

92. Solution of triangles by the law of cosines

The law of cosines is not well fitted for logarithmic computation. However, the formulas are used frequently without logarithms, particularly in physics. If a table of squares is available, or if convenient numbers are involved, problems of certain types can be solved efficiently by use of the law of cosines and natural values of the trigonometric functions.

OUTLINE. *Application of the law of cosines to solve* △*ABC under Case* IV, *that is, to find the angles when all sides are given.*

1. *Find each angle by use of its cosine, from* (4) *on page* 119.

2. *Check the solution by means of* $\alpha + \beta + \gamma = 180°$.

EXAMPLE 1. Solve △*ABC* if $a = 5$, $b = 7$, $c = 11$.

SOLUTION. 1. From (4) on page 119,

$$\cos \alpha = \frac{145}{154} = .9416; \quad \cos \beta = \frac{97}{110} = .8818; \quad \cos \gamma = -\frac{47}{70} = -.6714.$$

2. By use of Table VII, we find $\alpha = 19° 41'$; $\beta = 28° 8'$.

3. Since $\cos \gamma$ is negative, $\gamma > 90°$. Let θ be the reference angle for γ, so that θ is acute and $\gamma = 180° - \theta$. Then, $\cos \theta = .6714$. From Table VII, $\theta = 47° 50'$. Hence,

$$\gamma = 180° - 47° 50' = 132° 10'.$$

Check. $\alpha + \beta + \gamma = 19° 41' + 28° 8' + 132° 10' = 179° 59'.$

ILLUSTRATION 1. If $a = 5$, $b = 12$, and $\gamma = 60°$, then $\cos \gamma = \frac{1}{2}$ and, from (3) on page 119, we find

$$c^2 = 25 + 144 - 2(5)(12) \cos 60° = 109.$$

By use of logarithms or Table I, $c = \sqrt{109} = 10.4$.

EXERCISE 48

Find the obtuse angle α *by use of Table* VII.

1. $\sin \alpha = .2447.$ **2.** $\cos \alpha = -.1363.$ **3.** $\cos \alpha = -.7969.$

Solve without trigonometric tables if possible. Otherwise use Table VII.

4. $a = 3, b = 2, \gamma = 60°$; find c.
5. $b = 4, c = \sqrt{3}, \alpha = 30°$; find a.
6. $b = \sqrt{2}, a = 8, \gamma = 45°$; find c.
7. $b = 7, c = \sqrt{2}, \alpha = 135°$; find a.
8. $a = \sqrt{3}, c = 4, \beta = 150°$; find b.
9. $a = 2, c = 2, \beta = 120°$; find b.
10. $a = 3, b = 10, c = 8$; find γ.
11. $a = 7, b = 9, c = 4$; find α.
12. $a = 5, b = 6, c = 7$; find β.
13. $a = 9, b = 10, c = 7$; find γ.
14. $a = 13, b = 7, c = 8$; find α.
15. $a = 6, b = 12, c = 9$; find β.

By use of Table VII, solve $\triangle ABC$ and check, if all sides are given. Otherwise, just find the requested side. Use logarithms where pertinent in computing the angles.

16. $a = 5, b = 6, c = 4$.
17. $a = 8, b = 5, c = 7$.
18. $a = 6, b = 14, c = 10$.
19. $a = 13, b = 6, c = 9$.

20. $a = 5, b = 7, \gamma = 32°$; find c.
21. $a = 6, c = 10, \beta = 155° 30'$; find b.
22. $b = 5, c = 12, \alpha = 120° 40'$; find a.
23. $b = 4, c = 11, \alpha = 63° 28'$; find a.

24. Find the sides of a parallelogram if the lengths of its diagonals are 12 inches and 16 inches and one angle formed by the diagonals is 37°.

25. At 1 P.M., a train leaves a city T at 30 miles per hour in a direction due east, and a second train travels from T in the direction N 20° W at 40 miles per hour. How far apart are the trains at the end of 2 hours?

26. An enemy's camp at E cannot be seen from a battery of artillery at B. An observer at a location P finds that $PE = 7300$ yards, $PB = 6300$ yards, and $\angle BPE = 41° 27'$. Find the distance from the battery to E.

27. In a storm cloud, an airplane meets an air current flowing vertically upward at a rate of 100 miles per hour. The pilot aims his plane 58° from the horizontal downward and his instruments show that his airspeed is 250 miles per hour. Find the resultant speed of the plane and the inclination of its path to the horizontal.

Find the magnitude of the resultant of the given forces acting simultaneously on the same object.

28. 200 pounds and 300 pounds: angle between their directions is 78°.

29. 150 pounds and 250 pounds: angle between their directions is 67°.

30. 40 pounds and 70 pounds: angle between their directions is 123°.

93. Law of sines

In any triangle, the lengths of the sides are proportional to the sines of the opposite angles. That is,

$$a : b : c = \sin \alpha : \sin \beta : \sin \gamma, \text{ or} \qquad (1)$$

$$\frac{a}{\sin \alpha} = \frac{b}{\sin \beta} = \frac{c}{\sin \gamma}. \qquad (2)$$

In (2), we are abbreviating three equations:

$$\frac{a}{\sin \alpha} = \frac{b}{\sin \beta}; \qquad \frac{b}{\sin \beta} = \frac{c}{\sin \gamma}; \qquad \frac{c}{\sin \gamma} = \frac{a}{\sin \alpha}. \qquad (3)$$

Proof of (3). 1. Let b and c represent any two sides, and drop a perpendicular AD from A to side BC, or to this side extended.

FIG. 73

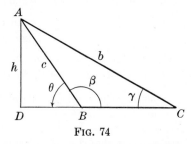

FIG. 74

2. *Suppose that neither β nor γ is obtuse,* as in Figure 73. Then, from the formulas for functions of acute angles, as related to right triangles, we obtain the following results:

From $\triangle ABD$, $\sin \beta = h/c$: $\qquad\qquad h = c \sin \beta.$ $\qquad (4)$

From $\triangle ACD$, $\sin \gamma = h/b$: $\qquad\qquad h = b \sin \gamma.$ $\qquad (5)$

From (4) and (5) we find

$$c \sin \beta = b \sin \gamma. \qquad (6)$$

On dividing both sides in (6) by $\sin \beta \sin \gamma$, we obtain

$$\frac{c}{\sin \gamma} = \frac{b}{\sin \beta}. \qquad (7)$$

3. *If one of β and γ is obtuse,* let β be the obtuse angle, as in Figure 74. Then, in $\triangle ABD$, $\sin \theta = h/c$. Since $\beta = 180° - \theta$,

$$\sin \beta = \sin (180° - \theta) = \sin \theta.$$

Hence, $\sin \beta = h/c$, or

$$h = c \sin \beta. \qquad (8)$$

We observe that (4) and (8) are identical. Also, (5) remains true in Figure 74. Hence, (7) is obtained again as a consequence of (5) and (8). Thus, (7) is true for any triangle. Since b, c represent any two sides, we have justified all equalities in (3).

Note 1. Equations (3) may be rewritten as follows:

$$\frac{a}{b} = \frac{\sin \alpha}{\sin \beta}; \qquad \frac{b}{c} = \frac{\sin \beta}{\sin \gamma}; \qquad \frac{a}{c} = \frac{\sin \alpha}{\sin \gamma}. \qquad (9)$$

We obtain new forms in (3) or (9) by inverting the fractions.

94. Solution of Case I by the law of sines

OUTLINE. *To solve $\triangle ABC$ if two angles and a side are given, for instance α, β, c.*

1. *Find the third angle by use of*

$$\alpha + \beta + \gamma = 180°.$$

2. *Find the unknown sides by use of the law of sines:*

$$a = \frac{c \sin \alpha}{\sin \gamma}; \qquad b = \frac{c \sin \beta}{\sin \gamma}. \tag{1}$$

3. *To check, use any one of formulas (15), page 121, which involves the angle which was not given:*[*]

Note 1. The third formula of the law of sines, involving a and b and not used in (1), has moderate value as a check on the solution if both sides are computed *without* logarithms, but is *practically worthless if logarithms are employed.* In that case, the formula would not detect an error in any logarithm met in (1) because the *same logarithms* would appear in checking.

EXAMPLE 1. Solve $\triangle ABC$ if $\beta = 37° 6'$, $\gamma = 42° 38'$, $c = 21.37$.

SOLUTION. We employ the four-place Tables V and VI.

Formulas	Computation
	Data: $\quad c = 21.37, \quad \beta = 37° 6', \quad \gamma = 42° 38'.$
$\alpha = 180° - (\beta + \gamma).$	$\alpha = 180° - (37° 6' + 42° 38') = 100° 16'.$
$\dfrac{b}{\sin \beta} = \dfrac{c}{\sin \gamma},$ or $b = \dfrac{c \sin \beta}{\sin \gamma}.$	$\begin{aligned} \log c &= 1.3298 &\text{(Table V)} \\ \log \sin \beta &= 9.7805 - 10\ (+) &\text{(Table VI)} \\ \hline \log c \sin \beta &= 11.1103 - 10 \\ \log \sin \gamma &= 9.8308 - 10\ (-) \\ \hline \log b &= 1.2795; \qquad b = 19.03. \end{aligned}$
$\dfrac{a}{\sin \alpha} = \dfrac{c}{\sin \gamma},$ or $a = \dfrac{c \sin \alpha}{\sin \gamma}.$	$\begin{aligned} \sin 100° 16' &= \sin (180° - 100° 16') = \sin 79° 44'. \\ \log c &= 1.3298 \\ \log \sin \alpha &= 9.9930 - 10\ (+) \\ \hline \log c \sin \alpha &= 11.3228 - 10 \\ \log \sin \gamma &= 9.8308 - 10\ (-) \\ \hline \log a &= 1.4920; \qquad a = 31.04. \end{aligned}$
Summary.	$a = 31.04, \qquad b = 19.03, \qquad \alpha = 100° 16'.$

Check. $\qquad c = a \cos \beta + b \cos \alpha.$

$\cos \alpha = \cos 100° 16' = -\cos (180° - 100° 16') = -\cos 79° 44'.$

$a \cos \beta = 31.04(.7976) = 24.76.$ (Table VII)

$b \cos \alpha = -19.03 \cos 79° 44' = -19.03(.1782) = -3.39.$

$a \cos \beta + b \cos \alpha = 24.76 - 3.39 = 21.37 \longrightarrow \longleftarrow c = 21.37;$ *satisfactory.*

---

[*] Other check formulas will be used for Case I later.

★*Comment.* Cologarithms may be used conveniently in Example 1.

$$b = \frac{c \sin \beta}{\sin \gamma} = c \sin \beta \frac{1}{\sin \gamma}: \qquad \log b = \log c + \log \sin \beta + \text{colog} \sin \gamma.$$

$\log \sin \gamma = 9.8308 - 10:$ *hence,*

$$\begin{array}{l} \log c = 1.3298 \\ \log \sin \beta = 9.7805 - 10 \\ \text{colog} \sin \gamma = 0.1692 \end{array} \Bigg\} (+)$$

$\log b = 1.2795; \qquad b = 19.03.$

$$a = \frac{c \sin \alpha}{\sin \gamma}:$$

$$\begin{array}{l} \log c = 1.3298 \\ \log \sin \alpha = 9.9930 - 10 \\ \text{colog} \sin \gamma = 0.1692 \end{array} \Bigg\} (+)$$

$\log a = 1.4920; \qquad a = 31.04.$

EXERCISE 49

Solve $\triangle ABC$ *without* logarithms by use of Table* VII.
1. $b = 5, \alpha = 75°, \beta = 30°.$ 2. $c = 3, \beta = 37°, \gamma = 30°.$
3. $a = 50, \alpha = 37° 30', \beta = 71° 10'.$ 4. $a = 200, \alpha = 32° 21', \gamma = 21° 39'.$

Solve by use of logarithms.† Check where directed by the instructor.
5. $c = 15.67; \alpha = 42° 20'; \gamma = 53° 40'.$
6. $b = 231.6; \alpha = 19° 10'; \beta = 82° 40'.$
7. $a = 1.056; \beta = 23° 20'; \gamma = 53° 50'.$
8. $c = 6019; \alpha = 16° 30'; \beta = 59° 20'.$
9. $\alpha = 19° 41'; \beta = 28° 8'; a = 5.37.$
10. $\alpha = 64° 9'; \beta = 13° 0'; a = 12.3.$
11. $\alpha = 23° 54'; \gamma = 85° 16'; b = .4317.$
12. $\beta = 101° 36'; \gamma = 21° 44'; c = .04198.$
13. $\alpha = 23° 42'; \beta = 98° 18'; a = .03152.$
14. $\alpha = 31° 18'; \gamma = 42° 32'; b = .01571.$
15. $\alpha = 21° 36.4'; \beta = 82° 13.6'; a = 13.159.$
16. $\beta = 48° 23.7'; \gamma = 17° 16.3'; b = 27.001.$
17. $\beta = 23° 19.2'; \gamma = 33° 40.8'; a = 513.52.$
18. $\alpha = 83° 45.1'; \beta = 24° 18.9'; c = .75846.$
19. $\alpha = 19° 34.5'; \beta = 80° 14.5'; c = .011105.$
20. $\alpha = 58° 11.4'; \gamma = 63° 25.6'; b = .0031478.$

21. A polygon is inscribed in a circle whose radius is 6 inches. One of the sides subtends an angle of 27° at the center of the circle; find the length of this side by use of the law of sines.

22. One side of a parallelogram is 56 inches long. The diagonals of the parallelogram make the angles 35° and 47°, respectively, with this side. Find the lengths of the diagonals.

* Division may sometimes be avoided by introducing cosecants.
† In Problems 5–14, results are given in the answer book for both *four-place* and *five-place* logarithmic computation.

23. In triangle ABC, suppose that $\gamma = 90°$. Show that in this case the equations of the law of sines give merely the well-known expressions for the sines of the two acute angles of the right triangle ABC.

24. A battery commander B is ordered to shoot at a target T from a position G, from which T is visible. To check on the range GT as found by a range finder, B locates an observation point H from which T is visible. The bearing of T from G is $N\ 12°\ 48'\ E$, of T from H is $N\ 6°\ 23'\ W$, and of H from G is $S\ 82°\ 53'\ E$. From a map, it is found that $GH = 3250$ yards. Find the range of the target from G.

95. Solution of Case II, the ambiguous case

If two sides of a triangle ABC and an angle opposite one of these sides are given, we shall find that there may exist *two* solutions, or just *one* solution, or *no* solution for the triangle, depending on the given values. Since there may be two solutions, Case II is called the *ambiguous case*.

Note 1. Recall that, if k is a positive number less than 1, the equation $\sin \alpha = k$ has *two* positive solutions less than 180°, one *acute* and the other *obtuse*. This existence of *two* solutions is the fact which accounts for the possibility of two triangles as solutions in Case II.

If the given parts of a triangle ABC are a, b, α, any triangle satisfying the data may be obtained geometrically as follows.

1. *Construct α with one side AD horizontal. On the other side, measure distance b from A to locate vertex C.*

2. *With C as center and radius equal to side a, strike an arc. The vertex B may then be located at any point where this arc cuts AD.*

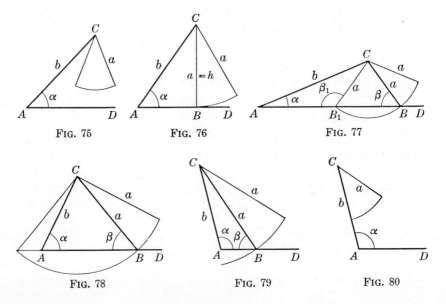

FIG. 75   FIG. 76   FIG. 77

FIG. 78   FIG. 79   FIG. 80

In Figures 75 and 80, the arc does *not meet* AD, and hence there is *no* solution. In Figure 76, the arc is tangent to AD and there is just *one* position for B, with $\beta = 90°$. In Figure 77, the arc cuts AD twice, at B and B_1; hence there are *two* solutions, triangles AB_1C and ABC. In Figure 78 and in Figure 79, there is just *one* solution.

In a triangle ABC, let h be the perpendicular distance from C to side AB. Then, as in Figure 76, $\sin \alpha = h/b$ or $h = b \sin \alpha$. In Figures 75–77 where $a < b$ and $\alpha < 90°$, we observe that we have *no* solution, *just one* solution, or *two* solutions according as side a, the radius of the arc, is *less than, equal to,* or *greater than* h.

Note 2. The preceding remarks and Figures 75–80 justify the following summary of possibilities in case the given parts under the ambiguous Case II are a, b, α:

$$\alpha < 90° \begin{cases} \boldsymbol{a < b \sin \alpha}; \ \textit{no solution (Figure 75).} \\ \boldsymbol{a = b \sin \alpha}; \ \textit{just one solution, with } \beta = 90° \textit{ (Figure 76).} \\ \boldsymbol{a > b \sin \alpha,} \textit{ but } \boldsymbol{a < b}; \ \textit{two solutions (Figure 77).} \\ \boldsymbol{a \geqq b}; \ \textit{just one solution (Figure 78).} \end{cases}$$

$$\alpha \geqq 90° \begin{cases} \boldsymbol{a > b}; \ \textit{just one solution (Figure 79).} \\ \boldsymbol{a \leqq b}; \ \textit{no solution (Figure 80).} \end{cases}$$

Instead of memorizing the preceding summary, the student is advised to *draw a figure roughly to scale for each problem.* Then, usually, the number of solutions to be expected can be determined easily without formulas.

OUTLINE.   *To solve* $\triangle ABC$ *under Case* II, *with the given parts* a, b, α:

1. *Construct the triangle approximately to scale.*

2. *Find* β *by use of* $\sin \beta = b \sin \alpha/a$. *If this gives*

   $\sin \beta > 1$, *or* $\log \sin \beta > 0$, *there is no solution;*

   $\sin \beta = 1$, *or* $\log \sin \beta = 0$, *then* $\beta = 90°$, *just one solution;*

   $\sin \beta < 1$, *find one acute and one obtuse value for* β.

3. *Discard any value of* β *for which* $\alpha + \beta \geqq 180°$; *for each value of* β, *compute* $\gamma = 180° - (\alpha + \beta)$.

4. *For each pair of values of* β *and* γ, *compute* $c = a \sin \gamma/\sin \alpha$.

Note 3. A solution under Case II may be checked as in Case I.

EXAMPLE 1.   How many triangles exist with $a = 4$, $b = 8$, $\alpha = 30°$?

SOLUTION.   1. A figure for this problem would look like Figure 76.

2. To find β:
$$\sin \beta = \frac{b \sin \alpha}{a} = \frac{8 \sin 30°}{4} = \frac{8(\frac{1}{2})}{4}.$$

Hence, $\sin \beta = 1$ and $\beta = 90°$. There is just *one* solution, a right $\triangle$.

EXAMPLE 2. Solve $\triangle ABC$ if $a = 20$, $b = 10$, and $\alpha = 30°$.

SOLUTION. A figure like Figure 78 indicates just one solution.

Formulas	Computation
	Data: $a = 20$, $b = 10$, $\alpha = 30°$.
$\dfrac{\sin \beta}{b} = \dfrac{\sin \alpha}{a}$, or $\sin \beta = \dfrac{b \sin \alpha}{a}.$	$\sin \beta = \dfrac{10 \sin 30°}{20} = .2500.$ $\beta = 14° \, 29'.$ (Table VII)

Comment. We also obtain $\beta = 180° - 14° \, 29'$, or $\beta = 165° \, 31'$. Figure 78 shows that this value cannot be used because there is only one solution, with β acute. To prove this otherwise, we compute

$$\alpha + \beta = 30° + 165° \, 31' = 195° \, 31';$$

since $195° \, 31' > 180°$, $\beta = 165° \, 31'$ is impossible.

$\gamma = 180° - (\alpha + \beta).$	$\gamma = 180° - (30° + 14° \, 29') = 135° \, 31'.$
$\dfrac{c}{\sin \gamma} = \dfrac{a}{\sin \alpha}$, or $c = \dfrac{a \sin \gamma}{\sin \alpha}.$	$\sin 135° \, 31' = \sin (180° - 135° \, 31') = \sin 44° \, 29'.$ $c = \dfrac{20 \sin 44° \, 29'}{\sin 30°} = 28.03.$ (Table VII)

Summary.   *One solution:* $c = 28.03$, $\beta = 14° \, 29'$, $\gamma = 135° \, 31'.$

EXAMPLE 3. Solve $\triangle ABC$ if $a = 2$, $b = 6$, and $\alpha = 30°$.

SOLUTION *without logarithms.* $\sin \beta = \dfrac{b \sin \alpha}{a} = \dfrac{6(\frac{1}{2})}{2} = 1.5 > 1.$

Hence, there is *no solution* because a sine is never greater than 1. A figure for this problem would look like Figure 75.

SOLUTION *with logarithms.*

$$\sin \beta = \frac{b \sin \alpha}{a}:$$

$\log b = 0.7782$
$\underline{\log \sin \alpha = 9.6990 - 10 \; (+)}$
$\overline{\log b \sin \alpha = 0.4772}$
$\underline{\quad \log a = 0.3010 \qquad (-)}$
$\overline{\log \sin \beta = 0.1762, \textit{ which is positive.}}$

If the logarithm of a number is *positive*, the number is *greater than* 1. Hence, if $\log \sin \beta = 0.1762$ then $\sin \beta > 1$, which is *impossible.* Therefore, there is *no solution.*

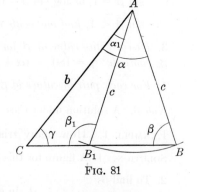

FIG. 81

EXAMPLE 4. Solve $\triangle ABC$ if $b = 4.157$, $c = 3.446$, $\gamma = 51° \, 48'$.

SOLUTION. From Figure 81, it appears that there are two solutions.

Formulas	Computation
	Data: $b = 4.157$, $c = 3.446$, $\gamma = 51° 48'$.
$\dfrac{\sin \beta}{b} = \dfrac{\sin \gamma}{c}$, or $\sin \beta = \dfrac{b \sin \gamma}{c}$.	$\log b = 0.6188$ (Table V) $\underline{\log \sin \gamma = 9.8953 - 10 \ (+)}$ (Table VI) $\log b \sin \gamma = 10.5141 - 10$ $\underline{\log c = 0.5373 \hspace{1.5em} (-)}$ $\log \sin \beta = 9.9768 - 10; \ \beta = 71° 26'$. (Table VI) $Hence, \quad \beta_1 = 180° - \beta = 108° 34'$.
●	Solution for $\triangle ABC$, Figure 81
$\alpha = 180° - (\beta + \gamma)$.	$\alpha = 180° - (71° 26' + 51° 48') = 56° 46'$.
$\dfrac{a}{\sin \alpha} = \dfrac{c}{\sin \gamma}$, or $a = \dfrac{c \sin \alpha}{\sin \gamma}$.	$\log c = 0.5373$ $\underline{\log \sin \alpha = 9.9224 - 10 \ (+)}$ $\log c \sin \alpha = 10.4597 - 10$ $\underline{\log \sin \gamma = 9.8953 - 10 \ (-)}$ $\log a = 0.5644; \qquad a = 3.668$.
	Solution for $\triangle AB_1C$, Figure 81
$\alpha_1 = 180° - (\beta_1 + \gamma)$.	$\alpha_1 = 180° - (108° 34' + 51° 48') = 19° 38'$.
$a_1 = \dfrac{c \sin \alpha_1}{\sin \gamma}$.	$\log c = 0.5373$ $\underline{\log \sin \alpha_1 = 9.5263 - 10 \ (+)}$ $\log c \sin \alpha_1 = 10.0636 - 10$ $\underline{\log \sin \gamma = 9.8953 - 10 \ (-)}$ $\log a_1 = 0.1683; \qquad a_1 = 1.473$.

Summary.   First solution: $a = 3.668$, $\alpha = 56° 46'$, $\beta = 71° 26'$.

           Second solution: $a_1 = 1.473$, $\alpha_1 = 19° 38'$, $\beta_1 = 108° 34'$.

EXERCISE 50

Solve $\triangle ABC$ without logarithms by use of Table VII.

1. $\beta = 30°$, $a = 4$, $b = 5$.   **2.** $\gamma = 22° 20'$, $a = 50$, $c = 38$.

3. $\gamma = 65° 30'$, $b = 97.5$, $c = 91$.   **4.** $\alpha = 30°$, $b = 3$, $a = 5$.

5. $\gamma = 75°$, $c = 7$, $b = 7$.   **6.** $\alpha = 150°$, $a = 5$, $c = 8$.

7. $\alpha = 31° 20'$, $b = .25$, $a = .13$.   **8.** $\alpha = 157° 40'$, $a = 38$, $b = 25$.

9. $\gamma = 148° 40'$, $a = 20$, $c = 26$.   **10.** $\beta = 114° 30'$, $b = 13$, $c = 10$.

Solve by use of five-place* logarithms.   Check as directed by the instructor.

         11. $\beta = 42° 30'$, $b = 16.7$, $c = 12.3$.

         12. $\alpha = 67° 40'$, $a = 2.39$, $c = 1.67$.

         13. $\alpha = 76° 19'$, $a = .0572$, $b = .139$.

         14. $\alpha = 71° 45'$, $a = .9632$, $b = .9632$.

         15. $\beta = 36° 53'$, $c = .07531$, $b = .05126$.

         16. $\gamma = 49° 46'$, $b = .9652$, $c = .4738$.

* Answers are given also for four-place computation in Problems 11–18.

17. $\alpha = 113° 20'$, $a = 11.56$, $c = 7.282$.

18. $\gamma = 147° 5'$, $b = 19.36$, $c = 15.17$.

19. $\alpha = 24° 7.4'$, $a = 1.2695$, $b = 1.5873$.

20. $\gamma = 36° 48.9'$, $c = 7.4261$, $b = 5.1379$.

21. $\beta = 44° 13.3'$, $c = 6.6260$, $b = 4.6212$.

22. $\alpha = 35° 28'$, $a = 9.8470$, $b = 5.7135$.

23. $\gamma = 127° 19'$, $a = .74215$, $c = .97316$.

24. $\beta = 52° 19' 8''$, $b = 2.4017$, $c = 2.6317$.

25. A telegraph pole is supported by two guy wires which run from the top of the pole to the ground on opposite sides. One wire is 53.6 feet long and makes an angle of 65° 20' with the ground. The other wire is 57.5 feet long. Find the acute angle which the second wire makes with the ground, if both wires are in the same vertical plane.

26. A force of 85 pounds pulls due east on P. A second force pulls N 37° W on P. The resultant force is 73 pounds. Find the second force and the direction of the resultant.

Without solving the triangle, construct all triangles which satisfy the data, and thus reach a conclusion geometrically concerning the number of solutions. Also, compute a perpendicular h, as referred to in Section 95, and apply a corresponding analytical test about the value of h to verify the geometrical conclusion.

27. $\alpha = 58°$, $a = 42$, $b = 50$.   **28.** $\gamma = 73°$, $a = 60$, $c = 58$.

29. $\beta = 115°$, $a = 35$, $b = 56$.   **30.** $\gamma = 41°$, $a = 200$, $c = 135$.

96. The law of tangents

In a triangle, the difference of any two sides, divided by their sum, equals the tangent of one half of the difference of the opposite angles divided by the tangent of one half of their sum:

$$\frac{a - b}{a + b} = \frac{\tan \frac{1}{2}(\alpha - \beta)}{\tan \frac{1}{2}(\alpha + \beta)}; \qquad \frac{c - a}{c + a} = \frac{\tan \frac{1}{2}(\gamma - \alpha)}{\tan \frac{1}{2}(\gamma + \alpha)}; \qquad (1)$$

$$\frac{b - c}{b + c} = \frac{\tan \frac{1}{2}(\beta - \gamma)}{\tan \frac{1}{2}(\beta + \gamma)}. \qquad (2)$$

Proof. 1. Let b and c be any two sides and let us prove (2).

2. By the law of sines,

$$\frac{b}{c} = \frac{\sin \beta}{\sin \gamma}. \qquad (3)$$

3. Subtract 1 on both sides of (3); also, add 1 on both sides:

$$\frac{b}{c} - 1 = \frac{\sin \beta}{\sin \gamma} - 1; \; or \qquad \frac{b - c}{c} = \frac{\sin \beta - \sin \gamma}{\sin \gamma}. \qquad (4)$$

$$\frac{b}{c} + 1 = \frac{\sin \beta}{\sin \gamma} + 1; \; or \qquad \frac{b + c}{c} = \frac{\sin \beta + \sin \gamma}{\sin \gamma}. \qquad (5)$$

4. Divide each side of (4) by the corresponding side of (5); then use (XVIII) and (XIX) from page 112:

$$\frac{b - c}{b + c} = \frac{\sin \beta - \sin \gamma}{\sin \beta + \sin \gamma} = \frac{2 \sin \frac{1}{2}(\beta - \gamma) \cos \frac{1}{2}(\beta + \gamma)}{2 \cos \frac{1}{2}(\beta - \gamma) \sin \frac{1}{2}(\beta + \gamma)}.$$

Hence, $$\frac{b - c}{b + c} = \tan \frac{1}{2}(\beta - \gamma) \cot \frac{1}{2}(\beta + \gamma) = \frac{\tan \frac{1}{2}(\beta - \gamma)}{\tan \frac{1}{2}(\beta + \gamma)}.$$

Note 1. Corresponding to (1) and (2), we obtain equivalent equations by changing the order of the letters. Thus, instead of (2), we find

$$\frac{c - b}{c + b} = \frac{\tan \frac{1}{2}(\gamma - \beta)}{\tan \frac{1}{2}(\gamma + \beta)}. \tag{6}$$

In any application, we use (6) if $c > b$ and (2) if $c < b$, in order to keep *the differences positive* for convenience in the formula employed.

97. Solution of Case III by the law of tangents

EXAMPLE 1. Solve $\triangle ABC$ if $\alpha = 78° 48'$, $b = 726$, $c = 938$.

SOLUTION. We solve by use of the four-place Tables V and VI.

Formulas	Computation
	Data: $\alpha = 78° 48'$, $b = 726$, $c = 938$.
$\frac{1}{2}(\gamma + \beta) = \frac{1}{2}(180° - \alpha)$.	$\frac{1}{2}(\gamma + \beta) = \frac{1}{2}(180° - 78° 48') = 50° 36'$.
$\frac{\tan \frac{1}{2}(\gamma - \beta)}{\tan \frac{1}{2}(\gamma + \beta)} = \frac{c - b}{c + b};$ *or,* $\tan \frac{1}{2}(\gamma - \beta) = \frac{(c - b) \tan \frac{1}{2}(\gamma + \beta)}{c + b}$.	$c - b = 212;$ $c + b = 1664.$ $\log (c - b) = \quad 2.3263$ $\log \tan \frac{1}{2}(\gamma + \beta) = \quad 0.0855 \quad (+)$ $\log \text{numerator} = 12.4118 - 10$ $\log (c + b) = \quad 3.2211 \quad (-)$ $\log \tan \frac{1}{2}(\gamma - \beta) = \quad 9.1907 - 10$ $\frac{1}{2}(\gamma - \beta) = \quad 8° 49'.$ (Table VI)
$\beta = \frac{1}{2}(\gamma + \beta) - \frac{1}{2}(\gamma - \beta)$. $\gamma = \frac{1}{2}(\gamma + \beta) + \frac{1}{2}(\gamma - \beta)$.	$\frac{1}{2}(\gamma + \beta) = 50° 36'$ ⎱ *Add to get* γ. $\frac{1}{2}(\gamma - \beta) = \quad 8° 49'$ ⎰ *Subtract to get* β. $\gamma = 59° 25';$ $\beta = 41° 47'.$
$\frac{a}{\sin \alpha} = \frac{c}{\sin \gamma}$, *or* $a = \frac{c \sin \alpha}{\sin \gamma}$.	$\log c = \quad 2.9722$ $\log \sin \alpha = \quad 9.9916 - 10 \ (+)$ $\log c \sin \alpha = 12.9638 - 10$ $\log \sin \gamma = \quad 9.9350 - 10 \ (-)$ $\log a = \quad 3.0288;$ $a = 1069.$
Summary.	$\beta = 41° 47',$ $\gamma = 59° 25',$ $a = 1069.$

Check. $\dfrac{a}{\sin \alpha} = \dfrac{b}{\sin \beta}.$

$\log a = 13.0289 - 10$ $\log b = 12.8609 - 10$
$\log \sin \alpha = \ \ 9.9916 - 10 \ (-)$ $\log \sin \beta = \ \ 9.8237 - 10 \ (-)$
$\log (a/\sin \alpha) = \ \ 3.0373 \longrightarrow$ $\longleftarrow \log (b/\sin \beta) = \ \ 3.0372;$ *satisfactory.*

OUTLINE. *Solution of $\triangle ABC$ with given parts a, b, γ.*

1. *Compute $\frac{1}{2}(\alpha + \beta) = \frac{1}{2}(180° - \gamma)$.*

2. *Find $\frac{1}{2}(\alpha - \beta)$ by use of the formula of the law of tangents involving a, b, α, β.*

3. *Compute α and β by use of*

$$\alpha = \tfrac{1}{2}(\alpha + \beta) + \tfrac{1}{2}(\alpha - \beta); \qquad \beta = \tfrac{1}{2}(\alpha + \beta) - \tfrac{1}{2}(\alpha - \beta). \qquad (1)$$

4. *Find c from the law of sines.*

5. *Check by a formula of the law of sines not used in solving.*

98. Refined checks on solutions of triangles

The formulas of the law of tangents provide sensitive checks on solutions of triangles obtained under Cases I, II, and III.

ILLUSTRATION 1. We could check the solution of Example 1, page 131, by use of any formula of the law of tangents not used in solving.

EXAMPLE 1. Check the first solution in Example 4, Section 95.

SOLUTION. The data were $b = 4.157$, $c = 3.446$, and $\gamma = 51° 48'$. The solution was $a = 3.668$, $\alpha = 56° 46'$, and $\beta = 71° 26'$.

Check formula:

$$\frac{b - a}{b + a} = \frac{\tan \frac{1}{2}(\beta - \alpha)}{\tan \frac{1}{2}(\beta + \alpha)}.$$

$b = 4.157$	$\beta = 71° 26'$
$a = 3.668$	$\alpha = 56° 46'$
$b + a = 7.825$	$\beta + \alpha = 128° 12'$
$b - a = .489$	$\beta - \alpha = 14° 40'$

$\frac{1}{2}(\beta + \alpha) = 64° 6'$; $\quad \frac{1}{2}(\beta - \alpha) = 7° 20'$.

$$\left\{ \begin{array}{l} \log (b - a) = 9.6893 - 10 \\ \log (b + a) = 0.8935 \qquad (-) \end{array} \right.$$

$$\left\{ \begin{array}{l} \log \tan \frac{1}{2}(\beta - \alpha) = 9.1096 - 10 \\ \log \tan \frac{1}{2}(\beta + \alpha) = 0.3137 \qquad (-) \end{array} \right.$$

$$\log \frac{b - a}{b + a} = 8.7958 - 10 \longrightarrow \qquad \longleftarrow \log \frac{\tan \frac{1}{2}(\beta - \alpha)}{\tan \frac{1}{2}(\beta + \alpha)} = 8.7959 - 10.$$

★*Note 1.* It can be proved that, in any triangle ABC,

$$\frac{a - b}{c} = \frac{\sin \frac{1}{2}(\alpha - \beta)}{\cos \frac{1}{2}\gamma}; \qquad \frac{b - c}{a} = \frac{\sin \frac{1}{2}(\beta - \gamma)}{\cos \frac{1}{2}\alpha}; \qquad \frac{c - a}{b} = \frac{\sin \frac{1}{2}(\gamma - \alpha)}{\cos \frac{1}{2}\beta}; \qquad (1)$$

$$\frac{a + b}{c} = \frac{\cos \frac{1}{2}(\alpha - \beta)}{\sin \frac{1}{2}\gamma}; \qquad \frac{b + c}{a} = \frac{\cos \frac{1}{2}(\beta - \gamma)}{\sin \frac{1}{2}\alpha}; \qquad \frac{a + c}{b} = \frac{\cos \frac{1}{2}(\gamma - \alpha)}{\sin \frac{1}{2}\beta}. \qquad (2)$$

These formulas are called **Mollweide's equations,** in recognition of their use by a German astronomer KARL MOLLWEIDE (1774–1825), although the formulas were known before his time. Equations (1) and (2) give sensitive checks on the solution of a triangle because each formula involves all parts of the triangle. The proofs of (1) and (2) are similar to the derivation of the law of tangents (see Note 11 of the Appendix).

EXERCISE 51

Solve $\triangle ABC$ *by use of five-place* logarithms and check as directed by the instructor.*

1. $b = 387, c = 136, \alpha = 68°.$

2. $a = 102, b = 437, \gamma = 43°.$

3. $a = .936, c = .348, \beta = 72°.$

4. $b = .657, c = .319, \alpha = 108°.$

5. $a = 13.16, c = 22.78, \alpha = 69° 40'.$

6. $a = 21.45, b = 9.36, \gamma = 70° 25'.$

7. $a = 773.6, \quad c = 993.4, \quad \beta = 120° 30'.$

8. $a = 21.467, \quad b = 13.218, \quad \gamma = 19° 20.6'.$

9. $b = 316.25, \quad c = 158.67, \quad \alpha = 61° 19.8'.$

10. $a = .98315, \quad c = 1.25670, \beta = 57° 35.7'.$

11. $b = .84107, \quad c = 1.36450, \alpha = 98° 16.8'.$

12. $a = 31024, \quad c = 65937, \quad \beta = 58° 7' 25''.$

13. $b = 13056.0, c = 8947.2, \quad \alpha = 105° 6' 29''.$

Find the other angles of $\triangle ABC$ *by use of Table VII and the law of tangents, without logarithms.*

14. $a = 12, b = 8, \gamma = 30°.$

15. $b = 30, c = 25, \alpha = 50°.$

16. $a = 50, c = 25, \beta = 110°.$

17. $a = 10, b = 15, \gamma = 150°.$

18. The sides of a parallelogram are 185 feet and 263 feet long, and one angle is 39°. Find the length of the longest diagonal.

19. Two forces whose magnitudes are 340.6 pounds and 263.5 pounds act simultaneously on an object. If the angle between the directions of the forces is 63° 48', find the magnitude of the resultant force.

20. A battery B is to fire at an invisible target T. An observation point H is located from which B and T are visible. With a range finder, it is determined that $\overline{HB} = 1250$ yards and $\overline{HT} = 5350$ yards. If the bearing of T from H is N 38° 16' W and of B from H is S 20° 5' W, find the range $\overline{BT}$ and the direction of T from B.

99. Tangents of the half-angles

We recall that the bisectors of the angles of a triangle ABC, as in Figure 82 on page 134, meet at the center O of the *inscribed circle*. Let r be its radius. Then, in Figure 82,

$$\overline{OD} = \overline{OE} = \overline{OF} = r.$$

Later, we shall obtain a formula for r in terms of sides a, b, c. Let s be one half of the perimeter of triangle ABC:

$$s = \tfrac{1}{2}(a + b + c). \tag{1}$$

Then, we shall show that

$$\tan \frac{\alpha}{2} = \frac{r}{s-a}; \qquad \tan \frac{\beta}{2} = \frac{r}{s-b}; \qquad \tan \frac{\gamma}{2} = \frac{r}{s-c}. \tag{2}$$

---

* Answers are given also for four-place computation in Problems 1–7.

Proof. 1. From right $\triangle ADO$ in Figure 82,

$$\tan \frac{\alpha}{2} = \frac{\overline{OD}}{\overline{AD}} = \frac{r}{\overline{AD}}. \tag{3}$$

2. The whole perimeter is

$$2s = (\overline{AD} + \overline{AF}) + (\overline{BE} + \overline{BD}) + (\overline{CE} + \overline{CF}).$$

But, from Figure 82, $\overline{AF} = \overline{AD}$; $\overline{BD} = \overline{BE}$; $\overline{CF} = \overline{CE}$. Therefore,

$$2s = 2\overline{AD} + 2\overline{BE} + 2\overline{CE}; \quad or$$

$$s = \overline{AD} + (\overline{BE} + \overline{CE}).$$

Since $\overline{BE} + \overline{CE} = \overline{BC} = a$, then

$$s = \overline{AD} + a, \text{ or}$$

$$\overline{AD} = s - a.$$

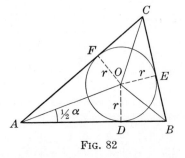

FIG. 82

3. Hence, from (3) we obtain (2) for $\alpha/2$. Or, *the tangent of one half of any angle equals r divided by the difference of s and the side opposite the angle.*

Note 1. Observe that (2) will not be useful until a formula for r is obtained in the following section, which also gives a second proof for (2). However, the preceding simple proof is very valuable for appreciation and memorization of formulas (2).

100. Sines, cosines, and tangents of the half-angles

Let α be any angle of triangle ABC. Then, without use of the preceding section, we shall show that

$$\sin \frac{\alpha}{2} = \sqrt{\frac{(s-b)(s-c)}{bc}}; \quad \cos \frac{\alpha}{2} = \sqrt{\frac{s(s-a)}{bc}}; \quad \tan \frac{\alpha}{2} = \frac{r}{s-a} \tag{1}$$

Proof. 1. Since $2s = a + b + c$, then $2s - 2b = a + c - b$. This proves the second equation in (2) below. Each equation in (3) is proved similarly.

$$a + b + c = 2s; \quad a + c - b = 2(s - b); \tag{2}$$

$$b + c - a = 2(s - a); \quad a + b - c = 2(s - c). \tag{3}$$

2. By the law of cosines,

$$\cos \alpha = \frac{b^2 + c^2 - a^2}{2bc}. \tag{4}$$

From page 109, $2 \cos^2 \frac{1}{2}\alpha = 1 + \cos \alpha$. Hence, from (4),

$$2 \cos^2 \frac{\alpha}{2} = 1 + \frac{b^2 + c^2 - a^2}{2bc} = \frac{(b^2 + 2bc + c^2) - a^2}{2bc};$$

$$\cos^2 \frac{\alpha}{2} = \frac{(b+c)^2 - a^2}{4bc} = \frac{(b+c+a)(b+c-a)}{4bc}. \qquad (5)$$

On using (2) and (3) in (5), we obtain

$$\cos^2 \frac{\alpha}{2} = \frac{s(s-a)}{bc}, \quad or \quad \cos \frac{\alpha}{2} = \sqrt{\frac{s(s-a)}{bc}}. \qquad (6)$$

3. Similarly, since $2 \sin^2 \frac{1}{2}\alpha = 1 - \cos \alpha$, from (4) we derive

$$\sin^2 \frac{\alpha}{2} = \frac{(a-b+c)(a+b-c)}{4bc} = \frac{(s-b)(s-c)}{bc};$$

$$\sin \frac{\alpha}{2} = \sqrt{\frac{(s-b)(s-c)}{bc}}. \qquad (7)$$

4. By use of (6) and (7),

$$\tan \tfrac{1}{2}\alpha = \frac{\sin \frac{1}{2}\alpha}{\cos \frac{1}{2}\alpha} = \sqrt{\frac{(s-b)(s-c)}{s(s-a)}}.$$

Multiply numerator and denominator of the radicand by $(s-a)$:

$$\tan \frac{\alpha}{2} = \sqrt{\frac{(s-a)(s-b)(s-c)}{s(s-a)^2}} = \frac{1}{s-a} \sqrt{\frac{(s-a)(s-b)(s-c)}{s}}. \qquad (8)$$

If we let

$$r = \sqrt{\frac{(s-a)(s-b)(s-c)}{s}}, \qquad (9)$$

then

$$\tan \frac{\alpha}{2} = \frac{r}{s-a}. \qquad (10)$$

In arriving at (10), we made no use of Section 99, and r was introduced in (9) *merely as an abbreviation for a radical*. But, we may now compare equation (10) above with $\tan \frac{1}{2}\alpha$ in (2) on page 134; since the denominators are the *same* in the right-hand members, the numerators must represent the *same quantity*. Hence, we have proved that *the radius r of the inscribed circle of a triangle ABC is given by* (9).

Note 1. By altering the letters in formulas (1) we obtain similar formulas for functions of $\beta/2$ and $\gamma/2$. Thus,

$$\sin \frac{\beta}{2} = \sqrt{\frac{(s-a)(s-c)}{ac}}; \qquad \cos \frac{\gamma}{2} = \sqrt{\frac{s(s-c)}{ab}}.$$

101. Solution of Case IV by the half-angle formulas

Suppose that all sides of triangle ABC are given. Then, if *just one* of its angles is desired, we may use the preceding formulas for the *sine* or *cosine* of half of the angle, because then it is *unnecessary to find r* or its logarithm. If *all* angles of the triangle are desired, it is best to use tangents of the half-angles, where we proceed as follows.

SUMMARY.   *To obtain the angles when the sides are known.*

1. *Compute s, (s − a), (s − b), (s − c), and then log r, by use of*

$$r = \sqrt{\frac{(s-a)(s-b)(s-c)}{s}}.$$

2. *Find α, β, γ by use of the tangents of the half-angles.*

3. *Check by use of α + β + γ = 180°.*

In checking, it will not be unusual for the sum of the angles to differ from 180° by several units in the last angular place employed. This is due to the fact that each angle is obtained by multiplying one half of the angle by 2, which *doubles* any previous error.

EXAMPLE 1.   Solve $\triangle ABC$ if $a = 173$, $b = 267$, $c = 412$.

SOLUTION.   We apply the preceding summary, and use four-place logarithms in the computation.

Formulas	*Computation*
$s = \frac{1}{2}(a + b + c)$. *To check here, notice that* $(s − a) + (s − b) + (s − c)$ $= 3s − (a + b + c) = s.$	$\begin{aligned}a &= 173 \\ b &= 267 \\ c &= 412 \\ \hline 2s &= 852 \longrightarrow\end{aligned}$ (+) $\qquad \begin{aligned}s − a &= 253 \\ s − b &= 159 \\ s − c &= \ \ 14 \\ \hline \longleftarrow s &= 426\end{aligned}$ (+)
$r = \sqrt{\dfrac{(s-a)(s-b)(s-c)}{s}}$; $r^2 = \dfrac{(s-a)(s-b)(s-c)}{s}$. $\log r = \frac{1}{2}\log r^2.$	$\log (s − a) = 2.4031$ $\log (s − b) = 2.2014$ (+) $\log (s − c) = 1.1461$ $\overline{\log \text{numerator} = 5.7506}$ $\log s = 2.6294 \quad (−)$ $\overline{\log r^2 = 3.1212; \ (\div \text{ by } 2)}$ $\log r = 1.5606.$
$\tan \dfrac{\alpha}{2} = \dfrac{r}{s-a}.$	$\log r = 11.5606 − 10$ $\log (s − a) = 2.4031 \qquad (−)$ $\overline{\log \tan \frac{1}{2}\alpha = 9.1575 − 10;}$ $\frac{1}{2}\alpha = 8° 11'; \quad \alpha = 16° 22'.$
$\tan \dfrac{\beta}{2} = \dfrac{r}{s-b}.$	$\log r = 11.5606 − 10$ $\log (s − b) = 2.2014 \qquad (−)$ $\overline{\log \tan \frac{1}{2}\beta = 9.3592 − 10;}$ $\frac{1}{2}\beta = 12° 53'; \quad \beta = 25° 46'.$
$\tan \dfrac{\gamma}{2} = \dfrac{r}{s-c}.$	$\log r = 1.5606$ $\log (s − c) = 1.1461 \quad (−)$ $\overline{\log \tan \frac{1}{2}\gamma = 0.4145;}$ $\frac{1}{2}\gamma = 68°56'; \quad \gamma = 137° 52'.$
Summary.	$\alpha = 16° 22', \quad \beta = 25° 46', \quad \gamma = 137° 52'.$

Check. $\alpha + \beta + \gamma = 16° 22' + 25° 46' + 137° 52' = 180° 0';$ *satisfactory.*

EXERCISE 52

Solve $\triangle ABC$ *by use of five-place * logarithms.*

1. $a = 17, b = 26, c = 25.$ **2.** $a = 8, b = 7, c = 11.$

3. $a = 5.26, b = 4.38, c = 9.34.$ **4.** $a = .986, b = .726, c = .648.$

5. $a = 136, b = 472, c = 450.$ **6.** $a = 4.614, b = 6.213, c = 5.709.$

7. $a = 73.09, b = 91.27, c = 59.86.$ **8.** $a = .1931, b = .1137, c = .2625.$

9. $a = 12.379, b = 26.423, c = 25.603.$

10. $a = 3812.6, b = 5372.4, c = 7635.8.$

11. $a = .91315, b = .80263, c = .74137.$

12. $a = .072130, b = .057387, c = .043002.$

13. $a = 9.8314, b = 6.1041, c = 7.0308.$

14. $a = 111.78, b = 235.67, c = 204.38.$

Find the desired angle by use of the sine or cosine of half of the angle.

15. $a = 13, b = 17, c = 9;$ find $\beta.$ **16.** $a = 27, b = 36, c = 42;$ find $\gamma.$

17. Two forces with the magnitudes 19 pounds and 21 pounds act simultaneously on an object. The magnitude of the resultant force is 35 pounds. Find the smallest positive angle between the directions in which the given forces act.

18. Two forces with the magnitudes 132.5 pounds and 217.3 pounds act simultaneously on an object. The magnitude of the resultant force is 265.3 pounds. Find the smallest positive angle between the directions in which the given forces act.

★19. An airplane heads in a northerly direction at an airspeed of 300 miles per hour while a wind is blowing due east at 50 miles per hour. The resultant groundspeed is 330 miles per hour. Find the heading.

102. Area of a triangle

The area K of a triangle ABC can be expressed in terms of two sides and their included angle:

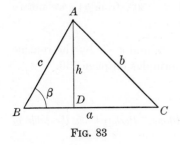

FIG. 83

$$K = \tfrac{1}{2}bc \sin \alpha;$$
$$K = \tfrac{1}{2}ac \sin \beta; \qquad (1)$$
$$K = \tfrac{1}{2}ab \sin \gamma.$$

Proof. Let a and c be any two sides, and let h be the altitude from A to BC, as in Figure 83. Then, regardless of the size of β, $h = c \sin \beta$, and

$$K = \tfrac{1}{2}ha = \tfrac{1}{2}ac \sin \beta.$$

Hence, the area is equal to *one half of the product of any two sides and the sine of their included angle.*

* Answers are given also for four-place computation in Problems 1–8.

The area K of triangle ABC is given by

$$K = \sqrt{s(s-a)(s-b)(s-c)}. \tag{2}$$

Proof. 1. From (1), $K = \frac{1}{2}bc \sin \alpha$. From (VII), page 108, we obtain $\sin \alpha = 2 \sin \frac{1}{2}\alpha \cos \frac{1}{2}\alpha$, and hence

$$K = bc \sin \tfrac{1}{2}\alpha \cos \tfrac{1}{2}\alpha. \tag{3}$$

2. By use of (3) and formulas (1), page 134,

$$K = bc\sqrt{\frac{(s-b)(s-c)}{bc}} \sqrt{\frac{s(s-a)}{bc}}$$

$$= \sqrt{s(s-a)(s-b)(s-c)}.$$

Note 1. Formula (2) is called **Heron's formula** for the area of a triangle. This famous result, which is sometimes proved in elementary geometry, is named after the Greek geometer HERON (or HERO) of ALEXANDRIA, who lived in the third century B.C.

The area K of a triangle ABC can be expressed in terms of any side and the angles:

$$K = \frac{a^2 \sin \beta \sin \gamma}{2 \sin \alpha}; \quad K = \frac{b^2 \sin \alpha \sin \gamma}{2 \sin \beta}; \quad K = \frac{c^2 \sin \alpha \sin \beta}{2 \sin \gamma}. \tag{4}$$

Proof. From (1), $K = \frac{1}{2}ac \sin \beta$. From the law of sines,

$$c = \frac{a \sin \gamma}{\sin \alpha}.$$

Hence, we obtain

$$K = \frac{1}{2} a \frac{a \sin \gamma}{\sin \alpha} \sin \beta = \frac{a^2 \sin \gamma \sin \beta}{2 \sin \alpha}.$$

Note 2. The exercises will emphasize (1) and (2). The student may prefer to derive any case of (1) instantaneously whenever it arises rather than to memorize the formula.

ILLUSTRATION 1. If $a = 12$, $c = 8$, and $\beta = 30°$, from (1) we obtain

$$K = \tfrac{1}{2}(12)(8) \sin 30° = 24.$$

In applying (2), we compute s, $s - a$, $s - b$, and $s - c$ by the routine introduced when employing the half-angle formulas on page 136.

EXERCISE 53

Find the area of the △ABC without logarithms. Perhaps use the table of square roots.

1. $a = 10$, $c = 8$, $\beta = 30°$.
2. $b = 2$, $c = \sqrt{3}$, $\alpha = 60°$.
3. $a = 3$, $b = \sqrt{3}$, $\gamma = 120°$.
4. $b = 15$, $c = 10$, $\alpha = 150°$.
5. $a = 7$, $b = 12$, $c = 13$.
6. $a = 9$, $b = 17$, $c = 10$.
7. $a = 21$, $b = 9$, $c = 20$.
8. $a = 11$, $b = 18$, $c = 25$.

Compute the area by use of four-place or five-place logarithms.

9. $a = 4.908, b = 3.578, c = 7.404.$

10. $a = 128.3, b = 140.7, c = 188.4.$

11. $a = .3158, b = .2893, c = .1642.$

12. $c = 31.42, \alpha = 37° 31', \beta = 63° 45'.$

13. $b = .0157, \alpha = 62° 17', \beta = 53° 25'.$

14. $a = 151.3, b = 206.3, \gamma = 42° 17'.$

★15. Find the area of the inscribed circle in Problem 9.

103. Summary concerning solution of triangles

I. *Given two angles and a side.*	*Solve by law of sines and check by law of tangents.*
II. *Given two sides and an opposite angle.*	*Solve by law of sines, with particular attention to the number of solutions. Check by law of tangents.**
III. *Given two sides and the included angle.*	1. *Find the angles by law of tangents and the third side by law of sines. Check by law of sines or law of tangents.** 2. *If* **only** *the third side is desired, perhaps use law of cosines (not adapted to logarithms).*
IV. *Given three sides.*	1. *Solve by half-angle formulas and check by* $\alpha + \beta + \gamma = 180°.$ 2. *Solve by law of cosines (not adapted to logarithms) and check by* $\alpha + \beta + \gamma = 180°.$

Note 1. Recall the suggestions on page 30 for outlining the solution of a problem with data described verbally.

MISCELLANEOUS EXERCISE 54

Solve △ABC completely except where only one part is requested.

Solve by use of Tables I, VII, XII without logarithms.

1. $b = 20, \beta = 30°, \gamma = 57°$; find only a.

2. $a = 3, b = 5, c = 7$; find only β (law of cosines).

3. $a = 4, b = 5, c = 8$; find only γ (law of cosines).

4. $a = 20, \alpha = 30°, \gamma = 42° 7'.$ **5.** $b = 81, c = 50, \beta = 164° 20'.$

6. $c = 910, \gamma = 65° 30', \beta = 100°.$ **7.** $c = 40, \beta = 90°, \gamma = 26° 12'.$

8. $a = 50, b = 38, \beta = 22° 20'.$ **9.** $a = 76, c = 20, \alpha = 157° 40'.$

10. $b = 10, c = 5, \alpha = 74° 20'$; find only a (law of cosines).

11. $a = 12, c = 5, \beta = 114° 50'$; find only b (law of cosines).

* Or, Mollweide's equations; or, formulas like $c = a \cos \beta + b \cos \alpha.$

Solve △ABC by use of five-place* logarithms, where needed.

12. $a = .956, b = .734, c = .526.$

13. $a = 1.315, b = 2.673, \gamma = 80° 19'.$

14. $b = 1573, c = 6132, \beta = 82° 14'.$

15. $a = 2395, c = 4647, \alpha = 25° 17'.$

16. $a = 863, c = 457, \gamma = 121° 53'.$

17. $a = 395.6, b = 524.7, \beta = 73° 6'.$

18. $a = 13.17, \alpha = 26° 33', \gamma = 82° 58'.$

19. $a = 31.48, b = 56.72, c = 40.09.$

20. $b = 21.54, c = 42.36, \alpha = 105° 16'.$

21. $b = 1498, \beta = 63° 18', \gamma = 15° 27'.$

Employ methods of this chapter in connection with at least one oblique triangle in the solution of each of the following problems. Use a figure. Employ logarithms where convenient. Answers should be obtained in reasonable agreement with the specifications of page 58.

22. The lengths of two sides and a diagonal of a parallelogram are, respectively, 30 feet, 40 feet, and 60 feet. Find the angles of the parallelogram without logarithms.

23. An aviator finds that, after traveling 300 miles in an easterly direction and then 250 miles in a southerly direction, he is 400 miles due east of his starting point. Without logarithms, find the direction in which he traveled on the first leg of his journey.

24. A telegraph pole, which leans 15° 10′ from the vertical toward the sun, casts a shadow 39.8 feet long when the angle of elevation of the sun is 63° 40′. Find the length of the pole.

25. At a point 3½ miles from one end of a lake and 5¾ miles from the other end, the lake subtends an angle of 78° 53′. How long is the lake?

26. Along one bank of a river (see Figure 84), a surveyor measures

$AB = 183.5$ *feet,*　$\angle BAC = 67° 45',$
　　and $\angle ABC = 43° 26',$

where C is a point on the opposite bank. Find the width of the river.

Outline. 1. In △ABC, find only $\log b$ from

$$b = \frac{c \sin \beta}{\sin \gamma}.$$

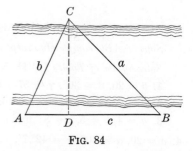

FIG. 84

2. From right △ADC, $CD = b \sin \alpha.$

27. From a ship, the angle of elevation of a point B at the top of a cliff is 21° 13′. After the ship has sailed 2500 feet directly toward B, its angle of elevation is found to be 47° 17′. Find the height of the cliff.

---

* Answers are given also for four-place computation in Problems 12–18.

28. From the top of an inclined road, 256 feet long, a vertical tower at the bottom subtends an angle of 22° 43′. Find the height of the tower if the road is inclined 39° 50′ from the horizontal.

29. A triangular building lot at the intersection of two streets has a frontage of 267 feet on one street and 135 feet on the other. If the third side of the lot is 356 feet long, find the acute angle between the streets.

30. A ship is sailing *N* 23° 25′ *W*. From *A* on the ship's track, the navigator sights a point of land *P* with bearing *N* 33° 40′ *E*. After sailing 2.85 miles farther to a point *B*, the bearing of *P* is *N* 42° 30′ *E*. Find the distance to *P* when it is nearest to the ship. (This is said to be the distance at which *P* is passed *abeam*.)

31. To find the range from a gun *G* to an inaccessible but visible target *T*, we measure a base line *AG* = 435 yards with a tape and transit; with a transit we measure ∠*TGA* = 88° 25.4′ and ∠*TAG* = 87° 46.7′. Find the range *GT*.

32. A surveyor runs a line *AB* = 1326 feet in the direction *N* 37° 28′ *E*, then *BC* = 1184 feet in a southerly direction, and then *CA* = 1016 feet, back to his starting point. As a check, he measures the direction of *CA*. Find this direction.

33. A surveyor desires to prolong an east-west line *AB* due east past an obstruction (see Figure 85). He measures *BC* = 785.4 feet, *S* 23° 17′ *E*, and then he runs *CD* in the direction *N* 47° 53′ *E*. Find the length of *CD* if *D* is to be due east of *B*.

FIG. 85

34. A boat is towing an artillery target 2000 feet behind it. From the guns on the shore, the direction of the boat is *N* 38° 10′ *E* and of the target is *N* 21° 43′ *E*. Find the distance from the guns to the target, if the boat and the target are traveling due east.

35. In Figure 86, to find the distance between the inaccessible points *C* and *D*, on one side of the river, a surveyor on the other side measures

$$AB = 157.8 \text{ feet}; \quad \delta = 32° 26′;$$

$$\theta = 27° 45′; \quad \beta = 40° 29′;$$

$$\gamma = 35° 18′.$$

Find *CD*.

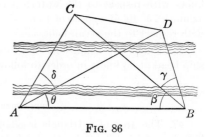

FIG. 86

Find the magnitude and direction of the resultant of the given forces which are acting together on an object.

36. 585 pounds directed *N* 26° 25′ *E*; 243 pounds directed *N* 78° 47′ *W*.

37. 41.7 pounds directed *S* 17° 5′ *E*; 39.4 pounds directed *N* 21° 14′ *E*.

38. One force of 8 pounds is directed due east. The magnitude of a second force is 12 pounds, and the magnitude of the resultant of these two forces is 15 pounds. Find the direction of the second force if it acts somewhat east of north, and find the direction of the resultant.

39. Four six-inch guns are emplaced in a straight line running east and west and facing north. The battery commander has measured the range of a target T as 10,300 yards and its azimuth as 337° 40′, with respect to the position of the first gun at the right. If the distance between consecutive guns is 90 yards, find the range and azimuth of T from the gun at the extreme left. Use four-place tables.

40. An airfield A is notified that enemy bombers are 400 miles away at B, whose azimuth from A is 30°; the bombers are flying on a track with azimuth 125°, with a groundspeed of 250 miles per hour. To intercept the bombers, what course should fighter planes follow if their groundspeed is 300 miles per hour, and how far from A will the interception occur?

41. At New York City, Navy headquarters learns that an enemy fleet, 600 miles away N 72° E, is sailing on a track with azimuth 190° at a speed of 25 knots.* Destroyers are dispatched at a speed of 35 knots to intercept the enemy. What course should the destroyers follow and how far from New York will the interception occur?

42. An airfield A is due east of a second field B. At a certain instant, an airplane takes off from B at a groundspeed of 270 miles per hour N 36° 50′ E, and a second airplane takes off from A at a groundspeed of 220 miles per hour. Find the course of the second airplane if it meets the first at the end of $2\frac{1}{2}$ hours.

Find the course, groundspeed, and drift angle for an airplane, corresponding to the specified airspeed, heading, and wind. All speeds are "per hour." Since three-place accuracy is sufficient, the student may desire to use the law of cosines. Each direction is an azimuth.

43. Airspeed = 200 miles; heading = 130°; wind = 40 miles, from 350°.

44. Airspeed = 300 miles; heading = 32°; wind = 50 miles, from 340°.

45. A ship heads in the direction with azimuth 141° 35′ at a speed of 36 knots with respect to the water; a current is flowing in the direction with azimuth 73° 40′ at a speed of 4 knots. Find the course of the ship and its speed with respect to the ocean floor.

46. Under the conditions in Problem 45, in which direction should the ship head at 36 knots in order to follow a track with azimuth 314° 30′?

Supplementary Problems

47. The area of a triangle is 8346 square feet and two of its angles are 37° 25′ and 56° 17′. Solve the triangle.

48. The building regulations in a city specify that a two-family dwelling may not be placed on a lot whose area is less than 15,000 square feet. The angle at the street corner of a triangular corner lot is 78° 36′ and the frontage of the lot on one street is 163 feet. What frontage must be obtained on the other street to permit the erection of a two-family dwelling?

49. The radius of the inscribed circle in a triangle is 6.8 feet and the triangle's area is 496 square feet. Find the sides if one angle is 57° 26′.

* A *knot* is a speed of one **nautical mile**, or 1.1515 statute miles, per hour.

50. Prove that the area of any parallelogram equals the product of the lengths of a pair of adjacent sides times the sine of their included angle.

51. Prove that the area of any convex quadrilateral is equal to one half of the product of the lengths of its diagonals times the sine of either angle formed by the diagonals.

52. Let R represent the radius of the *circumscribed* circle for a triangle ABC. Prove that

$$2R = \frac{a}{\sin \alpha} = \frac{b}{\sin \beta} = \frac{c}{\sin \gamma}.$$

HINT. Let α be any acute angle of the triangle. Draw the circle. Construct the diameter through C, meeting the circumference at D. Draw BC and notice that $\angle BDC = \alpha$. Then use right $\triangle BCD$.

53. Prove that, in any triangle ABC, $\quad \dfrac{s}{R} = \sin \alpha + \sin \beta + \sin \gamma.$

54. By use of half-angle formulas, prove that

$$R = \frac{abc}{4\sqrt{s(s-a)(s-b)(s-c)}}, \quad or \quad K = \frac{abc}{4R},$$

where K is the area of triangle ABC.

55. Prove that the radius of the inscribed circle of any triangle ABC is given by the formula $r = s \tan \frac{1}{2}\alpha \tan \frac{1}{2}\beta \tan \frac{1}{2}\gamma$.

56. In any triangle ABC, prove that $\quad K = \dfrac{abc}{s} \cos \dfrac{\alpha}{2} \cos \dfrac{\beta}{2} \cos \dfrac{\gamma}{2}.$

57. In any triangle ABC, prove that $\quad r = a \sin \dfrac{\beta}{2} \sin \dfrac{\gamma}{2} \sec \dfrac{\alpha}{2}.$

58. A flagpole of height h feet at the top of a wall inclines at an angle α from the vertical toward an observer. From a point A on a level with the base of the wall, the angles of elevation of the bottom and top of the pole are observed to be β and γ, respectively. Derive a formula for the height of the wall in terms of h, α, β, and γ.

59. A statue of height h feet stands on a pedestal whose height is k feet. At a certain point A on a level with the base of the pedestal, it and the statue subtend the same angle α. (1) Obtain a formula expressing the distance x from A to the pedestal in terms of h and α. (2) Obtain a trigonometric equation from which α could be found if h and k were given.

HINT. In Figure 87, eventually apply the law of sines to $\triangle ACD$. Write equations involving the letters in the figure and solve for the desired quantities.

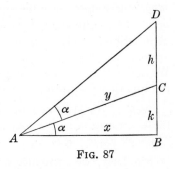

FIG. 87

60. A boat is sailing due north toward a shore which runs due east and west. The point of the shore nearest to the boat is A. On the shore, B is 16 miles east and C is 23 miles east of A. At what distance from the shore will an observer on the boat find that the line BC subtends an angle of $7° 20'$?

TEN

INVERSE TRIGONOMETRIC FUNCTIONS

104. The inverse trigonometric functions*

Let x and y be variables related by the equation $x = \sin y$. Then, y can be described as *"an angle whose sine is x,"* and we write $y = $ **arcsin** x, which is read *"arcsine x."* These remarks are summarized as follows.

DEFINITION I. *The expression "arcsin x" represents an angle whose sine is x, or the following equations are equivalent:*

$$x = \sin y \quad and \quad y = \textbf{arcsin } x. \tag{1}$$

ILLUSTRATION 1. To find the values of arcsin $\frac{1}{2}$, let $y = $ arcsin $\frac{1}{2}$. Then y satisfies $\sin y = \frac{1}{2}$, which has the solutions $y = 30°$ and $y = 150°$. Other solutions are $30° \pm 360°$, $30° \pm 720°$, $150° \pm 360°$, etc. Or, arcsin $\frac{1}{2}$ has infinitely many values given by

$$\text{arcsin } \tfrac{1}{2} = 30° + n \cdot 360° \quad and \quad \text{arcsin } \tfrac{1}{2} = 150° + n \cdot 360°, \tag{2}$$

where n is any integer, positive, negative, or zero.

In arcsin x, the variable x is the *sine of an angle*. Hence, arcsin x is not defined if $|x| > 1$, and the range for x is $-1 \leqq x \leqq 1$. If $|x| \leqq 1$, there are *infinitely many values* of arcsin x. The equation $x = \sin y$ *explicitly* describes x *as a function of y*, and *implicitly* defines y *as a function of x*. The equivalent equation $y = $ *arcsin x* serves the *inverse* purpose of describing y *explicitly as a function of x*. Hence, we call $\sin y$ and arcsin x *inverse functions*, and refer to either one as the *inverse* of the other. We notice that $x = \sin y$ defines x as a *single-valued* function of y, whereas the function $y = $ arcsin x is an *infinitely many-valued* function of x.

Note 1. In place of "arcsin x," a common notation for it is "$\sin^{-1} x$." Either arcsin x or $\sin^{-1} x$ may be read *"inverse sine of x,"* or *"arcsine x,"* or *"an angle whose sine is x."*

Similarly, we introduce **arccos x, arctan x, arccot x, arcsec x,** and **arccsc x** by paraphrasing Definition I for the various functions. Each inverse trigonometric function of x is an *infinitely many-valued* function of x for each value of x on its allowable range.

* Previously introduced on page 25. A completely fresh start is being made now.

ILLUSTRATION 2.   We read "arctan x" as "*arctangent x*." If $y =$ arctan x then $x =$ tan y. The variable x in arctan x represents the *tangent* of an angle, and hence may have *any real value;* or, the range for x is $-\infty < x < \infty$.

ILLUSTRATION 3.   If $y =$ arcsec x, then $x =$ sec y. Hence, we cannot have $|x| < 1$, and the range for x is all values such that $|x| \geqq 1$.

EXAMPLE 1.   Find an expression for all values of arccos $(-\frac{1}{2})$.

SOLUTION.   Let $y =$ arccos $(-\frac{1}{2})$. Then, cos $y = -\frac{1}{2}$. Hence, the solutions for y between $0°$ and $360°$ are $y = 120°$ and $y = 240°$. Any value of arccos $(-\frac{1}{2})$ is *coterminal* with either $120°$ or $240°$, or all values are given by the following expressions, where n may be any integer:

$$\text{arccos } (-\tfrac{1}{2}) = 120° + n(360°) \quad and \quad \text{arccos } (-\tfrac{1}{2}) = 240° + n(360°). \quad (3)$$

Comment 1.   Instead of (3), we could say that arccos $(-\frac{1}{2})$ is coterminal with either $120°$ or $-120°$, so that arccos $(-\frac{1}{2}) = n(360°) \pm 120°$.

Comment 2.   We may state the results in radian measure. Thus,

$$\text{arccos } (-\tfrac{1}{2}) = \tfrac{2}{3}\pi + 2n\pi \quad and \quad \text{arccos } (-\tfrac{1}{2}) = \tfrac{4}{3}\pi + 2n\pi.$$

EXAMPLE 2.   Find sec arctan $(-\frac{12}{5})$.

SOLUTION.   Let $\theta =$ arctan $(-\frac{12}{5})$. From page 93,

$$\sec \theta = \pm \sqrt{1 + \tan^2 \theta} = \pm \sqrt{1 + \tfrac{144}{25}} = \pm \tfrac{13}{5}.$$

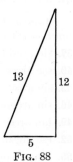

Hence, sec arctan $(-\frac{12}{5}) = \pm \frac{13}{5}$, where "$+$" or "$-$" would depend on the quadrant for the angle selected as the value of arctan $(-\frac{12}{5})$.

13   12

5

FIG. 88

Comment.   We could also obtain the *absolute value* of sec θ by means of the right triangle in Figure 88.

ILLUSTRATION 4.   Since sin $\theta = \pm \sqrt{1 - \cos^2 \theta}$,

$$\text{sin arccos } x = \pm \sqrt{1 - x^2}.$$

ILLUSTRATION 5.   For any value of x, we have sec arcsec $x = x$. That is, "*the secant of an angle whose secant is x is equal to x.*"

EXAMPLE 3.   Find all values of arccos $(-.2357)$ which are positive and less than $360°$.

SOLUTION.   Let $\theta =$ arccos $(-.2357)$. Then cos $\theta = -.2357$. Let α be the acute reference angle for θ. Then cos $\alpha = .2357$; from Table VII, $\alpha = 76° 22'$. Since θ is in quadrant II or quadrant III,

$$\theta = 180° - 76° 22' = 103° 38' \quad and \quad \theta = 180° + 76° 22' = 256° 22'.$$

Thus, arccos $(-.2357) = 103° 38'$ and arccos $(-.2357) = 256° 22'$.

★*Note 2.*   As a rule, any equation $f(x, y) = 0$ defines either variable as a function of the other. These two functions are called *inverse functions*, and either is called the *inverse* of the other. This terminology includes inverse trigonometric functions as special cases.

handwritten: principal value sin . 0 to 360 tan -90 to +90

EXERCISE 55

Write an equivalent equation in the notation of inverse functions.

1. $\tan y = \frac{3}{4}$.   **2.** $\csc y = -5$.   **3.** $\sin \theta = \frac{1}{3}$.   **4.** $\cot \theta = x$.

Find two positive or zero values and two negative values, if any, for each expression. State results in degree measure and radian measure.

5. arccos 1.   **6.** arctan 1.   **7.** arccos 0.   **8.** arcsec 2.

9. arcsin 1.   **10.** arccot (-1).   **11.** arccsc 1.   **12.** arcsin 0.

13. arccos (-1).   **14.** arctan ∞.   **15.** arcsec (-2).

16. arcsec $\sqrt{2}$.   **17.** arcsin $(-\frac{1}{2}\sqrt{2})$.   **18.** arccos $(\frac{1}{2}\sqrt{3})$.

19. arctan $\sqrt{3}$.   **20.** arccot $(-\sqrt{3})$.   **21.** arcsin $(-\frac{1}{2}\sqrt{3})$.

22. arcsec $\frac{2}{3}\sqrt{3}$.   **23.** arccsc (-1).   **24.** arccsc $(-\sqrt{2})$.

25. arcsin 3.   **26.** arccot ∞.   **27.** arcsec ∞.

28. arcsec $\frac{1}{2}$.   **29.** arccsc $(-\frac{2}{3}\sqrt{3})$.   **30.** arccsc ∞.

By use of Table VII, find two positive values for the expression.

31. arcsin .2051.   **32.** arctan .2247.   **33.** arccos $(-.4924)$.

34. arccos .9696.   **35.** arccot 1.560.   **36.** arcsin $(-.8371)$.

Assume that any angle involved is between $0°$ and $180°$, and find the specified function without using a table.

37. $\sin \arcsin \frac{3}{4}$.   **38.** $\cos \arccos \frac{1}{3}$.   **39.** $\tan \text{arccot} \frac{1}{2}$.

40. $\sec \arccos (-\frac{1}{4})$.   **41.** $\cot \arctan (-4)$.   **42.** $\cos \text{arcsec} \frac{5}{2}$.

43. $\sin \text{arccsc} \frac{4}{3}$.   **44.** $\cos \arcsin \frac{2}{3}$.   **45.** $\sin \arccos \frac{12}{13}$.

46. $\sin \arctan \frac{3}{4}$.   **47.** $\cos \text{arccot} \frac{8}{15}$.   **48.** $\sec \arctan (-\frac{5}{12})$.

49. $\tan \arccos (-\frac{4}{5})$.   **50.** $\sin \text{arccot} (-\frac{24}{7})$.   **51.** $\sec \arcsin \frac{5}{13}$.

52. $\csc \arcsin x$.   **53.** $\cot \text{arccot} x$.   **54.** $\sec \arccos x$.

55. $\tan \text{arccot} x$.   **56.** $\cos \arcsin x$.   **57.** $\sec \arctan z$.

58. $\csc \text{arccot} z$.   **59.** $\cos \arctan z$.   **60.** $\cos \text{arccot} x$.

Carry the solution of the equation only to a stage where all the values of x can be stated by use of inverse functions.

61. $3 \sin x = 2$.   **62.** $4 \cot x = 5$.   **63.** $5 \cos x + 3 = 0$.

64. $6 \sin^2 x - 7 \sin x - 3 = 0$.   **65.** $6 \sin x - \csc x + 1 = 0$.

66. $10 - 12 \sin^2 x + 5 \cos x = 0$.   **67.** $4 \cot x + 15 \tan x - 23 = 0$.

105. Principal values

We recall that, if $y = \arcsin x$, infinitely many values of y correspond to any assigned value of x. Sometimes it proves essential to fasten special attention on a particular one of these values of y, which is called the *principal value* of arcsin x. Similar remarks apply to the other inverse functions. Our definitions of principal values will follow the usage most prevalent in integral calculus, where important applications of principal values are met.

DEFINITION I. If $x \geqq 0$, *the principal value of any inverse trigonometric function of x is specified as that value which lies on the range 0 radians to $\pi/2$ radians, inclusive.*

ILLUSTRATION 1. The principal value of arcsin $\frac{1}{2}$ is $\frac{1}{6}\pi$ (or 30°).

DEFINITION II. *The principal value of* arctan x^* *or* arcsin x *is that value which lies on the range* $-\pi/2$ *radians to* $\pi/2$ *radians, inclusive.*

DEFINITION III. *The principal value of* arccos x *is that value which lies on the range* 0 *radians to* π *radians, inclusive.*

EXAMPLE 1. Find the principal value of arcsin $(-\frac{1}{2})$.

SOLUTION. Since sin 30° $= \frac{1}{2}$, values of arcsin $(-\frac{1}{2})$ are 210°, 330°, $-30°$, $-150°$, etc. The principal value of arcsin $(-\frac{1}{2})$ is $-\pi/6$ radians, or $-30°$.

In writing any inverse function, we shall commence its name with a *lower case* letter in case *an arbitrary value* of the function is involved, and with a *capital letter* to indicate the *principal value*.†

ILLUSTRATION 2. In Example 1, Arcsin $(-\frac{1}{2}) = -\frac{1}{6}\pi$.

★*Note 1.* We omit introducing principal value agreements for arccot x, arcsec x, arccsc x except as they are covered by Definition I. In texts on calculus, it is becoming common to avoid using these inverse functions.

★*Note 2.* The *single-valuedness* of Arcsin x, Arccos x, and Arctan x, in contrast to the fact that the *complete* inverse functions are *infinitely many-valued*, is a major reason for the importance of principal values.

EXERCISE 56

State each angle in degrees and radians. Use Table XIII if necessary.

1. Arcsin $\frac{1}{2}$.
2. Arctan 1.
3. Arccot $\sqrt{3}$.
4. Arccos 1.
5. Arcsin 0.
6. Arcsec 2.
7. Arccsc 2.
8. Arccos $\frac{1}{2}$.
9. Arcsin (-1).
10. Arccos $(-\frac{1}{2})$.
11. Arctan (-1).
12. Arcsin $(-\frac{1}{2})$.
13. Arccos $(-\frac{1}{2}\sqrt{2})$.
14. Arctan $(-\sqrt{3})$.
15. Arcsin $(-\frac{1}{2}\sqrt{2})$.
16. Arccos $(-\frac{1}{2}\sqrt{3})$.
17. Arctan $(-\frac{1}{3}\sqrt{3})$.
18. Arccos (-1).
19. Arcsin .36162.
20. Arccos .77125.
21. Arctan 1.3133.
22. Arcsin $(-.40776)$.
23. Arccos $(-.66746)$.

Find the value of each quantity without using a table.

24. sin Arccos 1.
25. cos Arcsin $\frac{1}{2}$.
26. sin Arccos $(-\frac{1}{2})$.
27. cos Arcsin $(-\frac{1}{2})$.
28. tan Arcsin $\frac{3}{4}$.
29. cot Arcsin $(-\frac{4}{5})$.
30. tan Arccos $(-\frac{1}{2})$.
31. cot Arccos $(-\frac{5}{13})$.
32. cos Arcsin $(-\frac{12}{13})$.
33. cos Arctan (-1).
34. sin Arctan $(-\sqrt{3})$.
35. sin Arctan $\frac{24}{7}$.

* For any value of x for which the function exists. This omits $\pm \pi/2$.
† There is no corresponding uniform custom in mathematical textbooks. In any book, the reader must learn what agreement applies.

36. tan Arcsin $(-\frac{24}{25})$.   **37.** cot Arccos $(-\frac{5}{13})$.   **38.** sec Arctan $\frac{7}{24}$.

39. cos $(\frac{1}{2}\pi + \text{Arcsin } \frac{3}{4})$.   **40.** sin $(\frac{1}{2}\pi - \text{Arcsin } \frac{1}{2})$.

HINT. Recall cos $(\frac{1}{2}\pi + \theta) = -\sin \theta$, and other reduction formulas.

41. tan $[\pi - \text{Arcsin } (-\frac{1}{2})]$.   **42.** sec $[\pi + \text{Arcsin } (-1)]$.

43. cos $[\frac{3}{2}\pi - \text{Arccos } (-\frac{1}{2}\sqrt{2})]$.   **44.** sin $[\frac{3}{2}\pi + \text{Arctan } (-\frac{4}{3})]$.

45. sin $(2 \text{ Arcsin } \frac{3}{5})$.   **46.** cos $(2 \text{ Arcsin } \frac{4}{5})$.   **47.** tan $(2 \text{ Arctan } 3)$.

HINT. If $\theta = \text{Arcsin } \frac{3}{5}$, we desire sin 2θ. Use a double-angle formula.

48. Arcsin (sin 140°).   **49.** Arccos (cos 250°).   **50.** Arctan (tan 105°).

51. sin $[\frac{1}{2} \text{ Arccos } (-\frac{3}{5})]$.   **52.** cos $[\frac{1}{2} \text{ Arcsin } \frac{4}{5}]$.

53. tan $[\frac{1}{2} \text{ Arcsin } (-\frac{5}{13})]$.   **54.** sin $[\text{Arcsin } \frac{3}{5} + \text{Arccos } (-\frac{5}{13})]$.

55. sin $(\text{Arcsin } \frac{3}{5} - \text{Arcsin } \frac{5}{13})$.   **56.** tan $(\text{Arctan } 1 + \text{Arctan } \frac{3}{4})$.

Find an expression for the quantity, provided that x, y, z are positive.

57. cos (Arccos x + Arcsin y).   **58.** tan (Arccot x − Arccot y).

59. cos (Arccos x − Arccos $3y$).   **60.** sin (Arccos $3y$ + Arccos $2x$).

61. sin (2 Arcsin x).   **62.** cot (2 Arctan x).   **63.** $\tan^2 (\frac{1}{2} \text{ Arccos } y)$.

64. cos (2 Arccos x).   **65.** $\sin^2 (\frac{1}{2} \text{ Arccos } x)$.   **66.** sin $(\frac{1}{2} \text{ Arcsin } x)$.

67. tan (2 Arctan x).   **68.** $\cos^2 (\frac{1}{2} \text{ Arccos } x)$.   **69.** cos $(\frac{1}{2} \text{ Arcsin } x)$.

106. Graphs of the inverse trigonometric functions

We recall that $y = \arcsin x$ is equivalent to $x = \sin y$. Hence, the graph of the function arcsin x, or of $y = \arcsin x$, in Figure 89, is a *sine curve along the vertical axis*. In Figure 89, the graph of the *principal value* $y = \text{Arcsin } x$ is simply arc *AOB*.

FIG. 89 $y = \arcsin x$ FIG. 90 $y = \arctan x$

Note 1. Look at Figure 89 through the reverse side of its sheet, rotated 90° clockwise and held against a light, to orient the curve as in Figure 54, page 80. A set of points for obtaining Figure 89 can be found by interchanging x and y in the table for Figure 54, with angles in radian measure.

ILLUSTRATION 1. A graph of $y = \arctan x$ is shown in Figure 90. Compare the graph as in Note 1 with the graph of $y = \tan x$ on page 81. In Figure 90, the graph of the principal value is simply branch AOB.

EXERCISE 57

Graph the function with y measured in radians, and the y-axis vertical. Use the same unit distance for the number scales on the two coordinate axes. Cover the range $-2\pi \leqq y \leqq 2\pi$. Clearly mark the graph of the principal value.

1. $y = \arcsin x$.   **2.** $y = \arccos x$.   **3.** $y = \arctan x$.

★*Solve for x.*

4. Arcsin $2x$ + Arcsin $x = 30°$.   **5.** Arcsin x = Arccos x.

HINT for Problem 4. 1. Solve for one function: Arcsin $2x = 30° -$ Arcsin x.

2. Take the sine of each side of the equation:

$$2x = \sin 30° \cos \text{Arcsin } x - \cos 30° \sin \text{Arcsin } x, \text{ or}$$
$$2x = \tfrac{1}{2}\sqrt{1 - x^2} - \tfrac{1}{2}x\sqrt{3}.$$

Rationalize, solve for x, and then test the results by substitution.

6. Arctan $3x$ + Arctan $x = 90°$.   **7.** Arcsin $(2x^2 + x) = \tfrac{1}{2}\pi$.

8. Arcsin x + Arccos $2x = 30°$.   **9.** Arccos $(1 - x)$ = Arccos $2x^2$.

10. Arcsin $\dfrac{3}{x}$ + Arcsin $\dfrac{4}{x} = \dfrac{\pi}{2}$.   **11.** Arcsin $\dfrac{8}{x}$ + Arccos $\dfrac{15}{x} = \dfrac{\pi}{2}$.

★*Prove the identity.*

12. Arccos x + Arcsin $x = 90°$.

HINT. Take the sine of each side.

13. Arcsec x + Arccsc $x = 90°$, if $x \geqq 1$.

14. $\tfrac{1}{2}$ Arccos x = Arcsin $\sqrt{\tfrac{1}{2}(1 + x)}$.   **15.** $\tfrac{1}{2}$ Arccos x = Arccos $\sqrt{\tfrac{1}{2}(1 + x)}$.

16. Arctan x = Arcsin $\dfrac{x}{\sqrt{1 + x^2}}$.   **17.** Arcsin x = Arctan $\dfrac{x}{\sqrt{1 - x^2}}$.

18. Arctan x + Arccos $\dfrac{x}{\sqrt{1 + x^2}} = \dfrac{\pi}{2}$.

Note 1. An equality involving general values of inverse trigonometric functions may be an identity in the sense that *any value of either side equals some value of the other side*, such as arctan x = arccot $1/x$; or, that *any value of a certain side equals some value of the other side*. In Problem 17, if "*Arctan*" and "*Arcsin*" are replaced by "*arctan*" and "*arcsin*," respectively, the resulting equality is not true in either of the preceding senses, as may be verified by writing values of the two sides when $x = \tfrac{1}{2}\sqrt{2}$.

ELEVEN

COMPLEX NUMBERS

107. Introduction to imaginary numbers

By definition, R is a square root of A if $R^2 = A$. Hence, -1 has no square root R which is zero, positive, or negative because, in such cases, $R^2 \geqq 0$ and cannot satisfy $R^2 = -1$. Accordingly, we extend the number system by introducing the symbol $\sqrt{-1}$ as a new variety of number, called an *imaginary number*, with the property that $\sqrt{-1} \cdot \sqrt{-1} = -1$. And, for contrast, we then call positive and negative numbers and zero *real* numbers. For convenience, we let $i = \sqrt{-1}$. Then, by definition, $i^2 = -1$. We agree that the operations of addition, subtraction, multiplication, and division may be applied to combinations of i and real numbers as if i were an ordinary real literal number, with $i^2 = -1$.* Thus, in particular, $(-i)^2 = i^2 = -1$, so that $-i$, as well as $+i$, is a square root of -1.

ILLUSTRATION 1.
$$(3 + 5i)(4 + i) = 12 + 23i + 5i^2$$
$$= 12 + 23i - 5 = 7 + 23i.$$

If P is any positive number, we verify that
$$(i\sqrt{P})^2 = (-i\sqrt{P})^2 = i^2 P = -P.$$

Hence, the negative number $-P$ has the two square roots $\pm i\sqrt{P}$. Hereafter, we agree that the symbol $\sqrt{-P}$ represents the particular square root $i\sqrt{P}$. Then, $-P$ has the two square roots $\pm\sqrt{-P}$. This agreement about the meaning of $\sqrt{-P}$ is equivalent to saying that we should proceed as follows in dealing with the square root of a negative number $-P$:

$$\sqrt{-P} = \sqrt{(-1)\cdot P} = \sqrt{-1}\,\sqrt{P} = i\sqrt{P}. \tag{1}$$

ILLUSTRATION 2. The square roots of -5 are
$$\pm\sqrt{-5} = \pm\sqrt{(-1)\cdot 5} = \pm\sqrt{-1}\,\sqrt{5} = \pm i\sqrt{5}.$$

ILLUSTRATION 3. $\sqrt{-4}\,\sqrt{-9} = (i\sqrt{4})(i\sqrt{9}) = (2i)(3i) = 6i^2 = -6.$

* This procedure can be justified by a more advanced discussion.

150

Note 1. The formula $\sqrt{a}\sqrt{b} = \sqrt{ab}$ was proved in algebra *only for the case where $\sqrt{a}$ and $\sqrt{b}$ are real.* We can verify that the formula does *not* hold if a and b are negative. Thus, by the formula,

$$\sqrt{-4}\,\sqrt{-9} = \sqrt{(-4)(-9)} = \sqrt{36} = 6, \tag{2}$$

which is wrong, because the correct result is -6 (in Illustration 3). The error in (2) shows the importance of expressing $\sqrt{-P}$ as $i\sqrt{P}$ before manipulating $\sqrt{-P}$ algebraically.

If a and b are *real* numbers, we call $(a + bi)$ a **complex number,** whose *real part* is a and *imaginary part* is bi. If $b \neq 0$, we call $(a + bi)$ an **imaginary number.** A **pure imaginary number** is one whose real part is *zero;* that is, $(a + bi)$ is a pure imaginary if $a = 0$ and $b \neq 0$. Any real number a is thought of as a complex number in which the coefficient of the imaginary part is *zero;* that is, $a = a + 0i$. In particular, 0 means $(0 + 0i)$.

ILLUSTRATION 4. $(2 - 3i)$ is an imaginary number. The real number 6 can be thought of as $(6 + 0i)$.

Note 2. In this book, unless otherwise stated, literal numbers represent real numbers, except that hereafter i will always represent $\sqrt{-1}$.

Any positive integral power of i can be expressed as either $\pm\, i$ or $\pm\, 1$, by use of $i^2 = -1$ and the laws of exponents. We notice that $i^4 = 1$.

ILLUSTRATION 5. $i^3 = i^2 i = (-1)i = -i.$

$$i^{13} = i^{12}i = (i^4)^3 i = 1 \cdot i = i.$$

DEFINITION I.   *Two complex numbers $(a + bi)$ and $(c + di)$ are called equal if and only if $a = c$ and $b = d$.*

Since $0 = 0 + 0i$, it follows from Definition I that

$$\textbf{if } a + bi = \textbf{0, then } a = \textbf{0 and } b = \textbf{0}. \tag{3}$$

108. Conjugate complex numbers

The numbers $(a + bi)$ and $(a - bi)$ are called *conjugate* complex numbers, and either is called *the conjugate* of the other. If it is known that $b \neq 0$, then $(a + bi)$ and $(a - bi)$ are called *conjugate imaginary numbers;* they differ only in the signs of their imaginary parts.

A quotient of two complex numbers can be expressed in the form $(a + bi)$ by multiplying both numerator and denominator by the conjugate of the denominator, if necessary.

ILLUSTRATION 1. $$\frac{5 + 2i}{3 - 4i} = \frac{5 + 2i}{3 - 4i} \cdot \frac{3 + 4i}{3 + 4i} \tag{1}$$

$$= \frac{15 + 26i + 8i^2}{9 - 16i^2} = \frac{15 + 26i - 8}{9 + 16} = \frac{7}{25} + \frac{26}{25}\, i.$$

EXERCISE 58

Simplify to the form a + bi.

1. i^6.   **2.** i^9.   **3.** i^4.   **4.** i^{10}.   **5.** i^{11}.   **6.** $i^7(5i^2)$.

7. $2 + 3i - \sqrt{-4}$.   **8.** $4 + \sqrt{-9} + \sqrt{-25}$.   **9.** $\sqrt{-3}\,\sqrt{-27}$.

10. $(2 + 5i)(6 - 7i)$.   **11.** $(\sqrt{-2} + 3)(\sqrt{-2} - 3)$.

12. $(4 - \sqrt{-5})(2 + 3\sqrt{-5})$.   **13.** $(2 - 4i)(3 + \sqrt{-4})$.

14. $\dfrac{2 + 3i}{5 + 4i}$.   **15.** $\dfrac{6 - i}{1 + i}$.   **16.** $\dfrac{3}{2i}$.   **17.** $\dfrac{8}{1 + 4i}$.

109. Geometrical representation of complex numbers

On a coordinate system, as in Figure 91, we may represent any complex number $(a + bi)$ by the point $P:(a, b)$. P falls on OX *when and only when* $b = 0$ and hence $(a + bi)$ is a *real* number; therefore, we call OX the *axis of real numbers*. Similarly, $(a + bi)$ falls on OY *when and only when* $a = 0$ and hence $(a + bi)$ is a *pure imaginary* number or *zero*. Therefore, we call OY the *axis of pure imaginaries*.

ILLUSTRATION 1. In Figure 91, A represents $(-3 + 6i)$; B represents $(-5 + 0 \cdot i)$, or -5; C represents $-3i$.

It is sometimes useful to think of the vector $\overrightarrow{OP}$, instead of merely the *point P*, as representing $(a + bi)$.

FIG. 91

110. Geometrical addition of complex numbers

Let M and N, in Figure 92, represent $(a + bi)$ and $(c + di)$, respectively. Complete the parallelogram with OM and ON as adjacent sides. Then, the fourth vertex, P, represents $[(a + c) + (b + d)i]$.

Proof. Let us agree that any line segment parallel to a coordinate axis is a *directed* segment, where the positive direction is the same as on the axis. Then, for any location of M and N, if the corresponding figure is labeled like Figure 92,

$$OR = OS + SR = a + c;$$
$$RP = SM + KN = b + d.$$

Or, P represents $[(a + c) + (b + d)i]$.

To *subtract* $(c + di)$ from $(a + bi)$ geometrically, we geometrically *add* $(-c - di)$ to $(a + bi)$.

FIG. 92

ILLUSTRATION 1. In Figure 93, we find

$$[(5 + 3i) - (3 - 2i)]$$

geometrically by adding $(5 + 3i)$ and $(- 3 + 2i)$. The result, $(2 + 5i)$, is represented by P. In Figure 93, think of the *vectors* $\overrightarrow{OM}$, $\overrightarrow{ON}$, and $\overrightarrow{OP}$, radiating from the origin, as representing

$$(- 3 + 2i), \quad (5 + 3i), \quad and \quad (2 + 5i),$$

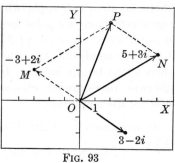

FIG. 93

respectively. Then, the construction for obtaining P is identical with the addition of vectors $\overrightarrow{OM}$ and $\overrightarrow{ON}$ by the *parallelogram law* of page 63.

Note 1. Imaginary numbers were introduced in the 16th century by CARDAN. The words *real* and *imaginary*, as now employed in references to numbers, were introduced by DESCARTES (1637), and the symbol i for $\sqrt{-1}$ by EULER (1748). A Norwegian surveyor, WESSEL (1797), was the first to employ the geometrical representation of complex numbers on a plane.

EXERCISE 59

Represent the complex number geometrically.

1. $5 + 2i$.   **2.** $- 3 + 4i$.   **3.** $- 2i - 3$.   **4.** $5 - 2i$.

5. 7.   **6.** $3i$.   **7.** $- 2i$.   **8.** $- 25$.   **9.** $- 8$.

Find the sum geometrically and read the result from the figure.

10. $(2 + i) + (1 + 3i)$.

11. $(3 - i) + (2 + 3i)$.

12. $(3 + 2i) + (2 + 3i)$.

13. $(3i - 2) + (- 4 - 3i)$.

14. $(2i - 3) + (3i - 1)$.

15. $(7 + 0i) + (0 + 3i)$.

16. $(- 2 - 4i) + (- 3 - 2i)$.

17. $(2 + (4i + 3)$.

111. Trigonometric form of a complex number

In Figure 94, P represents any complex number $z = a + bi$, and the units of length on the axes are the same. Let $r = \overline{OP}$, which will be *positive* or *zero* in all cases, and is called the *radius vector* for P. Let θ be any angle whose initial side is OX and terminal side is OP. Then,

$$r = \sqrt{a^2 + b^2}, \tag{1}$$

$$a = r\cos\theta, \qquad b = r\sin\theta, \tag{2}$$

$$\tan\theta = \frac{b}{a}, \tag{3}$$

$$z = a + bi = r(\cos\theta + i\sin\theta), \tag{4}$$

FIG. 94

where (3) does not apply when $a = 0$. We call $r(\cos \theta + i \sin \theta)$ the *trigonometric form* (or *polar form*) of z; the number r is called the *absolute value* (or *modulus*) of z, and θ is called the *amplitude* (or *argument*) of z. If θ is one amplitude, the other permissible amplitudes are $\theta + k \cdot 360°$, where k may be any integer. In writing a trigonometric form for z, unless otherwise necessary we choose the smallest permissible *positive* or *zero* value for the amplitude.

ILLUSTRATION 1. If $20°$ is one amplitude, others are $380°$, $-340°$, etc. Thus,
$$5(\cos 20° + i \sin 20°) = 5(\cos 380° + i \sin 380°) = etc.$$

ILLUSTRATION 2. The complex number 0 can be written in the form $0 \cdot (\cos \theta + i \sin \theta)$ where θ has *any* value; the absolute value of 0 is 0.

If two complex numbers are equal, they are represented by the same point in Figure 94, and hence have the *same absolute value*, and amplitudes which are *equal* or *differ merely by some integral multiple of* $360°$.

ILLUSTRATION 3. To change from the polar form to the form $(a + bi)$, we use trigonometric tables. Thus, by use of Table IV,
$$6(\cos 35° + i \sin 35°) = 6(.819 + .574i) = 4.914 + 3.444i.$$

To express a number $(a + bi)$ in trigonometric form, plot $(a + bi)$, notice the quadrant for θ, and then find r, θ from (1), (2), (3).

EXAMPLE 1. Find the trigonometric form of $(-5 + 6i)$.

SOLUTION. From (1), $r = \sqrt{61}$; θ is in quadrant II, and $\tan \theta = -\frac{6}{5}$. Hence, from Table IV, $\theta = 180° - 50.2° = 129.8°$, and
$$-5 + 6i = \sqrt{61} (\cos 129.8° + i \sin 129.8°).$$

★*Note 1.* If $z = a + bi$, we use $|z|$ or $|a + bi|$ for the absolute value of z. That is, $|z| = \sqrt{a^2 + b^2}$. This use of the absolute value terminology and notation is consistent with the usage for real numbers on page 3. Thus, if a is real, by our present agreement
$$|a| = |a + 0i| = \sqrt{a^2 + 0} = \sqrt{a^2},$$
which equals a if $a \geqq 0$ and equals $-a$ if $a < 0$. Hence, the present meaning of $|a|$ is the same as that introduced on page 3.

EXERCISE 60

Plot each number and also express it in the form $(a + bi)$:

1. $5(\cos 60° + i \sin 60°)$.
2. $7(\cos 270° + i \sin 270°)$.
3. $3(\cos 210° + i \sin 210°)$.
4. $2[\cos (-45°) + i \sin (-45°)]$.
5. $4(\cos 360° + i \sin 360°)$.
6. $3[\cos (-150°) + i \sin (-150°)]$.
7. $5(\cos 180° + i \sin 180°)$.
8. $\cos 147° + i \sin 147°$.
9. $\cos 249° + i \sin 249°$.
10. $6(\cos 0° + i \sin 0°)$.

Change each number to its trigonometric form.

11. $6 + 6i$.   **12.** $5i - 5$.   **13.** $i\sqrt{3} - 1$.   **14.** $\sqrt{3} - i$.

15. $3i$.   **16.** 4.   **17.** $-2i$.   **18.** -10.   **19.** $5i$.

20. $-4 - 3i$.   **21.** $-6 + 7i$.   **22.** $2 - 5i$.

23. Change $(3 - 3i)$ and its conjugate to trigonometric form.

24. Prove that the conjugate of $r(\cos \theta + i \sin \theta)$ is

$$r[\cos (-\theta) + i \sin (-\theta)].$$

112. Products in trigonometric form

The amplitude of a product of complex numbers is the sum of their amplitudes and the absolute value of the product is the product of the absolute values of the factors.

Proof. Consider a product of just two complex numbers:

$r_1(\cos \theta_1 + i \sin \theta_1) \cdot r_2(\cos \theta_2 + i \sin \theta_2)$

$= r_1 r_2(\cos \theta_1 \cos \theta_2 + i \sin \theta_1 \cos \theta_2 + i \cos \theta_1 \sin \theta_2 + i^2 \sin \theta_1 \sin \theta_2)$

$= r_1 r_2[(\cos \theta_1 \cos \theta_2 - \sin \theta_1 \sin \theta_2) + i(\sin \theta_1 \cos \theta_2 + \cos \theta_1 \sin \theta_2)].$

Hence, by the addition formulas (I) and (II) of Chapter Eight,

$r_1(\cos \theta_1 + i \sin \theta_1) \cdot r_2(\cos \theta_2 + i \sin \theta_2)$

$$= r_1 r_2[\cos (\theta_1 + \theta_2) + i \sin (\theta_1 + \theta_2)]. \qquad (1)$$

ILLUSTRATION 1. $3(\cos 40° + i \sin 40°) \cdot 5(\cos 170° + i \sin 170°)$

$$= 15(\cos 210° + i \sin 210°).$$

Note 1. We extend (1) to a product of any number of factors by successive applications of (1). Thus, we use (1) twice below:

$r_1(\cos \theta_1 + i \sin \theta_1) \cdot r_2(\cos \theta_2 + i \sin \theta_2) \cdot r_3(\cos \theta_3 + i \sin \theta_3)$

$= r_1 r_2[\cos (\theta_1 + \theta_2) + i \sin (\theta_1 + \theta_2)] \cdot r_3(\cos \theta_3 + i \sin \theta_3)$

$$= r_1 r_2 r_3[\cos (\theta_1 + \theta_2 + \theta_3) + i \sin (\theta_1 + \theta_2 + \theta_3)]. \qquad (2)$$

113. De Moivre's Theorem

If h is any positive integer,

$$[r(\cos \theta + i \sin \theta)]^h = r^h(\cos h\theta + i \sin h\theta). \qquad (1)$$

ILLUSTRATION 1.   From (2) in Section 112, with θ_1, θ_2, and θ_3 replaced by θ and r_1, r_2, and r_3 replaced by r,

$[r(\cos \theta + i \sin \theta)]^3$

$= r(\cos \theta + i \sin \theta) \cdot r(\cos \theta + i \sin \theta) \cdot r(\cos \theta + i \sin \theta)$

$= r \cdot r \cdot r[\cos (\theta + \theta + \theta) + i \sin (\theta + \theta + \theta)]$

$= r^3(\cos 3\theta + i \sin 3\theta).$

Proof of formula (1). $[r(\cos \theta + i \sin \theta)]^h$ indicates the product of h factors, each of which is $r(\cos \theta + i \sin \theta)$. Hence, by Section 112 the *absolute value* of this hth power is the product of h factors r, or r^h, an, the *amplitude* is the sum of h amplitudes θ, or $h\theta$. Hence, formula (1) is true.

EXAMPLE 1. Find $(1 - i)^4$ by use of De Moivre's Theorem.

SOLUTION. 1. Express $(1 - i)$ in trigonometric form:

$$r = \sqrt{2}; \qquad \tan \theta = -1, \textit{ with } \theta \textit{ in quadrant IV, so that } \theta = 315°.$$

2. Hence, $\qquad\qquad (1 - i)^4 = [\sqrt{2}(\cos 315° + i \sin 315°)]^4$

$$= (\sqrt{2})^4 (\cos 1260° + i \sin 1260°) = 4(\cos 180° + i \sin 180°) = -4.$$

In the preceding line we noticed that $1260° = 3 \cdot 360° + 180°$.

114. Division of complex numbers in trigonometric form

The absolute value of the quotient of two complex numbers is the quotient of their absolute values; the amplitude of the quotient is the amplitude of the dividend minus the amplitude of the divisor.*

Proof. Consider $r(\cos \alpha + i \sin \alpha)/s(\cos \beta + i \sin \beta)$ where $s \neq 0$. On multiplying by $(\cos \beta - i \sin \beta)$ in both numerator and denominator, we obtain

$$\frac{r(\cos \alpha + i \sin \alpha)}{s(\cos \beta + i \sin \beta)} = \frac{r}{s} \cdot \frac{(\cos \alpha + i \sin \alpha)(\cos \beta - i \sin \beta)}{(\cos \beta + i \sin \beta)(\cos \beta - i \sin \beta)} \qquad (1)$$

$$= \frac{r}{s} \cdot \frac{(\cos \alpha + i \sin \alpha)[\cos (-\beta) + i \sin (-\beta)]}{\cos^2 \beta + \sin^2 \beta}, \qquad (2)$$

because $\cos (-\beta) = \cos \beta$ and $\sin (-\beta) = -\sin \beta$. On using the result of Section 112 in the numerator of (2), we arrive at

$$\frac{r(\cos \alpha + i \sin \alpha)}{s(\cos \beta + i \sin \beta)} = \frac{r}{s} [\cos (\alpha - \beta) + i \sin (\alpha - \beta)]. \qquad (3)$$

ILLUSTRATION 1. $\quad \dfrac{15(\cos 350° + i \sin 350°)}{5(\cos 240° + i \sin 240°)} = 3(\cos 110° + i \sin 110°).$

EXERCISE 61

Give the result in trigonometric form except when the final sine and cosine are known without a table. Compute any power by De Moivre's Theorem.

1. $2(\cos 20° + i \sin 20°) \cdot 3(\cos 40° + i \sin 40°)$.

2. $5(\cos 30° + i \sin 30°) \cdot 2(\cos 120° + i \sin 120°)$.

3. $2(\cos 80° + i \sin 80°) \cdot 3(\cos 300° + i \sin 300°)$.

4. $3(\cos 40° + i \sin 40°) \cdot 4(\cos 350° + i \sin 350°)$.

* We assume that the divisor is *not zero*.

5. $[2(\cos 20° + i \sin 20°)]^3$.   **6.** $[2(\cos 120° + i \sin 120°)]^4$.

7. $[3(\cos 40° + i \sin 40°)]^5$.   **8.** $[3(\cos 315° + i \sin 315°)]^3$.

9. $(-3 + 3i)^4$.   **10.** $(2 - 2i)^5$.   **11.** $(1 - i\sqrt{3})^5$.   **12.** $(i - \sqrt{3})^6$.

13. $\dfrac{10(\cos 150° + i \sin 150°)}{5(\cos 30° + i \sin 30°)}$.

14. $\dfrac{8(\cos 135° + i \sin 135°)}{\sqrt{2} - i\sqrt{2}}$.

15. $\dfrac{24(\cos 160° + i \sin 160°)}{i + \sqrt{3}}$.

16. $\dfrac{2i\sqrt{3} - 2}{3(\cos 150° + i \sin 150°)}$.

115. The *n*th roots of a complex number

If n is a positive integer, to say that ρ is an nth root of a number H means that $H = \rho^n$. Thus, if ρ is a cube root of H, we have $H = \rho^3$.

THEOREM I. *If n is any positive integer and if $R > 0$, any complex number $R(\cos \alpha + i \sin \alpha)$ has just n distinct nth roots.*

Proof. 1. Suppose that $0 \le \theta < 360°$, and let $r(\cos \theta + i \sin \theta)$ be any nth root. Then,

$$R(\cos \alpha + i \sin \alpha) = [r(\cos \theta + i \sin \theta)]^n,$$

or, by De Moivre's Theorem,

$$R(\cos \alpha + i \sin \alpha) = r^n(\cos n\theta + i \sin n\theta). \tag{1}$$

2. Two complex numbers are equal if and only if their absolute values are equal, and their amplitudes differ at most by an integral multiple of $360°$. Hence, from (1), the values of r and θ which give nth roots satisfy $r^n = R$ and

$$n\theta = \alpha + k \cdot 360°,$$

where k is any integer, or

$$r = \sqrt[n]{R}; \qquad \theta = \frac{\alpha}{n} + k \cdot \frac{360°}{n}. \tag{2}$$

3. On placing $k = 0, 1, 2, \cdots, (n-1)$ in (2), we obtain the following n distinct values for θ, all less than $360°$:

$$\frac{\alpha}{n}; \quad \left(\frac{\alpha}{n} + \frac{360°}{n}\right); \quad \left(\frac{\alpha}{n} + 2 \cdot \frac{360°}{n}\right); \quad \cdots; \quad \left[\frac{\alpha}{n} + (n-1)\frac{360°}{n}\right]. \tag{3}$$

Corresponding to (3), we obtain the following n distinct nth roots:

$$\sqrt[n]{R}\left(\cos \frac{\alpha}{n} + i \sin \frac{\alpha}{n}\right); \quad \sqrt[n]{R}\left[\cos\left(\frac{\alpha}{n} + \frac{360°}{n}\right) + i \sin\left(\frac{\alpha}{n} + \frac{360°}{n}\right)\right]; \ etc.$$

4. If k is given any integral value besides $0, 1, \cdots, (n-1)$ in (2), the value of θ differs from one of the angles in (3) by an integral multiple of $360°$, and hence gives no additional nth root. Therefore, in (3) we have all the essentially different amplitudes θ which give nth roots. Hence, there exist *exactly* n distinct nth roots.

SUMMARY. *To obtain the nth roots of a complex number z.*

1. *Express z in its trigonometric form, $z = R(\cos\theta + i\sin\theta)$.*

2. *Place $k = 0, 1, 2, \cdots, (n-1)$ in the following formula:*

$$\sqrt[n]{R}\left[\cos\left(\frac{\alpha}{n} + k\cdot\frac{360°}{n}\right) + i\sin\left(\frac{\alpha}{n} + k\cdot\frac{360°}{n}\right)\right]. \tag{4}$$

EXAMPLE 1. Find the cube roots of $8(\cos 150° + i\sin 150°)$.

SOLUTION. We use $R = 8$, $\alpha = 150°$, and $n = 3$ in (4), and then place $k = 0, 1,$ and 2. The roots are

$$2(\cos 50° + i\sin 50°); \qquad 2(\cos 170° + i\sin 170°);$$
$$2(\cos 290° + i\sin 290°).$$

Comment. The cube roots are represented by P, Q, and S in Figure 95. P, Q, and S divide the circumference into three equal parts because the amplitudes of P, Q, and S, in succession, differ by 120°.

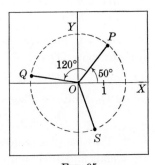

Note 1. All nth roots of $R(\cos\alpha + i\sin\alpha)$ have the same absolute value, $\sqrt[n]{R}$, and hence all of these roots will be located geometrically on the circumference of a circle whose center is the origin and radius is $\sqrt[n]{R}$. The points representing the roots divide the circumference into n equal parts, because adjacent amplitudes in (3) differ by $360°/n$. A special case of these remarks is illustrated in Figure 95.

FIG. 95

ILLUSTRATION 1. To find the 5th roots of -32, or to solve $x^5 = -32$, we first write -32 in trigonometric form:

$$-32 = 32(\cos 180° + i\sin 180°).$$

Hence, from (4), the five values of x which satisfy $x^5 = -32$ are

$$2(\cos 36° + i\sin 36°), \quad 2(\cos 108° + i\sin 108°),$$
$$2(\cos 180° + i\sin 180°), \textit{ etc.}$$

We notice that the root with amplitude 180° is -2.

EXERCISE 62

Leave each result in trigonometric form unless otherwise directed, or unless the sine and cosine involved are known without using tables.

Find the specified roots and plot them.

1. 5th roots of $32(\cos 100° + i\sin 100°)$.

2. 4th roots of $16(\cos 240° + i\sin 240°)$.

3. Cube roots of $1000(\cos 300° + i\sin 300°)$.

4. 5th roots of $32(\cos 200° + i \sin 200°)$.

5. 4th roots of $81(\cos 80° + i \sin 80°)$.

6. Cube roots of $125(\cos 210° + i \sin 210°)$.

7. Cube roots of 1. **8.** 6th roots of 1. **9.** Cube roots of -1.

10. Cube roots of $(4\sqrt{2} - 4i\sqrt{2})$. **11.** Square roots of i.

12. 4th roots of $(8 - 8i\sqrt{3})$. **13.** 5th roots of (-32).

14. Square roots of $(-i)$. **15.** Cube roots of i.

16. Cube roots of -8. **17.** 4th roots of 81.

18. Square roots of $-16i$. **19.** 4th roots of $8(\sqrt{2} - i\sqrt{2})$.

Find all the roots of each equation and plot them.

20. $x^4 = 16$.   **21.** $x^6 + 64 = 0$.   **22.** $x^5 = -243$.   **23.** $x^9 - 1 = 0$.

HINT. The solutions of $x^4 = 16$ are, by definition, the fourth roots of 16.

★**24.** Prove that $\dfrac{1}{r(\cos \theta + i \sin \theta)} = r^{-1}[\cos (-\theta) + i \sin (-\theta)]$.

★**25.** If $z = r(\cos \theta + i \sin \theta)$ and if n is a positive integer, prove that $z^{-n} = r^{-n}[\cos (-n\theta) + i \sin (-n\theta)]$, so that *De Moivre's Theorem holds if the exponent is a negative integer.*

★**26.** Suppose that m and n are integers, with $n > 0$ and m/n in lowest terms. If $R > 0$ and $z = R(\cos \alpha + i \sin \alpha)$, let $R^{\frac{m}{n}}$ be the positive nth root of R^m, and write z^m by use of page 155. Then, from (4) on page 158, write the n values of $z^{\frac{m}{n}}$, the nth roots of z^m; finally, place $k = 0$ in the formula to find a particular one of the roots. We may allow $m < 0$ in these details because of Problem 25.

Comment. The preceding result corresponds to (1) of Section 113, on page 155, with $h = m/n$. Thus, we have proved that *De Moivre's Theorem is true if the exponent is any rational number m/n,* in the sense that *just one* of the n values of $z^{\frac{m}{n}}$ is given by the formula of the theorem.

EXERCISE 63

Review of Chapters One through Ten

Except where otherwise specified, employ four-place or five-place logarithms in any problem where it appears that they would be useful.

1. Sketch an angle of 125° in its standard position on a coordinate system. Give the values of one negative and one positive coterminal angle.

2. Construct the acute angle α and find all of its functions from a triangle if (a) $\tan \alpha = \frac{5}{12}$; (b) $\sec \alpha = \frac{17}{8}$.

3. Prove that if θ is in quadrant III, then $\tan \theta$ and $\cot \theta$ are positive.

Find all functions of θ if the terminal side of θ, in its standard position, goes through the given point; do not use tables.

4. $(-3, 4)$.   **5.** $(15, -8)$.   **6.** $(0, 3)$.   **7.** $(-2, 0)$.   **8.** $(2, 5)$.

9. Determine the functions of 45° by use of a right triangle.

10. Find the functions of 30° and of 60° by use of a right triangle.

Find each function by use of Table VII.

11. $\tan 62° 37'$.   **12.** $\sin 79° 33'$.   **13.** $\sin 130°$.   **14.** $\tan 160°$.

15. $\tan 243°$.   **16.** $\sin (-15°)$.   **17.** $\cos (-115°)$.   **18.** $\sec 623°$.

19. Describe what is meant by writing $\tan 270° = \infty$.

20. Find the acute angle α to the nearest minute by interpolation in some table: (a) $\tan \alpha = 1.706$; (b) $\cos \alpha = .4138$; (c) $\sin \alpha = .9705$.

Find all functions of the angle without using a table.

21. 210°.   **22.** 150°.   **23.** $-135°$.   **24.** 315°.   **25.** $-120°$.   **26.** $-225°$.

27. Select a point on the terminal side of the angle, in standard position, and find its functions by use of their definitions: (a) 120°; (b) 225°.

Solve right $\triangle ABC$ without logarithms; use Table VII.

28. $c = 17.5$; $a = 10.5$.   **29.** $\alpha = 42° 36'$; $b = .45$.   **30.** $c = 63$; $\alpha = 6° 35'$.

31. Solve right $\triangle ABC$ without logarithms by interpolation in Table XI if $\beta = 69° 16.7'$ and $a = 250$.

32–35. Solve Problems 28 to 31, inclusive, by use of four-place or five-place logarithms and check the solutions.

36. For a right $\triangle ABC$, write a formula for a in terms of β and b; for finding α by use of a and c.

Solve for x on the range $0° \leqq x < 360°$.

37. $\sin x = \frac{1}{2}$.   **38.** $\tan x = 1$.   **39.** $\cot^2 x = 1$.   **40.** $\cos x = -\frac{1}{2}$.

41. $\sin^2 x = 1$.   **42.** $\sec x = -2$.   **43.** $\csc x = \sqrt{2}$.   **44.** $\cot x = \sqrt{3}$.

45. $\cos x = -\frac{1}{2}\sqrt{2}$.   **46.** $\sin x = -\frac{1}{2}\sqrt{3}$.   **47.** $\sin x = .4899$.

48. $\cos x = -.8192$.   **49.** $\tan x = -.4734$.   **50.** $\cot x = 1.492$.

51. $2 \cos^2 x = 5 \cos x$.   **52.** $\sin 3x = 1$.   **53.** $\cot x + \sin x \cot x = 0$.

54. $2 \sin^2 x + \sin x = 1$.   **55.** $\tan \frac{1}{2}x = -1$.   **56.** $1 + \csc^2 x = 7 \cot^2 x$.

Prove the identity by use of Definition I *on page* 10, *without using other identities.*

57. $\dfrac{\cos^2 \theta}{\cot^2 \theta} + \dfrac{\sin^2 \theta}{\tan^2 \theta} = 1.$ **58.** $\tan \theta = \dfrac{\sec \theta}{\csc \theta}.$ **59.** $\sec \theta = \dfrac{\tan \theta}{\sin \theta}.$

60. Without using a table or figure, find all functions of θ if θ is in quadrant III and $\tan \theta = 15/8$.

Obtain the number N whose logarithm is given.

61. $\log_3 N = 4.$ **62.** $\log_5 N = 2.$ **63.** $\log_2 N = -4.$ **64.** $\log_{16} N = \frac{3}{4}.$

Compute by use of four-place or five-place logarithms.

65. $(2.68)^3.$ **66.** $\sqrt[4]{.00314}.$ **67.** $1/.689.$

68. $\dfrac{21.9567}{86.7353}.$ **69.** $\dfrac{9.32(.0418)}{65(-.152613)}.$ **70.** $\dfrac{.739(10^{.215})}{432\sqrt[3]{.0185}}.$

71. Find N by use of Table V if $\log N = -3.0567$.

72. Find the length of arc subtended in a circle of radius 10 inches by a central angle of 3.7 radians.

73. Find the measure in radians of a central angle in a circle with radius 15 inches, if the angle subtends an arc 45 inches long.

74. Graph each trigonometric function of x from $x = -\pi$ to $x = \pi$ by use of only a few points, and then describe the variation of the function as x increases from $x = -\pi$ to $x = \pi$.

Prove the identity.

75. $\dfrac{\sec x - \cos x}{\csc x} = \sin^2 x \tan x.$ **76.** $\dfrac{\csc y - \sec y}{\csc y + \sec y} = \dfrac{\cos y - \sin y}{\cos y + \sin y}.$

77. $\dfrac{\cot^2 x + 1}{\tan^2 x + 1} = \cot^2 x.$ **78.** $1 + \cos x = \dfrac{\sin x}{\csc x - \cot x}.$

79. $\dfrac{\sin^2 x}{1 - \cos x} = 1 + \cos x.$ **80.** $\dfrac{\cot x - \sin x \tan x}{\sec x} = \dfrac{\cos x}{\tan x} - \dfrac{\sin x}{\csc x}.$

81. Change to radian measure: (*a*) $325°$; (*b*) $160° \, 35'$.

82. Change to degree measure: (*a*) 1.5 radians; (*b*) $\frac{11}{6}\pi$ radians.

83. What is meant by saying that $\sin \theta$ is a periodic function of θ, and what is the smallest period of $\sin \theta$? Also, tell another period of $\sin \theta$. Repeat the problem for $\tan \theta$.

84. The bearing of a point P as seen from A is N $26° \, 37'$ E. How far north and how far east is P from A if $PA = 36,723$ feet?

85. If P is 650 yards south and 316 yards west of A, find the bearing of A as seen from P.

Without tables, find the indicated function in radical form by using functions of the specified angle or angles, and Chapter Eight.

86. $\cos 165°$; use $45°, 120°$. **87.** $\sin 285°$; use $330°, 45°$.

88. $\sin 75°$; use $150°$. **89.** $\cos 120°$; use $60°$.

90. $\tan 240°$; use $120°$. **91.** $\tan 75°$; use $120°, 45°$.

92. Without tables, find the functions of $(\alpha + \beta)$ and of $(\alpha - \beta)$ if α is in quadrant II, β is in quadrant III, $\sin \alpha = \frac{8}{17}$, and $\cos \beta = -\frac{5}{13}$.

Prove the identity.

93. $\dfrac{2 \cot \theta}{\tan 2\theta} = \cot^2 \theta - 1.$

94. $\sec 2x = \dfrac{\sec^2 x \cot^2 x}{\cot^2 x - 1}.$

95. $\sec 2\theta = \dfrac{1}{\cos^2 \theta - \sin^2 \theta}.$

96. $\dfrac{\sin 5x - \sin 3x}{\cos 5x + \cos 3x} = \tan x.$

97. $\csc 2x = \dfrac{\csc^2 x}{2 \cot x}.$

98. $\tan (x - 45°) = \dfrac{1 - \cot x}{1 + \cot x}.$

99. $\sin (x - 30°) - \cos (120° - x) = 0.$ **100.** $\cos 3x = 4 \cos^3 x - 3 \cos x.$

Solve for x on the range $0° \leqq x < 360°$.

101. $\cos 2x + \cos x = 0.$

102. $\sin 2x - 2 \cos x = 0.$

103. $\sin 5x - \sin 3x = 0.$

104. $\cos 4x + \cos 2x = \cos x.$

105. For $\triangle ABC$, page 119, write a formula (1) for b in terms of a, α, β; (2) for a by use of b, c, α; (3) for β by use of a, b, α; (4) for α by use of a, b, c (give two formulas); (5) for the area in terms of a, b, γ; (6) for the area in terms of a, b, c.

Solve the oblique $\triangle ABC$ completely, except where just one part is requested. Use either four-place natural functions, or four-place or five-place logarithms as appears convenient.

106. $a = 50, \beta = 53°, \alpha = 67°$; find b.   **107.** $c = 35, b = 30, a = 25$; find γ.

108. $a = 25, b = 30, \alpha = 35°$; find β.   **109.** $a = 6, b = 5, c = 4$.

110. $a = 63.8, b = 96.4, \beta = 128° 17'$.   **111.** $a = .1568, b = .3349, \gamma = 69° 18'$.

112. $a = 1.9500, \alpha = 61° 42.3', \beta = 52° 19.7'$.

113. Without logarithms, find the angle of elevation of the sun when a tree 180 feet tall casts a horizontal shadow 240 feet long.

Express in terms of a function of an acute angle less than 45°.

114. $\sin 73°$.   **115.** $\tan 142°$.   **116.** $\sec 310°$.   **117.** $\csc 253°$.

118. $\sin (-153°)$.   **119.** $\cot (-220°)$.   **120.** $\sin 645°$.   **121.** $\csc (-895°)$.

Express the function in terms of a function of x.

122. $\sin (270° + x)$.   **123.** $\cot (90° + x)$.   **124.** $\sec (2\pi - x)$.

125. $\cos (180° + x)$.   **126.** $\tan (\frac{3}{2}\pi + x)$.   **127.** $\csc (-x)$.

128. Let θ be an obtuse angle and let $\beta = \theta - 90°$. Place θ and β in their standard positions on a coordinate system and, from the figure, prove the reduction formulas for functions of $(\theta - 90°)$.

129. From the top of a cliff, the angles of depression of two successive mileposts on a horizontal road running due north are $74° 15'$ and $25° 36'$, respectively. Find the elevation of the cliff above the road.

130. Find the length of the longest diagonal of a parallelogram whose sides are 175.3 and 286.5 feet long if one angle is $133° 22'$.

131. A tower at the top of an embankment casts a shadow 125.6 feet long, straight down one side, when the angle of elevation of the sun is 48° 25′. If the side of the embankment is inclined 33° 26′ from the horizontal, find the height of the tower.

132. Give two positive or zero values and one negative value for arcsin 1; arccos $(-\frac{1}{2}\sqrt{2})$; arctan $(-\sqrt{3})$. Indicate which is the principal value in each case.

Find the value of the expression.

133. Arcsin $\frac{1}{2}$. **134.** Arcsin (-1). **135.** sin arcsin $(-\frac{2}{3})$.

136. Arctan (-1). **137.** cos arccos $\frac{1}{5}$. **138.** sec Arctan (-1).

Prove the identity. If radicals occur, suppose that $0° \leqq x \leqq 90°$.

139. $\dfrac{\cos x}{\sec 4x} + \dfrac{\sin x}{\csc 4x} = \cos 3x.$

140. $\dfrac{1}{\cos x - 1} = \dfrac{2\cos x + 1}{\cos 2x - \cos x}.$

141. $\tan \dfrac{x}{2} = \dfrac{\sec x - 1}{\sin x \sec x}.$

142. $\dfrac{\cos 6x - 1}{\cos 6x + 1} = 1 - \sec^2 3x.$

143. $\sqrt{\dfrac{\csc x - 1}{\csc x + 1}} = \dfrac{1 - \sin x}{\cos x}.$

144. $\dfrac{1}{\cot x + \csc x} = \dfrac{1 - \cos x}{\sin x}.$

145. $\sin 5x + \sin 3x - \sin 2x = 4\cos x \cos \dfrac{5x}{2} \sin \dfrac{3x}{2}.$

Solve the equation.

146. $\csc x - \cot x = 1.$ **147.** $4\cos 2x = 5.$ **148.** $\tan 3x - \tan x = \sec 3x.$

149. $5\tan 3x - 2 = 0.$ **150.** $\cos x - \sqrt{3}\sin x = 0.$ **151.** $\cos x + 1 = \sin x.$

Compute the expression; assume that $x > 0$ and $y > 0$.

152. $\sin[90° + \text{Arccos}(-\frac{7}{25})].$ **153.** $\tan(\pi + \text{Arcsin} \frac{5}{13}).$

154. $\sin(\text{Arccos } x - \text{Arcsin } y).$ **155.** cot Arcsin x.

156. Graph $y = 3\sin \frac{1}{2}x$ from $x = 0$ to $x = 4\pi$.

157. Graph $y = \sin 2x - \cos x$ from $x = 0$ to $x = 2\pi$.

158. Find the unknown base: (1) $\log_a 8 = 3$; (2) $\log_a 125 = \frac{3}{2}$.

159. Find the specified logarithm: (1) $\log_6 216$; (2) $\log_{100} .0001$.

160. An object at P is acted upon simultaneously by the following horizontal forces in the specified directions: 168 pounds, $N\ 38°\ 15'\ E$; 157 pounds, $N\ 26°\ 42'\ W$. Find the magnitude and direction of the resultant force. Use Table I and five-place logarithms.

161. Find the vertical and horizontal components of a force of 216 pounds acting downward and inclined 18° 16′ from the horizontal.

162. Find the force which is exactly sufficient to keep a 500-pound weight from sliding down a plane inclined 26° 57′ from the horizontal.

163. A flywheel 36 inches in diameter is driven by a belt moving over the rim with a speed of 3000 feet per minute. Find the angular speed of a point on the rim of the wheel in radians per second.

164. Solve for x: $5(1.03)^{2x} = 15.731$.

FOR PLANE TRIGONOMETRY

NOTE 1

Accuracy of Computation

By illustrations, we could verify that the following rules do not *underestimate* the accuracy of computation. Also, it must be admitted that the rules sometimes *overestimate* the accuracy. We adopt these rules for computation in this text.

I. *In adding approximate values, round off the result in the first place where the last significant digit of any given value is found.*

II. *In multiplying or dividing approximate values, round off the result to the smallest number of significant figures found in any given value.*

ILLUSTRATION 1. Let $a = 35.64$, $b = 342.72$, and $c = .03147$ be approximate values. Then, $a + b + c$ is not reliable beyond the second decimal place because both a and b are subject to an unknown error which may be as large as 5 units in the third decimal place. Hence, we write

$$a + b + c = 378.39147 = 378.39, \text{ approximately.}$$

ILLUSTRATION 2. If $x = 31.27$ and $y = .021$ are approximate values, we state that $xy = .66$, because y has only two significant digits:

$$xy = 31.27(.021) = .65667 = .66, \text{ approximately.}$$

ILLUSTRATION 3. If a surveyor measures a rectangular field as 385.6' by 432.4', it would give an unjustified appearance of accuracy to write that the area is

$$(385.6)(432.4) = 166,733.44 \text{ square feet.}$$

For, an error of .05 foot in either dimension would cause an error of about 20 square feet in the area. By Rule II, a reasonably justified result would be that the area is 166,700 square feet, to the *nearest* 100 *square feet*.

In problems where approximate values enter, or where approximate results are obtained from exact data, the results should be rounded off so as to avoid giving a false appearance of accuracy. No hard and fast rules for such rounding off should be adopted, and the final decision as to the accuracy of a result should be made only after a careful examination of the details of the solution.

NOTE 2

A Logarithmic Scale

In Figure 96, after selecting the unit of length, HK, we lay off a scale above the line in the usual way. Below the line, each value of x is placed at the point under the value of X which equals $\log x$ (where "log" means "$\log_{10}$"); that is, if x is under X, then $\log x = X$.

FIG. 96

ILLUSTRATION 1. Since $\log 1 = 0$, $x = 1$ is under $X = 0$. Since $\log 4 = 0.6$, approximately, $x = 4$ is under $X = .6$.

If we blot out the upper numbers in Figure 96, we obtain the scale in Figure 97, called a **logarithmic scale**. For contrast, the upper scale in Figure 96 may be called a **uniform scale**. On a logarithmic scale, if the unit of distance is properly chosen, the distance from $x = 1$ to $x = N$ equals $\log N$. Since N has no real logarithm if $N \leq 0$, *we find neither zero nor negative numbers on a logarithmic scale.*

H *(unit of length)* K

| | | | | | | | | | | | | | |
| .4 | .5 | .6 | .8 | 1 | 2 | 3 | 4 5 | 6 | 8 10 | 20 | 30 40 | 60 80 100 | 200 300 | x |

FIG. 97

Note 1. Logarithmic scales are employed on the various scales on a slide rule.* The usual 10-inch slide rule permits rapid computation with about the accuracy obtained by using three-place logarithms. The *longer* the slide rule, the *greater* is the accuracy obtainable by using it. The fundamental principle involved in the primary use of a slide rule is illustrated in Figure 98. Scales A and B are logarithmic. To find, for instance, the product 3×4, we place the 1 of scale B under the 3 of A. Then, above the 4 of B we read the product 3×4 on A. We obtain this result because

$$OK = OH + HK = \log 3 + \log 4 = \log (3 \times 4).$$

A

| 1 | 2 | 3 | 4 | 5 | 6 | 7 | 8 | 10 | 12 | 20 |
| O | | H | | | | | | | K | |

B

| 1 | 2 | 3 | 4 | 5 | 6 | 7 |

FIG. 98

Note 2. Recall that, if a is any specified base for a system of logarithms, then $\log_{10} N = (\log_{10} a)(\log_a N)$. Hence, if the distance from $x = 1$ to $x = a$

* The detailed use of a slide rule is explained in the circular obtained on purchasing any of the standard rules.

on the scale in Figure 97 is selected as the positive unit of length, the distance from $x = 1$ to $x = N$ on the scale equals $\log_a N$. Thus, a logarithmic scale made by use of any specified system of logarithms may be used as the logarithmic scale with any other system.

NOTE 3

Logarithms of Functions of Angles Near 0° and 90°

The tabular differences increase rapidly in Table IX as we approach 0° in the columns headed log sin, log tan, and log cot. Hence, if a logarithm is determined by interpolation in these columns, the error is extremely large on page 36 of Table IX and remains undesirably large ($> .00001$) until we reach page 40. Table X is provided for avoiding these large errors of interpolation. In Table X, we let

$$\frac{\sin \alpha}{M} = s \quad and \quad \frac{\tan \alpha}{M} = t,$$

where M is the number of minutes in α. Then,

$$\sin \alpha = sM \quad and \quad \tan \alpha = tM;$$

$$\log \sin \alpha = \log s + \log M; \qquad \log \tan \alpha = \log t + \log M.$$

If we let $S = \log s$ and $T = \log t$, then

$$\log \sin \alpha = S + \log M; \qquad \log \tan \alpha = T + \log M. \tag{1}$$

S and T are computed by the methods of advanced mathematics; the values of S and T are tabulated in Table Xa for α between 0° and 3°.

I. *To find* **log sin α**, **log tan α**, *or* **log cot α** *for an acute angle α near* 0°:

1. *Express α in minutes and decimal parts of a minute, to find M.*

2. *Find* log M *from Table* VIII *and S and T from Table* Xa.

3. *Use* (1) *to find* log sin α *and* log tan α; *to find* log cot α, *recall*

$$\cot \alpha = \frac{1}{\tan \alpha}, \quad or \quad \log \cot \alpha = - \log \tan \alpha.$$

II. *To find* **log cos β**, **log tan β**, *or* **log cot β** *for an acute angle β near* 90°, *let $\alpha = 90° - \beta$. Recall* $\cos \beta = \sin \alpha$, $\tan \beta = \cot \alpha$, $\cot \beta = \tan \alpha$; *then use* (I).

III. *To find an acute angle α near* 0° *if* **log sin α** (*or* **log tan α**) *is given:*

1. *Find α* **to the nearest minute** *by inspection of Table* IX.

2. *Find S (or T) from Table* Xa; *substitute for S and* log sin α *in* (1), *and find* log M; *then obtain M from Table* VIII.

IV. *To find an acute angle β near* 90° *if* **log cos β**, **log tan β**, *or* **log cot β** *is given, write $\beta = 90° - \alpha$, and first find α by use of* (III).

EXAMPLE 1. Find log sin $1° 26' 12''$.

SOLUTION. 1. $\frac{12}{60} = .20$; $M = 86.20'$. From Table Xa, $S = 6.46368 - 10$.
2. From Table VIII, log $86.20 = 1.93551$. Hence,

$$\log \sin 1° 26' 12'' = 1.93551 + 6.46368 - 10 = 8.39919 - 10.$$

Note 1. If log cot α is given for α near $0°$, first find log tan α from log tan $\alpha = -$ log cot α, and then use (III).

ILLUSTRATION 1. If log cot $\beta = 8.65246 - 10$, then β is near $90°$; if $\alpha = 90° - \beta$, then log tan $\alpha = 8.65246 - 10$. By use of (III) we could find α and then obtain $\beta = 90° - \alpha$.

EXAMPLE 2. Find α if log sin $\alpha = 8.66345 - 10$.

SOLUTION. 1. By inspection of page 38 of Table IX, we find that α is nearer $2° 38'$ than $2° 39'$. Hence, approximately, $M = 158'$; from Table Xa, $S = 6.46357 - 10$.

2. In (1), substitute for log sin α and S:

$$8.66345 - 10 = 6.46357 - 10 + \log M;$$
$$\log M = 8.66345 - 6.46357 = 2.19988.$$

From Table VIII, $M = 158.44'$, or $\alpha = 2° 38.44' = 2° 38' 26''$.

Note 2. A second method for solving problems like Examples 1 and 2 is provided by Table Xb, for angles *very* near $0°$. If angles are expressed only to the nearest $.1'$, Table Xb demands no interpolation.

Note 3. A *slowly* changing function of an unknown angle α offers a poor means for determining α. Hence, when possible, we avoid using cos α in determining α if α is near $0°$, or sin α if α is near $90°$.

NOTE 4

Plane Surveying

At first, let us assume that all points involved are in the horizontal plane. Then, a line segment from M to P is referred to as **course MP.** The north-south projection of MP is called its **latitude,** and is considered *positive* or *negative* according as P is *north* or *south* of M. The east-west projection of MP is called its **departure** and is labeled *positive* or *negative* according as P is *east* or *west* of M. Then, from Figure 99, if β is the acute bearing angle of the direction MP, and $\overline{MP}$ is the length of MP,

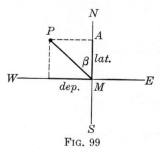

FIG. 99

$$\text{latitude} = \pm \overline{MP} \cos \beta; \Big\}$$
$$\text{departure} = \pm \overline{MP} \sin \beta; \Big\} \quad (1)$$

$$\tan \beta = \left| \frac{\text{departure}}{\text{latitude}} \right|. \quad (2)$$

ILLUSTRATION 1. A surveyor surveys the broken path $MPQR$, of Figure 100, where courses MP, PQ, QR have the lengths and bearings shown in the following table. He desires to find the bearing and length of the *closing course MR*, without measurement. To do this, he computes the latitudes and departures of MP, PQ, QR from (1), as given in the table, and combines the results to find the latitude and departure of MR. Then, with $AM = 128.5$ and $AR = 250.3$, he solves $\triangle AMR$ to find MR and its bearing angle β:

$$\tan \beta = \frac{128.5}{250.3}; \qquad \beta = 27° \, 10';$$

$$\overline{MR} = \frac{250.3}{\cos \beta} = 281.$$

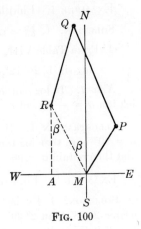

FIG. 100

COURSE	BEARING	LENGTH	LATITUDE	DEPARTURE
MP	$N\ 32°\ 10'\ E$	200 yd.	169.3 yd.	106.5 yd.
PQ	$N\ 22°\ 30'\ W$	400 yd.	369.6 yd.	$-\ 153.1$ yd.
QR	$S\ 15°\ 50'\ W$	300 yd.	$-\ 288.6$ yd.	$-\ 81.9$ yd.
MR	$N\ 27°\ 10'\ W$	281 yd.	250.3 yd.	$-\ 128.5$ yd.

As a general situation, suppose that a surveyor at M measures the distance from M to P, not necessarily at the same elevation as M. Then, the *horizontal projection of MP* is called **course MP**. In referring to the *direction of the inclined line MP*, the surveyor means *the direction of course MP*, and this direction is given automatically by his measurements in sighting from M to P with his transit. It also measures the acute angle α between MP and course MP; α is the inclination of MP from the horizontal. The length MH of course MP, the vertical projection of MP, and the inclination α of MP, as seen in Figure 101, are related by the following equations:

FIG. 101

$$MH = (\text{course } MP) = \overline{MP} \cos \alpha; \tag{3}$$

$$(\text{vertical projection of } MP) = \overline{MP} \sin \alpha; \tag{4}$$

$$\tan \alpha = \frac{\text{vertical projection of } MP}{\text{course } MP}. \tag{5}$$

When desired, a negative sign is placed beside the inclination and vertical projection of MP in tabulations when P is below M, but the sign is not used algebraically in (3), (4), (5).

EXAMPLE 1. Point E cannot be seen from A, and A and E are separated by a lake. In carrying out a survey from A to E by the broken line path $ABCDE$, a surveyor records the following entries in his note-book. Find the length and bearing of course AE, the length of AE, and the difference in elevation of A and E.

LINE	AB	BC	CD	DE
INCLIN.	6° 43′	(−) 3° 26′	5° 18′	(−) 4° 53′
BEARING	$N\ 27°\ 16'\ E$	$N\ 27°\ 16'\ E$	$S\ 53°\ 48'\ E$	$S\ 4°\ 17'\ W$
LENGTH	250 yd.	800 yd.	560 yd.	340 yd.

OUTLINE OF SOLUTION. 1. From (3) and (4), we augment the preceding table by computing items for two new rows, labeled *course* and *vertical projection* (signed, + or −). We combine these projections to get the vertical projection of AE.

2. We obtain course AE and its direction as in Illustration 1. Finally, from (3) and (5), we obtain the inclination and length of AE.

EXERCISE 64

Given that B, C, and D lie in the same direction from A. Find the length of AD, course AD, and the inclination of AD.

1.

LINE	INCLIN.	LENGTH
AB	9° 38′	650 yd.
BC	6° 20′	250 yd.
CD	− 5° 40′	300 yd.

2.

LINE	INCLIN.	LENGTH
AB	− 6° 25′	716 yd.
BC	8° 43′	267 yd.
CD	− 4° 20′	532 yd.

3. Complete the solution of Example 1 of Note 4.

NOTE 5

Proofs of the General Reduction Formulas

Let us suppose that, by the method of page 72, the reduction formulas have already been proved for functions of $(90° + \theta)$, $(90° − \theta)$, $(− \theta − 90°)$, and $(\theta − 90°)$. These results justify the following statement.

I. *The addition of $90°$ or $− 90°$ to θ or $− \theta$ gives an angle where each of its functions is numerically equal to the* **cofunction** *of θ.*

By successive applications of (I), we may then prove (1) and (2) of page 75.

ILLUSTRATION 1. By three applications of (I), we obtain

$$\sin (270° - \theta) = \sin [90° + (180° - \theta)] = \pm \cos (180° - \theta) \qquad \text{[using (I)]}$$
$$= \pm \cos [90° + (90° - \theta)] = \pm \sin (90° - \theta) \qquad \text{[using (I)]}$$
$$= \pm \cos \theta. \qquad \text{[using (I)]}$$

In passing from $(270° - \theta)$ to θ, three subtractions of 90° occurred, and thus we changed from *function* to *cofunction* three times, leaving the *cofunction* of the sine, or the *cosine* function, in the result.

To obtain a formula for any function of $(n \cdot 90° \pm \theta)$, where n is a positive integer, we could apply statement (I) in *subtracting* 90° a total of n times. Each of these steps would give a result changing from a *function* to the *cofunction*. If n is *even*, these n changes conclude with the *original named function* for θ, multiplied by ± 1. If n is *odd*, the conclusion involves the *cofunction* of the *original named function* for θ, multiplied by ± 1. That is, we have proved the following result for the case where n is positive:

$$[\text{any function of } (n \cdot 90° \pm \theta)] = \left\{ \begin{array}{l} \pm(\text{same function of } \theta), \ n \ even; \\ \pm(\text{cofunction of } \theta), \ n \ odd. \end{array} \right\} \ (1)$$

If n is a negative integer, we repeat the preceding remarks, with successive subtractions of $(- 90°)$ occurring in place of subtractions of 90°, and again obtain (1). If $n = 0$, and θ is involved on the left in the form $- \theta$, then (1) is true because of the results of page 71 for functions of $- \theta$. Thus, (1) is true for all integers n.

NOTE 6

Line Values of the Trigonometric Functions

Let θ be any angle, in its standard position on a coordinate system, as in Figures 102 and 103. Construct a circle with radius 1 and center at the origin, intersecting the positive halves of the x-axis and y-axis at U and V, respectively. Construct tangents to the circle at U and V. Let P, T, and C be the points where the terminal side of θ, or this side extended through O, intersects the circle and its tangents at U and V, respectively. In the reference $\triangle OAP$ for θ, OA and AP represent the coordinates of P.

In the resulting diagram we agree that all line segments will be considered as *directed segments*, and that the unit of length will be that which is used for the coordinates. A segment parallel to a coordinate axis will be considered positive or negative according as the direction is the same as or opposite to the positive direction on the axis. On OP, we define the positive direction as that from O to P. Then,*

* Special understandings are necessary if θ is a quadrantal angle.

$$\left.\begin{array}{lll} \sin \theta = AP; & \tan \theta = UT; & \sec \theta = OT; \\ \cos \theta = OA; & \cot \theta = VC; & \csc \theta = OC. \end{array}\right\} \quad (1)$$

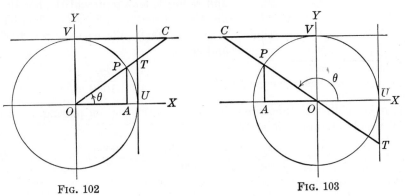

FIG. 102   FIG. 103

ILLUSTRATION 1. In Figure 103, OT is negative and hence $OT = -\overline{OT}$, where $\overline{OT}$ is the positive number of units of length in OT. Let α be the acute angle XOT. Then,

$$\sec \alpha = \frac{\overline{OT}}{\overline{OU}} = \overline{OT},$$

because $OU = 1$. But, $\sec \theta = -\sec \alpha = -\overline{OT} = OT$. Hence, if θ is in quadrant II, we have proved that $\sec \theta = OT$.

The terminal side of θ may fall in any one of the four quadrants, or on either half of either axis. In each of these possible cases, it would be necessary to give a separate proof, like that of Illustration 1, for each of equations (1).

NOTE 7

Mil Measure for Angles

In the artillery and certain other branches of the Army of the United States, as well as in the military services of various other nations, angles are measured frequently in terms of a unit called the **mil,** which is defined by the equation

$$1600 \text{ mils} = 90°. \quad (1)$$

$$1 \text{ mil} = \frac{90°}{1600} = 3.3750; \quad 1° = \frac{1600}{90} \text{ mils} = 17.7778 \text{ mils}. \quad (2)$$

$$1 \text{ radian} = \frac{180°}{\pi} = \frac{180}{\pi} \cdot \frac{1600}{90} \text{ mils} = 1018.6 \text{ mils}. \quad (3)$$

Thus, with only a small error, of about 2%,

$$(approximate) \qquad 1 \text{ radian} = 1000 \text{ mils}. \quad (4)$$

Equation (4) is the basis for certain approximations employing mils. Thus, assume that (4) is *exactly* true. Then, let θ be the radian measure of $\angle CAB$ in Figure 104, and let α be its value in mils. Let $AC = b$ and $CB = a$. On the circle with center A and radius b, let s represent the length of arc CD. Then, $s = b\theta$. Since θ radians is equal to 1000θ mils, we have $\alpha = 1000\theta$ and hence

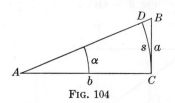

FIG. 104

$$s = \frac{b\alpha}{1000}. \tag{5}$$

If α is small, s is *approximately equal* to a. Then, on placing $s = a$ in (5) we obtain, approximately,

$$a = \frac{b\alpha}{1000}; \quad \frac{a}{b} = \frac{\alpha}{1000}; \quad \alpha = \frac{1000a}{b}. \tag{6}$$

From $\triangle ABC$, $\tan \alpha = a/b$. Hence, from (6),

$$\left\{ \begin{array}{c} approximate, \\ \alpha\ in\ mils \end{array} \right\} \qquad \tan\ \alpha = \frac{\alpha}{1000}. \tag{7}$$

ILLUSTRATION 1. If $a = 1$ and $b = 1000$ in (6), then $\alpha = 1$. Hence, 1 *foot at a distance of* 1000 *feet subtends an angle of approximately* 1 *mil.*

ILLUSTRATION 2. If a line segment 30 yards long is perpendicular to our line of sight at a distance of 8000 yards, the segment subtends an angle α whose value in mils is approximately, from (6), $\alpha = 1000(30)/8000$, or $\alpha = 3.75$ mils.

NOTE 8

Use of Reversible Operations in Proving an Identity

A trigonometric identity may sometimes be established as follows:

1. *Assume that the conjectured identity is true and manipulate it until an obvious identity is obtained.*

2. *Start anew with this final obvious identity and prove that, from it, the conjectured identity can be obtained.*

The action described in Part 2 usually amounts to verifying that each step involved in Part 1 can be *reversed,* to lead us *from* the obvious identity *back to* the conjectured identity. A by-product of the method is that, if Part 1 does *not* lead to an obvious identity, we may obtain some equality which we recognize as a *conditional equation.* Then, we might conclude that the conjectured identity is a conditional equation, and incidentally have a means for its solution. If the present method is to be used, it is a *prime necessity that the reversibility of each step be examined and commented upon,* as an essential part of the proof.

EXAMPLE 1. Prove the identity: $\dfrac{1 + \cos x}{\sin x} = \dfrac{\sin x}{1 - \cos x}.$

SOLUTION. 1. **Assume** that the identity is true and multiply both of its sides by sin $x(1 - \cos x)$:

$$(1 + \cos x)(1 - \cos x) = \sin^2 x;$$

or, $1 - \cos^2 x = \sin^2 x.$ (1)

We recognize that (1) is true because $\sin^2 x + \cos^2 x = 1.$

2. If x has any value such that $\sin x(1 - \cos x) \neq 0$, we may divide both sides of (1) by $\sin x(1 - \cos x)$. This division gives

$$\frac{1 - \cos^2 x}{\sin x(1 - \cos x)} = \frac{\sin^2 x}{\sin x(1 - \cos x)}, \quad or \quad \frac{1 + \cos x}{\sin x} = \frac{\sin x}{1 - \cos x}.$$

Hence, since (1) is true, the given identity has been proved because we have shown that *it is true if* (1) *is true.*

NOTE 9

General Proof of the Addition Formulas

Suppose that the following formulas have been proved geometrically in case α and β are on the range $0°$ to $90°$, inclusive:

$$\sin(\alpha + \beta) = \sin \alpha \cos \beta + \cos \alpha \sin \beta;$$ (1)

$$\cos(\alpha + \beta) = \cos \alpha \cos \beta - \sin \alpha \sin \beta.$$ (2)

THEOREM I. *If α and β are angles for which* (1) *and* (2) *are true, then they remain true if either α or β is increased or decreased by* $90°$.

Proof. 1. Let $\alpha' = \alpha + 90°$. Then $\sin \alpha' = \cos \alpha$; $\cos \alpha' = -\sin \alpha.$

2. $\sin(\alpha' + \beta) = \sin[(\alpha + \beta) + 90°] = \cos(\alpha + \beta)$

[using (2)] $= \cos \alpha \cos \beta - \sin \alpha \sin \beta.$ (3)

3. Replace α by α' on the right in (1) and use Step 1:

$$\sin \alpha' \cos \beta + \cos \alpha' \sin \beta = \cos \alpha \cos \beta - \sin \alpha \sin \beta.$$ (4)

We see that (3) and the right-hand side of (4) are identical. Hence

$$\sin(\alpha' + \beta) = \sin \alpha' \cos \beta + \cos \alpha' \sin \beta.$$ (5)

Since $\alpha' = \alpha + 90°$, (5) states that (1) is true if α is *increased* by $90°$.

4. Similarly, by starting with $\alpha' = \alpha - 90°$, it can be proved that (1) is true if α is *decreased* by $90°$. Similar facts can be proved about (2). To prove the theorem as it applies to β, we would similarly introduce β' by $\beta' = \beta + 90°$ or $\beta' = \beta - 90°$.

THEOREM II. *Formulas* (1) *and* (2) *hold for all values of α and β.*

Proof. 1. Let γ and θ be any angles not on the range $0°$ to $90°$, inclusive. Then, there exist angles α and β on the range $0°$ to $90°$, inclusive, such that $\gamma = \alpha + m \cdot 90°$ and $\theta = \beta + n \cdot 90°$, where m and n are appropriate integers. We know that (1) and (2) are true for α and β.

2. We can pass from α to γ through a sequence of angles, by successive *additions* of 90°, if $m > 0$, or *subtractions* of 90°, if $m < 0$. By Theorem I, formulas (1) and (2) remain true if α is replaced in turn by the successive angles of this sequence. Hence, finally, we may replace α by γ in (1) and (2). Similarly, we find that we may replace β by θ in (1) and (2). Thus, (1) and (2) are true if α and β are replaced by γ and θ, respectively.

NOTE 10

The Quadratic Formula

If a, b, c are constants, where $a \neq 0$, the quadratic equation

$$ax^2 + bx + c = 0 \tag{1}$$

has the solutions

$$x = \frac{-b \pm \sqrt{b^2 - 4ac}}{2a}. \tag{2}$$

If $b^2 - 4ac < 0$, the solutions in (2) are imaginary numbers. Otherwise, the solutions are real numbers, which are identical if and only if $b^2 - 4ac = 0$.

NOTE 11

Proof of Mollweide's Equations

Let us prove that, in any plane triangle ABC,

$$\frac{b - c}{a} = \frac{\sin \frac{1}{2}(\beta - \gamma)}{\cos \frac{1}{2}\alpha}. \tag{1}$$

From (4) on page 130,

$$\frac{b - c}{\sin \beta - \sin \gamma} = \frac{c}{\sin \gamma}. \tag{2}$$

Since $\dfrac{c}{\sin \gamma} = \dfrac{a}{\sin \alpha}$,

$$\frac{b - c}{\sin \beta - \sin \gamma} = \frac{a}{\sin \alpha}. \tag{3}$$

Hence,

$$\frac{b - c}{a} = \frac{\sin \beta - \sin \gamma}{\sin \alpha}. \tag{4}$$

From (XIX), page 112,

$$\sin \beta - \sin \gamma = 2 \cos \tfrac{1}{2}(\beta + \gamma) \sin \tfrac{1}{2}(\beta - \gamma). \tag{5}$$

By use of (VII), page 108, $\sin \alpha = 2 \sin \tfrac{1}{2}\alpha \cos \tfrac{1}{2}\alpha.$ (6)

Since $\alpha = 180° - (\beta + \gamma)$, $\tfrac{1}{2}\alpha = 90° - \tfrac{1}{2}(\beta + \gamma).$ (7)

From (7), $\sin \tfrac{1}{2}\alpha = \cos \tfrac{1}{2}(\beta + \gamma)$. Hence, (4), (5), and (6) give

$$\frac{b - c}{a} = \frac{2 \cos \tfrac{1}{2}(\beta + \gamma) \sin \tfrac{1}{2}(\beta - \gamma)}{2 \cos \tfrac{1}{2}\alpha \cos \tfrac{1}{2}(\beta + \gamma)} = \frac{\sin \tfrac{1}{2}(\beta - \gamma)}{\cos \tfrac{1}{2}\alpha}.$$

Similar proofs apply for the other Mollweide equations.

SPHERICAL TRIGONOMETRY

∠s of ⊙ > 180 ∠ 360°

$S = r \cdot \theta$

PRACTICAL TRIGONOMETRY

TWELVE

RIGHT SPHERICAL TRIANGLES

116. Results from the geometry of a sphere

A **sphere** is a closed surface which is the locus of all points equidistant from a point called the center of the sphere. On a sphere, let A, B, C be three points which are not on a great circle of the sphere. Then, if A, B, C are joined by arcs of great circles, the figure ABC is called a **spherical triangle** whose *sides* are the *arcs* AB, BC, and AC, and whose *angles* are the angles of intersection of these arcs. *Spherical trigonometry* is concerned with the development and application of trigonometric formulas involving the parts of a spherical triangle. The following facts concerning spherical geometry should be recalled.

A **great circle** of a sphere is its intersection with a plane through the center of the sphere, and has the same center and radius as the sphere.

The **poles** of a great circle of a sphere are the points P and P' in which a line through the center of the circle, perpendicular to its plane, intersects the sphere. If A is any point on the sphere, we can construct just one great circle having A as a pole.

If A and B are any two points on a sphere which are not diametrically opposite with respect to its center, we can construct just one great circle passing through A and B.

The **angle of intersection** BAC **of two arcs** AB and AC of great circles is defined as the angle TAM formed by the tangents AT and AM to these arcs at A. In Figure 105, where O is the center of the sphere, notice that AT and AM are perpendicular to AA', the intersection of planes $A'OAB$ and $A'OAC$. This angle TAM also measures the dihedral angle formed by the planes $A'OAB$ and $A'OAC$ in which the arcs lie.

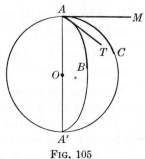

Fig. 105

The **angular measure of an arc** of a great circle is the measure of the angle subtended by the arc at the center of the sphere. The *length* of the arc can be found if we know its angular measure and the radius of the sphere.

117. Theorems concerning spherical triangles

Hereafter, we shall measure arcs of great circles in angular units. Therefore, both the *sides* and the *angles* of any spherical triangle will be described in *angular units*. Moreover, we agree to consider only spherical triangles each of whose sides and angles is *less than* 180°. As a standard notation for a spherical triangle ABC, we shall let α, β, and γ represent the angles at A, B, and C, respectively, and let a, b, and c be the corresponding opposite sides. The letter O will always represent the center of the sphere on which triangle ABC lies.

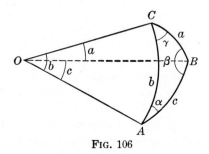

FIG. 106

Corresponding to any spherical triangle ABC, as in Figure 106, we can construct a *trihedral angle* O-ABC whose *dihedral* angles measure the *angles* and whose *face angles* AOB, COB, and COA measure the *sides* of the triangle ABC.

ILLUSTRATION 1. In Figure 106, the sides of $\triangle ABC$ lie in the planes OAB, OBC, and OAC, which form the faces of the trihedral angle O-ABC. From Section 116, $\angle ABC$ or β has the same measure as the dihedral angle whose edge is OB and whose faces are planes OAB and OBC. Also, we verify that $\angle AOC$ measures arc AC; that is,

$$b = \angle AOC; \quad c = \angle AOB; \quad a = \angle BOC.$$

The following theorems from geometry will be useful.

I. *The sum of the sides of a spherical triangle is less than* 360°.

II. *The sum of the angles of a spherical triangle is greater than* 180° *and less than* 540°.

DEFINITION I. *The **spherical excess** of a spherical triangle is the amount by which the sum of the angles of the triangle exceeds* 180°.

Two great circles on a sphere intersect to divide the sphere into four parts each of which is called a **lune** of the sphere. Any third great circle, not passing through the points of intersection of the first two circles, divides each lune into two spherical triangles. Hence, in general, *three* great circles on a sphere divide it into *eight* spherical triangles.

Note 1. If a spherical triangle ABC has a side or an angle *greater* than 180°, various arcs of the great circles which intersect to form triangle ABC also form related triangles each of whose sides and angles is *less* than 180°.

It can be verified later that any of the typical problems concerning the given triangle may be solved by investigating some one of these related triangles. Hence, our agreement to consider only those triangles whose sides and angles are all less than 180° is not an essential restriction on our results.

118. Polar triangles

If ABC is a spherical triangle, we can construct three great circles having A, B, and C, respectively, as poles. These circles intersect to form eight triangles, among which there is *just one* which may be lettered $A'B'C'$, as in Figure 107, so that

1. A, B, and C are, respectively, poles of the circles on which $B'C'$, $A'C'$, and $A'B'$ lie, and

2. A and A' are on the same side of* $B'C'$; B and B' are on the same side of $A'C'$; C and C' are on the same side of $A'B'$.

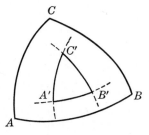

FIG. 107

We call triangle $A'B'C'$ the *polar triangle* of ABC. In geometry, the following theorems are proved about polar triangles.

I. *If $A'B'C'$ is the polar triangle of ABC, then ABC is the polar triangle of $A'B'C'$.*

II. *Each side of triangle ABC is the supplement of the corresponding angle of the polar triangle $A'B'C'$; each angle of ABC is the supplement of the corresponding side of $A'B'C'$.*

ILLUSTRATION 1. If $(a, b, c, \alpha, \beta, \gamma)$ and $(a', b', c', \alpha', \beta', \gamma')$ are the sides and angles of triangles ABC and $A'B'C'$, respectively, then

$$\left. \begin{aligned} a &= 180° - \alpha'; & b &= 180° - \beta'; & c &= 180° - \gamma'; \\ a' &= 180° - \alpha; & b' &= 180° - \beta; & c' &= 180° - \gamma. \end{aligned} \right\} \qquad (1)$$

119. Formulas for right spherical triangles

A *right* spherical triangle is one which has at least one angle equal to 90°. In such a triangle ABC, we shall always letter the vertices so that $\gamma = 90°$. Then, we shall prove the following formulas.

---

* That is, the same side of the great circle through the arc.

(I) $\sin \alpha = \dfrac{\sin a}{\sin c}$.   (III) $\sin \beta = \dfrac{\sin b}{\sin c}$.

(II) $\cos \alpha = \sin \beta \cos a$.   (IV) $\cos \beta = \sin \alpha \cos b$.

(V) $\cos c = \cos a \cos b$.

(VI) $\cos \alpha = \dfrac{\tan b}{\tan c}$.   (VIII) $\cos \beta = \dfrac{\tan a}{\tan c}$.

(VII) $\tan a = \sin b \tan \alpha$.   (IX) $\tan b = \sin a \tan \beta$.

(X) $\cos c = \cot \alpha \cot \beta$.

Proof when $a < 90°$ and $b < 90°$. 1. Through any point D on OB, in Figure 108, draw a plane perpendicular to OA, intersecting planes OAC, OBC, and OAB in EF, FD, and DE, respectively.

2. $DE \perp OA$ and $EF \perp OA$ because OA is perpendicular to plane DEF. Hence, $\angle DEF$ measures the *dihedral angle* whose edge is OA; therefore, $\angle DEF = \alpha$. Also, $\triangle OEF$ and OED have right angles at E.

3. Plane DEF is perpendicular to plane OAC because plane DEF is perpendicular to OA which lies in OAC. Thus, DF is perpendicular to plane OAC because DF is the intersection of planes OBC and DEF which are perpendicular to plane OAC. Hence, $DF \perp OC$, $DF \perp EF$, and $\triangle DOF$ and DEF have right angles at F.

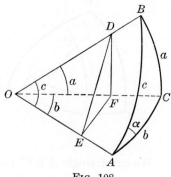

Fig. 108

4. From Figure 108, $a = \angle FOD$, $b = \angle FOE$, and $c = \angle EOD$.

5. Take OD as a unit for measuring lengths; or, let $OD = 1$.

6. From right $\triangle ODF$ and ODE, since $OD = 1$,

$\sin a = FD$; $\cos a = OF$; $\sin c = ED$; $\cos c = OE$.   (1)

7. From $\triangle OEF$, we find $OE = OF \cos b$, or $\cos c = \cos a \cos b$, which is (V).

8. From $\triangle OEF$, $EF = OF \sin b$ and $EF = OE \tan b$. Hence,

$EF = \cos a \sin b$; $EF = \cos c \tan b$.

9. Since $\angle DEF = \alpha$, from $\triangle DEF$ we obtain

$$\sin \alpha = \frac{FD}{ED} = \frac{\sin a}{\sin c};$$ (2)

$$\cos \alpha = \frac{EF}{ED} = \frac{\cos c \tan b}{\sin c} = \frac{\tan b}{\tan c};$$ (3)

$$\tan \alpha = \frac{FD}{EF} = \frac{\sin a}{\cos a \sin b} = \frac{\tan a}{\sin b}. \tag{4}$$

10. We observe that (2) gives (I), (3) gives (VI), and (4) gives (VII). By symmetrical reasoning, where we would interchange α with β, and a with b, we obtain (III) from (I), (VIII) from (VI), and (IX) from (VII).

11. From (VI) or (3),

$$\cos \alpha = \frac{\cos c \sin b}{\sin c \cos b} = \frac{\sin b}{\sin c} \cdot \frac{\cos c}{\cos b}; \tag{5}$$

by use of (III) and (V) in (5),

$$\cos \alpha = \sin \beta \cdot \frac{\cos a \cos b}{\cos b} = \sin \beta \cos a.$$

This establishes (II). By symmetry we obtain (IV) from (II).

12. We obtain (X) by solving (II) for $\cos a$, (IV) for $\cos b$, and substituting the results on the right side in (V).

Note 1. A moderate modification of the preceding proof, with Figure 108 altered, would establish (I) to (X) when one or both of the conditions $\alpha < 90°$, $\beta < 90°$ are not satisfied. It will be found that (I) to (V) inclusive are sufficient for most purposes. (I) and (III) may be remembered by analogy with corresponding formulas for right plane triangles.

120. Rules for species

We shall say that two angular magnitudes are of the *same* or of *different species* according as they terminate in the *same* or in *different quadrants*. In this statement the angles are thought of in their standard positions on a coordinate system.

ILLUSTRATION 1. 130° and 75° are of *different* species.

The following theorems are useful in discussing the species of parts of a spherical triangle. Theorems I and II are proved in texts on solid geometry.

I. *The sum of two sides of a spherical triangle is greater than the third side.*

II. *If two sides of a spherical triangle are unequal, the angles opposite are unequal and the greater angle is opposite the greater side. If two sides are equal, the angles opposite are equal.*

III. *In a right spherical triangle ABC,*

1. *a and α are of the same species;*

2. *b and β are of the same species;*

3. *if $c < 90°$, then a and b are of the same species;*

4. *if $c > 90°$, then a and b are of different species.*

Proof. From (VII) on page 180, tan a = sin b tan α. Since $b < 180°$, then sin $b > 0$. Hence, tan a and tan α are *both positive* and a and α are *both less than* 90°, or tan a and tan α are *both negative* and a and α are *both between* 90° *and* 180°. Thus, a and α are of the same species. (Parts 2, 3, and 4 will be proved by the student.)

EXERCISE 65

1. Prove Part 2 of Theorem III, Section 120, by use of (IV), page 180.

2. Prove Parts 3 and 4 of Theorem III, Section 120, by use of (V), page 180.

121. Solution of a right spherical triangle ABC

Suppose that values are assigned for any two parts of the triangle other than the right angle γ. Then, we shall find that there will exist just *one* solution for the unknown parts, or just *two* solutions, or *no* solution, depending on the nature of the data. Any solution which exists, or the conclusion that *no* solution exists, can be arrived at by use of formulas on page 180.* An inspection of the possibilities as to two given parts shows that two solutions cannot exist except when the given parts are (a and α) or (b and β); in either of these cases the data yield either two solutions or no solution.

EXAMPLE 1.   Solve $\triangle ABC$ if $a = 32° 24'$ and $c = 49° 15'$.

SOLUTION.   To find any unknown part, we use that formula which involves this part and the given parts. Thus, to find b, we use (V).

Formulas	*Computation*
	Data: $a = 32° 24'$, $c = 49° 15'$.
(V) cos $b = \dfrac{\cos c}{\cos a}$.	log cos c = 9.8148 − 10 (Table VI) log cos a = 9.9265 − 10 (−) log cos b = 9.8883 − 10; $b = 39° 21'$.
(I) sin $\alpha = \dfrac{\sin a}{\sin c}$.	log sin a = 9.7290 − 10 log sin c = 9.8794 − 10 (−) $\alpha = 45° 1'$ log sin α = 9.8496 − 10; or ~~134° 59′~~.

Note. 134° 59′ is ruled out by Part 1 of Theorem III, page 181: since $a < 90°$, it follows that $\alpha < 90°$.

(IV) cos β = sin α cos b.	The student should compute: $\beta = 56° 51'$.
Summary.	$\alpha = 45° 1'$, $\beta = 56° 51'$, $b = 39° 21'$.

Check. We could use (II), cos α = sin β cos a, as a check formula and compute the logarithm of both sides.

---

* We shall find it possible to solve any right spherical triangle by use of only formulas (I) to (V) on page 180.

In the logarithmic computation of a product or a quotient, the logarithm of the numerical value of any *negative factor F* will be labeled "**(n) log F.**" The logarithmic work will then give the *absolute value* of the product or quotient; its sign will be + or − according as an *even* or an *odd* number of factors are negative.

EXAMPLE 2.   Solve $\triangle ABC$ if $a = 63° 40'$ and $b = 117° 25'$.

Formulas	Computation
	Data: $a = 63° 40'$, $b = 117° 25'$.
(V) **cos c = cos a cos b.** cos $117° 25'$ = − cos $62° 35'$.	log cos a = 9.6470 − 10 (n) log cos b = 9.6632 − 10 (+) (n) log cos c = 9.3102 − 10; from Table VI, log cos $78° 13'$ = 9.3102 − 10; ∴ $c = 101° 47'$.
(I) **sin $\alpha = \dfrac{\sin a}{\sin c}$.** sin $101° 47'$ = sin $78° 13'$.	log sin a = 9.9524 − 10 log sin c = 9.9908 − 10 (−) $\alpha = 66° 16'$ log sin α = 9.9616 − 10; or ~~$113° 44'$~~.

Note. $\alpha = 113° 44'$ is ruled out because a and α always are of the same species.

Formula (III).	$\beta = 114° 57'$.
Summary.	$\alpha = 66° 16'$, $\beta = 114° 57'$, $c = 101° 47'$.

Check. We could use (II), sin β = cos α/cos a, with sin β from Table VII and the value of cos α/cos a computed by use of Tables V and VI.

EXAMPLE 3.   Solve $\triangle ABC$ if $\alpha = 43° 21'$ and $a = 36° 42'$.

Formulas	Computation
	Data: $\alpha = 43° 21'$, $a = 36° 42'$.
(II) **sin $\beta = \dfrac{\cos \alpha}{\cos a}$.**	log cos α = 9.8617 − 10 log cos a = 9.9040 − 10 (−) log sin β = 9.9577 − 10; $\beta = 65° 7'$ or $\beta = 114° 53'$.
(I) **sin $c = \dfrac{\sin a}{\sin \alpha}$.**	$c = 60° 31'$ or $c = 119° 29'$
(V) to find b.	When $c = 60° 31'$, $b = 52° 8'$. When $c = 119° 29'$, $b = 127° 52'$.

Grouping. Since b and β must be of the same species, we group the acute value of b with the acute value of β, etc. Parts 3 and 4 of Theorem III, page 181, dictate the choice of c.

Summary. First solution: $b_1 = 52° 8'$, $\beta_1 = 65° 7'$, $c_1 = 60° 31'$.
     Second solution: $b_2 = 127° 52'$, $\beta_2 = 114° 53'$, $c_2 = 119° 29'$.

Comment. In Figure 109, the first solution of Example 3 is represented by △ABC, and the second by △$A'BC$. The figure is not true to scale, but essential features are appropriately represented.

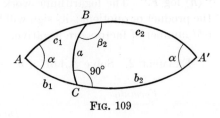

Fig. 109

If the given parts of triangle ABC are a and β, we could use (II) to determine α, (IV) to find b, and (V) to find c. A similar method of solution applies if b and α are the given parts.

If the given parts are α and c, we could use (I) to find a, (V) to find b, and (III) to find β. A similar method of solution applies if β and c are the given parts.

If the given parts are α and β, we could use (II), (IV), and (V) in succession to find a, b, and c.

EXERCISE 66

Solve the right spherical △ABC. If computation is necessary, use four-place or five-place logarithms, and check the solution.

1. $a = 45° 20'$, $c = 63° 10'$.
2. $b = 62° 10'$, $c = 75° 20'$.

3. $\alpha = 58° 20'$, $c = 85° 40'$.
4. $\beta = 73° 20'$, $c = 65° 30'$.

5. $a = 83° 45'$, $b = 45° 26'$.
6. $a = 61° 26'$, $b = 79° 32'$.

7. $b = 38° 15'$, $\beta = 52° 10'$.
8. $a = 43° 28'$, $\alpha = 57° 40'$.

9. $a = 61° 26'$, $b = 110° 30'$.
10. $a = 103° 15'$, $b = 58° 23'$.

11. $\alpha = 48° 26'$, $\beta = 100° 40'$.
12. $\alpha = 120° 15'$, $\beta = 70° 32'$.

13. $a = 63° 28'$, $\alpha = 48° 14'$.
14. $\alpha = 22° 10'$, $\beta = 37° 20'$.

15. $a = 127° 30'$, $\beta = 114° 27'$.
16. $b = 103° 18'$, $\beta = 135° 14'$.

17. $\alpha = 100° 15'$, $\beta = 160° 38'$.
18. $b = 67° 35'$, $\alpha = 108° 30'$.

19. $a = 114° 20'$, $\alpha = 96° 18'$.
20. $b = 126° 14'$, $\beta = 105° 30'$.

21. $b = 90°$, $a = 36°$.
22. $a = 90°$, $\beta = 90°$.

23. $a = 63°$, $\alpha = 128°$.
24. $c = 35° 25'$, $b = 63° 46'$.

Solve right △ABC by use of five-place logarithms and check.

25. $\alpha = 65° 27.3'$, $\beta = 49° 18.6'$.
26. $a = 35° 41.7'$, $c = 73° 24.5'$.

27. $\alpha = 124° 14.8'$, $a = 147° 15.2'$.
28. $\beta = 108° 19.4'$, $b = 157° 13.2'$.

29. $c = 128° 31.3'$, $\alpha = 36° 14.9'$.
30. $b = 36° 45.2'$, $\alpha = 131° 14.7'$.

What can be said about the other parts of the spherical △ABC under the given condition? Then check (I) to (V) for the triangle.

31. $\alpha = \gamma = 90°$.
32. $\gamma = a = 90°$.
33. $\gamma = c = 90°$.

34. $\gamma = a = b = 90°$.
35. $\alpha = \gamma = b = 90°$.
36. $a = b = c = 90°$.

122. Isosceles and quadrantal triangles

Suppose that the spherical triangle ABC is isosceles, with $a = b$; then it follows that $\alpha = \beta$. If a great circle is passed through C and the midpoint D of AB, as in Figure 110, triangles ADC and BDC are symmetric right triangles with right angles at D. By first solving one of these right triangles, we can solve triangle ABC if any two of its distinct parts (a, α, c, γ) are given.

Fig. 110

ILLUSTRATION 1. In Figure 110, if we are given $a = 75°$, $b = 75°$, and $\gamma = 58°$, then $\angle ACD = 29°$. Hence, we can find α and AD on solving $\triangle ADC$ by use of (I) to (V). Then $c = AB = 2(AD)$.

A *quadrantal triangle* ABC is a triangle with at least one *side* equal to $90°$; suppose that the triangle is lettered so that $c = 90°$. Then, from (1) on page 179, in the polar triangle $A'B'C'$, $\gamma' = 180° - 90° = 90°$. Thus, $A'B'C'$ is a *right* spherical triangle. Hence, if we are given two parts of a quadrantal triangle in addition to the $90°$ side, we can solve the triangle by first solving the polar triangle and then using (1) on page 179.

EXAMPLE 1. Solve $\triangle ABC$ if $c = 90°$, $\gamma = 43°$, and $a = 132°$.

SOLUTION. 1. In the polar $\triangle A'B'C'$,

$$\gamma' = 180° - c = 90°; \qquad c' = 180° - \gamma = 137°; \qquad \alpha' = 180° - a = 48°.$$

2. On solving $\triangle A'B'C'$ we obtain $a' = 30° 27'$; $b' = 148° 2'$; $\beta' = 129° 5'$. Hence, from (1) on page 179,

$$\alpha = 180° - a' = 149° 33'; \qquad \beta = 180° - b' = 31° 58'; \qquad b = 50° 55'.$$

EXERCISE 67

Solve the oblique $\triangle ABC$ by use of four-place or five-place logarithms.

1. $a = b = 80° 32'$, $c = 142° 40'$. **2.** $b = c = 68° 16'$, $a = 98° 36'$.

3. $\alpha = 94° 30'$, $b = c = 53° 27'$. **4.** $\alpha = \beta = 48° 21'$, $\gamma = 112° 18'$.

5. $\beta = \gamma = 53° 49'$, $c = 37° 32'$. **6.** $c = 90°$, $a = 28° 47'$, $b = 63° 57'$.

7. $b = 90°$, $\alpha = 128° 29'$, $\gamma = 133° 45'$.

8. $a = 90°$, $b = 121° 45'$, $\alpha = 143° 26'$.

Solve the oblique $\triangle ABC$ by use of auxiliary right triangles and four-place or five-place logarithms.

9. $b = 48° 27'$, $\alpha = 73° 29'$, $c = 128° 33'$.

HINT. First construct $\triangle ABC$ approximately to scale by starting with side c in a horizontal plane. Pass a great circle through C perpendicular to AB and solve the resulting right spherical triangles.

10. $a = 99° 26'$, $c = 43° 14'$, $\beta = 36° 57'$.

    11. $\beta = 57° 18'$, $c = 67° 26'$, $a = 18° 29'$.

    12. $\gamma = 23° 17'$, $\beta = 54° 16'$, $a = 115° 18'$.

    13.* $\alpha = \beta = 67° 19.8'$, $c = 94° 15.4'$.

    14.* $a = 90°$, $\alpha = 46° 17' 8''$, $b = 64° 11' 40''$.

123. Napier's rules

In the examples in this chapter, it has been assumed that formulas (I) to (V) have been memorized as a basis. However, if a student prefers, he may use all of (I) to (X). In such a case, it would be convenient for him to recall these formulas through rules formulated by Napier, the inventor of logarithms. To describe his method, we let $Co\text{-}\alpha$ equal $(90° - \alpha)$, and introduce $Co\text{-}\beta$ and $Co\text{-}c$ similarly. Then, we shall call $(a, b, Co\text{-}\alpha, Co\text{-}c, Co\text{-}\beta)$ the five **circular parts** for the triangle ABC. We shall think of these parts arranged around a *circle* or around the *triangle ABC* in the order (a, b, α, c, β). Thus, to each part there correspond two *adjacent* parts and two *opposite* parts. Then, if each of the following rules is applied to each circular part, we obtain formulas (I) to (X).

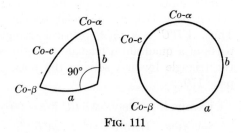

Fig. 111

Rule 1. *The sine of any circular part is equal to the product of the tangents of the two adjacent parts.*

Rule 2. *The sine of any circular part is equal to the product of the cosines of the two opposite parts.*

In applying these rules, recall that, for any angle θ, any function of $(90° - \theta)$ is equal to the *co*-function of θ.

Illustration 1. The parts *adjacent* to $Co\text{-}\beta$ are $Co\text{-}c$ and a; the parts *opposite* to $Co\text{-}\beta$ are $Co\text{-}\alpha$ and b. Hence, from Rules 1 and 2,

$$\sin (Co\text{-}\beta) = \tan (Co\text{-}c) \tan a; \quad or \quad \cos \beta = \cot c \tan a; \quad (1)$$

$$\sin (Co\text{-}\beta) = \cos (Co\text{-}\alpha) \cos b; \quad or \quad \cos \beta = \sin \alpha \cos b. \quad (2)$$

We verify that (1) is equivalent to (VIII) and (2) is (IV).

By Napier's rules, we can write a formula connecting any three of the parts (a, b, α, β, c) without referring to formulas (I) to (X).

Illustration 2. To write a formula connecting α, β, and a, we first notice that $Co\text{-}\beta$ and a are *opposite* to $Co\text{-}\alpha$. Hence, by use of Rule 2,

$$\sin (Co\text{-}\alpha) = \cos (Co\text{-}\beta) \cos a; \quad or \quad \cos \alpha = \sin \beta \cos a.$$

*Only five-place results are given.

THIRTEEN

OBLIQUE SPHERICAL TRIANGLES

124. The law of sines

In any spherical triangle ABC, the sines of the sides are proportional to the sines of the corresponding opposite angles. That is,

$$\frac{\sin a}{\sin \alpha} = \frac{\sin b}{\sin \beta} = \frac{\sin c}{\sin \gamma}. \tag{I}$$

Proof. 1. Let a and c be any two sides. Draw a great circle through B perpendicular to the plane of AC. This circle cuts AC at a point D (Figure 112), or cuts AC *extended* at a point D where $AD < 180°$ (Figure 113). Then, triangles ABD and CDB have right angles at D. In each figure, let the measure of BD be h.

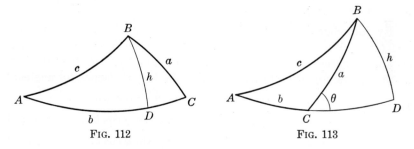

FIG. 112   FIG. 113

2. By use of formula (I), page 180,

| for $\triangle ADB$, | $\sin h = \sin \alpha \sin c;$ | (1) |

for $\triangle ADB$, $\sin h = \sin \alpha \sin c;$ (1)

for $\triangle DBC$, in Figure 112, $\sin h = \sin \gamma \sin a;$ (2)

for $\triangle DBC$, in Figure 113, $\sin h = \sin \theta \sin a.$ (3)

3. In Figure 113, $\theta = 180° - \gamma$; hence, $\sin \theta = \sin \gamma$ and (3) becomes (2). Thus, (1) and (2) are true for both figures, so that

$$\sin \alpha \sin c = \sin \gamma \sin a \quad or \quad \frac{\sin a}{\sin \alpha} = \frac{\sin c}{\sin \gamma}. \tag{4}$$

Since a and c represented any two sides, on using a, b instead of a, c in (4) we obtain the left-hand equality in (I), and thus complete its proof.

125. The law of cosines

In any spherical triangle ABC,

$$\cos a = \cos b \cos c + \sin b \sin c \cos \alpha; \qquad \text{(II)}$$

$$\cos b = \cos a \cos c + \sin a \sin c \cos \beta; \qquad \text{(III)}$$

$$\cos c = \cos a \cos b + \sin a \sin b \cos \gamma. \qquad \text{(IV)}$$

Proof (for the case of Figure 112 *on page* 187). By use of (V) on page 180, applied to $\triangle BDC$ and ADB, since $DC = b - AD$ we obtain

$$\cos a = \cos h \cos (b - AD); \qquad \cos c = \cos h \cos AD; \qquad (1)$$

$$\frac{\cos a}{\cos c} = \frac{\cos h \cos (b - AD)}{\cos h \cos AD} = \frac{\cos b \cos AD + \sin b \sin AD}{\cos AD},$$

where we used (V) of page 106. Hence,

$$\frac{\cos a}{\cos c} = \cos b + \sin b \tan AD. \qquad (2)$$

From (VI) on page 180, for $\triangle ABD$, $\tan AD = \tan c \cos \alpha$. From (2),

$$\cos a = \cos b \cos c + \sin b \cos c \tan c \cos \alpha;$$

or, $\cos a = \cos b \cos c + \sin b \sin c \cos \alpha.$

Note 1. In Figure 113, $CD = AD - b = -(b - AD)$. On repeating the details of the preceding proof and recalling the identity $\cos \theta = \cos (-\theta)$, we again obtain (II).

By interchanging the roles of the letters in (II), we obtain (III) and (IV). We call (II), (III), and (IV) the **law of cosines for sides.** On applying these formulas to the *polar* triangle $A'B'C'$ of triangle ABC, we obtain the following formulas, called the **law of cosines for angles:**

$$\cos \alpha = -\cos \beta \cos \gamma + \sin \beta \sin \gamma \cos a; \qquad \text{(V)}$$

$$\cos \beta = -\cos \alpha \cos \gamma + \sin \alpha \sin \gamma \cos b; \qquad \text{(VI)}$$

$$\cos \gamma = -\cos \alpha \cos \beta + \sin \alpha \sin \beta \cos c. \qquad \text{(VII)}$$

Proof. For triangle $A'B'C'$, from (II) we obtain

$$\cos a' = \cos b' \cos c' + \sin b' \sin c' \cos \alpha'. \qquad (3)$$

Recall that $a' = 180° - \alpha$; $b' = 180° - \beta$; $c' = 180° - \gamma$; $\alpha' = 180° - a$. Hence, $\sin \alpha' = \sin a$; $\cos a' = -\cos \alpha$; $\sin b' = \sin \beta$; etc. Therefore, from (3) we obtain (V). Similarly, we obtain (VI) and (VII).

126. Law of cosines in terms of haversines

If θ is any angle, we define a new trigonometric function called the **haversine of θ,** abbreviated **hav θ,** by the equation

$$\text{hav } \theta = \frac{1}{2}(1 - \cos \theta) \quad or \quad \cos \theta = 1 - 2 \text{ hav } \theta. \qquad (1)$$

Since cos $(-\theta)$ = cos θ, hav θ satisfies the identity

$$\text{hav } (-\boldsymbol{\theta}) = \text{hav } \boldsymbol{\theta}. \tag{2}$$

We shall prove that (II) to (IV) can be written in the form

$$\text{hav } a = \text{hav } (b - c) + \sin b \sin c \text{ hav } \alpha; \tag{II\,$'$}$$

$$\text{hav } b = \text{hav } (c - a) + \sin a \sin c \text{ hav } \beta; \tag{III\,$'$}$$

$$\text{hav } c = \text{hav } (a - b) + \sin a \sin b \text{ hav } \gamma. \tag{IV\,$'$}$$

Proof. In (II) on page 188, insert

$$\cos a = 1 - 2 \text{ hav } a \quad and \quad \cos \alpha = 1 - 2 \text{ hav } \alpha. \tag{3}$$

Then, (II) becomes

$$1 - 2 \text{ hav } a = (\cos b \cos c + \sin b \sin c) - 2 \text{ hav } \alpha \sin b \sin c;$$

$$1 - 2 \text{ hav } a = \cos (b - c) - 2 \text{ hav } \alpha \sin b \sin c. \tag{4}$$

From (1), we use cos $(b - c) = 1 - 2 \text{ hav } (b - c)$ in (4), which then simplifies to the form (II)$'$. Similarly, we find that (III) and (IV) give (III)$'$ and (IV)$'$.

Note 1. Each of (II)$'$ to (IV)$'$ expresses the haversine of a side in terms of the other two sides and their included angle. Values of haversines and their logarithms are provided in Table XVII. We could use $(c - b)$ instead of $(b - c)$ on the right in (II)$'$ because of identity (2). Thus, we may avoid using the haversine of a negative angle. Similar remarks are seen to apply in (III)$'$ and (IV)$'$.

Note 2. The principal applications of spherical triangles in the next chapter can be handled with convenience on the basis of formulas met up to this point. Hence, in a brief presentation of spherical trigonometry, Chapter Fourteen might be taken up immediately after the next exercise.

Note 3. Haversines could be introduced in various later formulas. We shall omit doing this. Such modifications will be found in more complete texts on spherical trigonometry where emphasis is given to navigation.

127. Solution of spherical triangles

The following cases arise in solving spherical triangles.*

I. *Given three sides.*

II. *Given three angles.*

III. *Given two sides and the included angle.*

IV. *Given two angles and the included side.*

V. *Given two sides and an angle opposite one of these sides.*

VI. *Given two angles and a side opposite one of these angles.*

* Hereafter, unless otherwise stated, any *triangle* referred to will be a *spherical triangle.*

If all *angles* of $\triangle ABC$ are given (Case II), by use of (1) on page 179 we can find all *sides* of the polar $\triangle A'B'C'$. Then, we could solve for the angles of $\triangle A'B'C'$, which is a problem under Case I. From these angles, we could then find the sides of $\triangle ABC$. Thus, Case II for $\triangle ABC$ could be solved under Case I for $\triangle A'B'C'$. Similarly, Cases IV and VI for $\triangle ABC$ could be solved under Cases III and V, respectively, applied to $\triangle A'B'C'$. Usually we shall not bring $\triangle A'B'C'$ into the discussion. Instead, available formulas for $\triangle ABC$ will apply directly to Cases II, IV, and VI.

128. Rules for species

If an angle $\theta \neq 90°$ is known to lie between $0°$ and $180°$, and $\sin \theta$ is given, we are aware that *two* values of θ correspond to the data. Thus, if the law of sines is used to find an unknown side or angle of a spherical triangle, in general two values will be obtained for the unknown part. Then, it becomes necessary to decide whether *neither* value, *one* of the values, or *both* values can be used for a solution. In making such a decision, or in grouping values obtained otherwise for various parts of a triangle, we usually employ Theorem II of page 181, or the rules for species applying to a right triangle.

Note 1. If an unknown angle $\theta \neq 90°$ between $0°$ and $180°$ is being found by use of $\tan \theta$, $\cos \theta$, or hav θ, then *just one value* for θ is obtained. This causes us to use $\tan \theta$, $\cos \theta$, or hav θ sometimes to remove an ambiguity resulting from previous use of $\sin \theta$.

★*Note 2.* The following rules for species are sometimes useful. These rules can be proved by use of later formulas.

RULE 1. *Half the sum of any two sides is of the same species as half the sum of the opposite angles.*

RULE 2. *A side (or angle) which differs from $90°$ by more than another side (or angle) has the same species as the angle (or side) opposite the first side (or angle).*

129. Solution of certain triangles by the laws of sines and cosines

Although later formulas are essential for a complete treatment of the solution of spherical triangles, certain types* of problems can be solved with reasonable accuracy by the laws of sines and cosines, with (II)′ to (IV)′ used in place of (II) to (IV). This remark assumes that a table of haversines and their logarithms is available (Table XVII). The following illustrations are restricted to the types of problems to be met in Chapter Fifteen. All triangle solutions fall under Case I or Case III.

* In a brief treatment of spherical trigonometry, Chapter Fifteen could be taken up immediately after Exercise 68.

Note 1. We shall not consider checking solutions of spherical triangles until other formulas are derived later in this chapter.

EXAMPLE 1. Solve $\triangle ABC$ if $a = 39°$, $b = 49°$, $c = 62°$.

SOLUTION. 1. *Formulas.* We use (II)′ to (IV)′, solved for the haversines of the angles and employing the differences $(c - b)$, $(b - a)$, $(c - a)$, to avoid negative angles:

$$\text{hav } \alpha = \frac{\text{hav } a - \text{hav } (c - b)}{\sin b \sin c}; \quad \text{hav } \beta = \frac{\text{hav } b - \text{hav } (c - a)}{\sin a \sin c}; \text{ etc.}$$

2. *Computation.* We employ Tables VIII, IX, XVII.

Data:	$a = 39°$, $b = 49°$, $c = 62°$.

$c - b = 13°$	$c - a = 23°$
hav $a = \quad .11143$	hav $b = \quad .17197$
hav $(c - b) = \quad .01281 \ (-)$	hav $(c - a) = \quad .03975 \ (-)$
difference $= \quad .09862$	difference $= \quad .13222$
log sin $b = 9.87778 - 10$	log sin $a = 9.79887 - 10$
log sin $c = 9.94593 - 10 \ (+)$	log sin $c = 9.94593 - 10 \ (+)$
log sin b sin $c = 9.82371 - 10 \mid (-)$	log sin a sin $c = 9.74480 - 10 \mid (-)$
log $.09862 = 8.99396 - 10 \downarrow$	log $.13222 = 9.12130 - 10 \downarrow$
log hav $\alpha = 9.17025 - 10$	log hav $\beta = 9.37650 - 10$
$\alpha = 45° \ 15'$.	$\beta = 58° \ 24'$.

Similarly, log hav $\gamma = 9.73440 - 10$; $\gamma = 94° 53'$.

Summary. $\alpha = 45° \ 15'$, $\beta = 58° \ 24'$, $\gamma = 94° \ 53'$.

Comment. 1. To find α, from Table XVII we obtain

log hav $45° 10' = 9.16872 - 10$;   log hav $45° 20' = 9.17175 - 10$.

Then, by interpolation above, log hav $\alpha = 9.17025 - 10$ gives $\alpha = 45° 15'$.

2. A certain inconsistency enters in employing five-place tables, with angular interpolation effective only to the nearest *minute* in Table XVII. We shall disregard this feature, with the viewpoint that later methods are better designed for refined computation, in view of the available tables.

Note 2. Notice the simplicity of the solution of the following example if *only the unknown side* is requested. This type of problem arises in applications.

EXAMPLE 2. Solve $\triangle ABC$ if $a = 125° \ 38'$, $c = 73° \ 24'$, $\beta = 102° \ 16'$.

SOLUTION. 1. *Formulas.* The problem falls under Case III. We use formula (III)′ to obtain b, and then the law of sines to find α and γ:

$$\text{hav } b = \text{hav } (a - c) + \sin a \sin c \text{ hav } \beta;$$

$$\sin \alpha = \frac{\sin a \sin \beta}{\sin b}; \quad \sin \gamma = \frac{\sin c \sin \beta}{\sin b}.$$

2. *Computation.* We use Tables VIII, IX, XVII.

Data: $a = 125°\ 38',$ $c = 73°\ 24',$ $\beta = 102°\ 16'.$

$\log \sin a = 9.90996 - 10$ ⎫	$a - c = 52°\ 14'$
$\log \sin c = 9.98151 - 10$ ⎬ $(+)$	$\mathrm{hav}\ (a - c) = .19378$
$\log \mathrm{hav}\ \beta = 9.78264 - 10$ ⎭	$\sin a \sin c\ \mathrm{hav}\ \beta = .47218$ $(+)$
$\log \mathrm{prod.} = 9.67411 - 10$	$\mathrm{hav}\ b = .66596$
$\sin a \sin c\ \mathrm{hav}\ \beta = .47218.$ (Table VIII)	(Table XVII) $b = 109°\ 23'.$

$\log \sin \beta = 9.98997 - 10$	$\log \dfrac{\sin \beta}{\sin b} = 0.01531$
$\log \sin b = 9.97466 - 10$ $(-)$	
$\log \sin \beta / \sin b = 0.01531$	$\log \sin c = 9.98151 - 10\ (+)$
$\log \sin a = 9.90996 - 10$ $(+)$	$\log \sin \gamma = 9.99682 - 10$
$\log \sin \alpha = 9.92527 - 10$	$\gamma_1 = 83°\ 4'$ *or* $\gamma_2 = 96°\ 56'.$
$\alpha_1 = 57°\ 21'$ *or* $\alpha_2 = 122°\ 39'.$	

Grouping. By Theorem II, page 181, $\alpha > \beta$ because $a > b$. Hence, we reject α_1 and use α_2. Since $c < b$, we must have $\gamma < \beta$. This fact does not indicate which of γ_1 and γ_2 should be used. In order to decide,* we compute $\log \mathrm{hav}\ \gamma = 9.64324 - 10$, as in Example 1; this gives $\gamma = 83°\ 5'$. Hence, we have found that $\gamma = \gamma_1 = 83°\ 4'$ should be used, and also we have obtained a check on the result. No means is at hand as yet for deciding which of $83°\ 5'$ and $83°\ 4'$ is the more accurate.

Summary. $b = 109°\ 23',$ $\alpha = 122°\ 39',$ $\gamma = 83°\ 4'.$

EXERCISE 68

Solve $\triangle ABC$ by use of Tables VIII, IX, XVII.

1–3. Use the data of Problems 2, 5, 8, respectively, of Exercise 71, page 197.

4–7. Use the data of Problems 2, 5, 8, 3, respectively, of Exercise 70, page 195.

130. Formulas for half-sides and half-angles

In any spherical triangle ABC, let

$$s = \tfrac{1}{2}(a + b + c) \quad and \quad S = \tfrac{1}{2}(\alpha + \beta + \gamma); \tag{1}$$

$$r = \sqrt{\frac{\sin\ (s - a)\ \sin\ (s - b)\ \sin\ (s - c)}{\sin s}}; \tag{2}$$

$$R = \sqrt{\frac{-\cos S}{\cos\ (S - \alpha)\ \cos\ (S - \beta)\ \cos\ (S - \gamma)}}. \tag{3}$$

Then, we shall prove that

$$\tan \frac{\alpha}{2} = \frac{r}{\sin\ (s - a)}; \tag{VIII}$$

$$\sin \frac{\alpha}{2} = \sqrt{\frac{\sin\ (s - b)\ \sin\ (s - c)}{\sin b \sin c}}; \quad \cos \frac{\alpha}{2} = \sqrt{\frac{\sin s \sin\ (s - a)}{\sin b \sin c}}. \tag{IX}$$

* See Note 1 on page 190.

Formulas symmetrical to (VIII) and (IX) hold for functions of $\beta/2$ and $\gamma/2$. Also, we shall prove that

$$\tan \tfrac{1}{2}a = R \cos (S - \alpha), \tag{X}$$

with symmetrical formulas for $\tan \tfrac{1}{2}b$ and $\tan \tfrac{1}{2}c$.

Proof of (VIII) *and* (IX). 1. On using the expression obtained on solving (II) of page 188 for $\cos \alpha$, and recalling (V) of page 106, we find

$$1 - \cos \alpha = \frac{\cos (b - c) - \cos a}{\sin b \sin c}$$

$[(XXI), \text{page } 112] \qquad = \dfrac{2 \sin \tfrac{1}{2}(a + b - c) \sin \tfrac{1}{2}(a - b + c)}{\sin b \sin c}, \text{ or }$

$$1 - \cos \alpha = \frac{2 \sin (s - c) \sin (s - b)}{\sin b \sin c}. \tag{4}$$

Similarly, $\qquad 1 + \cos \alpha = \dfrac{2 \sin s \sin (s - a)}{\sin b \sin c}. \tag{5}$

2. From (XIII) on page 109, with (4) and (5) we obtain

$$\tan \frac{\alpha}{2} = \sqrt{\frac{1 - \cos \alpha}{1 + \cos \alpha}} = \sqrt{\frac{\sin (s - b) \sin (s - c)}{\sin s \sin (s - a)}}$$

$$= \sqrt{\frac{\sin (s - a) \sin (s - b) \sin (s - c)}{\sin s} \cdot \frac{1}{\sin^2 (s - a)}} = \frac{r}{\sin (s - a)}.$$

Also, from (XII) on page 109, we obtain (IX) on extracting square roots in (4) and (5).

★*Outline for proof of* (X). The student may carry out the proof as follows. Consider the polar triangle $A'B'C'$, with sides a', b', c' and angles α', β', γ'. Express s', a', b', c', α', β', γ' in terms of parts of triangle ABC by use of (1) on page 179. Then, the expression for $\tan \tfrac{1}{2}\alpha'$ obtained from (VIII) simplifies to (X).

131. Gauss's formulas, or Delambre's analogies

If α and β are any two angles of a spherical triangle ABC, then

$$\sin \tfrac{1}{2}(\alpha + \beta) = \frac{\cos \tfrac{1}{2}(a - b)}{\cos \tfrac{1}{2}c} \cos \tfrac{1}{2}\gamma; \tag{XI}$$

$$\sin \tfrac{1}{2}(\alpha - \beta) = \frac{\sin \tfrac{1}{2}(a - b)}{\sin \tfrac{1}{2}c} \cos \tfrac{1}{2}\gamma; \tag{XII}$$

$$\cos \tfrac{1}{2}(\alpha + \beta) = \frac{\cos \tfrac{1}{2}(a + b)}{\cos \tfrac{1}{2}c} \sin \tfrac{1}{2}\gamma; \tag{XIII}$$

$$\cos \tfrac{1}{2}(\alpha - \beta) = \frac{\sin \tfrac{1}{2}(a + b)}{\sin \tfrac{1}{2}c} \sin \tfrac{1}{2}\gamma. \tag{XIV}$$

Any one of these formulas can be proved by expanding the left-hand member, inserting expressions for functions of $\frac{1}{2}\alpha$ and $\frac{1}{2}\beta$, and simplifying. Thus, by the addition formula for the sine,

$$\sin \tfrac{1}{2}(\alpha + \beta) = \sin \tfrac{1}{2}\alpha \cos \tfrac{1}{2}\beta + \cos \tfrac{1}{2}\alpha \sin \tfrac{1}{2}\beta. \tag{1}$$

Then, in (1) we would employ Section 130 and, later, (XVIII) of page 112, on the right to obtain (XI).

Note 1. Each of Delambre's analogies involves all parts of triangle ABC. Hence, these formulas are useful in checking solutions of triangles.

132. Napier's analogies

The following formulas, and the eight symmetrical equations involving $(\beta,\ \gamma;\ b,\ c)$ or $(\alpha,\ \gamma;\ a,\ c)$ on the left, are called *Napier's analogies.* Each of these involves five parts of triangle ABC. We obtain (XV) by dividing each side of (XII) by the corresponding side of (XI); etc.

$$\frac{\sin \tfrac{1}{2}(\alpha - \beta)}{\sin \tfrac{1}{2}(\alpha + \beta)} = \frac{\tan \tfrac{1}{2}(a - b)}{\tan \tfrac{1}{2}c}. \tag{XV}$$

$$\frac{\sin \tfrac{1}{2}(a - b)}{\sin \tfrac{1}{2}(a + b)} = \frac{\tan \tfrac{1}{2}(\alpha - \beta)}{\cot \tfrac{1}{2}\gamma}. \tag{XVI}$$

$$\frac{\cos \tfrac{1}{2}(\alpha - \beta)}{\cos \tfrac{1}{2}(\alpha + \beta)} = \frac{\tan \tfrac{1}{2}(a + b)}{\tan \tfrac{1}{2}c}. \tag{XVII}$$

$$\frac{\cos \tfrac{1}{2}(a - b)}{\cos \tfrac{1}{2}(a + b)} = \frac{\tan \tfrac{1}{2}(\alpha + \beta)}{\cot \tfrac{1}{2}\gamma}. \tag{XVIII}$$

★EXERCISE 69

Prove the formula in complete detail.

1. For $\tan \tfrac{1}{2}\beta$, as in (VIII).   **2.** For $\tan \tfrac{1}{2}a$ in (X).

3. For $\sin \tfrac{1}{2}\beta$ and $\cos \tfrac{1}{2}\beta$, as in (IX).   **4.** Formulas (XIV) and (XVI).

133. Solution in Cases I and II

To solve triangle ABC in Case I, where all sides are given, we use formulas of type (VIII), or (IX) if *just one angle* is desired. In Case II, where all angles are given, we use type (X). We check by use of the law of sines or a Delambre analogy.

EXAMPLE 1. Solve $\triangle ABC$ if $\alpha = 123° \ 56'$, $\beta = 72° \ 20'$, $\gamma = 81° \ 40'$.

SOLUTION. 1. *Formulas.* We use

$$S = \frac{1}{2}(\alpha + \beta + \gamma), \quad R = \sqrt{\frac{-\cos S}{\cos (S - \alpha) \cos (S - \beta) \cos (S - \gamma)}}. \tag{1}$$

$$\tan \tfrac{1}{2}a = R \cos (S - \alpha), \quad \tan \tfrac{1}{2}b = R \cos (S - \beta), \textit{ etc.} \tag{2}$$

2. *Computation.* We use Table VI.

Data:
$$\begin{aligned}\alpha &= 123°\ 56' \\ \beta &= 72°\ 20' \\ \gamma &= 81°\ 40'\end{aligned}\Big\}(+)$$

$$2S = 277°\ 56'.$$

$$\begin{aligned}S - \alpha &= 15°\ 2' \\ S - \beta &= 66°\ 38' \\ S - \gamma &= 57°\ 18'\end{aligned}\Big\}(+)$$

$$(check)\ S = 138°\ 58'.$$

$\cos 138°\ 58' = -\cos 41°\ 2'$;

hence, $-\cos S = \cos 41°\ 2'$.

$$\begin{aligned}\log \cos (S - \alpha) &= 9.9848 - 10 \\ \log \cos (S - \beta) &= 9.5984 - 10 \\ \log \cos (S - \gamma) &= 9.7326 - 10\end{aligned}\Big\}(+)$$

$$\log \text{prod.} = 9.3158 - 10 \mid (-)$$

$$\log (-\cos S) = \log \cos 41°\ 2' = 9.8776 - 10 \downarrow$$

[Formulas (1)] $\log R^2 = 0.5618$

$$\tfrac{1}{2}\log R^2 = \log R = 0.2809$$

$$\log \cos (S - \alpha) = 9.9848 - 10 \quad (+)$$

[Formulas (2)] $\log \tan \tfrac{1}{2}a = 0.2657$

$$\tfrac{1}{2}a = 61°\ 32'; \quad a = 123°\ 4'.$$

Similarly, from (2) we obtain $b = 74°\ 16'$ and $c = 91°\ 46'$.

Summary. $a = 123°\ 4', \quad b = 74°\ 16', \quad c = 91°\ 46'.$

Check. $\dfrac{\sin \alpha}{\sin a} = \dfrac{\sin \beta}{\sin b} = \dfrac{\sin \gamma}{\sin c}.$

$\log \sin \alpha = 9.9189 - 10$	$\log \sin \beta = 9.9790 - 10$	$\log \sin \gamma = 9.9954 - 10$
$\log \sin a = 9.9233 - 10\,(-)$	$\log \sin b = 9.9834 - 10\,(-)$	$\log \sin c = 9.9998 - 10\,(-)$
$\log \text{quot.} = 9.9956 - 10.$	$\log \text{quot.} = 9.9956 - 10.$	$\log \text{quot.} = 9.9956 - 10.$

★Comment. By use of the fact that $180° < \alpha + \beta + \gamma < 540°$, for any triangle ABC it can be proved that the radicand in (1) is positive. Similarly, the radicand in (2) on page 192 is positive. See Problem 11, page 200.

Note 1. Recall that Cases I and II can also be solved as in Section 129.

EXERCISE 70

Solve and check by use of four-place or five-place logarithms.

1. $a = 39°, b = 49°, c = 62°.$ 2. $a = 61°, b = 43°, c = 68°.$

3. $\alpha = 125°, \beta = 73°, \gamma = 84°.$ 4. $\alpha = 75°, \beta = 83°, \gamma = 69°.$

5. $a = 81°\ 27', b = 38°\ 50', c = 92°\ 43'.$

6. $\alpha = 116°\ 19', \beta = 55°\ 30', \gamma = 80°\ 37'.$

7. $\alpha = 124°\ 16', \beta = 53°\ 40', \gamma = 51°\ 24'.$

8. $a = 147°\ 40', b = 72°\ 10', c = 121°\ 36'.$

Solve and check by use of five-place logarithms.

9. $a = 48°\ 57.6', b = 69°\ 28.4', c = 83°\ 13.2'.$

10. $\alpha = 127°\ 39.4', \beta = 91°\ 16.2', \gamma = 75°\ 36.6'.$

11. $\alpha = 138°\ 26.7', \beta = 77°\ 27.3', \gamma = 81°\ 13.0'.$

12. $a = 48°\ 42.8', b = 106°\ 54.2', c = 84°\ 19.0'.$

134. Solution in Cases III and IV

In a problem under Case III, with the data consisting of two sides and the included angle, let the given parts be a, b, γ. Then, we may find α, β by use of Napier's analogies, and side c from (XVII).

EXAMPLE 1. Solve $\triangle ABC$ if $a = 125°\ 38'$, $c = 73°\ 24'$, $\beta = 102°\ 16'$.

SOLUTION. 1. *Formulas.* In Figure 114, points A, B, C are given, and hence there will be just one solution, because only one great circle connects A and C. We shall find $\tfrac{1}{2}(\alpha \pm \gamma)$ by use of (XVI), (XVIII) written for sides a, c:

$$\tan \tfrac{1}{2}(\alpha - \gamma) = \frac{\sin \tfrac{1}{2}(a - c) \cot \tfrac{1}{2}\beta}{\sin \tfrac{1}{2}(a + c)}; \quad (1)$$

$$\tan \tfrac{1}{2}(\alpha + \gamma) = \frac{\cos \tfrac{1}{2}(a - c) \cot \tfrac{1}{2}\beta}{\cos \tfrac{1}{2}(a + c)}. \quad (2)$$

To find b, we use (XVII), written for α, γ:

FIG. 114

$$\tan \tfrac{1}{2}b = \frac{\tan \tfrac{1}{2}(a + c) \cos \tfrac{1}{2}(\alpha + \gamma)}{\cos \tfrac{1}{2}(\alpha - \gamma)}. \quad (3)$$

2. *Computation.* We use Table VI.

Data: $a = 125°\ 38'$, $c = 73°\ 24'$, $\beta = 102°\ 16'$.

$$a - c = 52°\ 14'; \qquad a + c = 199°\ 2';$$
$$\tfrac{1}{2}(a - c) = 26°\ 7'; \qquad \tfrac{1}{2}(a + c) = 99°\ 31'; \qquad \tfrac{1}{2}\beta = 51°\ 8'.$$

From (1): $\log \cot \tfrac{1}{2}\beta = \ 9.9063 - 10$

$\underline{\log \sin \tfrac{1}{2}(a - c) = \ 9.6436 - 10 \ (+)}$

$\log \text{ product} = 19.5499 - 20$

$\underline{\log \sin \tfrac{1}{2}(a + c) = \ 9.9940 - 10 \ (-)}$

$\log \tan \tfrac{1}{2}(\alpha - \gamma) = \ 9.5559 - 10; \qquad \tfrac{1}{2}(\alpha - \gamma) = 19°\ 47'.$

From (2): $\log \cot \tfrac{1}{2}\beta = 9.9063 - 10$

$\underline{\log \cos \tfrac{1}{2}(a - c) = 9.9532 - 10 \ (+)}$

$\log \text{ product} = 9.8595 - 10$

$\underline{(n) \log \cos \tfrac{1}{2}(a + c) = 9.2184 - 10 \ (-)}$

$(n) \log \tan \tfrac{1}{2}(\alpha + \gamma) = 0.6411.$

From Table VI: $0.6411 = \log \tan 77°\ 8'$. Since $\tan \tfrac{1}{2}(\alpha + \gamma)$ is negative, $\tfrac{1}{2}(\alpha + \gamma)$ is an angle in quadrant II: $\tfrac{1}{2}(\alpha + \gamma) = 180° - 77°\ 8' = 102°\ 52'$.

$\left. \begin{array}{l} \tfrac{1}{2}(\alpha + \gamma) = 102°\ 52' \\ \tfrac{1}{2}(\alpha - \gamma) = \ 19°\ 47' \end{array} \right\}$ *add:* $\alpha = 122°\ 39'.$

                        subtract: $\gamma = \ 83°\ \ 5'.$

From (3), we find $\tfrac{1}{2}b = 54°\ 41'$; $b = 109°\ 22'.$

Summary. $\alpha = 122°\ 39'$, $\gamma = 83°\ 5'$, $b = 109°\ 22'.$

Check. We could use (XIII): $\dfrac{\cos \tfrac{1}{2}(\alpha + \beta)}{\sin \tfrac{1}{2}\gamma} = \dfrac{\cos \tfrac{1}{2}(a + b)}{\cos \tfrac{1}{2}c}.$

Note 1. From Section 129, recall that Case III may also be solved as follows: (*i*) use the law of cosines, preferably in haversine form, to find the third side; (*ii*) use the law of sines to find the unknown angles.

To solve in Case IV, with two angles and the included side given, we would use formulas of types (XV) and (XVII) to find the other sides, and then either (XVI) or (XVIII) to find the third angle.

EXERCISE 71

Solve $\triangle ABC$ *by use of four-place or five-place logarithms and check.*

1. $a = 93° 8', b = 46° 4', \gamma = 71° 6'$.
2. $a = 58° 6', b = 22° 8', \gamma = 112° 0'$.
3. $\alpha = 118° 4', \beta = 36° 2', c = 35° 6'$.
4. $\alpha = 108° 46', \beta = 40° 48', c = 80° 14'$.
5. $b = 127° 46', c = 65° 32', \alpha = 94° 38'$.
6. $\alpha = 126° 34', \gamma = 106° 24', b = 121° 47'$.
7. $\beta = 44° 28', \gamma = 116° 24', a = 63° 29'$.
8. $a = 64° 27', c = 104° 39', \beta = 64° 20'$.

Solve by use of five-place logarithms and check the solution.

9. $a = 124° 17.8', c = 83° 16.6', \beta = 63° 19.6'$.
10. $\alpha = 124° 16.3', \gamma = 52° 19.7', b = 56° 38.3'$.
11. $b = 84° 28' 10'', c = 137° 41' 44'', \alpha = 112° 10' 33''$.

135. Solution in Cases V and VI, the ambiguous cases

In Case V, with the data consisting of two sides and an angle opposite one of these sides, let the given parts be a, b, β. The possibilities bear a close resemblance to those for plane triangles in the ambiguous case. For the illustration in Figure 115 there are two solutions, triangles A_2BC and A_1BC. For any data, there will be either *no* solution, or *just one*, or *just two* solutions, depending on the given parts. With a, b, β as the given parts, we find α by use of the law of sines, where we meet the following possibilities:

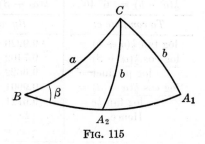

Fig. 115

1. *If we obtain* $\sin \alpha > 1$, *there is no solution.*

2. *If* $\sin \alpha = 1$, *there is just one solution, with* $\alpha = 90°$.

3. *If* $\sin \alpha < 1$, *we find an acute value* α_1 *from our tables, and a second value* $\alpha_2 = 180° - \alpha_1$. *Then,* α_1 *and* α_2 *must be tested, by Theorem* II *on page 181 or other means, to reject inadmissible values. Both, or just one, or neither of* α_1 *and* α_2 *may be admissible.*

Corresponding to each admissible value obtained for α, we find just one pair of values for the unknown side c and the opposite angle γ by use of the Napier analogies involving $\frac{1}{2}(a \pm b)$ and $\frac{1}{2}(\alpha \pm \beta)$.

EXAMPLE 1.   Solve $\triangle ABC$ if $a = 46° 39'$, $b = 33° 7'$, $\beta = 44° 28'$.

SOLUTION.   1. *To find α and the number of solutions.*   A figure for the data would appear like Figure 115 on page 197.

$\sin \alpha = \dfrac{\sin \beta \sin a}{\sin b}.$	$\log \sin \beta = \quad 9.8454 - 10$ $\log \sin a = \quad 9.8617 - 10 \ (+)$ $\overline{\log \text{ product} = 19.7071 - 20}$ $\log \sin b = \quad 9.7374 - 10 \ (-)$ $\overline{\log \sin \alpha = \quad 9.9697 - 10; \text{ hence,}}$ $\alpha_1 = 68° 50' \quad \text{or} \quad \alpha_2 = 111° 10'.$

By Theorem II on page 181, since $b < a$ we must have $\beta < \alpha$. We verify that $\beta < 68° 50'$ and $\beta < 111° 10'$. Therefore, both α_1 and α_2 are permissible; there are *two* solutions.

2. *To find c and γ we use* (XVI) *and* (XVII).

$$\tan \tfrac{1}{2}c = \frac{\tan \frac{1}{2}(a + b) \cos \frac{1}{2}(\alpha + \beta)}{\cos \frac{1}{2}(\alpha - \beta)}; \qquad \cot \tfrac{1}{2}\gamma = \frac{\tan \frac{1}{2}(\alpha - \beta) \sin \frac{1}{2}(a + b)}{\sin \frac{1}{2}(a - b)}.$$

$a = 46° 39'$	$\alpha_1 = \quad 68° 50'$	$\alpha_2 = 111° 10'$
$b = 33° \ 7'$	$\beta = \quad 44° 28'$	$\beta = \quad 44° 28'$
$a + b = 79° 46'$	$\alpha_1 + \beta = 113° 18'$	$\alpha_2 + \beta = 155° 38'$
$a - b = 13° 32'$	$\alpha_1 - \beta = \quad 24° 22'$	$\alpha_2 - \beta = \quad 66° 42'$
$\frac{1}{2}(a + b) = 39° 53'$	$\frac{1}{2}(\alpha_1 + \beta) = \quad 56° 39'$	$\frac{1}{2}(\alpha_2 + \beta) = \quad 77° 49'$
$\frac{1}{2}(a - b) = \quad 6° 46'$	$\frac{1}{2}(\alpha_1 - \beta) = \quad 12° 11'$	$\frac{1}{2}(\alpha_2 - \beta) = \quad 33° 21'$

To compute c:	By use of α_1:	By use of α_2:
$\log \tan \frac{1}{2}(a + b) =$	$9.9220 - 10$	$9.9220 - 10$
$\log \cos \frac{1}{2}(\alpha + \beta) =$	$9.7402 - 10 \ (+)$	$9.3244 - 10 \ (-)$
$\log \text{ product} =$	$9.6622 - 10$	$9.2464 - 10$
$\log \cos \frac{1}{2}(\alpha - \beta) =$	$9.9901 - 10 \ (-)$	$9.9218 - 10 \ (-)$
$\log \tan \frac{1}{2}c =$	$9.6721 - 10$	$9.3246 - 10$
Hence,	$\frac{1}{2}c_1 = 25° 10';$	$\frac{1}{2}c_2 = 11° 55';$
	$c_1 = 50° 20'.$	$c_2 = 23° 50'.$

From the formula for $\cot \frac{1}{2}\gamma$ we obtain $\gamma_1 = 80° 50'$ by use of α_1, and $\gamma_2 = 31° 14'$ by use of α_2.

Summary.   *First solution:* $\alpha_1 = \quad 68° 50'$, $c_1 = 50° 20'$, $\gamma_1 = 80° 50'$.
Second solution: $\alpha_2 = 111° 10'$, $c_2 = 23° 50'$, $\gamma_2 = 31° 14'$.

The details for the solution of triangle ABC under Case VI are similar to those of Case V. There may be no solution, just one, or just two solutions.

EXAMPLE 2. Determine how many solutions exist for $\triangle ABC$ if $\alpha = 36° 20'$, $\gamma = 104° 20'$, and $c = 133° 10'$.

SOLUTION. 1. *To find a:* $\qquad\qquad \sin a = \dfrac{\sin c \sin \alpha}{\sin \gamma}$.

$\log \sin c = 9.8629 - 10$ $\qquad$ $(\sin 133° 10' = \sin 46° 50')$
$\underline{\log \sin \alpha = 9.7727 - 10 \;(+)}$
$\log \text{product} = 9.6356 - 10$
$\underline{\log \sin \gamma = 9.9863 - 10 \;(-)}$ $\qquad$ $(\sin 104° 20' = \sin 75° 40')$
$\log \sin a = 9.6493 - 10$; hence $a_1 = 26° 29'$ and $a_2 = 153° 31'$.

2. *Test of the values of a by use of Theorem* II, *page* 181. Since $\gamma > \alpha$, hence $c > a$. We verify that $c > 26° 29'$ but $c < 153° 31'$. Therefore, a_2 is *not admissible*. There is just one solution, with $a = 26° 29'$.

EXERCISE 72

Only find the number of solutions for the spherical triangle ABC.

1. $a = 60°$, $b = 30°$, $\beta = 30°$. $\qquad$ 2. $c = 45°$, $\beta = 60°$, $\gamma = 30°$.
3. $b = 75°$, $c = 75°$, $\gamma = 40°$. $\qquad$ 4. $b = 150°$, $\beta = 45°$, $\gamma = 120°$.
5. $a = 30°$, $b = 60°$, $\alpha = 150°$. $\qquad$ 6. $a = 30°$, $\alpha = 75°$, $\gamma = 15°$.

Solve by use of four-place or five-place logarithms.

7. $a = 47° 20'$, $b = 34° 9'$, $\beta = 43° 20'$.
8. $b = 49° 20'$, $c = 37° 26'$, $\gamma = 42° 50'$.
9. $b = 39° 14'$, $c = 67° 20'$, $\gamma = 115° 10'$.
10. $a = 53° 30'$, $b = 82° 10'$, $\beta = 118° 16'$.
11. $c = 44° 50'$, $\beta = 61° 27'$, $\gamma = 18° 10'$.
12. $a = 39° 40'$, $\alpha = 105° 10'$, $\gamma = 143° 14'$.
13. $c = 147° 20'$, $\beta = 68° 12'$, $\gamma = 27° 10'$.

★136. Area of a spherical triangle

Let E be the *spherical excess* and H be the *area* of a triangle ABC, on a sphere whose radius is ρ. Then,

$$E = \alpha + \beta + \gamma - 180°; \qquad \textit{the area of the sphere is } 4\pi\rho^2. \qquad (1)$$

In geometry, it is proved that H is equal to *the area of a lune whose angle is* $\frac{1}{2}E$. The *area of a lune* is to *the area of the sphere* as *the angle of the lune* is to $360°$. Hence, if E is measured in degrees,

$$\frac{H}{4\pi\rho^2} = \frac{\frac{1}{2}E}{360°}, \quad or \quad H = \frac{\pi\rho^2 E}{180°}. \qquad (2)$$

Note 1. It can be proved that

$$\tan \tfrac{1}{4}E = \sqrt{\tan \tfrac{1}{2}s \, \tan \tfrac{1}{2}(s-a) \, \tan \tfrac{1}{2}(s-b) \, \tan \tfrac{1}{2}(s-c)}, \qquad (3)$$

which is called L'HUILIER'S THEOREM. We omit the proof of (3). To obtain H from (2), E is first computed from (3).

★EXERCISE 73

1–4. Find the areas of the triangles of Problems 3, 4, 5, and 8 in Exercise 70, if $\rho = 100$ feet.

MISCELLANEOUS EXERCISE 74

Solve the oblique $\triangle ABC$ by use of four-place or five-place logarithms.

1. $a = 131° 16', c = 78° 24', \beta = 107° 19'$.

2. $a = 81° 19', b = 103° 16', c = 39° 26'$.

3. $\alpha = 126° 39', \beta = 42° 18', \gamma = 53° 26'$.

4. $a = 113° 15', c = 71° 16', \gamma = 61° 47'$.

5. $a = 116° 53', \alpha = 61° 29', \beta = 81° 14'$.

6. $a = 116° 21', b = 77° 38', c = 108° 29'$.

7. $b = 47° 26', \beta = 118° 21', \gamma = 142° 16'$.

8. $b = 67° 13', \alpha = 47° 28', \gamma = 118° 19'$.

9. $a = 143° 20', \alpha = 137° 16', \beta = 103° 27'$.

10. $a = 129° 45', c = 61° 38', \beta = 97° 26'$.

★11. Prove the results stated in the comment on page 195.

FOURTEEN

APPLICATIONS OF SPHERICAL TRIANGLES

137. Latitude and longitude

For our purposes, no appreciable error is made in assuming that the earth's surface is a sphere with radius 3959 miles. The earth revolves on a diameter whose intersections with the surface are called the north pole, N, and the south pole, S. If an observer stands at A on the earth, the direction of N is called *north* and of S is called *south;* if he faces *north*, the perpendicular direction to the *right* is called *east* and the opposite direction is called *west*. The **equator** is the great circle on the earth whose poles are N and S. The **meridian** of a point A on the earth is the semi-circle NAS of the great circle through N, A, and S, as in Figure 116. The **latitude** of A is the angu-lar measure of the arc of the merid-ian of A extending from the equator to A. If O is the earth's center and L is the latitude of A, then, in Figure 116, $L = \angle HOA$. Latitude is measured from 0° to 90°, north or south of the equator. The **co-latitude** of A is the complement of its latitude and is the angular measure of arc AN, in Figure 116.

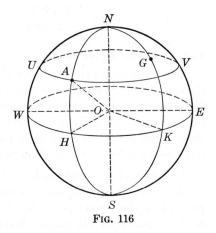

FIG. 116

ILLUSTRATION 1. For A in Fig-ure 116, $L = 40°\,N$ and the colatitude is 50°, approximately.

All points on the earth with the same latitude L lie on a small circle, with N and S as poles, in a plane parallel to the equator. This small circle is called a **parallel of latitude.** In Figure 116, the circle AUV is the parallel of latitude through A.

The **longitude** of a point A on the earth is the angle of intersection, λ, of the meridian of A and the prime meridian of Greenwich,* England,

* Used by many nations as the *zero meridian* for longitude.

indicated by G in Figure 116. Longitude is measured from $0°$ to $180°$, inclusive, east or west from Greenwich. The longitude λ is the measure of the smallest angle formed by the planes ONA and ONG; or, in Figure 116, $\lambda = \angle KOH$ in the plane of the equator.

ILLUSTRATION 2. In Figure 116, the longitude of A is approximately $100°\ W$, meaning west of Greenwich.

Any point A on the earth is definitely located by specifying two angular coordinates for A, its latitude L and longitude λ.

138. Nautical miles

A *nautical mile* is defined as the length of the arc which is subtended on a great circle on the earth by an angle of $1'$ at the center of the circle:

$$(1'\text{ of arc on a great circle on the earth}) = 1\text{ nautical mile;} \qquad (1)$$

$$\textbf{1 nautical mile = 6080 feet = 1.1515 statute miles.} \qquad (2)$$

To prove (2), we compute the circumference of a great circle on the earth and divide this by the number of minutes in $360°$:

$$360° = (360)(60') = 21,600 \text{ minutes.}$$

$$(\text{circumference of a great circle}) = 2\pi(3959) \text{ statute miles.}$$

$$1 \text{ nautical mile} = \frac{2\pi(3959)}{21,600} \text{ statute miles} = 1.152 \text{ statute miles.}$$

139. Directions on the earth

The horizontal plane at A on the earth is an *ideal plane* tangent to the earth at A. This plane consists of all lines tangent to the earth at A. Each direction from A on the earth corresponds to a direction arrow tangent to the earth at A; the arrow radiates from A in the horizontal plane. The directions N, S, E, W correspond to the arrows AN, AS, AE, AW, respectively, in the horizontal plane represented in Figure 117.

In referring to a path AB on the earth, we shall mean a *directed* path,* from the first point A to the second point B. At A, there is a line tangent to AB, and we direct this tangent from A toward B. The direction of the corresponding arrow AB in the horizontal plane, as in Figure 117, is called the *direction of the path AB at A*. The *bearing* of a point B from A is defined as the direction of the shortest *great-circle path* from A to B.

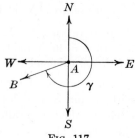

FIG. 117

In the horizontal plane, as in Figure 117, we shall describe any direc-

---

* Assumed to be so "smooth" that it has a tangent line at each point.

tion AB, indicated as an arrow, by specifying its *azimuth*. Recall that this is defined as the positive measure of the angle γ *between the north direction AN and AB*, measured to the *east* (clockwise) from the *north*. The direction of the track of a ship or airplane at any point A on the track is called the *course* of the ship or airplane, or the course of the track, at A. Thus, a *course* or any other direction is an *azimuth*, which is an angle on the range 0° to 360°, including 0° but not 360°.

ILLUSTRATION 1. If a ship sails on *course* 250°, indicated by AB in Figure 117, the track is in a southwesterly direction. The direction of AB is 70° west of south.

140. Great-circle distances

The shortest distance between points A and B on the earth is the length of the shortest arc AB of the great circle through A and B. This shortest distance is called the *great-circle distance* between A and B, and is on the range 0° to 180°, inclusive. Great-circle distances are of interest in geography and navigation. A fundamental problem of *great-circle navigation** for a ship or an airplane is the determination of the great-circle distance between given points A and B, and the *course* of the great-circle track AB at any point, particularly at A and at B.

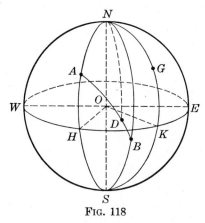

FIG. 118

ILLUSTRATION 1. In Figure 118, the course of AB at A is about 130°, and is called the *initial course* of AB. If D is any point on AB, and ND is the arc of the longitude circle through D, the course of AB at D is $\angle NDB$. The course changes continuously as we move from A to B. At B, the final course is $(180° - \angle ABN)$.

Many problems of great-circle navigation are solved by use of triangle NAB in Figure 118. If G represents Greenwich, $\angle GNA$ and $\angle GNB$ are the longitudes of A and B; $\angle BNA$ is found by subtraction if the longitudes are given. In Figure 118,

$$AN = colatitude\ of\ A\ ;$$

$$BN = 90° + (latitude\ of\ B),$$

since B is south of the equator. The angular measure of a great-circle arc AB can be translated into linear distance by recalling that 1′ *of arc on a great circle is* 1 *nautical mile in length*.

---

* Navigation when the paths to be followed *lie on great circles*.

EXAMPLE 1. Find the great-circle distance, the initial course, and the final course of the great-circle track from New York (40° 49′ N, 73° 58′ W) to Rio de Janeiro (22° 54′ S, 43° 10′ W), where latitude is given first and longitude second.

SOLUTION. 1. In Figure 118 on page 203, let A and B represent the cities. In $\triangle NAB$, act as if N were C in the standard notation ABC for a spherical triangle. Then, in $\triangle ABN$, where $\angle ANB = \gamma$,

$$\gamma = 73° 58′ - 43° 10′; \qquad b = AN = 90° - 40° 49′;$$

$$a = NB = 90° + 22° 54′.$$

Or, we have $a = 112° 54′$, $b = 49° 11′$, $\gamma = 30° 48′$. The solution of $\triangle ANB$ for its unknown parts is a problem under Case III.

2. By the haversine method of Example 2 on page 191, or the method of page 196 with four-place logarithms, we obtain $c = AB = 69° 51′$, $\alpha = 149° 50′$, $\beta = 24° 23′$. Since $69° 51′ = 4140′ + 51′ = 4191′$, the distance between the cities is 4191 nautical miles, or 4826 statute miles: $(4191)(1.1515) = 4826$.

3. The *initial course* is 149° 50′, which is the azimuth of Rio de Janeiro from New York. The *final course*, or the azimuth of the track at B, is seen to be $(180° - 24° 23′)$ or 155° 27′ (extend AB beyond B to verify this).

Comment. The azimuth of New York from Rio de Janeiro is $(360° - 24° 23′)$ or 335° 37′, or the bearing is $N\ 24° 23′\ W$.

EXERCISE 75

Find the great-circle distance in nautical miles between the cities. Also, find the initial course of the great-circle track from the first city to the second, and the direction of the first city from the second. Use the method of Section 129 on page 191, or Section 134 on page 196, as directed by the instructor.

1. New York (40° 49′ N, 73° 58′ W); Paris (48° 50′ N, 2° 20′ E).

2. Los Angeles (34° 3′ N, 118° 15′ W); Manila (14° 35′ N, 120° 59′ E).

3. Los Angeles; Tokyo (35° 39′ N, 139° 45′ E).

4. Honolulu (21° 18′ N, 157° 52′ W); Tokyo.

5. Seattle (47° 40′ N, 122° 19′ W); Tokyo.

6. Manila; Tokyo.   7. Los Angeles, Honolulu.

8. Gibraltar (36° 6′ N, 5° 21′ W); Rio de Janeiro (22° 54′ S, 43° 10′ W).

9. Sydney (33° 52′ S, 151° 12′ E); San Francisco (37° 47′ N, 122° 26′ W).

10. Liverpool (53° 24′ N, 3° 4′ W); Hongkong (22° 18′ N, 114° 10′ E).

11. San Francisco, New York.   12. New York; Los Angeles.

13. Moscow (55° 45′ N, 37° 37′ E); Paris.

14. Dakar (14° 40′ N, 17° 26′ W); Rio de Janeiro.

15. Moscow; Tokyo.   16. Liverpool; Berlin (52° 32′ N, 13° 25′ E).

17. Tokyo; Dutch Harbor, Alaska (53° 48′ N, 166° 25′ W).

18. Midway Island (28° 13′ N, 177° 23′ W); Dutch Harbor.

19. Minneapolis (44° 59′ N, 93° 17′ W); Dutch Harbor.

20. Minneapolis; Moscow.   **21.** New York; Moscow.

22. Vladivostok, Siberia (43° 11′ N, 131° 53′ E); Fairbanks, Alaska (64° 51′ N, 147° 44′ W).

23. Midway Island; Honolulu.   **24.** Minneapolis; Vladivostok.

Note 1. If ρ is the earth's radius (ρ = 3959 miles), and L is the latitude of a point A on the earth, the parallel of latitude through A is a circle with radius $\rho \cos L$, and is a great circle only when $L = 0°$.

25. Prove the result stated in Note 1.

Find the difference, in statute miles, between the great-circle distance and the distance along a parallel of latitude between the cities, approximately located.

26. New York (40° 50′ N, 74° 0′ W); Salt Lake City (40° 50′ N, 111° 50′ W).

27. San Diego (32° 40′ N, 117° 10′ W); Charleston (32° 40′ N, 79° 50′ W).

141. The celestial sphere

In the sky, we see the heavenly bodies as though they were on a *sphere* with our observation point as the center. This *celestial sphere* may be thought of as so large that, by comparison, the earth's radius is of negligible length. Hence, we refer to the earth as the center of the sphere. The **celestial north pole** P and **south pole** P' are the points where the earth's axis, extended through the earth's north and south poles, respectively, meets the celestial sphere. To any observer, this sphere appears to rotate *from east to west* about the axis PP', because the earth rotates *from west to east* about its axis.

Note 1. Any great circle referred to at present will be on the celestial sphere.

By the *position* of a celestial object, we mean the point where the line of sight from an observer to the object meets the celestial sphere. To discuss the positions of celestial objects, we introduce the following astronomical terms, illustrated in Figure 119 on page 206.

The **celestial equator** is the great circle whose poles are P and P', and is the intersection of the plane of the earth's equator and the celestial sphere.

At any instant, the **zenith** of an observer is the point Z vertically above him on the celestial sphere; the point Z' diametrically opposite to Z is called the **nadir.**

The **horizon** of an observer is the great circle whose poles are Z and Z'. The plane of the horizon is tangent to the earth's surface at the observer's position, and is called his *horizontal plane.*

The **celestial meridian** is the great circle through the zenith Z and the north pole P. The intersections N and S of this meridian and the horizon are called the **north point** and **south point,** respectively, where N is the intersection *nearest to* P. If the observer faces N, the points E and W to his right and left on the horizon are called the **east point** and **west point,** respectively. The equator and the horizon intersect at E and W.

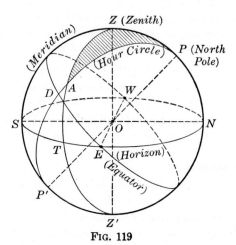

FIG. 119

The **hour circle** of a point A on the celestial sphere is the great circle through P and A.

The **hour angle*** of A is the angle ZPA between the meridian and the hour circle of A, measured east or west from the meridian from $0°$ to $180°$, inclusive. This angle is measured in *hours* or in *degrees*, where *one hour equals* $15°$.

Note 2. One *minute* in the hour system is $\frac{1}{60}$th of $15°$, or $15'$ in usual measure; one *second* in the hour system is $15''$. The hour system of measurement proves useful because the celestial sphere rotates through $15°$ in one *sidereal hour,* which is about $10''$ less than an ordinary *solar hour.*

The **declination** of A is the angular distance of A from the equator, measured along the *hour circle* of A. The declination, DA in Figure 119, is designated as *positive* or *negative* according as A is *north* or *south* of the equator.

The **vertical circle** of A is the great circle through Z and A.

The **altitude** of A is the angular distance of A from the horizon, measured along the vertical circle of A. The altitude, TA in Figure 119, is designated as *positive* or *negative* according as A is *above* or *below* the horizon.

---

* More properly, the *local* hour angle, as distinguished from the Greenwich and sidereal hour angles.

The **azimuth** of A is the angle NZA between the meridian and the vertical circle of A, counted from $0°$ to $360°$, including $0°$ but excluding $360°$, east (clockwise) from the north point. In Figure 119, arc NET measures the azimuth of A.

We notice that the altitude, azimuth, and hour angle of A depend not only on the position of A on the celestial sphere but also on the *time of observation* and the *position of the observer* on the earth. The declination depends *only on the position of A on the celestial sphere.*

At any instant, the position of A on the celestial sphere is uniquely determined with respect to an observer if the *altitude* and *azimuth* are known. This means of locating A can be referred to as the *altitude-azimuth coordinate system.* Also, the position of A can be described by specifying its *hour angle* and *declination;* this means is called the *declination-hour-angle system of coordinates.** Either system corresponds in its essential nature to the latitude-longitude system for indicating positions on the earth.

142. Location of the celestial north pole †

The altitude of the celestial north pole is the same as the latitude of the observer.

Proof. Consider the plane section of the earth, in Figure 120, where O is the observer, T is the earth's north pole, and T' is the earth's south pole. The reader should imagine himself standing with his feet at O and his head in the direction OZ. The arrows OZ, OP, and ON point at the zenith, north pole, and north point, respectively, on the celestial sphere. We verify that θ is the altitude of P. In Figure 120, we notice that ON is perpendicular to one side of angle L and OP to the other. Hence $\theta = L$, where L is the latitude of O.

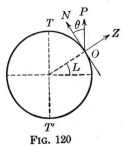

Fig. 120

143. The astronomical triangle

At any instant, for an observer at a given point on the earth, the *astronomical triangle* corresponding to a specified object A or point A on the celestial sphere is the spherical triangle ZPA of Figure 119, where

* Another coordinate (see texts on astronomy and navigation), called the *right ascension* of A, is paired with the declination to give a third system of coordinates, which is very important in astronomy and navigation.

† In Figure 119, associated remarks, and certain later formulas involving the pole P, we assume that the observer is in the northern hemisphere. Similar details relating to the pole P' would apply for an observer in the southern hemisphere.

$$ZP = 90° - (altitude\ of\ P) = colatitude\ of\ O;$$

$$AZ = 90° - (altitude\ of\ A) = coaltitude\ of\ A;$$

$$AP = 90° - (declination\ of\ A) = codeclination\ of\ A;$$

$$\angle ZPA = hour\ angle\ of\ A\ (east\ or\ west\ of\ meridian);$$

$$\angle PZA \begin{cases} = azimuth,\ if\ A\ is\ east\ of\ meridian; \\ = 360° - azimuth,\ if\ A\ is\ west\ of\ meridian. \end{cases}$$

Note 1. Problems associated with the astronomical triangle are important in navigation as well as in astronomy. It should not be assumed, however, that a navigator always carries out the trigonometric solution of spherical triangles as required in the exercises. Excellent navigation tables and special computing instruments enable him to eliminate much of the computation.

Note 2. The declination of the sun, certain planets, and prominent stars at all times during each year are available in American navigation tables. Also, when an observer's *longitude* is known, these tables give him the *local hour angle* of any one of these celestial bodies at any time.

For any observer, *solar noon* is the instant when the sun is on arc *PZS* of the meridian. Any *time* which we mention will be *local solar time*, specified as before or after solar noon. In Figure 119, if *A* represents the sun at *t* hours before noon, then $\angle ZPA = t$ hours; at *t* hours after noon, *A* is in the west and again $\angle ZPA = t$ hours.

144. Applications involving the astronomical triangle

I. *To find the time of day (solar time) of an observer whose latitude is known, when the sun's declination and altitude are given.*

In Problem I, the declination of the sun would be given by a nautical almanac and the altitude would be measured with a sextant. In the astronomical triangle *ZPA*, with *A* as the sun, all sides are given. Hence, the solution comes under Case I for spherical triangles. The results may be found by use of haversine formulas, as in Section 129 on page 190, or by the methods of Section 133 on page 194.

EXAMPLE 1. Find the solar time in New York $(L = 40° 50'\ N)$ at an instant in a morning when the sun's declination is $16° 30'$ and the sun's altitude is observed as $35° 20'$.

SOLUTION. 1. In $\triangle ZPA$ in Figure 119, where *A* is the sun,

$$ZP = 49° 10', \quad ZA = 54° 40', \quad AP = 73° 30'. \tag{1}$$

For convenience in applying triangle formulas, relabel *Z* as *B* and *P* as *C*; in standard notation, (1) becomes

$$a = 49° 10', \quad b = 73° 30', \quad c = 54° 40'. \tag{2}$$

We desire only the value of $\gamma = \angle ZPA$ in the triangle.

2. By use of Tables VIII, IX, and XVII, as on page 191, we obtain $\gamma = 57° 14'$; or, $\gamma = 3^{hr.} 49^{min.}$ in the astronomical hour unit. Since the celestial sphere turns through $1^{hr.}$ in one hour* of time, the observer took his observation at 3 hr. and 49 min. before noon, or 8:11 A.M.

Comment. We could also find γ by use of (IX), page 192.

A navigator at sea or in an airplane can use a result like that in Example 1 to determine his longitude, if he knows the solar time of Greenwich at the instant of observation. Greenwich time might be obtained by radio. Then, the difference in time would permit computation of the observer's longitude.

II. *To find the solar time of sunrise or sunset in a given latitude when the declination of the sun is known (from an ephemeris).*

Any instance of Problem II is a special case of Problem I, with the altitude of the sun as 0°. Then, in triangle ZPA, $ZA = 90°$ so that the triangle is quadrantal. The solution can still be obtained as in Example 1, but the method of page 185 also would apply.

III. *In a given latitude, to find the altitude and azimuth of a celestial object whose declination and hour angle are known.*

★*Note 1.* The preceding statement of Problem III is somewhat unnatural because no nautical almanac is available. In navigation, where Problem III is met, the data would consist of the observer's *latitude* and *longitude* and the *name of a star* A, whose altitude and azimuth are to be found. Then, a nautical almanac would give the declination, and also the hour angle for A because the longitude of the observer is known. Problem III arises when a navigator wishes to determine his latitude and longitude by observing the altitude and azimuth for each of two stars, A_1 and A_2. He starts by estimating his present latitude and longitude *roughly* on the basis of past information. Then, as in Problem III, he computes for each of A_1 and A_2 the altitude and azimuth which the star would have at the estimated position O corresponding to the *assumed* latitude and longitude. Also, the observer *measures* the altitudes of A_1 and A_2 with a sextant. Then, the computed azimuth of A_1, and the difference between its measured and its computed altitudes, determine approximately a *position circle* C_1 on the earth where the observer actually is located. Similarly, results for A_2 determine a second position circle C_2. Then, the observer's position is found as an intersection of C_1 and C_2, cleverly approximated by means of the famous *Sumner position lines.*†

In any example of Problem III, the solution of the astronomical triangle ZPA is found to come under Case III of Chapter Thirteen. Methods involving use of haversines prove to be convenient.

* We disregard the small difference between a solar and a sidereal hour.

† For a more complete discussion of navigation, see *Plane and Spherical Trigonometry with Applications*, by William L. Hart; D. C. Heath and Company. Or, see texts on navigation.

EXAMPLE 2. At a certain instant, an observer at O in latitude 44° 10′, who knows his longitude, reads in a nautical almanac that star A has declination 22° 57′ and hour angle 3 hours, 12 minutes east. Compute the altitude and azimuth of A.

SOLUTION. 1. In $\triangle ZPA$ of Figure 119,

$$PZ = 45° 50′, \quad PA = 90° - 22° 57′ = 67° 3′, \quad \angle ZPA = 48° 0′,$$

because 3 hours, 12 minutes equals 48°. We desire to find ZA, the coaltitude, and $\angle PZA$, which equals the azimuth, measured by arc NET.

2. Letter $\triangle ZPA$ with Z as B and P as C. Then, in the standard notation of Chapter Thirteen, we are given

$$a = 45° 50′, \quad b = 67° 3′, \quad \gamma = 48° 0′.$$

By the method of Section 129 on page 190, or Section 134 on page 196, we compute $c = AZ = 44° 28′$ and $\beta = \angle PZA = 102° 20′$. Hence, the desired altitude is 45° 32′ and the azimuth is 102° 20′.

IV. *To find the latitude of the observer if the altitude, hour angle, and declination of a celestial object are known.*

The altitude of the object A in Problem IV would be measured with a sextant, while the hour angle and declination would be read from a nautical almanac, under the assumption that the observer knows his longitude. In Problem IV, the data for triangle ZPA consists of two sides and an angle opposite one of these sides, so that the solution comes under Case V of Chapter Thirteen. Sometimes, an ambiguity in a formal solution may be eliminated by a figure showing triangle ZPA.

EXAMPLE 3. At 3:37 P.M. local solar time, when the sun's declination is − 16° 12′, an observer measures the sun's altitude as 22° 18′. Find his latitude.

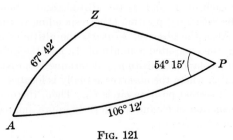

FIG. 121

SOLUTION. 1. In Figure 121, where A is the sun, $ZA = 67° 42′$; since the declination is negative, $PA = 90° + 16° 12′ = 106° 12′$. Since 3 hours, 37 minutes in angular measure equals 54° 15′, hence $\angle ZPA = 54° 15′$. On solving $\triangle ZPA$ by the method of Section 135 on page 197, we would obtain ZP, and then find the latitude $L = 90° - ZP$. If Section 135 has not been studied, $\triangle ZPA$ could be solved by the method of Problem 9 on page 185, after constructing an auxiliary great circle through A perpendicular to side ZP, to obtain related right triangles. On solving, we find $PZ = 63° 43'$. Hence, the latitude is 26° 17′.

Comment. In solving, an ambiguity about a second solution is eliminated because we must have $PZ \leqq 90°$, as seen in Figure 119, page 206.

EXERCISE 76

1.* Find the solar time in Chicago (latitude: 41° 50′ N) at a moment in a morning when the sun's declination is 14° 16′ if the sun's altitude is observed to be 38° 14′.

2.* Find the solar time in Washington, D.C. (latitude: 38° 55′ N), at a moment in an afternoon when the sun's declination is 18° 20′ if the sun's altitude is observed to be 49° 36′.

3. Find the Chicago time of sunrise on the morning of Problem 1, and the bearing of the sun at sunrise.

4. Find the Washington time of sunset on the afternoon of Problem 2, and the bearing of the sun at sunset.

Note 1. The sun's declination is 23° 27′ on the longest day of the year and − 23° 27′ on the shortest day of the year, for the northern hemisphere of the earth. We shall assume that all problems refer to this hemisphere. To find the length of a day, we first find the solar time at sunrise.

Find the lengths of the longest and the shortest days in each city and the bearing of the sun at sunrise on each of these days.

5. Fairbanks, Alaska (latitude: 64° 51′ N).

6. New Orleans (latitude: 29° 57′ N).

7. At 9:28 A.M., an observer finds that the sun's altitude is 37° 26′, on a day when the sun's declination is 6° 20′. Find his latitude.

8. At 2:36 P.M., an observer finds that the sun's altitude is 47° 32′, when the sun's declination is − 3° 16′. Find his latitude.

9. When the sun's declination is 11° 16′, an observer finds that the sun's azimuth is 311° 26′ and its altitude is 38° 22′. Find his latitude.

10. At 9:46 A.M. in Chicago (latitude: 41° 50′ N), the sun's altitude is observed to be 19° 20′. Find the sun's declination then.

Find the altitude and azimuth of a star A as observed from a point D whose latitude is L at an instant of time when δ is the declination and H is the local hour angle of A.

11. $L = 53° 20′ N$; $\delta = 28° 35′$; $H = 2$ hours, 17 minutes, east.

12. $L = 35° 16′ N$; $\delta = 48° 17′$; $H = 3$ hours, 25 minutes, east.

13. $L = 22° 25′ N$; $\delta = 76° 25′$; $H = 4$ hours, 40 minutes, west.

14. $L = 17° 40′ N$; $\delta = - 12° 50′$; $H = 4$ hours, 22 minutes, west.

15. $L = 35° 26′ S$; $\delta = - 25° 30′$; $H = 2$ hours, 10 minutes, east.

* These problems should be omitted if Chapter Thirteen has not been studied.

ANSWERS TO EXERCISES

EXERCISE 1. PAGE 6

15. On the line parallel to x-axis and 7 units above it; etc.

17. $<$.   **19.** $<$.   **21.** 81.   **23.** 5/3.

25. $-5 < 3$; $|3| < |-5|$.   **27.** $-14 < 18$; $|-14| < |18|$.

EXERCISE 3. PAGE 12

Note. Functions are in the order sine, cosine, tangent, cosecant, secant, cotangent.

1. $\frac{3}{5}, \frac{4}{5}, \frac{3}{4}, \frac{5}{3}, \frac{5}{4}, \frac{4}{3}$.   **3.** $\frac{24}{25}, \frac{7}{25}, \frac{24}{7}, \frac{25}{24}, \frac{25}{7}, \frac{7}{24}$.

5. $-\frac{2}{13}\sqrt{13}, -\frac{3}{13}\sqrt{13}, \frac{2}{3}, -\frac{1}{2}\sqrt{13}, -\frac{1}{3}\sqrt{13}, \frac{3}{2}$.

7. $\frac{8}{17}, -\frac{15}{17}, -\frac{8}{15}, \frac{17}{8}, -\frac{17}{15}, -\frac{15}{8}$.

9. $-\frac{4}{5}, \frac{3}{5}, -\frac{4}{3}, -\frac{5}{4}, \frac{5}{3}, -\frac{3}{4}$.

11. $-\frac{1}{2}\sqrt{3}, \frac{1}{2}, -\sqrt{3}, -\frac{2}{3}\sqrt{3}, 2, -\frac{1}{3}\sqrt{3}$.   **13.** 1, 0, none, 1, none, 0.

15. $-1, 0$, none, -1, none, 0.   **17.** $-\frac{1}{2}\sqrt{2}, -\frac{1}{2}\sqrt{2}, 1, -\sqrt{2}, -\sqrt{2}, 1$.

19. $\frac{5}{34}\sqrt{34}, -\frac{3}{34}\sqrt{34}, -\frac{5}{3}, \frac{1}{5}\sqrt{34}, -\frac{1}{3}\sqrt{34}, -\frac{3}{5}$.

23. $\sec \alpha = \frac{9}{4}$.   **25.** $\cos \gamma = \frac{3}{7}$.   **27.** II or IV.

29. I or III.   **31.** II.   **33.** III.   **35.** II.   **37.** III.

EXERCISE 4. PAGE 16

Note. Functions are in the order sine, cosine, tangent, cosecant, secant, cotangent.

1. 0, 1, 0, none, 1, none.

3. .5, .866, .577, 2, 1.155, 1.732.

5. .707, $-.707$, -1, 1.414, -1.414, -1.

7. .5, $-.866$, $-.577$, 2, -1.155, -1.732.

9. 0, 1, 0, none, 1, none.   **11.** Prob. 3, with signs for quad. IV.

13. $-1, 0$, none, -1, none, 0.

15. Prob. 5, with signs for quad. IV.   **17.** Prob. 5, with signs for quad. III.

19. Same as Prob. 3.   **21.** Prob. 5, with signs for quad. III.

23. 0, 1, 0, none, 1, none.   **25.** Prob. 5, with signs for quad. III.

EXERCISE 5. PAGE 17

Note. Only sine, cosine, tangent are given, in that order. Cosecant, secant, cotangent are equal to the corresponding reciprocals.

1. $\frac{5}{13}, \frac{12}{13}, \frac{5}{12}$.   **3.** $\frac{4}{5}, -\frac{3}{5}, -\frac{4}{3}$.   **5.** $\frac{3}{5}, \frac{4}{5}, \frac{3}{4}$.

7. $-\frac{5}{13}, -\frac{12}{13}, \frac{5}{12}$.   **9.** $\frac{8}{17}, -\frac{15}{17}, -\frac{8}{15}$.   **11.** $-\frac{1}{2}\sqrt{2}, -\frac{1}{2}\sqrt{2}, 1$.

13. $-\frac{1}{4}\sqrt{7}, \frac{3}{4}, -\frac{1}{3}\sqrt{7}$.   **15.** $\frac{3}{5}, \frac{4}{5}, \frac{3}{4}$.   **17.** $\frac{15}{17}, -\frac{8}{17}, -\frac{15}{8}$.

EXERCISE 6. PAGE 21

Note. See Note for Exercise 5.

1. $\frac{3}{5}, \frac{4}{5}, \frac{3}{4}$.   **3.** $\frac{24}{25}, \frac{7}{25}, \frac{24}{7}$.   **5.** $\frac{8}{17}, \frac{15}{17}, \frac{8}{15}$.

7. $\frac{2}{3}, \frac{1}{3}\sqrt{5}, \frac{2}{5}\sqrt{5}$.   **9.** See page 14.   **11.** $\sin 75°$.

13. tan 51° 50′.   **15.** sec 78°.   **17.** cot 50° 55′.
19. cos 23°.   **21.** cos 7° 37′.

EXERCISE 7. PAGE 23

1. .2079.   **3.** .6249.   **5.** 1.046.   **7.** .2334.   **9.** .0816.
11. 1.052.   **13.** 2.583.   **15.** 31.26.   **17.** .0963.   **19.** 1.133.
21. 22° 10′.   **23.** 31° 0′.   **25.** 22° 10′.   **27.** 75° 30′.   **29.** 72° 20′.
31. 64° 10′.   **33.** 38° 10′.   **35.** 69° 30′.   **37.** 32° 20′.

EXERCISE 8. PAGE 26

1. .0825.   **3.** .7298.   **5.** 1.957.   **7.** .9083.
9. .2487.   **11.** 1.426.   **13.** .9856.   **15.** 1.097.
17. .2259.   **19.** .0207.   **21.** 8.510.   **23.** .8189.
25. 1.001.   **27.** 7.012.   **29.** 4° 45′.   **31.** 22° 24′.
33. 20° 16′.   **35.** 48° 24′.   **37.** 52° 13′.   **39.** 45° 16′.
41. 32° 17′.   **43.** 50° 22′.   **45.** 45° 43′.   **47.** 12° 50′.
49. 12° 10′.   **51.** 42° 40′.   **53.** 60° 20′.   **55.** 52° 50′.
57. 16° 47′.   **59.** 47° 20′.   **61.** 64° 24′.

EXERCISE 9. PAGE 27

1. .99548.   **3.** 1.0359.   **5.** 8.4457.   **7.** 1.4988.
9. 32° 11′.   **11.** 11° 37′.   **13.** 70° 34′.   **15.** 17° 0′.
17. 47° 4′.   **19.** 33° 3′.   **21.** .53327.   **23.** 1.0500.
25. 1.0359.   **27.** .23842.   **29.** .32240.   **31.** .95261.
33. 17° .3′.   **35.** 47° 3.5′.   **37.** 33° 2.7′.   **39.** 31° 2′.
41. 80° 41′.   **43.** 60° 14′.

EXERCISE 10. PAGE 30

Note. Legitimately different methods of solution of a triangle may lead to slightly different results. The answers in this chapter are given as obtained by use of secants and cosecants, when applicable, in avoiding division.

1. $b = 115.0$, $c = 125.4$, 66° 30′.

3. $a = 121.6$, $b = 28.82$, 76° 40′.

5. $\alpha = 41° 53'$, $\beta = 48° 7'$, 599.2.

7. $\alpha = 52° 40'$, $\beta = 37° 20'$, 107.2.

9. $\alpha = 26° 32'$, $\beta = 63° 28'$, 1.038.

11. $\alpha = 61° 28'$, $\beta = 28° 32'$, 2.617.

13. $\alpha = 54° 24'$, $\beta = 35° 36'$, .5936.

15. $a = .01676$, $c = .02120$, 37° 49′.

17. $a = 1.577$, $b = .2723$, 9° 48′.   **19.** $\alpha = 58° 27'$, $\beta = 31° 33'$, 7329.

21. $\alpha = 61° 29'$, $\beta = 28° 31'$, 2.618.   **23.** See Prob. 13.

25. $a = .01675$, $c = .02120$, 37° 49′.   **27.** See Prob. 17.

29. See Prob. 19.   **31.** $b = 89.873$, $c = 96.446$, $21° 16.7'$.

33. $a = 13.089$, $b = 3.6943$, $15° 45.7'$.

35. $\alpha = 26° 31.3'$, $\beta = 63° 28.7'$, 1.0379.

EXERCISE 11. PAGE 31

1. 1.54 ft.   **3.** 44° 25'.   **5.** 1926 ft.   **7.** 1250 ft.

9. 272 ft.   **11.** 3988 ft.   **13.** 1° 43.1'; 269.9 ft.

15. 925 ft.   **17.** 283 yd.

EXERCISE 12. PAGE 35

1. $1/a^6$.   **3.** 1/16.   **5.** 1/9.   **7.** $b^{\frac{1}{4}}$.   **9.** $8^{\frac{1}{4}}$.

11. $\log_3 N = 5$.   **13.** $\log_4 64 = 3$.   **15.** 25.   **17.** 216.

19. 1.   **21.** 1/16.   **23.** 2.   **25.** 9.

27. 2.   **29.** 1/2.   **31.** 3.   **33.** 3.

35. 1/2.   **37.** -4.   **39.** 4.   **41.** 10.

43. 27.   **45.** 1/6.   **47.** 25.   **49.** -1.

EXERCISE 13. PAGE 37

1. .7781.   **3.** 1.4771.   **5.** .3680.   **7.** .5441.   **9.** $-.1549$.

11. 1.4065.   **13.** .9542.   **15.** 1.4313.   **17.** .2817.   **19.** $-.4771$.

21. .3820.   **23.** $-.2720$.

EXERCISE 14. PAGE 39

1. Ch. $= 3$; mant. $= .95$.   **3.** Ch. $= 0$; mant. $= .312$.

5. Ch. $= -1$; mant. $= .8439$.   **7.** 3.   **9.** -3.

11. 0.   **13.** 4.   **15.** -5.   **17.** 2.   **19.** -3.

EXERCISE 15. PAGE 41

1. 2.29820.   **3.** 0.14270.   **5.** $8.04844 - 10$.

7. $9.40875 - 10$.   **9.** 4.77525.   **11.** $6.25527 - 10$.

13. $9.90363 - 10$.   **15.** 3.61993.   **17.** 6.00000.

19. .69897.   **21.** 17.83.   **23.** .2674.

25. 297.2.   **27.** .03866.   **29.** 48,460.   **31.** .003097.

33. 5979.   **35.** .1237.   **37.** 1.7259.   **39.** $8.2122 - 10$.

41. $7.8609 - 10$.   **43.** 0.9269.   **45.** $5.6990 - 10$.   **47.** 242.

49. .838.   **51.** 4.66.   **53.** .0000795.

55. .0005031; .01322.

EXERCISE 16. PAGE 44

1. 4.26865.   **3.** 0.67374.   **5.** 1.78956.   **7.** $9.47898 - 10$.

9. $9.87715 - 10$.   **11.** 0.72605.   **13.** $8.86666 - 10$.

15. 5.95274.   **17.** $6.89570 - 10$.   **19.** $8.78763 - 20$.

21. 6.11414.
27. 1.0782(10⁶).
33. .0087124.
39. 1.9400.
45. 0.8431.
51. .001332.
57. 3.787(10⁴).

23. 8.69902.
29. .013267.
35. 9.3400.
41. 7.2448 − 10.
47. 8.4074 − 10.
53. 846.4.

25. .45007.
31. 2.8641(10⁵).
37. .60003.
43. 3.7261.
49. 5.7853 − 10.
55. 1.392(10⁻⁶).

EXERCISE 17. PAGE 46

Note. Results obtained by use of **four-place** logarithms will be given in heavy black type in all problems in the exercises where *both four-place and five-place logarithms are possibilities.*

1. **24.91**; 24.909.
5. **.2009**; .20086.
9. **51.10**; 51.098.
13. **.1406**; .14061.
17. **5542**; 5544.4.
21. **27.61**; 27.609.
25. **1.580(10⁻⁵)**; 1.5802(10⁻⁵).
27. **38.96**; 38.955.
29. (a) **4.792(10⁵)**; 4.7922(10⁵): (b) **8.065**; 8.0662.
31. (a) **5.616(10⁻⁴)**; 5.6160(10)⁻⁴: (b) **− .1626**; − .16263.
33. 4143.6; .0048460.

3. **.07942**; .079410.
7. **− .007667**; − .0076660.
11. **.8142**; .81422.
15. **.003069**; .0030681.
19. **1.047(10⁴)**; 10,464.
23. **− 2.627(10⁻⁸)**; − 2.6266(10⁻⁸).

EXERCISE 18. PAGE 48

1. **5358**; 5359.5.
5. **56.19**; 56.206.
9. **5.418**; 5.4169.
13. **.4199**; .41984.
17. **.1266**; .12658.
21. **1.169**; 1.1688.

3. **3.125(10⁻⁵)**; 3.1256(10⁻⁵).
7. **23.05**; 23.048.
11. **.9500**; .94986.
15. **.1176**; .11759.
19. **5.176(10⁻⁵)**; 5.1759(10⁻⁵).
23. **.8630**; .86258.

EXERCISE 19. PAGE 49

1. **95.80**; 95.848.
5. **93.74**; 93.722.
9. **.08468**; .084666.
13. **45.02**; 45.023.
17. **− .136**; − .1366.
21. **.2739**; .27392.
25. **− 940.2**; − 939.88.
29. $14,897.
31. (a) **3702**; 3702.5: (b) **334.5**; 334.54.
33. **.9824**; .98225 (sec.).
35. By use of Table V, (a) 2.219(10⁴); (b) 3.222(10⁻⁵).

3. **16.72**; 16.700.
7. **.007638**; .0076403.
11. **11.67**; 11.673.
15. **.1952**; .19522.
19. **7.662**; 7.6607.
23. **2.702**; 2.7031.
27. **19.231**; 19.219.

EXERCISE 20. PAGE 51

1. 1.3820. **3.** − 11.972. **5.** .68123.
7. 4.913.* **9.** − 6.9873. **11.** 25.18. **13.** 1.5208(10⁷).
15. (a) .002752, .5105; (b) $T = 623.3°$.
17. (a) 11.067; (b) .8412.

EXERCISE 21. PAGE 52

1. **4.317;** 4.3176. **3.** **1.291;** 1.2911.
5. **2.303;** 2.3026. **7.** − **1.449;** − 1.4496.
9. − **14.2;** − 14.20.
11. (a) **8.382;** 8.3822; (b) **1.474;** 1.4743.

EXERCISE 22. PAGE 54

1. (a) .2136; (b) 9.3296 − 10. **3.** 9.96817 − 10.
5. 9.82283 − 10. **7.** 9.99336 − 10. **9.** 9.82678 − 10.
11. 9.71946 − 10. **13.** 0.10215. **15.** 9.66350 − 10.
17. 17° 21.0′. **19.** 6° 19.0′. **21.** 83° 23.0′.
23. 82° 12.0′. **25.** 17° 4.8′. **27.** 14° 11.4′.
29. 9.8344 − 10. **31.** 9.8472 − 10. **33.** 47° 40′.
35. 75° 4′.

EXERCISE 23. PAGE 57

1. $b =$ **21.34,** 21.347; $c =$ **26.50,** 26.498; 53° 40′.
3. $\alpha =$ **28° 30′,** 28° 30.2′; $\beta =$ **61° 30′,** 61° 29.8′; **.7523,** .75228.
5. $a =$ **.3396,** .33956; $b =$ **.5950,** .59451; 60° 17′.
7. $\alpha =$ **42° 18′,** 42° 18.1′; $\beta =$ **47° 42′,** 47° 41.9′; **.8518,** .85153.
9. $b = 2.6715$; $c = 3.1304$; 58° 35.3′.
11. $\alpha = 26° 41.8′$; $\beta = 63° 18.2′$; 818.02.
13. $b = 40.445$; $c = 58.982$; 46° 42.4′.
15. $k =$ **512.2,** 512.18; $\alpha = 55° 50′$.
17. $\alpha =$ **45° 55′,** 45° 54.0′; $\gamma =$ **88° 10′,** 88° 12.0′.
19. $a =$ **402.5,** 402.58; $c =$ **539.3,** 539.34; $\beta = 29° 40′$.
21. $a =$ **43.50,** 43.507; $\beta =$ **19° 54′,** 19° 53.6′; $\gamma =$ **131° 50′,** 131° 50.8′.

EXERCISE 24. PAGE 58

1. 160 ft. **3.** 37° 40′; pitch .385.
5. Side 28.2 ft.; radius 34.0 ft. **7.** 94.5 ft.
9. 1.215(10⁴). **11.** 31.8 ft.

EXERCISE 25. PAGE 61

1. Ver. 40.9 ft.; hor. 131.3 ft. **3.** 52° 58′. **5.** 321°.
7. 252° 13′. **9.** 264 mi. W; 280 mi. N.

* No greater refinement possible with Table VIII.

11. 67.4 mi. *N* 29° 2' *E;* azimuth 29° 2'.

13. Range 8644 yd.; bearing *N* 48° 34' *W*, or azimuth 311° 26'.

15. 193 mi. *N* 50° 29' *W;* azimuth 309° 31'.

17. 215 mi.; azimuth 319° 43'.

EXERCISE 26. PAGE 64

1. Hor. 84.7 lb.; ver. 128.4 lb.

3. 22.07 lb. *W;* 36.49 lb. *S.*

5. 281 mi. *S;* 103 mi. *E.*

7. 37.1 mi.; 28° 38'.

9. 674 lb.; *S* 18° 47' *W.*

11. 221 mi.; course is azimuth 186° 29'; drift angle 6° 29'.

13. 8.8 mi. per hr.; 27° 9' from downstream.

15. 113 mi. per hr.

EXERCISE 27. PAGE 66

1. 111 lb. pressure; 100 lb. to drag.

3. 1123 lb.   **5.** (*a*) 202 lb.; (*b*) 208 lb.

7. 218 lb.   **9.** 33.3 ft.   **11.** 210 lb.; *N* 41° 57' *E.*

EXERCISE 28. PAGE 69

1. 59°.   **3.** 87°.   **5.** 70°.   **7.** -1.280.   **9.** $-\frac{1}{2}\sqrt{2}$.

11. -2.924.   **13.** -1.483.   **15.** -1.963.   **17.** $\frac{1}{2}\sqrt{3}$.

19. -1.280.   **21.** 5.759.   **23.** -2.   **25.** 1.305.

27. 1.743.   **29.** $-.052$.   **31.** 1.600.   **33.** $-\frac{1}{2}\sqrt{2}$.

35. $-.675$.   **37.** $-.993$.   **39.** .7262; .72617.

41. -3.558; -3.5576.   **43.** 2.261; 2.2602.

45. $-.95314$.   **47.** $-.28662$.   **49.** $-.086978$.

51. $-.24889$.

EXERCISE 29. PAGE 72

1. $-\sin 25°$.   **3.** $-\tan 12°$.   **5.** $\cos 128°$.

7. $\sec 35°$.   **9.** $-\csc 148°$.   **11.** $-\tan 130°$.

13. $\cos \alpha$.   **15.** $\sec H$.   **17.** $\sin 79°$.

19. $\cos 105°$.   **23.** -1.   **25.** $-4\frac{1}{3}$.

27. $4b - 12b^2$.   **29.** $x - \frac{3}{4}x^2$.

EXERCISE 30. PAGE 76

Note. Only sine, cosine, tangent are listed, in that order.

1. $\cos 43°$, $\sin 43°$, $\cot 43°$.   **3.** $\cos 39°$, $-\sin 39°$, $-\cot 39°$.

5. $-\sin 38°$, $-\cos 38°$, $\tan 38°$.   **7.** $-\cos 27°$, $-\sin 27°$, $\cot 27°$.

9. $-\cos 34°$, $\sin 34°$, $-\cot 34°$.   **11.** $-\sin 37°$, $\cos 37°$, $-\tan 37°$.

13. $-\cos 34°$, $-\sin 34°$, $\cot 34°$.   **15.** $\cos 40°$, $\sin 40°$, $\cot 40°$.

17. $\cos 37°$, $-\sin 37°$, $-\cot 37°$.   **19.** $\cos 23°$, $-\sin 23°$, $-\cot 23°$.

21. $-\cos 22°$, $-\sin 22°$, $\cot 22°$.　　**23.** $\sin 12°$, $-\cos 12°$, $-\tan 12°$.

25. $\cos 39°$, $-\sin 39°$, $-\cot 39°$.　　**27.** $-\cos \theta$.　　**29.** $-\sec \theta$.

31. $\csc \theta$.　　**33.** $-\csc \theta$.　　**35.** $\sec \theta$.　　**37.** $-\sin \theta$.

39. $\csc \theta$.　　**41.** $-\csc \theta$.　　**43.** $\cot \theta$.　　**45.** $\cot \theta$.

47. $\tan \theta$.　　**49.** $\csc \theta$.

EXERCISE 31. PAGE 80

7. If x increases from $-180°$ to $-90°$, $\sin x$ decreases from 0 to -1; etc.

EXERCISE 32. PAGE 83

7. $-270°$, $90°$.　　**9.** $-270°$, $-90°$, $90°$, $270°$.

11. $-225°$, $-45°$, $135°$, $315°$.　　**13.** $-270°$, $-90°$, $90°$, $270°$.

15. $-180°$, $0°$, $180°$.　　**17.** $0°$.　　**19.** $-180°$, $0°$, $180°$.

21. $-90°$, $270°$.

23. $270°$; $45°$ and $225°$; $90°$; $90°$ and $270°$; $135°$ and $315°$.

EXERCISE 33. PAGE 85

1. $\frac{1}{6}\pi$.　　**3.** $\frac{1}{3}\pi$.　　**5.** $\frac{2}{3}\pi$.　　**7.** $\frac{5}{6}\pi$.　　**9.** $-\frac{1}{2}\pi$.

11. $\frac{4}{3}\pi$.　　**13.** $\frac{5}{3}\pi$.　　**15.** $\frac{5}{2}\pi$.　　**17.** $60°$.　　**19.** $20°$.

21. $210°$.　　**23.** $240°$.　　**25.** $84°$.　　**27.** $114° 35'$.

29. $143° 14'$.　　**35.** $\frac{2}{15}\pi$.　　**37.** $\frac{5}{6}\pi$.　　**39.** 1.

41. 0.　　**43.** 1.　　**45.** 0.　　**47.** -1.　　**49.** $-\sqrt{2}$.

51. $\frac{1}{3}\sqrt{3}$.　　**53.** $-\frac{1}{2}\sqrt{2}$.　　**55.** .97572.

57. 1.6281.　　**59.** .6693.　　**61.** 4.779.

63. $-\sin \theta$.　　**65.** $\sin \theta$.　　**67.** $\cos \theta$.

69. $-\cot \theta$.　　**71.** $-\sec \theta$.　　**73.** $\cos \theta$.

75. $\tan \theta$.　　**77.** $-\sin \theta$.

EXERCISE 34. PAGE 88

1. 23.0 ft.　　**3.** 40.0 ft.　　**5.** 34.1 in.　　**7.** 179 in.

9. 3.65 rad.　　**11.** 37.7 in.　　**13.** 15 ft.　　**15.** 1.43 rad.

17. 642 yd.　　**19.** 5027 ft. per min.

21. 5.50 in.　　**23.** Belt, 36.7 ft. per sec.; large wheel, 168 rev. per min.

25. .291 mi.

EXERCISE 37. PAGE 94

7. $\tan \theta$.

Note. Only $\sin \theta$, $\cos \theta$, $\tan \theta$ are given, in that order.

19. $\frac{4}{5}$, $\frac{3}{5}$, $\frac{4}{3}$.　　**21.** $-\frac{5}{13}$, $-\frac{12}{13}$, $\frac{5}{12}$.　　**23.** $-\frac{3}{5}$, $\frac{4}{5}$, $-\frac{3}{4}$.

25. $-\frac{24}{25}$, $\frac{7}{25}$, $-\frac{24}{7}$.　　**27.** $\frac{5}{13}$, $-\frac{12}{13}$, $-\frac{5}{12}$.

29. $\frac{2}{3}$, $-\dfrac{\sqrt{5}}{3}$, $-\dfrac{2}{\sqrt{5}}$.　　**31.** -18.　　**33.** $\frac{1}{6}(5 + 3\sqrt{5})$.

35. $\cos^2 x$.　　**37.** $1/\sin x \cos x$.　　**39.** $\sin^2 x$.

41. $\cos^2 x$.   **43.** $\sin^2 x - \cos^2 x$.   **45.** $\cos x/\sin x$.

Note. Only sine, cosine, tangent are listed, in that order.

47. $\tan x/\pm \sqrt{1 + \tan^2 x},\ 1/\pm \sqrt{1 + \tan^2 x},\ \tan x$.

49. $\pm \sqrt{1 - \cos^2 x},\ \cos x,\ \pm \sqrt{1 - \cos^2 x}/\cos x$.

51. $1/\csc x,\ \pm\sqrt{\csc^2 x - 1}/\csc x,\ 1/\pm \sqrt{\csc^2 x - 1}$.

EXERCISE 39. PAGE 100

1. $45°, 225°$.   **3.** $180°$.   **5.** $90°, 270°$.   **7.** No sol.

9. $30°, 150°$.   **11.** $60°, 240°$.   **13.** $240°, 300°$.

15. $90°, 270°$.   **17.** No sol.   **19.** $45°, 135°, 225°, 315°$.

21. $60°, 120°, 240°, 300°$.   **23.** $77° 20', 257° 20'$.

25. $28° 50', 151° 10'$.   **27.** $172° 40', 352° 40'$.

29. $25° 35', 154° 25'$.   **31.** $30°, 150°, 270°$.

33. $60°, 135°, 240°, 315°$.   **35.** $90°$.

37. $120°, 180°, 240°$.   **39.** $0°, 90°, 180°$.   **41.** $0°, 60°, 300°$.

43. $0°, 225°, 180°, 315°$.   **45.** $0°, 45°, 135°, 180°, 225°, 315°$.

47. $45°, 90°, 135°, 225°, 270°, 315°$.   **49.** $60°, 120°, 240°, 300°$.

51. $28° 26', 100° 14', 208° 26', 280° 14'$.

EXERCISE 40. PAGE 102

1. $90°, 210°, 330°$.   **3.** $270°$.   **5.** No sol.

7. $0°, 45°, 180°, 225°$.   **9.** $270°$.

11. $63° 26', 116° 34', 243° 26', 296° 34'$.

13. $60°, 120°, 240°, 300°$.   **15.** $30°, 210°$.

17. $60°, 180°, 300°$.   **19.** $210°, 270°, 330°$.

21. $0°, 180°$.   **23.** $60°, 300°$.   **25.** $0°, 270°$.

27. $0°, 90°$.   **29.** $180°$.   **31.** $30°, 150°$.

33. $60°, 120°, 240°, 300°$.   **35.** $45°, 135°, 225°, 315°$.

37. $60°, 120°, 240°, 300°$.   **39.** $233° 8'$.

EXERCISE 41. PAGE 103

5. $\sin \theta = \pm 1/\sqrt{1 + \cot^2 \theta}$.   **7.** $60°, 300°$.

9. $163° 20', 196° 40'$.   **11.** $35° 39', 215° 39'$.

13. $120°, 240°$.   **15.** $180°$.   **17.** $18° 26', 198° 26'$.

19. $60°, 90°, 240°, 270°$.   **21.** No sol.

23. $106° 20', 253° 40'$.   **37.** $90°, 270°$.

39. $0°, 45°, 135°, 180°, 225°, 315°$.

EXERCISE 42. PAGE 107

Note. Functions are given in the order sine, cosine, tangent.

9. $\frac{1}{4}(\sqrt{2} + \sqrt{6}),\ \frac{1}{4}(\sqrt{6} - \sqrt{2}),\ (2 + \sqrt{3})$.

11. $\frac{1}{4}(\sqrt{6} - \sqrt{2}),\ -\frac{1}{4}(\sqrt{2} + \sqrt{6}),\ (\sqrt{3} - 2)$.

13. $-\frac{1}{4}(\sqrt{2} + \sqrt{6}),\ \frac{1}{4}(\sqrt{6} - \sqrt{2}),\ -(2 + \sqrt{3})$.

15. $\frac{1}{2}(\cos\alpha + \sqrt{3}\sin\alpha)$.

17. $(1 + \tan\beta)/(1 - \tan\beta)$.

19. $\frac{1}{2}\sqrt{2}\,(\cos A + \sin A)$.

21. $(\tan\alpha - \sqrt{3})/(1 + \sqrt{3}\tan\alpha)$.　　　**23.** $-\sin\alpha$.

25. $-\sin x$.　　　　**27.** (a) $\frac{1}{2}(1 + \sqrt{2})$; (b) $\frac{1}{4}(\sqrt{2} + \sqrt{6})$.

29. 1.　　　　**31.** 1.　　　　**33.** $\sin(A - 10°)$.

35. $\cos 75°$.　　　　**37.** $\tan 3x$.

39. $(\alpha + \beta)$, $(\frac{56}{65}, \frac{33}{65}, \frac{56}{33})$; $(\alpha - \beta)$, $(\frac{16}{65}, \frac{63}{65}, \frac{16}{63})$.

41. $(\alpha + \beta)$, $(\frac{220}{221}, -\frac{21}{221}, -\frac{220}{21})$; $(\alpha - \beta)$, $(-\frac{140}{221}, \frac{171}{221}, -\frac{140}{171})$.

45. IV.　　　　**53.** $\dfrac{\tan B + 3}{\tan A \tan B + 3\tan B}$.

EXERCISE 43. PAGE 110

11. $\sin 130°$.　　　　**13.** $\cos 160°$.　　　　**15.** $1 + \cos 40°$.

17. $2\cos^2 \frac{1}{2}B$.　　　　**19.** $1 + \cos 80°$.　　　　**21.** $2\sin^2 \frac{1}{2}B$.

23. $2\cos^2 25°$.　　　　**25.** $\tan 76°$.　　　　**27.** $\cot^2 70°$.

43. $2\sin 2\alpha\cos 2\alpha$, $(\cos^2 2\alpha - \sin^2 2\alpha)$, $2\tan 2\alpha/(1 - \tan^2 2\alpha)$.

45. $\pm\sqrt{\dfrac{1 - \cos 8x}{2}}$, $\pm\sqrt{\dfrac{1 + \cos 8x}{2}}$, $\pm\sqrt{\dfrac{1 - \cos 8x}{1 + \cos 8x}}$.

47. $\pm\sqrt{\dfrac{1 - \cos x}{2}}$, $\pm\sqrt{\dfrac{1 + \cos x}{2}}$, $\pm\sqrt{\dfrac{1 - \cos x}{1 + \cos x}}$.

49. $2\sin \frac{3}{2}\theta\cos \frac{3}{2}\theta$, $(\cos^2 \frac{3}{2}\theta - \sin^2 \frac{3}{2}\theta)$, $2\tan \frac{3}{2}\theta/(1 - \tan^2 \frac{3}{2}\theta)$.

51. $3\sin x - 4\sin^3 x$.

53. $\pm 4\sin x\,(1 - 2\sin^2 x)\sqrt{1 - \sin^2 x}$.

EXERCISE 44. PAGE 112

5. $\sin 7\theta - \sin 3\theta$.　　　　**7.** $\cos 2\theta - \cos 8\theta$.

9. $\cos 8\theta - \cos 10\theta$.　　　　**11.** $\cos 6\theta - \cos 8\theta$.

13. $2\sin 20°\cos 40°$.　　　　**15.** $-2\sin 25°\sin 55°$.

17. $2\sin 35°\cos 5°$.　　　　**19.** $2\cos x\cos 3x$.

21. $-2\sin \frac{7}{2}y\sin \frac{3}{2}y$.　　　　**23.** $2\sin x\sin 3x$.

25. $-2\sin x\sin 2x$.　　　　**27.** $2\cos \frac{5}{2}y\cos \frac{11}{2}y$.

41. $\tan \frac{13}{2}A$.　　　　**43.** $-\cot 30°\cot 45°$.　　　　**45.** $\cot \frac{1}{2}(\beta - \alpha)$.

EXERCISE 46. PAGE 117

1. $0°, 90°, 180°, 270°$.　　　　**3.** $90°, 270°$.　　　　**5.** $15°, 165°, 195°, 345°$.

7. $135°, 315°$.　　　　**9.** $45°, 75°, 165°, 195°, 285°, 315°$.

11. $45°, 105°, 165°, 225°, 285°, 345°$.

13. $60°, 300°$.　　　　**15.** $360°$.　　　　**17.** $300°$.　　　　**19.** $0°, 180°$.

21. $15°, 105°, 195°, 285°$.　　　　**23.** $30°, 90°, 150°, 270°$.

25. $60°, 180°, 300°$.　　　　**27.** $0°, 180°$.　　　　**29.** $90°, 270°$.

31. $6° 10', 83° 50', 186° 10', 263° 50'$.

33. $5° 18', 95° 18', 185° 18', 275° 18'$.

35. $60°, 90°, 270°, 300°$.　　　　**37.** $0°, 60°, 300°$.

39. $22\frac{1}{2}°$, $67\frac{1}{2}°$, $112\frac{1}{2}°$, $157\frac{1}{2}°$, $202\frac{1}{2}°$, $247\frac{1}{2}°$, $292\frac{1}{2}°$, $337\frac{1}{2}°$.

41. $0°$, $60°$, $120°$, $180°$, $240°$, $300°$.

43. $45°$, $135°$, $225°$, $315°$.

45. $0°$, $90°$, $180°$, $270°$. **47.** $0°$. **49.** $180°$.

51. $0°$, $90°$, $180°$, $270°$.

53. $0°$, $45°$, $90°$, $135°$, $180°$, $225°$, $270°$, $315°$.

55. $0°$, $60°$, $120°$, $180°$, $240°$, $300°$.

57. $0°$, $60°$, $120°$, $135°$, $180°$, $240°$, $300°$, $315°$.

59. $120°$. **61.** $20° 54'$, $69° 6'$, $200° 54'$, $249° 6'$.

63. $0°$, $180°$. **65.** $0°$, $45°$, $90°$, $135°$, $210°$, $225°$, $270°$, $315°$, $330°$.

67. $0°$, $30°$, $90°$, $150°$, $180°$, $210°$, $270°$, $330°$.

69. $0°$, $90°$, $180°$, $210°$, $270°$, $330°$.

EXERCISE 47. PAGE 118

Note. Functions are given in the order sine, cosine, tangent.

1. $\frac{1}{4}(\sqrt{2} + \sqrt{6})$, $\frac{1}{4}(\sqrt{6} - \sqrt{2})$, $(2 + \sqrt{3})$.

5. (a) $\frac{84}{85}$, $-\frac{13}{85}$, $-\frac{84}{13}$; (b) $\frac{24}{25}$, $\frac{7}{25}$, $\frac{24}{7}$; (c) $\frac{1}{10}\sqrt{10}$, $\frac{3}{10}\sqrt{10}$, $\frac{1}{3}$.

7. $2 \cos \frac{3}{2}\alpha \cos \frac{1}{2}\alpha$; $2 \sin 40° \cos 5°$; $2 \sin \alpha \sin 4\alpha$.

19. $30°$, $60°$, $210°$, $240°$. **21.** $45°$, $135°$, $225°$, $315°$.

23. $0°$, $180°$. **25.** $30°$, $60°$, $120°$, $150°$, $210°$, $240°$, $300°$, $330°$.

27. $15°$, $75°$, $105°$, $165°$, $195°$, $255°$, $285°$, $345°$.

29. $\sin \alpha \cos \beta \cos \gamma + \cos \alpha \sin \beta \cos \gamma - \cos \alpha \cos \beta \sin \gamma + \sin \alpha \sin \beta \sin \gamma$.

31. $8 \cos^4 x - 8 \cos^2 x + 1$.

EXERCISE 48. PAGE 121

1. $165° 50'$. **3.** $142° 50'$. **5.** 2.646. **7.** 8.062.

9. 2. **11.** $48° 11'$. **13.** $42° 50'$. **15.** $104° 29'$.

17. $\alpha = 81° 47'$, $\beta = 38° 13'$, $\gamma = 60° 0'$.

19. $\alpha = 118° 47'$, $\beta = 23° 52'$, $\gamma = 37° 21'$. **21.** 15.7.

23. 9.89. **25.** 115 mi.

27. 173 mi. per hr.; inclined $40° 13'$ downward. **29.** 338 lb.

EXERCISE 49. PAGE 125

1. $a = c = 9.659$, $75° 0'$.

3. $b = 77.75$, $c = 77.83$, $71° 20'$.

5. $a = 13.10$, 13.100; $b = 19.35$, 19.345; $84° 0'$.

7. $b = .4290$, $.42897$; $c = .8744$, $.87436$; $102° 50'$.

9. $b = 7.518$, 7.5175; $c = 11.81$, 11.814; $132° 11'$.

11. $a = .1852$, $.18517$; $c = .4556$, $.45548$; $70° 50'$.

13. $b = .07758$, $.077598$; $c = .06650$, $.066503$; $58° 0'$.

15. $b = 35.408$, $c = 34.700$, $76° 10'$.

17. $b = 242.39$, $c = 339.55$, $123° 0'$.

19. $a = .0037760$, $b = .011107$, $80° 11'$.

21. 2.80 in.

EXERCISE 50. PAGE 129

1. $\alpha = 23°\,35'$, $\gamma = 126°\,25'$, 8.048.

3. $\alpha = 37°\,20'$, $\beta = 77°\,10'$, 606.5; or,
$\alpha = 11°\,40'$, $\beta = 102°\,50'$, 202.2.

5. $\alpha = 30°\,0'$, $\beta = 75°\,0'$, 3.622.

7. $\beta = 90°\,0'$, $\gamma = 58°\,40'$, .2136.

9. $\alpha = 23°\,35'$, $\beta = 7°\,45'$, 6.740.

11. $\alpha = $ **107° 40'**, 107° 39.5'; **23.55**, 23.555; $\gamma = $ **29° 50'**, 29° 50.5'.

13. No solution.

15. $\alpha = $ **81° 15'**, 81° 15.6'; $\gamma = $ **61° 52'**, 61° 51.4'; **.08442**, .084415.
Or, $\alpha = $ **24° 59'**, 24° 58.4'; $\gamma = $ **118° 8'**, 118° 8.6'; **.03607**, .036058.

17. $\beta = $ **31° 21'**, 31° 19.7'; $\gamma = $ **35° 19'**, 35° 20.3'; **6.551**, 6.5460.

19. $\beta = $ 30° 43.9', $\gamma = $ 125° 8.7', 2.5399; or,
$\beta = $ 149° 16.1', $\gamma = $ 6° 36.5', .35745.

21. $\alpha = $ 45° 46.7', $\gamma = $ 90° 0', 4.7484.

23. $\alpha = $ 37° 20.2', $\beta = $ 15° 20.8', .32385.

25. 57° 54'.   **27.** No sol.   **29.** One sol.

EXERCISE 51. PAGE 133

1. $\beta = $ **91° 26'**, 91° 25.9'; $\gamma = $ **20° 34'**, 20° 34.1'; **358.9**, 358.94.

3. $\alpha = $ **86° 13'**, 86° 13.4'; $\gamma = $ **21° 47'**, 21° 46.6'; **.8922**, .89216.

5. $\beta = $ **34° 8'**, 34° 7.7'; $\gamma = $ **76° 12'**, 76° 12.3'; **22.00**, 21.995.

7. $\alpha = $ **25° 41'**, 25° 41.0'; $\gamma = $ **33° 49'**, 33° 49.0'; **1538**, 1538.0.

9. $\beta = $ 88° 34.0', $\gamma = $ 30° 6.2', 277.57.

11. $\beta = $ 29° 15.6', $\gamma = $ 52° 27.6', 1.7029.

13. $\beta = $ 45° 35.1', $\gamma = $ 29° 18.5', 17,646.

15. $\beta = $ 76° 2', $\gamma = $ 53° 58', 23.7.

17. $\alpha = $ 11° 56', $\beta = $ 18° 4', 24.2.

19. 514.5 lb.

EXERCISE 52. PAGE 137

1. $\alpha = $ **27° 40'**, 27° 39.6'; $\beta = $ **45° 14'**, 45° 14.2'; $\gamma = $ **107° 6'**, 107° 6.2'.

3. $\alpha = $ **15° 44'**, 15° 44.0'; $\beta = $ **13° 4'**, 13° 3.0'; $\gamma = $ **151° 12'**, 151° 12.8'.

5. $\alpha = $ **16° 44'**, 16° 44.6'; $\beta = $ **90° 50'**, 90° 50.2'; $\gamma = $ **72° 26'**, 72° 25.0'.

7. $\alpha = $ 53° 1.8', $\beta = $ 86° 6.0', $\gamma = $ 40° 52.2'.

9. $\alpha = $ 27° 28.2', $\beta = $ 79° 57.2', $\gamma = $ 72° 34.4'.

11. $\alpha = $ 72° 23.4', $\beta = $ 56° 54.4', $\gamma = $ 50° 42.0'.

13. $\alpha = $ 96° 40.0', $\beta = $ 38° 4.6', $\gamma = $ 45° 15.6'.

15. **99° 36'**, 99° 35.6'.   **17.** **122° 2'**, 122° 0.6'.

19. $N\ 33°\,8'\ W$.

EXERCISE 53. PAGE 138

1. 20.   **3.** 2.25.   **5.** 41.57.   **7.** 89.44.

9. **7.552**, 7.5502.   **11.** **.02359**, .023594.

13. **.0001225**, .00012243.   **15.** **2.837**, 2.8371.

EXERCISE 54. PAGE 139

1. 39.94. **3.** 125° 6'. **5.** $\alpha = 6° 4'$, $\gamma = 9° 36'$, 31.71.

7. $a = 81.28$, $b = 90.60$, 63° 48'.

9. $\beta = 16° 36'$, $\gamma = 5° 44'$, 57.14. **11.** 14.80.

13. $\alpha = 27° 52'$, 27° 51.9'; $\beta = 71° 48'$, 71° 49.1'; **2.774**, 2.7734.

15. $\beta = 30° 41'$, 30° 40.8'; $\gamma = 124° 2'$, 124° 2.2'; **2861**, 2861.3.
Or, $\beta = 98° 45'$, 98° 45.2'; $\gamma = 55° 58'$, 55° 57.8'; **5542**, 5542.6.

17. $\alpha = 46° 10'$, 46° 10.2'; $\gamma = 60° 44'$, 60° 43.8'; **478.4**, 478.37.

19. $\alpha = 32° 33.2'$, $\beta = 104° 11.8'$, $\gamma = 43° 15.2'$.

21. $a = 1644.6$, $c = 446.69$, 101° 15'.

23. $N\ 51° 20'\ E.$ **25.** 6.128 mi. **27.** 1513 ft.

29. 58° 55'. **31.** 6562 yd. **33.** 1076 ft.

35. 89.08 ft. **37.** 27.6 lb.; $S\ 83° 16'\ E.$

39. Az., 339° 4'; 1.02(10⁴) yd.

41. Az. of track, 111° 6'; distance, 530 mi.

43. Az. of track, 136° 22'; groundspeed, 232.1 mi. per hr.; drift angle, 6° 22'.

45. 37.7 knots, $S\ 44° 4'\ E.$

47. 181.5 ft.; 151.3 ft.; 110.5 ft.

49. 68.0 ft.; 17.3 ft.; 60.5 ft.

59. Distance, $h \cos 2\alpha \cot \alpha$; equation, $k = h \cos 2\alpha$.

EXERCISE 55. PAGE 146

1. $y = \arctan \frac{3}{4}$. **3.** $\theta = \arcsin \frac{1}{3}$.

5. 0°, 360°, − 360°, − 720°; or, 0, 2π, − 2π, − 4π.

7. $\pm \frac{1}{2}\pi$, $\pm \frac{3}{2}\pi$. **9.** $\frac{1}{2}\pi$, $\frac{5}{2}\pi$, − $\frac{3}{2}\pi$, − $\frac{7}{2}\pi$.

11. $\frac{1}{2}\pi$, − $\frac{3}{2}\pi$, etc. **13.** $\pm \pi$, $\pm 3\pi$.

15. $\pm \frac{2}{3}\pi$, $\pm \frac{4}{3}\pi$. **17.** $\frac{5}{4}\pi$, $\frac{7}{4}\pi$, − $\frac{1}{4}\pi$, − $\frac{3}{4}\pi$.

19. $\frac{1}{3}\pi$, $\frac{4}{3}\pi$, − $\frac{2}{3}\pi$, − $\frac{5}{3}\pi$. **21.** $\frac{4}{3}\pi$, $\frac{5}{3}\pi$, − $\frac{1}{3}\pi$, − $\frac{2}{3}\pi$.

23. $\frac{3}{2}\pi$, − $\frac{1}{2}\pi$, etc. **25.** Does not exist.

27. $\pm \frac{1}{2}\pi$, $\pm \frac{3}{2}\pi$. **29.** $\frac{4}{3}\pi$, $\frac{5}{3}\pi$, − $\frac{1}{3}\pi$, − $\frac{2}{3}\pi$.

31. 11° 50', 168° 10'. **33.** 119° 30', 240° 30'.

35. 32° 40', 212° 40'. **37.** $\frac{3}{4}$. **39.** 2.

41. − $\frac{1}{4}$. **43.** $\frac{3}{4}$. **45.** $\frac{5}{13}$. **47.** $\frac{8}{17}$.

49. − $\frac{3}{4}$. **51.** $\pm \frac{12}{13}$. **53.** x. **55.** $1/x$.

57. $\pm \sqrt{1 + z^2}$. **59.** $\pm 1/\sqrt{1 + z^2}$.

61. $x = \arcsin \frac{2}{3}$. **63.** $x = \arccos (- \frac{3}{5})$.

65. $x = \arcsin (- \frac{1}{2})$ and $x = \arcsin \frac{1}{3}$.

67. $x = \arctan \frac{1}{5}$ and $x = \arctan \frac{4}{3}$.

EXERCISE 56. PAGE 147

Note. Answers will be given only in radian measure.

1. $\frac{1}{6}\pi$. **3.** $\frac{1}{6}\pi$. **5.** 0. **7.** $\frac{1}{6}\pi$.

9. − $\frac{1}{2}\pi$. **11.** − $\frac{1}{4}\pi$. **13.** $\frac{3}{4}\pi$. **15.** − $\frac{1}{4}\pi$.

17. $-\frac{1}{6}\pi$.

19. .37 rad.; 21° 12.0′.

21. .92 rad.; 52° 42.7′.

23. 2.30 rad.; 131° 52.3′.

25. $\frac{1}{2}\sqrt{3}$.

27. $\frac{1}{2}\sqrt{3}$.

29. $-\frac{3}{4}$.

31. $-\frac{5}{12}$.

33. $\frac{1}{2}\sqrt{2}$.

35. $\frac{24}{25}$.

37. $-\frac{5}{12}$.

39. $-\frac{3}{4}$.

41. $\frac{1}{3}\sqrt{3}$.

43. $-\frac{1}{2}\sqrt{2}$.

45. $\frac{24}{25}$.

47. $-\frac{3}{4}$.

49. 110°.

51. $\frac{2}{5}\sqrt{5}$.

53. $-\frac{1}{5}$.

55. $\frac{16}{65}$.

57. $x\sqrt{1-y^2} - y\sqrt{1-x^2}$.

59. $3xy + \sqrt{(1-x^2)(1-9y^2)}$.

61. $2x\sqrt{1-x^2}$.

63. $(1-y)/(1+y)$.

65. $\frac{1}{2}(1-x)$.

67. $2x/(1-x^2)$.

69. $\sqrt{\dfrac{1+\sqrt{1-x^2}}{2}}$.

EXERCISE 57. PAGE 149

5. $\frac{1}{2}\sqrt{2}$.

7. $\frac{1}{2}$; -1.

9. $\frac{1}{2}$.

11. No solution.

EXERCISE 58. PAGE 152

1. -1.

3. 1.

5. $-i$.

7. $2+i$.

9. -9.

11. -11.

13. $14-8i$.

15. $\frac{7}{2} - \frac{7}{2}i$.

17. $\frac{8}{17} - \frac{32}{17}i$.

EXERCISE 60. PAGE 154

1. $\frac{5}{2} + \frac{5}{2}i\sqrt{3}$.

3. $-\frac{3}{2}\sqrt{3} - \frac{3}{2}i$.

5. 4.

7. -5.

9. By Table VII, $-.3584 - .9336i$.

11. $6\sqrt{2}(\cos 45° + i \sin 45°)$.

13. $2(\cos 120° + i \sin 120°)$.

15. $3(\cos 90° + i \sin 90°)$.

17. $2(\cos 270° + i \sin 270°)$.

19. $5(\cos 90° + i \sin 90°)$.

21. $\sqrt{85}(\cos 130° 36′ + i \sin 130° 36′)$.

23. $3\sqrt{2}(\cos 315° + i \sin 315°)$; conj., $3\sqrt{2}(\cos 45° + i \sin 45°)$.

EXERCISE 61. PAGE 156

1. $3 + 3i\sqrt{3}$.

3. $6(\cos 20° + i \sin 20°)$.

5. $4 + 4i\sqrt{3}$.

7. $243(\cos 200° + i \sin 200°)$.

9. -324.

11. $16 + 16i\sqrt{3}$.

13. $-1 + i\sqrt{3}$.

15. $12(\cos 130° + i \sin 130°)$.

EXERCISE 62. PAGE 158

1. $2(\cos 20° + i \sin 20°)$, $2(\cos 92° + i \sin 92°)$, etc.

3. $10(\cos 100° + i \sin 100°)$, $10(\cos 220° + i \sin 220°)$, etc.

5. $3(\cos 20° + i \sin 20°)$, $3(\cos 110° + i \sin 110°)$, etc.

7. 1, $(-\frac{1}{2} \pm \frac{1}{2}i\sqrt{3})$.

9. $(\frac{1}{2} \pm \frac{1}{2}i\sqrt{3})$, -1.

11. $(\frac{1}{2}\sqrt{2} + \frac{1}{2}i\sqrt{2})$, $(-\frac{1}{2}\sqrt{2} - \frac{1}{2}i\sqrt{2})$.

13. $2(\cos 36° + i \sin 36°)$, $2(\cos 108° + i \sin 108°)$, etc.

15. $(\frac{1}{2}\sqrt{3} + \frac{1}{2}i)$, $(-\frac{1}{2}\sqrt{3} + \frac{1}{2}i)$, $-i$.

17. ± 3, $\pm 3i$.

19. $2(\cos 78.75° + i \sin 78.75°)$, $2(\cos 168.75° + i \sin 168.75°)$, etc.

21. $(\sqrt{3} \pm i)$, $\pm 2i$, $(-\sqrt{3} \pm i)$.

23. 1, $(\cos 40° + i \sin 40°)$, $(\cos 80° + i \sin 80°)$, $\cdots$, $(\cos 320° + i \sin 320°)$.

EXERCISE 63. PAGE 160

Note. Where all trigonometric functions are requested, they are given in the order sine, cosine, tangent, cosecant, secant, cotangent.

5. $-\frac{8}{17}, \frac{15}{17}, -\frac{8}{15}, -\frac{17}{8}, \frac{17}{15}, -\frac{15}{8}$.

7. $0, -1, 0, \infty, -1, \infty$.　　　　　**11.** 1.931.　　　　　**13.** .7660.

15. 1.963.　　　　**17.** $-.4226$.　　　　**21.** $-\frac{1}{2}, -\frac{1}{2}\sqrt{3}, \frac{1}{3}\sqrt{3}, -2, -\frac{2}{3}\sqrt{3}, \sqrt{3}$.

23. $-\frac{1}{2}\sqrt{2}, -\frac{1}{2}\sqrt{2}, 1, -\sqrt{2}, -\sqrt{2}, 1$.

25. $-\frac{1}{2}\sqrt{3}, -\frac{1}{2}, \sqrt{3}, -\frac{2}{3}\sqrt{3}, -2, \frac{1}{3}\sqrt{3}$.

27. (a) See Prob. 25 with signs for quad. II. (b) See Prob. 23, with signs for quad. III.

29. $a = .4138$, $c = .6111$, $47° 24'$.　　　　**31.** $b = 66.085$, $c = 70.655$, $20° 43.3'$.

33. $a = .4138$, .41379; $c = .6114$, .61132; $47° 24'$.

35. $b = 661.0$, 660.86; $c = 706.7$, 706.57; $20° 43'$, $20° 43.3'$.

37. $30°, 150°$.　　　　**39.** $45°, 135°, 225°, 315°$.

41. $90°, 270°$.　　　　**43.** $45°, 135°$.　　　　**45.** $135°, 225°$.

47. $29° 20', 150° 40'$.　　　　**49.** $154° 40', 334° 40'$.

51. $90°, 270°$.　　　　**53.** $90°, 270°$.　　　　**55.** $270°$.

61. 81.　　　　**63.** $\frac{1}{16}$.　　　　**65.** 19.24, 19.248.

67. 1.451, 1.4514.　　　　**69.** $-.03928, -.039275$.

71. .0008776.　　　　**73.** 3.　　　　**81.** (a) $\frac{65}{36}\pi$; (b) 2.803.

85. $N\ 25° 56'\ E$.　　　　**87.** $-\frac{1}{4}(\sqrt{2} + \sqrt{6})$.

89. $-\frac{1}{2}$.　　　　**91.** $2 + \sqrt{3}$.　　　　**101.** $60°, 180°, 300°$.

103. $0°, 22\frac{1}{2}°, 67\frac{1}{2}°, 112\frac{1}{2}°, 157\frac{1}{2}°, 180°, 202\frac{1}{2}°, 247\frac{1}{2}°, 292\frac{1}{2}°, 337\frac{1}{2}°$.

107. $78° 28'$.

109. $\alpha = 82° 49'$, $\beta = 55° 46'$, $\gamma = 41° 25'$.　　　　**111.** $\alpha = 27° 42'$, $\beta = 83° 0'$, .3155.

113. $36° 52'$.　　　　**115.** $-\tan 38°$.　　　　**117.** $-\sec 27°$.

119. $-\cot 40°$.　　　　**121.** $-\csc 5°$.

123. $-\tan x$.　　　　**125.** $-\cos x$.　　　　**127.** $-\csc x$.

129. 2925.　　　　**131.** 48.92, 48.924.　　　　**133.** $\frac{1}{6}\pi$.

135. $-\frac{2}{3}$.　　　　**137.** $\frac{1}{5}$.　　　　**147.** No sol.

149. $7° 16', 67° 16', 127° 16', 187° 16', 247° 16', 307° 16'$.

151. $90°, 180°$.　　　　**153.** $\frac{5}{12}$.　　　　**155.** $\sqrt{1-x^2}/x$.　　　　**159.** $3, -2$.

161. Ver., 67.7 lb.; hor., 205.1 lb.　　　　**163.** $33\frac{1}{3}$.

EXERCISE 64. PAGE 169

1. $\overline{AD} = 1193$ yd.; (*course AD*) $= 1188$ yd.; incl. $= 5° 8'$.

3. Diff. in elev. is $+ 4$ yd.; $\overline{AE} = 941$ yd.;
(*course AE*) $= 941$ yd.; bearing $N\ 73° 50'\ E$.
There is less than 1 yd. difference between $\overline{AE}$ and *course AE*.

EXERCISE 66. PAGE 184

1. $b = \mathbf{50° 3'}$, 50° 3.0'; $\alpha = \mathbf{52° 51'}$, 52° 50.9'; $\beta = \mathbf{59° 13'}$, 59° 13.0'.

3. $a = \mathbf{58° 5'}$, 58° 4.1'; $b = \mathbf{81° 47'}$, 81° 47.2'; $\beta = \mathbf{83° 1'}$, 83° 1.0'.

5. $c = \mathbf{85° 37'}$, 85° 37.1'; $\alpha = \mathbf{85° 32'}$, 85° 32.3'; $\beta = \mathbf{45° 36'}$, 45° 36.2'.

7. $a = \mathbf{37° 45'}$, 37° 45.0'; $c = \mathbf{51° 38'}$, 51° 36.9'; $\alpha = \mathbf{51° 22'}$, 51° 21.4'.
Or, $a = \mathbf{142° 15'}$, 142° 15.0'; $c = \mathbf{128° 22'}$, 128° 23.1'; $\alpha = \mathbf{128° 38'}$, 128° 38.6'.

9. $c = \mathbf{99° 38'}$, 99° 38.4'; $\alpha = \mathbf{62° 59'}$, 62° 58.7'; $\beta = \mathbf{108° 10'}$, 108° 10.7'.

11. $a = \mathbf{47° 31'}$, 47° 32.0'; $b = \mathbf{104° 19'}$, 104° 19.4'; $c = \mathbf{99° 37'}$, 99° 36.9'.

13. No sol.

15. $b = \mathbf{119° 49'}$, 119° 49.0'; $c = \mathbf{72° 23'}$, 72° 22.8'; $\alpha = \mathbf{123° 39'}$, 123° 39.3'.

17. $a = \mathbf{122° 28'}$, 122° 27.2'; $b = \mathbf{163° 30'}$, 163° 28.8'; $c = \mathbf{59° 2'}$, 59° 2.4'.

19. $b = \mathbf{14° 8'}$, 14° 7.8'; $c = \mathbf{113° 32'}$, 113° 33.0'; $\beta = \mathbf{15° 27'}$, 15° 26.7'.
Or, $b = \mathbf{165° 52'}$, 165° 52.2'; $c = \mathbf{66° 28'}$, 66° 27.0'; $\beta = \mathbf{164° 33'}$, 164° 33.3'.

21. $c = 90°$, $\alpha = 36°$, $\beta = 90°$.

23. No sol. **25.** $a = 56° 46.8'$, $b = 44° 12.8'$, $c = 66° 52.8'$.

27. $b = 25° 58.0'$, $c = 139° 7.6'$, $\beta = 41° 59.8'$; or,
$b = 154° 2.0'$, $c = 40° 52.4'$, $\beta = 138° 0.2'$.

29. $a = 27° 33.3'$, $b = 134° 37.7'$, $\beta = 114° 32.6'$. **31.** $a = c = 90°$; $b = \beta$.

33. $a = \alpha = 90°$ and $b = \beta$; or, $b = \beta = 90°$ and $a = \alpha$. **35.** $\beta = a = c = 90°$.

EXERCISE 67. PAGE 185

1. $\alpha = \beta = \mathbf{60° 26'}$, 60° 25.6'; $\gamma = \mathbf{147° 40'}$, 147° 40.6'.

3. $a = \mathbf{72° 18'}$, 72° 18.2'; $\beta = \gamma = \mathbf{57° 12'}$, 57° 12.6'.

5. $a = \mathbf{48° 48'}$, 48° 47.6'; $b = \mathbf{37° 32'}$; $\alpha = \mathbf{85° 22'}$, 85° 22.6'.

7. $a = \mathbf{119° 52'}$, 119° 52.0'; $c = \mathbf{126° 50'}$, 126° 50.7'; $\beta = \mathbf{115° 29'}$, 115° 29.3'.

9. $a = \mathbf{104° 18'}$, 104° 17.2'; $\beta = \mathbf{47° 46'}$, 47° 46.1'; $\gamma = \mathbf{129° 18'}$, 129° 18.4'.

11. $b = \mathbf{58° 31'}$, 58° 31.5'; $\alpha = \mathbf{18° 13'}$, 18° 13.8'; $\gamma = \mathbf{114° 21'}$, 114° 20.3'.

13. $a = 70° 18.8'$, $\gamma = 102° 13.4'$.

EXERCISE 68. PAGE 192

1. $c = 68° 18'$, $\alpha = 57° 54'$, $\beta = 22° 6'$.

3. $b = 74° 24'$, $\alpha = 57° 36'$, $\gamma = 115° 8'$.

5. $\alpha = 72° 46'$, $\beta = 37° 16'$, $\gamma = 105° 16'$.

7. $a = 124° 49'$, $b = 73° 25'$, $c = 94° 38'$.

EXERCISE 70. PAGE 195

1. $\alpha = \mathbf{45° 16'}$, 45° 14.8'; $\beta = \mathbf{58° 24'}$, 58° 23.6'; $\gamma = \mathbf{94° 52'}$, 94° 52.6'.

3. $a = \mathbf{124° 50'}$, 124° 49.0'; $b = \mathbf{73° 26'}$, 73° 25.4'; $c = \mathbf{94° 38'}$, 94° 37.4'.

5. $\alpha = \mathbf{72° 46'}$, 72° 45.8'; $\beta = \mathbf{37° 16'}$, 37° 16.4'; $\gamma = \mathbf{105° 16'}$, 105° 15.6'.

7. $a = \mathbf{107° 54'}$, 107° 53.4'; $b = \mathbf{68° 4'}$, 68° 4.2'; $c = \mathbf{64° 10'}$, 64° 9.0'.

9. $\alpha = 48° 35.0'$, $\beta = 68° 36.8'$, $\gamma = 99° 8.2'$.

11. $a = 137° 50.8'$, $b = 80° 58.0'$, $c = 90° 52.2'$.

EXERCISE 71. PAGE 197

1. $c = 78° 46'$, $78° 45.4'$; $\alpha = 105° 36'$, $105° 36.0'$; $\beta = 44° 0'$, $44° 0.0'$.
3. $a = 58° 49'$, $58° 49.2'$; $b = 34° 47'$, $34° 46.4'$; $\gamma = 36° 22'$, $36° 22.6'$.
5. $a = 108° 10'$, $108° 9.8'$; $\beta = 123° 59'$, $123° 58.7'$; $\gamma = 72° 43'$, $72° 42.7'$.
7. $b = 51° 25'$, $51° 24.6'$; $c = 91° 51'$, $91° 51.8'$; $\alpha = 53° 16'$, $53° 18.8'$.
9. $b = 72° 24.0'$, $\alpha = 129° 14.7'$, $\gamma = 68° 35.5'$.
11. $a = 108° 54.8'$, $\beta = 103° 0.7'$, $\gamma = 138° 47.3'$.

EXERCISE 72. PAGE 199

1. Two.   5. None.
7. $c = 21° 46'$, $21° 43.6'$; $\alpha = 115° 58'$, $115° 59.2'$; $\gamma = 26° 56'$, $26° 54.4'$.
Or, $c = 54° 50'$, $54° 49.8'$; $\alpha = 64° 2'$, $64° 0.8'$; $\gamma = 87° 56'$, $87° 54.0'$.
9. $a = 42° 48'$, $42° 49.0'$; $\alpha = 41° 48'$, $41° 48.4'$; $\beta = 38° 20'$, $38° 20.5'$.
11. No solution.   13. No solution.

EXERCISE 73. PAGE 200

1. $1.780(10^4)$ sq. ft.   3. $6.16(10^3)$ sq. ft.

EXERCISE 74. PAGE 200

1. $b = 110° 36'$, $110° 35.8'$; $\alpha = 129° 58'$, $129° 57.2'$; $\gamma = 92° 32'$, $92° 31.2'$.
3. $a = 106° 50'$, $106° 48.4'$; $b = 53° 26'$, $53° 25.2'$; $c = 73° 26'$, $73° 24.0'$.
5. No solution.
7. $a = 155° 2'$, $155° 4.8'$; $c = 149° 11'$, $149° 11.6'$; $\alpha = 149° 44'$, $149° 46.0'$.
9. $b = 58° 51'$, $58° 51.2'$; $c = 139° 16'$, $139° 16.2'$; $\gamma = 132° 10'$, $132° 8.6'$.
Or, $b = 121° 9'$, $121° 8.8'$; $c = 60° 26'$, $60° 22.4'$; $\gamma = 81° 6'$, $81° 3.6'$.

EXERCISE 75. PAGE 204

Note. Each direction is specified by giving its azimuth.
1. 3144 mi.; $53° 49'$; $291° 53'$.   3. 4755 mi.; $306° 0'$; $55° 35'$.
5. 4151 mi.; $300° 34'$; $45° 32'$.   7. 2223 mi.; $260° 22'$; $61° 15'$.
9. 6447 mi.; $55° 46'$; $240° 18'$.   11. 2229 mi.; $69° 44'$; $281° 34'$.
13. 1343 mi.; $266° 55'$; $58° 37'$.   15. 4039 mi.; $59° 26'$; $323° 23'$.
17. 2466 mi.; $46° 30'$; $266° 16'$.   19. 2774 mi.; $308° 30'$; $69° 35'$.
21. 4047 mi.; $34° 31'$; $310° 21'$ 23. 1125 mi.; $106° 39'$; $294° 47'$.
27. Great-circle distance is 12 mi. shorter.

EXERCISE 76. PAGE 211

1. 8:36 A.M.   3. 5:07 A.M.; bearing (azimuth), $70° 41'$.
5. Longest, 21 hr. and 0 min.; bearing, $20° 33'$.
   Shortest, 3 hr. and 0 min.; bearing, $159° 27'$.
7. $47° 48'$.   9. $53° 52'$.   11. Alt., $54° 48'$; az., $120° 58'$.
13. Alt., $26° 25'$; az., $345° 44'$.   15. Alt., $60° 26'$; az., $79° 25'$.

Numbers Refer to Pages

I. SQUARES AND SQUARE ROOTS:* 1—200

N	N²	√N	N	N²	√N	N	N²	√N	N	N²	√N
1	1	1.000	51	2,601	7.141	101	10,201	10.050	151	22,801	12.288
2	4	1.414	52	2,704	7.211	102	10,404	10.100	152	23,104	12.329
3	9	1.732	53	2,809	7.280	103	10,609	10.149	153	23,409	12.369
4	16	2.000	54	2,916	7.348	104	10,816	10.198	154	23,716	12.410
5	25	2.236	55	3,025	7.416	105	11,025	10.247	155	24,025	12.450
6	36	2.449	56	3,136	7.483	106	11,236	10.296	156	24,336	12.490
7	49	2.646	57	3,249	7.550	107	11,449	10.344	157	24,649	12.530
8	64	2.828	58	3,364	7.616	108	11,664	10.392	158	24,964	12.570
9	81	3.000	59	3,481	7.681	109	11,881	10.440	159	25,281	12.610
10	100	3.162	60	3,600	7.746	110	12,100	10.488	160	25,600	12.649
11	121	3.317	61	3,721	7.810	111	12,321	10.536	161	25,921	12.689
12	144	3.464	62	3,844	7.874	112	12,544	10.583	162	26,244	12.728
13	169	3.606	63	3,969	7.937	113	12,769	10.630	163	26,569	12.767
14	196	3.742	64	4,096	8.000	114	12,996	10.677	164	26,896	12.806
15	225	3.873	65	4,225	8.062	115	13,225	10.724	165	27,225	12.845
16	256	4.000	66	4,356	8.124	116	13,456	10.770	166	27,556	12.884
17	289	4.123	67	4,489	8.185	117	13,689	10.817	167	27,889	12.923
18	324	4.243	68	4,624	8.246	118	13,924	10.863	168	28,224	12.962
19	361	4.359	69	4,761	8.307	119	14,161	10.909	169	28,561	13.000
20	400	4.472	70	4,900	8.367	120	14,400	10.954	170	28,900	13.038
21	441	4.583	71	5,041	8.426	121	14,641	11.000	171	29,241	13.077
22	484	4.690	72	5,184	8.485	122	14,884	11.045	172	29,584	13.115
23	529	4.796	73	5,329	8.544	123	15,129	11.091	173	29,929	13.153
24	576	4.899	74	5,476	8.602	124	15,376	11.136	174	30,276	13.191
25	625	5.000	75	5,625	8.660	125	15,625	11.180	175	30,625	13.229
26	676	5.099	76	5,776	8.718	126	15,876	11.225	176	30,976	13.266
27	729	5.196	77	5,929	8.775	127	16,129	11.269	177	31,329	13.304
28	784	5.292	78	6,084	8.832	128	16,384	11.314	178	31,684	13.342
29	841	5.385	79	6,241	8.888	129	16,641	11.358	179	32,041	13.379
30	900	5.477	80	6,400	8.944	130	16,900	11.402	180	32,400	13.416
31	961	5.568	81	6,561	9.000	131	17,161	11.446	181	32,761	13.454
32	1,024	5.657	82	6,724	9.055	132	17,424	11.489	182	33,124	13.491
33	1,089	5.745	83	6,889	9.110	133	17,689	11.533	183	33,489	13.528
34	1,156	5.831	84	7,056	9.165	134	17,956	11.576	184	33,856	13.565
35	1,225	5.916	85	7,225	9.220	135	18,225	11.619	185	34,225	13.601
36	1,296	6.000	86	7,396	9.274	136	18,496	11.662	186	34,596	13.638
37	1,369	6.083	87	7,569	9.327	137	18,769	11.705	187	34,969	13.675
38	1,444	6.164	88	7,744	9.381	138	19,044	11.747	188	35,344	13.711
39	1,521	6.245	89	7,921	9.434	139	19,321	11.790	189	35,721	13.748
40	1,600	6.325	90	8,100	9.487	140	19,600	11.832	190	36,100	13.784
41	1,681	6.403	91	8,281	9.539	141	19,881	11.874	191	36,481	13.820
42	1,764	6.481	92	8,464	9.592	142	20,164	11.916	192	36,864	13.856
43	1,849	6.557	93	8,649	9.644	143	20,449	11.958	193	37,249	13.892
44	1,936	6.633	94	8,836	9.695	144	20,736	12.000	194	37,636	13.928
45	2,025	6.708	95	9,025	9.747	145	21,025	12.042	195	38,025	13.964
46	2,116	6.782	96	9,216	9.798	146	21,316	12.083	196	38,416	14.000
47	2,209	6.856	97	9,409	9.849	147	21,609	12.124	197	38,809	14.036
48	2,304	6.928	98	9,604	9.899	148	21,904	12.166	198	39,204	14.071
49	2,401	7.000	99	9,801	9.950	149	22,201	12.207	199	39,601	14.107
50	2,500	7.071	100	10,000	10.000	150	22,500	12.247	200	40,000	14.142
N	N²	√N	N	N²	√N	N	N²	√N	N	N²	√N

* A more extensive table is found commencing on page 115.

II. THREE-PLACE LOGARITHMS OF NUMBERS

N	Log N	N	Log N
1.0	.000	5.5	.740
1.1	.041	5.6	.748
1.2	.079	5.7	.756
1.3	.114	5.8	.763
1.4	.146	5.9	.771
1.5	.176	6.0	.778
1.6	.204	6.1	.785
1.7	.230	6.2	.792
1.8	.255	6.3	.799
1.9	.279	6.4	.806
2.0	.301	6.5	.813
2.1	.322	6.6	.820
2.2	.342	6.7	.826
2.3	.362	6.8	.833
2.4	.380	6.9	.839
2.5	.398	7.0	.845
2.6	.415	7.1	.851
2.7	.431	7.2	.857
2.8	.447	7.3	.863
2.9	.462	7.4	.869
3.0	.477	7.5	.875
3.1	.491	7.6	.881
3.2	.505	7.7	.886
3.3	.519	7.8	.892
3.4	.531	7.9	.898
3.5	.544	8.0	.903
3.6	.556	8.1	.908
3.7	.568	8.2	.914
3.8	.580	8.3	.919
3.9	.591	8.4	.924
4.0	.602	8.5	.929
4.1	.613	8.6	.935
4.2	.623	8.7	.940
4.3	.633	8.8	.944
4.4	.643	8.9	.949
4.5	.653	9.0	.954
4.6	.663	9.1	.959
4.7	.672	9.2	.964
4.8	.681	9.3	.968
4.9	.690	9.4	.973
5.0	.699	9.5	.978
5.1	.708	9.6	.982
5.2	.716	9.7	.987
5.3	.724	9.8	.991
5.4	.732	9.9	.996
5.5	.740	1.00	1.000
N	Log N	N	Log N

III. THREE-PLACE LOGARITHMS OF FUNCTIONS

→	L Sin *	L Tan *	L Cot	L Cos *	
0°	——	——	——	10.000	90°
1°	8.242	8.242	1.758	10.000	89°
2°	.543	.543	.457	10.000	88°
3°	.719	.719	.281	9.999	87°
4°	.844	.845	.155	.999	86°
5°	8.940	8.942	1.058	9.998	85°
6°	9.019	9.022	0.978	9.998	84°
7°	.086	.089	.911	.997	83°
8°	.144	.148	.852	.996	82°
9°	.194	.200	.800	.995	81°
10°	9.240	9.246	0.754	9.993	80°
11°	9.281	9.289	0.711	9.992	79°
12°	.318	.327	.673	.990	78°
13°	.352	.363	.637	.989	77°
14°	.384	.397	.603	.987	76°
15°	9.413	9.428	0.572	9.985	75°
16°	9.440	9.458	0.543	9.983	74°
17°	.466	.485	.515	.981	73°
18°	.490	.512	.488	.978	72°
19°	.513	.537	.463	.976	71°
20°	9.534	9.561	0.439	9.973	70°
21°	9.554	9.584	0.416	9.970	69°
22°	.574	.606	.394	.967	68°
23°	.592	.628	.372	.964	67°
24°	.609	.649	.351	.961	66°
25°	9.626	9.669	0.331	9.957	65°
26°	9.642	9.688	0.312	9.954	64°
27°	.657	.707	.293	.950	63°
28°	.672	.726	.274	.946	62°
29°	.686	.744	.256	.942	61°
30°	9.699	9.761	0.239	9.938	60°
31°	9.712	9.779	0.221	9.933	59°
32°	.724	.796	.204	.928	58°
33°	.736	.813	.187	.924	57°
34°	.748	.829	.171	.919	56°
35°	9.759	9.845	0.155	9.913	55°
36°	9.769	9.861	0.139	9.908	54°
37°	.779	.877	.123	.902	53°
38°	.789	.893	.107	.897	52°
39°	.799	.908	.092	.891	51°
40°	9.808	9.924	0.076	9.884	50°
41°	9.817	9.939	0.061	9.878	49°
42°	.826	.954	.046	.871	48°
43°	.834	.970	.030	.864	47°
44°	.842	.985	.015	.857	46°
45°	9.849	10.000	0.000	9.849	45°
	L Cos *	L Cot *	L Tan	L Sin *	←

* Subtract 10 from each entry in this column.

IV. THREE-PLACE VALUES OF TRIGONOMETRIC FUNCTIONS AND DEGREES IN RADIAN MEASURE

Rad.	Deg.	Sin	Tan	Sec	Csc	Cot	Cos	Deg.	Rad.
.000	0°	.000	.000	1.000	——	——	1.000	90°	1.571
.017	1°	.017	.017	1.000	57.30	57.29	1.000	89°	1.553
.035	2°	.035	.035	1.001	28.65	28.64	0.999	88°	1.536
.052	3°	.052	.052	1.001	19.11	19.08	.999	87°	1.518
.070	4°	.070	.070	1.002	14.34	14.30	.998	86°	1.501
.087	5°	.087	.087	1.004	11.47	11.43	.996	85°	1.484
.105	6°	.105	.105	1.006	9.567	9.514	.995	84°	1.466
.122	7°	.122	.123	1.008	8.206	8.144	.993	83°	1.449
.140	8°	.139	.141	1.010	7.185	7.115	.990	82°	1.431
.157	9°	.156	.158	1.012	6.392	6.314	.988	81°	1.414
.175	10°	.174	.176	1.015	5.759	5.671	.985	80°	1.396
.192	11°	.191	.194	1.019	5.241	5.145	.982	79°	1.379
.209	12°	.208	.213	1.022	4.810	4.705	.978	78°	1.361
.227	13°	.225	.231	1.026	4.445	4.331	.974	77°	1.344
.244	14°	.242	.249	1.031	4.134	4.011	.970	76°	1.326
.262	15°	.259	.268	1.035	3.864	3.732	.966	75°	1.309
.279	16°	.276	.287	1.040	3.628	3.487	.961	74°	1.292
.297	17°	.292	.306	1.046	3.420	3.271	.956	73°	1.274
.314	18°	.309	.325	1.051	3.236	3.078	.951	72°	1.257
.332	19°	.326	.344	1.058	3.072	2.904	.946	71°	1.239
.349	20°	.342	.364	1.064	2.924	2.747	.940	70°	1.222
.367	21°	.358	.384	1.071	2.790	2.605	.934	69°	1.204
.384	22°	.375	.404	1.079	2.669	2.475	.927	68°	1.187
.401	23°	.391	.424	1.086	2.559	2.356	.921	67°	1.169
.419	24°	.407	.445	1.095	2.459	2.246	.914	66°	1.152
.436	25°	.423	.466	1.103	2.366	2.145	.906	65°	1.134
.454	26°	.438	.488	1.113	2.281	2.050	.899	64°	1.117
.471	27°	.454	.510	1.122	2.203	1.963	.891	63°	1.100
.489	28°	.469	.532	1.133	2.130	1.881	.883	62°	1.082
.506	29°	.485	.554	1.143	2.063	1.804	.875	61°	1.065
.524	30°	.500	.577	1.155	2.000	1.732	.866	60°	1.047
.541	31°	.515	.601	1.167	1.942	1.664	.857	59°	1.030
.559	32°	.530	.625	1.179	1.887	1.600	.848	58°	1.012
.576	33°	.545	.649	1.192	1.836	1.540	.839	57°	0.995
.593	34°	.559	.675	1.206	1.788	1.483	.829	56°	0.977
.611	35°	.574	.700	1.221	1.743	1.428	.819	55°	0.960
.628	36°	.588	.727	1.236	1.701	1.376	.809	54°	0.942
.646	37°	.602	.754	1.252	1.662	1.327	.799	53°	0.925
.663	38°	.616	.781	1.269	1.624	1.280	.788	52°	0.908
.681	39°	.629	.810	1.287	1.589	1.235	.777	51°	0.890
.698	40°	.643	.839	1.305	1.556	1.192	.766	50°	0.873
.716	41°	.656	.869	1.325	1.524	1.150	.755	49°	0.855
.733	42°	.669	.900	1.346	1.494	1.111	.743	48°	0.838
.750	43°	.682	.933	1.367	1.466	1.072	.731	47°	0.820
.768	44°	.695	0.966	1.390	1.440	1.036	.719	46°	0.803
.785	45°	.707	1.000	1.414	1.414	1.000	.707	45°	0.785
Rad.	Deg.	Cos	Cot	Csc	Sec	Tan	Sin	Deg.	Rad.

V. FOUR-PLACE LOGARITHMS OF NUMBERS

N	0	1	2	3	4	5	6	7	8	9
10	.0000	0043	0086	0128	0170	0212	0253	0294	0334	0374
11	.0414	0453	0492	0531	0569	0607	0645	0682	0719	0755
12	.0792	0828	0864	0899	0934	0969	1004	1038	1072	1106
13	.1139	1173	1206	1239	1271	1303	1335	1367	1399	1430
14	.1461	1492	1523	1553	1584	1614	1644	1673	1703	1732
15	.1761	1790	1818	1847	1875	1903	1931	1959	1987	2014
16	.2041	2068	2095	2122	2148	2175	2201	2227	2253	2279
17	.2304	2330	2355	2380	2405	2430	2455	2480	2504	2529
18	.2553	2577	2601	2625	2648	2672	2695	2718	2742	2765
19	.2788	2810	2833	2856	2878	2900	2923	2945	2967	2989
20	.3010	3032	3054	3075	3096	3118	3139	3160	3181	3201
21	.3222	3243	3263	3284	3304	3324	3345	3365	3385	3404
22	.3424	3444	3464	3483	3502	3522	3541	3560	3579	3598
23	.3617	3636	3655	3674	3692	3711	3729	3747	3766	3784
24	.3802	3820	3838	3856	3874	3892	3909	3927	3945	3962
25	.3979	3997	4014	4031	4048	4065	4082	4099	4116	4133
26	.4150	4166	4183	4200	4216	4232	4249	4265	4281	4298
27	.4314	4330	4346	4362	4378	4393	4409	4425	4440	4456
28	.4472	4487	4502	4518	4533	4548	4564	4579	4594	4609
29	.4624	4639	4654	4669	4683	4698	4713	4728	4742	4757
30	.4771	4786	4800	4814	4829	4843	4857	4871	4886	4900
31	.4914	4928	4942	4955	4969	4983	4997	5011	5024	5038
32	.5051	5065	5079	5092	5105	5119	5132	5145	5159	5172
33	.5185	5198	5211	5224	5237	5250	5263	5276	5289	5302
34	.5315	5328	5340	5353	5366	5378	5391	5403	5416	5428
35	.5441	5453	5465	5478	5490	5502	5514	5527	5539	5551
36	.5563	5575	5587	5599	5611	5623	5635	5647	5658	5670
37	.5682	5694	5705	5717	5729	5740	5752	5763	5775	5786
38	.5798	5809	5821	5832	5843	5855	5866	5877	5888	5899
39	.5911	5922	5933	5944	5955	5966	5977	5988	5999	6010
40	.6021	6031	6042	6053	6064	6075	6085	6096	6107	6117
41	.6128	6138	6149	6160	6170	6180	6191	6201	6212	6222
42	.6232	6243	6253	6263	6274	6284	6294	6304	6314	6325
43	.6335	6345	6355	6365	6375	6385	6395	6405	6415	6425
44	.6435	6444	6454	6464	6474	6484	6493	6503	6513	6522
45	.6532	6542	6551	6561	6571	6580	6590	6599	6609	6618
46	.6628	6637	6646	6656	6665	6675	6684	6693	6702	6712
47	.6721	6730	6739	6749	6758	6767	6776	6785	6794	6803
48	.6812	6821	6830	6839	6848	6857	6866	6875	6884	6893
49	.6902	6911	6920	6928	6937	6946	6955	6964	6972	6981
50	.6990	6998	7007	7016	7024	7033	7042	7050	7059	7067
N	0	1	2	3	4	5	6	7	8	9

Prop. Parts

	28	27	26
1	2.8	2.7	2.6
2	5.6	5.4	5.2
3	8.4	8.1	7.8
4	11.2	10.8	10.4
5	14.0	13.5	13.0
6	16.8	16.2	15.6
7	19.6	18.9	18.2
8	22.4	21.6	20.8
9	25.2	24.3	23.4

	22	21	20
1	2.2	2.1	2.0
2	4.4	4.2	4.0
3	6.6	6.3	6.0
4	8.8	8.4	8.0
5	11.0	10.5	10.0
6	13.2	12.6	12.0
7	15.4	14.7	14.0
8	17.6	16.8	16.0
9	19.8	18.9	18.0

	16	15	14
1	1.6	1.5	1.4
2	3.2	3.0	2.8
3	4.8	4.5	4.2
4	6.4	6.0	5.6
5	8.0	7.5	7.0
6	9.6	9.0	8.4
7	11.2	10.5	9.8
8	12.8	12.0	11.2
9	14.4	13.5	12.6

	13	12	11
1	1.3	1.2	1.1
2	2.6	2.4	2.2
3	3.9	3.6	3.3
4	5.2	4.8	4.4
5	6.5	6.0	5.5
6	7.8	7.2	6.6
7	9.1	8.4	7.7
8	10.4	9.6	8.8
9	11.7	10.8	9.9

	43	42	41	40	39		38	37	36	35	34		33	32	31	30	29	
1	4.3	4.2	4.1	4.0	3.9	1	3.8	3.7	3.6	3.5	3.4	1	3.3	3.2	3.1	3.0	2.9	1
2	8.6	8.4	8.2	8.0	7.8	2	7.6	7.4	7.2	7.0	6.8	2	6.6	6.4	6.2	6.0	5.8	2
3	12.9	12.6	12.3	12.0	11.7	3	11.4	11.1	10.8	10.5	10.2	3	9.9	9.6	9.3	9.0	8.7	3
4	17.2	16.8	16.4	16.0	15.6	4	15.2	14.8	14.4	14.0	13.6	4	13.2	12.8	12.4	12.0	11.6	4
5	21.5	21.0	20.5	20.0	19.5	5	19.0	18.5	18.0	17.5	17.0	5	16.5	16.0	15.5	15.0	14.5	5
6	25.8	25.2	24.6	24.0	23.4	6	22.8	22.2	21.6	21.0	20.4	6	19.8	19.2	18.6	18.0	17.4	6
7	30.1	29.4	28.7	28.0	27.3	7	26.6	25.9	25.2	24.5	23.8	7	23.1	22.4	21.7	21.0	20.3	7
8	34.4	33.6	32.8	32.0	31.2	8	30.4	29.6	28.8	28.0	27.2	8	26.4	25.6	24.8	24.0	23.2	8
9	38.7	37.8	36.9	36.0	35.1	9	34.2	33.3	32.4	31.5	30.6	9	29.7	28.8	27.9	27.0	26.1	9

Prop. Parts			N	0	1	2	3	4	5	6	7	8	9
			50	.6990	6998	7007	7016	7024	7033	7042	7050	7059	7067

	25	**24**	**23**
1	2.5	2.4	2.3
2	5.0	4.8	4.6
3	7.5	7.2	6.9
4	10.0	9.6	9.2
5	12.5	12.0	11.5
6	15.0	14.4	13.8
7	17.5	16.8	16.1
8	20.0	19.2	18.4
9	22.5	21.6	20.7

	19	**18**	**17**
1	1.9	1.8	1.7
2	3.8	3.6	3.4
3	5.7	5.4	5.1
4	7.6	7.2	6.8
5	9.5	9.0	8.5
6	11.4	10.8	10.2
7	13.3	12.6	11.9
8	15.2	14.4	13.6
9	17.1	16.2	15.3

	10	**9**
1	1.0	0.9
2	2.0	1.8
3	3.0	2.7
4	4.0	3.6
5	5.0	4.5
6	6.0	5.4
7	7.0	6.3
8	8.0	7.2
9	9.0	8.1

	8	**7**
1	0.8	0.7
2	1.6	1.4
3	2.4	2.1
4	3.2	2.8
5	4.0	3.5
6	4.8	4.2
7	5.6	4.9
8	6.4	5.6
9	7.2	6.3

	6	**5**	**4**
1	0.6	0.5	0.4
2	1.2	1.0	0.8
3	1.8	1.5	1.2
4	2.4	2.0	1.6
5	3.0	2.5	2.0
6	3.6	3.0	2.4
7	4.2	3.5	2.8
8	4.8	4.0	3.2
9	5.4	4.5	3.6

N	0	1	2	3	4	5	6	7	8	9
51	.7076	7084	7093	7101	7110	7118	7126	7135	7143	7152
52	.7160	7168	7177	7185	7193	7202	7210	7218	7226	7235
53	.7243	7251	7259	7267	7275	7284	7292	7300	7308	7316
54	.7324	7332	7340	7348	7356	7364	7372	7380	7388	7396
55	.7404	7412	7419	7427	7435	7443	7451	7459	7466	7474
56	.7482	7490	7497	7505	7513	7520	7528	7536	7543	7551
57	.7559	7566	7574	7582	7589	7597	7604	7612	7619	7627
58	.7634	7642	7649	7657	7664	7672	7679	7686	7694	7701
59	.7709	7716	7723	7731	7738	7745	7752	7760	7767	7774
60	.7782	7789	7796	7803	7810	7818	7825	7832	7839	7846
61	.7853	7860	7868	7875	7882	7889	7896	7903	7910	7917
62	.7924	7931	7938	7945	7952	7959	7966	7973	7980	7987
63	.7993	8000	8007	8014	8021	8028	8035	8041	8048	8055
64	.8062	8069	8075	8082	8089	8096	8102	8109	8116	8122
65	.8129	8136	8142	8149	8156	8162	8169	8176	8182	8189
66	.8195	8202	8209	8215	8222	8228	8235	8241	8248	8254
67	.8261	8267	8274	8280	8287	8293	8299	8306	8312	8319
68	.8325	8331	8338	8344	8351	8357	8363	8370	8376	8382
69	.8388	8395	8401	8407	8414	8420	8426	8432	8439	8445
70	.8451	8457	8463	8470	8476	8482	8488	8494	8500	8506
71	.8513	8519	8525	8531	8537	8543	8549	8555	8561	8567
72	.8573	8579	8585	8591	8597	8603	8609	8615	8621	8627
73	.8633	8639	8645	8651	3657	8663	8669	8675	8681	8686
74	.8692	8698	8704	8710	8716	8722	8727	8733	8739	8745
75	.8751	8756	8762	8768	8774	8779	8785	8791	8797	8802
76	.8808	8814	8820	8825	8831	8837	8842	8848	8854	8859
77	.8865	8871	8876	8882	8887	8893	8899	8904	8910	8915
78	.8921	8927	8932	8938	8943	8949	8954	8960	8965	8971
79	.8976	8982	8987	8993	8998	9004	9009	9015	9020	9025
80	.9031	9036	9042	9047	9053	9058	9063	9069	9074	9079
81	.9085	9090	9096	9101	9106	9112	9117	9122	9128	9133
82	.9138	9143	9149	9154	9159	9165	9170	9175	9180	9186
83	.9191	9196	9201	9206	9212	9217	9222	9227	9232	9238
84	.9243	9248	9253	9258	9263	9269	9274	9279	9284	9289
85	.9294	9299	9304	9309	9315	9320	9325	9330	9335	9340
86	.9345	9350	9355	9360	9365	9370	9375	9380	9385	9390
87	.9395	9400	9405	9410	9415	9420	9425	9430	9435	9440
88	.9445	9450	9455	9460	9465	9469	9474	9479	9484	9489
89	.9494	9499	9504	9509	9513	9518	9523	9528	9533	9538
90	.9542	9547	9552	9557	9562	9566	9571	9576	9581	9586
91	.9590	9595	9600	9605	9609	9614	9619	9624	9628	9633
92	.9638	9643	9647	9652	9657	9661	9666	9671	9675	9680
93	.9685	9689	9694	9699	9703	9708	9713	9717	9722	9727
94	.9731	9736	9741	9745	9750	9754	9759	9763	9768	9773
95	.9777	9782	9786	9791	9795	9800	9805	9809	9814	9818
96	.9823	9827	9832	9836	9841	9845	9850	9854	9859	9863
97	.9868	9872	9877	9881	9886	9890	9894	9899	9903	9908
98	.9912	9917	9921	9926	9930	9934	9939	9943	9948	9952
99	.9956	9961	9965	9969	9974	9978	9983	9987	9991	9996
N	0	1	2	3	4	5	6	7	8	9

	L Sin*	d	L Tan*	c d	L Cot	L Cos*		Prop. Parts
0° 00′						10.0000	**90° 00′**	*To avoid interpolating, for angles between 0° and 3°, or between 87° and 90°, use Table IX.*
10′	7.4637		7.4637		2.5363	.0000	89° 50′	
20′	.7648		.7648		.2352	.0000	40′	
30′	7.9408		7.9409		2.0591	.0000	30′	
40′	8.0658		8.0658		1.9342	.0000	20′	
0° 50′	.1627		.1627		.8373	10.0000	10′	

	L Sin*	d	L Tan*	c d	L Cot	L Cos*			**2**	**223**	**222**	**213**
1° 00′	8.2419		8.2419		1.7581	9.9999	**89° 00′**					
10′	.3088		.3089		.6911	.9999	88° 50′	**1**	0.2	22	22	21
20′	.3668		.3669		.6331	.9999	40′	**2**	0.4	45	44	43
30′	.4179		.4181		.5819	.9999	30′	**3**	0.6	67	67	64
40′	.4637		.4638		.5362	.9998	20′	**4**	0.8	89	89	85
1° 50′	.5050		.5053		.4947	.9998	10′	**5**	1.0	112	111	106
2° 00′	8.5428		8.5431		1.4569	9.9997	**88° 00′**	**6**	1.2	134	133	128
10′	.5776		.5779		.4221	.9997	87° 50′	**7**	1.4	156	155	149
20′	.6097		.6101		.3899	.9996	40′	**8**	1.6	178	178	170
30′	.6397		.6401		.3599	.9996	30′	**9**	1.8	201	200	192
40′	.6677		.6682		.3318	.9995	20′					
2° 50′	.6940		.6945		.3055	.9995	10′			**3**	**212**	**202**	**194**
3° 00′	8.7188		8.7194		1.2806	9.9994	**87° 00′**					
10′	.7423	222	.7429	223	.2571	.9993	86° 50′	**1**	0.3	21	20	19
20′	.7645	212	.7652	213	.2348	.9993	40′	**2**	0.6	42	40	39
30′	.7857	202	.7865	202	.2135	.9992	30′	**3**	0.9	64	61	58
40′	.8059	192	.8067	194	.1933	.9991	20′	**4**	1.2	85	81	78
3° 50′	.8251	185	.8261	185	.1739	.9990	10′	**5**	1.5	106	101	97
4° 00′	8.8436	177	8.8446	178	1.1554	9.9989	**86° 00′**	**6**	1.8	127	121	116
10′	.8613	170	.8624	171	.1376	.9989	85° 50′	**7**	2.1	148	141	136
20′	.8783	163	.8795	165	.1205	.9988	40′	**8**	2.4	170	162	155
30′	.8946	158	.8960	158	.1040	.9987	30′	**9**	2.7	191	182	175
40′	.9104	152	.9118	154	.0882	.9986	20′					
4° 50′	.9256	147	.9272	148	.0728	.9985	10′			**192**	**185**	**178**
5° 00′	8.9403	142	8.9420	143	1.0580	9.9983	**85° 00′**	**1**		19	18	18
10′	.9545	137	.9563	138	.0437	.9982	84° 50′	**2**		38	37	36
20′	.9682	134	.9701	135	.0299	.9981	40′	**3**		58	56	53
30′	.9816	129	.9836	130	.0164	.9980	30′	**4**		77	74	71
40′	8.9945	125	8.9966	127	1.0034	.9979	20′	**5**		96	92	89
5° 50′	9.0070	122	9.0093	123	0.9907	.9977	10′	**6**		115	111	107
6° 00′	9.0192		9.0216		0.9784	9.9976	**84° 00′**	**7**		134	130	125
	L Cos*	d	L Cot*	c d	L Tan	L Sin*	←	**8**		154	148	142
								9		173	166	160

	177	**171**	**170**	**165**	**163**		**158**	**154**	**152**	**148**	**147**		**143**	**142**	**138**	**137**	**135**	
1	18	17	17	16	16	**1**	16	15	15	15	15	**1**	14	14	14	14	14	**1**
2	35	34	34	33	33	**2**	32	31	30	30	29	**2**	29	28	28	27	27	**2**
3	53	51	51	50	49	**3**	47	46	46	44	44	**3**	43	43	41	41	40	**3**
4	71	68	68	66	65	**4**	63	62	61	59	59	**4**	57	57	55	55	54	**4**
5	88	86	85	82	82	**5**	79	77	76	74	74	**5**	72	71	69	68	68	**5**
6	106	103	102	99	98	**6**	95	92	91	89	88	**6**	86	85	83	82	81	**6**
7	124	120	119	116	114	**7**	111	108	106	104	103	**7**	100	99	97	96	94	**7**
8	142	137	136	132	130	**8**	126	123	122	118	118	**8**	114	114	110	110	108	**8**
9	159	154	153	148	147	**9**	142	139	137	133	132	**9**	129	128	124	123	122	**9**

	134	**130**	**129**	**127**	**125**		**123**	**122**	**120**	**119**	**117**		**115**	**114**	**113**	**111**	**109**	
1	13	13	13	13	12	**1**	12	12	12	12	12	**1**	12	11	11	11	11	**1**
2	27	26	26	25	25	**2**	25	24	24	24	23	**2**	23	23	23	22	22	**2**
3	40	39	39	38	38	**3**	37	37	36	36	35	**3**	34	34	34	33	33	**3**
4	54	52	52	51	50	**4**	49	49	48	48	47	**4**	46	46	45	44	44	**4**
5	67	65	64	64	62	**5**	62	61	60	60	58	**5**	58	57	56	56	54	**5**
6	80	78	77	76	75	**6**	74	73	72	71	70	**6**	69	68	68	67	65	**6**
7	94	91	90	89	88	**7**	86	85	84	83	82	**7**	80	80	79	78	76	**7**
8	107	104	105	102	100	**8**	98	98	96	95	94	**8**	92	91	90	89	87	**8**
9	121	117	116	114	112	**9**	111	110	108	107	105	**9**	104	103	102	100	98	**9**

VI. FOUR-PLACE LOGARITHMS OF FUNCTIONS: 6°—12°; 78°—84°

Prop. Parts	→	L Sin*	d	L Tan*	c d	L Cot	L Cos*	
	6° 00′	9.0192	119	9.0216	120	0.9784	9.9976	84° 00′
Subtract 10 from each	10′	.0311	115	.0336	117	.9664	.9975	83° 50′
entry in the columns	20′	.0426	113	.0453	114	.9547	.9973	40′
marked with "" through-*	30′	.0539	109	.0567	111	.9433	.9972	30′
out the table.	40′	.0648	107	.0678	108	.9322	.9971	20′
	6° 50′	.0755	104	.0786	105	.9214	.9969	10′
	7° 00′	9.0859	102	9.0891	104	0.9109	9.9968	83° 00′

	108	107	105
1	10.8	10.7	10.5
2	21.6	21.4	21.0
3	32.4	32.1	31.5
4	43.2	42.8	42.0
5	54.0	53.5	52.5
6	64.8	64.2	63.0
7	75.6	74.9	73.5
8	86.4	85.6	84.0
9	97.2	96.3	94.5

	10′	.0961	99	.0995	101	.9005	.9966	82° 50′
	20′	.1060	97	.1096	98	.8904	.9964	40′
	30′	.1157	95	.1194	97	.8806	.9963	30′
	40′	.1252	93	.1291	94	.8709	.9961	20′
	7° 50′	.1345	91	.1385	93	.8615	.9959	10′
	8° 00′	9.1436	89	9.1478	91	0.8522	9.9958	82° 00′

	104	102	101
1	10.4	10.2	10.1
2	20.8	20.4	20.2
3	31.2	30.6	30.3
4	41.6	40.8	40.4
5	52.0	51.0	50.5
6	62.4	61.2	60.6
7	72.8	71.4	70.7
8	83.2	81.6	80.8
9	93.6	91.8	90.9

	10′	.1525	87	.1569	89	.8431	.9956	81° 50′
	20′	.1612	85	.1658	87	.8342	.9954	40′
	30′	.1697	84	.1745	86	.8255	.9952	30′
	40′	.1781	82	.1831	84	.8169	.9950	20′
	8° 50′	.1863	80	.1915	82	.8085	.9948	10′
	9° 00′	9.1943	79	9.1997	81	0.8003	9.9946	81° 00′
	10′	.2022	78	.2078	80	.7922	.9944	80° 50′
	20′	.2100	76	.2158	78	.7842	.9942	40′
	30′	.2176	75	.2236	77	.7764	.9940	30′
	40′	.2251	73	.2313	76	.7687	.9938	20′
	9° 50′	.2324	73	.2389	74	.7611	.9936	10′
	10° 00′	9.2397	71	9.2463	73	0.7537	9.9934	80° 00′

	99	98	97	95
1	9.9	9.8	9.7	9.5
2	19.8	19.6	19.4	19.0
3	29.7	29.4	29.1	28.5
4	39.6	39.2	38.8	38.0
5	49.5	49.0	48.5	47.5
6	59.4	58.8	58.2	57.0
7	69.3	68.6	67.9	66.5
8	79.2	78.4	77.6	76.0
9	89.1	88.2	87.3	85.5

	10′	.2468	70	.2536	73	.7464	.9931	79° 50′
	20′	.2538	68	.2609	71	.7391	.9929	40′
	30′	.2606	68	.2680	70	.7320	.9927	30′
	40′	.2674	66	.2750	69	.7250	.9924	20′
	10° 50′	.2740	66	.2819	68	.7181	.9922	10′
	11° 00′	9.2806	64	9.2887	66	0.7113	9.9919	79° 00′
	10′	.2870	64	.2953	67	.7047	.9917	78° 50′
	20′	.2934	63	.3020	65	.6980	.9914	40′
	30′	.2997	61	.3085	64	.6915	.9912	30′
	40′	.3058	61	.3149	63	.6851	.9909	20′
	11° 50′	.3119	60	.3212	63	.6788	.9907	10′
	12° 00′	9.3179		9.3275		0.6725	9.9904	78° 00′
		L Cos*	d	L Cot*	c d	L Tan	L Sin*	←

	94	93	91	89		87	86	85	84	82		81	80	79	78	77	
1	9.4	9.3	9.1	8.9	1	8.7	8.6	8.5	8.4	8.2	1	8.1	8	7.9	7.8	7.7	1
2	18.8	18.6	18.2	17.8	2	17.4	17.2	17.0	16.8	16.4	2	16.2	16	15.8	15.6	15.4	2
3	28.2	27.9	27.3	26.7	3	26.1	25.8	25.5	25.2	24.6	3	24.3	24	23.7	23.4	23.1	3
4	37.6	37.2	36.4	35.6	4	34.8	34.4	34.0	33.6	32.8	4	32.4	32	31.6	31.2	30.8	4
5	47.0	46.5	45.5	44.5	5	43.5	43.0	42.5	42.0	41.0	5	40.5	40	39.5	39.0	38.5	5
6	56.4	55.8	54.6	53.4	6	52.2	51.6	51.0	50.4	49.2	6	48.6	48	47.4	46.8	46.2	6
7	65.8	65.1	63.7	62.3	7	60.9	60.2	59.5	58.8	57.4	7	56.7	56	55.3	54.6	53.9	7
8	75.2	74.4	72.8	71.2	8	69.6	68.8	68.0	67.2	65.6	8	64.8	64	63.2	62.4	61.6	8
9	84.6	83.7	81.9	80.1	9	78.3	77.4	76.5	75.6	73.8	9	72.9	72	71.1	70.2	69.3	9

	76	75	74	73	71		70	69	68	67	66		65	64	63	61	60	
1	7.6	7.5	7.4	7.3	7.1	1	7	6.9	6.8	6.7	6.6	1	6.5	6.4	6.3	6.1	6	1
2	15.2	15.0	14.8	14.6	14.2	2	14	13.8	13.6	13.4	13.2	2	13.0	12.8	12.6	12.2	12	2
3	22.8	22.5	22.2	21.9	21.3	3	21	20.7	20.4	20.1	19.8	3	19.5	19.2	18.9	18.3	18	3
4	30.4	30.0	29.6	29.2	28.4	4	28	27.6	27.2	26.8	26.4	4	26.0	25.6	25.2	24.4	24	4
5	38.0	37.5	37.0	36.5	35.5	5	35	34.5	34.0	33.5	33.0	5	32.5	32.0	31.5	30.5	30	5
6	45.6	45.0	44.4	43.8	42.6	6	42	41.4	40.8	40.2	39.6	6	39.0	38.4	37.8	36.6	36	6
7	53.2	52.5	51.8	51.1	49.7	7	49	48.3	47.6	46.9	46.2	7	45.5	44.8	44.1	42.7	42	7
8	60.8	60.0	59.2	58.4	56.8	8	56	55.2	54.4	53.6	52.8	8	52.0	51.2	50.4	48.8	48	8
9	68.4	67.5	66.6	65.7	63.9	9	63	62.1	61.2	60.3	59.4	9	58.5	57.6	56.7	54.9	54	9

	L Sin *	d	L Tan *	c d	L Cot	L Cos *		Prop. Parts
12° 00′	9.3179		9.3275		0.6725	9.9904	78° 00′	
10′	.3238	59	.3336	61	.6664	.9901	77° 50′	
20′	.3296	58	.3397	61	.6603	.9899	40′	
30′	.3353	57	.3458	61	.6542	.9896	30′	
40′	.3410	57	.3517	59	.6483	.9893	20′	
12° 50′	.3466	56	.3576	59	.6424	.9890	10′	
13° 00′	9.3521	55	9.3634	58	0.6366	9.9887	77° 00′	
10′	.3575	54	.3691	57	.6309	.9884	76° 50′	
20′	.3629	54	.3748	57	.6252	.9881	40′	
30′	.3682	53	.3804	56	.6196	.9878	30′	
40′	.3734	52	.3859	55	.6141	.9875	20′	
13° 50′	.3786	52	.3914	55	.6086	.9872	10′	
14° 00′	9.3837	51	9.3968	54	0.6032	9.9869	76° 00′	
10′	.3887	50	.4021	53	.5979	.9866	75° 50′	
20′	.3937	50	.4074	53	.5926	.9863	40′	
30′	.3986	49	.4127	53	.5873	.9859	30′	
40′	.4035	49	.4178	51	.5822	.9856	20′	
14° 50′	.4083	48	.4230	52	.5770	.9853	10′	
15° 00′	9.4130	47	9.4281	51	0.5719	9.9849	75° 00′	
10′	.4177	47	.4331	50	.5669	.9846	74° 50′	
20′	.4223	46	.4381	50	.5619	.9843	40′	
30′	.4269	46	.4430	49	.5570	.9839	30′	
40′	.4314	45	.4479	49	.5521	.9836	20′	
15° 50′	.4359	45	.4527	48	.5473	.9832	10′	
16° 00′	9.4403	44	9.4575	48	0.5425	9.9828	74° 00′	
10′	.4447	44	.4622	47	.5378	.9825	73° 50′	
20′	.4491	44	.4669	47	.5331	.9821	40′	
30′	.4533	42	.4716	47	.5284	.9817	30′	
40′	.4576	43	.4762	46	.5238	.9814	20′	
16° 50′	.4618	42	.4808	46	.5192	.9810	10′	
17° 00′	9.4659	41	9.4853	45	0.5147	9.9806	73° 00′	
10′	.4700	41	.4898	45	.5102	.9802	72° 50′	
20′	.4741	41	.4943	45	.5057	.9798	40′	
30′	.4781	40	.4987	44	.5013	.9794	30′	
40′	.4821	40	.5031	44	.4969	.9790	20′	
17° 50′	.4861	40	.5075	44	.4925	.9786	10′	
18° 00′	9.4900	39	9.5118	43	0.4882	9.9782	72° 00′	
10′	.4939	39	.5161	43	.4839	.9778	71° 50′	
20′	.4977	38	.5203	42	.4797	.9774	40′	
30′	.5015	38	.5245	42	.4755	.9770	30′	
40′	.5052	37	.5287	42	.4713	.9765	20′	
18° 50′	.5090	38	.5329	42	.4671	.9761	10′	
19° 00′	9.5126	36	9.5370	41	0.4630	9.9757	71° 00′	
	L Cos *	d	L Cot *	c d	L Tan	L Sin *	←	

Prop. Parts:

	61	59	58
1	6.1	5.9	5.8
2	12.2	11.8	11.6
3	18.3	17.7	17.4
4	24.4	23.6	23.2
5	30.5	29.5	29.0
6	36.6	35.4	34.8
7	42 7	41.3	40.6
8	48.8	47.2	46.4
9	54.9	53.1	52.2

	57	56	55
1	5.7	5.6	5.5
2	11.4	11.2	11.0
3	17.1	16.8	16.5
4	22.8	22.4	22.0
5	28.5	28.0	27.5
6	34.2	33.6	33.0
7	39.9	39.2	38.5
8	45.6	44.8	44.0
9	51.3	50.4	49.5

	54	53	52
1	5.4	5.3	5.2
2	10.8	10.6	10.4
3	16.2	15.9	15.6
4	21.6	21.2	20.8
5	27.0	26.5	26.0
6	32.4	31.8	31.2
7	37.8	37.1	36.4
8	43.2	42.4	41.6
9	48.6	47.7	46.8

	51	50	49
1	5.1	5	4.9
2	10.2	10	9.8
3	15.3	15	14.7
4	20.4	20	19.6
5	25.5	25	24.5
6	30.6	30	29.4
7	35.7	35	34.3
8	40.8	40	39.2
9	45.9	45	44.1

	48	47	46		45	44	43	42		41	40	39	
1	4.8	4.7	4.6	1	4.5	4.4	4.3	4.2	1	4.1	4	3.9	1
2	9.6	9.4	9.2	2	9.0	8.8	8.6	8.4	2	8.2	8	7.8	2
3	14.4	14.1	13.8	3	13.5	13.2	12.9	12.6	3	12.3	12	11.7	3
4	19.2	18.8	18.4	4	18.0	17.6	17.2	16.8	4	16.4	16	15.6	4
5	24.0	23.5	23.0	5	22.5	22.0	21.5	21.0	5	20.5	20	19.5	5
6	28.8	28.2	27.6	6	27.0	26.4	25.8	25.2	6	24.6	24	23.4	6
7	33.6	32.9	32.2	7	31.5	30.8	30.1	29.4	7	28.7	28	27.3	7
8	38.4	37.6	36.8	8	36.0	35.2	34.4	33.6	8	32.8	32	31.2	8
9	43.2	42.3	41.4	9	40.5	39.6	38.7	37.8	9	36.9	36	35.1	9

* Subtract 10 from each entry in this column.

VI. FOUR–PLACE LOGARITHMS OF FUNCTIONS: 19° — 27°; 63° — 71°

Prop. Parts

	2	3	4
1	0.2	0.3	0.4
2	0.4	0.6	0.8
3	0.6	0.9	1.2
4	0.8	1.2	1.6
5	1.0	1.5	2.0
6	1.2	1.8	2.4
7	1.4	2.1	2.8
8	1.6	2.4	3.2
9	1.8	2.7	3.6

	5	6	7
1	0.5	0.6	0.7
2	1.0	1.2	1.4
3	1.5	1.8	2.1
4	2.0	2.4	2.8
5	2.5	3.0	3.5
6	3.0	3.6	4.2
7	3.5	4.2	4.9
8	4.0	4.8	5.6
9	4.5	5.4	6.3

	38	37	36
1	3.8	3.7	3.6
2	7.6	7.4	7.2
3	11.4	11.1	10.8
4	15.2	14.8	14.4
5	19.0	18.5	18.0
6	22.8	22.2	21.6
7	26.6	25.9	25.2
8	30.4	29.6	28.8
9	34.2	33.3	32.4

	35	34	33
1	3.5	3.4	3.3
2	7.0	6.8	6.6
3	10.5	10.2	9.9
4	14.0	13.6	13.2
5	17.5	17.0	16.5
6	21.0	20.4	19.8
7	24.5	23.8	23.1
8	28.0	27.2	26.4
9	31.5	30.6	29.7

Main table

	L Sin *	d	L Tan *	c d	L Cot	L Cos *	
19° 00'	9.5126	37	9.5370	41	0.4630	9.9757	71° 00'
10'	.5163	36	.5411	4C	.4589	.9752	70° 50'
20'	.5199	36	.5451	40	.4549	.9748	40'
30'	.5235	35	.5491	40	.4509	.9743	30'
40'	.5270	36	.5531	40	.4469	.9739	20'
19° 50'	.5306	35	.5571	40	.4429	.9734	10'
20° 00'	9.5341	34	9.5611	40	0.4389	9.9730	70° 00'
10'	.5375	34	.5650	39	.4350	.9725	69° 50'
20'	.5409	34	.5689	39	.4311	.9721	40'
30'	.5443	34	.5727	38	.4273	.9716	30'
40'	.5477	33	.5766	39	.4234	.9711	20'
20° 50'	.5510	33	.5804	38	.4196	.9706	10'
21° 00'	9.5543	33	9.5842	38	0.4158	9.9702	69° 00'
10'	.5576	33	.5879	38	.4121	.9697	68° 50'
20'	.5609	32	.5917	37	.4083	.9692	40'
30'	.5641	32	.5954	37	4046	.9687	30'
40'	.5673	31	.5991	37	.4009	.9682	20'
21° 50'	.5704	32	.6028	37	.3972	.9677	10'
22° 00'	9.5736	31	9.6064	36	0.3936	9.9672	68° 00'
10'	.5767	31	.6100	36	.3900	.9667	67° 50'
20'	.5798	30	.6136	36	.3864	.9661	40'
30'	.5828	31	.6172	36	.3828	.9656	30'
40'	.5859	30	.6208	36	.3792	.9651	20'
22° 50'	.5889	30	.6243	35	.3757	.9646	10'
23° 00'	9.5919	30	9.6279	36	0.3721	9.9640	67° 00'
10'	.5948	29	.6314	35	.3686	.9635	66° 50'
20'	.5978	30	.6348	35	.3652	.9629	40'
30'	.6007	29	.6383	34	.3617	.9624	30'
40'	.6036	29	.6417	35	.3583	.9618	20'
23° 50'	.6065	29	.6452	34	.3548	.9613	10'
24° 00'	9.6093	28	9.6486	34	0.3514	9.9607	66° 00'
10'	.6121	28	.6520	33	.3480	.9602	65° 50'
20'	.6149	28	.6553	34	.3447	.9596	40'
30'	.6177	28	.6587	33	.3413	.9590	30'
40'	.6205	27	.6620	34	.3380	.9584	20'
24° 50'	.6232	27	.6654	33	.3346	.9579	10'
25° 00'	9.6259	27	9.6687	33	0.3313	9.9573	65° 00'
10'	.6286	27	.6720	32	.3280	.9567	64° 50'
20'	.6313	26	.6752	33	.3248	.9561	40'
30'	.6340	26	.6785	32	.3215	.9555	30'
40'	.6366	26	.6817	33	.3183	.9549	20'
25° 50'	.6392	26	.6850	32	.3150	.9543	10'
26° 00'	9.6418	26	9.6882	32	0.3118	9.9537	64° 00'
10'	.6444	26	.6914	32	.3086	.9530	63° 50'
20'	.6470	25	.6946	31	.3054	.9524	40'
30'	.6495	26	.6977	32	.3023	.9518	30'
40'	.6521	25	.7009	31	.2991	.9512	20'
26° 50'	.6546	24	.7040	32	.2960	.9505	10'
27° 00'	9.6570		9.7072		0.2928	9.9499	63° 00'
	L Cos *	d	L Cot *	c d	L Tan	L Sin *	←

	32	31	30	29		28	27	26	25	24	
1	3.2	3.1	3	2.9	1	2.8	2.7	2.6	2.5	2.4	1
2	6.4	6.2	6	5.8	2	5.6	5.4	5.2	5.0	4.8	2
3	9.6	9.3	9	8.7	3	8.4	8.1	7.8	7.5	7.2	3
4	12.8	12.4	12	11.6	4	11.2	10.8	10.4	10.0	9.6	4
5	16.0	15.5	15	14.5	5	14.0	13.5	13.0	12.5	12.0	5
6	19.2	18.6	18	17.4	6	16.8	16.2	15.6	15.0	14.4	6
7	22.4	21.7	21	20.3	7	19.6	18.9	18.2	17.5	16.8	7
8	25.6	24.8	24	23.2	8	22.4	21.6	20.8	20.0	19.2	8
9	28.8	27.9	27	26.1	9	25.2	24.3	23.4	22.5	21.6	9

VI. FOUR–PLACE LOGARITHMS OF FUNCTIONS: 27° — 36°; 54° — 63°

	L Sin *	d	L Tan *	c d	L Cot	L Cos *	
27° 00'	9.6570		9.7072		0.2928	9.9499	**63° 00'**
10'	.6595	25	.7103	31	.2897	.9492	62° 50'
20'	.6620	25	.7134	31	.2866	.9486	40'
30'	.6644	24	.7165	31	.2835	.9479	30'
40'	.6668	24	.7196	31	.2804	.9473	20'
27° 50'	.6692	24	.7226	30	.2774	.9466	10'
28° 00'	9.6716	24	9.7257	31	0.2743	9.9459	**62° 00'**
10'	.6740	24	.7287	30	.2713	.9453	61° 50'
20'	.6763	23	.7317	30	.2683	.9446	40'
30'	.6787	24	.7348	31	.2652	.9439	30'
40'	.6810	23	.7378	30	.2622	.9432	20'
28° 50'	.6833	23	.7408	30	.2592	.9425	10'
29° 00'	9.6856	23	9.7438	30	0.2562	9.9418	**61° 00'**
10'	.6878	22	.7467	29	.2533	.9411	60° 50'
20'	.6901	23	.7497	30	.2503	.9404	40'
30'	.6923	22	.7526	29	.2474	.9397	30'
40'	.6946	23	.7556	30	.2444	.9390	20'
29° 50'	.6968	22	.7585	29	.2415	.9383	10'
30° 00'	9.6990	22	9.7614	29	0.2386	9.9375	**60° 00'**
10'	.7012	22	.7644	30	.2356	.9368	59° 50'
20'	.7033	21	.7673	29	.2327	.9361	40'
30'	.7055	22	.7701	28	.2299	.9353	30'
40'	.7076	21	.7730	29	.2270	.9346	20'
30° 50'	.7097	21	.7759	29	.2241	.9338	10'
31° 00'	9.7118	21	9.7788	29	0.2212	9.9331	**59° 00'**
10'	.7139	21	.7816	29	.2184	.9323	58° 50'
20'	.7160	21	.7845	28	.2155	.9315	40'
30'	.7181	21	.7873	29	.2127	.9308	30'
40'	.7201	20	.7902	28	.2098	.9300	20'
31° 50'	.7222	21	.7930	28	.2070	.9292	10'
32° 00'	9.7242	20	9.7958	28	0.2042	9.9284	**58° 00'**
10'	.7262	20	.7986	28	.2014	.9276	57° 50'
20'	.7282	20	.8014	28	.1986	.9268	40'
30'	.7302	20	.8042	28	.1958	.9260	30'
40'	.7322	20	.8070	27	.1930	.9252	20'
32° 50'	.7342	19	.8097	28	.1903	.9244	10'
33° 00'	9.7361	19	9.8125	28	0.1875	9.9236	**57° 00'**
10'	.7380	20	.8153	27	.1847	.9228	56° 50'
20'	.7400	19	.8180	28	.1820	.9219	40'
30'	.7419	19	.8208	27	1792	.9211	30'
40'	.7438	19	.8235	28	.1765	.9203	20'
33° 50'	.7457	19	.8263	27	.1737	.9194	10'
34° 00'	9.7476	18	9.8290	27	0.1710	9.9186	**56° 00'**
10'	.7494	19	.8317	27	.1683	.9177	55° 50'
20'	.7513	18	.8344	27	.1656	.9169	40'
30'	.7531	19	.8371	27	.1629	.9160	30'
40'	.7550	18	.8398	27	.1602	.9151	20'
34° 50'	.7568	18	.8425	27	.1575	.9142	10'
35° 00'	9.7586	18	9.8452	27	0.1548	9.9134	**55° 00'**
10'	.7604	18	.8479	27	.1521	.9125	54° 50'
20'	.7622	18	.8506	27	.1494	.9116	40'
30'	.7640	17	.8533	26	.1467	.9107	30'
40'	.7657	18	.8559	27	.1441	.9098	20'
35° 50'	.7675	17	.8586	27	.1414	.9089	10'
36° 00'	9.7692		9.8613		0.1387	9.9080	**54° 00'**
	L Cos *	d	L Cot *	c d	L Tan	L Sin *	←

Prop. Parts

	31	30	29
1	3.1	3	2.9
2	6.2	6	5.8
3	9.3	9	8.7
4	12.4	12	11.6
5	15.5	15	14.5
6	18.6	18	17.4
7	21.7	21	20.3
8	24.8	24	23.2
9	27.9	27	26.1

	28	27	26
1	2.8	2.7	2.6
2	5.6	5.4	5.2
3	8.4	8.1	7.8
4	11.2	10.8	10.4
5	14.0	13.5	13.0
6	16.8	16.2	15.6
7	19.6	18.9	18.2
8	22.4	21.6	20.8
9	25.2	24.3	23.4

	25	24
1	2.5	2.4
2	5.0	4.8
3	7.5	7.2
4	10.0	9.6
5	12.5	12.0
6	15.0	14.4
7	17.5	16.8
8	20.0	19.2
9	22.5	21.6

	23	22
1	2.3	2.2
2	4.6	4.4
3	6.9	6.6
4	9.2	8.8
5	11.5	11.0
6	13.8	13.2
7	16.1	15.4
8	18.4	17.6
9	20.7	19.8

	21	20
1	2.1	2
2	4.2	4
3	6.3	6
4	8.4	8
5	10.5	10
6	12.6	12
7	14.7	14
8	16.8	16
9	18.9	18

* Subtract 10 from each entry in this column.

Prop. Parts

	19	18
1	1.9	1.8
2	3.8	3.6
3	5.7	5.4
4	7.6	7.2
5	9.5	9.0
6	11.4	10.8
7	13.3	12.6
8	15.2	14.4
9	17.1	16.2

	17	16	15
1	1.7	1.6	1.5
2	3.4	3.2	3.0
3	5.1	4.8	4.5
4	6.8	6.4	6.0
5	8.5	8.0	7.5
6	10.2	9.6	9.0
7	11.9	11.2	10.5
8	13.6	12.8	12.0
9	15.3	14.4	13.5

	14	13	12
1	1.4	1.3	1.2
2	2.8	2.6	2.4
3	4.2	3.9	3.6
4	5.6	5.2	4.8
5	7.0	6.5	6.0
6	8.4	7.8	7.2
7	9.8	9.1	8.4
8	11.2	10.4	9.6
9	12.6	11.7	10.8

	11	10	9
1	1.1	1.0	0.9
2	2.2	2.0	1.8
3	3.3	3.0	2.7
4	4.4	4.0	3.6
5	5.5	5.0	4.5
6	6.6	6.0	5.4
7	7.7	7.0	6.3
8	8.8	8.0	7.2
9	9.9	9.0	8.1

	8	7	6
1	0.8	0.7	0.6
2	1.6	1.4	1.2
3	2.4	2.1	1.8
4	3.2	2.8	2.4
5	4.0	3.5	3.0
6	4.8	4.2	3.6
7	5.6	4.9	4.2
8	6.4	5.6	4.8
9	7.2	6.3	5.4

——→	L Sin *	d	L Tan *	c d	L Cot	L Cos *	
36° 00'	9.7692		9.8613		0.1387	9.9080	54° 00'
10'	.7710	18	.8639	26	.1361	.9070	53° 50'
20'	.7727	17	.8666	27	.1334	.9061	40'
30'	.7744	17	.8692	26	.1308	.9052	30'
40'	.7761	17	.8718	26	.1282	.9042	20'
36° 50'	.7778	17	.8745	27	.1255	.9033	10'
37° 00'	9.7795	17	9.8771	26	0.1229	9.9023	53° 00'
10'	.7811	16	.8797	26	.1203	.9014	52° 50'
20'	.7828	17	.8824	27	.1176	.9004	40'
30'	.7844	16	.8850	26	.1150	.8995	30'
40'	.7861	17	.8876	26	.1124	.8985	20'
37° 50'	.7877	16	.8902	26	.1098	.8975	10'
38° 00'	9.7893	16	9.8928	26	0.1072	9.8965	52° 00'
10'	.7910	17	.8954	26	.1046	.8955	51° 50'
20'	.7926	16	.8980	26	.1020	.8945	40'
30'	.7941	15	.9006	26	.0994	.8935	30'
40'	.7957	16	.9032	26	.0968	.8925	20'
38° 50'	.7973	16	.9058	26	.0942	.8915	10'
39° 00'	9.7989	16	9.9084	26	0.0916	9.8905	51° 00'
10'	.8004	15	.9110	26	.0890	.8895	50° 50'
20'	.8020	16	.9135	25	.0865	.8884	40'
30'	.8035	15	.9161	26	.0839	.8874	30'
40'	.8050	15	.9187	26	.0813	.8864	20'
39° 50'	.8066	16	.9212	25	.0788	.8853	10'
40° 00'	9.8081	15	9.9238	26	0.0762	9.8843	50° 00'
10'	.8096	15	.9264	26	.0736	.8832	49° 50'
20'	.8111	15	.9289	25	.0711	.8821	40'
30'	.8125	14	.9315	26	.0685	.8810	30'
40'	.8140	15	.9341	26	.0659	.8800	20'
40° 50'	.8155	15	.9366	25	.0634	.8789	10'
41° 00'	9.8169	14	9.9392	26	0.0608	9.8778	49° 00'
10'	.8184	15	.9417	25	.0583	.8767	48° 50'
20'	.8198	14	.9443	26	.0557	.8756	40'
30'	.8213	15	.9468	26	.0532	•.8745	30'
40'	.8227	14	.9494	25	.0506	.8733	20'
41° 50'	.8241	14	.9519	26	.0481	.8722	10'
42° 00'	9.8255	14	9.9544	25	0.0456	9.8711	48° 00'
10'	.8269	14	.9570	26	.0430	.8699	47° 50'
20'	.8283	14	.9595	25	.0405	.8688	40'
30'	.8297	14	.9621	25	.0379	.8676	30'
40'	.8311	14	.9646	25	.0354	.8665	20'
42° 50'	.8324	13	.9671	25	.0329	.8653	10'
43° 00'	9.8338	14	9.9697	26	0.0303	9.8641	47° 00'
10'	.8351	13	.9722	25	.0278	.8629	46° 50'
20'	.8365	14	.9747	25	.0253	.8618	40'
30'	.8378	13	.9772	26	.0228	.8606	30'
40'	.8391	14	.9798	25	.0202	.8594	20'
43° 50'	.8405	13	.9823	25	.0177	.8582	10'
44° 00'	9.8418	13	9.9848	26	0.0152	9.8569	46° 00'
10'	.8431	13	.9874	25	.0126	.8557	45° 50'
20'	.8444	13	.9899	25	.0101	.8545	40'
30'	.8457	12	.9924	25	.0076	.8532	30'
40'	.8469	13	.9949	26	.0051	.8520	20'
44° 50'	.8482	13	.9975	25	.0025	.8507	10'
45° 00'	9.8495		10.0000		0.0000	9.8495	45° 00'
	L Cos *	d	L Cot *	c d	L Tan	L Sin *	←——

*Subtract 10 from each entry in this column.

→	Sin	Cos	Tan	Cot	Sec	Csc	
0° 00′	.0000	1.000	.0000	——	1.000	——	90° 00′
10′	029	000	029	343.8	000	343.8	89° 50′
20′	058	000	058	171.9	000	171.9	40′
30′	.0087	1.000	.0087	114.6	1.000	114.6	30′
40′	116	.9999	116	85.94	000	85.95	20′
0° 50′	145	999	145	68.75	000	68.76	10′
1° 00′	.0175	.9998	.0175	57.29	1.000	57.30	89° 00′
10′	204	998	204	49.10	000	49.11	88° 50′
20′	233	997	233	42.96	000	42.98	40′
30′	.0262	.9997	.0262	38.19	1.000	38.20	30′
40′	291	996	291	34.37	000	34.38	20′
1° 50′	320	995	320	31.24	001	31.26	10′
2° 00′	.0349	.9994	.0349	28.64	1.001	28.65	88° 00′
10′	378	993	378	26.43	001	26.45	87° 50′
20′	407	992	407	24.54	001	24.56	40′
30′	.0436	.9990	.0437	22.90	001	22.93	30′
40′	465	989	466	21.47	001	21.49	20′
2° 50′	494	988	495	20.21	001	20.23	10′
3° 00′	.0523	.9986	.0524	19.08	1.001	19.11	87° 00′
10′	552	985	553	18.07	002	18.10	86° 50′
20′	581	983	582	17.17	002	17.20	40′
30′	.0610	.9981	.0612	16.35	1.002	16.38	30′
40′	640	980	641	15.60	002	15.64	20′
3° 50′	669	978	670	14.92	002	14.96	10′
4° 00′	.0698	.9976	.0699	14.30	1.002	14.34	86° 00′
10′	727	974	729	13.73	003	13.76	85° 50′
20′	756	971	758	13.20	003	13.23	40′
30′	.0785	.9969	.0787	12.71	1.003	12.75	30′
40′	814	967	816	12.25	003	12.29	20′
4° 50′	843	964	846	11.83	004	11.87	10′
5° 00′	.0872	.9962	.0875	11.43	1.004	11.47	85° 00′
10′	901	959	904	11.06	004	11.10	84° 50′
20′	929	957	934	10.71	004	10.76	40′
30′	.0958	.9954	.0963	10.39	1.005	10.43	30′
40′	.0987	951	.0992	10.08	005	10.13	20′
5° 50′	.1016	948	.1022	9.788	005	9.839	10′
6° 00′	.1045	.9945	.1051	9.514	1.006	9.567	84° 00′
	Cos	Sin	Cot	Tan	Csc	Sec	←

Prop. Parts *

	28	29	30	31
1	2.8	2.9	3	3.1
2	5.6	5.8	6	6.2
3	8.4	8.7	9	9.3
4	11.2	11.6	12	12.4
5	14.0	14.5	15	15.5
6	16.8	17.4	18	18.6
7	19.6	20.3	21	21.7
8	22.4	23.2	24	24.8
9	25.2	26.1	27	27.9

	32	33	34	35
1	3.2	3.3	3.4	3.5
2	6.4	6.6	6.8	7.0
3	9.6	9.9	10.2	10.5
4	12.8	13.2	13.6	14.0
5	16.0	16.5	17.0	17.5
6	19.2	19.8	20.4	21.0
7	22.4	23.1	23.8	24.5
8	25.6	26.4	27.2	28.0
9	28.8	29.7	30.6	31.5

	48	49	53	57
1	4.8	4.9	5.3	5.7
2	9.6	9.8	10.6	11.4
3	14.4	14.7	15.9	17.1
4	19.2	19.6	21.2	22.8
5	24.0	24.5	26.5	28.5
6	28.8	29.4	31.8	34.2
7	33.6	34.3	37.1	39.9
8	38.4	39.2	42.4	45.6
9	43.2	44.1	47.7	51.3

	69	70	71	72
1	6.9	7	7.1	7.2
2	13.8	14	14.2	14.4
3	20.7	21	21.3	21.6
4	27.6	28	28.4	28.8
5	34.5	35	35.5	36.0
6	41.4	42	42.6	43.2
7	48.3	49	49.7	50.4
8	55.2	56	56.8	57.6
9	62.1	63	63.9	64.8

	79	81	82	83	84	87	88	89		90	91	94	95	96	98	100	101	
1	7.9	8.1	8.2	8.3	8.4	8.7	8.8	8.9	1	9	9.1	9.4	9.5	9.6	9.8	10	10.1	1
2	15.8	16.2	16.4	16.6	16.8	17.4	17.6	17.8	2	18	18.2	18.8	19.0	19.2	19.6	20	20.2	2
3	23.7	24.3	24.6	24.9	25.2	26.1	26.4	26.7	3	27	27.3	28.2	28.5	28.8	29.4	30	30.3	3
4	31.6	32.4	32.8	33.2	33.6	34.8	35.2	35.6	4	36	36.4	37.6	38.0	38.4	39.2	40	40.4	4
5	39.5	40.5	41.0	41.5	42.0	43.5	44.0	44.5	5	45	45.5	47.0	47.5	48.0	49.0	50	50.5	5
6	47.4	48.6	49.2	49.8	50.4	52.2	52.8	53.4	6	54	54.6	56.4	57.0	57.6	58.8	60	60.6	6
7	55.3	56.7	57.4	58.1	58.8	60.9	61.6	62.3	7	63	63.7	65.8	66.5	67.2	68.6	70	70.7	7
8	63.2	64.8	65.6	66.4	67.2	69.6	70.4	71.2	8	72	72.8	75.2	76.0	76.8	78.4	80	80.8	8
9	71.1	72.9	73.8	74.7	75.6	78.3	79.2	80.1	9	81	81.9	84.6	85.5	86.4	88.2	90	90.9	9

	102	104	105	107	108	111	113	115		117	120	121	124	126	129	130	135	
1	10.2	10.4	10.5	10.7	10.8	11	11	12	1	12	12	12	12	13	13	13	14	1
2	20.4	20.8	21.0	21.4	21.6	22	23	23	2	23	24	24	25	25	26	26	27	2
3	30.6	31.2	31.5	32.1	32.4	33	34	34	3	35	36	36	37	38	39	39	40	3
4	40.8	41.6	42.0	42.8	43.2	44	45	46	4	47	48	48	50	50	52	52	54	4
5	51.0	52.0	52.5	53.5	54.0	56	56	58	5	58	60	60	62	63	64	65	68	5
6	61.2	62.4	63.0	64.2	64.8	67	68	69	6	70	72	73	74	76	77	78	81	6
7	71.4	72.8	73.5	74.9	75.6	78	79	80	7	82	84	85	87	88	90	91	94	7
8	81.6	83.2	84.0	85.6	86.4	89	90	92	8	94	96	97	99	101	103	104	108	8
9	91.8	93.6	94.5	96.3	97.2	100	102	104	9	105	108	109	112	113	116	117	122	9

* If the difference is > 1.00, use Table XI to avoid interpolation.

VII. FOUR-PLACE VALUES OF FUNCTIONS: 6° — 12°; 78° — 84°

	Sin	Cos	Tan	Cot	Sec	Csc	
6° 00'	.1045	.9945	.1051	9.514	1.006	9.567	84° 00'
10'	074	942	080	255	006	309	83° 50'
20'	103	939	110	9.010	006	9.065	40'
30'	.1132	.9936	.1139	8.777	1.006	8.834	30'
40	161	932	169	556	007	614	20'
6° 50'	190	929	198	345	007	405	10'
7° 00'	.1219	.9925	.1228	8.144	1.008	8.206	83° 00'
10'	248	922	257	7.953	008	8.016	82° 50'
20'	276	918	287	770	008	7.834	40'
30'	.1305	.9914	.1317	7.596	1.009	7.661	30'
40'	334	911	346	429	009	496	20'
7° 50'	363	907	376	269	009	337	10'
8° 00'	.1392	.9903	.1405	7.115	1.010	7.185	82° 00'
10'	421	899	435	6.968	010	7.040	81° 50'
20'	449	894	465	827	011	6.900	40'
30'	.1478	.9890	.1495	6.691	1.011	6.765	30'
40'	507	886	524	561	012	636	20'
8° 50'	536	881	554	435	012	512	10'
9° 00'	.1564	.9877	.1584	6.314	1.012	6.392	81° 00'
10'	593	872	614	197	013	277	80° 50'
20'	622	868	644	6.084	013	166	40'
30'	.1650	.9863	.1673	5.976	1.014	6.059	30'
40'	679	858	703	871	014	5.955	20'
9° 50'	708	853	733	769	015	855	10'
10° 00'	.1736	.9848	.1763	5.671	1.015	5.759	80° 00'
10'	765	843	793	576	016	665	79° 50'
20'	794	838	823	485	016	575	40'
30'	.1822	.9833	.1853	5.396	1.017	5.487	30'
40'	851	827	883	309	018	403	20'
10° 50'	880	822	914	226	018	320	10'
11° 00'	.1908	.9816	.1944	5.145	1.019	5.241	79° 00'
10'	937	811	.1974	5.066	019	164	78° 50'
20'	965	805	.2004	4.989	020	089	40'
30'	.1994	.9799	.2035	4.915	1.020	5.016	30'
40'	.2022	793	065	843	021	4.945	20'
11° 50'	051	787	095	773	022	876	10'
12° 00'	.2079	.9781	.2126	4.705	1.022	4.810	78° 00'
	Cos	Sin	Cot	Tan	Csc	Sec	←

Prop. Parts

	2	3	4	5	6
1	0.2	0.3	0.4	0.5	0.6
2	0.4	0.6	0.8	1.0	1.2
3	0.6	0.9	1.2	1.5	1.8
4	0.8	1.2	1.6	2 0	2.4
5	1.0	1.5	2.0	2.5	3.0
6	1.2	1.8	2.4	3.0	3.6
7	1.4	2.1	2.8	3.5	4.2
8	1.6	2.4	3.2	4.0	4.8
9	1.8	2.7	3.6	4.5	5.4

	37	40	42	46
1	3.7	4	4.2	4.6
2	7.4	8	8.4	9.2
3	11.1	12	12.6	13.8
4	14.8	16	16.8	18.4
5	18.5	20	21.0	23.0
6	22.2	24	25.2	27.6
7	25.9	28	29.4	32.2
8	29.6	32	33.6	36.8
9	33.3	36	37.8	41.4

	58	62	66	68
1	5.8	6.2	6.6	6.8
2	11.6	12.4	13.2	13.6
3	17.4	18.6	19.8	20.4
4	23.2	24.8	26.4	27.2
5	29.0	31.0	33.0	34.0
6	34.8	37.2	39.6	40.8
7	40.6	43.4	46.2	47.6
8	46.4	49.6	52.8	54.4
9	52.2	55.8	59.4	61.2

	73	74	75	77
1	7.3	7.4	7.5	7.7
2	14.6	14.8	15.0	15.4
3	21.9	22.2	22.5	23.1
4	29.2	29.6	30.0	30.8
5	36.5	37.0	37.5	38.5
6	43.8	44.4	45.0	46.2
7	51.1	51 8	52.5	53.9
8	58.4	59.2	60.0	61.6
9	65.7	66.6	67.5	69.3

	136	140	141	145	147	152	154	159		160	165	167	173	174	182	183	190	
1	14	14	14	14	15	15	15	16	1	16	16	17	17	17	18	18	19	1
2	27	28	28	29	29	30	31	32	2	32	33	33	35	35	36	37	38	2
3	41	42	42	44	44	46	46	48	3	48	50	50	52	52	55	55	57	3
4	54	56	56	58	59	61	62	64	4	64	66	67	69	70	73	73	76	4
5	68	70	70	72	74	76	77	80	5	80	82	84	86	87	91	92	95	5
6	82	84	85	87	88	91	92	95	6	96	99	100	104	104	109	110	114	6
7	95	98	99	102	103	106	108	111	7	112	116	117	121	122	127	128	133	7
8	109	112	113	116	118	122	123	127	8	128	132	134	138	139	146	146	152	8
9	122	126	127	130	132	137	139	143	9	144	148	150	156	157	164	165	171	9

	191	199	201	209	211	220	221	231		233	244	245	258	259	272	274	
1	19	20	20	21	21	22	22	23	1	23	24	24	26	26	27	27	1
2	38	40	40	42	42	44	44	46	2	47	49	49	52	52	54	55	2
3	57	60	60	63	63	66	66	69	3	70	73	74	77	78	82	82	3
4	76	80	80	84	84	88	88	92	4	93	98	98	103	104	109	110	4
5	96	100	100	104	106	110	110	116	5	116	122	122	129	130	136	137	5
6	115	119	121	125	127	132	133	139	6	140	146	147	155	155	163	164	6
7	134	139	141	146	148	154	155	162	7	163	171	172	181	181	190	192	7
8	153	159	161	167	169	176	177	185	8	186	195	196	206	207	218	219	8
9	172	179	181	188	190	198	199	208	9	210	220	220	232	233	245	247	9

→	Sin	Cos	Tan	Cot	Sec	Csc	
12° 00'	.2079	.9781	.2126	4.705	1.022	4.810	78° 00'
10'	108	775	156	638	023	745	77° 50'
20'	136	769	186	574	024	682	40'
30'	.2164	.9763	.2217	4.511	1.024	4.620	30'
40'	193	757	247	449	025	560	20'
12° 50'	221	750	278	390	026	502	10'
13° 00'	.2250	.9744	.2309	4.331	1.026	4.445	77° 00'
10'	278	737	339	275	027	390	76° 50'
20'	306	730	370	219	028	336	40'
30'	.2334	.9724	.2401	4.165	1.028	4.284	30'
40'	363	717	432	113	029	232	20'
13° 50'	391	710	462	061	030	182	10'
14° 00'	.2419	.9703	.2493	4.011	1.031	4.134	76° 00'
10'	447	696	524	3.962	031	086	75° 50'
20'	476	689	555	914	032	4.039	40'
30'	.2504	.9681	.2586	3.867	1.033	3.994	30'
40'	532	674	617	821	034	950	20'
14° 50'	560	667	648	776	034	906	10'
15° 00'	.2588	.9659	.2679	3.732	1.035	3.864	75° 00'
10'	616	652	711	689	036	822	74° 50'
20'	644	644	742	647	037	782	40'
30'	.2672	.9636	.2773	3.606	1.038	3.742	30'
40'	700	628	805	566	039	703	20'
15° 50'	728	621	836	526	039	665	10'
16° 00'	.2756	.9613	.2867	3.487	1.040	3.628	74° 00'
10'	784	605	899	450	041	592	73° 50'
20'	812	596	931	412	042	556	40'
30'	.2840	.9588	.2962	3.376	1.043	3.521	30'
40'	868	580	.2994	340	044	487	20'
16° 50'	896	572	.3026	305	045	453	10'
17° 00'	.2924	.9563	.3057	3.271	1.046	3.420	73° 00'
10'	952	555	089	237	047	388	72° 50'
20'	.2979	546	121	204	048	356	40'
30'	.3007	.9537	.3153	3.172	1.049	3.326	30'
40'	035	528	185	140	049	295	20'
17° 50'	062	520	217	108	050	265	10'
18° 00'	.3090	.9511	.3249	3.078	1.051	3.236	72° 00'
10'	118	502	281	047	052	207	71° 50'
20'	145	492	314	3.018	053	179	40'
30'	.3173	.9483	.3346	2.989	1.054	3.152	30'
40'	201	474	378	960	056	124	20'
18° 50'	228	465	411	932	057	098	10'
19° 00'	.3256	.9455	.3443	2.904	1.058	3.072	71° 00'
10'	283	446	476	877	059	046	70° 50'
20'	311	436	508	850	060	3.021	40'
30'	.3338	.9426	.3541	2.824	1.061	2.996	30'
40'	365	417	574	798	062	971	20'
19° 50'	393	407	607	773	063	947	10'
20° 00'	.3420	.9397	.3640	2.747	1.064	2.924	70° 00'
	Cos	Sin	Cot	Tan	Csc	Sec	←

Prop. Parts

	2	6	7	8
1	0.2	0.6	0.7	0.8
2	0.4	1.2	1.4	1.6
3	0.6	1.8	2.1	2.4
4	0.8	2.4	2.8	3.2
5	1.0	3.0	3.5	4.0
6	1.2	3.6	4.2	4.8
7	1.4	4.2	4.9	5.6
8	1.6	4.8	5.6	6.4
9	1.8	5.4	6.3	7.2

	13	14	15	16
1	1.3	1.4	1.5	1.6
2	2.6	2.8	3.0	3.2
3	3.9	4.2	4.5	4.8
4	5.2	5.6	6.0	6.4
5	6.5	7.0	7.5	8.0
6	7.8	8.4	9.0	9.6
7	9.1	9.8	10.5	11.2
8	10.4	11.2	12.0	12.8
9	11.7	12.6	13.5	14.4

	21	22	23	24
1	2.1	2.2	2.3	2.4
2	4.2	4.4	4.6	4.8
3	6.3	6.6	6.9	7.2
4	8.4	8.8	9.2	9.6
5	10.5	11.0	11.5	12.0
6	12.6	13.2	13.8	14.4
7	14.7	15.4	16.1	16.8
8	16.8	17.6	18.4	19.2
9	18.9	19.8	20.7	21.6

	29	30	31	32
1	2.9	3	3.1	3.2
2	5.8	6	6.2	6.4
3	8.7	9	9.3	9.6
4	11.6	12	12.4	12.8
5	14.5	15	15.5	16.0
6	17.4	18	18.6	19.2
7	20.3	21	21.7	22.4
8	23.2	24	24.8	25.6
9	26.1	27	27.9	28.8

	37	38	39	40	41	42	43		44	45	46	47	48	49	50	
1	3.7	3.8	3.9	4	4.1	4.2	4.3	1	4.4	4.5	4.6	4.7	4.8	4.9	5	1
2	7.4	7.6	7.8	8	8.2	8.4	8.6	2	8.8	9.0	9.2	9.4	9.6	9.8	10	2
3	11.1	11.4	11.7	12	12.3	12.6	12.9	3	13.2	13.5	13.8	14.1	14.4	14.7	15	3
4	14.8	15.2	15.6	16	16.4	16.8	17.2	4	17.6	18.0	18.4	18.8	19.2	19.6	20	4
5	18.5	19.0	19.5	20	20.5	21.0	21.5	5	22.0	22.5	23.0	23.5	24.0	24.5	25	5
6	22.2	22.8	23.4	24	24.6	25.2	25.8	6	26.4	27.0	27.6	28.2	28.8	29.4	30	6
7	25.9	26.6	27.3	28	28.7	29.4	30.1	7	30.8	31.5	32.2	32.9	33.6	34.3	35	7
8	29.6	30.4	31.2	32	32.8	33.6	34.4	8	35.2	36.0	36.8	37.6	38.4	39.2	40	8
9	33.3	34.2	35.1	36	36.9	37.8	38.7	9	39.6	40.5	41.4	42.3	43.2	44.1	45	9

VII. FOUR–PLACE VALUES OF FUNCTIONS: 20° — 28°; 62° — 70°

→	Sin	Cos	Tan	Cot	Sec	Csc	
20° 00′	.3420	.9397	.3640	2.747	1.064	2.924	70° 00′
10′	448	387	673	723	065	901	69° 50′
20′	475	377	706	699	066	878	40′
30′	.3502	.9367	.3739	2.675	1.068	2.855	30′
40′	529	356	772	651	069	833	20′
20° 50′	557	346	805	628	070	812	10′
21° 00′	.3584	.9336	.3839	2.605	1.071	2.790	69° 00′
10′	611	325	872	583	072	769	68° 50′
20′	638	315	906	560	074	749	40′
30′	.3665	.9304	.3939	2.539	1.075	2.729	30′
40′	692	293	.3973	517	076	709	20′
21° 50′	719	283	.4006	496	077	689	10′
22° 00′	.3746	.9272	.4040	2.475	1.079	2.669	68° 00′
10′	773	261	074	455	080	650	67° 50′
20′	800	250	108	434	081	632	40′
30′	.3827	.9239	.4142	2.414	1.082	2.613	30′
40′	854	228	176	394	084	595	20′
22° 50′	881	216	210	375	085	577	10′
23° 00′	.3907	.9205	.4245	2.356	1.086	2.559	67° 00′
10′	934	194	279	337	088	542	66° 50′
20′	961	182	314	318	089	525	40′
30′	.3987	.9171	.4348	2.300	1.090	2.508	30′
40′	.4014	159	383	282	092	491	20′
23° 50′	041	147	417	264	093	475	10′
24° 00′	.4067	.9135	.4452	2.246	1.095	2.459	66° 00′
10′	094	124	487	229	096	443	65° 50′
20′	120	112	522	211	097	427	40′
30′	.4147	.9100	.4557	2.194	1.099	2.411	30′
40′	173	088	592	177	100	396	20′
24° 50′	200	075	628	161	102	381	10′
25° 00′	.4226	.9063	.4663	2.145	1.103	2.366	65° 00′
10′	253	051	699	128	105	352	64° 50′
20′	279	038	734	112	106	337	40′
30′	.4305	.9026	.4770	2.097	1.108	2.323	30′
40′	331	013	806	081	109	309	20′
25° 50′	358	.9001	841	066	111	295	10′
26° 00′	.4384	.8988	.4877	2.050	1.113	2.281	64° 00′
10′	410	975	913	035	114	268	63° 50′
20′	436	962	950	020	116	254	40′
30′	.4462	.8949	.4986	2.006	1.117	2.241	30′
40′	488	936	.5022	1.991	119	228	20′
26° 50′	514	923	059	977	121	215	10′
27° 00′	.4540	.8910	.5095	1.963	1.122	2.203	63° 00′
10′	566	897	132	949	124	190	62° 50′
20′	592	884	169	935	126	178	40′
30′	.4617	.8870	.5206	1.921	1.127	2.166	30′
40′	643	857	243	907	129	154	20′
27° 50′	669	843	280	894	131	142	10′
28° 00′	.4695	.8829	.5317	1.881	1.133	2.130	62° 00′
	Cos	Sin	Cot	Tan	Csc	Sec	←

Prop. Parts

	9	10	11	12
1	0.9	1.0	1.1	1.2
2	1.8	2.0	2.2	2.4
3	2.7	3.0	3.3	3.6
4	3.6	4.0	4.4	4.8
5	4.5	5.0	5.5	6.0
6	5.4	6.0	6.6	7.2
7	6.3	7.0	7.7	8.4
8	7.2	8.0	8.8	9.6
9	8.1	9.0	9.9	10.8

	17	18	19	20
1	1.7	1.8	1.9	2
2	3.4	3.6	3.8	4
3	5.1	5.4	5.7	6
4	6.8	7.2	7.6	8
5	8.5	9.0	9.5	10
6	10.2	10 8	11.4	12
7	11.9	12.6	13.3	14
8	13.6	14.4	15.2	16
9	15.3	16.2	17.1	18

	25	26	27	28
1	2.5	2.6	2.7	2.8
2	5 0	5.2	5.4	5.6
3	7.5	7.8	8.1	8.4
4	10.0	10.4	10.8	11.2
5	12.5	13.0	13.5	14.0
6	15.0	15.6	16.2	16.8
7	17.5	18.2	18.9	19.6
8	20.0	20.8	21.6	22.4
9	22.5	23.4	24.3	25.2

	33	34	35	36
1	3.3	3.4	3.5	3.6
2	6.6	6.8	7.0	7.2
3	9.9	10.2	10.5	10.8
4	13.2	13.6	14.0	14.4
5	16.5	17.0	17.5	18.0
6	19.8	20.4	21.0	21.6
7	23.1	23.8	24.5	25.2
8	26.4	27.2	28.0	28.8
9	29.7	30.6	31.5	32.4

	52	54	55	56	57	58	59		60	62	63	64	65	67	
1	5.2	5.4	5.5	5.6	5.7	5.8	5.9	1	6	6.2	6.3	6.4	6.5	6.7	1
2	10.4	10.8	11.0	11.2	11.4	11.6	11.8	2	12	12.4	12.6	12.8	13.0	13.4	2
3	15.6	16.2	16.5	16.8	17.1	17.4	17.7	3	18	18.6	18.9	19.2	19.5	20.1	3
4	20.8	21.6	22.0	22.4	22.8	23.2	23.6	4	24	24.8	25.2	25.6	26.0	26.8	4
5	26.0	27.0	27.5	28.0	28.5	29.0	29.5	5	30	31.0	31.5	32.0	32.5	33.5	5
6	31.2	32.4	33.0	33.6	34.2	34.8	35.4	6	36	37.2	37.8	38.4	39.0	40.2	6
7	36.4	37.8	38.5	39.2	39.9	40.6	41.3	7	42	43.4	44.1	44.8	45.5	46.9	7
8	41.6	43.2	44.0	44.8	45.6	46.4	47.2	8	48	49.6	50.4	51.2	52.0	53.6	8
9	46.8	48.6	49.5	50.4	51.3	52.2	53.1	9	54	55.8	56.7	57.6	58.5	60.3	9

→	Sin	Cos	Tan	Cot	Sec	Csc	
28° 00′	.4695	.8829	.5317	1.881	1.133	2.130	**62° 00′**
10′	720	816	354	868	134	118	61° 50′
20′	746	802	392	855	136	107	40′
30′	.4772	.8788	.5430	1.842	1.138	2.096	30′
40′	797	774	467	829	140	085	20′
28° 50′	823	760	505	816	142	074	10′
29° 00′	.4848	.8746	.5543	1.804	1.143	2.063	**61° 00′**
10′	874	732	581	792	145	052	60° 50′
20′	899	718	619	780	147	041	40′
30′	.4924	.8704	.5658	1.767	1.149	2.031	30′
40′	950	689	696	756	151	020	20′
29° 50′	.4975	675	735	744	153	010	10′
30° 00′	.5000	.8660	.5774	1.732	1.155	2.000	**60° 00′**
10′	025	646	812	720	157	1.990	59° 50′
20′	050	631	851	709	159	980	40′
30′	.5075	.8616	.5890	1.698	1.161	1.970	30′
40′	100	601	930	686	163	961	20′
30° 50′	125	587	.5969	675	165	951	10′
31° 00′	.5150	.8572	.6009	1.664	1.167	1.942	**59° 00′**
19′	175	557	048	653	169	932	58° 50′
20′	200	542	088	643	171	923	40′
30′	.5225	.8526	.6128	1.632	1.173	1.914	30′
40′	250	511	168	621	175	905	20′
31° 50′	275	496	208	611	177	896	10′
32° 00′	.5299	.8480	.6249	1.600	1.179	1.887	**58° 00′**
10′	324	465	289	590	181	878	57° 50′
20′	348	450	330	580	184	870	40′
30′	.5373	.8434	.6371	1.570	1.186	1.861	30′
40′	398	418	412	560	188	853	20′
32° 50′	422	403	453	550	190	844	10′
33° 00′	.5446	.8387	.6494	1.540	1.192	1.836	**57° 00′**
10′	471	371	536	530	195	828	56° 50′
20′	495	355	577	520	197	820	40′
30′	.5519	.8339	.6619	1.511	1.199	1.812	30′
40′	544	323	661	501	202	804	20′
33° 50′	568	307	703	492	204	796	10′
34° 00′	.5592	.8290	.6745	1.483	1.206	1.788	**56° 00′**
10′	616	274	787	473	209	781	55° 50′
20′	640	258	830	464	211	773	40′
30	.5664	.8241	.6873	1.455	1.213	1.766	30′
40	688	225	916	446	216	758	20′
34° 50	712	208	.6959	437	218	751	10′
35° 00′	.5736	.8192	.7002	1.428	1.221	1.743	**55° 00′**
10′	760	175	046	419	223	736	54° 50′
20′	783	158	089	411	226	729	40′
30′	.5807	.8141	.7133	1.402	1.228	1.722	30′
40′	831	124	177	393	231	715	20′
35° 50′	854	107	221	385	233	708	10′
36° 00′	.5878	.8090	.7265	1.376	1.236	1.701	**54° 00′**
	Cos	Sin	Cot	Tan	Csc	Sec	←

Prop. Parts

	2	3	4	5	6
1	0.2	0.3	0.4	0.5	0.6
2	0.4	0.6	0.8	1.0	1.2
3	0.6	0.9	1.2	1.5	1.8
4	0.8	1.2	1.6	2.0	2.4
5	1.0	1.5	2.0	2.5	3.0
6	1.2	1.8	2.4	3.0	3.6
7	1.4	2.1	2.8	3.5	4.2
8	1.6	2.4	3.2	4.0	4.8
9	1.8	2.7	3.6	4.5	5.4

	11	12	13	14
1	1.1	1.2	1.3	1.4
2	2.2	2.4	2.6	2.8
3	3.3	3.6	3.9	4.2
4	4.4	4.8	5.2	5.6
5	5.5	6.0	6.5	7.0
6	6.6	7.2	7.8	8.4
7	7.7	8.4	9.1	9.8
8	8.8	9.6	10.4	11.2
9	9.9	10.8	11.7	12.6

	19	20	21	22
1	1.9	2	2.1	2.2
2	3.8	4	4.2	4.4
3	5.7	6	6.3	6.6
4	7.6	8	8.4	8.8
5	9.5	10	10.5	11.0
6	11.4	12	12.6	13.2
7	13.3	14	14.7	15.4
8	15.2	16	16.8	17.6
9	17.1	18	18.9	19.8

	37	38	39	40
1	3.7	3.8	3.9	4
2	7.4	7.6	7.8	8
3	11.1	11.4	11.7	12
4	14.8	15.2	15.6	16
5	18.5	19.0	19.5	20
6	22.2	22.8	23.4	24
7	25.9	26.6	27.3	28
8	29.6	30.4	31.2	32
9	33.3	34.2	35.1	36

	44	45	46	47	48	49		50	51	52	53	54	55	
1	4.4	4.5	4.6	4.7	4.8	4.9	1	5	5.1	5.2	5.3	5.4	5.5	1
2	8.8	9.0	9.2	9.4	9.6	9.8	2	10	10.2	10.4	10.6	10.8	11.0	2
3	13.2	13.5	13.8	14.1	14.4	14.7	3	15	15.3	15.6	15.9	16.2	16.5	3
4	17.6	18.0	18.4	18.8	19.2	19.6	4	20	20.4	20.8	21.2	21.6	22.0	4
5	22.0	22.5	23.0	23.5	24.0	24.5	5	25	25.5	26.0	26.5	27.0	27.5	5
6	26.4	27.0	27.6	28.2	28.8	29.4	6	30	30.6	31.2	31.8	32.4	33.0	6
7	30.8	31.5	32.2	32.9	33.6	34.3	7	35	35.7	36.4	37.1	37.8	38.5	7
8	35.2	36.0	36.8	37.6	38.4	39.2	8	40	40.8	41.6	42.4	43.2	44.0	8
9	39.6	40.5	41.4	42.3	43.2	44.1	9	45	45.9	46.8	47.7	48.6	49.5	9

Prop. Parts

	7	8	9	10
1	0.7	0.8	0.9	1.0
2	1.4	1.6	1.8	2.0
3	2.1	2.4	2.7	3.0
4	2.8	3.2	3.6	4.0
5	3.5	4.0	4.5	5.0
6	4.2	4.8	5.4	6.0
7	4.9	5.6	6.3	7.0
8	5.6	6.4	7.2	8.0
9	6.3	7.2	8.1	9.0

	15	16	17	18
1	1.5	1.6	1.7	1.8
2	3.0	3.2	3.4	3.6
3	4.5	4.8	5.1	5.4
4	6.0	6.4	6.8	7.2
5	7.5	8.0	8.5	9.0
6	9.0	9.6	10.2	10.8
7	10.5	11.2	11.9	12.6
8	12.0	12.8	13.6	14.4
9	13.5	14.4	15.3	16.2

	23	24	25	26
1	2.3	2.4	2.5	2.6
2	4.6	4.8	5.0	5.2
3	6.9	7.2	7.5	7.8
4	9.2	9.6	10.0	10.4
5	11.5	12.0	12.5	13.0
6	13.8	14.4	15.0	15.6
7	16.1	16.8	17.5	18.2
8	18.4	19.2	20.0	20.8
9	20.7	21.6	22.5	23.4

	41	42	43
1	4.1	4.2	4.3
2	8.2	8.4	8.6
3	12.3	12.6	12.9
4	16.4	16.8	17.2
5	20.5	21.0	21.5
6	24.6	25.2	25.8
7	28.7	29.4	30.1
8	32.8	33.6	34.4
9	36.9	37.8	38.7

	56	57	58
1	5.6	5.7	5.8
2	11.2	11.4	11.6
3	16.8	17.1	17.4
4	22.4	22.8	23.2
5	28.0	28.5	29.0
6	33.6	34.2	34.8
7	39.2	39.9	40.6
8	44.8	45.6	46.4
9	50.4	51.3	52.2

→→→	Sin	Cos	Tan	Cot	Sec	Csc	
36° 00'	.5878	.8090	.7265	1.376	1.236	1.701	54° 00'
10'	901	073	319	368	239	695	53° 50'
20'	925	056	355	360	241	688	40'
30'	.5948	.8039	.7400	1.351	1.244	1.681	30'
40'	972	021	445	343	247	675	20'
36° 50'	.5995	.8004	490	335	249	668	10'
37° 00'	.6018	.7986	.7536	1.327	1.252	1.662	53° 00'
10'	041	969	581	319	255	655	52° 50'
20'	065	951	627	311	258	649	40'
30'	.6088	.7934	.7673	1.303	1.260	1.643	30'
40'	111	916	720	295	263	636	20'
37° 50'	134	898	766	288	266	630	10'
38° 00'	.6157	.7880	.7813	1.280	1.269	1.624	52° 00'
10'	180	862	860	272	272	618	51° 50'
20'	202	844	907	265	275	612	40'
30'	.6225	.7826	.7954	1.257	1.278	1.606	30'
40'	248	808	.8002	250	281	601	20'
38° 50'	271	790	050	242	284	595	10'
39° 00'	.6293	.7771	.8098	1.235	1.287	1.589	51° 00'
10'	316	753	146	228	290	583	50° 50'
20'	338	735	195	220	293	578	40'
30'	.6361	.7716	.8243	1.213	1.296	1.572	30'
40'	383	698	292	206	299	567	20'
39° 50'	406	679	342	199	302	561	10'
40° 00'	.6428	.7660	.8391	1.192	1.305	1.556	50° 00
10	450	642	441	185	309	550	49° 40'
20'	472	623	491	178	312	545	40'
30'	.6494	.7604	.8541	1.171	1.315	1.540	30'
40'	517	585	591	164	318	535	20'
40° 50'	539	566	642	157	322	529	10'
41° 00'	.6561	.7547	.8693	1.150	1.325	1.524	49° 00'
10'	583	528	744	144	328	519	48° 50'
20'	604	509	796	137	332	514	40'
30'	.6626	.7490	.8847	1.130	1.335	1.509	30'
40'	648	470	899	124	339	504	20'
41° 50'	670	451	.8952	117	342	499	10'
42° 00'	.6691	.7431	.9004	1.111	1.346	1.494	48° 00'
10'	713	412	057	104	349	490	47° 50'
20'	734	392	110	098	353	485	40'
30'	.6756	.7373	.9163	1.091	1.356	1.480	30'
40'	777	353	217	085	360	476	20'
42° 50'	799	333	271	079	364	471	10'
43° 00'	.6820	.7314	.9325	1.072	1.367	1.466	47° 00'
10'	841	294	380	066	371	462	46° 50'
20'	862	274	435	060	375	457	40'
30'	.6884	.7254	.9490	1.054	1.379	1.453	30'
40'	905	234	545	048	382	448	20'
43° 50'	926	214	601	042	386	444	10'
44° 00'	.6947	.7193	.9657	1.036	1.390	1.440	46° 00'
10'	967	173	713	030	394	435	45° 50'
20'	.6988	153	770	024	398	431	40'
30'	.7009	.7133	.9827	1.018	1.402	1.427	30'
40'	030	112	884	012	406	423	20'
44° 50'	050	092	.9942	006	410	418	10'
45° 00'	.7071	.7071	1.000	1.000	1.414	1.414	45° 00'
	Cos	Sin	Cot	Tan	Csc	Sec	←——

VIII. FIVE–PLACE LOGARITHMS: 100 — 150

N	0	1	2	3	4	5	6	7	8	9
100	00 000	043	087	130	173	217	260	303	346	389
01	432	475	518	561	604	647	689	732	775	817
02	00 860	903	945	988	*030	*072	*115	*157	*199	*242
03	01 284	326	368	410	452	494	536	578	620	662
04	01 703	745	787	828	870	912	953	995	*036	*078
05	02 119	160	202	243	284	325	366	407	449	490
06	531	572	612	653	694	735	776	816	857	898
07	02 938	979	*019	*060	*100	*141	*181	*222	*262	*302
08	03 342	383	423	463	503	543	583	623	663	703
09	03 743	782	822	862	902	941	981	*021	*060	*100
110	04 139	179	218	258	297	336	376	415	454	493
11	532	571	610	650	689	727	766	805	844	883
12	04 922	961	999	*038	*077	*115	*154	*192	*231	*269
13	05 308	346	385	423	461	500	538	576	614	652
14	05 690	729	767	805	843	881	918	956	994	*032
15	06 070	108	145	183	221	258	296	333	371	408
16	446	483	521	558	595	633	670	707	744	781
17	06 819	856	893	930	967	*004	*041	*078	*115	*151
18	07 188	225	262	298	335	372	408	445	482	518
19	555	591	628	664	700	737	773	809	846	882
120	07 918	954	990	*027	*063	*099	*135	*171	*207	*243
21	08 279	314	350	386	422	458	493	529	565	600
22	636	672	707	743	778	814	849	884	920	955
23	08 991	*026	*061	*096	*132	*167	*202	*237	*272	*307
24	09 342	377	412	447	482	517	552	587	621	656
25	09 691	726	760	795	830	864	899	934	968	*003
26	10 037	072	106	140	175	209	243	278	312	346
27	380	415	449	483	517	551	585	619	653	687
28	10 721	755	789	823	857	890	924	958	992	*025
29	11 059	093	126	160	193	227	261	294	327	361
130	394	428	461	494	528	561	594	628	661	694
31	11 727	760	793	826	860	893	926	959	992	*024
32	12 057	090	123	156	189	222	254	287	320	352
33	385	418	450	483	516	548	581	613	646	678
34	12 710	743	775	808	840	872	905	937	969	*001
35	13 033	066	098	130	162	194	226	258	290	322
36	354	386	418	450	481	513	545	577	609	640
37	672	704	735	767	799	830	862	893	925	956
38	13 988	*019	*051	*082	*114	*145	*176	*208	*239	*270
39	14 301	333	364	395	426	457	489	520	551	582
140	613	644	675	706	737	768	799	829	860	891
41	14 922	953	983	*014	*045	*076	*106	*137	*168	*198
42	15 229	259	290	320	351	381	412	442	473	503
43	534	564	594	625	655	685	715	746	776	806
44	15 836	866	897	927	957	987	*017	*047	*077	*107
45	16 137	167	197	227	256	286	316	346	376	406
46	435	465	495	524	554	584	613	643	673	702
47	16 732	761	791	820	850	879	909	938	967	997
48	17 026	056	085	114	143	173	202	231	260	289
49	319	348	377	406	435	464	493	522	551	580
150	17 609	638	667	696	725	754	782	811	840	869
N	0	1	2	3	4	5	6	7	8	9

Prop. Parts

	44	43	42
1	4.4	4.3	4.2
2	8.8	8.6	8.4
3	13.2	12.9	12.6
4	17.6	17.2	16.8
5	22.0	21.5	21.0
6	26.4	25.8	25.2
7	30.8	30.1	29.4
8	35.2	34.4	33.6
9	39.6	38.7	37.8

	41	40	39
1	4.1	4	3.9
2	8.2	8	7.8
3	12.3	12	11.7
4	16.4	16	15.6
5	20.5	20	19.5
6	24.6	24	23.4
7	28.7	28	27.3
8	32.8	32	31.2
9	36.9	36	35.1

	38	37	36
1	3.8	3.7	3.6
2	7.6	7.4	7.2
3	11.4	11.1	10.8
4	15.2	14.8	14.4
5	19.0	18.5	18.0
6	22.8	22.2	21.6
7	26.6	25.9	25.2
8	30.4	29.6	28.8
9	34.2	33.3	32.4

	35	34	33
1	3.5	3.4	3.3
2	7.0	6.8	6.6
3	10.5	10.2	9.9
4	14.0	13.6	13.2
5	17.5	17.0	16.5
6	21.0	20.4	19.8
7	24.5	23.8	23.1
8	28.0	27.2	26.4
9	31.5	30.6	29.7

	32	31	30
1	3.2	3.1	3
2	6.4	6.2	6
3	9.6	9.3	9
4	12.8	12.4	12
5	16.0	15.5	15
6	19.2	18.6	18
7	22.4	21.7	21
8	25.6	24.8	24
9	28.8	27.9	27

Prop. Parts

	29	28
1	2.9	2.8
2	5.8	5.6
3	8.7	8.4
4	11.6	11.2
5	14.5	14.0
6	17.4	16.8
7	20.3	19.6
8	23.2	22.4
9	26.1	25.2

	27	26
1	2.7	2.6
2	5.4	5.2
3	8.1	7.8
4	10.8	10.4
5	13.5	13.0
6	16.2	15.6
7	18.9	18.2
8	21.6	20.8
9	24.3	23.4

	25
1	2.5
2	5.0
3	7.5
4	10.0
5	12.5
6	15.0
7	17.5
8	20.0
9	22.5

	24	23
1	2.4	2.3
2	4.8	4.6
3	7.2	6.9
4	9.6	9.2
5	12.0	11.5
6	14.4	13.8
7	16.8	16.1
8	19.2	18.4
9	21.6	20.7

	22	21
1	2.2	2.1
2	4.4	4.2
3	6.6	6.3
4	8.8	8.4
5	11.0	10.5
6	13.2	12.6
7	15.4	14.7
8	17.6	16.8
9	19.8	18.9

N	0	1	2	3	4	5	6	7	8	9
150	17 609	638	667	696	725	754	782	811	840	869
51	17 898	926	955	984	*013	*041	*070	*099	*127	*156
52	18 184	213	241	270	298	327	355	384	412	441
53	469	498	526	554	583	611	639	667	696	724
54	18 752	780	808	837	865	893	921	949	977	*005
55	19 033	061	089	117	145	173	201	229	257	285
56	312	340	368	396	424	451	479	507	535	562
57	590	618	645	673	700	728	756	783	811	838
58	19 866	893	921	948	976	*003	*030	*058	*085	*112
59	20 140	167	194	222	249	276	303	330	358	385
160	412	439	466	493	520	548	575	602	629	656
61	683	710	737	763	790	817	844	871	898	925
62	20 952	978	*005	*032	*059	*085	*112	*139	*165	*192
63	21 219	245	272	299	325	352	378	405	431	458
64	484	511	537	564	590	617	643	669	696	722
65	21 748	775	801	827	854	880	906	932	958	985
66	22 011	037	063	089	115	141	167	194	220	246
67	272	298	324	350	376	401	427	453	479	505
68	531	557	583	608	634	660	686	712	737	763
69	22 789	814	840	866	891	917	943	968	994	*019
170	23 045	070	096	121	147	172	198	223	249	274
71	300	325	350	376	401	426	452	477	502	528
72	553	578	603	629	654	679	704	729	754	779
73	23 805	830	855	880	905	930	955	980	*005	*030
74	24 055	080	105	130	155	180	204	229	254	279
75	304	329	353	378	403	428	452	477	502	527
76	551	576	601	625	650	674	699	724	748	773
77	24 797	822	846	871	895	920	944	969	993	*018
78	25 042	066	091	115	139	164	188	212	237	261
79	285	310	334	358	382	406	431	455	479	503
180	527	551	575	600	624	648	672	696	720	744
81	25 768	792	816	840	864	888	912	935	959	983
82	26 007	031	055	079	102	126	150	174	198	221
83	245	269	293	316	340	364	387	411	435	458
84	482	505	529	553	576	600	623	647	670	694
85	717	741	764	788	811	834	858	881	905	928
86	26 951	975	998	*021	*045	*068	*091	*114	*138	*161
87	27 184	207	231	254	277	300	323	346	370	393
88	416	439	462	485	508	531	554	577	600	623
89	646	669	692	715	738	761	784	807	830	852
190	27 875	898	921	944	967	989	*012	*035	*058	*081
91	28 103	126	149	171	194	217	240	262	285	307
92	330	353	375	398	421	443	466	488	511	533
93	556	578	601	623	646	668	691	713	735	758
94	28 780	803	825	847	870	892	914	937	959	981
95	29 003	026	048	070	092	115	137	159	181	203
96	226	248	270	292	314	336	358	380	403	425
97	447	469	491	513	535	557	579	601	623	645
98	667	688	710	732	754	776	798	820	842	863
99	29 885	907	929	951	973	994	*016	*038	*060	*081
200	30 103	125	146	168	190	211	233	255	276	298

| Prop. Parts | N | 0 | 1 | 2 | 3 | 4 | 5 | 6 | 7 | 8 | 9 |

N	0	1	2	3	4	5	6	7	8	9
200	30 103	125	146	168	190	211	233	255	276	298
01	320	341	363	384	406	428	449	471	492	514
02	535	557	578	600	621	643	664	685	707	728
03	750	771	792	814	835	856	878	899	920	942
04	30 963	984	*006	*027	*048	*069	*091	*112	*133	*154
05	31 175	197	218	239	260	281	302	323	345	366
06	387	408	429	450	471	492	513	534	555	576
07	597	618	639	660	681	702	723	744	765	785
08	31 806	827	848	869	890	911	931	952	973	994
09	32 015	035	056	077	098	118	139	160	181	201
210	222	243	263	284	305	325	346	366	387	408
11	428	449	469	490	510	531	552	572	593	613
12	634	654	675	695	715	736	756	777	797	818
13	32 838	858	879	899	919	940	960	980	*001	*021
14	33 041	062	082	102	122	143	163	183	203	224
15	244	264	284	304	325	345	365	385	405	425
16	445	465	486	506	526	546	566	586	606	626
17	646	666	686	706	726	746	766	786	806	826
18	33 846	866	885	905	925	945	965	985	*005	*025
19	34 044	064	084	104	124	143	163	183	203	223
220	242	262	282	301	321	341	361	380	400	420
21	439	459	479	498	518	537	557	577	596	616
22	635	655	674	694	713	733	753	772	792	811
23	34 830	850	869	889	908	928	947	967	986	*005
24	35 025	044	064	083	102	122	141	160	180	199
25	218	238	257	276	295	315	334	353	372	392
26	411	430	449	468	488	507	526	545	564	583
27	603	622	641	660	679	698	717	736	755	774
28	793	813	832	851	870	889	908	927	946	965
29	35 984	*003	*021	*040	*059	*078	*097	*116	*135	*154
230	36 173	192	211	229	248	267	286	305	324	342
31	361	380	399	418	436	455	474	493	511	530
32	549	568	586	605	624	642	661	680	698	717
33	736	754	773	791	810	829	847	866	884	903
34	36 922	940	959	977	996	*014	*033	*051	*070	*088
35	37 107	125	144	162	181	199	218	236	254	273
36	291	310	328	346	365	383	401	420	438	457
37	475	493	511	530	548	566	585	603	621	639
38	658	676	694	712	731	749	767	785	803	822
39	37 840	858	876	894	912	931	949	967	985	*003
240	38 021	039	057	075	093	112	130	148	166	184
41	202	220	238	256	274	292	310	328	346	364
42	382	399	417	435	453	471	489	507	525	543
43	561	578	596	614	632	650	668	686	703	721
44	739	757	775	792	810	828	846	863	881	899
45	38 917	934	952	970	987	*005	*023	*041	*058	*076
46	39 094	111	129	146	164	182	199	217	235	252
47	270	287	295	322	340	358	375	393	410	428
48	445	463	480	498	515	533	550	568	585	602
49	620	637	655	672	690	707	724	742	759	777
250	39 794	811	829	846	863	881	898	915	933	950
N	0	1	2	3	4	5	6	7	8	9

Prop. Parts

	22	21
1	2.2	2.1
2	4.4	4.2
3	6.6	6.3
4	8.8	8.4
5	11.0	10.5
6	13.2	12.6
7	15.4	14.7
8	17.6	16.8
9	19.8	18.9

	20
1	2
2	4
3	6
4	8
5	10
6	12
7	14
8	16
9	18

	19
1	1.9
2	3.8
3	5.7
4	7.6
5	9.5
6	11.4
7	13.3
8	15.2
9	17.1

	18
1	1.8
2	3.6
3	5.4
4	7.2
5	9.0
6	10.8
7	12.6
8	14.4
9	16.2

	17
1	1.7
2	3.4
3	5.1
4	6.8
5	8.5
6	10.2
7	11.9
8	13.6
9	15.3

VIII. FIVE-PLACE LOGARITHMS: 250 — 300

N	0	1	2	3	4	5	6	7	8	9
250	39 794	811	829	846	863	881	898	915	933	950
51	39 967	985	*002	*019	*037	*054	*071	*088	*106	*123
52	40 140	157	175	192	209	226	243	261	278	295
53	312	329	346	364	381	398	415	432	449	466
54	483	500	518	535	552	569	586	603	620	637
55	654	671	688	705	722	739	756	773	790	807
56	824	841	858	875	892	909	926	943	960	976
57	40 993	*010	*027	*044	*061	*078	*095	*111	*128	*145
58	41 162	179	196	212	229	246	263	280	296	313
59	330	347	363	380	397	414	430	447	464	481
260	497	514	531	547	564	581	597	614	631	647
61	664	681	697	714	731	747	764	780	797	814
62	830	847	863	880	896	913	929	946	963	979
63	41 996	*012	*029	*045	*062	*078	*095	*111	*127	*144
64	42 160	177	193	210	226	243	259	275	292	308
65	325	341	357	374	390	406	423	439	455	472
66	488	504	521	537	553	570	586	602	619	635
67	651	667	684	700	716	732	749	765	781	797
68	813	830	846	862	878	894	911	927	943	959
69	42 975	991	*008	*024	*040	*056	*072	*088	*104	*120
270	43 136	152	169	185	201	217	233	249	265	281
71	297	313	329	345	361	377	393	409	425	441
72	457	473	489	505	521	537	553	569	584	600
73	616	632	648	664	680	696	712	727	743	759
74	775	791	807	823	838	854	870	886	902	917
75	43 933	949	965	981	996	*012	*028	*044	*059	*075
76	44 091	107	122	138	154	170	185	201	217	232
77	248	264	279	295	311	326	342	358	373	389
78	404	420	436	451	467	483	498	514	529	545
79	560	576	592	607	623	638	654	669	685	700
280	716	731	747	762	778	793	809	824	840	855
81	44 871	886	902	917	932	948	963	979	994	*010
82	45 025	040	056	071	086	102	117	133	148	163
83	179	194	209	225	240	255	271	286	301	317
84	332	347	362	378	393	408	423	439	454	469
85	484	500	515	530	545	561	576	591	606	621
86	637	652	667	682	697	712	728	743	758	773
87	788	803	818	834	849	864	879	894	909	924
88	45 939	954	969	984	*000	*015	*030	*045	*060	*075
89	46 090	105	120	135	150	165	180	195	210	225
290	240	255	270	285	300	315	330	345	359	374
91	389	404	419	434	449	464	479	494	509	523
92	538	553	568	583	598	613	627	642	657	672
93	687	702	716	731	746	761	776	790	805	820
94	835	850	864	879	894	909	923	938	953	967
95	46 982	997	*012	*026	*041	*056	*070	*085	*100	*114
96	47 129	144	159	173	188	202	217	232	246	261
97	276	290	305	319	334	349	363	378	392	407
98	422	436	451	465	480	494	509	524	538	553
99	567	582	596	611	625	640	654	669	683	698
300	47 712	727	741	756	770	784	799	813	828	842

Prop. Parts

18

1	1.8
2	3.6
3	5.4
4	7.2
5	9.0
6	10.8
7	12.6
8	14.4
9	16.2

17

1	1.7
2	3.4
3	5.1
4	6.8
5	8.5
6	10.2
7	11.9
8	13.6
9	15.3

16

1	1.6
2	3.2
3	4.8
4	6.4
5	8.0
6	9.6
7	11.2
8	12.8
9	14.4

15

1	1.5
2	3.0
3	4.5
4	6.0
5	7.5
6	9.0
7	10.5
8	12.0
9	13.5

14

1	1.4
2	2.8
3	4.2
4	5.6
5	7.0
6	8.4
7	9.8
8	11.2
9	12.6

N	0	1	2	3	4	5	6	7	8	9	Prop. Parts	
300	47 712	727	741	756	770	784	799	813	828	842		
01	47 857	871	885	900	914	929	943	958	972	986		
02	48 001	015	029	044	058	073	087	101	116	130		
03	144	159	173	187	202	216	230	244	259	273		
04	287	302	316	330	344	359	373	387	401	416		**15**
05	430	444	458	473	487	501	515	530	544	558	1	1.5
06	572	586	601	615	629	643	657	671	686	700	2	3.0
											3	4.5
07	714	728	742	756	770	785	799	813	827	841	4	6.0
08	855	869	883	897	911	926	940	954	968	982	5	7.5
09	48 996	*010	*024	*038	*052	*066	*080	*094	*108	*122	6	9.0
											7	10.5
310	49 136	150	164	178	192	206	220	234	248	262	8	12.0
11	276	290	304	318	332	346	360	374	388	402	9	13.5
12	415	429	443	457	471	485	499	513	527	541		
13	554	568	582	596	610	624	638	651	665	679		
14	693	707	721	734	748	762	776	790	803	817		
15	831	845	859	872	886	900	914	927	941	955		**14**
16	49 969	982	996	*010	*024	*037	*051	*065	*079	*092	1	1.4
17	50 106	120	133	147	161	174	188	202	215	229	2	2.8
18	243	256	270	284	297	311	325	338	352	365	3	4.2
19	379	393	406	420	433	447	461	474	488	501	4	5.6
320	515	529	542	556	569	583	596	610	623	637	5	7.0
											6	8.4
21	651	664	678	691	705	718	732	745	759	772	7	9.8
22	786	799	813	826	840	853	866	880	893	907	8	11.2
23	50 920	934	947	961	974	987	*001	*014	*028	*041	9	12.6
24	51 055	068	081	095	108	121	135	148	162	175		
25	188	202	215	228	242	255	268	282	295	308		
26	322	335	348	362	375	388	402	415	428	441		
27	455	468	481	495	508	521	534	548	561	574		**13**
28	587	601	614	627	640	654	667	680	693	706		
29	720	733	746	759	772	786	799	812	825	838	1	1.3
											2	2.6
330	851	865	878	891	904	917	930	943	957	970	3	3.9
											4	5.2
31	51 983	996	*009	*022	*035	*048	*061	*075	*088	*101	5	6.5
32	52 114	127	140	153	166	179	192	205	218	231	6	7.8
33	244	257	270	284	297	310	323	336	349	362	7	9.1
											8	10.4
34	375	388	401	414	427	440	453	466	479	492	9	11.7
35	504	517	530	543	556	569	582	595	608	621		
36	634	647	660	673	686	699	711	724	737	750		
37	763	776	789	802	815	827	840	853	866	879		
38	52 892	905	917	930	943	956	969	982	994	*007		
39	53 020	033	046	058	071	084	097	110	122	135		**12**
340	148	161	173	186	199	212	224	237	250	263	1	1.2
41	275	288	301	314	326	339	352	364	377	390	2	2.4
42	403	415	428	441	453	466	479	491	504	517	3	3.6
43	529	542	555	567	580	593	605	618	631	643	4	4.8
											5	6.0
44	656	668	681	694	706	719	732	744	757	769	6	7.2
45	782	794	807	820	832	845	857	870	882	895	7	8.4
46	53 908	920	933	945	958	970	983	995	*008	*020	8	9.6
											9	10.8
47	54 033	045	058	070	083	095	108	120	133	145		
48	158	170	183	195	208	220	233	245	258	270		
49	283	295	307	320	332	345	357	370	382	394		
350	54 407	419	432	444	456	469	481	494	506	518		
N	0	1	2	3	4	5	6	7	8	9	Prop. Parts	

Prop. Parts		N	0	1	2	3	4	5	6	7	8	9
		350	54 407	419	432	444	456	469	481	494	506	518
		51	531	543	555	568	580	593	605	617	630	642
		52	654	667	679	691	704	716	728	741	753	765
		53	777	790	802	814	827	839	851	864	876	888
13		54	54 900	913	925	937	949	962	974	986	998	*011
1	1.3	**55**	55 023	035	047	060	072	084	096	108	121	133
2	2.6	56	145	157	169	182	194	206	218	230	242	255
3	3.9											
4	5.2	57	267	279	291	303	315	328	340	352	364	376
5	6.5	58	388	400	413	425	437	449	461	473	485	497
6	7.8	59	509	522	534	546	558	570	582	594	606	618
7	9.1											
8	10.4	**360**	630	642	654	666	678	691	703	715	727	739
9	11.7	61	751	763	775	787	799	811	823	835	847	859
		62	871	883	895	907	919	931	943	955	967	979
		63	55 991	*003	*015	*027	*038	*050	*062	*074	*086	*098
		64	56 110	122	134	146	158	170	182	194	205	217
		65	229	241	253	265	277	289	301	312	324	336
12		66	348	360	372	384	396	407	419	431	443	455
1	1.2	67	467	478	490	502	514	526	538	549	561	573
2	2.4	68	585	597	608	620	632	644	656	667	679	691
3	3.6	69	703	714	726	738	750	761	773	785	797	808
4	4.8											
5	6.0	**370**	820	832	844	855	867	879	891	902	914	926
6	7.2											
7	8.4	71	56 937	949	961	972	984	996	*008	*019	*031	*043
8	9.6	72	57 054	066	078	089	101	113	124	136	148	159
9	10.8	73	171	183	194	206	217	229	241	252	264	276
		74	287	299	310	322	334	345	357	368	380	392
		75	403	415	426	438	449	461	473	484	496	507
		76	519	530	542	553	565	576	588	600	611	623
		77	634	646	657	669	680	692	703	715	726	738
11		78	749	761	772	784	795	807	818	830	841	852
1	1.1	79	864	875	887	898	910	921	933	944	955	967
2	2.2	**380**	57 978	990	*001	*013	*024	*035	*047	*058	*070	*081
3	3.3	81	58 092	104	115	127	138	149	161	172	184	195
4	4.4	82	206	218	229	240	252	263	274	286	297	309
5	5.5	83	320	331	343	354	365	377	388	399	410	422
6	6.6											
7	7.7	84	433	444	456	467	478	490	501	512	524	535
8	8.8	**85**	546	557	569	580	591	602	614	625	636	647
9	9.9	86	659	670	681	692	704	715	726	737	749	760
		87	771	782	794	805	816	827	838	850	861	872
		88	883	894	906	917	928	939	950	961	973	984
		89	58 995	*006	*017	*028	*040	*051	*062	*073	*084	*095
10		**390**	59 106	118	129	140	151	162	173	184	195	207
1	1.0	91	218	229	240	251	262	273	284	295	306	318
2	2.0	92	329	340	351	362	373	384	395	406	417	428
3	3.0	93	439	450	461	472	483	494	506	517	528	539
4	4.0											
5	5.0	94	550	561	572	583	594	605	616	627	638	649
6	6.0	**95**	660	671	682	693	704	715	726	737	748	759
7	7.0	96	770	780	791	802	813	824	835	846	857	868
8	8.0	97	879	890	901	912	923	934	945	956	966	977
9	9.0	98	59 988	999	*010	*021	*032	*043	*054	*065	*076	*086
		99	60 097	108	119	130	141	152	163	173	184	195
		400	60 206	217	228	239	249	260	271	282	293	304
Prop. Parts		N	0	1	2	3	4	5	6	7	8	9

N	0	1	2	3	4	5	6	7	8	9	Prop. Parts
400	60 206	217	228	239	249	260	271	282	293	304	
01	314	325	336	347	358	369	379	390	401	412	
02	423	433	444	455	466	477	487	498	509	520	
03	531	541	552	563	574	584	595	606	617	627	
04	638	649	660	670	681	692	703	713	724	735	
05	746	756	767	778	788	799	810	821	831	842	
06	853	863	874	885	895	906	917	927	938	949	
07	60 959	970	981	991	*002	*013	*023	*034	*045	*055	
08	61 066	077	087	098	109	119	130	140	151	162	
09	172	183	194	204	215	225	236	247	257	268	
410	278	289	300	310	321	331	342	352	363	374	
11	384	395	405	416	426	437	448	458	469	479	
12	490	500	511	521	532	542	553	563	574	584	
13	595	606	616	627	637	648	658	669	679	690	
14	700	711	721	731	742	752	763	773	784	794	
15	805	815	826	836	847	857	868	878	888	899	
16	61 909	920	930	941	951	962	972	982	993	*003	
17	62 014	024	034	045	055	066	076	086	097	107	
18	118	128	138	149	159	170	180	190	201	211	
19	221	232	242	252	263	273	284	294	304	315	
420	325	335	346	356	366	377	387	397	408	418	
21	428	439	449	459	469	480	490	500	511	521	
22	531	542	552	562	572	583	593	603	613	624	
23	634	644	655	665	675	685	696	706	716	726	
24	737	747	757	767	778	788	798	808	818	829	
25	839	849	859	870	880	890	900	910	921	931	
26	62 941	951	961	972	982	992	*002	*012	*022	*033	
27	63 043	053	063	073	083	094	104	114	124	134	
28	144	155	165	175	185	195	205	215	225	236	
29	246	256	266	276	286	296	306	317	327	337	
430	347	357	367	377	387	397	407	417	428	438	
31	448	458	468	478	488	498	508	518	528	538	
32	548	558	568	579	589	599	609	619	629	639	
33	649	659	669	679	689	699	709	719	729	739	
34	749	759	769	779	789	799	809	819	829	839	
35	849	859	869	879	889	899	909	919	929	939	
36	63 949	959	969	979	988	998	*008	*018	*028	*038	
37	64 048	058	068	078	088	098	108	118	128	137	
38	147	157	167	177	187	197	207	217	227	237	
39	246	256	266	276	286	296	306	316	326	335	
440	345	355	365	375	385	395	404	414	424	434	
41	444	454	464	473	483	493	503	513	523	532	
42	542	552	562	572	582	591	601	611	621	631	
43	640	650	660	670	680	689	699	709	719	729	
44	738	748	758	768	777	787	797	807	816	826	
45	836	846	856	865	875	885	895	904	914	924	
46	64 933	943	953	963	972	982	992	*002	*011	*021	
47	65 031	040	050	060	070	079	089	099	108	118	
48	128	137	147	157	167	176	186	196	205	215	
49	225	234	244	254	263	273	283	292	302	312	
450	65 321	331	341	350	360	369	379	389	398	408	
N	0	1	2	3	4	5	6	7	8	9	Prop. Parts

Prop. Parts:

11

1	1.1
2	2.2
3	3.3
4	4.4
5	5.5
6	6.6
7	7.7
8	8.8
9	9.9

10

1	1.0
2	2.0
3	3.0
4	4.0
5	5.0
6	6.0
7	7.0
8	8.0
9	9.0

9

1	0.9
2	1.8
3	2.7
4	3.6
5	4.5
6	5.4
7	6.3
8	7.2
9	8.1

Prop. Parts	N	0	1	2	3	4	5	6	7	8	9
	450	65 321	331	341	350	360	369	379	389	398	408
	51	418	427	437	447	456	466	475	485	495	504
	52	514	523	533	543	552	562	571	581	591	600
	53	610	619	629	639	648	658	667	677	686	696
	54	706	715	725	734	744	753	763	772	782	792
	55	801	811	820	830	839	849	858	868	877	887
	56	896	906	916	925	935	944	954	963	973	982
10	57	65 992	*001	*011	*020	*030	*039	*049	*058	*068	*077
1 1.0	58	66 087	096	106	115	124	134	143	153	162	172
2 2.0	59	181	191	200	210	219	229	238	247	257	266
3 3.0 4 4.0	**460**	276	285	295	304	314	323	332	342	351	361
5 5.0	61	370	380	389	398	408	417	427	436	445	455
6 6.0	62	464	474	483	492	502	511	521	530	539	549
7 7.0	63	558	567	577	586	596	605	614	624	633	642
8 8.0	64	652	661	671	680	689	699	708	717	727	736
9 9.0	**65**	745	755	764	773	783	792	801	811	820	829
	66	839	848	857	867	876	885	894	904	913	922
	67	66 932	941	950	960	969	978	987	997	*006	*015
	68	67 025	034	043	052	062	071	080	089	099	108
	69	117	127	136	145	154	164	173	182	191	201
	470	210	219	228	237	247	256	265	274	284	293
9	71	302	311	321	330	339	348	357	367	376	385
1 0.9	72	394	403	413	422	431	440	449	459	468	477
2 1 8	73	486	495	504	514	523	532	541	550	560	569
3 2.7	74	578	587	596	605	614	624	633	642	651	660
4 3.6	**75**	669	679	688	697	706	715	724	733	742	752
5 4.5	76	761	770	779	788	797	806	815	825	834	843
6 5.4	77	852	861	870	879	888	897	906	916	925	934
7 6.3	78	67 943	952	961	970	979	988	997	*006	*015	*024
8 7.2	79	68 034	043	052	061	070	079	088	097	106	115
9 8.1	**480**	124	133	142	151	160	169	178	187	196	205
	81	215	224	233	242	251	260	269	278	287	296
	82	305	314	323	332	341	350	359	368	377	386
	83	395	404	413	422	431	440	449	458	467	476
	84	485	494	502	511	520	529	538	547	556	565
	85	574	583	592	601	610	619	628	637	646	655
8	86	664	673	681	690	699	708	717	726	735	744
1 0.8	87	753	762	771	780	789	797	806	815	824	833
2 1.6	88	842	851	860	869	878	886	895	904	913	922
3 2.4	89	68 931	940	949	958	966	975	984	993	*002	*011
4 3.2	**490**	69 020	028	037	046	055	064	073	082	090	099
5 4.0	91	108	117	126	135	144	152	161	170	179	188
6 4.8	92	197	205	214	223	232	241	249	258	267	276
7 5.6	93	285	294	302	311	320	329	338	346	355	364
8 6.4	94	373	381	390	399	408	417	425	434	443	452
9 7.2	**95**	461	469	478	487	496	504	513	522	531	539
	96	548	557	566	574	583	592	601	609	618	627
	97	636	644	653	662	671	679	688	697	705	714
	98	723	732	740	749	758	767	775	784	793	801
	99	810	819	827	836	845	854	862	871	880	888
	500	69 897	906	914	923	932	940	949	958	966	975
Prop. Parts	N	0	1	2	3	4	5	6	7	8	9

[25]

N	0	1	2	3	4	5	6	7	8	9	Prop. Parts
500	69 897	906	914	923	932	940	949	958	966	975	
01	69 984	992	*001	*010	*018	*027	*036	*044	*053	*062	
02	70 070	079	088	096	105	114	122	131	140	148	
03	157	165	174	183	191	200	209	217	226	234	
04	243	252	260	269	278	286	295	303	312	321	
05	329	338	346	355	364	372	381	389	398	406	
06	415	424	432	441	449	458	467	475	484	492	
07	501	509	518	526	535	544	552	561	569	578	
08	586	595	603	612	621	629	638	646	655	663	
09	672	680	689	697	706	714	723	731	740	749	
510	757	766	774	783	791	800	808	817	825	834	
11	842	851	859	868	876	885	893	902	910	919	
12	70 927	935	944	952	961	969	978	986	995	*003	
13	71 012	020	029	037	046	054	063	071	079	088	
14	096	105	113	122	130	139	147	155	164	172	
15	181	189	198	206	214	223	231	240	248	257	
16	265	273	282	290	299	307	315	324	332	341	
17	349	357	366	374	383	391	399	408	416	425	
18	433	441	450	458	466	475	483	492	500	508	
19	517	525	533	542	550	559	567	575	584	592	
520	600	609	617	625	634	642	650	659	667	675	
21	684	692	700	709	717	725	734	742	750	759	
22	767	775	784	792	800	809	817	825	834	842	
23	850	858	867	875	883	892	900	908	917	925	
24	71 933	941	950	958	966	975	983	991	999	*008	
25	72 016	024	032	041	049	057	066	074	082	090	
26	099	107	115	123	132	140	148	156	165	173	
27	181	189	198	206	214	222	230	239	247	255	
28	263	272	280	288	296	304	313	321	329	337	
29	346	354	362	370	378	387	395	403	411	419	
530	428	436	444	452	460	469	477	485	493	501	
31	509	518	526	534	542	550	558	567	575	583	
32	591	599	607	616	624	632	640	648	656	665	
33	673	681	689	697	705	713	722	730	738	746	
34	754	762	770	779	787	795	803	811	819	827	
35	835	843	852	860	868	876	884	892	900	908	
36	916	925	933	941	949	957	965	973	981	989	
37	72 997	*006	*014	*022	*030	*038	*046	*054	*062	*070	
38	73 078	086	094	102	111	119	127	135	143	151	
39	159	167	175	183	191	199	207	215	223	231	
540	239	247	255	263	272	280	288	296	304	312	
41	320	328	336	344	352	360	368	376	384	392	
42	400	408	416	424	432	440	448	456	464	472	
43	480	488	496	504	512	520	528	536	544	552	
44	560	568	576	584	592	600	608	616	624	632	
45	640	648	656	664	672	679	687	695	703	711	
46	719	727	735	743	751	759	767	775	783	791	
47	799	807	815	823	830	838	846	854	862	870	
48	878	886	894	902	910	918	926	933	941	949	
49	73 957	965	973	981	989	997	*005	*013	*020	*028	
550	74 036	044	052	060	068	076	084	092	099	107	
N	0	1	2	3	4	5	6	7	8	9	Prop. Parts

Prop. Parts

	9
1	0.9
2	1.8
3	2.7
4	3.6
5	4.5
6	5.4
7	6.3
8	7.2
9	8.1

	8
1	0.8
2	1.6
3	2.4
4	3.2
5	4.0
6	4.8
7	5.6
8	6.4
9	7.2

	7
1	0.7
2	1.4
3	2.1
4	2.8
5	3.5
6	4.2
7	4.9
8	5.6
9	6.3

N	0	1	2	3	4	5	6	7	8	9
550	74 036	044	052	060	068	076	084	092	099	107
51	115	123	131	139	147	155	162	170	178	186
52	194	202	210	218	225	233	241	249	257	265
53	273	280	288	296	304	312	320	327	335	343
54	351	359	367	374	382	390	398	406	414	421
55	429	437	445	453	461	468	476	484	492	500
56	507	515	523	531	539	547	554	562	570	578
57	586	593	601	609	617	624	632	640	648	656
58	663	671	679	687	695	702	710	718	726	733
59	741	749	757	764	772	780	788	796	803	811
560	819	827	834	842	850	858	865	873	881	889
61	896	904	912	920	927	935	943	950	958	966
62	74 974	981	989	997	*005	*012	*020	*028	*035	*043
63	75 051	059	066	074	082	089	097	105	113	120
64	128	136	143	151	159	166	174	182	189	197
65	205	213	220	228	236	243	251	259	266	274
66	282	289	297	305	312	320	328	335	343	351
67	358	366	374	381	389	397	404	412	420	427
68	435	442	450	458	465	473	481	488	496	504
69	511	519	526	534	542	549	557	565	572	580
570	587	595	603	610	618	626	633	641	648	656
71	664	671	679	686	694	702	709	717	724	732
72	740	747	755	762	770	778	785	793	800	808
73	815	823	831	838	846	853	861	868	876	884
74	891	899	906	914	921	929	937	944	952	959
75	75 967	974	982	989	997	*005	*012	*020	*027	*035
76	76 042	050	057	065	072	080	087	095	103	110
77	118	125	133	140	148	155	163	170	178	185
78	193	200	208	215	223	230	238	245	253	260
79	268	275	283	290	298	305	313	320	328	335
580	343	350	358	365	373	380	388	395	403	410
81	418	425	433	440	448	455	462	470	477	485
82	492	500	507	515	522	530	537	545	552	559
83	567	574	582	589	597	604	612	619	626	634
84	641	649	656	664	671	678	686	693	701	708
85	716	723	730	738	745	753	760	768	775	782
86	790	797	805	812	819	827	834	842	849	856
87	864	871	879	886	893	901	908	916	923	930
88	76 938	945	953	960	967	975	982	989	997	*004
89	77 012	019	026	034	041	048	056	063	070	078
590	085	093	100	107	115	122	129	137	144	151
91	159	166	173	181	188	195	203	210	217	225
92	232	240	247	254	262	269	276	283	291	298
93	305	313	320	327	335	342	349	357	364	371
94	379	386	393	401	408	415	422	430	437	444
95	452	459	466	474	481	488	495	503	510	517
96	525	532	539	546	554	561	568	576	583	590
97	597	605	612	619	627	634	641	648	656	663
98	670	677	685	692	699	706	714	721	728	735
99	743	750	757	764	772	779	786	793	801	808
600	77 815	822	830	837	844	851	859	866	873	880

Prop. Parts

8

1	0.8
2	1.6
3	2.4
4	3.2
5	4.0
6	4.8
7	5.6
8	6.4
9	7.2

7

1	0.7
2	1.4
3	2.1
4	2.8
5	3.5
6	4.2
7	4.9
8	5.6
9	6.3

N	0	1	2	3	4	5	6	7	8	9	Prop. Parts	
600	77 815	822	830	837	844	851	859	866	873	880		
01	887	895	902	909	916	924	931	938	945	952		
02	77 960	967	974	981	988	996	*003	*010	*017	*025		
03	78 032	039	046	053	061	068	075	082	089	097		
04	104	111	118	125	132	140	147	154	161	168		
05	176	183	190	197	204	211	219	226	233	240		
06	247	254	262	269	276	283	290	297	305	312		**8**
07	319	326	333	340	347	355	362	369	376	383	1	0.8
08	390	398	405	412	419	426	433	440	447	455	2	1.6
09	462	469	476	483	490	497	504	512	519	526	3	2.4
610	533	540	547	554	561	569	576	583	590	597	4	3.2
11	604	611	618	625	633	640	647	654	661	668	5	4.0
											6	4.8
12	675	682	689	696	704	711	718	725	732	739	7	5 6
13	746	753	760	767	774	781	789	796	803	810	8	6.4
14	817	824	831	838	845	852	859	866	873	880	9	7.2
15	888	895	902	909	916	923	930	937	944	951		
16	78 958	965	972	979	986	993	*000	*007	*014	*021		
17	79 029	036	043	050	057	064	071	078	085	092		
18	099	106	113	120	127	134	141	148	155	162		
19	169	176	183	190	197	204	211	218	225	232		
620	239	246	253	260	267	274	281	288	295	302		
21	309	316	323	330	337	344	351	358	365	372		**7**
22	379	386	393	400	407	414	421	428	435	442	1	0.7
23	449	456	463	470	477	484	491	498	505	511	2	1.4
24	518	525	532	539	546	553	560	567	574	581	3	2.1
											4	2.8
25	588	595	602	609	616	623	630	637	644	650	5	3.5
26	657	664	671	678	685	692	699	706	713	720	6	4.2
27	727	734	741	748	754	761	768	775	782	789	7	4.9
28	796	803	810	817	824	831	837	844	851	858	8	5.6
29	865	872	879	886	893	900	906	913	920	927	9	6.3
630	79 934	941	948	955	962	969	975	982	989	996		
31	80 003	010	017	024	030	037	044	051	058	065		
32	072	079	085	092	099	106	113	120	127	134		
33	140	147	154	161	168	175	182	188	195	202		
34	209	216	223	229	236	243	250	257	264	271		
35	277	284	291	298	305	312	318	325	332	339		
36	346	353	359	366	373	380	387	393	400	407		**6**
37	414	421	428	434	441	448	455	462	468	475	1	0.6
38	482	489	496	502	509	516	523	530	536	543	2	1.2
39	550	557	564	570	577	584	591	598	604	611	3	1.8
											4	2.4
640	618	625	632	638	645	652	659	665	672	679	5	3.0
41	686	693	699	706	713	720	726	733	740	747	6	3.6
42	754	760	767	774	781	787	794	801	808	814	7	4.2
43	821	828	835	841	848	855	862	868	875	882	8	4.8
44	889	895	902	909	916	922	929	936	943	949	9	5.4
45	80 956	963	969	976	983	990	996	*003	*010	*017		
46	81 023	030	037	043	050	057	064	070	077	084		
47	090	097	104	111	117	124	131	137	144	151		
48	158	164	171	178	184	191	198	204	211	218		
49	224	231	238	245	251	258	265	271	278	285		
650	81 291	298	305	311	318	325	331	338	345	351		
N	0	1	2	3	4	5	6	7	8	9	Prop. Parts	

Prop. Parts	N	0	1	2	3	4	5	6	7	8	9
	650	81 291	298	305	311	318	325	331	338	345	351
	51	358	365	371	378	385	391	398	405	411	418
	52	425	431	438	445	451	458	465	471	478	485
	53	491	498	505	511	518	525	531	538	544	551
	54	558	564	571	578	584	591	598	604	611	617
	55	624	631	637	644	651	657	664	671	677	684
	56	690	697	704	710	717	723	730	737	743	750
	57	757	763	770	776	783	790	796	803	809	816
	58	823	829	836	842	849	856	862	869	875	882
	59	889	895	902	908	915	921	928	935	941	948
	660	81 954	961	968	974	981	987	994	*000	*007	*014
	61	82 020	027	033	040	046	053	060	066	073	079
	62	086	092	099	105	112	119	125	132	138	145
	63	151	158	164	171	178	184	191	197	204	210
	64	217	223	230	236	243	249	256	263	269	276
	65	282	289	295	302	308	315	321	328	334	341
	66	347	354	360	367	373	380	387	393	400	406
	67	413	419	426	432	439	445	452	458	465	471
	68	478	484	491	497	504	510	517	523	530	536
	69	543	549	556	562	569	575	582	588	595	601
	670	607	614	620	627	633	640	646	653	659	666
	71	672	679	685	692	698	705	711	718	724	730
	72	737	743	750	756	763	769	776	782	789	795
	73	802	808	814	821	827	834	840	847	853	860
	74	866	872	879	885	892	898	905	911	918	924
	75	930	937	943	950	956	963	969	975	982	988
	76	82 995	*001	*008	*014	*020	*027	*033	*040	*046	*052
	77	83 059	065	072	078	085	091	097	104	110	117
	78	123	129	136	142	149	155	161	168	174	181
	79	187	193	200	206	213	219	225	232	238	245
	680	251	257	264	270	276	283	289	296	302	308
	81	315	321	327	334	340	347	353	359	366	372
	82	378	385	391	398	404	410	417	423	429	436
	83	442	448	455	461	467	474	480	487	493	499
	84	506	512	518	525	531	537	544	550	556	563
	85	569	575	582	588	594	601	607	613	620	626
	86	632	639	645	651	658	664	670	677	683	689
	87	696	702	708	715	721	727	734	740	746	753
	88	759	765	771	778	784	790	797	803	809	816
	89	822	828	835	841	847	853	860	866	872	879
	690	885	891	897	904	910	916	923	929	935	942
	91	83 948	954	960	967	973	979	985	992	998	*004
	92	84 011	017	023	029	036	042	048	055	061	067
	93	073	080	086	092	098	105	111	117	123	130
	94	136	142	148	155	161	167	173	180	186	192
	95	198	205	211	217	223	230	236	242	248	255
	96	261	267	273	280	286	292	298	305	311	317
	97	323	330	336	342	348	354	361	367	373	379
	98	386	392	398	404	410	417	423	429	435	442
	99	448	454	460	466	473	479	485	491	497	504
	700	84 510	516	522	528	535	541	547	553	559	566
Prop. Parts	N	0	1	2	3	4	5	6	7	8	9

Prop. Parts

7

1	0.7
2	1.4
3	2.1
4	2.8
5	3.5
6	4.2
7	4.9
8	5.6
9	6.3

6

1	0.6
2	1.2
3	1.8
4	2.4
5	3.0
6	3.6
7	4.2
8	4.8
9	5.4

N	0	1	2	3	4	5	6	7	8	9
700	84 510	516	522	528	535	541	547	553	559	566
01	572	578	584	590	597	603	609	615	621	628
02	634	640	646	652	658	665	671	677	683	689
03	696	702	708	714	720	726	733	739	745	751
04	757	763	770	776	782	788	794	800	807	813
05	819	825	831	837	844	850	856	862	868	874
06	880	887	893	899	905	911	917	924	930	936
07	84 942	948	954	960	967	973	979	985	991	997
08	85 003	009	016	022	028	034	040	046	052	058
09	065	071	077	083	089	095	101	107	114	120
710	126	132	138	144	150	156	163	169	175	181
11	187	193	199	205	211	217	224	230	236	242
12	248	254	260	266	272	278	285	291	297	303
13	309	315	321	327	333	339	345	352	358	364
14	370	376	382	388	394	400	406	412	418	425
15	431	437	443	449	455	461	467	473	479	485
16	491	497	503	509	516	522	528	534	540	546
17	552	558	564	570	576	582	588	594	600	606
18	612	618	625	631	637	643	649	655	661	667
19	673	679	685	691	697	703	709	715	721	727
720	733	739	745	751	757	763	769	775	781	788
21	794	800	806	812	818	824	830	836	842	848
22	854	860	866	872	878	884	890	896	902	908
23	914	920	926	932	938	944	950	956	962	968
24	85 974	980	986	992	998	*004	*010	*016	*022	*028
25	86 034	040	046	052	058	064	070	076	082	088
26	094	100	106	112	118	124	130	136	141	147
27	153	159	165	171	177	183	189	195	201	207
28	213	219	225	231	237	243	249	255	261	267
29	273	279	285	291	297	303	308	314	320	326
730	332	338	344	350	356	362	368	374	380	386
31	392	398	404	410	415	421	427	433	439	445
32	451	457	463	469	475	481	487	493	499	504
33	510	516	522	528	534	540	546	552	558	564
34	570	576	581	587	593	599	605	611	617	623
35	629	635	641	646	652	658	664	670	676	682
36	688	694	700	705	711	717	723	729	735	741
37	747	753	759	764	770	776	782	788	794	800
38	806	812	817	823	829	835	841	847	853	859
39	864	870	876	882	888	894	900	906	911	917
740	923	929	935	941	947	953	958	964	970	976
41	86 982	988	994	999	*005	*011	*017	*023	*029	*035
42	87 040	046	052	058	064	070	075	081	087	093
43	099	105	111	116	122	128	134	140	146	151
44	157	163	169	175	181	186	192	198	204	210
45	216	221	227	233	239	245	251	256	262	268
46	274	280	286	291	297	303	309	315	320	326
47	332	338	344	349	355	361	367	373	379	384
48	390	396	402	408	413	419	425	431	437	442
49	448	454	460	466	471	477	483	489	495	500
750	87 506	512	518	523	529	535	541	547	552	558
N	0	1	2	3	4	5	6	7	8	9

Prop. Parts

7	
1	0.7
2	1.4
3	2.1
4	2.8
5	3.5
6	4.2
7	4.9
8	5.6
9	6.3

6	
1	0.6
2	1.2
3	1.8
4	2.4
5	3.0
6	3.6
7	4.2
8	4.8
9	5.4

5	
1	0.5
2	1.0
3	1.5
4	2.0
5	2.5
6	3.0
7	3.5
8	4.0
9	4.5

N	0	1	2	3	4	5	6	7	8	9
750	87 506	512	518	523	529	535	541	547	552	558
51	564	570	576	581	587	593	599	604	610	616
52	622	628	633	639	645	651	656	662	668	674
53	679	685	691	697	703	708	714	720	726	731
54	737	743	749	754	760	766	772	777	783	789
55	795	800	806	812	818	823	829	835	841	846
56	852	858	864	869	875	881	887	892	898	904
57	910	915	921	927	933	938	944	950	955	961
58	87 967	973	978	984	990	996	*001	*007	*013	*018
59	88 024	030	036	041	047	053	058	064	070	076
760	081	087	093	098	104	110	116	121	127	133
61	138	144	150	156	161	167	173	178	184	190
62	195	201	207	213	218	224	230	235	241	247
63	252	258	264	270	275	281	287	292	298	304
64	309	315	321	326	332	338	343	349	355	360
65	366	372	377	383	389	395	400	406	412	417
66	423	429	434	440	446	451	457	463	468	474
67	480	485	491	497	502	508	513	519	525	530
68	536	542	547	553	559	564	570	576	581	587
69	593	598	604	610	615	621	627	632	638	643
770	649	655	660	666	672	677	683	689	694	700
71	705	711	717	722	728	734	739	745	750	756
72	762	767	773	779	784	790	795	801	807	812
73	818	824	829	835	840	846	852	857	863	868
74	874	880	885	891	897	902	908	913	919	925
75	930	936	941	947	953	958	964	969	975	981
76	88 986	992	997	*003	*009	*014	*020	*025	*031	*037
77	89 042	048	053	059	064	070	076	081	087	092
78	098	104	109	115	120	126	131	137	143	148
79	154	159	165	170	176	182	187	193	198	204
780	209	215	221	226	232	237	243	248	254	260
81	265	271	276	282	287	293	298	304	310	315
82	321	326	332	337	343	348	354	360	365	371
83	376	382	387	393	398	404	409	415	421	426
84	432	437	443	448	454	459	465	470	476	481
85	487	492	498	504	509	515	520	526	531	537
86	542	548	553	559	564	570	575	581	586	592
87	597	603	609	614	620	625	631	636	642	647
88	653	658	664	669	675	680	686	691	697	702
89	708	713	719	724	730	735	741	746	752	757
790	763	768	774	779	785	790	796	801	807	812
91	818	823	829	834	840	845	851	856	862	867
92	873	878	883	889	894	900	905	911	916	922
93	927	933	938	944	949	955	960	966	971	977
94	89 982	988	993	998	*004	*009	*015	*020	*026	*031
95	90 037	042	048	053	059	064	069	075	080	086
96	091	097	102	108	113	119	124	129	135	140
97	146	151	157	162	168	173	179	184	189	195
98	200	206	211	217	222	227	233	238	244	249
99	255	260	266	271	276	282	287	293	298	304
800	90 309	314	320	325	331	336	342	347	352	358

Prop. Parts

6

1	0.6
2	1.2
3	1.8
4	2.4
5	3.0
6	3.6
7	4.2
8	4.8
9	5.4

5

1	0.5
2	1.0
3	1.5
4	2.0
5	2.5
6	3.0
7	3.5
8	4.0
9	4.5

N	0	1	2	3	4	5	6	7	8	9	Prop. Parts
800	90 309	314	320	325	331	336	342	347	352	358	
01	363	369	374	380	385	390	396	401	407	412	
02	417	423	428	434	439	445	450	455	461	466	
03	472	477	482	488	493	499	504	509	515	520	
04	526	531	536	542	547	553	558	563	569	574	
05	580	585	590	596	601	607	612	617	623	628	
06	634	639	644	650	655	660	666	671	677	682	
07	687	693	698	703	709	714	720	725	730	736	
08	741	747	752	757	763	768	773	779	784	789	
09	795	800	806	811	816	822	827	832	838	843	
810	849	854	859	865	870	875	881	886	891	897	
11	902	907	913	918	924	929	934	940	945	950	
12	90 956	961	966	972	977	982	988	993	998	*004	
13	91 009	014	020	025	030	036	041	046	052	057	
14	062	068	073	078	084	089	094	100	105	110	
15	116	121	126	132	137	142	148	153	158	164	
16	169	174	180	185	190	196	201	206	212	217	
17	222	228	233	238	243	249	254	259	265	270	
18	275	281	286	291	297	302	307	312	318	323	
19	328	334	339	344	350	355	360	365	371	376	
820	381	387	392	397	403	408	413	418	424	429	
21	434	440	445	450	455	461	466	471	477	482	
22	487	492	498	503	508	514	519	524	529	535	
23	540	545	551	556	561	566	572	577	582	587	
24	593	598	603	609	614	619	624	630	635	640	
25	645	651	656	661	666	672	677	682	687	693	
26	698	703	709	714	719	724	730	735	740	745	
27	751	756	761	766	772	777	782	787	793	798	
28	803	808	814	819	824	829	834	840	845	850	
29	855	861	866	871	876	882	887	892	897	903	
830	908	913	918	924	929	934	939	944	950	955	
31	91 960	965	971	976	981	986	991	997	*002	*007	
32	92 012	018	023	028	033	038	044	049	054	059	
33	065	070	075	080	085	091	096	101	106	111	
34	117	122	127	132	137	143	148	153	158	163	
35	169	174	179	184	189	195	200	205	210	215	
36	221	226	231	236	241	247	252	257	262	267	
37	273	278	283	288	293	298	304	309	314	319	
38	324	330	335	340	345	350	355	361	366	371	
39	376	381	387	392	397	402	407	412	418	423	
840	428	433	438	443	449	454	459	464	469	474	
41	480	485	490	495	500	505	511	516	521	526	
42	531	536	542	547	552	557	562	567	572	578	
43	583	588	593	598	603	609	614	619	624	629	
44	634	639	645	650	655	660	665	670	675	681	
45	686	691	696	701	706	711	716	722	727	732	
46	737	742	747	752	758	763	768	773	778	783	
47	788	793	799	804	809	814	819	824	829	834	
48	840	845	850	855	860	865	870	875	881	886	
49	891	896	901	906	911	916	921	927	932	937	
850	92 942	947	952	957	962	967	973	978	983	988	
N	**0**	**1**	**2**	**3**	**4**	**5**	**6**	**7**	**8**	**9**	Prop. Parts

Prop. Parts:

	6
1	0.6
2	1.2
3	1.8
4	2.4
5	3.0
6	3.6
7	4.2
8	4.8
9	5.4

	5
1	0.5
2	1.0
3	1.5
4	2.0
5	2.5
6	3.0
7	3.5
8	4.0
9	4.5

N	0	1	2	3	4	5	6	7	8	9
850	92 942	947	952	957	962	967	973	978	983	988
51	92 993	998	*003	*008	*013	*018	*024	*029	*034	*039
52	93 044	049	054	059	064	069	075	080	085	090
53	095	100	105	110	115	120	125	131	136	141
54	146	151	156	161	166	171	176	181	186	192
55	197	202	207	212	217	222	227	232	237	242
56	247	252	258	263	268	273	278	283	288	293
57	298	303	308	313	318	323	328	334	339	344
58	349	354	359	364	369	374	379	384	389	394
59	399	404	409	414	420	425	430	435	440	445
860	450	455	460	465	470	475	480	485	490	495
61	500	505	510	515	520	526	531	536	541	546
62	551	556	561	566	571	576	581	586	591	596
63	601	606	611	616	621	626	631	636	641	646
64	651	656	661	666	671	676	682	687	692	697
65	702	707	712	717	722	727	732	737	742	747
66	752	757	762	767	772	777	782	787	792	797
67	802	807	812	817	822	827	832	837	842	847
68	852	857	862	867	872	877	882	887	892	897
69	902	907	912	917	922	927	932	937	942	947
870	93 952	957	962	967	972	977	982	987	992	997
71	94 002	007	012	017	022	027	032	037	042	047
72	052	057	062	067	072	077	082	086	091	096
73	101	106	111	116	121	126	131	136	141	146
74	151	156	161	166	171	176	181	186	191	196
75	201	206	211	216	221	226	231	236	240	245
76	250	255	260	265	270	275	280	285	290	295
77	300	305	310	315	320	325	330	335	340	345
78	349	354	359	364	369	374	379	384	389	394
79	399	404	409	414	419	424	429	433	438	443
880	448	453	458	463	468	473	478	483	488	493
81	498	503	507	512	517	522	527	532	537	542
82	547	552	557	562	567	571	576	581	586	591
83	596	601	606	611	616	621	626	630	635	640
84	645	650	655	660	665	670	675	680	685	689
85	694	699	704	709	714	719	724	729	734	738
86	743	748	753	758	763	768	773	778	783	787
87	792	797	802	807	812	817	822	827	832	836
88	841	846	851	856	861	866	871	876	880	885
89	890	895	900	905	910	915	919	924	929	934
890	939	944	949	954	959	963	968	973	978	983
91	94 988	993	998	*002	*007	*012	*017	*022	*027	*032
92	95 036	041	046	051	056	061	066	071	075	080
93	085	090	095	100	105	109	114	119	124	129
94	134	139	143	148	153	158	163	168	173	177
95	182	187	192	197	202	207	211	216	221	226
96	231	236	240	245	250	255	260	265	270	274
97	279	284	289	294	299	303	308	313	318	323
98	328	332	337	342	347	352	357	361	366	371
99	376	381	386	390	395	400	405	410	415	419
900	95 424	429	434	439	444	448	453	458	463	468

Prop. Parts

6	
1	0.6
2	1.2
3	1.8
4	2.4
5	3.0
6	3.6
7	4.2
8	4.8
9	5.4

5	
1	0.5
2	1.0
3	1.5
4	2.0
5	2.5
6	3.0
7	3.5
8	4.0
9	4.5

4	
1	0.4
2	0.8
3	1.2
4	1.6
5	2.0
6	2.4
7	2.8
8	3.2
9	3.6

N	0	1	2	3	4	5	6	7	8	9	Prop. Parts
900	95 424	429	434	439	444	448	453	458	463	468	
01	472	477	482	487	492	497	501	506	511	516	
02	521	525	530	535	540	545	550	554	559	564	
03	569	574	578	583	588	593	598	602	607	612	
04	617	622	626	631	636	641	646	650	655	660	
05	665	670	674	679	684	689	694	698	703	708	
06	713	718	722	727	732	737	742	746	751	756	
07	761	766	770	775	780	785	789	794	799	804	
08	809	813	818	823	828	832	837	842	847	852	
09	856	861	866	871	875	880	885	890	895	899	
910	904	909	914	918	923	928	933	938	942	947	
11	952	957	961	966	971	976	980	985	990	995	**5**
12	95 999	*004	*009	*014	*019	*023	*028	*033	*038	*042	
13	96 047	052	057	061	066	071	076	080	085	090	1 0.5
14	095	099	104	109	114	118	123	128	133	137	2 1.0 3 1.5
15	142	147	152	156	161	166	171	175	180	185	4 2.0
16	190	194	199	204	209	213	218	223	227	232	5 2.5 6 3.0
17	237	242	246	251	256	261	265	270	275	280	7 3.5
18	284	289	294	298	303	308	313	317	322	327	8 4.0
19	332	336	341	346	350	355	360	365	369	374	9 4.5
920	379	384	388	393	398	402	407	412	417	421	
21	426	431	435	440	445	450	454	459	464	468	
22	473	478	483	487	492	497	501	506	511	515	
23	520	525	530	534	539	544	548	553	558	562	
24	567	572	577	581	586	591	595	600	605	609	
25	614	619	624	628	633	638	642	647	652	656	
26	661	666	670	675	680	685	689	694	699	703	
27	708	713	717	722	727	731	736	741	745	750	
28	755	759	764	769	774	778	783	788	792	797	
29	802	806	811	816	820	825	830	834	839	844	
930	848	853	858	862	867	872	876	881	886	890	
31	895	900	904	909	914	918	923	928	932	937	**4**
32	942	946	951	956	960	965	970	974	979	984	
33	96 988	993	997	*002	*007	*011	*016	*021	*025	*030	1 0.4
34	97 035	039	044	049	053	058	063	067	072	077	2 0.8 3 1.2
35	081	086	090	095	100	104	109	114	118	123	4 1.6
36	128	132	137	142	146	151	155	160	165	169	5 2.0 6 2.4
37	174	179	183	188	192	197	202	206	211	216	7 2.8
38	220	225	230	234	239	243	248	253	257	262	8 3.2
39	267	271	276	280	285	290	294	299	304	308	9 3.6
940	313	317	322	327	331	336	340	345	350	354	
41	359	364	368	373	377	382	387	391	396	400	
42	405	410	414	419	424	428	433	437	442	447	
43	451	456	460	465	470	474	479	483	488	493	
44	497	502	506	511	516	520	525	529	534	539	
45	543	548	552	557	562	566	571	575	580	585	
46	589	594	598	603	607	612	617	621	626	630	
47	635	640	644	649	653	658	663	667	672	676	
48	681	685	690	695	699	704	708	713	717	722	
49	727	731	736	740	745	749	754	759	763	768	
950	97 772	777	782	786	791	795	800	804	809	813	
N	0	1	2	3	4	5	6	7	8	9	Prop. Parts

Prop. Parts		N	0	1	2	3	4	5	6	7	8	9
		950	97 772	777	782	786	791	795	800	804	809	813
		51	818	823	827	832	836	841	845	850	855	859
		52	864	868	873	877	882	886	891	896	900	905
		53	909	914	918	923	928	932	937	941	946	950
		54	97 955	959	964	968	973	978	982	987	991	996
		55	98 000	005	009	014	019	023	028	032	037	041
		56	046	050	055	059	064	068	073	078	082	087
		57	091	096	100	105	109	114	118	123	127	132
		58	137	141	146	150	155	159	164	168	173	177
		59	182	186	191	195	200	204	209	214	218	223
		960	227	232	236	241	245	250	254	259	263	268
	5	61	272	277	281	286	290	295	299	304	308	313
		62	318	322	327	331	336	340	345	349	354	358
1	0.5	63	363	367	372	376	381	385	390	394	399	403
2	1.0											
3	1.5	64	408	412	417	421	426	430	435	439	444	448
4	2.0	**65**	453	457	462	466	471	475	480	484	489	493
5	2.5	66	498	502	507	511	516	520	525	529	534	538
6	3.0											
7	3.5	67	543	547	552	556	561	565	570	574	579	583
8	4.0	68	588	592	597	601	605	610	614	619	623	628
9	4.5	69	632	637	641	646	650	655	659	664	668	673
		970	677	682	686	691	695	700	704	709	713	717
		71	722	726	731	735	740	744	749	753	758	762
		72	767	771	776	780	784	789	793	798	802	807
		73	811	816	820	825	829	834	838	843	847	851
		74	856	860	865	869	874	878	883	887	892	896
		75	900	905	909	914	918	923	927	932	936	941
		76	945	949	954	958	963	967	972	976	981	985
		77	98 989	994	998	*003	*007	*012	*016	*021	*025	*029
		78	99 034	038	043	047	052	056	061	065	069	074
		79	078	083	087	092	096	100	105	109	114	118
		980	123	127	131	136	140	145	149	154	158	162
	4	81	167	171	176	180	185	189	193	198	202	207
		82	211	216	220	224	229	233	238	242	247	251
1	0.4	83	255	260	264	269	273	277	282	286	291	295
2	0.8											
3	1.2	84	300	304	308	313	317	322	326	330	335	339
4	1.6	**85**	344	348	352	357	361	366	370	374	379	383
5	2.0	86	388	392	396	401	405	410	414	419	423	427
6	2.4											
7	2.8	87	432	436	441	445	449	454	458	463	467	471
8	3.2	88	476	480	484	489	493	498	502	506	511	515
9	3.6	89	520	524	528	533	537	542	546	550	555	559
		990	564	568	572	577	581	585	590	594	599	603
		91	607	612	616	621	625	629	634	638	642	647
		92	651	656	660	664	669	673	677	682	686	691
		93	695	699	704	708	712	717	721	726	730	734
		94	739	743	747	752	756	760	765	769	774	778
		95	782	787	791	795	800	804	808	813	817	822
		96	826	830	835	839	843	848	852	856	861	865
		97	870	874	878	883	887	891	896	900	904	909
		98	913	917	922	926	930	935	939	944	948	952
		99	99 957	961	965	970	974	978	983	987	991	996
		1000	00 000	004	009	013	017	022	026	030	035	039
Prop. Parts		N	0	1	2	3	4	5	6	7	8	9

′	L Sin *	d	L Tan *	c d	L Cot	L Cos *		Prop. Parts
0	......		......		......	10.00 000	60	*Avoid inaccurate interpolation by using Table X on page 83.*
1	6.46 373		6.46 373		3.53 627	000	59	
2	6.76 476		6.76 476		3.23 524	000	58	
3	6.94 085		6.94 085		3.05 915	000	57	*Subtract* 10 *from each*
4	7.06 579		7.06 579		2.93 421	000	56	*entry in the columns marked*
5	7.16 270		7.16 270		2.83 730	10.00 000	55	*with "*" in the table.*
6	7.24 188		7.24 188		2.75 812	000	54	
7	7.30 882		7.30 882		2.69 118	000	53	
8	7.36 682		7.36 682		2.63 318	000	52	
9	7.41 797		7.41 797		2.58 203	000	51	
10	7.46 373		7.46 373		2.53 627	10.00 000	50	

Prop. Parts

	717	706	695	684	673
1	72	71	70	68	67
2	143	141	139	137	135
3	215	212	208	205	202
4	287	282	278	274	269
5	358	353	348	342	336
6	430	424	417	410	404
7	502	494	486	479	471
8	574	565	556	547	538
9	645	635	626	616	606

′	L Sin *	d	L Tan *	c d	L Cot	L Cos *	
11	7.50 512		7.50 512		2.49 488	000	49
12	7.54 291		7.54 291		2.45 709	000	48
13	7.57 767		7.57 767		2.42 233	000	47
14	7.60 985		7.60 986		2.39 014	000	46
15	7.63 982		7.63 982		2.36 018	10.00 000	45
16	7.66 784		7.66 785		2.33 215	10.00 000	44
17	7.69 417		7.69 418		2.30 582	9.99 999	43
18	7.71 900		7.71 900		2.28 100	999	42
19	7.74 248		7.74 248		2.25 752	999	41
20	7.76 475		7.76 476		2.23 524	9.99 999	40

	663	653	643	634	625
1	66	65	64	63	62
2	133	130	129	127	125
3	199	196	193	190	188
4	265	261	257	254	250
5	332	326	322	317	312
6	398	392	386	380	375
7	464	457	450	444	438
8	530	522	514	507	500
9	597	588	579	571	562

′	L Sin *	d	L Tan *	c d	L Cot	L Cos *	
21	7.78 594		7.78 595		2.21 405	999	39
22	7.80 615		7.80 615		2.19 385	999	38
23	7.82 545		7.82 546		2.17 454	999	37
24	7.84 393		7.84 394		2.15 606	999	36
25	7.86 166		7.86 167		2.13 833	9.99 999	35
26	7.87 870		7.87 871		2.12 129	999	34
27	7.89 509		7.89 510		2.10 490	999	33
28	7.91 088		7.91 089		2.08 911	999	32
29	7.92 612		7.92 613		2.07 387	998	31
30	7.94 084		7.94 086		2.05 914	9.99 998	30

	616	608	599	590	583
1	62	61	60	59	58
2	123	122	120	118	117
3	185	182	180	177	175
4	246	243	240	236	233
5	308	304	300	295	292
6	370	365	359	354	350
7	431	426	419	413	408
8	493	486	479	472	466
9	554	547	539	531	525

′	L Sin *	d	L Tan *	c d	L Cot	L Cos *	
31	7.95 508		7.95 510		2.04 490	998	29
32	7.96 887		7.96 889		2.03 111	998	28
33	7.98 223		7.98 225		2.01 775	998	27
34	7.99 520		7.99 522		2.00 478	998	26
35	8.00 779		8.00 781		1.99 219	9.99 998	25
36	8.02 002		8.02 004		1.97 996	998	24
37	8.03 192		8.03 194		1.96 806	997	23
38	8.04 350		8.04 353		1.95 647	997	22
39	8.05 478		8.05 481		1.94 519	997	21
40	8.06 578		8.06 581		1.93 419	9.99 997	20

	575	568	560	553	546
1	58	57	56	55	55
2	115	114	112	111	109
3	172	170	168	166	164
4	230	227	224	221	218
5	288	284	280	276	273
6	345	341	336	332	328
7	402	398	392	387	382
8	460	454	448	442	437
9	518	511	504	498	491

′	L Sin *	d	L Tan *	c d	L Cot	L Cos *	
41	8.07 650		8.07 653		1.92 347	997	19
42	8.08 696		8.08 700		1.91 300	997	18
43	8.09 718		8.09 722		1.90 278	997	17
44	8.10 717	999	8.10 720	998	1.89 280	996	16
45	8.11 693	976	8.11 696	976	1.88 304	9.99 996	15

	540	533	526	520	514
1	54	53	53	52	51
2	108	107	105	104	103
3	162	160	158	156	154
4	216	213	210	208	206
5	270	266	263	260	257
6	324	320	316	312	308
7	378	373	368	364	360
8	432	426	421	416	411
9	486	480	473	468	463

′	L Sin *	d	L Tan *	c d	L Cot	L Cos *	
46	8.12 647	954	8.12 651	955	1.87 349	996	14
47	8.13 581	934	8.13 585	934	1.86 415	996	13
48	8.14 495	914	8.14 500	915	1.85 500	996	12
49	8.15 391	896	8.15 395	895	1.84 605	996	11
50	8.16 268	877	8.16 273	878	1.83 727	9.99 995	10

	508	502	496	491	485
1	51	50	50	49	48
2	102	100	99	98	97
3	152	151	149	147	146
4	203	201	198	196	194
5	254	251	248	246	242
6	305	301	298	295	291
7	356	351	347	344	340
8	406	402	397	393	388
9	457	452	446	442	436

′	L Sin *	d	L Tan *	c d	L Cot	L Cos *	
51	8.17 128	860	8.17 133	860	1.82 867	995	9
52	8.17 971	843	8.17 976	843	1.82 024	995	8
53	8.18 798	827	8.18 804	828	1.81 196	995	7
54	8.19 610	812	8.19 616	812	1.80 384	995	6
55	8.20 407	797	8.20 413	797	1.79 587	9.99 994	5

	480	475	470	464	460
1	48	48	47	46	46
2	96	95	94	93	92
3	144	142	141	139	138
4	192	190	188	186	184
5	240	238	235	232	230
6	288	285	282	278	276
7	336	332	329	325	322
8	384	380	376	371	368
9	432	428	423	418	414

′	L Sin *	d	L Tan *	c d	L Cot	L Cos *	
56	8.21 189	782	8.21 195	782	1.78 805	994	4
57	8.21 958	769	8.21 964	769	1.78 036	994	3
58	8.22 713	755	8.22 720	756	1.77 280	994	2
59	8.23 456	743	8.23 462	742	1.76 538	994	1
60	8.24 186	730	8.24 192	730	1.75 808	9.99 993	0

	L Cos *	d	L Cot *	c d	L Tan	L Sin *	′

89°

[36]

IX. FIVE–PLACE LOGARITHMS OF FUNCTIONS — 1°

*Use the proportional parts of the number below or at the left which is **nearest** to the actual tabular difference; the error will be at most **2** units in the last place. For greater accuracy, use Table X on page 83.*

Proportional Parts

	455	450	446	445	441
1	46	45	45	44	44
2	91	90	89	89	88
3	136	135	134	134	132
4	182	180	178	178	176
5	228	225	223	222	220
6	273	270	268	267	265
7	318	315	312	312	309
8	364	360	357	356	353
9	410	405	401	400	397

	437	436	433	432	428
1	44	44	43	43	43
2	87	87	87	86	86
3	131	131	130	130	128
4	175	174	173	173	171
5	218	218	216	216	214
6	262	262	260	259	257
7	306	305	303	302	300
8	350	349	346	346	342
9	393	392	390	389	385

	427	424	420	419	416
1	43	42	42	42	42
2	85	85	84	84	83
3	128	127	126	126	125
4	171	170	168	168	166
5	214	212	210	210	208
6	256	254	252	251	250
7	299	297	294	293	291
8	342	339	336	335	333
9	384	382	378	377	374

	412	411	408	404	401
1	41	41	41	40	40
2	82	82	82	81	80
3	124	123	122	121	120
4	165	164	163	162	160
5	206	206	204	202	200
6	247	247	245	242	241
7	288	288	286	283	281
8	330	329	326	323	321
9	371	370	367	364	361

	397	396	393	390	386
1	40	40	39	39	39
2	79	79	79	78	77
3	119	119	118	117	116
4	159	158	157	156	154
5	198	198	196	195	193
6	238	238	236	234	232
7	278	277	275	273	270
8	318	317	314	312	309
9	357	356	354	351	347

	383	382	380	379	376
1	38	38	38	38	38
2	77	76	76	76	75
3	115	115	114	114	113
4	153	153	152	152	150
5	192	191	190	190	188
6	230	229	228	227	226
7	268	267	266	265	263
8	306	306	304	303	301
9	345	344	342	341	338

	373	370	369	367	363
1	37	37	37	37	36
2	75	74	74	73	73
3	112	111	111	110	109
4	149	148	148	147	145
5	186	185	184	184	182
6	224	222	221	220	218
7	261	259	258	257	254
8	298	296	295	294	290
9	336	333	332	330	327

′	L Sin *	d	L Tan *	c d	L Cot	L Cos *	
0	8.24 186		8.24 192		1.75 808	9.99 993	60
1	8.24 903	717	8.24 910	718	1.75 090	993	59
2	8.25 609	706	8.25 616	706	1.74 384	993	58
3	8.26 304	695	8.26 312	696	1.73 688	993	57
4	8.26 988	684	8.26 996	684	1.73 004	992	56
5	8.27 661	673	8.27 669	673	1.72 331	9.99 992	55
6	8.28 324	663	8.28 332	663	1.71 668	992	54
7	8.28 977	653	8.28 986	654	1.71 014	992	53
8	8.29 621	644	8.29 629	643	1.70 371	992	52
9	8.30 255	634	8.30 263	634	1.69 737	991	51
10	8.30 879	624	8.30 888	625	1.69 112	9.99 991	50
11	8.31 495	616	8.31 505	617	1.68 495	991	49
12	8.32 103	608	8.32 112	607	1.67 888	990	48
13	8.32 702	599	8.32 711	599	1.67 289	990	47
14	8.33 292	590	8.33 302	591	1.66 698	990	46
15	8.33 875	583	8.33 886	584	1.66 114	9.99 990	45
16	8.34 450	575	8.34 461	575	1.65 539	989	44
17	8.35 018	568	8.35 029	568	1.64 971	989	43
18	8.35 578	560	8.35 590	561	1.64 410	989	42
19	8.36 131	553	8.36 143	553	1.63 857	989	41
20	8.36 678	547	8.36 689	546	1.63 311	9.99 988	40
21	8.37 217	539	8.37 229	540	1.62 771	988	39
22	8.37 750	533	8.37 762	533	1.62 238	988	38
23	8.38 276	526	8.38 289	527	1.61 711	987	37
24	8.38 796	520	8.38 809	520	1.61 191	987	36
25	8.39 310	514	8.39 323	514	1.60 677	9.99 987	35
26	8.39 818	508	8.39 832	509	1.60 168	986	34
27	8.40 320	502	8.40 334	502	1.59 666	986	33
28	8.40 816	496	8.40 830	496	1.59 170	986	32
29	8.41 307	491	8.41 321	491	1.58 679	985	31
30	8.41 792	485	8.41 807	486	1.58 193	9.99 985	30
31	8.42 272	480	8.42 287	480	1.57 713	985	29
32	8.42 746	474	8.42 762	475	1.57 238	984	28
33	8.43 216	470	8.43 232	470	1.56 768	984	27
34	8.43 680	464	8.43 696	464	1.56 304	984	26
35	8.44 139	459	8.44 156	460	1.55 844	9.99 983	25
36	8.44 594	455	8.44 611	455	1.55 389	983	24
37	8.45 044	450	8.45 061	450	1.54 939	983	23
38	8.45 489	445	8.45 507	446	1.54 493	982	22
39	8.45 930	441	8.45 948	441	1.54 052	982	21
40	8.46 366	436	8.46 385	437	1.53 615	9.99 982	20
41	8.46 799	433	8.46 817	432	1.53 183	981	19
42	8.47 226	427	8.47 245	428	1.52 755	981	18
43	8.47 650	424	8.47 669	424	1.52 331	981	17
44	8.48 069	419	8.48 089	420	1.51 911	980	16
45	8.48 485	416	8.48 505	416	1.51 495	9.99 980	15
46	8.48 896	411	8.48 917	412	1.51 083	979	14
47	8.49 304	408	8.49 325	408	1.50 675	979	13
48	8.49 708	404	8.49 729	404	1.50 271	979	12
49	8.50 108	400	8.50 130	401	1.49 870	978	11
50	8.50 504	396	8.50 527	397	1.49 473	9.99 978	10
51	8.50 897	393	8.50 920	393	1.49 080	977	9
52	8.51 287	390	8.51 310	390	1.48 690	977	8
53	8.51 673	386	8.51 696	386	1.48 304	977	7
54	8.52 055	382	8.52 079	383	1.47 921	976	6
55	8.52 434	379	8.52 459	380	1.47 541	9.99 976	5
56	8.52 810	376	8.52 835	376	1.47 165	975	4
57	8.53 183	373	8.53 208	373	1.46 792	975	3
58	8.53 552	369	8.53 578	370	1.46 422	974	2
59	8.53 919	367	8.53 945	367	1.46 055	974	1
60	8.54 282	363	8.54 308	363	1.45 692	9.99 974	0
	L Cos *	d	L Cot *	c d	L Tan	L Sin *	′

88°

′	L Sin *	d	L Tan *	c d	L Cot	L Cos *	
0	8.54 282		8.54 308		1.45 692	9.99 974	60
1	8.54 642	360	8.54 669	361	1.45 331	973	59
2	8.54 999	357	8.55 027	358	1.44 973	973	58
3	8.55 354	355	382	355	618	972	57
4	8.55 705	351	8.55 734	352	1.44 266	972	56
5	8.56 054	349	8.56 083	349	1.43 917	9.99 971	55
6	400	346	429	346	571	971	54
7	8.56 743	343	8.56 773	344	1.43 227	970	53
8	8.57 084	341	8.57 114	341	1.42 886	970	52
9	421	337	452	338	548	969	51
10	8.57 757	336	8.57 788	336	1.42 212	9.99 969	50
11	8.58 089	332	8.58 121	333	1.41 879	968	49
12	419	330	451	330	549	968	48
13	8.58 747	328	8.58 779	328	1.41 221	967	47
14	8.59 072	325	8.59 105	326	1.40 895	967	46
15	8.59 395	323	8.59 428	323	1.40 572	9.99 967	45
16	8.59 715	320	8.59 749	321	1.40 251	966	44
17	8.60 033	318	8.60 068	319	1.39 932	966	43
18	349	316	384	316	616	965	42
19	662	313	8.60 698	314	1.39 302	964	41
20	8.60 973	311	8.61 009	311	1.38 991	9.99 964	40
21	8.61 282	309	319	310	681	963	39
22	589	307	626	307	374	963	38
23	8.61 894	305	8.61 931	305	1.38 069	962	37
24	8.62 196	302	8.62 234	303	1.37 766	962	36
25	8.62 497	301	8.62 535	301	1.37 465	9.99 961	35
26	8.62 795	298	8.62 834	299	1.37 166	961	34
27	8.63 091	296	8.63 131	297	1.36 869	960	33
28	385	294	426	295	574	960	32
29	678	293	8.63 718	292	1.36 282	959	31
30	8.63 968	290	8.64 009	291	1.35 991	9.99 959	30
31	8.64 256	288	298	289	702	958	29
32	543	287	585	287	415	958	28
33	8.64 827	284	8.64 870	285	1.35 130	957	27
34	8.65 110	283	8.65 154	284	1.34 846	956	26
35	8.65 391	281	8.65 435	281	1.34 565	9.99 956	25
36	670	279	715	280	285	955	24
37	8.65 947	277	8.65 993	278	1.34 007	955	23
38	8.66 223	276	8.66 269	276	1.33 731	954	22
39	497	274	543	274	457	954	21
40	8.66 769	272	8.66 816	273	1.33 184	9.99 953	20
41	8.67 039	270	8.67 087	271	1.32 913	952	19
42	308	269	356	269	644	952	18
43	575	267	624	268	376	951	17
44	8.67 841	266	8.67 890	266	1.32 110	951	16
45	8.68 104	263	8.68 154	264	1.31 846	9.99 950	15
46	367	263	417	263	583	949	14
47	627	260	678	261	322	949	13
48	8.68 886	259	8.68 938	260	1.31 062	948	12
49	8.69 144	258	8.69 196	258	1.30 804	948	11
50	8.69 400	256	8.69 453	257	1.30 547	9.99 947	10
51	654	254	708	255	292	946	9
52	8.69 907	253	8.69 962	254	1.30 038	946	8
53	8.70 159	252	8.70 214	252	1.29 786	945	7
54	409	250	465	251	535	944	6
55	8.70 658	249	8.70 714	249	1.29 286	9.99 944	5
56	8.70 905	247	8.70 962	248	1.29 038	943	4
57	8.71 151	246	8.71 208	246	1.28 792	942	3
58	395	244	453	245	547	942	2
59	638	243	697	244	303	941	1
60	8.71 880	242	8.71 940	243	1.28 060	9.99 940	0
	L Cos *	d	L Cot *	c d	L Tan	L Sin *	′

87°

Prop. Parts

Subtract 10 *from each entry in the columns marked with "*".*

See opposite page for additional tables.

	361	360	358
1	36	36	36
2	72	72	72
3	108	108	107
4	144	144	143
5	180	180	179
6	217	216	215
7	253	252	251
8	289	288	286
9	325	324	322

	357	355	352
1	36	36	35
2	71	71	70
3	107	106	106
4	143	142	141
5	178	178	176
6	214	213	211
7	250	248	246
8	286	284	282
9	321	320	317

	351	349	346
1	35	35	35
2	70	70	69
3	105	105	104
4	140	140	138
5	176	174	173
6	211	209	208
7	246	244	242
8	281	279	277
9	316	314	311

	344	343	341
1	34	34	34
2	69	69	68
3	103	103	102
4	138	137	136
5	172	172	170
6	206	206	205
7	241	240	239
8	275	274	273
9	310	309	307

	338	337	336
1	34	34	34
2	68	67	67
3	101	101	101
4	135	135	134
5	169	168	168
6	203	202	202
7	237	236	235
8	270	270	269
9	304	303	302

	333	332	330
1	33	33	33
2	67	66	66
3	100	100	99
4	133	133	132
5	166	166	165
6	200	199	198
7	233	232	231
8	266	266	264
9	300	299	297

	328	326	325	323	321	320		319	318	316	314	313	311	
1	33	33	32	32	32	32	1	32	32	32	31	31	31	1
2	66	65	65	65	64	64	2	64	64	63	63	63	62	2
3	98	98	98	97	96	96	3	96	95	95	94	94	93	3
4	131	130	130	129	128	128	4	128	127	126	126	125	124	4
5	164	163	162	162	160	160	5	160	159	158	157	156	156	5
6	197	196	195	194	193	192	6	191	191	190	188	188	187	6
7	230	228	228	226	225	224	7	223	223	221	220	219	218	7
8	262	261	260	258	257	256	8	255	254	253	251	250	249	8
9	295	293	292	291	289	288	9	287	286	284	283	282	280	9

	310	309	307	305	303	302		301	299	298	297	296	295	
1	31	31	31	30	30	30	1	30	30	30	30	30	30	1
2	62	62	61	61	61	60	2	60	60	60	59	59	59	2
3	93	93	92	92	91	91	3	90	90	89	89	89	88	3
4	124	124	123	122	121	121	4	120	120	119	119	118	118	4
5	155	154	154	152	152	151	5	150	150	149	148	148	148	5
6	186	185	184	183	182	181	6	181	179	179	178	178	177	6
7	217	216	215	214	212	211	7	211	209	209	208	207	206	7
8	248	247	246	244	242	242	8	241	239	238	238	237	236	8
9	279	278	276	274	273	272	9	271	269	268	267	266	266	9

	294	293	292	291	290	289		288	287	285	284	283	281	
1	29	29	29	29	29	29	1	29	29	28	28	28	28	1
2	59	59	58	58	58	58	2	58	57	57	57	57	56	2
3	88	88	88	87	87	87	3	86	86	86	85	85	84	3
4	118	117	117	116	116	116	4	115	115	114	114	113	112	4
5	147	146	146	146	145	144	5	144	144	142	142	142	140	5
6	176	176	175	175	174	173	6	173	172	171	170	170	169	6
7	206	205	204	204	203	202	7	202	201	200	199	198	197	7
8	235	234	234	233	232	231	8	230	230	228	227	226	225	8
9	265	264	263	262	261	260	9	259	258	256	256	255	253	9

	280	279	278	277	276	274		273	272	271	270	269	268	
1	28	28	28	28	28	27	1	27	27	27	27	27	27	1
2	56	56	56	55	55	55	2	55	54	54	54	54	54	2
3	84	84	83	83	83	82	3	82	82	81	81	81	80	3
4	112	112	111	111	110	110	4	109	109	108	108	108	107	4
5	140	140	139	138	138	137	5	136	136	136	135	134	134	5
6	168	167	167	166	166	164	6	164	163	163	162	161	161	6
7	196	195	195	194	193	192	7	191	190	190	189	188	188	7
8	224	223	222	222	221	219	8	218	218	217	216	215	214	8
9	252	251	250	249	248	247	9	246	245	244	243	242	241	9

	267	266	264	263	261	260		259	258	257	256	255	254	
1	27	27	26	26	26	26	1	26	26	26	26	26	25	1
2	53	53	53	53	52	52	2	52	52	51	51	51	51	2
3	80	80	79	79	78	78	3	78	77	77	77	76	76	3
4	107	106	106	105	104	104	4	104	103	103	102	102	102	4
5	134	133	132	132	130	130	5	130	129	128	128	128	127	5
6	160	160	158	158	157	156	6	155	155	154	154	153	152	6
7	187	186	185	184	183	182	7	181	181	180	179	178	178	7
8	214	213	211	210	209	208	8	207	206	206	205	204	203	8
9	240	239	238	237	235	234	9	233	232	231	230	230	229	9

	253	252	251	250	249	248		247	246	245	244	243	242	
1	25	25	25	25	25	25	1	25	25	24	24	24	24	1
2	51	50	50	50	50	50	2	49	49	49	49	49	48	2
3	76	76	75	75	75	74	3	74	74	74	73	73	73	3
4	101	101	100	100	100	99	4	99	98	98	98	97	97	4
5	126	126	126	125	124	124	5	124	123	122	122	122	121	5
6	152	151	151	150	149	149	6	148	148	147	146	146	145	6
7	177	176	176	175	174	174	7	173	172	172	171	170	169	7
8	202	202	201	200	199	198	8	198	197	196	195	194	194	8
9	228	227	226	225	224	223	9	222	221	220	220	219	218	9

′	L Sin *	d	L Tan *	c d	L Cot	L Cos *		Prop. Parts
0	8.71 880		8.71 940		1.28 060	9.99 940	60	Subtract 10 *from each en-*
1	8.72 120	240	8.72 181	241	1.27 819	940	59	*try in the columns marked*
2	359	239	420	239	580	939	58	*with "*."*
3	597	238	659	239	341	938	57	
4	8.72 834	237	8.72 896	237	1.27 104	938	56	*See opposite page for ad-*
5	8.73 069	235	8.73 132	236	1.26 868	9.99 937	55	*ditional tables.*
6	303	234	366	234	634	936	54	
7	535	232	600	234	400	936	53	
8	767	232	8.73 832	232	1.26 168	935	52	
9	8.73 997	230	8.74 063	231	1.25 937	934	51	
10	8.74 226	229	8.74 292	229	1.25 708	9.99 934	50	
								241 **240**
11	454	228	521	229	479	933	49	**1** 24.1 24
12	680	226	748	227	252	932	48	**2** 48.2 48
13	8.74 906	226	8.74 974	226	1.25 026	932	47	**3** 72.3 72
14	8.75 130	224	8.75 199	225	1.24 801	931	46	**4** 96.4 96
15	8.75 353	223	8.75 423	224	1.24 577	9.99 930	45	**5** 120.5 120
								6 144.6 144
16	575	222	645	222	355	929	44	**7** 168.7 168
17	8.75 795	220	8.75 867	222	1.24 133	929	43	**8** 192.8 192
18	8.76 015	220	8.76 087	220	1.23 913	928	42	**9** 216.9 216
19	234	219	306	219	694	927	41	
20	8.76 451	217	8.76 525	219	1.23 475	9.99 926	40	
21	667	216	742	217	258	926	39	
22	8.76 883	216	8.76 958	216	1.23 042	925	38	**239** **238**
23	8.77 097	214	8.77 173	215	1.22 827	924	37	
24	310	213	387	214	613	923	36	**1** 23.9 23.8
25	8.77 522	212	8.77 600	213	1.22 400	9.99 923	35	**2** 47.8 47.6
								3 71.7 71.4
26	733	211	8.77 811	211	1.22 189	922	34	**4** 95.6 95.2
27	8.77 943	210	8.78 022	211	1.21 978	921	33	**5** 119.5 119.0
28	8.78 152	209	232	210	768	920	32	**6** 143.4 142.8
29	360	208	441	209	559	920	31	**7** 167.3 166.6
30	8.78 568	208	8.78 649	208	1.21 351	9.99 919	30	**8** 191.2 190.4
								9 215.1 214.2
31	774	206	8.78 855	206	1.21 145	918	29	
32	8.78 979	205	8.79 061	206	1.20 939	917	28	
33	8.79 183	204	266	205	734	917	27	
34	386	203	470	204	530	916	26	
35	8.79 588	202	8.79 673	203	1.20 327	9.99 915	25	
36	789	201	8.79 875	202	1.20 125	914	24	**237**
37	8.79 990	201	8.80 076	201	1.19 924	913	23	
38	8.80 189	199	277	201	723	913	22	**1** 23.7
39	388	199	476	199	524	912	21	**2** 47.4
40	8.80 585	197	8.80 674	198	1.19 326	9.99 911	20	**3** 71.1
								4 94.8
41	782	197	8.80 872	198	1.19 128	910	19	**5** 118.5
42	8.80 978	196	8.81 068	196	1.18 932	909	18	**6** 142.2
43	8.81 173	195	264	196	736	909	17	**7** 165.9
44	367	194	459	195	541	908	16	**8** 189.6
45	8.81 560	193	8.81 653	194	1.18 347	9.99 907	15	**9** 213.3
46	752	192	8.81 846	193	1.18 154	906	14	
47	8.81 944	192	8.82 038	192	1.17 962	905	13	
48	8.82 134	190	230	192	770	904	12	
49	324	190	420	190	580	904	11	
50	8.82 513	189	8.82 610	190	1.17 390	9.99 903	10	**236** **235**
51	701	188	799	189	201	902	9	**1** 23.6 23.5
52	8.82 888	187	8.82 987	188	1.17 013	901	8	**2** 47.2 47.0
53	8.83 075	187	8.83 175	188	1.16 825	900	7	**3** 70.8 70.5
54	261	186	361	186	639	899	6	**4** 94.4 94.0
55	8.83 446	185	8.83 547	186	1.16 453	9.99 898	5	**5** 118.0 117.5
								6 141.6 141.0
56	630	184	732	185	268	898	4	**7** 165.2 164.5
57	813	183	8.83 916	184	1.16 084	897	3	**8** 188.8 188.0
58	8.83 996	183	8.84 100	184	1.15 900	896	2	**9** 212.4 211.5
59	8.84 177	181	282	182	718	895	1	
60	8.84 358	181	8.84 464	182	1.15 536	9.99 894	0	
	L Cos *	d	L Cot *	c d	L Tan	L Sin *	′	

86°

	234	232	231	230		229	228	227	226	
1	23.4	23.2	23.1	23	1	22.9	22.8	22.7	22.6	1
2	46.8	46.4	46.2	46	2	45.8	45.6	45.4	45.2	2
3	70.2	69.6	69.3	69	3	68.7	68.4	68.1	67.8	3
4	93.6	92.8	92.4	92	4	91.6	91.2	90.8	90.4	4
5	117.0	116.0	115.5	115	5	114.5	114.0	113.5	113.0	5
6	140.4	139.2	138.6	138	6	137.4	136.8	136.2	135.6	6
7	163.8	162.4	161.7	161	7	160.3	159.6	158.9	158.2	7
8	187.2	185.6	184.8	184	8	183.2	182.4	181.6	180.8	8
9	210.6	208.8	207.9	207	9	206.1	205.2	204.3	203.4	9

	225	224	223	222		220	219	217	216	
1	22.5	22.4	22.3	22.2	1	22	21.9	21.7	21.6	1
2	45.0	44.8	44.6	44.4	2	44	43.8	43.4	43.2	2
3	67.5	67.2	66.9	66.6	3	66	65.7	65.1	64.8	3
4	90.0	89.6	89.2	88.8	4	88	87.6	86.8	86.4	4
5	112.5	112.0	111.5	111.0	5	110	109.5	108.5	108.0	5
6	135.0	134.4	133.8	133.2	6	132	131.4	130.2	129.6	6
7	157.5	156.8	156.1	155.4	7	154	153.3	151.9	151.2	7
8	180.0	179.2	178.4	177.6	8	176	175.2	173.6	172.8	8
9	202.5	201.6	200.7	199.8	9	198	197.1	195.3	194.4	9

	215	214	213	212		211	210	209	208	
1	21.5	21.4	21.3	21.2	1	21.1	21	20.9	20.8	1
2	43.0	42.8	42.6	42.4	2	42.2	42	41.8	41.6	2
3	64.5	64.2	63.9	63.6	3	63.3	63	62.7	62.4	3
4	86.0	85.6	85.2	84.8	4	84.4	84	83.6	83.2	4
5	107.5	107.0	106.5	106.0	5	105.5	105	104.5	104.0	5
6	129.0	128.4	127.8	127.2	6	126.6	126	125.4	124.8	6
7	150.5	149.8	149.1	148.4	7	147.7	147	146.3	145.6	7
8	172.0	171.2	170.4	169.6	8	168.8	168	167.2	166.4	8
9	193.5	192.6	191.7	190.8	9	189.9	189	188.1	187.2	9

	206	205	204	203		202	201	199	198	
1	20.6	20.5	20.4	20.3	1	20.2	20.1	19.9	19.8	1
2	41.2	41.0	40.8	40.6	2	40.4	40.2	39.8	39.6	2
3	61.8	61.5	61.2	60.9	3	60.6	60.3	59.7	59.4	3
4	82.4	82.0	81.6	81.2	4	80.8	80.4	79.6	79.2	4
5	103.0	102.5	102.0	101.5	5	101.0	100.5	99.5	99.0	5
6	123.6	123.0	122.4	121.8	6	121.2	120.6	119.4	118.8	6
7	144.2	143.5	142.8	142.1	7	141.4	140.7	139.3	138.6	7
8	164.8	164.0	163.2	162.4	8	161.6	160.8	159.2	158.4	8
9	185.4	184.5	183.6	182.7	9	181.8	180.9	179.1	178.2	9

	197	196	195	194		193	192	190	189	
1	19.7	19.6	19.5	19.4	1	19.3	19.2	19	18.9	1
2	39.4	39.2	39.0	38.8	2	38.6	38.4	38	37.8	2
3	59.1	58.8	58.5	58.2	3	57.9	57.6	57	56.7	3
4	78.8	78.4	78.0	77.6	4	77.2	76.8	76	75.6	4
5	98.5	98.0	97.5	97.0	5	96.5	96.0	95	94.5	5
6	118.2	117.6	117.0	116.4	6	115.8	115.2	114	113.4	6
7	137.9	137.2	136.5	135.8	7	135.1	134.4	133	132.3	7
8	157.6	156.8	156.0	155.2	8	154.4	153.6	152	151.2	8
9	177.3	176.4	175.5	174.6	9	173.7	172.8	171	170.1	9

	188	187	186	185		184	183	182	181	
1	18.8	18.7	18.6	18.5	1	18.4	18.3	18.2	18.1	1
2	37.6	37.4	37.2	37.0	2	36.8	36.6	36.4	36.2	2
3	56.4	56.1	55.8	55.5	3	55.2	54.9	54.6	54.3	3
4	75.2	74.8	74.4	74.0	4	73.6	73.2	72.8	72.4	4
5	94.0	93.5	93.0	92.5	5	92.0	91.5	91.0	90.5	5
6	112.8	112.2	111.6	111.0	6	110.4	109.8	109.2	108.6	6
7	131.6	130.9	130.2	129.5	7	128.8	128.1	127.4	126.7	7
8	150.4	149.6	148.8	148.0	8	147.2	146.4	145.6	144.8	8
9	169.2	168.3	167.4	166.5	9	165.6	164.7	163.8	162.9	9

IX. FIVE–PLACE LOGARITHMS OF FUNCTIONS — 4°

′	L Sin *	d	L Tan *	c d	L Cot	L Cos *	
0	8.84 358		8.84 464		1.15 536	9.99 894	60
1	539	181	646	182	354	893	59
2	718	179	8.84 826	180	1.15 174	892	58
3	8.84 897	179	8.85 006	180	1.14 994	891	57
4	8.85 075	178	185	179	815	891	56
5	8.85 252	177	8.85 363	178	1.14 637	9.99 890	55
6	429	177	540	177	460	889	54
7	605	176	717	177	283	888	53
8	780	175	8.85 893	176	1.14 107	887	52
9	8.85 955	175	8.86 069	176	1.13 931	886	51
10	8.86 128	173	8.86 243	174	1.13 757	9.99 885	50
11	301	173	417	174	583	884	49
12	474	173	591	174	409	883	48
13	645	171	763	172	237	882	47
14	816	171	8.86 935	172	1.13 065	881	46
15	8.86 987	171	8.87 106	171	1.12 894	9.99 880	45
16	8.87 156	169	277	171	723	879	44
17	325	169	447	170	553	879	43
18	494	169	616	169	384	878	42
19	661	167	785	169	215	877	41
20	8.87 829	168	8.87 953	168	1.12 047	9.99 876	40
21	8.87 995	166	8.88 120	167	1.11 880	875	39
22	8.88 161	166	287	167	713	874	38
23	326	165	453	166	547	873	37
24	490	164	618	165	382	872	36
25	8.88 654	164	8.88 783	165	1.11 217	9.99 871	35
26	817	163	8.88 948	165	1.11 052	870	34
27	8.88 980	163	8.89 111	163	1.10 889	869	33
28	8.89 142	162	274	163	726	868	32
29	304	162	437	163	563	867	31
30	8.89 464	160	8.89 598	161	1.10 402	9.99 866	30
31	625	161	760	162	240	865	29
32	784	159	8.89 920	160	1.10 080	864	28
33	8.89 943	159	8.90 080	160	1.09 920	863	27
34	8.90 102	159	240	160	760	862	26
35	8.90 260	158	8.90 399	159	1.09 601	9.99 861	25
36	417	157	557	158	443	860	24
37	574	157	715	158	285	859	23
38	730	156	8.90 872	157	1.09 128	858	22
39	8.90 885	155	8.91 029	157	1.08 971	857	21
40	8.91 040	155	8.91 185	156	1.08 815	9.99 856	20
41	195	155	340	155	660	855	19
42	349	154	495	155	505	854	18
43	502	153	650	155	350	853	17
44	655	153	803	153	197	852	16
45	8.91 807	152	8.91 957	154	1.08 043	9.99 851	15
46	8.91 959	152	8.92 110	153	1.07 890	850	14
47	8.92 110	151	262	152	738	848	13
48	261	151	414	152	586	847	12
49	411	150	565	151	435	846	11
50	8.92 561	150	8.92 716	151	1.07 284	9.99 845	10
51	710	149	8.92 866	150	1.07 134	844	9
52	8.92 859	149	8.93 016	150	1.06 984	843	8
53	8.93 007	148	165	149	835	842	7
54	154	147	313	148	687	841	6
55	8.93 301	147	8.93 462	149	1.06 538	9.99 840	5
56	448	147	609	147	391	839	4
57	594	146	756	147	244	838	3
58	740	146	8.93 903	147	1.06 097	837	2
59	8.93 885	145	8.94 049	146	1.05 951	836	1
60	8.94 030	145	8.94 195	146	1.05 805	9.99 834	0
	L Cos *	d	L Cot *	c d	L Tan	L Sin *	′

Prop. Parts

	182	181	180	179
1	18.2	18.1	18	17.9
2	36.4	36.2	36	35.8
3	54.6	54.3	54	53.7
4	72.8	72.4	72	71.6
5	91.0	90.5	90	89.5
6	109.2	108.6	108	107.4
7	127.4	126.7	126	125.3
8	145.6	144.8	144	143.2
9	163.8	162.9	162	161.1

	178	177	176	175
1	17.8	17.7	17.6	17.5
2	35.6	35.4	35.2	35.0
3	53.4	53.1	52.8	52.5
4	71.2	70.8	70.4	70.0
5	89.0	88.5	88.0	87.5
6	106.8	106.2	105.6	105.0
7	124.6	123.9	123.2	122.5
8	142.4	141.6	140.8	140.0
9	160.2	159.3	158.4	157.5

	174	173	172	171
1	17.4	17.3	17.2	17.1
2	34.8	34.6	34.4	34.2
3	52.2	51.9	51.6	51.3
4	69.6	69.2	68.8	68.4
5	87.0	86.5	86.0	85.5
6	104.4	103.8	103.2	102.6
7	121.8	121.1	120.4	119.7
8	139.2	138.4	137.6	136.8
9	156.6	155.7	154.8	153.9

	170	169	168	167
1	17	16.9	16.8	16.7
2	34	33.8	33.6	33.4
3	51	50.7	50.4	50.1
4	68	67.6	67.2	66.8
5	85	84.5	84.0	83.5
6	102	101.4	100.8	100.2
7	119	118.3	117.6	116.9
8	136	135.2	134.4	133.6
9	153	152.1	151.2	150.3

	166	165	164	163
1	16.6	16.5	16.4	16.3
2	33.2	33.0	32.8	32.6
3	49.8	49.5	49.2	48.9
4	66.4	66.0	65.6	65.2
5	83.0	82.5	82.0	81.5
6	99.6	99.0	98.4	97.8
7	116.2	115.5	114.8	114.1
8	132.8	132.0	131.2	130.4
9	149.4	148.5	147.6	146.7

	162	161	160	159
1	16.2	16.1	16	15.9
2	32.4	32.2	32	31.8
3	48.6	48.3	48	47.7
4	64.8	64.4	64	63.6
5	81.0	80.5	80	79.5
6	97.2	96.6	96	95.4
7	113.4	112.7	112	111.3
8	129.6	128.8	128	127.2
9	145.8	144.9	144	143.1

	158	157	156	155
1	15.8	15.7	15.6	15.5
2	31.6	31.4	31.2	31.0
3	47.4	47.1	46.8	46.5
4	63.2	62.8	62.4	62.0
5	79.0	78.5	78.0	77.5
6	94.8	94.2	93.6	93.0
7	110.6	109.9	109.2	108.5
8	126.4	125.6	124.8	124.0
9	142.2	141.3	140.4	139.5

	154	153	152	151
1	15.4	15.3	15.2	15.1
2	30.8	30.6	30.4	30.2
3	46.2	45.9	45.6	45.3
4	61.6	61.2	60.8	60.4
5	77.0	76.5	76.0	75.5
6	92.4	91.8	91.2	90.6
7	107.8	107.1	106.4	105.7
8	123.2	122.4	121.6	120.8
9	138.6	137.7	136.8	135.9

85°

Prop. Parts

	150	149	148	147
1	15	14.9	14.8	14.7
2	30	29.8	29.6	29.4
3	45	44.7	44.4	44.1
4	60	59.6	59.2	58.8
5	75	74.5	74.0	73.5
6	90	89.4	88.8	88.2
7	105	104.3	103.6	102.9
8	120	119.2	118.4	117.6
9	135	134.1	133.2	132.3

	146	145	144	143
1	14.6	14.5	14.4	14.3
2	29.2	29.0	28.8	28.6
3	43.8	43.5	43.2	42.9
4	58.4	58.0	57.6	57.2
5	73.0	72.5	72.0	71.5
6	87.6	87.0	86.4	85.8
7	102.2	101.5	100.8	100.1
8	116.8	116.0	115.2	114.4
9	131.4	130.5	129.6	128.7

	142	141	140	139
1	14.2	14.1	14	13.9
2	28.4	28.2	28	27.8
3	42.6	42.3	42	41.7
4	56.8	56.4	56	55.6
5	71.0	70.5	70	69.5
6	85.2	84.6	84	83.4
7	99.4	98.7	98	97.3
8	113.6	112.8	112	111.2
9	127.8	126.9	126	125.1

	138	137	136	135
1	13.8	13.7	13.6	13.5
2	27.6	27.4	27.2	27.0
3	41.4	41.1	40.8	40.5
4	55.2	54.8	54.4	54.0
5	69.0	68.5	68.0	67.5
6	82.8	82.2	81.6	81.0
7	96.6	95.9	95.2	94.5
8	110.4	109.6	108.8	108.0
9	124.2	123.3	122.4	121.5

	134	133	132	131
1	13.4	13.3	13.2	13.1
2	26.8	26.6	26.4	26.2
3	40.2	39.9	39.6	39.3
4	53.6	53.2	52.8	52.4
5	67.0	66.5	66.0	65.5
6	80.4	79.8	79.2	78.6
7	93.8	93.1	92.4	91.7
8	107.2	106.4	105.6	104.8
9	120.6	119.7	118.8	117.9

	130	129	128	127
1	13	12.9	12.8	12.7
2	26	25.8	25.6	25.4
3	39	38.7	38.4	38.1
4	52	51.6	51.2	50.8
5	65	64.5	64.0	63.5
6	78	77.4	76.8	76.2
7	91	90.3	89.6	88.9
8	104	103.2	102.4	101.6
9	117	116.1	115.2	114.3

	126	125	124	123
1	12.6	12.5	12.4	12.3
2	25.2	25.0	24.8	24.6
3	37.8	37.5	37.2	36.9
4	50.4	50.0	49.6	49.2
5	63.0	62.5	62.0	61.5
6	75.6	75.0	74.4	73.8
7	88.2	87.5	86.8	86.1
8	100.8	100.0	99.2	98.4
9	113.4	112.5	111.6	110.7

	122	121	120
1	12.2	12.1	12
2	24.4	24.2	24
3	36.6	36.3	36
4	48.8	48.4	48
5	61.0	60.5	60
6	73.2	72.6	72
7	85.4	84.7	84
8	97.6	96.8	96
9	109.8	108.9	108

'	L Sin *	d	L Tan *	c d	L Cot	L Cos *	
0	8.94 030		8.94 195		1.05 805	9.99 834	60
1	174	144	340	145	660	833	59
2	317	143	485	145	515	832	58
3	461	144	630	145	370	831	57
4	603	142	773	143	227	830	56
5	8.94 746	143	8.94 917	144	1.05 083	9.99 829	55
6	8.94 887	141	8.95 060	143	1.04 940	828	54
7	8.95 029	142	202	142	798	827	53
8	170	141	344	142	656	825	52
9	310	140	486	142	514	824	51
10	8.95 450	140	8.95 627	141	1.04 373	9.99 823	50
11	589	139	767	140	233	822	49
12	728	139	8.95 908	141	1.04 092	821	48
13	8.95 867	139	8.96 047	139	1.03 953	820	47
14	8.96 005	138	187	140	813	819	46
15	8.96 143	138	8.96 325	138	1.03 675	9.99 817	45
16	280	137	464	139	536	816	44
17	417	137	602	138	398	815	43
18	553	136	739	137	261	814	42
19	689	136	8.96 877	138	1.03 123	813	41
20	8.96 825	136	8.97 013	136	1.02 987	9.99 812	40
21	8.96 960	135	150	137	850	810	39
22	8.97 095	135	285	135	715	809	38
23	229	134	421	136	579	808	37
24	363	134	556	135	444	807	36
25	8.97 496	133	8.97 691	135	1.02 309	9.99 806	35
26	629	133	825	134	175	804	34
27	762	133	8.97 959	134	1.02 041	803	33
28	8.97 894	132	8.98 092	133	1.01 908	802	32
29	8.98 026	132	225	133	775	801	31
30	8.98 157	131	8.98 358	133	1.01 642	9.99 800	30
31	288	131	490	132	510	798	29
32	419	131	622	132	378	797	28
33	549	130	753	131	247	796	27
34	679	130	884	131	116	795	26
35	8.98 808	129	8.99 015	131	1.00 985	9.99 793	25
36	8.98 937	129	145	130	855	792	24
37	8.99 066	129	275	130	725	791	23
38	194	128	405	130	595	790	22
39	322	128	534	129	466	788	21
40	8.99 450	128	8.99 662	128	1.00 338	9.99 787	20
41	577	127	791	129	209	786	19
42	704	127	8.99 919	128	1.00 081	785	18
43	830	126	9.00 046	127	0.99 954	783	17
44	8.99 956	126	174	128	826	782	16
45	9.00 082	126	9.00 301	127	0.99 699	9.99 781	15
46	207	125	427	126	573	780	14
47	332	125	553	126	447	778	13
48	456	124	679	126	321	777	12
49	581	125	805	126	195	776	11
50	9.00 704	123	9.00 930	125	0.99 070	9.99 775	10
51	828	124	9.01 055	125	0.98 945	773	9
52	9.00 951	123	179	124	821	772	8
53	9.01 074	123	303	124	697	771	7
54	196	122	427	124	573	769	6
55	9.01 318	122	9.01 550	123	0.98 450	9.99 768	5
56	440	122	673	123	327	767	4
57	561	121	796	123	204	765	3
58	682	121	9.01 918	122	0.98 082	764	2
59	803	121	9.02 040	122	0.97 960	763	1
60	9.01 923	120	9.02 162	122	0.97 838	9.99 761	0
	L Cos *	d	L Cot *	c d	L Tan	L Sin *	'

84°

′	L Sin *	d	L Tan *	c d	L Cot	L Cos *	
0	9.01 923		9.02 162		0.97 838	9.99 761	60
1	9.02 043	120	283	121	717	760	59
2	163	120	404	121	596	759	58
3	283	120	525	121	475	757	57
4	402	119	645	120	355	756	56
5	9.02 520	118	9.02 766	121	0.97 234	9.99 755	55
6	639	119	9.02 885	119	0.97 115	753	54
7	757	118	9.03 005	120	0.96 995	752	53
8	874	117	124	119	876	751	52
9	9.02 992	118	242	118	758	749	51
10	9.03 109	117	9.03 361	119	0.96 639	9.99 748	50
11	226	117	479	118	521	747	49
12	342	116	597	118	403	745	48
13	458	116	714	117	286	744	47
14	574	116	832	118	168	742	46
15	9.03 690	116	9.03 948	116	0.96 052	9.99 741	45
16	805	115	9.04 065	117	0.95 935	740	44
17	9.03 920	115	181	116	819	738	43
18	9.04 034	114	297	116	703	737	42
19	149	115	413	116	587	736	41
20	9.04 262	113	9.04 528	115	0.95 472	9.99 734	40
21	376	114	643	115	357	733	39
22	490	114	758	115	242	731	38
23	603	113	873	115	127	730	37
24	715	112	9.04 987	114	0.95 013	728	36
25	9.04 828	113	9.05 101	114	0.94 899	9.99 727	35
26	9.04 940	112	214	113	786	726	34
27	9.05 052	112	328	114	672	724	33
28	164	112	441	113	559	723	32
29	275	111	553	112	447	721	31
30	9.05 386	111	9.05 666	113	0.94 334	9.99 720	30
31	497	111	778	112	222	718	29
32	607	110	9.05 890	112	0.94 110	717	28
33	717	110	9.06 002	112	0.93 998	716	27
34	827	110	113	111	887	714	26
35	9.05 937	110	9.06 224	111	0.93 776	9.99 713	25
36	9.06 046	109	335	111	665	711	24
37	155	109	445	110	555	710	23
38	264	109	556	111	444	708	22
39	372	108	666	110	334	707	21
40	9.06 481	109	9.06 775	109	0.93 225	9.99 705	20
41	589	108	885	110	115	704	19
42	696	107	9.06 994	109	0.93 006	702	18
43	804	108	9.07 103	109	0.92 897	701	17
44	9.06 911	107	211	108	789	699	16
45	9.07 018	107	9.07 320	109	0.92 680	9.99 698	15
46	124	106	428	108	572	696	14
47	231	107	536	108	464	695	13
48	337	106	643	107	357	693	12
49	442	105	751	108	249	692	11
50	9.07 548	106	9.07 858	107	0.92 142	9.99 690	10
51	653	105	9.07 964	106	0.92 036	689	9
52	758	105	9.08 071	107	0.91 929	687	8
53	863	105	177	106	823	686	7
54	9.07 968	105	283	106	717	684	6
55	9.08 072	104	9.08 389	106	0.91 611	9.99 683	5
56	176	104	495	106	505	681	4
57	280	104	600	105	400	680	3
58	383	103	705	105	295	678	2
59	486	103	810	105	190	677	1
60	9.08 589	103	9.08 914	104	0.91 086	9.99 675	0
	L Cos *	d	L Cot *	c d	L Tan	L Sin *	′

Prop. Parts

Subtract 10 from each entry in the columns marked with "."*

	121	120	119
1	12.1	12	11.9
2	24.2	24	23.8
3	36.3	36	35.7
4	48.4	48	47.6
5	60.5	60	59.5
6	72.6	72	71.4
7	84.7	84	83.3
8	96.8	96	95.2
9	108.9	108	107.1

	118	117	116
1	11.8	11.7	11.6
2	23.6	23.4	23.2
3	35.4	35.1	34.8
4	47.2	46.8	46.4
5	59.0	58.5	58.0
6	70.8	70.2	69.6
7	82.6	81.9	81.2
8	94.4	93.6	92.8
9	106.2	105.3	104.4

	115	114	113
1	11.5	11.4	11.3
2	23.0	22.8	22.6
3	34.5	34.2	33.9
4	46.0	45.6	45.2
5	57.5	57.0	56.5
6	69.0	68.4	67.8
7	80.5	79.8	79.1
8	92.0	91.2	90.4
9	103.5	102.6	101.7

	112	111	110
1	11.2	11.1	11
2	22.4	22.2	22
3	33.6	33.3	33
4	44.8	44.4	44
5	56.0	55.5	55
6	67.2	66.6	66
7	78.4	77.7	77
8	89.6	88.8	88
9	100.8	99.9	99

	109	108	107	106
1	10.9	10.8	10.7	10.6
2	21.8	21.6	21.4	21.2
3	32.7	32.4	32.1	31.8
4	43.6	43.2	42.8	42.4
5	54.5	54.0	53.5	53.0
6	65.4	64.8	64.2	63.6
7	76.3	75.6	74.9	74.2
8	87.2	86.4	85.6	84.8
9	98.1	97.2	96.3	95.4

83°

Prop. Parts

	105	104	103
1	10.5	10.4	10.3
2	21.0	20.8	20.6
3	31.5	31.2	30.9
4	42.0	41.6	41.2
5	52.5	52.0	51.5
6	63.0	62.4	61.8
7	73.5	72.8	72.1
8	84.0	83.2	82.4
9	94.5	93.6	92.7

	102	101	99
1	10.2	10.1	9.9
2	20.4	20.2	19.8
3	30.6	30.3	29.7
4	40.8	40.4	39.6
5	51.0	50.5	49.5
6	61.2	60.6	59.4
7	71.4	70.7	69.3
8	81.6	80.8	79.2
9	91.8	90.9	89.1

	98	97	96
1	9.8	9.7	9.6
2	19.6	19.4	19.2
3	29.4	29.1	28.8
4	39.2	38.8	38.4
5	49.0	48.5	48.0
6	58.8	58.2	57.6
7	68.6	67.9	67.2
8	78.4	77.6	76.8
9	88.2	87.3	86.4

-	95	94	93
1	9.5	9.4	9.3
2	19.0	18.8	18.6
3	28.5	28.2	27.9
4	38.0	37.6	37.2
5	47.5	47.0	46.5
6	57.0	56.4	55.8
7	66.5	65.8	65.1
8	76.0	75.2	74.4
9	85.5	84.6	83.7

	92	91	90
1	9.2	9.1	9
2	18.4	18.2	18
3	27.6	27.3	27
4	36.8	36.4	36
5	46.0	45.5	45
6	55.2	54.6	54
7	64.4	63.7	63
8	73.6	72.8	72
9	82.8	81.9	81

′	L Sin *	d	L Tan *	c d	L Cot	L Cos *	
0	9.08 589		9.08 914		0.91 086	9.99 675	60
1	692	103	9.09 019	105	0.90 981	674	59
2	795	103	123	104	877	672	58
3	897	102	227	104	773	670	57
4	9.08 999	102	330	103	670	669	56
5	9.09 101	102	9.09 434	104	0.90 566	9.99 667	55
6	202	101	537	103	463	666	54
7	304	102	640	103	360	664	53
8	405	101	742	102	258	663	52
9	506	101	845	103	155	661	51
10	9.09 606	100	9.09 947	102	0.90 053	9.99 659	50
11	707	101	9.10 049	102	0.89 951	658	49
12	807	100	150	101	850	656	48
13	9.09 907	100	252	102	748	655	47
14	9.10 006	99	353	101	647	653	46
15	9.10 106	100	9.10 454	101	0.89 546	9.99 651	45
16	205	99	555	101	445	650	44
17	304	99	656	101	344	648	43
18	402	98	756	100	244	647	42
19	501	99	856	100	144	645	41
20	9.10 599	98	9.10 956	100	0.89 044	9.99 643	40
21	697	98	9.11 056	100	0.88 944	642	39
22	795	98	155	99	845	640	38
23	893	98	254	99	746	638	37
24	9.10 990	97	353	99	647	637	36
25	9.11 087	97	9.11 452	99	0.88 548	9.99 635	35
26	184	97	551	99	449	633	34
27	281	97	649	98	351	632	33
28	377	96	747	98	253	630	32
29	474	97	845	98	155	629	31
30	9.11 570	96	9.11 943	98	0.88 057	9.99 627	30
31	666	96	9.12 040	97	0.87 960	625	29
32	761	95	138	98	862	624	28
33	857	96	235	97	765	622	27
34	9.11 952	95	332	97	668	620	26
35	9.12 047	95	9.12 428	96	0.87 572	9.99 618	25
36	142	95	525	97	475	617	24
37	236	94	621	96	379	615	23
38	331	95	717	96	283	613	22
39	425	94	813	96	187	612	21
40	9.12 519	94	9.12 909	96	0.87 091	9.99 610	20
41	612	93	9.13 004	95	0.86 996	608	19
42	706	94	099	95	901	607	18
43	799	93	194	95	806	605	17
44	892	93	289	95	711	603	16
45	9.12 985	93	9.13 384	95	0.86 616	9.99 601	15
46	9.13 078	93	478	94	522	600	14
47	171	93	573	95	427	598	13
48	263	92	667	94	333	596	12
49	355	92	761	94	239	595	11
50	9.13 447	92	9.13 854	93	0.86 146	9.99 593	10
51	539	92	9.13 948	94	0.86 052	591	9
52	630	91	9.14 041	93	0.85 959	589	8
53	722	92	134	93	866	588	7
54	813	91	227	93	773	586	6
55	9.13 904	91	9.14 320	93	0.85 680	9.99 584	5
56	9.13 994	90	412	92	588	582	4
57	9.14 085	91	504	92	496	581	3
58	175	90	597	93	403	579	2
59	266	91	688	91	312	577	1
60	9.14 356	90	9.14 780	92	0.85 220	9.99 575	0
	L Cos *	d	L Cot *	c d	L Tan	L Sin *	′

82°

IX. FIVE–PLACE LOGARITHMS OF FUNCTIONS — 8°

′	L Sin *	d	L Tan *	c d	L Cot	L Cos *	
0	9.14 356		9.14 780		0.85 220	9.99 575	60
1	445	89	872	92	128	574	59
2	535	90	9.14 963	91	0.85 037	572	58
3	624	89	9.15 054	91	0.84 946	570	57
4	714	90	145	91	855	568	56
5	9.14 803	89	9.15 236	91	0.84 764	9.99 566	55
6	891	88	327	91	673	565	54
7	9.14 980	89	417	90	583	563	53
8	9.15 069	89	508	91	492	561	52
9	157	88	598	90	402	559	51
10	9.15 245	88	9.15 688	90	0.84 312	9.99 557	50
11	333	88	777	89	223	556	49
12	421	88	867	90	133	554	48
13	508	87	9.15 956	89	0.84 044	552	47
14	596	88	9.16 046	90	0.83 954	550	46
15	9.15 683	87	9.16 135	89	0.83 865	9.99 548	45
16	770	87	224	89	776	546	44
17	857	87	312	88	688	545	43
18	9.15 944	87	401	89	599	543	42
19	9.16 030	86	489	88	511	541	41
20	9.16 116	86	9.16 577	88	0.83 423	9.99 539	40
21	203	87	665	88	335	537	39
22	289	86	753	88	247	535	38
23	374	85	841	88	159	533	37
24	460	86	9.16 928	87	0.83 072	532	36
25	9.16 545	85	9.17 016	88	0.82 984	9.99 530	35
26	631	86	103	87	897	528	34
27	716	85	190	87	810	526	33
28	801	85	277	87	723	524	32
29	886	85	363	86	637	522	31
30	9.16 970	84	9.17 450	87	0.82 550	9.99 520	30
31	9.17 055	85	536	86	464	518	29
32	139	84	622	86	378	517	28
33	223	84	708	86	292	515	27
34	307	84	794	86	206	513	26
35	9.17 391	84	9.17 880	86	0.82 120	9.99 511	25
36	474	83	9.17 965	85	0.82 035	509	24
37	558	84	9.18 051	86	0.81 949	507	23
38	641	83	136	85	864	505	22
39	724	83	221	85	779	503	21
40	9.17 807	83	9.18 306	85	0.81 694	9.99 501	20
41	890	83	391	85	609	499	19
42	9.17 973	83	475	84	525	497	18
43	9.18 055	82	560	85	440	495	17
44	137	82	644	84	356	494	16
45	9.18 220	83	9.18 728	84	0.81 272	9.99 492	15
46	302	82	812	84	188	490	14
47	383	81	896	84	104	488	13
48	465	82	9.18 979	83	0.81 021	486	12
49	547	82	9.19 063	84	0.80 937	484	11
50	9.18 628	81	9.19 146	83	0.80 854	9.99 482	10
51	709	81	229	83	771	480	9
52	790	81	312	83	688	478	8
53	871	81	395	83	605	476	7
54	9.18 952	81	478	83	522	474	6
55	9.19 033	81	9.19 561	83	0.80 439	9.99 472	5
56	113	80	643	82	357	470	4
57	193	80	725	82	275	468	3
58	273	80	807	82	193	466	2
59	353	80	889	82	111	464	1
60	9.19 433	80	9.19 971	82	0.80 029	9.99 462	0
	L Cos *	d	L Cot *	c d	L Tan	L Sin *	′

Prop. Parts

Subtract 10 from each entry in the columns marked with "."*

	92	91	90	89
1	9.2	9.1	9	8.9
2	18.4	18.2	18	17.8
3	27.6	27.3	27	26.7
4	36.8	36.4	36	35.6
5	46.0	45.5	45	44.5
6	55.2	54.6	54	53.4
7	64.4	63.7	63	62.3
8	73.6	72.8	72	71.2
9	82.8	81.9	81	80.1

	88	87	86
1	8.8	8.7	8.6
2	17.6	17.4	17.2
3	26.4	26.1	25.8
4	35.2	34.8	34.4
5	44.0	43.5	43.0
6	52.8	52.2	51.6
7	61.6	60.9	60.2
8	70.4	69.6	68.8
9	79.2	78.3	77.4

	85	84	83
1	8.5	8.4	8.3
2	17.0	16.8	16.6
3	25.5	25.2	24.9
4	34.0	33.6	33.2
5	42.5	42.0	41.5
6	51.0	50.4	49.8
7	59.5	58.8	58.1
8	68.0	67.2	66.4
9	76.5	75.6	74.7

	82	81	80
1	8.2	8.1	8
2	16.4	16.2	16
3	24.6	24.3	24
4	32.8	32.4	32
5	41.0	40.5	40
6	49.2	48.6	48
7	57.4	56.7	56
8	65.6	64.8	64
9	73.8	72.9	72

81°

Prop. Parts

	82	81	80
1	8.2	8.1	8
2	16.4	16.2	16
3	24.6	24.3	24
4	32.8	32.4	32
5	41.0	40.5	40
6	49.2	48.6	48
7	57.4	56.7	56
8	65.6	64.8	64
9	73.8	72.9	72

	79	78	77
1	7.9	7.8	7.7
2	15.8	15.6	15.4
3	23.7	23.4	23.1
4	31.6	31.2	30.8
5	39.5	39.0	38.5
6	47.4	46.8	46.2
7	55.3	54.6	53.9
8	63.2	62.4	61.6
9	71.1	70.2	69.3

	76	75	74
1	7.6	7.5	7.4
2	15.2	15.0	14.8
3	22.8	22.5	22.2
4	30.4	30.0	29.6
5	38.0	37.5	37.0
6	45.6	45.0	44.4
7	53.2	52.5	51.8
8	60.8	60.0	59.2
9	68.4	67.5	66.6

	73	72	71
1	7.3	7.2	7.1
2	14.6	14.4	14.2
3	21.9	21.6	21.3
4	29.2	28.8	28.4
5	36.5	36.0	35.5
6	43.8	43.2	42.6
7	51.1	50.4	49.7
8	58.4	57.6	56.8
9	65.7	64.8	63.9

′	L Sin *	d	L Tan *	c d	L Cot	L Cos *	d	
0	9.19 433		9.19 971		0.80 029	9.99 462		60
1	513	80	9.20 053	82	0.79 947	460	2	59
2	592	79	134	81	866	458	2	58
3	672	80	216	82	784	456	2	57
4	751	79	297	81	703	454	2	56
5	9.19 830	79	9.20 378	81	0.79 622	9.99 452	2	55
6	909	79	459	81	541	450	2	54
7	9.19 988	79	540	81	460	448	2	53
8	9.20 067	79	621	81	379	446	2	52
9	145	78	701	80	299	444	2	51
10	9.20 223	78	9.20 782	81	0.79 218	9.99 442	2	50
11	302	79	862	80	138	440	2	49
12	380	78	9.20 942	80	0.79 058	438	2	48
13	458	78	9.21 022	80	0.78 978	436	2	47
14	535	77	102	80	898	434	2	46
15	9.20 613	78	9.21 182	80	0.78 818	9.99 432	2	45
16	691	78	261	79	739	429	3	44
17	768	77	341	80	659	427	2	43
18	845	77	420	79	580	425	2	42
19	922	77	499	79	501	423	2	41
20	9.20 999	77	9.21 578	79	0.78 422	9.99 421	2	40
21	9.21 076	77	657	79	343	419	2	39
22	153	77	736	79	264	417	2	38
23	229	76	814	78	186	415	2	37
24	306	77	893	79	107	413	2	36
25	9.21 382	76	9.21 971	78	0.78 029	9.99 411	2	35
26	458	76	9.22 049	78	0.77 951	409	2	34
27	534	76	127	78	873	407	2	33
28	610	75	205	78	795	404	3	32
29	685	76	283	78	717	402	2	31
30	9.21 761		9.22 361		0.77 639	9.99 400	2	30
31	836	75	438	77	562	398	2	29
32	912	76	516	78	484	396	2	28
33	9.21 987	75	593	77	407	394	2	27
34	9.22 062	75	670	77	330	392	2	26
35	9.22 137	75	9.22 747	77	0.77 253	9.99 390	2	25
36	211	74	824	77	176	388	3	24
37	286	75	901	77	099	385	2	23
38	361	74	9.22 977	76	0.77 023	383	2	22
39	435	74	9.23 054	77	0.76 946	381	2	21
40	9.22 509	74	9.23 130	76	0.76 870	9.99 379		20
41	583	74	206	76	794	377	2	19
42	657	74	283	77	717	375	3	18
43	731	74	359	76	641	372	2	17
44	805	73	435	75	565	370	2	16
45	9.22 878	74	9.23 510	76	0.76 490	9.99 368	2	15
46	9.22 952	73	586	75	414	366	2	14
47	9.23 025	73	661	76	339	364	2	13
48	098	73	737	75	263	362	3	12
49	171	73	812	75	188	359	2	11
50	9.23 244	73	9.23 887	75	0.76 113	9.99 357	2	10
51	317	73	9.23 962	75	0.76 038	355	2	9
52	390	72	9.24 037	75	0.75 963	353	2	8
53	462	73	112	74	888	351	3	7
54	535	72	186	75	814	348	2	6
55	9.23 607	72	9.24 261	74	0.75 739	9.99 346	2	5
56	679	72	335	75	665	344	2	4
57	752	73	410	74	590	342	2	3
58	823	71	484	74	516	340	3	2
59	895	72	558	74	442	337	2	1
60	9.23 967		9.24 632		0.75 368	9.99 335		0
	L Cos *	d	L Cot *	c d	L Tan	L Sin *	d	′

80°

′	L Sin *	d	L Tan *	c d	L Cot	L Cos *	d	
0	9.23 967		9.24 632		0.75 368	9.99 335		60
1	9.24 039	72	706	74	294	333	2	59
2	110	71	779	73	221	331	2	58
3	181	71	853	74	147	328	3	57
4	253	72	9.24 926	73	074	326	2	56
5	9.24 324	71	9.25 000	74	0.75 000	9.99 324	2	55
6	395	71	073	73	0.74 927	322	2	54
7	466	71	146	73	854	319	3	53
8	536	70	219	73	781	317	2	52
9	607	71	292	73	708	315	2	51
10	9.24 677	70	9.25 365	73	0.74 635	9.99 313	2	50
11	748	71	437	72	563	310	3	49
12	818	70	510	73	490	308	2	48
13	888	70	582	72	418	306	2	47
14	9.24 958	70	655	73	345	304	2	46
15	9.25 028	70	9.25 727	72	0.74 273	9.99 301	3	45
16	098	70	799	72	201	299	2	44
17	168	70	871	72	129	297	2	43
18	237	69	9.25 943	72	0.74 057	294	3	42
19	307	70	9.26 015	72	0.73 985	292	2	41
20	9.25 376	69	9.26 086	71	0.73 914	9.99 290	2	40
21	445	69	158	72	842	288	3	39
22	514	69	229	71	771	285	3	38
23	583	69	301	72	699	283	2	37
24	652	69	372	71	628	281	3	36
25	9.25 721	69	9.26 443	71	0.73 557	9.99 278	3	35
26	790	69	514	71	486	276	2	34
27	858	68	585	71	415	274	2	33
28	927	69	655	70	345	271	3	32
29	9.25 995	68	726	71	274	269	2	31
30	9.26 063	68	9.26 797	71	0.73 203	9.99 267	2	30
31	131	68	867	70	133	264	3	29
32	199	68	9.26 937	70	0.73 063	262	2	28
33	267	68	9.27 008	71	0.72 992	260	2	27
34	335	68	078	70	922	257	3	26
35	9.26 403	68	9.27 148	70	0.72 852	9.99 255	2	25
36	470	67	218	70	782	252	3	24
37	538	68	288	70	712	250	2	23
38	605	67	357	69	643	248	2	22
39	672	67	427	70	573	245	3	21
40	9.26 739	67	9.27 496	69	0.72 504	9.99 243	2	20
41	806	67	566	70	434	241	2	19
42	873	67	635	69	365	238	2	18
43	9.26 940	67	704	69	296	236	3	17
44	9.27 007	67	773	69	227	233	2	16
45	9.27 073	66	9.27 842	69	0.72 158	9.99 231	2	15
46	140	67	911	69	089	229	3	14
47	206	66	9.27 980	69	0.72 020	226	2	13
48	273	67	9.28 049	69	0.71 951	224	3	12
49	339	66	117	68	883	221	2	11
50	9.27 405	66	9.28 186	69	0.71 814	9.99 219	2	10
51	471	66	254	68	746	217	3	9
52	537	66	323	69	677	214	2	8
53	602	65	391	68	609	212	3	7
54	668	66	459	68	541	209	2	6
55	9.27 734	66	9.28 527	68	0.71 473	9.99 207	3	5
56	799	65	595	68	405	204	2	4
57	864	65	662	67	338	202	2	3
58	930	66	730	68	270	200	3	2
59	9.27 995	65	798	68	202	197	2	1
60	9.28 060	65	9.28 865	67	0.71 135	9.99 195		0
	L Cos *	d	L Cot *	c d	L Tan	L Sin *	d	′

Prop. Parts

	74	73	72
1	7.4	7.3	7.2
2	14.8	14.6	14.4
3	22.2	21.9	21.6
4	29.6	29.2	28.8
5	37.0	36.5	36.0
6	44.4	43.8	43.2
7	51.8	51.1	50.4
8	59.2	58.4	57.6
9	66.6	65.7	64.8

	71	70	69
1	7.1	7	6.9
2	14.2	14	13.8
3	21.3	21	20.7
4	28.4	28	27.6
5	35.5	35	34.5
6	42.6	42	41.4
7	49.7	49	48.3
8	56.8	56	55.2
9	63.9	63	62.1

	68	67	66
1	6.8	6.7	6.6
2	13.6	13.4	13.2
3	20.4	20.1	19.8
4	27.2	26.8	26.4
5	34.0	33.5	33.0
6	40.8	40.2	39.6
7	47.6	46.9	46.2
8	54.4	53.6	52.8
9	61.2	60.3	59.4

	65	3	2
1	6.5	0.3	0.2
2	13.0	0.6	0.4
3	19.5	0.9	0.6
4	26.0	1.2	0.8
5	32.5	1.5	1.0
6	39.0	1.8	1.2
7	45.5	2.1	1.4
8	52.0	2.4	1.6
9	58.5	2.7	1.8

79°

IX. FIVE-PLACE LOGARITHMS OF FUNCTIONS — 11°

Prop. Parts

	68	67	66
1	6.8	6.7	6.6
2	13.6	13.4	13.2
3	20.4	20.1	19.8
4	27.2	26.8	26.4
5	34.0	33.5	33.0
6	40.8	40.2	39.6
7	47.6	46.9	46.2
8	54.4	53.6	52.8
9	61.2	60.3	59.4

	65	64	63
1	6.5	6.4	6.3
2	13.0	12.8	12.6
3	19.5	19.2	18.9
4	26.0	25.6	25.2
5	32.5	32.0	31.5
6	39.0	38.4	37.8
7	45.5	44.8	44.1
8	52.0	51.2	50.4
9	58.5	57.6	56.7

	62	61	60
1	6.2	6.1	6
2	12.4	12.2	12
3	18.6	18.3	18
4	24.8	24.4	24
5	31.0	30.5	30
6	37.2	36.6	36
7	43.4	42.7	42
8	49.6	48.8	48
9	55.8	54.9	54

	59	3	2
1	5.9	0.3	0.2
2	11.8	0.6	0.4
3	17.7	0.9	0.6
4	23.6	1.2	0.8
5	29.5	1.5	1.0
6	35.4	1.8	1.2
7	41.3	2.1	1.4
8	47.2	2.4	1.6
9	53.1	2.7	1.8

′	L Sin *	d	L Tan *	c d	L Cot	L Cos *	d	
0	9.28 060		9.28 865		0.71 135	9.99 195		60
1	125	65	9.28 933	68	067	192	3	59
2	190	65	9.29 000	67	0.71 000	190	2	58
3	254	64	067	67	0.70 933	187	3	57
4	319	65	134	67	866	185	2	56
5	9.28 384	65	9.29 201	67	0.70 799	9.99 182	3	55
6	448	64	268	67	732	180	2	54
7	512	64	335	67	665	177	3	53
8	577	65	402	67	598	175	2	52
9	641	64	468	66	532	172	3	51
10	9.28 705	64	9.29 535	67	0.70 465	9.99 170	2	50
11	769	64	601	66	399	167	3	49
12	833	64	668	67	332	165	2	48
13	896	63	734	66	266	162	3	47
14	9.28 960	64	800	66	200	160	2	46
15	9.29 024	64	9.29 866	66	0.70 134	9.99 157	3	45
16	087	63	932	66	068	155	2	44
17	150	63	9.29 998	66	0.70 002	152	3	43
18	214	64	9.30 064	66	0.69 936	150	2	42
19	277	63	130	66	870	147	2	41
20	9.29 340	63	9.30 195	65	0.69 805	9.99 145	2	40
21	403	63	261	66	739	142	3	39
22	466	63	326	65	674	140	2	38
23	529	63	391	65	609	137	3	37
24	591	62	457	66	543	135	2	36
25	9.29 654	63	9.30 522	65	0.69 478	9.99 132	3	35
26	716	62	587	65	413	130	2	34
27	779	63	652	65	348	127	3	33
28	841	62	717	65	283	124	3	32
29	903	62	782	65	218	122	2	31
30	9.29 966	63	9.30 846	64	0.69 154	9.99 119	3	30
31	9.30 028	62	911	65	089	117	2	29
32	090	62	9.30 975	64	0.69 025	114	2	28
33	151	61	9.31 040	65	0.68 960	112	2	27
34	213	62	104	64	896	109	3	26
35	9.30 275	62	9.31 168	64	0.68 832	9.99 106	3	25
36	336	61	233	65	767	104	2	24
37	398	62	297	64	703	101	3	23
38	459	61	361	64	639	099	2	22
39	521	62	425	64	575	096	3	21
40	9.30 582	61	9.31 489	64	0.68 511	9.99 093	3	20
41	643	61	552	63	448	091	2	19
42	704	61	616	64	384	088	3	18
43	765	61	679	63	321	086	2	17
44	826	61	743	64	257	083	3	16
45	9.30 887	61	9.31 806	63	0.68 194	9.99 080	3	15
46	9.30 947	60	870	64	130	078	2	14
47	9.31 008	61	933	63	067	075	3	13
48	068	60	9.31 996	63	0.68 004	072	2	12
49	129	61	9.32 059	63	0.67 941	070	3	11
50	9.31 189	60	9.32 122	63	0.67 878	9.99 067	3	10
51	250	61	185	63	815	064	2	9
52	310	60	248	63	752	062	3	8
53	370	60	311	63	689	059	3	7
54	430	60	373	62	627	056	3	6
55	9.31 490	60	9.32 436	63	0.67 564	9.99 054	2	5
56	549	59	498	62	502	051	3	4
57	609	60	561	63	439	048	3	3
58	669	60	623	62	377	046	2	2
59	728	59	685	62	315	043	3	1
60	9.31 788	60	9.32 747	62	0.67 253	9.99 040		0
	L Cos *	d	L Cot *	c d	L Tan	L Sin *	d	′

78°

[49]

′	L Sin *	d	L Tan *	c d	L Cot	L Cos *	d		Prop. Parts

′	L Sin *	d	L Tan *	c d	L Cot	L Cos *	d	
0	9.31 788		9.32 747		0.67 253	9.99 040		**60**
1	847	59	810	63	190	038	2	59
2	907	60	872	62	128	035	3	58
3	9.31 966	59	933	61	067	032	3	57
4	9.32 025	59	9.32 995	62	0.67 005	030	2	56
5	9.32 084	59	9.33 057	62	0.66 943	9.99 027	3	**55**
6	143	59	119	62	881	024	3	54
7	202	59	180	61	820	022	2	53
8	261	59	242	62	758	019	3	52
9	319	58	303	61	697	016	3	51
10	9.32 378	59	9.33 365	62	0.66 635	9.99 013	3	**50**
11	437	59	426	61	574	011	2	49
12	495	58	487	61	513	008	3	48
13	553	58	548	61	452	005	3	47
14	612	59	609	61	391	002	3	46
15	9.32 670	58	9.33 670	61	0.66 330	9.99 000	2	**45**
16	728	58	731	61	269	9.98 997	3	44
17	786	58	792	61	208	994	3	43
18	844	58	853	61	147	991	3	42
19	902	58	913	60	087	989	2	41
20	9.32 960	58	9.33 974	61	0.66 026	9.98 986	3	**40**
21	9.33 018	58	9.34 034	60	0.65 966	983	3	39
22	075	57	095	61	905	980	3	38
23	133	58	155	60	845	978	2	37
24	190	57	215	60	785	975	3	36
25	9.33 248	58	9.34 276	61	0.65 724	9.98 972	3	**35**
26	305	57	336	60	664	969	3	34
27	362	57	396	60	604	967	2	33
28	420	58	456	60	544	964	3	32
29	477	57	516	60	484	961	3	31
30	9.33 534	57	9.34 576	60	0.65 424	9.98 958	3	**30**
31	591	57	635	59	365	955	3	29
32	647	56	695	60	305	953	2	28
33	704	57	755	60	245	950	3	27
34	761	57	814	59	186	947	3	26
35	9.33 818	57	9.34 874	60	0.65 126	9.98 944	3	**25**
36	874	56	933	59	067	941	3	24
37	931	57	9.34 992	59	0.65 008	938	3	23
38	9.33 987	56	9.35 051	59	0.64 949	936	2	22
39	9.34 043	56	111	60	889	933	3	21
40	9.34 100	57	9.35 170	59	0.64 830	9.98 930	3	**20**
41	156	56	229	59	771	927	3	19
42	212	56	288	59	712	924	3	18
43	268	56	347	59	653	921	2	17
44	324	56	405	58	595	919	3	16
45	9.34 380	56	9.35 464	59	0.64 536	9.98 916	3	**15**
46	436	56	523	59	477	913	3	14
47	491	55	581	58	419	910	3	13
48	547	56	640	59	360	907	3	12
49	602	55	698	58	302	904	3	11
50	9.34 658	56	9.35 757	59	0.64 243	9.98 901	3	**10**
51	713	55	815	58	185	898	2	9
52	769	56	873	58	127	896	3	8
53	824	55	931	58	069	893	3	7
54	879	55	9.35 989	58	0.64 011	890	3	6
55	9.34 934	55	9.36 047	58	0.63 953	9.98 887	3	**5**
56	9.34 989	55	105	58	895	884	3	4
57	9.35 044	55	163	58	837	881	3	3
58	099	55	221	58	779	878	3	2
59	154	55	279	58	721	875	3	1
60	9.35 209	55	9.36 336	57	0.63 664	9.98 872	3	**0**
	L Cos *	d	L Cot *	c d	L Tan	L Sin *	d	′

Prop. Parts

	63	62	61
1	6.3	6.2	6.1
2	12.6	12.4	12.2
3	18.9	18.6	18.3
4	25.2	24.8	24.4
5	31.5	31.0	30.5
6	37.8	37.2	36.6
7	44.1	43.4	42.7
8	50.4	49.6	48.8
9	56.7	55.8	54.9

	60	59	58
1	6	5.9	5.8
2	12	11.8	11.6
3	18	17.7	17.4
4	24	23.6	23.2
5	30	29.5	29.0
6	36	35.4	34.8
7	42	41.3	40.6
8	48	47.2	46.4
9	54	53.1	52.2

	57	56	55
1	5.7	5.6	5.5
2	11.4	11.2	11.0
3	17.1	16.8	16.5
4	22.8	22.4	22.0
5	28.5	28.0	27.5
6	34.2	33.6	33.0
7	39.9	39.2	38.5
8	45.6	44.8	44.0
9	51.3	50.4	49.5

	3	2
1	0.3	0.2
2	0.6	0.4
3	0.9	0.6
4	1.2	0.8
5	1.5	1.0
6	1.8	1.2
7	2.1	1.4
8	2.4	1.6
9	2.7	1.8

77°

Prop. Parts

Subtract 10 from each entry in the columns marked with "*."

	58	57	56
1	5.8	5.7	5.6
2	11.6	11.4	11.2
3	17.4	17.1	16.8
4	23.2	22.8	22.4
5	29.0	28.5	28.0
6	34.8	34.2	33.6
7	40.6	39.9	39.2
8	46.4	45.6	44.8
9	52.2	51.3	50.4

	55	54	53
1	5.5	5.4	5.3
2	11.0	10.8	10.6
3	16.5	16.2	15.9
4	22.0	21.6	21.2
5	27.5	27.0	26.5
6	33.0	32.4	31.8
7	38.5	37.8	37.1
8	44.0	43.2	42.4
9	49.5	48.6	47.7

	52	51
1	5.2	5.1
2	10.4	10.2
3	15.6	15.3
4	20.8	20.4
5	26.0	25.5
6	31.2	30.6
7	36.4	35.7
8	41.6	40.8
9	46.8	45.9

	4	3	2
1	0.4	0.3	0.2
2	0.8	0.6	0.4
3	1.2	0.9	0.6
4	1.6	1.2	0.8
5	2.0	1.5	1.0
6	2.4	1.8	1.2
7	2.8	2.1	1.4
8	3.2	2.4	1.6
9	3.6	2.7	1.8

′	L Sin *	d	L Tan *	c d	L Cot	L Cos *	d	′
0	9.35 209		9.36 336		0.63 664	9.98 872		60
1	263	54	394	58	606	869	3	59
2	318	55	452	58	548	867	2	58
3	373	55	509	57	491	864	3	57
4	427	54	566	57	434	861	3	56
5	9.35 481	54	9.36 624	58	0.63 376	9.98 858	3	55
6	536	55	681	57	319	855	3	54
7	590	54	738	57	262	852	3	53
8	644	54	795	57	205	849	3	52
9	698	54	852	57	148	846	3	51
10	9.35 752	54	9.36 909	57	0.63 091	9.98 843	3	50
11	806	54	9.36 966	57	0.63 034	840	3	49
12	860	54	9.37 023	57	0.62 977	837	3	48
13	914	54	080	57	920	834	3	47
14	9.35 968	54	137	56	863	831	3	46
15	9.36 022	54	9.37 193	56	0.62 807	9.98 828	3	45
16	075	53	250	57	750	825	3	44
17	129	54	306	56	694	822	3	43
18	182	53	363	57	637	819	3	42
19	236	54	419	56	581	816	3	41
20	9.36 289	53	9.37 476	57	0.62 524	9.98 813	3	40
21	342	53	532	56	468	810	3	39
22	395	53	588	56	412	807	3	38
23	449	54	644	56	356	804	3	37
24	502	53	700	56	300	801	3	36
25	9.36 555	53	9.37 756	56	0.62 244	9.98 798	3	35
26	608	53	812	56	188	795	3	34
27	660	52	868	56	132	792	3	33
28	713	53	924	56	076	789	3	32
29	766	53	9.37 980	56	0.62 020	786	3	31
30	9.36 819	53	9.38 035	55	0.61 965	9.98 783	3	30
31	871	52	091	56	909	780	3	29
32	924	53	147	56	853	777	3	28
33	9.36 976	52	202	55	798	774	3	27
34	9.37 028	52	257	55	743	771	3	26
35	9.37 081	53	9.38 313	56	0.61 687	9.98 768	3	25
36	133	52	368	55	632	765	3	24
37	185	52	423	55	577	762	3	23
38	237	52	479	56	521	759	3	22
39	289	52	534	55	466	756	3	21
40	9.37 341	52	9.38 589	55	0.61 411	9.98 753	3	20
41	393	52	644	55	356	750	3	19
42	445	52	699	55	301	746	4	18
43	497	52	754	55	246	743	3	17
44	549	51	808	54	192	740	3	16
45	9.37 600	52	9.38 863	55	0.61 137	9.98 737	3	15
46	652	51	918	55	082	734	3	14
47	703	52	9.38 972	54	0.61 028	731	3	13
48	755	51	9.39 027	55	0.60 973	728	3	12
49	806	51	082	54	918	725	3	11
50	9.37 858	52	9.39 136	54	0.60 864	9.98 722	3	10
51	909	51	190	54	810	719	3	9
52	9.37 960	51	245	55	755	715	4	8
53	9.38 011	51	299	54	701	712	3	7
54	062	51	353	54	647	709	3	6
55	9.38 113	51	9.39 407	54	0.60 593	9.98 706	3	5
56	164	51	461	54	539	703	3	4
57	215	51	515	54	485	700	3	3
58	266	51	569	54	431	697	3	2
59	317	51	623	54	377	694	4	1
60	9.38 368		9.39 677		0.60 323	9.98 690		0
	L Cos *	d	L Cot *	c d	L Tan	L Sin *	d	′

76°

′	L Sin *	d	L Tan *	c d	L Cot	L Cos *	d		Prop. Parts
0	9.38 368		9.39 677		0.60 323	9.98 690		60	*Subtract* 10 *from each entry in the columns marked with* "*."
1	418	50	731	54	269	687	3	59	
2	469	51	785	54	215	684	3	58	
3	519	50	838	53	162	681	3	57	
4	570	51	892	54	108	678	3	56	
5	9.38 620	50	9.39 945	53	0.60 055	9.98 675	3	55	
6	670	50	9.39 999	54	0.60 001	671	4	54	
7	721	51	9.40 052	53	0.59 948	668	3	53	
8	771	50	106	54	894	665	3	52	
9	821	50	159	53	841	662	3	51	
10	9.38 871	50	212	53	0.59 788	9.98 659	3	50	

Prop. Parts

	54	53	52
1	5.4	5.3	5.2
2	10.8	10.6	10.4
3	16.2	15.9	15.6
4	21.6	21.2	20.8
5	27.0	26.5	26.0
6	32.4	31.8	31.2
7	37.8	37.1	36.4
8	43.2	42.4	41.6
9	48.6	47.7	46.8

′	L Sin *	d	L Tan *	c d	L Cot	L Cos *	d	
11	921	50	266	54	734	656	3	49
12	9.38 971	50	319	53	681	652	4	48
13	9.39 021	50	372	53	628	649	3	47
14	071	50	425	53	575	646	3	46
15	9.39 121	50	9.40 478	53	0.59 522	9.98 643	3	45
16	170	49	531	53	469	640	3	44
17	220	50	584	53	416	636	4	43
18	270	50	636	52	364	633	3	42
19	319	49	689	53	311	630	3	41
20	9.39 369	50	9.40 742	53	0.59 258	9.98 627	3	40
21	418	49	795	53	205	623	4	39
22	467	49	847	52	153	620	3	38
23	517	50	900	53	100	617	3	37
24	566	49	9.40 952	52	0.59 048	614	3	36
25	9.39 615	49	9.41 005	53	0.58 995	9.98 610	4	35

	51	50	49
1	5.1	5	4.9
2	10.2	10	9.8
3	15.3	15	14.7
4	20.4	20	19.6
5	25.5	25	24.5
6	30.6	30	29.4
7	35.7	35	34.3
8	40.8	40	39.2
9	45.9	45	44.1

′	L Sin *	d	L Tan *	c d	L Cot	L Cos *	d	
26	664	49	057	52	943	607	3	34
27	713	49	109	52	891	604	3	33
28	762	49	161	52	839	601	3	32
29	811	49	214	53	786	597	4	31
30	9.39 860	49	9.41 266	52	0.58 734	9.98 594	3	30
31	909	49	318	52	682	591	3	29
32	9.39 958	49	370	52	630	588	4	28
33	9.40 006	48	422	52	578	584	3	27
34	055	49	474	52	526	581	3	26
35	9.40 103	48	9.41 526	52	0.58 474	9.98 578	4	25
36	152	49	578	52	422	574	3	24
37	200	48	629	51	371	571	3	23
38	249	49	681	52	319	568	3	22
39	297	48	733	52	267	565	4	21
40	9.40 346	49	9.41 784	51	0.58 216	9.98 561		20

	48	47
1	4.8	4.7
2	9.6	9.4
3	14.4	14.1
4	19.2	18.8
5	24.0	23.5
6	28.8	28.2
7	33.6	32.9
8	38.4	37.6
9	43.2	42.3

′	L Sin *	d	L Tan *	c d	L Cot	L Cos *	d	
41	394	48	836	52	164	558	3	19
42	442	48	887	51	113	555	3	18
43	490	48	939	52	061	551	4	17
44	538	48	9.41 990	51	0.58 010	548	3	16
45	9.40 586	48	9.42 041	51	0.57 959	9.98 545	3	15
46	634	48	093	52	907	541	4	14
47	682	48	144	51	856	538	3	13
48	730	48	195	51	805	535	3	12
49	778	48	246	51	754	531	4	11
50	9.40 825	47	9.42 297	51	0.57 703	9.98 528	3	10

	4	3
1	0.4	0.3
2	0.8	0.6
3	1.2	0.9
4	1.6	1.2
5	2.0	1.5
6	2.4	1.8
7	2.8	2.1
8	3.2	2.4
9	3.6	2.7

′	L Sin *	d	L Tan *	c d	L Cot	L Cos *	d	
51	873	48	348	51	652	525	3	9
52	921	48	399	51	601	521	4	8
53	9.40 968	47	450	51	550	518	3	7
54	9.41 016	48	501	51	499	515	3	6
55	9.41 063	47	9.42 552	51	0.57 448	9.98 511	4	5
56	111	48	603	51	397	508	3	4
57	158	47	653	50	347	505	3	3
58	205	47	704	51	296	501	4	2
59	252	47	755	51	245	498	3	1
60	9.41 300	48	9.42 805	50	0.57 195	9.98 494	4	0

	L Cos *	d	L Cot *	c d	L Tan	L Sin *	d	′

75°

IX. FIVE–PLACE LOGARITHMS OF FUNCTIONS — 15°

′	L Sin *	d	L Tan *	c d	L Cot	L Cos *	d	
0	9.41 300		9.42 805		0.57 195	9.98 494		60
1	347	47	856	51	144	491	3	59
2	394	47	906	50	094	488	3	58
3	441	47	9.42 957	51	0.57 043	484	4	57
4	488	47	9.43 007	50	0.56 993	481	3	56
5	9.41 535	47	9.43 057	50	0.56 943	9.98 477	4	55
6	582	47	108	51	892	474	3	54
7	628	46	158	50	842	471	3	53
8	675	47	208	50	792	467	4	52
9	722	47	258	50	742	464	3	51
10	9.41 768	46	9.43 308	50	0.56 692	9.98 460	4	50
11	815	47	358	50	642	457	3	49
12	861	46	408	50	592	453	4	48
13	908	47	458	50	542	450	3	47
14	9.41 954	46	508	50	492	447	3	46
15	9.42 001	47	9.43 558	50	0.56 442	9.98 443	4	45
16	047	46	607	49	393	440	3	44
17	093	46	657	50	343	436	4	43
18	140	47	707	50	293	433	3	42
19	186	46	756	49	244	429	4	41
20	9.42 232	46	9.43 806	50	0.56 194	9.98 426	3	40
21	278	46	855	49	145	422	4	39
22	324	46	905	50	095	419	3	38
23	370	46	9.43 954	49	0.56 046	415	4	37
24	416	46	9.44 004	50	0.55 996	412	3	36
25	9.42 461	45	9.44 053	49	0.55 947	9.98 409	4	35
26	507	46	102	49	898	405	3	34
27	553	46	151	49	849	402	3	33
28	599	46	201	50	799	398	4	32
29	644	45	250	49	750	395	3	31
30	9.42 690	46	9.44 299	49	0.55 701	9.98 391	4	30
31	735	45	348	49	652	388	3	29
32	781	46	397	49	603	384	4	28
33	826	45	446	49	554	381	3	27
34	872	46	495	49	505	377	4	26
35	9.42 917	45	9.44 544	49	0.55 456	9.98 373	4	25
36	9.42 962	45	592	48	408	370	3	24
37	9.43 008	46	641	49	359	366	4	23
38	053	45	690	49	310	363	3	22
39	098	45	738	48	262	359	4	21
40	9.43 143	45	9.44 787	49	0.55 213	9.98 356	3	20
41	188	45	836	49	164	352	4	19
42	233	45	884	48	116	349	3	18
43	278	45	933	49	067	345	4	17
44	323	45	9.44 981	48	0.55 019	342	3	16
45	9.43 367	44	9.45 029	48	0.54 971	9.98 338	4	15
46	412	45	078	49	922	334	4	14
47	457	45	126	48	874	331	3	13
48	502	45	174	48	826	327	4	12
49	546	44	222	48	778	324	3	11
50	9.43 591	45	9.45 271	49	0.54 729	9.98 320	4	10
51	635	44	319	48	681	317	3	9
52	680	45	367	48	633	313	4	8
53	724	44	415	48	585	309	4	7
54	769	45	463	48	537	306	3	6
55	9.43 813	44	9.45 511	48	0.54 489	9.98 302	4	5
56	857	44	559	48	441	299	3	4
57	901	44	606	47	394	295	4	3
58	946	45	654	48	346	291	4	2
59	9.43 990	44	702	48	298	288	3	1
60	9.44 034	44	9.45 750	48	0.54 250	9.98 284	4	0
	L Cos *	d	L Cot *	c d	L Tan	L Sin *	d	′

Prop. Parts

	51	50	49
1	5.1	5	4.9
2	10.2	10	9.8
3	15.3	15	14.7
4	20.4	20	19.6
5	25.5	25	24.5
6	30.6	30	29.4
7	35.7	35	34.3
8	40.8	40	39.2
9	45.9	45	44.1

	48	47	46
1	4.8	4.7	4.6
2	9.6	9.4	9.2
3	14.4	14.1	13.8
4	19.2	18.8	18.4
5	24.0	23.5	23.0
6	28.8	28.2	27.6
7	33.6	32.9	32.2
8	38.4	37.6	36.8
9	43.2	42.3	41.4

	45	44
1	4.5	4.4
2	9.0	8.8
3	13.5	13.2
4	18.0	17.6
5	22.5	22.0
6	27.0	26.4
7	31.5	30.8
8	36.0	35.2
9	40.5	39.6

	4	3
1	0.4	0.3
2	0.8	0.6
3	1.2	0.9
4	1.6	1.2
5	2.0	1.5
6	2.4	1.8
7	2.8	2.1
8	3.2	2.4
9	3.6	2.7

74°

�'	L Sin *	d	L Tan *	c d	L Cot	L Cos *	d		Prop. Parts
0	9.44 034		9.45 750		0.54 250	9.98 284		**60**	
1	078	44	797	47	203	281	3	59	
2	122	44	845	48	155	277	4	58	
3	166	44	892	47	108	273	4	57	
4	210	44	940	48	060	270	3	56	
5	9.44 253	43	9.45 987	47	0.54 013	9.98 266	4	**55**	
6	297	44	9.46 035	48	0.53 965	262	4	54	**48** **47** **46**
7	341	44	082	47	918	259	3	53	
8	385	44	130	48	870	255	4	52	1 4.8 4.7 4.6
9	428	43	177	47	823	251	4	51	2 9.6 9.4 9.2
10	9.44 472	44	9.46 224	47	0.53 776	9.98 248	3	**50**	3 14.4 14.1 13.8
									4 19.2 18.8 18.4
11	516	44	271	47	729	244	4	49	5 24.0 23.5 23.0
12	559	43	319	48	681	240	4	48	6 28.8 28.2 27.6
13	602	43	366	47	634	237	4	47	7 33.6 32.9 32.2
14	646	44	413	47	587	233	4	46	8 38.4 37.6 36.8
15	9.44 689	43	9.46 460	47	0.53 540	9.98 229	4	**45**	9 43.2 42.3 41.4
16	733	44	507	47	493	226	3	44	
17	776	43	554	47	446	222	4	43	
18	819	43	601	47	399	218	4	42	
19	862	43	648	47	352	215	3	41	
20	9.44 905	43	9.46 694	46	0.53 306	9.98 211	4	**40**	
									45 **44** **43**
21	948	43	741	47	259	207	4	39	
22	9.44 992	43	788	47	212	204	3	38	1 4.5 4.4 4.3
23	9.45 035	43	835	47	165	200	4	37	2 9.0 8.8 8.6
24	077	42	881	46	119	196	4	36	3 13.5 13.2 12.9
25	9.45 120	43	9.46 928	47	0.53 072	9.98 192	4	**35**	4 18.0 17.6 17.2
									5 22.5 22.0 21.5
26	163	43	9.46 975	47	0.53 025	189	3	34	6 27.0 26.4 25.8
27	206	43	9.47 021	46	0.52 979	185	4	33	7 31.5 30.8 30.1
28	249	43	068	47	932	181	4	32	8 36.0 35.2 34.4
29	292	43	114	46	886	177	4	31	9 40.5 39.6 38.7
30	9.45 334	42	9.47 160	46	0.52 840	9.98 174	3	**30**	
31	377	43	207	47	793	170	4	29	
32	419	42	253	46	747	166	4	28	
33	462	43	299	46	701	162	4	27	
34	504	42	346	47	654	159	3	26	**42** **41**
35	9.45 547	43	9.47 392	46	0.52 608	9.98 155	4	**25**	
36	589	42	438	46	562	151	4	24	1 4.2 4.1
37	632	43	484	46	516	147	4	23	2 8.4 8.2
38	674	42	530	46	470	144	3	22	3 12.6 12.3
39	716	42	576	46	424	140	4	21	4 16.8 16.4
40	9.45 758	42	9.47 622	46	0.52 378	9.98 136	4	**20**	5 21.0 20.5
									6 25.2 24.6
41	801	43	668	46	332	132	4	19	7 29.4 28.7
42	843	42	714	46	286	129	3	18	8 33.6 32.8
43	885	42	760	46	240	125	4	17	9 37.8 36.9
44	927	42	806	46	194	121	4	16	
45	9.45 969	42	9.47 852	46	0.52 148	9.98 117	4	**15**	
46	9.46 011	42	897	45	103	113	3	14	
47	053	42	943	46	057	110	4	13	
48	095	42	9.47 989	46	0.52 011	106	4	12	**4** **3**
49	136	41	9.48 035	46	0.51 965	102	4	11	
50	9.46 178	42	9.48 080	45	0.51 920	9.98 098	4	**10**	1 0.4 0.3
									2 0.8 0.6
51	220	42	126	46	874	094	4	9	3 1.2 0.9
52	262	42	171	45	829	090	4	8	4 1.6 1.2
53	303	41	217	46	783	087	3	7	5 2.0 1.5
54	345	42	262	45	738	083	4	6	6 2.4 1.8
55	9.46 386	41	9.48 307	45	0.51 693	9.98 079	4	**5**	7 2.8 2.1
56	428	42	353	46	647	075	4	4	8 3.2 2.4
57	469	41	398	45	602	071	4	3	9 3.6 2.7
58	511	42	443	45	557	067	4	2	
59	552	41	489	46	511	063	4	1	
60	9.46 594	42	9.48 534	45	0.51 466	9.98 060	3	**0**	
	L Cos *	d	L Cot *	c d	L Tan	L Sin *	d	✗	

73°

Prop. Parts

Subtract 10 from each entry in the columns marked with "."*

1	45	44	43
1	4.5	4.4	4.3
2	9.0	8.8	8.6
3	13.5	13.2	12.9
4	18.0	17.6	17.2
5	22.5	22.0	21.5
6	27.0	26.4	25.8
7	31.5	30.8	30.1
8	36.0	35.2	34.4
9	40.5	39.6	38.7

	42	41
1	4.2	4.1
2	8.4	8.2
3	12.6	12.3
4	16.8	16.4
5	21.0	20.5
6	25.2	24.6
7	29.4	28.7
8	33.6	32.8
9	37.8	36.9

	40	39
1	4	3.9
2	8	7.8
3	12	11.7
4	16	15.6
5	20	19.5
6	24	23.4
7	28	27.3
8	32	31.2
9	36	35.1

	5	4	3
1	0.5	0.4	0.3
2	1.0	0.8	0.6
3	1.5	1.2	0.9
4	2.0	1.6	1.2
5	2.5	2.0	1.5
6	3.0	2.4	1.8
7	3.5	2.8	2.1
8	4.0	3.2	2.4
9	4.5	3.6	2.7

′	L Sin *	d	L Tan *	c d	L Cot	L Cos *	d	
0	9.46 594		9.48 534		0.51 466	9.98 060		60
1	635	41	579	45	421	056	4	59
2	676	41	624	45	376	052	4	58
3	717	41	669	45	331	048	4	57
4	758	41	714	45	286	044	4	56
5	9.46 800	42	9.48 759	45	0.51 241	9.98 040	4	55
6	841	41	804	45	196	036	4	54
7	882	41	849	45	151	032	4	53
8	923	41	894	45	106	029	3	52
9	9.46 964	41	939	45	061	025	4	51
10	9.47 005	41	9.48 984	45	0.51 016	9.98 021	4	50
11	045	40	9.49 029	45	0.50 971	017	4	49
12	086	41	073	45	927	013	4	48
13	127	41	118	45	882	009	4	47
14	168	41	163	45	837	005	4	46
15	9.47 209	41	9.49 207	44	0.50 793	9.98 001	4	45
16	249	40	252	45	748	9.97 997	4	44
17	290	41	296	44	704	993	4	43
18	330	40	341	45	659	989	4	42
19	371	41	385	44	615	986	3	41
20	9.47 411	40	9.49 430	45	0.50 570	9.97 982	4	40
21	452	41	474	44	526	978	4	39
22	492	40	519	45	481	974	4	38
23	533	41	563	44	437	970	4	37
24	573	40	607	45	393	966	4	36
25	9.47 613	40	9.49 652	44	0.50 348	9.97 962	4	35
26	654	41	696	44	304	958	4	34
27	694	40	740	44	260	954	4	33
28	734	40	784	44	216	950	4	32
29	774	40	828	44	172	946	4	31
30	9.47 814	40	9.49 872	44	0.50 128	9.97 942	4	30
31	854	40	916	44	084	938	4	29
32	894	40	9.49 960	44	0.50 040	934	4	28
33	934	40	9.50 004	44	0.49 996	930	4	27
34	9.47 974	40	048	44	952	926	4	26
35	9.48 014	40	9.50 092	44	0.49 908	9.97 922	4	25
36	054	40	136	44	864	918	4	24
37	094	39	180	43	820	914	4	23
38	133	40	223	44	777	910	4	22
39	173	40	267	44	733	906	4	21
40	9.48 213	40	9.50 311	44	0.49 689	9.97 902	4	20
41	252	39	355	44	645	898	4	19
42	292	40	398	43	602	894	4	18
43	332	40	442	44	558	890	4	17
44	371	39	485	43	515	886	4	16
45	9.48 411	40	9.50 529	44	0.49 471	9.97 882	4	15
46	450	39	572	44	428	878	4	14
47	490	40	616	43	384	874	4	13
48	529	39	659	44	341	870	4	12
49	568	39	703	43	297	866	5	11
50	9.48 607	39	9.50 746	43	0.49 254	9.97 861	4	10
51	647	40	789	44	211	857	4	9
52	686	39	833	43	167	853	4	8
53	725	39	876	43	124	849	4	7
54	764	39	919	43	081	845	4	6
55	9.48 803	39	9.50 962	43	0.49 038	9.97 841	4	5
56	842	39	9.51 005	43	0.48 995	837	4	4
57	881	39	048	43	952	833	4	3
58	920	39	092	44	908	829	4	2
59	959	39	135	43	865	825	4	1
60	9.48 998	39	9.51 178	43	0.48 822	9.97 821	4	0
	L Cos *	d	L Cot *	c d	L Tan	L Sin *	d	′

72°

[55]

′	L Sin *	d	L Tan *	c d	L Cot	L Cos *	d		Prop. Parts
0	9.48 998		9.51 178		0.48 822	9.97 821		60	
1	9.49 037	39	221	43	779	817	4	59	
2	076	39	264	43	736	812	5	58	
3	115	39	306	42	694	808	4	57	
4	153	38	349	43	651	804	4	56	
5	9.49 192	39	9.51 392	43	0.48 608	9.97 800	4	55	
6	231	39	435	43	565	796	4	54	
7	269	38	478	43	522	792	4	53	
8	308	39	520	42	480	788	4	52	
9	347	39	563	43	437	784	4	51	
10	9.49 385	38	9.51 606	43	0.48 394	9.97 779	5	50	
11	424	39	648	42	352	775	4	49	
12	462	38	691	43	309	771	4	48	
13	500	38	734	43	266	767	4	47	
14	539	39	776	42	224	763	4	46	
15	9.49 577	38	9.51 819	43	0.48 181	9.97 759	4	45	
16	615	38	861	42	139	754	5	44	
17	654	39	903	42	097	750	4	43	
18	692	38	946	43	054	746	4	42	
19	730	38	9.51 988	42	0.48 012	742	4	41	
20	9.49 768	38	9.52 031	43	0.47 969	9.97 738	4	40	
21	806	38	073	42	927	734	4	39	
22	844	38	115	42	885	729	5	38	
23	882	38	157	43	843	725	4	37	
24	920	38	200	42	800	721	4	36	
25	9.49 958	38	9.52 242	42	0.47 758	9.97 717	4	35	
26	9.49 996	38	284	42	716	713	4	34	
27	9.50 034	38	326	42	674	708	5	33	
28	072	38	368	42	632	704	4	32	
29	110	38	410	42	590	700	4	31	
30	9.50 148	38	9.52 452	42	0.47 548	9.97 696	4	30	
31	185	37	494	42	506	691	5	29	
32	223	38	536	42	464	687	4	28	
33	261	38	578	42	422	683	4	27	
34	298	37	620	42	380	679	4	26	
35	9.50 336	38	9.52 661	41	0.47 339	9.97 674	5	25	
36	374	38	703	42	297	670	4	24	
37	411	37	745	42	255	666	4	23	
38	449	38	787	42	213	662	4	22	
39	486	37	829	42	171	657	5	21	
40	9.50 523	37	9.52 870	41	0.47 130	9.97 653	4	20	
41	561	38	912	42	088	649	4	19	
42	598	37	953	41	047	645	4	18	
43	635	37	9.52 995	42	0.47 005	640	5	17	
44	673	38	9.53 037	42	0.46 963	636	4	16	
45	9.50 710	37	9.53 078	41	0.46 922	9.97 632	4	15	
46	747	37	120	42	880	628	4	14	
47	784	37	161	41	839	623	5	13	
48	821	37	202	41	798	619	4	12	
49	858	37	244	42	756	615	4	11	
50	9.50 896	38	9.53 285	41	0.46 715	9.97 610	5	10	
51	933	37	327	42	673	606	4	9	
52	9.50 970	37	368	41	632	602	4	8	
53	9.51 007	37	409	41	591	597	5	7	
54	043	36	450	41	550	593	4	6	
55	9.51 080	37	9.53 492	42	0.46 508	9.97 589	4	5	
56	117	37	533	41	467	584	5	4	
57	154	37	574	41	426	580	4	3	
58	191	37	615	41	385	576	4	2	
59	227	36	656	41	344	571	5	1	
60	9.51 264	37	9.53 697	41	0.46 303	9.97 567	4	0	
	L Cos *	d	L Cot *	c d	L Tan	L Sin *	d	′	

Prop. Parts

	43	42	41
1	4.3	4.2	4.1
2	8.6	8.4	8.2
3	12.9	12.6	12.3
4	17.2	16.8	16.4
5	21.5	21.0	20.5
6	25.8	25.2	24.6
7	30.1	29.4	28.7
8	34.4	33.6	32.8
9	38.7	37.8	36.9

	39	38
1	3.9	3.8
2	7.8	7.6
3	11.7	11.4
4	15.6	15.2
5	19.5	19.0
6	23.4	22.8
7	27.3	26.6
8	31.2	30.4
9	35.1	34.2

	37	36
1	3.7	3.6
2	7.4	7.2
3	11.1	10.8
4	14.8	14.4
5	18.5	18.0
6	22.2	21.6
7	25.9	25.2
8	29.6	28.8
9	33.3	32.4

	5	4
1	0.5	0.4
2	1.0	0.8
3	1.5	1.2
4	2.0	1.6
5	2.5	2.0
6	3.0	2.4
7	3.5	2.8
8	4.0	3.2
9	4.5	3.6

71°

Prop. Parts

	41	40	39
1	4.1	4	3.9
2	8.2	8	7.8
3	12.3	12	11.7
4	16.4	16	15.6
5	20.5	20	19.5
6	24.6	24	23.4
7	28.7	28	27.3
8	32.8	32	31.2
9	36.9	36	35.1

	37	36
1	3.7	3.6
2	7.4	7.2
3	11.1	10.8
4	14.8	14.4
5	18.5	18.0
6	22.2	21.6
7	25.9	25.2
8	29.6	28.8
9	33.3	32.4

	35	34
1	3.5	3.4
2	7.0	6.8
3	10.5	10.2
4	14.0	13.6
5	17.5	17.0
6	21.0	20.4
7	24.5	23.8
8	28.0	27.2
9	31.5	30.6

	5	4
1	0.5	0.4
2	1.0	0.8
3	1.5	1.2
4	2.0	1.6
5	2.5	2.0
6	3.0	2.4
7	3.5	2.8
8	4.0	3.2
9	4.5	3.6

′	L Sin *	d	L Tan *	c d	L Cot	L Cos *	d	
0	9.51 264		9.53 697		0.46 303	9.97 567		60
1	301	37	738	41	262	563	4	59
2	338	37	779	41	221	558	5	58
3	374	36	820	41	180	554	4	57
4	411	37	861	41	139	550	4	56
5	9.51 447	36	9.53 902	41	0.46 098	9.97 545	5	55
6	484	37	943	41	057	541	4	54
7	520	36	9.53 984	41	0.46 016	536	5	53
8	557	37	9.54 025	41	0.45 975	532	4	52
9	593	36	065	40	935	528	4	51
10	9.51 629	36	9.54 106	41	0.45 894	9.97 523	5	50
11	666	37	147	41	853	519	4	49
12	702	36	187	40	813	515	4	48
13	738	36	228	41	772	510	5	47
14	774	36	269	41	731	506	4	46
15	9.51 811	37	9.54 309	40	0.45 691	9.97 501	5	45
16	847	36	350	41	650	497	4	44
17	883	36	390	40	610	492	5	43
18	919	36	431	41	569	488	4	42
19	955	36	471	40	529	484	4	41
20	9.51 991	36	9.54 512	41	0.45 488	9.97 479	5	40
21	9.52 027	36	552	40	448	475	4	39
22	063	36	593	41	407	470	5	38
23	099	36	633	40	367	466	4	37
24	135	36	673	40	327	461	5	36
25	9.52 171	36	9.54 714	41	0.45 286	9.97 457	4	35
26	207	36	754	40	246	453	4	34
27	242	35	794	40	206	448	5	33
28	278	36	835	41	165	444	4	32
29	314	36	875	40	125	439	5	31
30	9.52 350	36	9.54 915	40	0.45 085	9.97 435	4	30
31	385	35	955	40	045	430	5	29
32	421	36	9.54 995	40	0.45 005	426	4	28
33	456	36	9.55 035	40	0.44 965	421	5	27
34	492	35	075	40	925	417	4	26
35	9.52 527	35	9.55 115	40	0.44 885	9.97 412	5	25
36	563	36	155	40	845	408	4	24
37	598	35	195	40	805	403	5	23
38	634	36	235	40	765	399	4	22
39	669	35	275	40	725	394	5	21
40	9.52 705	36	9.55 315	40	0.44 685	9.97 390	4	20
41	740	35	355	40	645	385	5	19
42	775	35	395	39	605	381	4	18
43	811	36	434	40	566	376	5	17
44	846	35	474	40	526	372	4	16
45	9.52 881	35	9.55 514	40	0.44 486	9.97 367	5	15
46	916	35	554	40	446	363	4	14
47	951	35	593	39	407	358	5	13
48	9.52 986	35	633	40	367	353	4	12
49	9.53 021	35	673	40	327	349	5	11
50	9.53 056	35	9.55 712	39	0.44 288	9.97 344	4	10
51	092	36	752	40	248	340	5	9
52	126	34	791	39	209	335	4	8
53	161	35	831	40	169	331	5	7
54	196	35	870	39	130	326	4	6
55	9.53 231	35	9.55 910	40	0.44 090	9.97 322	5	5
56	266	35	949	39	051	317	5	4
57	301	35	9.55 989	40	0.44 011	312	4	3
58	336	34	9.56 028	39	0.43 972	308	5	2
59	370	35	067	39	933	303	4	1
60	9.53 405		9.56 107	40	0.43 893	9.97 299		0
	L Cos *	d	L Cot *	c d	L Tan	L Sin *	d	′

70°

′	L Sin *	d	L Tan *	c d	L Cot	L Cos *	d		Prop. Parts
0	9.53 405		9.56 107		0.43 893	9.97 299		60	*Subtract* 10 *from each en-*
1	440	35	146	39	854	294	5	59	*try in the columns marked*
2	475	35	185	39	815	289	5	58	*with "*."*
3	509	34	224	39	776	285	4	57	
4	544	35	264	40	736	280	5	56	
5	9.53 578	34	9.56 303	39	0.43 697	9.97 276	4	55	
6	613	35	342	39	658	271	5	54	
7	647	34	381	39	619	266	5	53	
8	682	35	420	39	580	262	4	52	
9	716	34	459	39	541	257	5	51	
10	9.53 751	35	9.56 498	39	0.43 502	9.97 252	5	50	
11	785	34	537	39	463	248	5	49	
12	819	34	576	39	424	243	5	48	
13	854	35	615	39	385	238	4	47	
14	888	34	654	39	346	234	5	46	
15	9.53 922	34	9.56 693	39	0.43 307	9.97 229	5	45	
16	957	35	732	39	268	224	4	44	
17	9.53 991	34	771	39	229	220	5	43	
18	9.54 025	34	810	39	190	215	5	42	
19	059	34	849	38	151	210	4	41	
20	9.54 093	34	9.56 887	39	0.43 113	9.97 206	5	40	
21	127	34	926	39	074	201	5	39	
22	161	34	9.56 965	39	0.43 035	196	4	38	
23	195	34	9.57 004	38	0.42 996	192	5	37	
24	229	34	042	39	958	187	5	36	
25	9.54 263	34	9.57 081	39	0.42 919	9.97 182	4	35	
26	297	34	120	38	880	178	5	34	
27	331	34	158	39	842	173	5	33	
28	365	34	197	38	803	168	5	32	
29	399	34	235	39	765	163	4	31	
30	9.54 433	33	9.57 274	38	0.42 726	9.97 159	5	30	
31	466	34	312	39	688	154	5	29	
32	500	34	351	38	649	149	4	28	
33	534	33	389	39	611	145	5	27	
34	567	34	428	38	572	140	5	26	
35	9.54 601	34	9.57 466	38	0.42 534	9.97 135	5	25	
36	635	33	504	39	496	130	4	24	
37	668	34	543	38	457	126	5	23	
38	702	33	581	38	419	121	5	22	
39	735	34	619	39	381	116	5	21	
40	9.54 769	33	9.57 658	38	0.42 342	9.97 111	4	20	
41	802	34	696	38	304	107	5	19	
42	836	33	734	38	266	102	5	18	
43	869	34	772	38	228	097	5	17	
44	903	33	810	39	190	092	5	16	
45	9.54 936	33	9.57 849	38	0.42 151	9.97 087	4	15	
46	9.54 969	34	887	38	113	083	5	14	
47	9.55 003	33	925	38	075	078	5	13	
48	036	33	9.57 963	38	0.42 037	073	5	12	
49	069	33	9.58 001	38	0.41 999	068	5	11	
50	9.55 102	33	9.58 039	38	0.41 961	9.97 063	4	10	
51	136	34	077	38	923	059	5	9	
52	169	33	115	38	885	054	5	8	
53	202	33	153	38	847	049	5	7	
54	235	33	191	38	809	044	5	6	
55	9.55 268	33	9.58 229	38	0.41 771	9.97 039	4	5	
56	301	33	267	38	733	035	5	4	
57	334	33	304	37	696	030	5	3	
58	367	33	342	38	658	025	5	2	
59	400	33	380	38	620	020	5	1	
60	9.55 433		9.58 418		0.41 582	9.97 015		0	
	L Cos *	d	L Cot *	c d	L Tan	L Sin *	d	′	

Prop. Parts

	40	39	38
1	4	3.9	3.8
2	8	7.8	7.6
3	12	11.7	11.4
4	16	15.6	15.2
5	20	19.5	19.0
6	24	23.4	22.8
7	28	27.3	26.6
8	32	31.2	30.4
9	36	35.1	34.2

	37	35
1	3.7	3.5
2	7.4	7.0
3	11.1	10.5
4	14.8	14.0
5	18.5	17.5
6	22.2	21.0
7	25.9	24.5
8	29.6	28.0
9	33.3	31.5

	34	33
1	3.4	3.3
2	6.8	6.6
3	10.2	9.9
4	13.6	13.2
5	17.0	16.5
6	20.4	19.8
7	23.8	23.1
8	27.2	26.4
9	30.6	29.7

	5	4
1	0.5	0.4
2	1.0	0.8
3	1.5	1.2
4	2.0	1.6
5	2.5	2.0
6	3.0	2.4
7	3.5	2.8
8	4.0	3.2
9	4.5	3.6

69°

Prop. Parts

	38	37	36
1	3.8	3.7	3.6
2	7.6	7.4	7.2
3	11.4	11.1	10.8
4	15.2	14.8	14.4
5	19.0	18.5	18.0
6	22.8	22.2	21.6
7	26.6	25.9	25.2
8	30.4	29.6	28.8
9	34.2	33.3	32.4

	33	32	31
1	3.3	3.2	3.1
2	6.6	6.4	6.2
3	9.9	9.6	9.3
4	13.2	12.8	12.4
5	16.5	16.0	15.5
6	19.8	19.2	18.6
7	23.1	22.4	21.7
8	26.4	25.6	24.8
9	29.7	28.8	27.9

	6	5	4
1	0.6	0.5	0.4
2	1.2	1.0	0.8
3	1.8	1.5	1.2
4	2.4	2.0	1.6
5	3.0	2.5	2.0
6	3.6	3.0	2.4
7	4.2	3.5	2.8
8	4.8	4.0	3.2
9	5.4	4.5	3.6

′	L Sin *	d	L Tan *	c d	L Cot	L Cos *	d	
0	9.55 433		9.58 418		0.41 582	9.97 015		60
1	466	33	455	37	545	010	5	59
2	499	33	493	38	507	005	5	58
3	532	33	531	38	469	9.97 001	4	57
4	564	32	569	38	431	9.96 996	5	56
5	9.55 597	33	9.58 606	37	0.41 394	9.96 991	5	55
6	630	33	644	38	356	986	5	54
7	663	33	681	37	319	981	5	53
8	695	32	719	38	281	976	5	52
9	728	33	757	38	243	971	5	51
10	9.55 761	33	9.58 794	37	0.41 206	9.96 966	5	50
11	793	32	832	38	168	962	4	49
12	826	33	869	37	131	957	5	48
13	858	32	907	38	093	952	5	47
14	891	33	944	37	056	947	5	46
15	9.55 923	32	9.58 981	37	0.41 019	9.96 942	5	45
16	956	33	9.59 019	38	0.40 981	937	5	44
17	9.55 988	32	056	37	944	932	5	43
18	9.56 021	33	094	38	906	927	5	42
19	053	32	131	37	869	922	5	41
20	9.56 085	32	9.59 168	37	0.40 832	9.96 917	5	40
21	118	33	205	37	795	912	5	39
22	150	32	243	38	757	907	5	38
23	182	32	280	37	720	903	4	37
24	215	33	317	37	683	898	5	36
25	9.56 247	32	9.59 354	37	0.40 646	9.96 893	5	35
26	279	32	391	37	609	888	5	34
27	311	32	429	38	571	883	5	33
28	343	32	466	37	534	878	5	32
29	375	33	503	37	497	873	5	31
30	9.56 408	32	9.59 540	37	0.40 460	9.96 868	5	30
31	440	32	577	37	423	863	5	29
32	472	32	614	37	386	858	5	28
33	504	32	651	37	349	853	5	27
34	536	32	688	37	312	848	5	26
35	9.56 568	32	9.59 725	37	0.40 275	9.96 843	5	25
36	599	31	762	37	238	838	5	24
37	631	32	799	36	201	833	5	23
38	663	32	835	37	165	828	5	22
39	695	32	872	37	128	823	5	21
40	9.56 727	32	9.59 909	37	0.40 091	9.96 818	5	20
41	759	32	946	37	054	813	5	19
42	790	31	9.59 983	37	0.40 017	808	5	18
43	822	32	9.60 019	36	0.39 981	803	5	17
44	854	32	056	37	944	798	5	16
45	9.56 886	32	9.60 093	37	0.39 907	9.96 793	5	15
46	917	31	130	37	870	788	5	14
47	949	32	166	36	834	783	5	13
48	9.56 980	31	203	37	797	778	5	12
49	9.57 012	32	240	37	760	772	6	11
50	9.57 044	32	9.60 276	36	0.39 724	9.96 767	5	10
51	075	31	313	37	687	762	5	9
52	107	32	349	36	651	757	5	8
53	138	31	386	37	614	752	5	7
54	169	31	422	36	578	747	5	6
55	9.57 201	32	9.60 459	37	0.39 541	9.96 742	5	5
56	232	31	495	36	505	737	5	4
57	264	31	532	36	468	732	5	3
58	295	31	568	37	432	727	5	2
59	326	31	605	36	395	722	5	1
60	9.57 358	32	9.60 641	36	0.39 359	9.96 717		0
	L Cos *	d	L Cot *	c d	L Tan	L Sin *	d	′

68°

′	L Sin *	d	L Tan *	c d	L Cot	L Cos *	d	
0	9.57 358		9.60 641		0.39 359	9.96 717		60
1	389	31	677	36	323	711	6	59
2	420	31	714	37	286	706	5	58
3	451	31	750	36	250	701	5	57
4	482	31	786	36	214	696	5	56
5	9.57 514	32	9.60 823	37	0.39 177	9.96 691	5	55
6	545	31	859	36	141	686	5	54
7	576	31	895	36	105	681	5	53
8	607	31	931	36	069	676	5	52
9	638	31	9.60 967	36	0.39 033	670	6	51
10	9.57 669	31	9.61 004	37	0.38 996	9.96 665	5	50
11	700	31	040	36	960	660	5	49
12	731	31	076	36	924	655	5	48
13	762	31	112	36	888	650	5	47
14	793	31	148	36	852	645	5	46
15	9.57 824	31	9.61 184	36	0.38 816	9.96 640	5	45
16	855	31	220	36	780	634	6	44
17	885	30	256	36	744	629	5	43
18	916	31	292	36	708	624	5	42
19	947	31	328	36	672	619	5	41
20	9.57 978	31	9.61 364	36	0.38 636	9.96 614	5	40
21	9.58 008	30	400	36	600	608	6	39
22	039	31	436	36	564	603	5	38
23	070	31	472	36	528	598	5	37
24	101	31	508	36	492	593	5	36
25	9.58 131	30	9.61 544	36	0.38 456	9.96 588	5	35
26	162	31	579	35	421	582	6	34
27	192	30	615	36	385	577	5	33
28	223	31	651	36	349	572	5	32
29	253	30	687	36	313	567	5	31
30	9.58 284	31	9.61 722	35	0.38 278	9.96 562	5	30
31	314	30	758	36	242	556	6	29
32	345	31	794	36	206	551	5	28
33	375	30	830	36	170	546	5	27
34	406	31	865	35	135	541	5	26
35	9.58 436	30	9.61 901	36	0.38 099	9.96 535	6	25
36	467	31	936	35	064	530	5	24
37	497	30	9.61 972	36	0.38 028	525	5	23
38	527	30	9.62 008	36	0.37 992	520	5	22
39	557	31	043	35	957	514	6	21
40	9.58 588	30	9.62 079	36	0.37 921	9.96 509	5	20
41	618	30	114	35	886	504	5	19
42	648	30	150	36	850	498	6	18
43	678	31	185	35	815	493	5	17
44	709	30	221	36	779	488	5	16
45	9.58 739	30	9.62 256	35	0.37 744	9.96 483	5	15
46	769	30	292	36	708	477	6	14
47	799	30	327	35	673	472	5	13
48	829	30	362	35	638	467	5	12
49	859	30	398	36	602	461	6	11
50	9.58 889	30	9.62 433	35	0.37 567	9.96 456	5	10
51	919	30	468	35	532	451	5	9
52	949	30	504	36	496	445	6	8
53	9.58 979	30	539	35	461	440	5	7
54	9.59 009	30	574	35	426	435	5	6
55	9.59 039	30	9.62 609	35	0.37 391	9.96 429	6	5
56	069	30	645	36	355	424	5	4
57	098	29	680	35	320	419	5	3
58	128	30	715	35	285	413	6	2
59	158	30	750	35	250	408	5	1
60	9.59 188	30	9.62 785	35	0.37 215	9.96 403	5	0
	L Cos *	d	L Cot *	c d	L Tan	L Sin *	d	′

Prop. Parts

	37	36	35
1	3.7	3.6	3.5
2	7.4	7.2	7.0
3	11.1	10.8	10.5
4	14.8	14.4	14.0
5	18.5	18.0	17.5
6	22.2	21.6	21.0
7	25.9	25.2	24.5
8	29.6	28.8	28.0
9	33.3	32.4	31.5

	32	31
1	3.2	3.1
2	6.4	6.2
3	9.6	9.3
4	12.8	12.4
5	16.0	15.5
6	19.2	18.6
7	22.4	21.7
8	25.6	24.8
9	28.8	27.9

	30	29
1	3	2.9
2	6	5.8
3	9	8.7
4	12	11.6
5	15	14.5
6	18	17.4
7	21	20.3
8	24	23.2
9	27	26.1

	6	5
1	0.6	0.5
2	1.2	1.0
3	1.8	1.5
4	2.4	2.0
5	3.0	2.5
6	3.6	3.0
7	4.2	3.5
8	4.8	4.0
9	5.4	4.5

67°

Prop. Parts

	36	35	34
1	3.6	3.5	3.4
2	7.2	7.0	6.8
3	10.8	10.5	10.2
4	14.4	14.0	13.6
5	18.0	17.5	17.0
6	21.6	21.0	20.4
7	25.2	24.5	23.8
8	28.8	28.0	27.2
9	32.4	31.5	30.6

	30	29	28
1	3	2.9	2.8
2	6	5.8	5.6
3	9	8.7	8.4
4	12	11.6	11.2
5	15	14.5	14.0
6	18	17.4	16.8
7	21	20.3	19.6
8	24	23.2	22.4
9	27	26.1	25.2

	6	5
1	0.6	0.5
2	1.2	1.0
3	1.8	1.5
4	2.4	2.0
5	3.0	2.5
6	3.6	3.0
7	4.2	3.5
8	4.8	4.0
9	5.4	4.5

′	L Sin *	d	L Tan *	c d	L Cot	L Cos *	d	
0	9.59 188		9.62 785		0.37 215	9.96 403		60
1	218	30	820	35	180	397	6	59
2	247	29	855	35	145	392	5	58
3	277	30	890	35	110	387	5	57
4	307	30	926	36	074	381	6	56
5	9.59 336	29	9.62 961	35	0.37 039	9.96 376	5	55
6	366	30	9.62 996	35	0.37 004	370	6	54
7	396	30	9.63 031	35	0.36 969	365	5	53
8	425	29	066	35	934	360	5	52
9	455	30	101	35	899	354	6	51
10	9.59 484	29	9.63 135	34	0.36 865	9.96 349	5	50
11	514	30	170	35	830	343	6	49
12	543	29	205	35	795	338	5	48
13	573	30	240	35	760	333	5	47
14	602	29	275	35	725	327	6	46
15	9.59 632	30	9 63 310	35	0.36 690	9.96 322	5	45
16	661	29	345	35	655	316	6	44
17	690	29	379	34	621	311	5	43
18	720	30	414	35	586	305	6	42
19	749	29	449	35	551	300	5	41
20	9.59 778	29	9.63 484	35	0.36 516	9.96 294	6	40
21	808	30	519	35	481	289	5	39
22	837	29	553	34	447	284	5	38
23	866	29	588	35	412	278	6	37
24	895	29	623	35	377	273	5	36
25	9.59 924	29	9.63 657	34	0.36 343	9.96 267	6	35
26	954	30	692	35	308	262	5	34
27	9.59 983	29	726	34	274	256	5	33
28	9.60 012	29	761	35	239	251	5	32
29	041	29	796	35	204	245	6	31
30	9.60 070	29	9.63 830	34	0.36 170	9.96 240	5	30
31	099	29	865	35	135	234	6	29
32	128	29	899	34	101	229	5	28
33	157	29	934	35	066	223	6	27
34	186	29	9.63 968	34	0.36 032	218	5	26
35	9.60 215	29	9.64 003	35	0.35 997	9.96 212	6	25
36	244	29	037	34	963	207	5	24
37	273	29	072	35	928	201	6	23
38	302	29	106	34	894	196	5	22
39	331	28	140	34	860	190	6	21
40	9.60 359	29	9.64 175	35	0.35 825	9.96 185	5	20
41	388	29	209	34	791	179	6	19
42	417	29	243	34	757	174	5	18
43	446	28	278	35	722	168	6	17
44	474	29	312	34	688	162	6	16
45	9.60 503	29	9.64 346	34	0.35 654	9.96 157	5	15
46	532	29	381	35	619	151	6	14
47	561	28	415	34	585	146	5	13
48	589	29	449	34	551	140	6	12
49	618	28	483	34	517	135	5	11
50	9.60 646	29	9.64 517	35	0.35 483	9.96 129	6	10
51	675	29	552	34	448	123	5	9
52	704	28	586	34	414	118	6	8
53	732	29	620	34	380	112	5	7
54	761	28	654	34	346	107	6	6
55	9.60 789	29	9.64 688	34	0.35 312	9.96 101		5
56	818	29	722	34	278	095	6	4
57	846	28	756	34	244	090	5	3
58	875	29	790	34	210	084	6	2
59	903	28	824	34	176	079	5	1
60	9.60 931	28	9.64 858		0.35 142	9.96 073	6	0
	L Cos *	d	L Cot *	c d	L Tan	L Sin *	d	′

66°

′	L Sin *	d	L Tan *	c d	L Cot	L Cos *	d		Prop. Parts
0	9.60 931		9.64 858		0.35 142	9.96 073		60	*Subtract* 10 *from each entry in the columns marked with* " * ."
1	960	29	892	34	108	067	6	59	
2	9.60 988	28	926	34	074	062	5	58	
3	9.61 016	28	960	34	040	056	6	57	
4	045	29	9.64 994	34	0.35 006	050	6	56	
5	9.61 073	28	9.65 028	34	0.34 972	9.96 045	5	55	
6	101	28	062	34	938	039	6	54	
7	129	28	096	34	904	034	5	53	
8	158	29	130	34	870	028	6	52	
9	186	28	164	34	836	022	6	51	
10	9.61 214	28	9.65 197	33	0.34 803	9.96 017	5	50	
11	242	28	231	34	769	011	6	49	
12	270	28	265	34	735	005	6	48	
13	298	28	299	34	701	9.96 000	5	47	
14	326	28	333	34	667	9.95 994	6	46	
15	9.61 354	28	9.65 366	33	0.34 634	9.95 988	6	45	
16	382	28	400	34	600	982	5	44	
17	411	29	434	34	566	977	6	43	
18	438	27	467	33	533	971	6	42	
19	466	28	501	34	499	965	5	41	
20	9.61 494	28	9.65 535	34	0.34 465	9.95 960	6	40	
21	522	28	568	33	432	954	6	39	
22	550	28	602	34	398	948	6	38	
23	578	28	636	34	364	942	5	37	
24	606	28	669	33	331	937	6	36	
25	9.61 634	28	9.65 703	34	0.34 297	9.95 931	6	35	
26	662	28	736	33	264	925	5	34	
27	689	27	770	34	230	920	6	33	
28	717	28	803	33	197	914	6	32	
29	745	28	837	34	163	908	6	31	
30	9.61 773	28	9.65 870	33	0.34 130	9.95 902	5	30	
31	800	27	904	34	096	897	6	29	
32	828	28	937	33	063	891	6	28	
33	856	27	9.65 971	34	0.34 029	885	6	27	
34	883	28	9.66 004	33	0.33 996	879	6	26	
35	9.61 911	28	9.66 038	34	0.33 962	9.95 873	5	25	
36	939	28	071	33	929	868	6	24	
37	966	27	104	33	896	862	6	23	
38	9.61 994	28	138	34	862	856	6	22	
39	9.62 021	27	171	33	829	850	6	21	
40	9.62 049	28	9.66 204	33	0.33 796	9.95 844	5	20	
41	076	27	238	34	762	839	6	19	
42	104	28	271	33	729	833	6	18	
43	131	27	304	33	696	827	6	17	
44	159	28	337	33	663	821	6	16	
45	9.62 186	27	9.66 371	34	0.33 629	9.95 815	5	15	
46	214	28	404	33	596	810	6	14	
47	241	27	437	33	563	804	6	13	
48	268	27	470	33	530	798	6	12	
49	296	28	503	33	497	792	6	11	
50	9.62 323	27	9.66 537	34	0.33 463	9.95 786	6	10	
51	350	27	570	33	430	780	6	9	
52	377	27	603	33	397	775	6	8	
53	405	28	636	33	364	769	6	7	
54	432	27	669	33	331	763	6	6	
55	9.62 459	27	9.66 702	33	0.33 298	9.95 757	6	5	
56	486	27	735	33	265	751	6	4	
57	513	27	768	35	232	745	6	3	
58	541	28	801	33	199	739	6	2	
59	568	27	834	33	166	733	6	1	
60	9.62 595	27	9.66 867	33	0.33 133	9.95 728	5	0	
	L Cos *	d	L Cot *	c d	L Tan	L Sin *	d	′	

Prop. Parts:

	34	33
1	3.4	3.3
2	6.8	6.6
3	10.2	9.9
4	13.6	13.2
5	17.0	16.5
6	20.4	19.8
7	23.8	23.1
8	27.2	26.4
9	30.6	29.7

	29	28	27
1	2.9	2.8	2.7
2	5.8	5.6	5.4
3	8.7	8.4	8.1
4	11.6	11.2	10.8
5	14.5	14.0	13.5
6	17.4	16.8	16.2
7	20.3	19.6	18.9
8	23.2	22.4	21.6
9	26.1	25.2	24.3

	6	5
1	0.6	0.5
2	1.2	1.0
3	1.8	1.5
4	2.4	2.0
5	3.0	2.5
6	3.6	3.0
7	4.2	3.5
8	4.8	4.0
9	5.4	4.5

65°

Prop. Parts			′	L Sin *	d	L Tan *	c d	L Cot	L Cos *	d	
			0	9.62 595		9.66 867		0.33 133	9.95 728		60
			1	622	27	900	33	100	722	6	59
			2	649	27	933	33	067	716	6	58
			3	676	27	966	33	034	710	6	57
			4	703	27	9.66 999	33	0.33 001	704	6	56
			5	9.62 730	27	9.67 032	33	0.32 968	9.95 698	6	55
	33	**32**	6	757	27	065	33	935	692	6	54
			7	784	27	098	33	902	686	6	53
			8	811	27	131	33	869	680	6	52
			9	838	27	163	32	837	674	6	51
1	3.3	3.2	10	9.62 865	27	9.67 196	33	0.32 804	9.95 668	6	50
2	6.6	6.4	11	892	27	229	33	771	663	5	49
3	9.9	9.6	12	918	26	262	33	738	657	6	48
4	13.2	12.8	13	945	27	295	33	705	651	6	47
5	16.5	16.0	14	972	27	327	32	673	645	6	46
6	19.8	19.2	15	9.62 999	27	9.67 360	33	0.32 640	9.95 639	6	45
7	23.1	22.4	16	9.63 026	27	393	33	607	633	6	44
8	26.4	25.6	17	052	26	426	33	574	627	6	43
9	29.7	28.8	18	079	27	458	32	542	621	6	42
			19	106	27	491	33	509	615	6	41
			20	9.63 133	27	9.67 524	33	0.32 476	9.95 609	6	40
			21	159	26	556	32	444	603	6	39
			22	186	27	589	33	411	597	6	38
			23	213	27	622	33	378	591	6	37
			24	239	26	654	32	346	585	6	36
			25	9.63 266	27	9.67 687	33	0.32 313	9.95 579	6	35
	27	**26**	26	292	26	719	32	281	573	6	34
			27	319	27	752	33	248	567	6	33
			28	345	26	785	33	215	561	6	32
1	2.7	2.6	29	372	27	817	32	183	555	6	31
2	5.4	5.2	30	9.63 398	26	9.67 850	33	0.32 150	9.95 549	6	30
3	8.1	7.8	31	425	27	882	32	118	543	6	29
4	10.8	10.4	32	451	26	915	33	085	537	6	28
5	13.5	13.0	33	478	27	947	32	053	531	6	27
6	16.2	15.6	34	504	26	9.67 980	33	0.32 020	525	6	26
7	18.9	18.2	35	9.63 531	27	9.68 012	32	0.31 988	9.95 519	6	25
8	21.6	20.8	36	557	26	044	32	956	513	6	24
9	24.3	23.4	37	583	26	077	33	923	507	6	23
			38	610	27	109	32	891	500	7	22
			39	636	26	142	33	858	494	6	21
			40	9.63 662	26	9.68 174	32	0.31 826	9.95 488	6	20
			41	689	27	206	32	794	482	6	19
			42	715	26	239	33	761	476	6	18
			43	741	26	271	32	729	470	6	17
			44	767	26	303	32	697	464	6	16
	7	**6**	**5**	45	9.63 794	27	9.68 336	33	0.31 664	9.95 458	6	15
1	0.7	0.6	0.5	46	820	26	368	32	632	452	6	14
2	1.4	1.2	1.0	47	846	26	400	32	600	446	6	13
3	2.1	1.8	1.5	48	872	26	432	32	568	440	6	12
4	2.8	2.4	2.0	49	898	26	465	33	535	434	7	11
5	3.5	3.0	2.5	50	9.63 924	26	9.68 497	32	0.31 503	9.95 427	6	10
6	4.2	3.6	3.0	51	950	26	529	32	471	421	6	9
7	4.9	4.2	3.5	52	9.63 976	26	561	32	439	415	6	8
8	5.6	4.8	4.0	53	9.64 002	26	593	33	407	409	6	7
9	6.3	5.4	4.5	54	028	26	626	32	374	403	6	6
			55	9.64 054	26	9.68 658	32	0.31 342	9.95 397	6	5
			56	080	26	690	32	310	391	6	4
			57	106	26	722	32	278	384	7	3
			58	132	26	754	32	246	378	6	2
			59	158	26	786	32	214	372	6	1
			60	9.64 184		9.68 818		0.31 182	9.95 366		0
				L Cos *	d	L Cot *	c d	L Tan	L Sin *	d	′

64°

′	L Sin *	d	L Tan *	c d	L Cot	L Cos *	d		Prop. Parts
0	9.64 184		9.68 818		0.31 182	9.95 366		60	
1	210	26	850	32	150	360	6	59	
2	236	26	882	32	118	354	6	58	
3	262	26	914	32	086	348	6	57	
4	288	26	946	32	054	341	7	56	
5	9.64 313	25	9.68 978	32	0.31 022	9.95 335	6	55	
6	339	26	9.69 010	32	0.30 990	329	6	54	
7	365	26	042	32	958	323	6	53	
8	391	26	074	32	926	317	6	52	
9	417	26	106	32	894	310	7	51	
10	9.64 442	25	9.69 138	32	0.30 862	9.95 304	6	50	
11	468	26	170	32	830	298	6	49	
12	494	26	202	32	798	292	6	48	
13	519	25	234	32	766	286	6	47	
14	545	26	266	32	734	279	7	46	
15	9.64 571	26	9.69 298	32	0.30 702	9.95 273	6	45	
16	596	25	329	31	671	267	6	44	
17	622	26	361	32	639	261	6	43	
18	647	25	393	32	607	254	7	42	
19	673	26	425	32	575	248	6	41	
20	9.64 698	25	9.69 457	32	0.30 543	9.95 242	6	40	
21	724	26	488	31	512	236	6	39	
22	749	25	520	32	480	229	7	38	
23	775	26	552	32	448	223	6	37	
24	800	25	584	32	416	217	6	36	
25	9.64 826	26	9.69 615	31	0.30 385	9.95 211	6	35	
26	851	25	647	32	353	204	7	34	
27	877	26	679	32	321	198	6	33	
28	902	25	710	31	290	192	6	32	
29	927	25	742	32	258	185	7	31	
30	9.64 953	26	9.69 774	32	0.30 226	9.95 179	6	30	
31	9.64 978	25	805	31	195	173	6	29	
32	9.65 003	25	837	32	163	167	6	28	
33	029	26	868	31	132	160	7	27	
34	054	25	900	32	100	154	6	26	
35	9.65 079	25	9.69 932	32	0.30 068	9.95 148	6	25	
36	104	25	963	31	037	141	7	24	
37	130	26	9.69 995	32	0.30 005	135	6	23	
38	155	25	9.70 026	31	0.29 974	129	6	22	
39	180	25	058	32	942	122	7	21	
40	9.65 205	25	9.70 089	31	0.29 911	9.95 116	6	20	
41	230	25	121	32	879	110	6	19	
42	255	26	152	31	848	103	7	18	
43	281	25	184	32	816	097	6	17	
44	306	25	215	31	785	090	7	16	
45	9.65 331	25	9.70 247	32	0.29 753	9.95 084	6	15	
46	356	25	278	31	722	078	7	14	
47	381	25	309	31	691	071	6	13	
48	406	25	341	32	659	065	6	12	
49	431	25	372	31	628	059	7	11	
50	9.65 456	25	9.70 404	32	0.29 596	9.95 052	6	10	
51	481	25	435	31	565	046	7	9	
52	506	25	466	31	534	039	6	8	
53	531	25	498	32	502	033	6	7	
54	556	24	529	31	471	027	7	6	
55	9.65 580	25	9.70 560	31	0.29 440	9.95 020	6	5	
56	605	25	592	32	408	014	6	4	
57	630	25	623	31	377	007	7	3	
58	655	25	654	31	346	9.95 001	6	2	
59	680	25	685	31	315	9.94 995	6	1	
60	9.65 705		9.70 717	32	0.29 283	9.94 988	7	0	
	L Cos *	d	L Cot *	c d	L Tan	L Sin *	d	′	

Prop. Parts

	32	31
1	3.2	3.1
2	6.4	6.2
3	9.6	9.3
4	12.8	12.4
5	16.0	15.5
6	19.2	18.6
7	22.4	21.7
8	25.6	24.8
9	28.8	27.9

	26	25	24
1	2.6	2.5	2.4
2	5.2	5.0	4.8
3	7.8	7.5	7.2
4	10.4	10.0	9.6
5	13.0	12.5	12.0
6	15.6	15.0	14.4
7	18.2	17.5	16.8
8	20.8	20.0	19.2
9	23.4	22.5	21.6

	7	6
1	0.7	0.6
2	1.4	1.2
3	2.1	1.8
4	2.8	2.4
5	3.5	3.0
6	4.2	3.6
7	4.9	4.2
8	5.6	4.8
9	6.3	5.4

63°

Prop. Parts

	32	31	30
1	3.2	3.1	3
2	6.4	6.2	6
3	9.6	9.3	9
4	12.8	12.4	12
5	16.0	15.5	15
6	19.2	18.6	18
7	22.4	21.7	21
8	25.6	24.8	24
9	28.8	27.9	27

	25	24	23
1	2.5	2.4	2.3
2	5.0	4.8	4.6
3	7.5	7.2	6.9
4	10.0	9.6	9.2
5	12.5	12.0	11.5
6	15.0	14.4	13.8
7	17.5	16.8	16.1
8	20.0	19.2	18.4
9	22.5	21.6	20.7

	7	6
1	0.7	0.6
2	1.4	1.2
3	2.1	1.8
4	2.8	2.4
5	3.5	3.0
6	4.2	3.6
7	4.9	4.2
8	5.6	4.8
9	6.3	5.4

′	L Sin *	d	L Tan *	c d	L Cot	L Cos *	d	′
0	9.65 705		9.70 717		0.29 283	9.94 988		60
1	729	24	748	31	252	982	6	59
2	754	25	779	31	221	975	7	58
3	779	25	810	31	190	969	6	57
4	804	25	841	31	159	962	7	56
5	9.65 828	24	9.70 873	32	0.29 127	9.94 956	6	55
6	853	25	904	31	096	949	7	54
7	878	25	935	31	065	943	6	53
8	902	24	966	31	034	936	7	52
9	927	25	9.70 997	31	0.29 003	930	6	51
10	9.65 952	25	9.71 028	31	0.28 972	9.94 923	7	50
11	9.65 976	24	059	31	941	917	6	49
12	9.66 001	25	090	31	910	911	6	48
13	025	24	121	32	879	904	7	47
14	050	25	153	31	847	898	6	46
15	9.66 075	25	9.71 184	31	0.28 816	9.94 891	7	45
16	099	24	215	31	785	885	6	44
17	124	25	246	31	754	878	7	43
18	148	24	277	31	723	871	6	42
19	173	25	308	31	692	865	7	41
20	9.66 197	24	9.71 339	31	0.28 661	9.94 858	6	40
21	221	24	370	31	630	852	7	39
22	246	25	401	30	599	845	6	38
23	270	24	431	31	569	839	7	37
24	295	25	462	31	538	832	6	36
25	9.66 319	24	9.71 493	31	0.28 507	9.94 826		35
26	343	24	524	31	476	819	7	34
27	368	25	555	31	445	813	6	33
28	392	24	586	31	414	806	7	32
29	416	24	617	31	383	799	7	31
30	9.66 441	25	9.71 648	31	0.28 352	9.94 793	6	30
31	465	24	679	31	321	786	7	29
32	489	24	709	30	291	780	6	28
33	513	24	740	31	260	773	7	27
34	537	24	771	31	229	767	7	26
35	9.66 562	25	9.71 802	31	0.28 198	9.94 760		25
36	586	24	833	31	167	753	7	24
37	610	24	863	30	137	747	6	23
38	634	24	894	31	106	740	7	22
39	658	24	925	31	075	734	6	21
40	9.66 682	24	9.71 955	30	0.28 045	9.94 727	7	20
41	706	24	9.71 986	31	0.28 014	720	7	19
42	731	25	9.72 017	31	0.27 983	714	6	18
43	755	24	048	31	952	707	7	17
44	779	24	078	30	922	700	7	16
45	9.66 803	24	9.72 109	31	0.27 891	9.94 694	6	15
46	827	24	140	31	860	687	7	14
47	851	24	170	30	830	680	7	13
48	875	24	201	31	799	674	6	12
49	899	24	231	30	769	667	7	11
50	9.66 922	23	9.72 262	31	0.27 738	9.94 660	7	10
51	946	24	293	30	707	654	6	9
52	970	24	323	31	677	647	7	8
53	9.66 994	24	354	30	646	640	7	7
54	9.67 018	24	384	31	616	634	6	6
55	9.67 042	24	9.72 415	30	0.27 585	9.94 627	7	5
56	066	24	445	31	555	620	6	4
57	090	24	476	30	524	614	7	3
58	113	23	506	31	494	607	7	2
59	137	24	537	30	463	600	7	1
60	9.67 161	24	9.72 567		0.27 433	9.94 593		0
	L Cos *	d	L Cot *	c d	L Tan	L Sin *	d	′

62°

′	L Sin *	d	L Tan *	c d	L Cot	L Cos *	d	′
0	9.67 161		9.72 567		0.27 433	9.94 593		60
1	185	24	598	31	402	587	6	59
2	208	23	628	30	372	580	7	58
3	232	24	659	31	341	573	7	57
4	256	24	689	30	311	567	6	56
5	9.67 280	24	9.72 720	31	0.27 280	9.94 560	7	55
6	303	23	750	30	250	553	7	54
7	327	24	780	30	220	546	7	53
8	350	23	811	31	189	540	6	52
9	374	24	841	30	159	533	7	51
10	9.67 398	24	9.72 872	31	0.27 128	9.94 526	7	50
11	421	23	902	30	098	519	7	49
12	445	24	932	30	068	513	6	48
13	468	23	963	31	037	506	7	47
14	492	24	9.72 993	30	0.27 007	499	7	46
15	9.67 515	23	9.73 023	30	0.26 977	9.94 492	7	45
16	539	24	054	31	946	485	7	44
17	562	23	084	30	916	479	6	43
18	586	24	114	30	886	472	7	42
19	609	23	144	30	856	465	7	41
20	9.67 633	24	9.73 175	31	0.26 825	9.94 458	7	40
21	656	23	205	30	795	451	7	39
22	680	24	235	30	765	445	6	38
23	703	23	265	30	735	438	7	37
24	726	23	295	30	705	431	7	36
25	9.67 750	24	9.73 326	31	0.26 674	9.94 424	7	35
26	773	23	356	30	644	417	7	34
27	796	23	386	30	614	410	7	33
28	820	24	416	30	584	404	6	32
29	843	23	446	30	554	397	7	31
30	9.67 866	23	9 73 476	30	0.26 524	9.94 390	7	30
31	890	24	507	31	493	383	7	29
32	913	23	537	30	463	376	7	28
33	936	23	567	30	433	369	7	27
34	959	23	597	30	403	362	7	26
35	9.67 982	23	9.73 627	30	0.26 373	9.94 355	7	25
36	9.68 006	24	657	30	343	349	6	24
37	029	23	687	30	313	342	7	23
38	052	23	717	30	283	335	7	22
39	075	23	747	30	253	328	7	21
40	9.68 098	23	9.73 777	30	0.26 223	9.94 321	7	20
41	121	23	807	30	193	314	7	19
42	144	23	837	30	163	307	7	18
43	167	23	867	30	133	300	7	17
44	190	23	897	30	103	293	7	16
45	9.68 213	23	9.73 927	30	0.26 073	9.94 286	7	15
46	237	24	957	30	043	279	7	14
47	260	23	9.73 987	30	0.26 013	273	6	13
48	283	23	9.74 017	30	0.25 983	266	7	12
49	305	22	047	30	953	259	7	11
50	9.68 328	23	9.74 077	30	0.25 923	9.94 252	7	10
51	351	23	107	30	893	245	7	9
52	374	23	137	30	863	238	7	8
53	397	23	166	29	834	231	7	7
54	420	23	196	30	804	224	7	6
55	9.68 443	23	9.74 226	30	0.25 774	9.94 217	7	5
56	466	23	256	30	744	210	7	4
57	489	23	286	30	714	203	7	3
58	512	22	316	30	684	196	7	2
59	534	23	345	29	655	189	7	1
60	9.68 557		9.74 375	30	0.25 625	9.94 182		0
	L Cos *	d	L Cot *	c d	L Tan	L Sin *	d	′

Prop. Parts

Subtract 10 from each entry in the columns marked with "."*

	31	30	29
1	3.1	3	2.9
2	6.2	6	5.8
3	9.3	9	8.7
4	12.4	12	11.6
5	15.5	15	14.5
6	18.6	18	17.4
7	21.7	21	20.3
8	24.8	24	23.2
9	27.9	27	26.1

	24	23	22
1	2.4	2.3	2.2
2	4.8	4.6	4.4
3	7.2	6.9	6.6
4	9.6	9.2	8.8
5	12.0	11.5	11.0
6	14.4	13.8	13.2
7	16.8	16.1	15.4
8	19.2	18.4	17.6
9	21.6	20.7	19.8

	7	6
1	0.7	0.6
2	1.4	1.2
3	2.1	1.8
4	2.8	2.4
5	3.5	3.0
6	4.2	3.6
7	4.9	4.2
8	5.6	4.8
9	6.3	5.4

61°

Prop. Parts

	30	29
1	3	2.9
2	6	5 8
3	9	8.7
4	12	11.6
5	15	14.5
6	18	17.4
7	21	20.3
8	24	23.2
9	27	26.1

	23	22
1	2.3	2.2
2	4.6	4.4
3	6.9	6.6
4	9.2	8.8
5	11.5	11.0
6	13.8	13.2
7	16.1	15.4
8	18.4	17.6
9	20.7	19.8

	8	7
1	0.8	0.7
2	1.6	1.4
3	2.4	2.1
4	3.2	2.8
5	4.0	3.5
6	4.8	4.2
7	5.6	4.9
8	6.4	5.6
9	7.2	6.3

′	L Sin *	d	L Tan *	c d	L Cot	L Cos *	d	
0	9.68 557		9.74 375		0.25 625	9.94 182		60
1	580	23	405	30	595	175	7	59
2	603	23	435	30	565	168	7	58
3	625	22	465	30	535	161	7	57
4	648	23	494	29	506	154	7	56
5	9.68 671	23	9.74 524	30	0.25 476	9.94 147	7	55
6	694	23	554	30	446	140	7	54
7	716	22	583	29	417	133	7	53
8	739	23	613	30	387	126	7	52
9	762	23	643	30	357	119	7	51
10	9.68 784	22	9.74 673	30	0.25 327	9.94 112	7	50
11	807	23	702	29	298	105	7	49
12	829	22	732	30	268	098	7	48
13	852	23	762	30	238	090	8	47
14	875	23	791	29	209	083	7	46
15	9.68 897	22	9.74 821	30	0.25 179	9.94 076	7	45
16	920	23	851	30	149	069	7	44
17	942	22	880	29	120	062	7	43
18	965	23	910	30	090	055	7	42
19	9.68 987	22	939	29	061	048	7	41
20	9.69 010	23	9.74 969	30	0.25 031	9.94 041	7	40
21	032	22	9.74 998	29	0.25 002	034	7	39
22	055	22	9.75 028	30	0.24 972	027	7	38
23	077	23	058	30	942	020	7	37
24	100	22	087	29	913	012	8	36
25	9.69 122	22	9.75 117	30	0.24 883	9.94 005	7	35
26	144	23	146	29	854	9.93 998	7	34
27	167	22	176	30	824	991	7	33
28	189	23	205	29	795	984	7	32
29	212	22	235	30	765	977	7	31
30	9.69 234	22	9.75 264	29	0.24 736	9.93 970	7	30
31	256	22	294	30	706	963	7	29
32	279	23	323	29	677	955	8	28
33	301	22	353	30	647	948	7	27
34	323	22	382	29	618	941	7	26
35	9.69 345	22	9.75 411	29	0.24 589	9.93 934	7	25
36	368	23	441	30	559	927	7	24
37	390	22	470	29	530	920	7	23
38	412	22	500	30	500	912	8	22
39	434	22	529	29	471	905	7	21
40	9.69 456	22	9.75 558	29	0.24 442	9.93 898	7	20
41	479	23	588	30	412	891	7	19
42	501	22	617	29	383	884	7	18
43	523	22	647	30	353	876	8	17
44	545	22	676	29	324	869	7	16
45	9.69 567	22	9.75 705	29	0.24 295	9.93 862	7	15
46	589	22	735	30	265	855	7	14
47	611	22	764	29	236	847	8	13
48	633	22	793	29	207	840	7	12
49	655	22	822	29	178	833	7	11
50	9.69 677	22	9.75 852	30	0.24 148	9.93 826	7	10
51	699	22	881	29	119	819	7	9
52	721	22	910	29	090	811	8	8
53	743	22	939	29	061	804	7	7
54	765	22	969	30	031	797	7	6
55	9.69 787	22	9.75 998	29	0.24 002	9.93 789	8	5
56	809	22	9.76 027	29	0.23 973	782	7	4
57	831	22	056	29	944	775	7	3
58	853	22	086	30	914	768	7	2
59	875	22	115	29	885	760	8	1
60	9.69 897	22	9.76 144	29	0.23 856	9.93 753	7	0
	L Cos *	d	L Cot *	c d	L Tan	L Sin *	d	′

60°

IX. FIVE-PLACE LOGARITHMS OF FUNCTIONS — 30°

′	L Sin *	d	L Tan *	c d	L Cot	L Cos *	d	′
0	9.69 897		9.76 144		0.23 856	9.93 753		60
1	919	22	173	29	827	746	7	59
2	941	22	202	29	798	738	8	58
3	963	22	231	29	769	731	7	57
4	9.69 984	21	261	30	739	724	7	56
5	9.70 006	22	9.76 290	29	0.23 710	9.93 717	7	55
6	028	22	319	29	681	709	8	54
7	050	22	348	29	652	702	7	53
8	072	22	377	29	623	695	8	52
9	093	21	406	29	594	687	7	51
10	9.70 115	22	9.76 435	29	0.23 565	9.93 680	7	50
11	137	22	464	29	536	673	8	49
12	159	22	493	29	507	665	7	48
13	180	21	522	29	478	658	8	47
14	202	22	551	29	449	650	7	46
15	9.70 224	22	9.76 580	29	0.23 420	9.93 643	7	45
16	245	21	609	29	391	636	8	44
17	267	22	639	30	361	628	7	43
18	288	21	668	29	332	621	7	42
19	310	22	697	29	303	614	8	41
20	9.70 332	22	9.76 725	28	0.23 275	9.93 606	7	40
21	353	21	754	29	246	599	8	39
22	375	22	783	29	217	591	7	38
23	396	21	812	29	188	584	7	37
24	418	22	841	29	159	577	8	36
25	9.70 439	21	9.76 870	29	0.23 130	9.93 569	7	35
26	461	22	899	29	101	562	8	34
27	482	21	928	29	072	554	7	33
28	504	22	957	29	043	547	8	32
29	525	21	9.76 986	29	0.23 014	539	7	31
30	9.70 547	22	9.77 015	29	0.22 985	9.93 532	7	30
31	568	21	044	29	956	525	8	29
32	590	22	073	28	927	517	7	28
33	611	21	101	29	899	510	8	27
34	633	22	130	29	870	502	7	26
35	9.70 654	21	9.77 159	29	0.22 841	9.93 495	8	25
36	675	22	188	29	812	487	7	24
37	697	21	217	29	783	480	8	23
38	718	21	246	28	754	472	7	22
39	739	22	274	29	726	465	8	21
40	9.70 761	21	9.77 303	29	0.22 697	9.93 457	7	20
41	782	21	332	29	668	450	8	19
42	803	21	361	29	639	442	7	18
43	824	22	390	28	610	435	8	17
44	846	21	418	29	582	427	7	16
45	9.70 867	21	9.77 447	29	0.22 553	9.93 420	8	15
46	888	21	476	29	524	412	7	14
47	909	22	505	28	495	405	8	13
48	931	21	533	29	467	397	7	12
49	952	21	562	29	438	390	8	11
50	9.70 973	21	9.77 591	28	0.22 409	9.93 382	7	10
51	9.70 994	21	619	29	381	375	8	9
52	9.71 015	21	648	29	352	367	7	8
53	036	22	677	29	323	360	8	7
54	058	21	706	28	294	352	8	6
55	9.71 079	21	9.77 734	29	0.22 266	9.93 344	7	5
56	100	21	763	28	237	337	8	4
57	121	21	791	29	209	329	7	3
58	142	21	820	29	180	322	8	2
59	163	21	849	28	151	314	7	1
60	9.71 184		9.77 877		0.22 123	9.93 307		0
	L Cos *	d	L Cot *	c d	L Tan	L Sin *	d	′

Prop. Parts

	30	29	28
1	3	2.9	2.8
2	6	5.8	5.6
3	9	8.7	8.4
4	12	11.6	11.2
5	15	14.5	14.0
6	18	17.4	16.8
7	21	20.3	19.6
8	24	23.2	22.4
9	27	26.1	25.2

	22	21
1	2.2	2.1
2	4.4	4.2
3	6.6	6.3
4	8.8	8.4
5	11.0	10.5
6	13.2	12.6
7	15.4	14.7
8	17.6	16.8
9	19.8	18.9

	8	7
1	0.8	0.7
2	1.6	1.4
3	2.4	2.1
4	3.2	2.8
5	4.0	3.5
6	4.8	4.2
7	5.6	4.9
8	6.4	5.6
9	7.2	6.3

59°

Prop. Parts	′	L Sin *	d	L Tan *	c d	L Cot	L Cos *	d	
Subtract 10 *from each entry in the columns marked with* "*."	0	9.71 184		9.77 877		0.22 123	9.93 307		60
	1	205	21	906	29	094	299	8	59
	2	226	21	935	29	065	291	8	58
	3	247	21	963	28	037	284	7	57
	4	268	21	9.77 992	29	0.22 008	276	8	56
	5	9.71 289	21	9.78 020	28	0.21 980	9.93 269	7	55
	6	310	21	049	29	951	261	8	54
	7	331	21	077	28	923	253	8	53
	8	352	21	106	29	894	246	8	52
	9	373	21	135	29	865	238	8	51
	10	9.71 393	20	9.78 163	28	0.21 837	9.93 230	8	50
	11	414	21	192	29	808	223	7	49
	12	435	21	220	28	780	215	8	48
	13	456	21	249	29	751	207	8	47
	14	477	21	277	28	723	200	7	46
	15	9.71 498	21	9.78 306	29	0.21 694	9.93 192	8	45
	16	519	21	334	28	666	184	7	44
	17	539	20	363	29	637	177	8	43
	18	560	21	391	28	609	169	8	42
	19	581	21	419	28	581	161	8	41
	20	9.71 602	21	9.78 448	29	0.21 552	9.93 154	7	40
	21	622	20	476	28	524	146	8	39
	22	643	21	505	29	495	138	8	38
	23	664	21	533	28	467	131	7	37
	24	685	20	562	29	438	123	8	36
	25	9.71 705	21	9.78 590	28	0.21 410	9.93 115	8	35
	26	726	21	618	28	382	108	7	34
	27	747	20	647	29	353	100	8	33
	28	767	21	675	28	325	092	8	32
	29	788	21	704	29	296	084	8	31
	30	9.71 809	20	9.78 732	28	0.21 268	9.93 077	7	30
	31	829	21	760	29	240	069	8	29
	32	850	20	789	28	211	061	8	28
	33	870	21	817	28	183	053	7	27
	34	891	20	845	29	155	046	8	26
	35	9.71 911	21	9.78 874	28	0.21 126	9.93 038	8	25
	36	932	20	902	28	098	030	8	24
	37	952	21	930	29	070	022	8	23
	38	973	21	959	28	041	014	7	22
	39	9.71 994	20	9.78 987	28	0.21 013	9.93 007	8	21
	40	9.72 014	20	9.79 015	28	0.20 985	9.92 999		20
	41	034	21	043	29	957	991	8	19
	42	055	20	072	28	928	983	8	18
	43	075	21	100	28	900	976	7	17
	44	096	20	128	28	872	968	8	16
	45	9.72 116	21	9.79 156	29	0.20 844	9.92 960	8	15
	46	137	20	185	28	815	952	8	14
	47	157	20	213	28	787	944	8	13
	48	177	21	241	28	759	936	7	12
	49	198	20	269	28	731	929	8	11
	50	9.72 218	20	9.79 297	29	0.20 703	9.92 921	8	10
	51	238	21	326	28	674	913	8	9
	52	259	20	354	28	646	905	8	8
	53	279	20	382	28	618	897	8	7
	54	299	21	410	28	590	889	8	6
	55	9.72 320	20	9.79 438	28	0.20 562	9.92 881	7	5
	56	340	20	466	29	534	874	8	4
	57	360	20	495	28	505	866	8	3
	58	381	21	523	28	477	858	8	2
	59	401	20	551	28	449	850	8	1
	60	9.72 421	20	9.79 579		0.20 421	9.92 842		0
		L Cos *	d	L Cot *	c d	L Tan	L Sin *	d	′

Prop. Parts

	29	28
1	2.9	2.8
2	5.8	5.6
3	8.7	8.4
4	11.6	11.2
5	14.5	14.0
6	17.4	16.8
7	20.3	19.6
8	23.2	22.4
9	26.1	25.2

	21	20
1	2.1	2
2	4.2	4
3	6.3	6
4	8.4	8
5	10.5	10
6	12.6	12
7	14.7	14
8	16 8	16
9	18.9	18

	8	7
1	0.8	0.7
2	1.6	1.4
3	2.4	2.1
4	3.2	2.8
5	4.0	3.5
6	4.8	4.2
7	5.6	4.9
8	6.4	5.6
9	7.2	6.3

58°

′	L Sin *	d	L Tan *	c d	L Cot	L Cos *	d		Prop. Parts		
0	9.72 421		9.79 579		0.20 421	9.92 842		**60**			
1	441	20	607	28	393	834	8	59			
2	461	20	635	28	365	826	8	58			
3	482	21	663	28	337	818	8	57			
4	502	20	691	28	309	810	8	56			
5	9.72 522	20	9.79 719	28	0.20 281	9.92 803	7	**55**			
6	542	20	747	28	253	795	8	54			
7	562	20	776	29	224	787	8	53			
8	582	20	804	28	196	779	8	52		**29**	**28**	**27**
9	602	20	832	28	168	771	8	51				
10	9.72 622	20	9.79 860	28	0.20 140	9.92 763	8	**50**	**1**	2.9	2.8	2.7
11	643	21	888	28	112	755	8	49	**2**	5.8	5.6	5.4
12	663	20	916	28	084	747	8	48	**3**	8.7	8.4	8.1
13	683	20	944	28	056	739	8	47	**4**	11.6	11.2	10.8
14	703	20	9.79 972	28	028	731	8	46	**5**	14.5	14.0	13.5
15	9.72 723	20	9.80 000	28	0.20 000	9.92 723	8	**45**	**6**	17.4	16.8	16.2
16	743	20	028	28	0.19 972	715	8	44	**7**	20.3	19.6	18.9
17	763	20	056	28	944	707	8	43	**8**	23.2	22.4	21.6
18	783	20	084	28	916	699	8	42	**9**	26.1	25.2	24.3
19	803	20	112	28	888	691	8	41				
20	9.72 823	20	9.80 140	28	0.19 860	9.92 683	8	**40**				
21	843	20	168	28	832	675	8	39				
22	863	20	195	27	805	667	8	38				
23	883	20	223	28	777	659	8	37				
24	902	19	251	28	749	651	8	36				
25	9.72 922	20	9.80 279	28	0.19 721	9.92 643	8	**35**		**21**	**20**	**19**
26	942	20	307	28	693	635	8	34				
27	962	20	335	28	665	627	8	33	**1**	2.1	2	1.9
28	9.72 982	20	363	28	637	619	8	32	**2**	4.2	4	3.8
29	9.73 002	20	391	28	609	611	8	31	**3**	6.3	6	5.7
30	9.73 022	20	9.80 419	28	0.19 581	9.92 603	8	**30**	**4**	8.4	8	7.6
31	041	19	447	28	553	595	8	29	**5**	10.5	10	9.5
32	061	20	474	27	526	587	8	28	**6**	12.6	12	11.4
33	081	20	502	28	498	579	8	27	**7**	14.7	14	13.3
34	101	20	530	28	470	571	8	26	**8**	16.8	16	15.2
35	9.73 121	20	9.80 558	28	0.19 442	9.92 563	8	**25**	**9**	18.9	18	17.1
36	140	19	586	28	414	555	9	24				
37	160	20	614	28	386	546	8	23				
38	180	20	642	27	358	538	8	22				
39	·200	19	669	28	331	530	8	21				
40	9.73 219	20	9.80 697	28	0.19 303	9.92 522	8	**20**				
41	239	20	725	28	275	514	8	19				
42	259	19	753	28	247	506	8	18				
43	278	20	781	27	219	498	8	17				
44	298	20	808	28	192	490	8	16		**9**	**8**	**7**
45	9.73 318	19	9.80 836	28	0.19 164	9.92 482	9	**15**				
46	337	20	864	28	136	473	8	14	**1**	0.9	0.8	0.7
47	357	20	892	27	108	465	8	13	**2**	1.8	1.6	1.4
48	377	19	919	28	081	457	8	12	**3**	2.7	2.4	2.1
49	396	20	947	28	053	449	8	11	**4**	3.6	3.2	2.8
50	9.73 416	19	9.80 975	28	0.19 025	9.92 441	8	**10**	**5**	4.5	4.0	3.5
51	435	20	9.81 003	27	0.18 997	433	8	9	**6**	5.4	4.8	4.2
52	455	19	030	28	970	425	9	8	**7**	6.3	5.6	4.9
53	474	20	058	28	942	416	8	7	**8**	7.2	6.4	5.6
54	494	19	086	27	914	408	8	6	**9**	8.1	7.2	6.3
55	9.73 513	20	9.81 113	28	0.18 887	9.92 400	8	**5**				
56	533	19	141	28	859	392	8	4				
57	552	20	169	27	831	384	8	3				
58	572	19	196	28	804	376	9	2				
59	591	20	224	28	776	367	8	1				
60	9.73 611		9.81 252		0.18 748	9.92 359		**0**				
	L Cos *	d	L Cot *	c d	L Tan	L Sin *	d	′			

Prop. Parts

	28	27
1	2.8	2.7
2	5.6	5.4
3	8.4	8.1
4	11.2	10.8
5	14.0	13.5
6	16.8	16.2
7	19.6	18.9
8	22.4	21.6
9	25.2	24.3

	20	19	18
1	2	1.9	1.8
2	4	3.8	3.6
3	6	5.7	5.4
4	8	7.6	7.2
5	10	9.5	9.0
6	12	11.4	10.8
7	14	13.3	12.6
8	16	15.2	14.4
9	18	17.1	16.2

	9	8
1	0.9	0.8
2	1.8	1.6
3	2.7	2.4
4	3.6	3.2
5	4.5	4.0
6	5.4	4.8
7	6.3	5.6
8	7.2	6.4
9	8.1	7.2

′	L Sin *	d	L Tan *	c d	L Cot	L Cos *	d	′
0	9.73 611		9.81 252		0.18 748	9.92 359		60
1	630	19	279	27	721	351	8	59
2	650	20	307	28	693	343	8	58
3	669	19	335	28	665	335	8	57
4	689	20	362	27	638	326	9	56
5	9.73 708	19	9.81 390	28	0.18 610	9.92 318	8	55
6	727	19	418	28	582	310	8	54
7	747	20	445	27	555	302	8	53
8	766	19	473	28	527	293	9	52
9	785	19	500	27	500	285	8	51
10	9.73 805	20	9.81 528	28	0.18 472	9.92 277	8	50
11	824	19	556	28	444	269	8	49
12	843	19	583	27	417	260	9	48
13	863	20	611	28	389	252	8	47
14	882	19	638	27	362	244	8	46
15	9.73 901	19	9.81 666	28	0.18 334	9.92 235	9	45
16	921	20	693	27	307	227	8	44
17	940	19	721	28	279	219	8	43
18	959	19	748	27	252	211	9	42
19	978	19	776	28	224	202	8	41
20	9.73 997	19	9.81 803	27	0.18 197	9.92 194	8	40
21	9.74 017	20	831	28	169	186	8	39
22	036	19	858	27	142	177	9	38
23	055	19	886	28	114	169	8	37
24	074	19	913	27	087	161	8	36
25	9.74 093	19	9.81 941	28	0.18 059	9.92 152	9	35
26	113	20	968	27	032	144	8	34
27	132	19	9.81 996	28	0.18 004	136	8	33
28	151	19	9.82 023	27	0.17 977	127	9	32
29	170	19	051	28	949	119	8	31
30	9.74 189	19	9.82 078	27	0.17 922	9.92 111	8	30
31	208	19	106	28	894	102	9	29
32	227	19	133	28	867	094	8	28
33	246	19	161	27	839	086	9	27
34	265	19	188	27	812	077	8	26
35	9.74 284	19	9.82 215	28	0.17 785	9.92 069	9	25
36	303	19	243	27	757	060	8	24
37	322	19	270	28	730	052	8	23
38	341	19	298	27	702	044	9	22
39	360	19	325	27	675	035	8	21
40	9.74 379	19	9.82 352	28	0.17 648	9.92 027	9	20
41	398	19	380	27	620	018	8	19
42	417	19	407	28	593	010	8	18
43	436	19	435	27	565	9.92 002	9	17
44	455	19	462	27	538	9.91 993	8	16
45	9.74 474	19	9.82 489	28	0.17 511	9.91 985	9	15
46	493	19	517	28	483	976	8	14
47	512	19	544	27	456	968	9	13
48	531	18	571	28	429	959	8	12
49	549	19	599	27	401	951	9	11
50	9.74 568	19	9.82 626	27	0.17 374	9.91 942	8	10
51	587	19	653	28	347	934	9	9
52	606	19	681	27	319	925	8	8
53	625	19	708	27	292	917	9	7
54	644	18	735	27	265	908	8	6
55	9.74 662	19	9.82 762	28	0.17 238	9.91 900	9	5
56	681	19	790	27	210	891	8	4
57	700	19	817	27	183	883	9	3
58	719	18	844	27	156	874	8	2
59	737	19	871	28	129	866	9	1
60	9.74 756		9.82 899		0.17 101	9.91 857		0
	L Cos *	d	L Cot *	c d	L Tan	L Sin *	d	′

56°

,	L Sin *	d	L Tan *	c d	L Cot	L Cos *	d		Prop. Parts		
0	9.74 756		9.82 899		0.17 101	9.91 857		60			
1	775	19	926	27	074	849	8	59			
2	794	19	953	27	047	840	9	58			
3	812	18	9.82 980	27	0.17 020	832	8	57			
4	831	19	9.83 008	28	0.16 992	823	9	56			
5	9.74 850	19	9.83 035	27	0.16 965	9.91 815	8	55			
6	868	18	062	27	938	806	8	54			
7	887	19	089	27	911	798	9	53			
8	906	19	117	28	883	789	9	52		28	27	26
9	924	18	144	27	856	781	8	51	1	2.8	2.7	2.6
10	9.74 943	19	9.83 171	27	0.16 829	9.91 772	9	50	2	5.6	5.4	5.2
11	961	18	198	27	802	763	9	49	3	8.4	8.1	7.8
12	980	19	225	27	775	755	8	48	4	11.2	10.8	10.4
13	9.74 999	19	252	27	748	746	9	47	5	14.0	13.5	13.0
14	9.75 017	18	280	28	720	738	8	46	6	16.8	16.2	15.6
15	9.75 036	19	9.83 307	27	0.16 693	9.91 729	9	45	7	19.6	18.9	18.2
16	054	18	334	27	666	720	9	44	8	22.4	21.6	20.8
17	073	19	361	27	639	712	8	43	9	25.2	24.3	23.4
18	091	18	388	27	612	703	9	42				
19	110	19	415	27	585	695	8	41				
20	9.75 128	18	9.83 442	27	0.16 558	9.91 686	9	40				
21	147	19	470	28	530	677	9	39				
22	165	18	497	27	503	669	8	38				
23	184	19	524	27	476	660	9	37				
24	202	18	551	27	449	651	9	36				
25	9.75 221	19	9.83 578	27	0.16 422	9.91 643	8	35				
26	239	18	605	27	395	634	9	34				
27	258	19	632	27	368	625	9	33		19	18
28	276	18	659	27	341	617	8	32				
29	294	18	686	27	314	608	9	31	1	1.9	1.8
30	9.75 313	19	9.83 713	27	0.16 287	9.91 599	9	30	2	3.8	3.6
31	331	18	740	27	260	591	8	29	3	5.7	5.4
32	350	19	768	28	232	582	9	28	4	7.6	7.2
33	368	18	795	27	205	573	9	27	5	9.5	9.0
34	386	18	822	27	178	565	8	26	6	11.4	10.8
35	9.75 405	19	9.83 849	27	0.16 151	9.91 556	9	25	7	13.3	12.6
36	423	18	876	27	124	547	9	24	8	15.2	14.4
37	441	18	903	27	097	538	9	23	9	17.1	16.2
38	459	18	930	27	070	530	8	22				
39	478	19	957	27	043	521	9	21				
40	9.75 496	18	9.83 984	27	0.16 016	9.91 512	9	20				
41	514	18	9.84 011	27	0.15 989	504	8	19				
42	533	19	038	27	962	495	9	18				
43	551	18	065	27	935	486	9	17				
44	569	18	092	27	908	477	9	16				
45	9.75 587	18	9.84 119	27	0.15 881	9.91 469	8	15		9	8
46	605	18	146	27	854	460	9	14				
47	624	19	173	27	827	451	9	13	1	0.9	0.8
48	642	18	200	27	800	442	9	12	2	1.8	1.6
49	660	18	227	27	773	433	8	11	3	2.7	2.4
50	9.75 678	18	9.84 254	27	0.15 746	9.91 425	9	10	4	3.6	3.2
51	696	18	280	26	720	416	9	9	5	4.5	4.0
52	714	18	307	27	693	407	9	8	6	5.4	4.8
53	733	19	334	27	666	398	9	7	7	6.3	5.6
54	751	18	361	27	639	389	8	6	8	7.2	6.4
55	9.75 769	18	9.84 388	27	0.15 612	9.91 381	9	5	9	8.1	7.2
56	787	18	415	27	585	372	9	4				
57	805	18	442	27	558	363	9	3				
58	823	18	469	27	531	354	9	2				
59	841	18	496	27	504	345	9	1				
60	9.75 859	18	9.84 523	27	0.15 477	9.91 336	9	0				
	L Cos *	d	L Cot *	c d	L Tan	L Sin *	d	,			

55°

Prop. Parts		′	L Sin *	d	L Tan *	c d	L Cot	L Cos *	d	
		0	9.75 859		9.84 523		0.15 477	9.91 336		60
		1	877	18	550	27	450	328	8	59
		2	895	18	576	26	424	319	9	58
		3	913	18	603	27	397	310	9	57
		4	931	18	630	27	370	301	9	56
		5	9.75 949	18	9.84 657	27	0.15 343	9.91 292	9	55
		6	967	18	684	27	316	283	9	54
27	**26**	7	9.75 985	18	711	27	289	274	8	53
		8	9.76 003	18	738	27	262	266	9	52
1 2.7	2.6	9	021	18	764	26	236	257	9	51
2 5.4	5.2	10	9.76 039	18	9.84 791	27	0.15 209	9.91 248		50
3 8.1	7.8	11	057	18	818	27	182	239	9	49
4 10.8	10.4	12	075	18	845	27	155	230	9	48
5 13.5	13.0	13	093	18	872	27	128	221	9	47
6 16.2	15.6	14	111	18	899	27	101	212	9	46
7 18.9	18.2	15	9.76 129	18	9.84 925	26	0.15 075	9.91 203	9	45
8 21.6	20.8	16	146	17	952	27	048	194	9	44
9 24.3	23.4	17	164	18	9.84 979	27	0.15 021	185	9	43
		18	182	18	9.85 006	27	0.14 994	176	9	42
		19	200	18	033	27	967	167	9	41
		20	9.76 218	18	9.85 059	26	0.14 941	9.91 158	9	40
		21	236	18	086	27	914	149	8	39
		22	253	17	113	27	887	141	9	38
		23	271	18	140	27	860	132	9	37
		24	289	18	166	26	834	123	9	36
		25	9.76 307	18	9.85 193	27	0.14 807	9.91 114	9	35
		26	324	17	220	27	780	105	9	34
18	**17**	27	342	18	247	27	753	096	9	33
		28	360	18	273	26	727	087	9	32
1 1.8	1.7	29	378	17	300	27	700	078	9	31
2 3.6	3.4	30	9.76 395	18	9.85 327	27	0.14 673	9.91 069		30
3 5.4	5.1	31	413	18	354	27	646	060	9	29
4 7.2	6.8	32	431	18	380	26	620	051	9	28
5 9.0	8.5	33	448	17	407	27	593	042	9	27
6 10.8	10.2	34	466	18	434	26	566	033	10	26
7 12.6	11.9	35	9.76 484	18	9.85 460	27	0.14 540	9.91 023		25
8 14.4	13.6	36	501	17	487	27	513	014	9	24
9 16.2	15.3	37	519	18	514	26	486	9.91 005	9	23
		38	537	18	540	27	460	9.90 996	9	22
		39	554	17	567	27	433	987	9	21
		40	9.76 572	18	9.85 594	26	0.14 406	9.90 978	9	20
		41	590	18	620	27	380	969	9	19
		42	607	17	647	27	353	960	9	18
		43	625	18	674	26	326	951	9	17
		44	642	17	700	27	300	942	9	16
10	**9** **8**	45	9.76 660	18	9.85 727	27	0.14 273	9.90 933	9	15
		46	677	17	754	26	246	924	9	14
1 1.0 0.9	0.8	47	695	18	780	27	220	915	9	13
2 2.0 1.8	1.6	48	712	17	807	27	193	906	10	12
3 3.0 2.7	2.4	49	730	18	834	26	166	896	9	11
4 4.0 3.6	3.2	50	9.76 747	17	9.85 860	27	0.14 140	9.90 887		10
5 5.0 4.5	4.0	51	765	18	887	26	113	878	9	9
6 6.0 5.4	4.8	52	782	17	913	27	087	869	9	8
7 7.0 6.3	5.6	53	800	18	940	27	060	860	9	7
8 8.0 7.2	6.4	54	817	17	967	26	033	851	9	6
9 9.0 8.1	7.2	55	9.76 835	18	9.85 993	27	0.14 007	9.90 842	10	5
		56	852	17	9.86 020	27	0.13 980	832	9	4
		57	870	18	046	26	954	823	9	3
		58	887	17	073	27	927	814	9	2
		59	904	17	100	27	900	805	9	1
		60	9.76 922	18	9.86 126	26	0.13 874	9.90 796		0
			L Cos *	d	L Cot *	c d	L Tan	L Sin *	d	′

54°

′	L Sin *	d	L Tan *	c d	L Cot	L Cos *	d		Prop. Parts
0	9.76 922		9.86 126		0.13 874	9.90 796		60	*Subtract* 10 *from each en-*
1	939	17	153	27	847	787	9	59	*try in the columns marked*
2	957	18	179	26	821	777	10	58	*with* "*."
3	974	17	206	27	794	768	9	57	
4	9.76 991	17	232	26	768	759	9	56	
5	9.77 009	18	9.86 259	27	0.13 741	9.90 750	9	55	
6	026	17	285	26	715	741	9	54	
7	043	17	312	27	688	731	10	53	
8	061	18	338	26	662	722	9	52	
9	078	17	365	27	635	713	9	51	
10	9.77 095	17	9.86 392	27	0.13 608	9.90 704	9	50	
11	112	17	418	26	582	694	10	49	
12	130	18	445	27	555	685	9	48	
13	147	17	471	26	529	676	9	47	
14	164	17	498	27	502	667	9	46	
15	9.77 181	17	9.86 524	26	0.13 476	9.90 657	10	45	
16	199	18	551	27	449	648	9	44	
17	216	17	577	26	423	639	9	43	
18	233	17	603	26	397	630	9	42	
19	250	17	630	27	370	620	10	41	
20	9.77 268	18	9.86 656	26	0.13 344	9.90 611	9	40	
21	285	17	683	27	317	602	10	39	
22	302	17	709	26	291	592	9	38	
23	319	17	736	27	264	583	9	37	
24	336	17	762	26	238	574	9	36	
25	9.77 353	17	9.86 789	27	0.13 211	9.90 565	10	35	
26	370	17	815	26	185	555	9	34	
27	387	17	842	27	158	546	9	33	
28	405	18	868	26	132	537	10	32	
29	422	17	894	26	106	527	9	31	
30	9.77 439	17	9.86 921	27	0.13 079	9.90 518		30	
31	456	17	947	26	053	509	9	29	
32	473	17	9.86 974	27	026	499	10	28	
33	490	17	9.87 000	26	0.13 000	490	10	27	
34	507	17	027	27	0.12 973	480	9	26	
35	9.77 524	17	9.87 053	26	0.12 947	9.90 471	9	25	
36	541	17	079	26	921	462	9	24	
37	558	17	106	27	894	452	10	23	
38	575	17	132	26	868	443	9	22	
39	592	17	158	27	842	434	10	21	
40	9.77 609	17	9.87 185	26	0.12 815	9.90 424	9	20	
41	626	17	211	27	789	415	10	19	
42	643	17	238	26	762	405	9	18	
43	660	17	264	26	736	396	10	17	
44	677	17	290	27	710	386	9	16	
45	9.77 694	17	9.87 317	26	0.12 683	9.90 377	9	15	
46	711	17	343	26	657	368	10	14	
47	728	16	369	27	631	358	9	13	
48	744	17	396	26	604	349	10	12	
49	761	17	422	26	578	339	9	11	
50	9.77 778	17	9.87 448	27	0.12 552	9.90 330	10	10	
51	795	17	475	26	525	320	9	9	
52	812	17	501	26	499	311	10	8	
53	829	17	527	27	473	301	9	7	
54	846	16	554	26	446	292	10	6	
55	9.77 862	17	9.87 580	26	0.12 420	9.90 282	9	5	
56	879	17	606	27	394	273	10	4	
57	896	17	633	26	367	263	9	3	
58	913	17	659	26	341	254	10	2	
59	930	16	685	26	315	244	9	1	
60	9.77 946		9.87 711		0.12 289	9.90 235		0	
	L Cos *	d	L Cot *	c d	L Tan	L Sin *	d	′	

Prop. Parts

	27	26
1	2.7	2.6
2	5.4	5.2
3	8.1	7.8
4	10.8	10.4
5	13.5	13.0
6	16.2	15.6
7	18.9	18.2
8	21.6	20.8
9	24.3	23.4

	18	17	16
1	1.8	1.7	1.6
2	3.6	3.4	3.2
3	5.4	5.1	4.8
4	7.2	6.8	6.4
5	9.0	8.5	8.0
6	10.8	10.2	9.6
7	12.6	11.9	11.2
8	14.4	13.6	12.8
9	16.2	15.3	14.4

	10	9
1	1.0	0.9
2	2.0	1.8
3	3.0	2.7
4	4.0	3.6
5	5.0	4.5
6	6.0	5.4
7	7.0	6.3
8	8.0	7.2
9	9.0	8.1

53°

Prop. Parts

	27	26
1	2.7	2.6
2	5.4	5.2
3	8.1	7.8
4	10.8	10.4
5	13.5	13.0
6	16.2	15.6
7	18.9	18.2
8	21.6	20.8
9	24.3	23.4

	17	16
1	1.7	1.6
2	3.4	3.2
3	5.1	4.8
4	6.8	6.4
5	8.5	8.0
6	10.2	9.6
7	11.9	11.2
8	13.6	12.8
9	15.3	14.4

	10	9
1	1.0	0.9
2	2.0	1.8
3	3.0	2.7
4	4.0	3.6
5	5.0	4.5
6	6.0	5.4
7	7.0	6.3
8	8.0	7.2
9	9.0	8.1

′	L Sin *	d	L Tan *	c d	L Cot	L Cos *	d	
0	9.77 946		9.87 711		0.12 289	9.90 235		60
1	963	17	738	27	262	225	10	59
2	980	17	764	26	236	216	9	58
3	9.77 997	17	790	26	210	206	10	57
4	9.78 013	16	817	27	183	197	9	56
5	9.78 030	17	9.87 843	26	0.12 157	9.90 187	10	55
6	047	17	869	26	131	178	9	54
7	063	16	895	26	105	168	10	53
8	080	17	922	27	078	159	9	52
9	097	17	948	26	052	149	10	51
10	9.78 113	16	9.87 974	26	0.12 026	9.90 139	10	50
11	130	17	9.88 000	26	0.12 000	130	9	49
12	147	17	027	27	0.11 973	120	10	48
13	163	16	053	26	947	111	10	47
14	180	17	079	26	921	101	10	46
15	9.78 197	17	9.88 105	26	0.11 895	9.90 091	10	45
16	213	16	131	26	869	082	9	44
17	230	17	158	27	842	072	10	43
18	246	16	184	26	816	063	9	42
19	263	17	210	26	790	053	10	41
20	9.78 280	17	9.88 236	26	0.11 764	9.90 043	10	40
21	296	16	262	26	738	034	9	39
22	313	17	289	27	711	024	10	38
23	329	16	315	26	685	014	10	37
24	346	17	341	26	659	9.90 005	9	36
25	9.78 362	16	9.88 367	26	0.11 633	9.89 995	10	35
26	379	17	393	26	607	985	10	34
27	395	16	420	27	580	976	9	33
28	412	17	446	26	554	966	10	32
29	428	16	472	26	528	956	9	31
30	9.78 445	17	9.88 498	26	0.11 502	9.89 947	10	30
31	461	16	524	26	476	937	10	29
32	478	17	550	26	450	927	10	28
33	494	16	577	27	423	918	10	27
34	510	16	603	26	397	908	10	26
35	9.78 527	17	9.88 629	26	0.11 371	9.89 898	10	25
36	543	16	655	26	345	888	9	24
37	560	17	681	26	319	879	10	23
38	576	16	707	26	293	869	10	22
39	592	16	733	26	267	859	10	21
40	9.78 609	17	9.88 759	27	0.11 241	9.89 849	10	20
41	625	16	786	26	214	840	9	19
42	642	17	812	26	188	830	10	18
43	658	16	838	26	162	820	10	17
44	674	16	864	26	136	810	10	16
45	9.78 691	17	9.88 890	26	0.11 110	9.89 801	9	15
46	707	16	916	26	084	791	10	14
47	723	16	942	26	058	781	10	13
48	739	16	968	26	032	771	10	12
49	756	17	9.88 994	26	0.11 006	761	9	11
50	9.78 772	16	9.89 020	26	0.10 980	9.89 752	10	10
51	788	16	046	26	954	742	10	9
52	805	17	073	27	927	732	10	8
53	821	16	099	26	901	722	10	7
54	837	16	125	26	875	712	10	6
55	9.78 853	16	9.89 151	26	0.10 849	9.89 702	10	5
56	869	16	177	26	823	693	9	4
57	886	17	203	26	797	683	10	3
58	902	16	229	26	771	673	10	2
59	918	16	255	26	745	663	10	1
60	9.78 934	16	9.89 281	26	0.10 719	9.89 653	10	0
	L Cos *	d	L Cot *	c d	L Tan	L Sin *	d	′

52°

′	L Sin *	d	L Tan *	c d	L Cot	L Cos *	d		Prop. Parts
0	9.78 934		9.89 281		0.10 719	9.89 653		**60**	
1	950	16	307	26	693	643	10	59	
2	967	17	333	26	667	633	10	58	
3	983	16	359	26	641	624	9	57	
4	9.78 999	16	385	26	615	614	10	56	
5	9.79 015	16	9.89 411	26	0.10 589	9.89 604	10	**55**	
6	031	16	437	26	563	594	10	54	
7	047	16	463	26	537	584	10	53	
8	063	16	489	26	511	574	10	52	
9	079	16	515	26	485	564	10	51	
10	9.79 095	16	9.89 541	26	0.10 459	9.89 554	10	**50**	

	26	**25**
1	2.6	2.5
2	5.2	5.0
3	7.8	7.5
4	10.4	10.0
5	13.0	12.5
6	15.6	15.0
7	18.2	17.5
8	20.8	20.0
9	23.4	22.5

′	L Sin *	d	L Tan *	c d	L Cot	L Cos *	d	
11	111	16	567	26	433	544	10	49
12	128	17	593	26	407	534	10	48
13	144	16	619	26	381	524	10	47
14	160	16	645	26	355	514	10	46
15	9.79 176	16	9.89 671	26	0.10 329	9.89 504	10	**45**
16	192	16	697	26	303	495	9	44
17	208	16	723	26	277	485	10	43
18	224	16	749	26	251	475	10	42
19	240	16	775	26	225	465	10	41
20	9.79 256	16	9.89 801	26	0.10 199	9.89 455	10	**40**
21	272	16	827	26	173	445	10	39
22	288	16	853	26	147	435	10	38
23	304	16	879	26	121	425	10	37
24	319	15	905	26	095	415	10	36
25	9.79 335	16	9.89 931	26	0.10 069	9.89 405	10	**35**
26	351	16	957	26	043	395	10	34
27	367	16	9.89 983	26	0.10 017	385	10	33
28	383	16	9.90 009	26	0.09 991	375	11	32
29	399	16	035	26	965	364	10	31
30	9.79 415	16	9.90 061	26	0.09 939	9.89 354	10	**30**

	17	**16**	**15**
1	1.7	1.6	1.5
2	3.4	3.2	3.0
3	5.1	4.8	4.5
4	6.8	6.4	6.0
5	8.5	8.0	7.5
6	10.2	9.6	9.0
7	11.9	11.2	10.5
8	13.6	12.8	12.0
9	15.3	14.4	13.5

′	L Sin *	d	L Tan *	c d	L Cot	L Cos *	d	
31	431	16	086	25	914	344	10	29
32	447	16	112	26	888	334	10	28
33	463	15	138	26	862	324	10	27
34	478	16	164	26	836	314	10	26
35	9.79 494	16	9.90 190	26	0.09 810	9.89 304	10	**25**
36	510	16	216	26	784	294	10	24
37	526	16	242	26	758	284	10	23
38	542	16	268	26	732	274	10	22
39	558	15	294	26	706	264	10	21
40	9.79 573	16	9.90 320	26	0.09 680	9.89 254	10	**20**
41	589	16	346	26	654	244	10	19
42	605	16	371	25	629	233	11	18
43	621	15	397	26	603	223	10	17
44	636	16	423	26	577	213	10	16
45	9.79 652	16	9.90 449	26	0.09 551	9.89 203	10	**15**

	11	**10**	**9**
1	1.1	1.0	0.9
2	2.2	2.0	1.8
3	3.3	3.0	2.7
4	4.4	4.0	3.6
5	5.5	5.0	4.5
6	6.6	6.0	5.4
7	7.7	7.0	6.3
8	8.8	8.0	7.2
9	9.9	9.0	8.1

′	L Sin *	d	L Tan *	c d	L Cot	L Cos *	d	
46	668	16	475	26	525	193	10	14
47	684	16	501	26	499	183	10	13
48	699	15	527	26	473	173	10	12
49	715	16	553	25	447	162	11	11
50	9.79 731	16	9.90 578		0.09 422	9.89 152	10	**10**
51	746	15	604	26	396	142	10	9
52	762	16	630	26	370	132	10	8
53	778	16	656	26	344	122	10	7
54	793	15	682	26	318	112	10	6
55	9.79 809	16	9.90 708	26	0.09 292	9.89 101	11	**5**
56	825	16	734	26	266	091	10	4
57	840	15	759	25	241	081	10	3
58	856	16	785	26	215	071	10	2
59	872	16	811	26	189	060	11	1
60	9.79 887	15	9.90 837	26	0.09 163	9.89 050	10	**0**
	L Cos *	d	L Cot *	c d	L Tan	L Sin *	d	′

′	L Sin *	d	L Tan *	c d	L Cot	L Cos *	d	′
0	9.79 887		9.90 837		0.09 163	9.89 050		60
1	903	16	863	26	137	040	10	59
2	918	15	889	26	111	030	10	58
3	934	16	914	25	086	020	10	57
4	950	16	940	26	060	9.89 009	11	56
5	9.79 965	15	9.90 966	26	0.09 034	9.88 999	10	55
6	981	16	9.90 992	26	0.09 008	989	10	54
7	9.79 996	15	9.91 018	26	0.08 982	978	11	53
8	9.80 012	16	043	25	957	968	10	52
9	027	15	069	26	931	958	10	51
10	9.80 043	16	9.91 095	26	0.08 905	9.88 948	10	50
11	058	15	121	26	879	937	11	49
12	074	16	147	26	853	927	10	48
13	089	15	172	25	828	917	10	47
14	105	16	198	26	802	906	11	46
15	9.80 120	15	9.91 224	26	0.08 776	9.88 896	10	45
16	136	16	250	26	750	886	10	44
17	151	15	276	26	724	875	11	43
18	166	15	301	25	699	865	10	42
19	182	16	327	26	673	855	10	41
20	9.80 197	15	9.91 353	26	0.08 647	9.88 844	11	40
21	213	16	379	26	621	834	10	39
22	228	15	404	25	596	824	10	38
23	244	16	430	26	570	813	10	37
24	259	15	456	26	544	803	10	36
25	9.80 274	15	9.91 482	26	0.08 518	9.88 793	10	35
26	290	16	507	25	493	782	11	34
27	305	15	533	26	467	772	11	33
28	320	15	559	26	441	761	10	32
29	336	16	585	26	415	751	10	31
30	9.80 351	15	9.91 610	25	0.08 390	9.88 741		30
31	366	15	636	26	364	730	11	29
32	382	16	662	26	338	720	11	28
33	397	15	688	25	312	709	10	27
34	412	15	713	26	287	699	11	26
35	9.80 428	16	9.91 739	26	0.08 261	9.88 688		25
36	443	15	765	26	235	678	10	24
37	458	15	791	26	209	668	10	23
38	473	15	816	25	184	657	11	22
39	489	16	842	26	158	647	10	21
40	9.80 504	15	9.91 868	26	0.08 132	9.88 636	11	20
41	519	15	893	25	107	626	10	19
42	534	15	919	26	081	615	11	18
43	550	16	945	26	055	605	11	17
44	565	15	971	26	029	594	11	16
45	9.80 580	15	9.91 996	25	0.08 004	9.88 584	10	15
46	595	15	9.92 022	26	0.07 978	573	11	14
47	610	15	048	26	952	563	11	13
48	625	15	073	25	927	552	11	12
49	641	16	099	26	901	542	10	11
50	9.80 656	15	9.92 125	26	0.07 875	9.88 531	11	10
51	671	15	150	25	850	521	10	9
52	686	15	176	26	824	510	11	8
53	701	15	202	26	798	499	11	7
54	716	15	227	25	773	489	10	6
55	9.80 731	15	9.92 253	26	0.07 747	9.88 478	11	5
56	746	15	279	26	721	468	10	4
57	762	16	304	25	696	457	11	3
58	777	15	330	26	670	447	10	2
59	792	15	356	26	644	436	11	1
60	9.80 807	15	9.92 381	25	0.07 619	9.88 425	11	0
	L Cos *	d	L Cot *	c d	L Tan	L Sin *	d	′

Prop. Parts

	26	25
1	2.6	2.5
2	5.2	5.0
3	7.8	7.5
4	10.4	10.0
5	13.0	12.5
6	15.6	15.0
7	18.2	17.5
8	20.8	20.0
9	23.4	22.5

	16	15
1	1.6	1.5
2	3.2	3.0
3	4.8	4.5
4	6.4	6.0
5	8.0	7.5
6	9.6	9.0
7	11.2	10.5
8	12.8	12.0
9	14.4	13.5

	11	10
1	1.1	1.0
2	2.2	2.0
3	3.3	3.0
4	4.4	4.0
5	5.5	5.0
6	6.6	6.0
7	7.7	7.0
8	8.8	8.0
9	9.9	9.0

50°

′	L Sin *	d	L Tan *	c d	L Cot	L Cos *	d		Prop. Parts
0	9.80 807		9.92 381		0.07 619	9.88 425		60	
1	822	15	407	26	593	415	10	59	*Subtract 10 from each en-*
2	837	15	433	26	567	404	11	58	*try in the columns marked*
3	852	15	458	25	542	394	10	57	*with "*."*
4	867	15	484	26	516	383	11	56	
5	9.80 882	15	9.92 510	26	0.07 490	9.88 372	11	55	
6	897	15	535	25	465	362	10	54	
7	912	15	561	26	439	351	11	53	
8	927	15	587	26	413	340	11	52	
9	942	15	612	25	388	330	10	51	
10	9.80 957	15	9.92 638	26	0.07 362	9.88 319	11	50	
										26	25
11	972	15	663	25	337	308	11	49	1	2.6	2.5
12	9.80 987	15	689	26	311	298	10	48	2	5.2	5.0
13	9.81 002	15	715	26	285	287	11	47	3	7.8	7.5
14	017	15	740	25	260	276	11	46	4	10.4	10.0
15	9.81 032	15	9.92 766	26	0.07 234	9.88 266	10	45	5	13.0	12.5
16	047	15	792	26	208	255	11	44	6	15.6	15.0
17	061	14	817	25	183	244	11	43	7	18.2	17.5
18	076	15	843	26	157	234	10	42	8	20.8	20.0
19	091	15	868	25	132	223	11	41	9	23.4	22.5
20	9.81 106	15	9.92 894	26	0.07 106	9.88 212	11	40	
21	121	15	920	26	080	201	11	39	
22	136	15	945	25	055	191	10	38	
23	151	15	971	26	029	180	11	37	
24	166	15	9.92 996	25	0.07 004	169	11	36	
25	9.81 180	14	9.93 022	26	0.06 978	9.88 158	11	35	
26	195	15	048	26	952	148	10	34	
27	210	15	073	25	927	137	11	33		15	14
28	225	15	099	26	901	126	11	32	1	1.5	1.4
29	240	15	124	25	876	115	11	31	2	3.0	2.8
30	9.81 254	14	9.93 150	26	0.06 850	9.88 105	10	30	3	4.5	4.2
31	269	15	175	25	825	094	11	29	4	6.0	5.6
32	284	15	201	26	799	083	11	28	5	7.5	7.0
33	299	15	227	26	773	072	11	27	6	9.0	8.4
34	314	15	252	25	748	061	11	26	7	10.5	9.8
35	9.81 328	14	9.93 278	26	0.06 722	9.88 051	10	25	8	12.0	11.2
36	343	15	303	25	697	040	11	24	9	13.5	12.6
37	358	15	329	26	671	029	11	23	
38	372	14	354	25	646	018	11	22	
39	387	15	380	26	620	9.88 007	11	21	
40	9.81 402	15	9.93 406	26	0.06 594	9.87 996	11	20	
41	417	15	431	25	569	985	11	19	
42	431	14	457	26	543	975	10	18	
43	446	15	482	25	518	964	11	17	
44	461	15	508	26	492	953	11	16	
45	9.81 475	14	9.93 533	25	0.06 467	9.87 942	11	15		11	10
46	490	15	559	26	441	931	11	14	1	1.1	1.0
47	505	15	584	25	416	920	11	13	2	2.2	2.0
48	519	14	610	26	390	909	11	12	3	3.3	3.0
49	534	15	636	26	364	898	11	11	4	4.4	4.0
50	9.81 549	15	9.93 661	25	0.06 339	9.87 887	11	10	5	5.5	5.0
51	563	14	687	26	313	877	10	9	6	6.6	6.0
52	578	15	712	25	288	866	11	8	7	7.7	7.0
53	592	14	738	26	262	855	11	7	8	8.8	8.0
54	607	15	763	25	237	844	11	6	9	9.9	9.0
55	9.81 622	15	9.93 789	26	0.06 211	9.87 833	11	5	
56	636	14	814	25	186	822	11	4	
57	651	15	840	26	160	811	11	3	
58	665	14	865	25	135	800	11	2	
59	680	15	891	26	109	789	11	1	
60	9.81 694	14	9.93 916	25	0.06 084	9.87 778	11	0	
	L Cos *	d	L Cot *	c d	L Tan	L Sin *	d	′	

49°

Prop. Parts

	26	25
1	2.6	2.5
2	5.2	5.0
3	7.8	7.5
4	10.4	10.0
5	13.0	12.5
6	15.6	15.0
7	18.2	17.5
8	20.8	20.0
9	23.4	22.5

	15	14
1	1.5	1.4
2	3.0	2.8
3	4.5	4.2
4	6.0	5.6
5	7.5	7.0
6	9.0	8.4
7	10.5	9.8
8	12.0	11.2
9	13.5	12.6

	12	11
1	1.2	1.1
2	2.4	2.2
3	3.6	3.3
4	4.8	4.4
5	6.0	5.5
6	7.2	6.6
7	8.4	7.7
8	9.6	8.8
9	10.8	9.9

′	L Sin *	d	L Tan *	c d	L Cot	L Cos *	d	′
0	9.81 694		9.93 916		0.06 084	9.87 778		60
1	709	15	942	26	058	767	11	59
2	723	14	967	25	033	756	11	58
3	738	15	9.93 993	26	0.06 007	745	11	57
4	752	14	9.94 018	25	0.05 982	734	11	56
5	9.81 767	15	9.94 044	26	0.05 956	9.87 723	11	55
6	781	14	069	25	931	712	11	54
7	796	15	095	26	905	701	11	53
8	810	14	120	25	880	690	11	52
9	825	15	146	26	854	679	11	51
10	9.81 839	14	9.94 171	25	0.05 829	9.87 668	11	50
11	854	15	197	26	803	657	11	49
12	868	14	222	25	778	646	11	48
13	882	14	248	26	752	635	11	47
14	897	15	273	25	727	624	11	46
15	9.81 911	14	9.94 299	26	0.05 701	9.87 613	11	45
16	926	15	324	25	676	601	12	44
17	940	14	350	26	650	590	11	43
18	955	15	375	25	625	579	11	42
19	969	14	401	26	599	568	11	41
20	9.81 983	14	9.94 426	25	0.05 574	9 87 557	11	40
21	9.81 998	15	452	26	548	546	11	39
22	9.82 012	14	477	25	523	535	11	38
23	026	14	503	26	497	524	11	37
24	041	15	528	25	472	513	11	36
25	9.82 055	14	9.94 554	26	0.05 446	9.87 501	12	35
26	069	15	579	25	421	490	11	34
27	084	14	604	25	396	479	11	33
28	098	14	630	26	370	468	11	32
29	112	14	655	25	345	457	11	31
30	9.82 126	14	9.94 681	26	0.05 319	9 87 446	11	30
31	141	15	706	25	294	434	12	29
32	155	14	732	26	268	423	11	28
33	169	14	757	25	243	412	11	27
34	184	15	783	26	217	401	11	26
35	9.82 198	14	9.94 808	25	0.05 192	9.87 390	11	25
36	212	14	834	26	166	378	12	24
37	226	14	859	25	141	367	11	23
38	240	14	884	26	116	356	11	22
39	255	15	910	25	090	345	11	21
40	9.82 269	14	9.94 935	26	0.05 065	9.87 334	11	20
41	283	14	961	25	039	322	12	19
42	297	14	9.94 986	26	0.05 014	311	11	18
43	311	14	9.95 012	25	0.04 988	300	11	17
44	326	15	037	25	963	288	12	16
45	9.82 340	14	9.95 062	26	0.04 938	9.87 277	11	15
46	354	14	088	25	912	266	11	14
47	368	14	113	26	887	255	12	13
48	382	14	139	25	861	243	11	12
49	396	14	164	26	836	232	11	11
50	9.82 410	14	9.95 190	25	0.04 810	9.87 221	12	10
51	424	15	215	25	785	209	11	9
52	439	14	240	26	760	198	11	8
53	453	14	266	25	734	187	12	7
54	467	14	291	23	709	175	11	6
55	9.82 481	14	9.95 317	25	0.04 683	9.87 164	11	5
56	495	14	342	26	658	153	12	4
57	509	14	368	25	632	141	11	3
58	523	14	393	25	607	130	11	2
59	537	14	418	26	582	119	12	1
60	9.82 551		9.95 444		0.04 556	9.87 107		0
	L Cos *	d	L Cot *	c d	L Tan	L Sin *	d	′

48°

′	L Sin *	d	L Tan *	c d	L Cot	L Cos *	d		Prop. Parts
0	9.82 551		9.95 444		0.04 556	9.87 107		60	
1	565	14	469	25	531	096	11	59	
2	579	14	495	26	505	085	11	58	
3	593	14	520	25	480	073	12	57	
4	607	14	545	25	455	062	11	56	
5	9.82 621	14	9.95 571	26	0.04 429	9.87 050	12	55	
6	635	14	596	25	404	039	11	54	
7	649	14	622	26	378	028	11	53	
8	663	14	647	25	353	016	12	52	
9	677	14	672	25	328	9.87 005	11	51	
10	9.82 691	14	9.95 698	26	0.04 302	9.86 993	12	50	
11	705	14	723	25	277	982	11	49	
12	719	14	748	25	252	970	12	48	
13	733	14	774	26	226	959	11	47	
14	747	14	799	25	201	947	12	46	
15	9.82 761	14	9.95 825	26	0.04 175	9.86 936	11	45	
16	775	14	850	25	150	924	12	44	
17	788	13	875	25	125	913	11	43	
18	802	14	901	26	099	902	11	42	
19	816	14	926	25	074	890	12	41	
20	9.82 830	14	9.95 952	26	0.04 048	9.86 879	11	40	
21	844	14	9.95 977	25	0.04 023	867	12	39	
22	858	14	9.96 002	25	0.03 998	855	12	38	
23	872	14	028	26	972	844	11	37	
24	885	13	053	25	947	832	12	36	
25	9.82 899	14	9.96 078	25	0.03 922	9.86 821	11	35	
26	913	14	104	26	896	809	12	34	
27	927	14	129	25	871	798	11	33	
28	941	14	155	26	845	786	12	32	
29	955	14	180	25	820	775	11	31	
30	9.82 968	13	9.96 205	25	0.03 795	9.86 763	12	30	
31	982	14	231	26	769	752	11	29	
32	9.82 996	14	256	25	744	740	12	28	
33	9.83 010	14	281	25	719	728	12	27	
34	023	13	307	26	693	717	11	26	
35	9.83 037	14	9.96 332	25	0.03 668	9.86 705	12	25	
36	051	14	357	25	643	694	11	24	
37	065	14	383	26	617	682	12	23	
38	078	13	408	25	592	670	12	22	
39	092	14	433	25	567	659	11	21	
40	9.83 106	14	9.96 459	26	0.03 541	9.86 647	12	20	
41	120	14	484	25	516	635	12	19	
42	133	13	510	26	490	624	11	18	
43	147	14	535	25	465	612	12	17	
44	161	14	560	25	440	600	12	16	
45	9.83 174	13	9.96 586	26	0.03 414	9.86 589	11	15	
46	188	14	611	25	389	577	12	14	
47	202	14	636	25	364	565	12	13	
48	215	13	662	26	338	554	11	12	
49	229	14	687	25	313	542	12	11	
50	9.83 242	13	9.96 712	25	0.03 288	9.86 530	12	10	
51	256	14	738	26	262	518	12	9	
52	270	14	763	25	237	507	11	8	
53	283	13	788	25	212	495	12	7	
54	297	14	814	26	186	483	12	6	
55	9.83 310	13	9.96 839	25	0.03 161	9.86 472	11	5	
56	324	14	864	25	136	460	12	4	
57	338	14	890	26	110	448	12	3	
58	351	13	915	25	085	436	12	2	
59	365	14	940	25	060	425	11	1	
60	9.83 378	13	9.96 966	26	0.03 034	9.86 413	12	0	
	L Cos *	d	L Cot *	c d	L Tan	L Sin *	d	′	

Prop. Parts

	26	25
1	2.6	2.5
2	5.2	5.0
3	7.8	7.5
4	10.4	10.0
5	13.0	12.5
6	15.6	15.0
7	18.2	17.5
8	20.8	20.0
9	23.4	22.5

	14	13
1	1.4	1.3
2	2.8	2.6
3	4.2	3.9
4	5.6	5.2
5	7.0	6.5
6	8.4	7.8
7	9.8	9.1
8	11.2	10.4
9	12.6	11.7

	12	11
1	1.2	1.1
2	2.4	2.2
3	3.6	3.3
4	4.8	4.4
5	6.0	5.5
6	7.2	6.6
7	8.4	7.7
8	9.6	8.8
9	10.8	9.9

47°

Prop. Parts

	26	25
1	2.6	2.5
2	5.2	5.0
3	7.8	7.5
4	10.4	10.0
5	13.0	12.5
6	15.6	15.0
7	18.2	17.5
8	20.8	20.0
9	23.4	22.5

	14	13
1	1.4	1.3
2	2.8	2.6
3	4.2	3.9
4	5.6	5.2
5	7.0	6.5
6	8.4	7.8
7	9.8	9.1
8	11.2	10.4
9	12.6	11.7

	12	11
1	1.2	1.1
2	2.4	2.2
3	3.6	3.3
4	4.8	4.4
5	6.0	5.5
6	7.2	6.6
7	8.4	7.7
8	9.6	8.8
9	10.8	9.9

′	L Sin *	d	L Tan *	c d	L Cot	L Cos *	d	
0	9.83 378		9.96 966		0.03 034	9.86 413		60
1	392	14	9.96 991	25	0.03 009	401	12	59
2	405	13	9.97 016	25	0.02 984	389	12	58
3	419	14	042	26	958	377	12	57
4	432	13	067	25	933	366	11	56
5	9.83 446	14	9.97 092	25	0.02 908	9.86 354	12	55
6	459	13	118	26	882	342	12	54
7	473	14	143	25	857	330	12	53
8	486	13	168	25	832	318	12	52
9	500	14	193	25	807	306	11	51
10	9.83 513	13	9.97 219	26	0.02 781	9.86 295		50
11	527	14	244	25	756	283	12	49
12	540	13	269	25	731	271	12	48
13	554	14	295	26	705	259	12	47
14	567	13	320	25	680	247	12	46
15	9.83 581	14	9.97 345	25	0.02 655	9.86 235	12	45
16	594	13	371	26	629	223	12	44
17	608	14	396	25	604	211	12	43
18	621	13	421	25	579	200	11	42
19	634	13	447	26	553	188	12	41
20	9.83 648	14	9.97 472	25	0.02 528	9.86 176	12	40
21	661	13	497	25	503	164	12	39
22	674	13	523	26	477	152	12	38
23	688	14	548	25	452	140	12	37
24	701	13	573	25	427	128	12	36
25	9.83 715	14	9.97 598	25	0.02 402	9.86 116	12	35
26	728	13	624	26	376	104	12	34
27	741	13	649	25	351	092	12	33
28	755	14	674	25	326	080	12	32
29	768	13	700	26	300	068	12	31
30	9.83 781	13	9.97 725	25	0.02 275	9.86 056	12	30
31	795	14	750	25	250	044	12	29
32	808	13	776	26	224	032	12	28
33	821	13	801	25	199	020	12	27
34	834	13	826	25	174	9.86 008	12	26
35	9.83 848	14	9.97 851	25	0.02 149	9.85 996	12	25
36	861	13	877	26	123	984	12	24
37	874	13	902	25	098	972	12	23
38	887	13	927	25	073	960	12	22
39	901	14	953	26	047	948	12	21
40	9.83 914	13	9.97 978	25	0.02 022	9.85 936	12	20
41	927	13	9.98 003	25	0.01 997	924	12	19
42	940	13	029	26	971	912	12	18
43	954	14	054	25	946	900	12	17
44	967	13	079	25	921	888	12	16
45	9.83 980	13	9.98 104	25	0.01 896	9.85 876	12	15
46	9.83 993	13	130	26	870	864	12	14
47	9.84 006	13	155	25	845	851	13	13
48	020	14	180	25	820	839	12	12
49	033	13	206	26	794	827	12	11
50	9.84 046	13	9.98 231	25	0.01 769	9.85 815	12	10
51	059	13	256	25	744	803	12	9
52	072	13	281	25	719	791	12	8
53	085	13	307	26	693	779	13	7
54	098	13	332	25	668	766	12	6
55	9.84 112	14	9.98 357	25	0.01 643	9.85 754	12	5
56	125	13	383	26	617	742	12	4
57	138	13	408	25	592	730	12	3
58	151	13	433	25	567	718	12	2
59	164	13	458	25	542	706	13	1
60	9.84 177	13	9.98 484	26	0.01 516	9.85 693		0
	L Cos *	d	L Cot *	c d	L Tan	L Sin *	d	′

46°

′	L Sin *	d	L Tan *	c d	L Cot	L Cos *	d		Prop. Parts
0	9.84 177		9.98 484		0.01 516	9.85 693		60	*Subtract* 10 *from each entry in the columns marked with* "*."
1	190	13	509	25	491	681	12	59	
2	203	13	534	25	466	669	12	58	
3	216	13	560	26	440	657	12	57	
4	229	13	585	25	415	645	12	56	
5	9.84 242	13	9.98 610	25	0.01 390	9.85 632	13	55	
6	255	13	635	25	365	620	12	54	
7	269	14	661	26	339	608	12	53	
8	282	13	686	25	314	596	12	52	
9	295	13	711	26	289	583	13	51	
10	9.84 308	13	9.98 737		0.01 263	9.85 571	12	50	
11	321	13	762	25	238	559	12	49	
12	334	13	787	25	213	547	12	48	
13	347	13	812	25	188	534	13	47	
14	360	13	838	26	162	522	12	46	
15	9.84 373	13	9.98 863	25	0.01 137	9.85 510	12	45	
16	385	12	888	25	112	497	13	44	
17	398	13	913	25	087	485	12	43	
18	411	13	939	26	061	473	12	42	
19	424	13	964	25	036	460	13	41	
20	9.84 437	13	9.98 989	25	0.01 011	9.85 448	12	40	
21	450	13	9.99 015	26	0.00 985	436	12	39	
22	463	13	040	25	960	423	13	38	
23	476	13	065	25	935	411	12	37	
24	489	13	090	26	910	399	12	36	
25	9.84 502	13	9.99 116		0.00 884	9.85 386	13	35	
26	515	13	141	25	859	374	12	34	
27	528	13	166	25	834	361	13	33	
28	540	12	191	25	809	349	12	32	
29	553	13	217	26	783	337	13	31	
30	9.84 566	13	9.99 242	25	0.00 758	9.85 324		30	
31	579	13	267	25	733	312	12	29	
32	592	13	293	26	707	299	13	28	
33	605	13	318	25	682	287	12	27	
34	618	13	343	25	657	274	13	26	
35	9.84 630	12	9.99 368	25	0.00 632	9.85 262	12	25	
36	643	13	394	26	606	250	12	24	
37	656	13	419	25	581	237	13	23	
38	669	13	444	25	556	225	12	22	
39	682	13	469	25	531	212	13	21	
40	9.84 694	12	9.99 495	26	0.00 505	9.85 200	12	20	
41	707	13	520	25	480	187	13	19	
42	720	13	545	25	455	175	12	18	
43	733	13	570	25	430	162	13	17	
44	745	12	596	26	404	150	12	16	
45	9.84 758	13	9.99 621	25	0.00 379	9.85 137	13	15	
46	771	13	646	25	354	125	12	14	
47	784	13	672	26	328	112	13	13	
48	796	12	697	25	303	100	12	12	
49	809	13	722	25	278	087	13	11	
50	9.84 822	13	9.99 747	25	0.00 253	9.85 074	13	10	
51	835	13	773	26	227	062	12	9	
52	847	12	798	25	202	049	13	8	
53	860	13	823	25	177	037	12	7	
54	873	13	848	25	152	024	13	6	
55	9.84 885	12	9.99 874	26	0.00 126	9.85 012	12	5	
56	898	13	899	25	101	9.84 999	13	4	
57	911	13	924	25	076	986	13	3	
58	923	12	949	25	051	974	12	2	
59	936	13	9.99 975	26	025	961	13	1	
60	9.84 949	13	10.00 000	25	0.00 000	9.84 949	12	0	
	L Cos *	d	L Cot *	c d	L Tan	L Sin *	d	′	

Prop. Parts:

	26	25
1	2.6	2.5
2	5.2	5.0
3	7.8	7.5
4	10.4	10.0
5	13.0	12.5
6	15.6	15.0
7	18.2	17.5
8	20.8	20.0
9	23.4	22.5

	14
1	1.4
2	2.8
3	4.2
4	5.6
5	7.0
6	8.4
7	9.8
8	11.2
9	12.6

	13	12
1	1.3	1.2
2	2.6	2.4
3	3.9	3.6
4	5.2	4.8
5	6.5	6.0
6	7.8	7.2
7	9.1	8.4
8	10.4	9.6
9	11.7	10.8

45°

X. AUXILIARY TABLES FOR ANGLES NEAR 0° OR 90°

NOTE 1.   On account of large tabular differences, results obtained by interpolation in the preceding table are particularly inaccurate if we are determining **log sin, log tan,** or **log cot for an angle near 0°**, or **log cos, log tan, or log cot for an angle near 90°**.   To avoid such interpolation in Table IX, we use Table Xa or Table Xb.

Table Xb applies without interpolation *if the angle is expressed to the nearest tenth of a minute,* and if the angle differs from 0°, or 90°, by at most 2°.   If angles are expressible to the nearest *second,* interpolation in Table Xb is sufficiently accurate except on the upper parts of pages 84 and 85.

Table Xa applies for the indicated values of the angle M in connection with the following formulas.*

A. Angle α near 0°.   Let M be the number of **minutes** in α.   Then,

$$\log \sin \alpha = S + \log M; \qquad \log \tan \alpha = T + \log M. \tag{1}$$

B. Angle α near 90°.   Let M be the number of **minutes** in $(90° - \alpha)$.   Then,

$$\log \cos \alpha = S + \log M; \qquad \log \cot \alpha = T + \log M. \tag{2}$$

In using (1) and (2), we find S and T from Table Xa below and log M from Table VIII.

NOTE 2.   If log cot α is desired in (**A**), or log tan α in (**B**), recall that $\tan \alpha = \dfrac{1}{\cot \alpha}$.

Table Xa.   Auxiliary Table for S and T

To find S or T, subtract 10 *from the given entry.*

M	$S + 10$		M	$T + 10$		M	$T + 10$
0′ — 13′	6.46373		0′ — 26′	6.46373		131′ — 133′	6.46394
14′ — 42′	72		27′ — 39′	74		134′ — 136′	95
43′ — 58′	71		40′ — 48′	75		137′ — 139′	96
59′ — 71′	6.46370		49′ — 56′	6.46376		140′ — 142′	6.46397
72′ — 81′	69		57′ — 63′	77		143′ — 145′	98
82′ — 91′	68		64′ — 69′	78		146′ — 148′	99
92′ — 99′	6.46367		70′ — 74′	6.46379		149′ — 150′	6.46400
100′ — 107′	66		75′ — 80′	80		151′ — 153′	01
108′ — 115′	65		81′ — 85′	81		154′ — 156′	02
116′ — 121′	6.46364		86′ — 89′	6.46382		157′ — 158′	6.46403
122′ — 128′	63		90′ — 94′	83		159′ — 161′	04
129′ — 134′	62		95′ — 98′	84		162′ — 163′	05
135′ — 140′	6.46361		99′ — 102′	6.46385		164′ — 166′	6.46406
141′ — 146′	60		103′ — 106′	86		167′ — 168′	07
147′ — 151′	59		107′ — 110′	87		169′ — 171′	08
152′ — 157′	6.46358		111′ — 113′	6.46388		172′ — 173′	6.46409
158′ — 162′	57		114′ — 117′	89		174′ — 175′	10
163′ — 167′	56		118′ — 120′	90		176′ — 178′	11
168′ — 171′	6.46355		121′ — 124′	6.46391		179′ — 180′	6.46412
172′ — 176′	54		125′ — 127′	92		181′ — 182′	13
177′ — 180′	53		128′ — 130′	93		183′ — 184′	14

* For an explanation of these formulas, see page 176 of William L. Hart's *Plane Trigonometry,* or page 176 of William L. Hart's *Plane and Spherical Trigonometry,* or page 166 of William L. Hart's *College Trigonometry,* all published by D. C. Heath and Company.

↓				10 + log sin:			0°					
′	.0	.1	.2	.3	.4	.5	.6	.7	.8	.9	1.0	
0	5. ——	46373	76476	94085	*06579	*16270	*24188	*30882	*36682	*41797	*46373	59
1	6. 46373	50512	54291	57767	60985	63982	66785	69418	71900	74248	76476	58
2	6. 76476	78595	80615	82545	84394	86167	87870	89509	91088	92612	94085	57
3	6. 94085	95509	96888	98224	99520	*00779	*02003	*03193	*04351	*05479	*06579	56
4	7. 06579	07651	08698	09719	10718	11694	12648	13582	14497	15392	16270	55
5	7. 16270	17130	17973	18800	19612	20409	21191	21960	22715	23458	24188	54
6	7. 24188	24906	25612	26307	26991	27664	28327	28980	29623	30257	30882	53
7	7. 30882	31498	32106	32705	33296	33879	34454	35022	35582	36135	36682	52
8	7. 36682	37221	37754	38280	38800	39314	39822	40324	40821	41312	41797	51
9	7. 41797	42277	42751	43221	43685	44145	44600	45050	45495	45936	46373	50
10	7. 46373	46805	47233	47656	48076	48491	48903	49311	49715	50115	50512	49
11	7. 50512	50905	51294	51680	52063	52442	52818	53191	53561	53927	54291	48
12	7. 54291	54651	55009	55363	55715	56064	56410	56753	57094	57431	57767	47
13	7. 57767	58100	58430	58758	59083	59406	59726	60045	60360	60674	60985	46
14	7. 60985	61294	61601	61906	62209	62509	62808	63104	63399	63691	63982	45
15	7. 63982	64270	64557	64842	65125	65406	65685	65962	66238	66512	66784	44
16	7. 66784	67055	67324	67591	67857	68121	68383	68644	68903	69161	69417	43
17	7. 69417	69672	69925	70177	70427	70676	70924	71170	71414	71658	71900	42
18	7. 71900	72140	72380	72618	72854	73090	73324	73557	73788	74019	74248	41
19	7. 74248	74476	74703	74928	75153	75376	75599	75819	76039	76258	76475	40
20	7.7 6475	6692	6907	7122	7335	7548	7759	7969	8179	8387	8594	39
21	7.7 8594	8801	9006	9210	9414	9616	9818	*0018	*0218	*0417	*0615	38
22	7.8 0615	0812	1008	1203	1397	1591	1783	1975	2166	2356	2545	37
23	7.8 2545	2733	2921	3108	3294	3479	3663	3847	4030	4212	4393	36
24	7.8 4393	4574	4754	4933	5111	5289	5466	5642	5817	5992	6166	35
25	7.8 6166	6340	6512	6684	6856	7026	7196	7366	7534	7702	7870	34
26	7.8 7870	8036	8202	8368	8533	8697	8860	9023	9186	9347	9509	33
27	7.8 9509	9669	9829	9988	*0147	*0305	*0463	*0620	*0777	*0933	*1088	32
28	7.9 1088	1243	1397	1551	1704	1857	2009	2160	2311	2462	2612	31
29	7.9 2612	2761	2910	3059	3207	3354	3501	3648	3794	3939	4084	30
30	7.9 4084	4229	4373	4516	4659	4802	4944	5086	5227	5368	5508	29
31	7.9 5508	5648	5787	5926	6065	6203	6341	6478	6615	6751	6887	28
32	7.9 6887	7022	7158	7292	7426	7560	7694	7827	7959	8092	8223	27
33	7.9 8223	8355	8486	8616	8747	8876	9006	9135	9264	9392	9520	26
34	7.9 9520	9647	9775	9901	*0028	*0154	*0279	*0405	*0530	*0654	*0779	25
35	8.0 0779	0903	1026	1149	1272	1395	1517	1639	1760	1881	2002	24
36	8.0 2002	2123	2243	2362	2482	2601	2720	2838	2957	3074	3192	23
37	8.0 3192	3309	3426	3543	3659	3775	3891	4006	4121	4236	4350	22
38	8.0 4350	4464	4578	4692	4805	4918	5030	5143	5255	5367	5478	21
39	8.0 5478	5589	5700	5811	5921	6031	6141	6251	6360	6469	6578	20
40	8.0 6578	6686	6794	6902	7010	7117	7224	7331	7438	7544	7650	19
41	8.0 7650	7756	7861	7967	8072	8176	8281	8385	8489	8593	8696	18
42	8.0 8696	8800	8903	9006	9108	9210	9312	9414	9516	9617	9718	17
43	8.0 9718	9819	9920	*0020	*0120	*0220	*0320	*0420	*0519	*0618	*0717	16
44	8.1 0717	0815	0914	1012	1110	1207	1305	1402	1499	1596	1693	15
45	8.1 1693	1789	1885	1981	2077	2172	2268	2363	2458	2553	2647	14
46	8.1 2647	2741	2836	2929	3023	3117	3210	3303	3396	3489	3581	13
47	8.1 3581	3673	3765	3857	3949	4041	4132	4223	4314	4405	4495	12
48	8.1 4495	4586	4676	4766	4856	4945	5035	5124	5213	5302	5391	11
49	8.1 5391	5479	5568	5656	5744	5832	5919	6007	6094	6181	6268	10
50	8.1 6268	6355	6441	6528	6614	6700	6786	6872	6957	7043	7128	9
51	8.1 7128	7213	7298	7383	7467	7552	7636	7720	7804	7888	7971	8
52	8.1 7971	8055	8138	8221	8304	8387	8469	8552	8634	8716	8798	7
53	8.1 8798	8880	8962	9044	9125	9206	9287	9368	9449	9530	9610	6
54	8.1 9610	9691	9771	9851	9931	*0010	*0090	*0170	*0249	*0328	*0407	5
55	8.2 0407	0486	0565	0643	0722	0800	0878	0956	1034	1112	1189	4
56	8.2 1189	1267	1344	1422	1499	1576	1652	1729	1805	1882	1958	3
57	8.2 1958	2034	2110	2186	2262	2337	2413	2488	2563	2638	2713	2
58	8.2 2713	2788	2863	2937	3012	3086	3160	3234	3308	3382	3456	1
59	8.2 3456	3529	3603	3676	3749	3822	3895	3968	4041	4113	4186	0
	1.0	.9	.8	.7	.6	.5	.4	.3	.2	.1	.0	′

10 + log cos: 89°   ↑

✓					10 + log tan:		0°					
′	.0	.1	.2	.3	.4	.5	.6	.7	.8	.9	1.0	
0	5. ——	46373	76476	94085	*06579	*16270	*24188	*30882	*36682	*41797	*46373	59
1	6. 46373	50512	54291	57767	60985	63982	66785	69418	71900	74248	76476	58
2	6. 76476	78595	80615	82545	84394	86167	87870	89509	91088	92612	94085	57
3	6. 94085	95509	96888	98224	99521	*00779	*02003	*03193	*04351	*05479	*06579	56
4	7. 06579	07651	08698	09719	10718	11694	12648	13582	14497	15392	16270	55
5	7. 16270	17130	17973	18800	19612	20409	21191	21960	22715	23458	24188	54
6	7. 24188	24906	25612	26307	26991	27664	28327	28980	29624	30258	30882	53
7	7. 30882	31499	32106	32705	33296	33879	34454	35022	35582	36135	36682	52
8	7. 36682	37221	37754	38281	38801	39315	39823	40325	40821	41312	41797	51
9	7. 41797	42277	42751	43221	43686	44145	44600	45050	45495	45936	46373	50
10	7. 46373	46805	47233	47656	48076	48492	48903	49311	49715	50115	50512	49
11	7. 50512	50905	51295	51681	52063	52443	52819	53191	53561	53927	54291	48
12	7. 54291	54651	55009	55363	55715	56064	56410	56753	57094	57432	57767	47
13	7. 57767	58100	58430	58758	59083	59406	59727	60045	60361	60674	60986	46
14	7. 60986	61295	61602	61906	62209	62510	62808	63105	63399	63692	63982	45
15	7. 63982	64271	64557	64842	65125	65406	65685	65963	66239	66513	66785	44
16	7. 66785	67056	67324	67592	67857	68121	68384	68645	68904	69162	69418	43
17	7. 69418	69673	69926	70178	70428	70677	70924	71170	71415	71658	71900	42
18	7. 71900	72141	72380	72618	72855	73090	73324	73557	73789	74019	74248	41
19	7. 74248	74476	74703	74929	75153	75377	75599	75820	76040	76258	76476	40
20	7.7 6476	6693	6908	7123	7336	7549	7760	7970	8179	8388	8595	39
21	7.7 8595	8801	9007	9211	9415	9617	9819	*0019	*0219	*0418	*0615	38
22	7.8 0615	0812	1009	1204	1398	1591	1784	1976	2167	2357	2546	37
23	7.8 2546	2734	2922	3109	3295	3480	3664	3848	4031	4213	4394	36
24	7.8 4394	4575	4755	4934	5112	5290	5467	5643	5819	5993	6167	35
25	7.8 6167	6341	6513	6685	6857	7027	7197	7367	7535	7703	7871	34
26	7.8 7871	8037	8204	8369	8534	8698	8862	9025	9187	9349	9510	33
27	7.8 9510	9670	9830	9990	*0149	*0307	*0464	*0622	*0778	*0934	*1089	32
28	7.9 1089	1244	1398	1552	1705	1858	2010	2162	2313	2463	2613	31
29	7.9 2613	2763	2912	3060	3208	3356	3503	3649	3795	3941	4086	30
30	7.9 4086	4230	4374	4518	4661	4804	4946	5088	5229	5370	5510	29
31	7.9 5510	5650	5789	5928	6067	6205	6343	6480	6617	6753	6889	28
32	7.9 6889	7024	7159	7294	7428	7562	7696	7829	7961	8094	8225	27
33	7.9 8225	8357	8488	8618	8749	8878	9008	9137	9266	9394	9522	26
34	7.9 9522	9649	9777	9903	*0030	*0156	*0282	*0407	*0532	*0657	*0781	25
35	8.0 0781	0905	1028	1152	1274	1397	1519	1641	1762	1884	2004	24
36	8.0 2004	2125	2245	2365	2484	2604	2722	2841	2959	3077	3194	23
37	8.0 3194	3312	3429	3545	3661	3777	3893	4008	4124	4238	4353	22
38	8.0 4353	4467	4581	4694	4808	4921	5033	5146	5258	5369	5481	21
39	8.0 5481	5592	5703	5814	5924	6034	6144	6254	6363	6472	6581	20
40	8.0 6581	6689	6797	6905	7013	7120	7227	7334	7441	7547	7653	19
41	8.0 7653	7759	7864	7970	8075	8180	8284	8388	8492	8596	8700	18
42	8.0 8700	8803	8906	9009	9111	9214	9316	9418	9519	9621	9722	17
43	8.0 9722	9823	9923	*0024	*0124	*0224	*0324	*0423	*0522	*0621	*0720	16
44	8.1 0720	0819	0917	1015	1113	1211	1309	1406	1503	1600	1696	15
45	8.1 1696	1793	1889	1985	2081	2176	2272	2367	2462	2556	2651	14
46	8.1 2651	2745	2839	2933	3027	3121	3214	3307	3400	3493	3585	13
47	8.1 3585	3677	3770	3861	3953	4045	4136	4227	4318	4409	4500	12
48	8.1 4500	4590	4680	4770	4860	4950	5039	5128	5218	5306	5395	11
49	8.1 5395	5484	5572	5660	5748	5836	5924	6011	6099	6186	6273	10
50	8.1 6273	6359	6446	6533	6619	6705	6791	6877	6962	7048	7133	9
51	8.1 7133	7218	7303	7388	7472	7557	7641	7725	7809	7893	7976	8
52	8.1 7976	8060	8143	8226	8309	8392	8475	8557	8639	8722	8804	7
53	8.1 8804	8886	8967	9049	9130	9211	9293	9374	9454	9535	9616	6
54	8.1 9616	9696	9776	9856	9936	*0016	*0096	*0175	*0254	*0334	*0413	5
55	8.2 0413	0491	0570	0649	0727	0806	0884	0962	1040	1118	1195	4
56	8.2 1195	1273	1350	1427	1504	1581	1658	1735	1811	1888	1964	3
57	8.2 1964	2040	2116	2192	2268	2343	2419	2494	2569	2645	2720	2
58	8.2 2720	2794	2869	2944	3018	3092	3167	3241	3315	3388	3462	1
59	8.2 3462	3536	3609	3682	3756	3829	3902	3974	4047	4120	4192	0
	1.0	.9	.8	.7	.6	.5	.4	.3	.2	.1	.0	′

					10 + log cot:		89°					↑

↓	10 + log sin:						1°					
′	.0	.1	.2	.3	.4	.5	.6	.7	.8	.9	1.0	
0	8.2 4186	4258	4330	4402	4474	4546	4618	4689	4761	4832	4903	59
1	8.2 4903	4974	5045	5116	5187	5258	5328	5399	5469	5539	5609	58
2	8.2 5609	5679	5749	5819	5889	5958	6028	6097	6166	6235	6304	57
3	8.2 6304	6373	6442	6511	6579	6648	6716	6784	6852	6920	6988	56
4	8.2 6988	7056	7124	7191	7259	7326	7393	7460	7528	7595	7661	55
5	8.2 7661	7728	7795	7861	7928	7994	8060	8127	8193	8258	8324	54
6	8.2 8324	8390	8456	8521	8587	8652	8717	8782	8848	8912	8977	53
7	8.2 8977	9042	9107	9171	9236	9300	9364	9429	9493	9557	9621	52
8	8.2 9621	9684	9748	9812	9875	9939	*0002	*0065	*0129	*0192	*0255	51
9	8.3 0255	0317	0380	0443	0506	0568	0631	0693	0755	0817	0879	50
10	8.3 0879	0941	1003	1065	1127	1188	1250	1311	1373	1434	1495	49
11	8.3 1495	1556	1618	1678	1739	1800	1861	1921	1982	2042	2103	48
12	8.3 2103	2163	2223	2283	2343	2403	2463	2523	2583	2642	2702	47
13	8.3 2702	2761	2820	2880	2939	2998	3057	3116	3175	3234	3292	46
14	8.3 3292	3351	3410	3468	3527	3585	3643	3701	3759	3817	3875	45
15	8.3 3875	3933	3991	4049	4106	4164	4221	4279	4336	4393	4450	44
16	8.3 4450	4508	4565	4621	4678	4735	4792	4849	4905	4962	5018	43
17	8.3 5018	5074	5131	5187	5243	5299	5355	5411	5467	5523	5578	42
18	8.3 5578	5634	5690	5745	5800	5856	5911	5966	6021	6076	6131	41
19	8.3 6131	6186	6241	6296	6351	6405	6460	6515	6569	6623	6678	40
20	8.3 6678	6732	6786	6840	6894	6948	7002	7056	7110	7163	7217	39
21	8.3 7217	7271	7324	7378	7431	7484	7538	7591	7644	7697	7750	38
22	8.3 7750	7803	7856	7908	7961	8014	8066	8119	8171	8224	8276	37
23	8.3 8276	8328	8381	8433	8485	8537	8589	8641	8693	8744	8796	36
24	8.3 8796	8848	8899	8951	9002	9054	9105	9157	9208	9259	9310	35
25	8.3 9310	9361	9412	9463	9514	9565	9616	9666	9717	9767	9818	34
26	8.3 9818	9868	9919	9969	*0019	*0070	*0120	*0170	*0220	*0270	*0320	33
27	8.4 0320	0370	0420	0469	0519	0569	0618	0668	0717	0767	0816	32
28	8.4 0816	0865	0915	0964	1013	1062	1111	1160	1209	1258	1307	31
29	8.4 1307	1356	1404	1453	1501	1550	1598	1647	1695	1744	1792	30
30	8.4 1792	1840	1888	1936	1984	2032	2080	2128	2176	2224	2272	29
31	8.4 2272	2319	2367	2415	2462	2510	2557	2604	2652	2699	2746	28
32	8.4 2746	2793	2840	2888	2935	2982	3028	3075	3122	3169	3216	27
33	8.4 3216	3262	3309	3355	3402	3448	3495	3541	3588	3634	3680	26
34	8.4 3680	3726	3772	3818	3864	3910	3956	4002	4048	4094	4139	25
35	8.4 4139	4185	4231	4276	4322	4367	4413	4458	4504	4549	4594	24
36	8.4 4594	4639	4684	4730	4775	4820	4865	4910	4954	4999	5044	23
37	8.4 5044	5089	5133	5178	5223	5267	5312	5356	5401	5445	5489	22
38	8.4 5489	5534	5578	5622	5666	5710	5754	5798	5842	5886	5930	21
39	8.4 5930	5974	6018	6061	6105	6149	6192	6236	6280	6323	6366	20
40	8.4 6366	6410	6453	6497	6540	6583	6626	6669	6712	6755	6799	19
41	8.4 6799	6841	6884	6927	6970	7013	7056	7098	7141	7184	7226	18
42	8.4 7226	7269	7311	7354	7396	7439	7481	7523	7565	7608	7650	17
43	8.4 7650	7692	7734	7776	7818	7860	7902	7944	7986	8028	8069	16
44	8.4 8069	8111	8153	8194	8236	8278	8319	8361	8402	8443	8485	15
45	8.4 8485	8526	8567	8609	8650	8691	8732	8773	8814	8855	8896	14
46	8.4 8896	8937	8978	9019	9060	9101	9141	9182	9223	9263	9304	13
47	8.4 9304	9345	9385	9426	9466	9506	9547	9587	9627	9668	9708	12
48	8.4 9708	9748	9788	9828	9868	9908	9948	9988	*0028	*0068	*0108	11
49	8.5 0108	0148	0188	0227	0267	0307	0346	0386	0425	0465	0504	10
50	8.5 0504	0544	0583	0623	0662	0701	0741	0780	0819	0858	0897	9
51	8.5 0897	0936	0976	1015	1054	1092	1131	1170	1209	1248	1287	8
52	8.5 1287	1325	1364	1403	1442	1480	1519	1557	1596	1634	1673	7
53	8.5 1673	1711	1749	1788	1826	1864	1903	1941	1979	2017	2055	6
54	8.5 2055	2093	2131	2169	2207	2245	2283	2321	2359	2397	2434	5
55	8.5 2434	2472	2510	2547	2585	2623	2660	2698	2735	2773	2810	4
56	8.5 2810	2848	2885	2922	2960	2997	3034	3071	3109	3146	3183	3
57	8.5 3183	3220	3257	3294	3331	3368	3405	3442	3479	3515	3552	2
58	8.5 3552	3589	3626	3663	3699	3736	3772	3809	3846	3882	3919	1
59	8.5 3919	3955	3992	4028	4064	4101	4137	4173	4210	4246	4282	0
	1.0	.9	.8	.7	.6	.5	.4	.3	.2	.1	.0	′

10 + log cos: 88°

↓	10 + log tan:					1°						
′	.0	.1	.2	.3	.4	.5	.6	.7	.8	.9	1.0	
0	8.2 4192	4264	4337	4409	4481	4553	4624	4696	4767	4839	4910	59
1	8.2 4910	4981	5052	5123	5194	5265	5335	5406	5476	5546	5616	58
2	8.2 5616	5686	5756	5826	5896	5965	6035	6104	6173	6243	6312	57
3	8.2 6312	6380	6449	6518	6586	6655	6723	6792	6860	6928	6996	56
4	8.2 6996	7063	7131	7199	7266	7334	7401	7468	7535	7602	7669	**55**
5	8.2 7669	7736	7803	7869	7936	8002	8068	8134	8201	8266	8332	54
6	8.2 8332	8398	8464	8529	8595	8660	8725	8791	8856	8921	8986	53
7	8.2 8986	9050	9115	9180	9244	9309	9373	9437	9501	9565	9629	52
8	8.2 9629	9693	9757	9820	9884	9947	*0011	*0074	*0137	*0200	*0263	51
9	8.3 0263	0326	0389	0452	0514	0577	0639	0702	0764	0826	0888	**50**
10	8.3 0888	0950	1012	1074	1136	1198	1259	1321	1382	1443	1505	49
11	8.3 1505	1566	1627	1688	1749	1809	1870	1931	1991	2052	2112	48
12	8.3 2112	2173	2233	2293	2353	2413	2473	2533	2592	2652	2711	47
13	8.3 2711	2771	2830	2890	2949	3008	3067	3126	3185	3244	3302	46
14	8.3 3302	3361	3420	3478	3537	3595	3653	3712	3770	3828	3886	**45**
15	8.3 3886	3944	4001	4059	4117	4174	4232	4289	4347	4404	4461	44
16	8.3 4461	4518	4575	4632	4689	4746	4803	4859	4916	4972	5029	43
17	8.3 5029	5085	5142	5198	5254	5310	5366	5422	5478	5534	5590	42
18	8.3 5590	5645	5701	5756	5812	5867	5922	5978	6033	6088	6143	41
19	8.3 6143	6198	6253	6308	6362	6417	6472	6526	6581	6635	6689	**40**
20	8.3 6689	6744	6798	6852	6906	6960	7014	7068	7122	7175	7229	39
21	8.3 7229	7283	7336	7390	7443	7497	7550	7603	7656	7709	7762	38
22	8.3 7762	7815	7868	7921	7974	8026	8079	8132	8184	8236	8289	37
23	8.3 8289	8341	8393	8446	8498	8550	8602	8654	8706	8757	8809	36
24	8.3 8809	8861	8913	8964	9016	9067	9118	9170	9221	9272	9323	**35**
25	8.3 9323	9374	9425	9476	9527	9578	9629	9680	9730	9781	9832	34
26	8.3 9832	9882	9932	9983	*0033	*0083	*0134	*0184	*0234	*0284	*0334	33
27	8.4 0334	0384	0434	0483	0533	0583	0632	0682	0732	0781	0830	32
28	8.4 0830	0880	0929	0978	1027	1077	1126	1175	1224	1272	1321	31
29	8.4 1321	1370	1419	1468	1516	1565	1613	1662	1710	1758	1807	**30**
30	8.4 1807	1855	1903	1951	1999	2048	2095	2143	2191	2239	2287	29
31	8.4 2287	2335	2382	2430	2477	2525	2572	2620	2667	2715	2762	28
32	8.4 2762	2809	2856	2903	2950	2997	3044	3091	3138	3185	3232	27
33	8.4 3232	3278	3325	3371	3418	3464	3511	3557	3604	3650	3696	26
34	8.4 3696	3742	3789	3835	3881	3927	3973	4019	4064	4110	4156	**25**
35	8.4 4156	4202	4247	4293	4339	4384	4430	4475	4520	4566	4611	24
36	8.4 4611	4656	4701	4747	4792	4837	4882	4927	4972	5016	5061	23
37	8.4 5061	5106	5151	5195	5240	5285	5329	5374	5418	5463	5507	22
38	8.4 5507	5551	5596	5640	5684	5728	5772	5816	5860	5904	5948	21
39	8.4 5948	5992	6036	6080	6123	6167	6211	6254	6298	6341	6385	**20**
40	8.4 6385	6428	6472	6515	6558	6602	6645	6688	6731	6774	6817	19
41	8.4 6817	6860	6903	6946	6989	7032	7075	7117	7160	7203	7245	18
42	8.4 7245	7288	7330	7373	7415	7458	7500	7543	7585	7627	7669	17
43	8.4 7669	7712	7754	7796	7838	7880	7922	7964	8006	8047	8089	16
44	8.4 8089	8131	8173	8214	8256	8298	8339	8381	8422	8464	8505	**15**
45	8.4 8505	8546	8588	8629	8670	8711	8753	8794	8835	8876	8917	14
46	8.4 8917	8958	8999	9040	9081	9121	9162	9203	9244	9284	9325	13
47	8.4 9325	9366	9406	9447	9487	9528	9568	9608	9649	9689	9729	12
48	8.4 9729	9769	9810	9850	9890	9930	9970	*0010	*0050	*0090	*0130	11
49	8.5 0130	0170	0209	0249	0289	0329	0368	0408	0448	0487	0527	**10**
50	8.5 0527	0566	0606	0645	0684	0724	0763	0802	0842	0881	0920	9
51	8.5 0920	0959	0998	1037	1076	1115	1154	1193	1232	1271	1310	8
52	8.5 1310	1349	1387	1426	1465	1503	1542	1581	1619	1658	1696	7
53	8.5 1696	1735	1773	1811	1850	1888	1926	1964	2003	2041	2079	6
54	8.5 2079	2117	2155	2193	2231	2269	2307	2345	2383	2421	2459	**5**
55	8.5 2459	2496	2534	2572	2610	2647	2685	2722	2760	2797	2835	4
56	8.5 2835	2872	2910	2947	2985	3022	3059	3096	3134	3171	3208	3
57	8.5 3208	3245	3282	3319	3356	3393	3430	3467	3504	3541	3578	2
58	8.5 3578	3615	3651	3688	3725	3762	3798	3835	3872	3908	3945	1
59	8.5 3945	3981	4018	4054	4091	4127	4163	4200	4236	4272	4308	**0**
	1.0	.9	.8	.7	.6	.5	.4	.3	.2	.1	.0	′
	10 + log cot:					88°						↑

→	0°		1°		2°		3°		4°		
′	Sin	Cos	Sin	Cos	Sin	Cos	Sin	Cos	Sin	Cos	
0	.00000	1.0000	.01745	.99985	.03490	.99939	.05234	.99863	.06976	.99756	60
1	029	000	774	984	519	938	263	861	.07005	754	59
2	058	000	803	984	548	937	292	860	034	752	58
3	087	000	832	983	577	936	321	858	063	750	57
4	116	000	862	983	606	935	350	857	092	748	56
5	.00145	1.0000	.01891	.99982	.03635	.99934	.05379	.99855	.07121	.99746	55
6	175	000	920	982	664	933	408	854	150	744	54
7	204	000	949	981	693	932	437	852	179	742	53
8	233	000	.01978	980	723	931	466	851	208	740	52
9	262	000	.02007	980	752	930	495	849	237	738	51
10	.00291	1.0000	.02036	.99979	.03781	.99929	.05524	.99847	.07266	.99736	50
11	320	.99999	065	979	810	927	553	846	295	734	49
12	349	999	094	978	839	926	582	844	324	731	48
13	378	999	123	977	868	925	611	842	353	729	47
14	407	999	152	977	897	924	640	841	382	727	46
15	.00436	.99999	.02181	.99976	.03926	.99923	.05669	.99839	.07411	.99725	45
16	465	999	211	976	955	922	698	838	440	723	44
17	495	999	240	975	.03984	921	727	836	469	721	43
18	524	999	269	974	.04013	919	756	834	498	719	42
19	553	998	298	974	042	918	785	833	527	716	41
20	.00582	.99998	.02327	.99973	.04071	.99917	.05814	.99831	.07556	.99714	40
21	611	998	356	972	100	916	844	829	585	712	39
22	640	998	385	972	129	915	873	827	614	710	38
23	669	998	414	971	159	913	902	826	643	708	37
24	698	998	443	970	188	912	931	824	672	705	36
25	.00727	.99997	.02472	.99969	.04217	.99911	.05960	.99822	.07701	.99703	35
26	756	997	501	969	246	910	.05989	821	730	701	34
27	785	997	530	968	275	909	.06018	819	759	699	33
28	814	997	560	967	304	907	047	817	788	696	32
29	844	996	589	966	333	906	076	815	817	694	31
30	.00873	.99996	.02618	.99966	.04362	.99905	.06105	.99813	.07846	.99692	30
31	902	996	647	965	391	904	134	812	875	689	29
32	931	996	676	964	420	902	163	810	904	687	28
33	960	995	705	963	449	901	192	808	933	685	27
34	.00989	995	734	963	478	900	221	806	962	683	26
35	.01018	.99995	.02763	.99962	.04507	.99898	.06250	.99804	.07991	.99680	25
36	047	995	792	961	536	897	279	803	.08020	678	24
37	076	994	821	960	565	896	308	801	049	676	23
38	105	994	850	959	594	894	337	799	078	673	22
39	134	994	879	959	623	893	366	797	107	671	21
40	.01164	.99993	.02908	.99958	.04653	.99892	.06395	.99795	.08136	.99668	20
41	193	993	938	957	682	890	424	793	165	666	19
42	222	993	967	956	711	889	453	792	194	664	18
43	251	992	.02996	955	740	888	482	790	223	661	17
44	280	992	.03025	954	769	886	511	788	252	659	16
45	.01309	.99991	.03054	.99953	.04798	.99885	.06540	.99786	.08281	.99657	15
46	338	991	083	952	827	883	569	784	310	654	14
47	367	991	112	952	856	882	598	782	339	652	13
48	396	990	141	951	885	881	627	780	368	649	12
49	425	990	170	950	914	879	656	778	397	647	11
50	.01454	.99989	.03199	.99949	.04943	.99878	.06685	.99776	.08426	.99644	10
51	483	989	228	948	.04972	876	714	774	455	642	9
52	513	989	257	947	.05001	875	743	772	484	639	8
53	542	988	286	946	030	873	773	770	513	637	7
54	571	988	316	945	059	872	802	768	542	635	6
55	.01600	.99987	.03345	.99944	.05088	.99870	.06831	.99766	.08571	.99632	5
56	629	987	374	943	117	869	860	764	600	630	4
57	658	986	403	942	146	867	889	762	629	627	3
58	687	986	432	941	175	866	918	760	658	625	2
59	716	985	461	940	205	864	947	758	687	622	1
60	.01745	.99985	.03490	.99939	.05234	.99863	.06976	.99756	.08716	.99619	0
	Cos	Sin	Cos	Sin	Cos	Sin	Cos	Sin	Cos	Sin	′
	89°		88°		87°		86°		85°		←

XI. FIVE–PLACE VALUES: TANGENT AND COTANGENT

→	0°		1°		2°		3°		4°		
′	Tan	Cot	Tan	Cot	Tan	Cot	Tan	Cot	Tan	Cot	
0	.00000	——	.01746	57.290	.03492	28.636	.05241	19.081	.06993	14.301	60
1	029	3437.7	775	56.351	521	.399	270	18.976	.07022	.241	59
2	058	1718.9	804	55.442	550	28.166	299	.871	051	.182	58
3	087	1145.9	833	54.561	579	27.937	328	.768	080	.124	57
4	116	859.44	862	53.709	609	.712	357	.666	110	.065	56
5	.00145	687.55	.01891	52.882	.03638	27.490	.05387	18.564	.07139	14.008	55
6	175	572.96	920	52.081	667	.271	416	.464	168	13.951	54
7	204	491.11	949	51.303	696	27.057	445	.366	197	.894	53
8	233	429.72	.01978	50.549	725	26.845	474	.268	227	.838	52
9	262	381.97	.02007	49.816	754	.637	503	.171	256	.782	51
10	.00291	343.77	.02036	49.104	.03783	26.432	.05533	18.075	.07285	13.727	50
11	320	312.52	066	48.412	812	.230	562	17.980	314	.672	49
12	349	286.48	095	47.740	842	26.031	591	.886	344	.617	48
13	378	264.44	124	47.085	871	25.835	620	.793	373	.563	47
14	407	245.55	153	46.449	900	.642	649	.702	402	.510	46
15	.00436	229.18	.02182	45.829	.03929	25.452	05678	17.611	.07431	13.457	45
16	465	214.86	211	45.226	958	.264	708	.521	461	.404	44
17	495	202.22	240	44.639	.03987	25.080	737	.431	490	.352	43
18	524	190.98	269	44.066	.04016	24.898	766	.343	519	.300	42
19	553	180.93	298	43.508	046	.719	795	.256	548	.248	41
20	.00582	171.89	.02328	42.964	.04075	24.542	.05824	17.169	.07578	13.197	40
21	611	163.70	357	42.433	104	.368	854	17.084	607	.146	39
22	640	156.26	386	41.916	133	.196	883	16.999	636	.096	38
23	669	149.47	415	41.411	162	24.026	912	.915	665	13.046	37
24	698	143.24	444	40.917	191	23.859	941	.832	695	12.996	36
25	.00727	137.51	.02473	40.436	.04220	23.695	.05970	16.750	.07724	12.947	35
26	756	132.22	502	39.965	250	.532	.05999	.668	753	.898	34
27	785	127.32	531	39.506	279	.372	.06029	.587	782	.850	33
28	815	122.77	560	39.057	308	.214	058	.507	812	.801	32
29	844	118.54	589	38.618	337	23.058	087	.428	841	.754	31
30	.00873	114.59	.02619	38.188	.04366	22.904	.06116	16.350	.07870	12.706	30
31	902	110.89	648	37.769	395	.752	145	.272	899	.659	29
32	931	107.43	677	37.358	424	.602	175	.195	929	.612	28
33	960	104.17	706	36.956	454	.454	204	.119	958	.566	27
34	.00989	101.11	735	36.563	483	.308	233	16.043	.07987	.520	26
35	.01018	98.218	.02764	36.178	.04512	22.164	.06262	15.969	.08017	12.474	25
36	047	95.489	793	35.801	541	22.022	291	.895	046	.429	24
37	076	92.908	822	35.431	570	21.881	321	.821	075	.384	23
38	105	90.463	851	35.070	599	.743	350	.748	104	.339	22
39	135	88.144	881	34.715	628	.606	379	.676	134	.295	21
40	.01164	85.940	.02910	34.368	.04658	21.470	.06408	15.605	.08163	12.251	20
41	193	83.844	939	34.027	687	.337	438	.534	192	.207	19
42	222	81.847	968	33.694	716	.205	467	.464	221	.163	18
43	251	79.943	.02997	33.366	745	21.075	496	.394	251	.120	17
44	280	78.126	.03026	33.045	774	20.946	525	.325	280	.077	16
45	.01309	76.390	.03055	32.730	.04803	20.819	.06554	15.257	.08309	12.035	15
46	338	74.729	084	32.421	833	.693	584	.189	339	11.992	14
47	367	73.139	114	32.118	862	.569	613	.122	368	.950	13
48	396	71.615	143	31.821	891	.446	642	15.056	397	.909	12
49	425	70.153	172	31.528	920	.325	671	14.990	427	.867	11
50	.01455	68.750	.03201	31.242	.04949	20.206	.06700	14.924	.08456	11.826	10
51	484	67.402	230	30.960	.04978	20.087	730	.860	485	.785	9
52	513	66.105	259	30.683	.05007	19.970	759	.795	514	.745	8
53	542	64.858	288	30.412	037	.855	788	.732	544	.705	7
54	571	63.657	317	30.145	066	.740	817	.669	573	.664	6
55	.01600	62.499	.03346	29.882	.05095	19.627	.06847	14.606	.08602	11.625	5
56	629	61.383	376	29.624	124	.516	876	.544	632	.585	4
57	658	60.306	405	29.371	153	.405	905	.482	661	.546	3
58	687	59.266	434	29.122	182	.296	934	.421	690	.507	2
59	716	58.261	463	28.877	212	.188	963	.361	720	.468	1
60	.01746	57.290	.03492	28.636	.05241	19.081	.06993	14.301	.08749	11.430	0
	Cot	Tan	Cot	Tan	Cot	Tan	Cot	Tan	Cot	Tan	′
	89°		88°		87°		86°		85°		←

'	5° Sin	5° Cos	6° Sin	6° Cos	7° Sin	7° Cos	8° Sin	8° Cos	9° Sin	9° Cos	
0	.08716	.99619	.10453	.99452	.12187	.99255	.13917	.99027	.15643	.98769	60
1	745	617	482	449	216	251	946	023	672	764	59
2	774	614	511	446	245	248	.13975	019	701	760	58
3	803	612	540	443	274	244	.14004	015	730	755	57
4	831	609	569	440	302	240	033	011	758	751	56
5	.08860	.99607	.10597	.99437	.12331	.99237	.14061	.99006	.15787	.98746	55
6	889	604	626	434	360	233	090	.99002	816	741	54
7	918	602	655	431	389	230	119	.98998	845	737	53
8	947	599	684	428	418	226	148	994	873	732	52
9	.08976	596	713	424	447	222	177	990	902	728	51
10	.09005	.99594	.10742	.99421	.12476	.99219	.14205	.98986	.15931	.98723	50
11	034	591	771	418	504	215	234	982	959	718	49
12	063	588	800	415	533	211	263	978	.15988	714	48
13	092	586	829	412	562	208	292	973	.16017	709	47
14	121	583	858	409	591	204	320	969	046	704	46
15	.09150	.99580	.10887	.99406	.12620	.99200	.14349	.98965	.16074	.98700	45
16	179	578	916	402	649	197	378	961	103	695	44
17	208	575	945	399	678	193	407	957	132	690	43
18	237	572	.10973	396	706	189	436	953	160	686	42
19	266	570	.11002	393	735	186	464	948	189	681	41
20	.09295	.99567	.11031	.99390	.12764	.99182	.14493	.98944	.16218	.98676	40
21	324	564	060	386	793	178	522	940	246	671	39
22	353	562	089	383	822	175	551	936	275	667	38
23	382	559	118	380	851	171	580	931	304	662	37
24	411	556	147	377	880	167	608	927	333	657	36
25	.09440	.99553	.11176	.99374	.12908	.99163	.14637	.98923	.16361	.98652	35
26	469	551	205	370	937	160	666	919	390	648	34
27	498	548	234	367	966	156	695	914	419	643	33
28	527	545	263	364	.12995	152	723	910	447	638	32
29	556	542	291	360	.13024	148	752	906	476	633	31
30	.09585	.99540	.11320	.99357	.13053	.99144	.14781	.98902	.16505	.98629	30
31	614	537	349	354	081	141	810	897	533	624	29
32	642	534	378	351	110	137	838	893	562	619	28
33	671	531	407	347	139	133	867	889	591	614	27
34	700	528	436	344	168	129	896	884	620	609	26
35	.09729	.99526	.11465	.99341	.13197	.99125	.14925	.98880	.16648	.98604	25
36	758	523	494	337	226	122	954	876	677	600	24
37	787	520	523	334	254	118	.14982	871	706	595	23
38	816	517	552	331	283	114	.15011	867	734	590	22
39	845	514	580	327	312	110	040	863	763	585	21
40	.09874	.99511	.11609	.99324	.13341	.99106	.15069	.98858	.16792	.98580	20
41	903	508	638	320	370	102	097	854	820	575	19
42	932	506	667	317	399	098	126	849	849	570	18
43	961	503	696	314	427	094	155	845	878	565	17
44	.09990	500	725	310	456	091	184	841	906	561	16
45	.10019	.99497	.11754	.99307	.13485	.99087	.15212	.98836	.16935	.98556	15
46	048	494	783	303	514	083	241	832	964	551	14
47	077	491	812	300	543	079	270	827	.16992	546	13
48	106	488	840	297	572	075	299	823	.17021	541	12
49	135	485	869	293	600	071	327	818	050	536	11
50	.10164	.99482	.11898	.99290	.13629	.99067	.15356	.98814	.17078	.98531	10
51	192	479	927	286	658	063	385	809	107	526	9
52	221	476	956	283	687	059	414	805	136	521	8
53	250	473	.11985	279	716	055	442	800	164	516	7
54	279	470	.12014	276	744	051	471	796	193	511	6
55	.10308	.99467	.12043	.99272	.13773	.99047	.15500	.98791	.17222	.98506	5
56	337	464	071	269	802	043	529	787	250	501	4
57	366	461	100	265	831	039	557	782	279	496	3
58	395	458	129	262	860	035	586	778	308	491	2
59	424	455	158	258	889	031	615	773	336	486	1
60	.10453	.99452	.12187	.99255	.13917	.99027	.15643	.98769	.17365	.98481	0
	Cos	Sin	Cos	Sin	Cos	Sin	Cos	Sin	Cos	Sin	'
	84°		83°		82°		81°		80°		←

XI. FIVE–PLACE VALUES: TANGENT AND COTANGENT

→	5°		6°		7°		8°		9°		
′	Tan	Cot	Tan	Cot	Tan	Cot	Tan	Cot	Tan	Cot	
0	.08749	11.430	.10510	9.5144	.12278	8.1443	.14054	7.1154	.15838	6.3138	60
1	778	.392	540	.4878	308	.1248	084	.1004	868	.3019	59
2	807	.354	569	.4614	338	.1054	113	.0855	898	.2901	58
3	837	.316	599	.4352	367	.0860	143	.0706	928	.2783	57
4	866	.279	628	.4090	397	.0667	173	.0558	958	.2666	56
5	.08895	11.242	.10657	9.3831	.12426	8.0476	.14202	7.0410	.15988	6.2549	55
6	925	.205	687	.3572	456	.0285	232	.0264	.16017	.2432	54
7	954	.168	716	.3315	485	8.0095	262	7.0117	047	.2316	53
8	.08983	.132	746	.3060	515	7.9906	291	6.9972	077	.2200	52
9	.09013	.095	775	.2806	544	.9718	321	.9827	107	.2085	51
10	.09042	11.059	.10805	9.2553	.12574	7.9530	.14351	6.9682	.16137	6.1970	50
11	071	11.024	834	.2302	603	.9344	381	.9538	167	.1856	49
12	101	10.988	863	.2052	633	.9158	410	.9395	196	.1742	48
13	130	.953	893	.1803	662	.8973	440	.9252	226	.1628	47
14	159	.918	922	.1555	692	.8789	470	.9110	256	.1515	46
15	.09189	10.883	.10952	9.1309	.12722	7.8606	.14499	6.8969	.16286	6.1402	45
16	218	.848	.10981	.1065	751	.8424	529	.8828	316	.1290	44
17	247	.814	.11011	.0821	781	.8243	559	.8687	346	.1178	43
18	277	.780	040	.0579	810	.8062	588	.8548	376	.1066	42
19	306	.746	070	.0338	840	.7882	618	.8408	405	.0955	41
20	.09335	10.712	.11099	9.0098	.12869	7.7704	.14648	6.8269	.16435	6.0844	40
21	365	.678	128	8.9860	899	.7525	678	.8131	465	.0734	39
22	394	.645	158	.9623	929	.7348	707	.7994	495	.0624	38
23	423	.612	187	.9387	958	.7171	737	.7856	525	.0514	37
24	453	.579	217	.9152	.12988	.6996	767	.7720	555	.0405	36
25	.09482	10.546	.11246	8.8919	.13017	7.6821	.14796	6.7584	.16585	6.0296	35
26	511	.514	276	.8686	047	.6647	826	.7448	615	.0188	34
27	541	.481	305	.8455	076	.6473	856	.7313	645	6.0080	33
28	570	.449	335	.8225	106	.6301	886	.7179	674	5.9972	32
29	600	.417	364	.7996	136	.6129	915	.7045	704	.9865	31
30	.09629	10.385	.11394	8.7769	.13165	7.5958	.14945	6.6912	.16734	5.9758	30
31	658	.354	423	.7542	195	.5787	.14975	.6779	764	.9651	29
32	688	.322	452	.7317	224	.5618	.15005	.6646	794	.9545	28
33	717	.291	482	.7093	254	.5449	034	.6514	824	.9439	27
34	746	.260	511	.6870	284	.5281	064	.6383	854	.9333	26
35	.09776	10.229	.11541	8.6648	.13313	7.5113	.15094	6.6252	.16884	5.9228	25
36	805	.199	570	.6427	343	.4947	124	.6122	914	.9124	24
37	834	.168	600	.6208	372	.4781	153	.5992	944	.9019	23
38	864	.138	629	.5989	402	.4615	183	.5863	.16974	.8915	22
39	893	.108	659	.5772	432	.4451	213	.5734	.17004	.8811	21
40	.09923	10.078	.11688	8.5555	.13461	7.4287	.15243	6.5606	.17033	5.8708	20
41	952	.048	718	.5340	491	.4124	272	.5478	063	.8605	19
42	.09981	10.019	747	.5126	521	.3962	302	.5350	093	.8502	18
43	.10011	9.9893	777	.4913	550	.3800	332	.5223	123	.8400	17
44	040	.9601	806	.4701	580	.3639	362	.5097	153	.8298	16
45	.10069	9.9310	.11836	8.4490	.13609	7.3479	.15391	6.4971	.17183	5.8197	15
46	099	.9021	865	.4280	639	.3319	421	.4846	213	.8095	14
47	128	.8734	895	.4071	669	.3160	451	.4721	243	.7994	13
48	158	.8448	924	.3863	698	.3002	481	.4596	273	.7894	12
49	187	.8164	954	.3656	728	.2844	511	.4472	303	.7794	11
50	.10216	9.7882	.11983	8.3450	.13758	7.2687	.15540	6.4348	.17333	5.7694	10
51	246	.7601	.12013	.3245	787	.2531	570	.4225	363	.7594	9
52	275	.7322	042	.3041	817	.2375	600	.4103	393	.7495	8
53	305	.7044	072	.2838	846	.2220	630	.3980	423	.7396	7
54	334	.6768	101	.2636	876	.2066	660	.3859	453	.7297	6
55	.10363	9.6493	.12131	8.2434	.13906	7.1912	.15689	6.3737	.17483	5.7199	5
56	393	.6220	160	.2234	935	.1759	719	.3617	513	.7101	4
57	422	.5949	190	.2035	965	.1607	749	.3496	543	.7004	3
58	452	.5679	219	.1837	.13995	.1455	779	.3376	573	.6906	2
59	481	.5411	249	.1640	.14024	.1304	809	.3257	603	.6809	1
60	.10510	9.5144	.12278	8.1443	.14054	7.1154	.15838	6.3138	.17633	5.6713	0
	Cot	Tan	Cot	Tan	Cot	Tan	Cot	Tan	Cot	Tan	′
	84°		83°		82°		81°		80°		←

[91]

XI. FIVE–PLACE VALUES: SINE AND COSINE

→	10°		11°		12°		13°		14°		
′	Sin	Cos	Sin	Cos	Sin	Cos	Sin	Cos	Sin	Cos	
0	.17365	.98481	.19081	.98163	.20791	.97815	.22495	.97437	.24192	.97030	60
1	393	476	109	157	820	809	523	430	220	023	59
2	422	471	138	152	848	803	552	424	249	015	58
3	451	466	167	146	877	797	580	417	277	008	57
4	479	461	195	140	905	791	608	411	305	.97001	56
5	.17508	.98455	.19224	.98135	.20933	.97784	.22637	.97404	.24333	.96994	55
6	537	450	252	129	962	778	665	398	362	987	54
7	565	445	281	124	.20990	772	693	391	390	980	53
8	594	440	309	118	.21019	766	722	384	418	973	52
9	623	435	338	112	047	760	750	378	446	966	51
10	.17651	.98430	.19366	.98107	.21076	.97754	.22778	.97371	.24474	.96959	50
11	680	425	395	101	104	748	807	365	503	952	49
12	708	420	423	096	132	742	835	358	531	945	48
13	737	414	452	090	161	735	863	351	559	937	47
14	766	409	481	084	189	729	892	345	587	930	46
15	.17794	.98404	.19509	.98079	.21218	.97723	.22920	.97338	.24615	.96923	45
16	823	399	538	073	246	717	948	331	644	916	44
17	852	394	566	067	275	711	.22977	325	672	909	43
18	880	389	595	061	303	705	.23005	318	700	902	42
19	909	383	623	056	331	698	033	311	728	894	41
20	.17937	.98378	.19652	.98050	.21360	.97692	.23062	.97304	.24756	.96887	40
21	966	373	680	044	388	686	090	298	784	880	39
22	.17995	368	709	039	417	680	118	291	813	873	38
23	.18023	362	737	033	445	673	146	284	841	866	37
24	052	357	766	027	474	667	175	278	869	858	36
25	.18081	.98352	.19794	.98021	.21502	.97661	.23203	.97271	.24897	.96851	35
26	109	347	823	016	530	655	231	264	925	844	34
27	138	341	851	010	559	648	260	257	954	837	33
28	166	336	880	.98004	587	642	288	251	.24982	829	32
29	195	331	908	.97998	616	636	316	244	.25010	822	31
30	.18224	.98325	.19937	.97992	.21644	.97630	.23345	.97237	.25038	.96815	30
31	252	320	965	987	672	623	373	230	066	807	29
32	281	315	.19994	981	701	617	401	223	094	800	28
33	309	310	.20022	975	729	611	429	217	122	793	27
34	338	304	051	969	758	604	458	210	151	786	26
35	.18367	.98299	.20079	.97963	.21786	.97598	.23486	.97203	.25179	.96778	25
36	395	294	108	958	814	592	514	196	207	771	24
37	424	288	136	952	843	585	542	189	235	764	23
38	452	283	165	946	871	579	571	182	263	756	22
39	481	277	193	940	899	573	599	176	291	749	21
40	.18509	.98272	.20222	.97934	.21928	.97566	.23627	.97169	.25320	.96742	20
41	538	267	250	928	956	560	656	162	348	734	19
42	567	261	279	922	.21985	553	684	155	376	727	18
43	595	256	307	916	.22013	547	712	148	404	719	17
44	624	250	336	910	041	541	740	141	432	712	16
45	.18652	.98245	.20364	.97905	.22070	.97534	.23769	.97134	.25460	.96705	15
46	681	240	393	899	098	528	797	127	488	697	14
47	710	234	421	893	126	521	825	120	516	690	13
48	738	229	450	887	155	515	853	113	545	682	12
49	767	223	478	881	183	508	882	106	573	675	11
50	.18795	.98218	.20507	.97875	.22212	.97502	.23910	.97100	.25601	.96667	10
51	824	212	535	869	240	496	938	093	629	660	9
52	852	207	563	863	268	489	966	086	657	653	8
53	881	201	592	857	297	483	.23995	079	685	645	7
54	910	196	620	851	325	476	.24023	072	713	638	6
55	.18938	.98190	.20649	.97845	.22353	.97470	.24051	.97065	.25741	.96630	5
56	967	185	677	839	382	463	079	058	769	623	4
57	.18995	179	706	833	410	457	108	051	798	615	3
58	.19024	174	734	827	438	450	136	044	826	608	2
59	052	168	763	821	467	444	164	037	854	600	1
60	.19081	.98163	.20791	.97815	.22495	.97437	.24192	.97030	.25882	.96593	0
	Cos	Sin	Cos	Sin	Cos	Sin	Cos	Sin	Cos	Sin	′
	79°		78°		77°		76°		75°		←

→	10°		11°		12°		13°		14°		
′	Tan	Cot	Tan	Cot	Tan	Cot	Tan	Cot	Tan	Cot	
0	.17633	5.6713	.19438	5.1446	.21256	4.7046	.23087	4.3315	.24933	4.0108	60
1	663	.6617	468	.1366	286	.6979	117	.3257	964	.0058	59
2	693	.6521	498	.1286	316	.6912	148	.3200	.24995	4.0009	58
3	723	.6425	529	.1207	347	.6845	179	.3143	.25026	3.9959	57
4	753	.6329	559	.1128	377	.6779	209	.3086	056	.9910	56
5	.17783	5.6234	.19589	5.1049	.21408	4.6712	.23240	4.3029	.25087	3.9861	55
6	813	.6140	619	.0970	438	.6646	271	.2972	118	.9812	54
7	843	.6045	649	.0892	469	.6580	301	.2916	149	.9763	53
8	873	.5951	680	.0814	499	.6514	332	.2859	180	.9714	52
9	903	.5857	710	.0736	529	.6448	363	.2803	211	.9665	51
10	.17933	5.5764	.19740	5.0658	.21560	4.6382	.23393	4.2747	.25242	3.9617	50
11	963	.5671	770	.0581	590	.6317	424	.2691	273	.9568	49
12	.17993	5.5578	801	.0504	621	.6252	455	.2635	304	.9520	48
13	.18023	5.5485	831	.0427	651	.6187	485	.2580	335	.9471	47
14	053	.5393	861	.0350	682	.6122	516	.2524	366	.9423	46
15	.18083	5.5301	.19891	5.0273	.21712	4.6057	.23547	4.2468	.25397	3.9375	45
16	113	.5209	921	.0197	743	.5993	578	.2413	428	.9327	44
17	143	.5118	952	.0121	773	.5928	608	.2358	459	.9279	43
18	173	.5026	.19982	5.0045	804	.5864	639	.2303	490	.9232	42
19	203	.4936	.20012	4.9969	834	.5800	670	.2248	521	.9184	41
20	.18233	5.4845	.20042	4.9894	.21864	4.5736	.23700	4.2193	.25552	3.9136	40
21	263	.4755	073	.9819	895	.5673	731	.2139	583	.9089	39
22	293	.4665	103	.9744	925	.5609	762	.2084	614	.9042	38
23	323	.4575	133	.9669	956	.5546	793	.2030	645	.8995	37
24	353	.4486	164	.9594	.21986	.5483	823	.1976	676	.8947	36
25	.18384	5.4397	.20194	4.9520	.22017	4.5420	.23854	4.1922	.25707	3.8900	35
26	414	.4308	224	.9446	047	.5357	885	.1868	738	.8854	34
27	444	.4219	254	.9372	078	.5294	916	.1814	769	.8807	33
28	474	.4131	285	.9298	108	.5232	946	.1760	800	.8760	32
29	504	.4043	315	.9225	139	.5169	.23977	.1706	831	.8714	31
30	.18534	5.3955	.20345	4.9152	.22169	4.5107	.24008	4.1653	.25862	3.8667	30
31	564	.3868	376	.9078	200	.5045	039	.1600	893	.8621	29
32	594	.3781	406	.9006	231	.4983	069	.1547	924	.8575	28
33	624	.3694	436	.8933	261	.4922	100	.1493	955	.8528	27
34	654	.3607	466	.8860	292	.4860	131	.1441	.25986	.8482	26
35	.18684	5.3521	.20497	4.8788	.22322	4.4799	.24162	4.1388	.26017	3.8436	25
36	714	.3435	527	.8716	353	.4737	193	.1335	048	.8391	24
37	745	.3349	557	.8644	383	.4676	223	.1282	079	.8345	23
38	775	.3263	588	.8573	414	.4615	254	.1230	110	.8299	22
39	805	.3178	618	.8501	444	.4555	285	.1178	141	.8254	21
40	.18835	5.3093	.20648	4.8430	.22475	4.4494	.24316	4.1126	.26172	3.8208	20
41	865	.3008	679	.8359	505	.4434	347	.1074	203	.8163	19
42	895	.2924	709	.8288	536	.4373	377	.1022	235	.8118	18
43	925	.2839	739	.8218	567	.4313	408	.0970	266	.8073	17
44	955	.2755	770	.8147	597	.4253	439	.0918	297	.8028	16
45	.18986	5.2672	.20800	4.8077	.22628	4.4194	.24470	4.0867	.26328	3.7983	15
46	.19016	.2588	830	.8007	658	.4134	501	.0815	359	.7938	14
47	046	.2505	861	.7937	689	.4075	532	.0764	390	.7893	13
48	076	.2422	891	.7867	719	.4015	562	.0713	421	.7848	12
49	106	.2339	921	.7798	750	.3956	593	.0662	452	.7804	11
50	.19136	5.2257	.20952	4.7729	.22781	4.3897	.24624	4.0611	.26483	3.7760	10
51	166	.2174	.20982	.7659	811	.3838	655	.0560	515	.7715	9
52	197	.2092	.21013	.7591	842	.3779	686	.0509	546	.7671	8
53	227	.2011	043	.7522	872	.3721	717	.0459	577	.7627	7
54	257	.1929	073	.7453	903	.3662	747	.0408	608	.7583	6
55	.19287	5.1848	.21104	4.7385	.22934	4.3604	.24778	4.0358	.26639	3.7539	5
56	317	.1767	134	.7317	964	.3546	809	.0308	670	.7495	4
57	347	.1686	164	.7249	.22995	.3488	840	.0257	701	.7451	3
58	378	.1606	195	.7181	.23026	.3430	871	.0207	733	.7408	2
59	408	.1526	225	.7114	056	.3372	902	.0158	764	.7364	1
60	.19438	5.1446	.21256	4.7046	.23087	4.3315	.24933	4.0108	.26795	3.7321	0
	Cot	Tan	Cot	Tan	Cot	Tan	Cot	Tan	Cot	Tan	′
	79°		78°		77°		76°		75°		←

XI. FIVE–PLACE VALUES: SINE AND COSINE

→	15°		16°		17°		18°		19°		
′	Sin	Cos	Sin	Cos	Sin	Cos	Sin	Cos	Sin	Cos	
0	.25882	.96593	.27564	.96126	.29237	.95630	.30902	.95106	.32557	.94552	60
1	910	585	592	118	265	622	929	097	584	542	59
2	938	578	620	110	293	613	957	088	612	533	58
3	966	570	648	102	321	605	.30985	079	639	523	57
4	.25994	562	676	094	348	596	.31012	070	667	514	56
5	.26022	.96555	.27704	.96086	.29376	.95588	.31040	.95061	.32694	.94504	55
6	050	547	731	078	404	579	068	052	722	495	54
7	079	540	759	070	432	571	095	043	749	485	53
8	107	532	787	062	460	562	123	033	777	476	52
9	135	524	815	054	487	554	151	024	804	466	51
10	.26163	.96517	.27843	.96046	.29515	.95545	.31178	.95015	.32832	.94457	50
11	191	509	871	037	543	536	206	.95006	859	447	49
12	219	502	899	029	571	528	233	.94997	887	438	48
13	247	494	927	021	599	519	261	988	914	428	47
14	275	486	955	013	626	511	289	979	942	418	46
15	.26303	.96479	.27983	.96005	.29654	.95502	.31316	.94970	.32969	.94409	45
16	331	471	.28011	.95997	682	493	344	961	.32997	399	44
17	359	463	039	989	710	485	372	952	.33024	390	43
18	387	456	067	981	737	476	399	943	051	380	42
19	415	448	095	972	765	467	427	933	079	370	41
20	.26443	.96440	.28123	.95964	.29793	.95459	.31454	.94924	.33106	.94361	40
21	471	433	150	956	821	450	482	915	134	351	39
22	500	425	178	948	849	441	510	906	161	342	38
23	528	417	206	940	876	433	537	897	189	332	37
24	556	410	234	931	904	424	565	888	216	322	36
25	.26584	.96402	.28262	.95923	.29932	.95415	.31593	.94878	.33244	.94313	35
26	612	394	290	915	960	407	620	869	271	303	34
27	640	386	318	907	.29987	398	648	860	298	293	33
28	668	379	346	898	.30015	389	675	851	326	284	32
29	696	371	374	890	043	380	703	842	353	274	31
30	.26724	.96363	.28402	.95882	.30071	.95372	.31730	.94832	.33381	.94264	30
31	752	355	429	874	098	363	758	823	408	254	29
32	780	347	457	865	126	354	786	814	436	245	28
33	808	340	485	857	154	345	813	805	463	235	27
34	836	332	513	849	182	337	841	795	490	225	26
35	.26864	.96324	.28541	.95841	.30209	.95328	.31868	.94786	.33518	.94215	25
36	892	316	569	832	237	319	896	777	545	206	24
37	920	308	597	824	265	310	923	768	573	196	23
38	948	301	625	816	292	301	951	758	600	186	22
39	.26976	293	652	807	320	293	.31979	749	627	176	21
40	.27004	.96285	.28680	.95799	.30348	.95284	.32006	.94740	.33655	.94167	20
41	032	277	708	791	376	275	034	730	682	157	19
42	060	269	736	782	403	266	061	721	710	147	18
43	088	261	764	774	431	257	089	712	737	137	17
44	116	253	792	766	459	248	116	702	764	127	16
45	.27144	.96246	.28820	.95757	.30486	.95240	.32144	.94693	.33792	.94118	15
46	172	238	847	749	514	231	171	684	819	108	14
47	200	230	875	740	542	222	199	674	846	098	13
48	228	222	903	732	570	213	227	665	874	088	12
49	256	214	931	724	597	204	254	656	901	078	11
50	.27284	.96206	.28959	.95715	.30625	.95195	.32282	.94646	.33929	.94068	10
51	312	198	.28987	707	653	186	309	637	956	058	9
52	340	190	.29015	698	680	177	337	627	.33983	049	8
53	368	182	042	690	708	168	364	618	.34011	039	7
54	396	174	070	681	736	159	392	609	038	029	6
55	.27424	.96166	.29098	.95673	.30763	.95150	.32419	.94599	.34065	.94019	5
56	452	158	126	664	791	142	447	590	093	.94009	4
57	480	150	154	656	819	133	474	580	120	.93999	3
58	508	142	182	647	846	124	502	571	147	989	2
59	536	134	209	639	874	115	529	561	175	979	1
60	.27564	.96126	.29237	.95630	.30902	.95106	.32557	.94552	.34202	.93969	0
	Cos	Sin	Cos	Sin	Cos	Sin	Cos	Sin	Cos	Sin	′
	74°		73°		72°		71°		70°		←

XI. FIVE–PLACE VALUES: TANGENT AND COTANGENT

→	15°		16°		17°		18°		19°		
′	Tan	Cot	Tan	Cot	Tan	Cot	Tan	Cot	Tan	Cot	
0	.26795	3.7321	.28675	3.4874	.30573	3.2709	.32492	3.0777	.34433	2.9042	60
1	826	.7277	706	.4836	605	.2675	524	.0746	465	.9015	59
2	857	.7234	738	.4798	637	.2641	556	.0716	498	.8987	58
3	888	.7191	769	.4760	669	.2607	588	.0686	530	.8960	57
4	920	.7148	801	.4722	700	.2573	621	.0655	563	.8933	56
5	.26951	3.7105	.28832	3.4684	.30732	3.2539	.32653	3.0625	.34596	2.8905	55
6	.26982	.7062	864	.4646	764	.2506	685	.0595	628	.8878	54
7	.27013	.7019	895	.4608	796	.2472	717	.0565	661	.8851	53
8	044	.6976	927	.4570	828	.2438	749	.0535	693	.8824	52
9	076	.6933	958	.4533	860	.2405	782	.0505	726	.8797	51
10	.27107	3.6891	.28990	3.4495	.30891	3.2371	.32814	3.0475	.34758	2.8770	50
11	138	.6848	.29021	.4458	923	.2338	846	.0445	791	.8743	49
12	169	.6806	053	.4420	955	.2305	878	.0415	824	.8716	48
13	201	.6764	084	.4383	.30987	.2272	911	.0385	856	.8689	47
14	232	.6722	116	.4346	.31019	.2238	943	.0356	889	.8662	46
15	.27263	3.6680	.29147	3.4308	.31051	3.2205	.32975	3.0326	.34922	2.8636	45
16	294	.6638	179	.4271	083	.2172	.33007	.0296	954	.8609	44
17	326	.6596	210	.4234	115	.2139	040	.0267	.34987	.8582	43
18	357	.6554	242	.4197	147	.2106	072	.0237	.35020	.8556	42
19	388	.6512	274	.4160	178	.2073	104	.0208	052	.8529	41
20	.27419	3.6470	.29305	3.4124	.31210	3.2041	.33136	3.0178	.35085	2.8502	40
21	451	.6429	337	.4087	242	.2008	169	.0149	118	.8476	39
22	482	.6387	368	.4050	274	.1975	201	.0120	150	.8449	38
23	513	.6346	400	.4014	306	.1943	233	.0090	183	.8423	37
24	545	.6305	432	.3977	338	.1910	266	.0061	216	.8397	36
25	.27576	3.6264	.29463	3.3941	.31370	3.1878	.33298	3.0032	.35248	2.8370	35
26	607	.6222	495	.3904	402	.1845	330	3.0003	281	.8344	34
27	638	.6181	526	.3868	434	.1813	363	2.9974	314	.8318	33
28	670	.6140	558	.3832	466	.1780	395	.9945	346	.8291	32
29	701	.6100	590	.3796	498	.1748	427	.9916	379	.8265	31
30	.27732	3.6059	.29621	3.3759	.31530	3.1716	.33460	2.9887	.35412	2.8239	30
31	764	.6018	653	.3723	562	.1684	492	.9858	445	.8213	29
32	795	.5978	685	.3687	594	.1652	524	.9829	477	.8187	28
33	826	.5937	716	.3652	626	.1620	557	.9800	510	.8161	27
34	858	.5897	748	.3616	658	.1588	589	.9772	543	.8135	26
35	.27889	3.5856	.29780	3.3580	.31690	3.1556	.33621	2.9743	.35576	2.8109	25
36	921	.5816	811	.3544	722	.1524	654	.9714	608	.8083	24
37	952	.5776	843	.3509	754	.1492	686	.9686	641	.8057	23
38	.27983	.5736	875	.3473	786	.1460	718	.9657	674	.8032	22
39	.28015	.5696	906	.3438	818	.1429	751	.9629	707	.8006	21
40	.28046	3.5656	.29938	3.3402	.31850	3.1397	.33783	2.9600	.35740	2.7980	20
41	077	.5616	.29970	.3367	882	.1366	816	.9572	772	.7955	19
42	109	.5576	.30001	.3332	914	.1334	848	.9544	805	.7929	18
43	140	.5536	033	.3297	946	.1303	881	.9515	838	.7903	17
44	172	.5497	065	.3261	.31978	.1271	913	.9487	871	.7878	16
45	.28203	3.5457	.30097	3.3226	.32010	3.1240	.33945	2.9459	.35904	2.7852	15
46	234	.5418	128	.3191	042	.1209	.33978	.9431	937	.7827	14
47	266	.5379	160	.3156	074	.1178	.34010	.9403	.35969	.7801	13
48	297	.5339	192	.3122	106	.1146	043	.9375	.36002	.7776	12
49	329	.5300	224	.3087	139	.1115	075	.9347	035	.7751	11
50	.28360	3.5261	.30255	3.3052	.32171	3.1084	.34108	2.9319	.36068	2.7725	10
51	391	.5222	287	.3017	203	.1053	140	.9291	101	.7700	9
52	423	.5183	319	.2983	235	.1022	173	.9263	134	.7675	8
53	454	.5144	351	.2948	267	.0991	205	.9235	167	.7650	7
54	486	.5105	382	.2914	299	.0961	238	.9208	199	.7625	6
55	.28517	3.5067	.30414	3.2879	.32331	3.0930	.34270	2.9180	.36232	2.7600	5
56	549	.5028	446	.2845	363	.0899	303	.9152	265	.7575	4
57	580	.4989	478	.2811	396	.0868	335	.9125	298	.7550	3
58	612	.4951	509	.2777	428	.0838	368	.9097	331	.7525	2
59	643	.4912	541	.2743	460	.0807	400	.9070	364	.7500	1
60	.28675	3.4874	.30573	3.2709	.32492	3.0777	.34433	2.9042	.36397	2.7475	0
	Cot	Tan	Cot	Tan	Cot	Tan	Cot	Tan	Cot	Tan	′
	74°		73°		72°		71°		70°		←

→	20°		21°		22°		23°		24°		
′	Sin	Cos	Sin	Cos	Sin	Cos	Sin	Cos	Sin	Cos	
0	.34202	.93969	.35837	.93358	.37461	.92718	.39073	.92050	.40674	.91355	60
1	229	959	864	348	488	707	100	039	700	343	59
2	257	949	891	337	515	697	127	028	727	331	58
3	284	939	918	327	542	686	153	016	753	319	57
4	311	929	945	316	569	675	180	.92005	780	307	56
5	.34339	.93919	.35973	.93306	.37595	.92664	.39207	.91994	.40806	.91295	55
6	366	909	.36000	295	622	653	234	982	833	283	54
7	393	899	027	285	649	642	260	971	860	272	53
8	421	889	054	274	676	631	287	959	886	260	52
9	448	879	081	264	703	620	314	948	913	248	51
10	.34475	.93869	.36108	.93253	.37730	.92609	.39341	.91936	.40939	.91236	50
11	503	859	135	243	757	598	367	925	966	224	49
12	530	849	162	232	784	587	394	914	.40992	212	48
13	557	839	190	222	811	576	421	902	.41019	200	47
14	584	829	217	211	838	565	448	891	045	188	46
15	.34612	.93819	.36244	.93201	.37865	.92554	.39474	.91879	.41072	.91176	45
16	639	809	271	190	892	543	501	868	098	164	44
17	666	799	298	180	919	532	528	856	125	152	43
18	694	789	325	169	946	521	555	845	151	140	42
19	721	779	352	159	973	510	581	833	178	128	41
20	.34748	.93769	.36379	.93148	.37999	.92499	.39608	.91822	.41204	.91116	40
21	775	759	406	137	.38026	488	635	810	231	104	39
22	803	748	434	127	053	477	661	799	257	092	38
23	830	738	461	116	080	466	688	787	284	080	37
24	857	728	488	106	107	455	715	775	310	068	36
25	.34884	.93718	.36515	.93095	.38134	.92444	.39741	.91764	.41337	.91056	35
26	912	708	542	084	161	432	768	752	363	044	34
27	939	698	569	074	188	421	795	741	390	032	33
28	966	688	596	063	215	410	822	729	416	020	32
29	.34993	677	623	052	241	399	848	718	443	.91008	31
30	.35021	.93667	.36650	.93042	.33268	.92388	.39875	.91706	.41469	.90996	30
31	048	657	677	031	295	377	902	694	496	984	29
32	075	647	704	020	322	366	928	683	522	972	28
33	102	637	731	.93010	349	355	955	671	549	960	27
34	130	626	758	.92999	376	343	.39982	660	575	948	26
35	.35157	.93616	.36785	.92988	.38403	.92332	.40008	.91648	.41602	.90936	25
36	184	606	812	978	430	321	035	636	628	924	24
37	211	596	839	967	456	310	062	625	655	911	23
38	239	585	867	956	483	299	088	613	681	899	22
39	266	575	894	945	510	287	115	601	707	887	21
40	.35293	.93565	.36921	.92935	.38537	.92276	.40141	.91590	.41734	.90875	20
41	320	555	948	924	564	265	168	578	760	863	19
42	347	544	.36975	913	591	254	195	566	787	851	18
43	375	534	.37002	902	617	243	221	555	813	839	17
44	402	524	029	892	644	231	248	543	840	826	16
45	.35429	.93514	.37056	.92881	.38671	.92220	.40275	.91531	.41866	.90814	15
46	456	503	083	870	698	209	301	519	892	802	14
47	484	493	110	859	725	198	328	508	919	790	13
48	511	483	137	849	752	186	355	496	945	778	12
49	538	472	164	838	778	175	381	484	972	766	11
50	.35565	.93462	.37191	.92827	.38805	.92164	.40408	.91472	.41998	.90753	10
51	592	452	218	816	832	152	434	461	.42024	741	9
52	619	441	245	805	859	141	461	449	051	729	8
53	647	431	272	794	886	130	488	437	077	717	7
54	674	420	299	784	912	119	514	425	104	704	6
55	.35701	.93410	.37326	.92773	.38939	.92107	.40541	.91414	.42130	.90692	5
56	728	400	353	762	966	096	567	402	156	680	4
57	755	389	380	751	.38993	085	594	390	183	668	3
58	782	379	407	740	.39020	073	621	378	209	655	2
59	810	368	434	729	046	062	647	366	235	643	1
60	.35837	.93358	.37461	.92718	.39073	.92050	.40674	.91355	.42262	.90631	0
	Cos	Sin	Cos	Sin	Cos	Sin	Cos	Sin	Cos	Sin	′
	69°		68°		67°		66°		65°		←

→	20°		21°		22°		23°		24°		
′	Tan	Cot	Tan	Cot	Tan	Cot	Tan	Cot	Tan	Cot	
0	.36397	2.7475	.38386	2.6051	.40403	2.4751	.42447	2.3559	.44523	2.2460	60
1	430	.7450	420	.6028	436	.4730	482	.3539	558	.2443	59
2	463	.7425	453	.6006	470	.4709	516	.3520	593	.2425	58
3	496	.7400	487	.5983	504	.4689	551	.3501	627	.2408	57
4	529	.7376	520	.5961	538	.4668	585	.3483	662	.2390	56
5	.36562	2.7351	.38553	2.5938	.40572	2.4648	.42619	2.3464	.44697	2.2373	55
6	595	.7326	587	.5916	606	.4627	654	.3445	732	.2355	54
7	628	.7302	620	.5893	640	.4606	688	.3426	767	.2338	53
8	661	.7277	654	.5871	674	.4586	722	.3407	802	.2320	52
9	694	.7253	687	.5848	707	.4566	757	.3388	837	.2303	51
10	.36727	2.7228	.38721	2.5826	.40741	2.4545	.42791	2.3369	.44872	2.2286	50
11	760	.7204	754	.5804	775	.4525	826	.3351	907	.2268	49
12	793	.7179	787	.5782	809	.4504	860	.3332	942	.2251	48
13	826	.7155	821	.5759	843	.4484	894	.3313	.44977	.2234	47
14	859	.7130	854	.5737	877	.4464	929	.3294	.45012	.2216	46
15	.36892	2.7106	.38888	2.5715	.40911	2.4443	.42963	2.3276	.45047	2.2199	45
16	925	.7082	921	.5693	945	.4423	.42998	.3257	082	.2182	44
17	958	.7058	955	.5671	.40979	.4403	.43032	.3238	117	.2165	43
18	.36991	.7034	.38988	.5649	.41013	.4383	067	.3220	152	.2148	42
19	.37024	.7009	.39022	.5627	047	.4362	101	.3201	187	.2130	41
20	.37057	2.6985	.39055	2.5605	.41081	2.4342	.43136	2.3183	.45222	2.2113	40
21	090	.6961	089	.5583	115	.4322	170	.3164	257	.2096	39
22	123	.6937	122	.5561	149	.4302	205	.3146	292	.2079	38
23	157	.6913	156	.5539	183	.4282	239	.3127	327	.2062	37
24	190	.6889	190	.5517	217	.4262	274	.3109	362	.2045	36
25	.37223	2.6865	.39223	2.5495	.41251	2.4242	.43308	2.3090	.45397	2.2028	35
26	256	.6841	257	.5473	285	.4222	343	.3072	432	.2011	34
27	289	.6818	290	.5452	319	.4202	378	.3053	467	.1994	33
28	322	.6794	324	.5430	353	.4182	412	.3035	502	.1977	32
29	355	.6770	357	.5408	387	.4162	447	.3017	538	.1960	31
30	.37388	2.6746	.39391	2.5386	.41421	2.4142	.43481	2.2998	.45573	2.1943	30
31	422	.6723	425	.5365	455	.4122	516	.2980	608	.1926	29
32	455	.6699	458	.5343	490	.4102	550	.2962	643	.1909	28
33	488	.6675	492	.5322	524	.4083	585	.2944	678	.1892	27
34	521	.6652	526	.5300	558	.4063	620	.2925	713	.1876	26
35	.37554	2.6628	.39559	2.5279	.41592	2.4043	.43654	2.2907	.45748	2.1859	25
36	588	.6605	593	.5257	626	.4023	689	.2889	784	.1842	24
37	621	.6581	626	.5236	660	.4004	724	.2871	819	.1825	23
38	654	.6558	660	.5214	694	.3984	758	.2853	854	.1808	22
39	687	.6534	694	.5193	728	.3964	793	.2835	889	.1792	21
40	.37720	2.6511	.39727	2.5172	.41763	2.3945	.43828	2.2817	.45924	2.1775	20
41	754	.6488	761	.5150	797	.3925	862	.2799	960	.1758	19
42	787	.6464	795	.5129	831	.3906	897	.2781	.45995	.1742	18
43	820	.6441	829	.5108	865	.3886	932	.2763	.46030	.1725	17
44	853	.6418	862	.5086	899	.3867	.43966	.2745	065	.1708	16
45	.37887	2.6395	.39896	2.5065	.41933	2.3847	.44001	2.2727	.46101	2.1692	15
46	920	.6371	930	.5044	.41968	.3828	036	.2709	136	.1675	14
47	953	.6348	963	.5023	.42002	.3808	071	.2691	171	.1659	13
48	.37986	.6325	.39997	.5002	036	.3789	105	.2673	206	.1642	12
49	.38020	.6302	.40031	.4981	070	.3770	140	.2655	242	.1625	11
50	.38053	2.6279	.40065	2.4960	.42105	2.3750	.44175	2.2637	.46277	2.1609	10
51	086	.6256	098	.4939	139	.3731	210	.2620	312	.1592	9
52	120	.6233	132	.4918	173	.3712	244	.2602	348	.1576	8
53	153	.6210	166	.4897	207	.3693	279	.2584	383	.1560	7
54	186	.6187	200	.4876	242	.3673	314	.2566	418	.1543	6
55	.38220	2.6165	.40234	2.4855	.42276	2.3654	.44349	2.2549	.46454	2.1527	5
56	253	.6142	267	.4834	310	.3635	384	.2531	489	.1510	4
57	286	.6119	301	.4813	345	.3616	418	.2513	525	.1494	3
58	320	.6096	335	.4792	379	.3597	453	.2496	560	.1478	2
59	353	.6074	369	.4772	413	.3578	488	.2478	595	.1461	1
60	.38386	2.6051	.40403	2.4751	.42447	2.3559	.44523	2.2460	.46631	2.1445	0
	Cot	Tan	Cot	Tan	Cot	Tan	Cot	Tan	Cot	Tan	′
	69°		68°		67°		66°		65°		←

XI. FIVE–PLACE VALUES: SINE AND COSINE

→	25°		26°		27°		28°		29°		
′	Sin	Cos	Sin	Cos	Sin	Cos	Sin	Cos	Sin	Cos	
0	.42262	.90631	.43837	.89879	.45399	.89101	.46947	.88295	.48481	.87462	60
1	288	618	863	867	425	087	973	281	506	448	59
2	315	606	889	854	451	074	.46999	267	532	434	58
3	341	594	916	841	477	061	.47024	254	557	420	57
4	367	582	942	828	503	048	050	240	583	406	56
5	.42394	.90569	.43968	.89816	.45529	.89035	.47076	.88226	.48608	.87391	55
6	420	557	.43994	803	554	021	101	213	634	377	54
7	446	545	.44020	790	580	.89008	127	199	659	363	53
8	473	532	046	777	606	.88995	153	185	684	349	52
9	499	520	072	764	632	981	178	172	710	335	51
10	.42525	.90507	.44098	.89752	.45658	.88968	.47204	.88158	.48735	.87321	50
11	552	495	124	739	684	955	229	144	761	306	49
12	578	483	151	726	710	942	255	130	786	292	48
13	604	470	177	713	736	928	281	117	811	278	47
14	631	458	203	700	762	915	306	103	837	264	46
15	.42657	.90446	.44229	.89687	.45787	.88902	.47332	.88089	.48862	.87250	45
16	683	433	255	674	813	888	358	075	888	235	44
17	709	421	281	662	839	875	383	062	913	221	43
18	736	408	307	649	865	862	409	048	938	207	42
19	762	396	333	636	891	848	434	034	964	193	41
20	.42788	.90383	.44359	.89623	.45917	.88835	.47460	.88020	.48989	.87178	40
21	815	371	385	610	942	822	486	.88006	.49014	164	39
22	841	358	411	597	968	808	511	.87993	040	150	38
23	867	346	437	584	.45994	795	537	979	065	136	37
24	894	334	464	571	.46020	782	562	965	090	121	36
25	.42920	.90321	.44490	.89558	.46046	.88768	.47588	.87951	.49116	.87107	35
26	946	309	516	545	072	755	614	937	141	093	34
27	972	296	542	532	097	741	639	923	166	079	33
28	.42999	284	568	519	123	728	665	909	192	064	32
29	.43025	271	594	506	149	715	690	896	217	050	31
30	.43051	.90259	.44620	.89493	.46175	.88701	.47716	.87882	.49242	.87036	30
31	077	246	646	480	201	688	741	868	268	021	29
32	104	233	672	467	226	674	767	854	293	.87007	28
33	130	221	698	454	252	661	793	840	318	.86993	27
34	156	208	724	441	278	647	818	826	344	978	26
35	.43182	.90196	.44750	.89428	.46304	.88634	.47844	.87812	.49369	.86964	25
36	209	183	776	415	330	620	869	798	394	949	24
37	235	171	802	402	355	607	895	784	419	935	23
38	261	158	828	389	381	593	920	770	445	921	22
39	287	146	854	376	407	580	946	756	470	906	21
40	.43313	.90133	.44880	.89363	.46433	.88566	.47971	.87743	.49495	.86892	20
41	340	120	906	350	458	553	.47997	729	521	878	19
42	366	108	932	337	484	539	.48022	715	546	863	18
43	392	095	958	324	510	526	048	701	571	849	17
44	418	082	.44984	311	536	512	073	687	596	834	16
45	.43445	.90070	.45010	.89298	.46561	.88499	.48099	.87673	.49622	.86820	15
46	471	057	036	285	587	485	124	659	647	805	14
47	497	045	062	272	613	472	150	645	672	791	13
48	523	032	088	259	639	458	175	631	697	777	12
49	549	019	114	245	664	445	201	617	723	762	11
50	.43575	.90007	.45140	.89232	.46690	.88431	.48226	.87603	.49748	.86748	10
51	602	.89994	166	219	716	417	252	589	773	733	9
52	628	981	192	206	742	404	277	575	798	719	8
53	654	968	218	193	767	390	303	561	824	704	7
54	680	956	243	180	793	377	328	546	849	690	6
55	.43706	.89943	.45269	.89167	.46819	.88363	.48354	.87532	.49874	.86675	5
56	733	930	295	153	844	349	379	518	899	661	4
57	759	918	321	140	870	336	405	504	924	646	3
58	785	905	347	127	896	322	430	490	950	632	2
59	811	892	373	114	921	308	456	476	.49975	617	1
60	.43837	.89879	.45399	.89101	.46947	.88295	.48481	.87462	.50000	.86603	0
	Cos	Sin	Cos	Sin	Cos	Sin	Cos	Sin	Cos	Sin	′
	64°		63°		62°		61°		60°		←

XI. FIVE–PLACE VALUES: TANGENT AND COTANGENT

→	25°		26°		27°		28°		29°		
′	Tan	Cot	Tan	Cot	Tan	Cot	Tan	Cot	Tan	Cot	
0	.46631	2.1445	.48773	2.0503	.50953	1.9626	.53171	1.8807	.55431	1.8040	60
1	666	.1429	809	.0488	.50989	.9612	208	.8794	469	.8028	59
2	702	.1413	845	.0473	.51026	.9598	246	.8781	507	.8016	58
3	737	.1396	881	.0458	063	.9584	283	.8768	545	.8003	57
4	772	.1380	917	.0443	099	.9570	320	.8755	583	.7991	56
5	.46808	2.1364	.48953	2.0428	.51136	1.9556	.53358	1.8741	.55621	1.7979	55
6	843	.1348	.48989	.0413	173	.9542	395	.8728	659	.7966	54
7	879	.1332	.49026	.0398	209	.9528	432	.8715	697	.7954	53
8	914	.1315	062	.0383	246	.9514	470	.8702	736	.7942	52
9	950	.1299	098	.0368	283	.9500	507	.8689	774	.7930	51
10	.46985	2.1283	.49134	2.0353	.51319	1.9486	.53545	1.8676	.55812	1.7917	50
11	.47021	.1267	170	.0338	356	.9472	582	.8663	850	.7905	49
12	056	.1251	206	.0323	393	.9458	620	.8650	888	.7893	48
13	092	.1235	242	.0308	430	.9444	657	.8637	926	.7881	47
14	128	.1219	278	.0293	467	.9430	694	.8624	.55964	.7868	46
15	.47163	2.1203	.49315	2.0278	.51503	1.9416	.53732	1.8611	.56003	1.7856	45
16	199	.1187	351	.0263	540	.9402	769	.8598	041	.7844	44
17	234	.1171	387	.0248	577	.9388	807	.8585	079	.7832	43
18	270	.1155	423	.0233	614	.9375	844	.8572	117	.7820	42
19	305	.1139	459	.0219	651	.9361	882	.8559	156	.7808	41
20	.47341	2.1123	.49495	2.0204	.51688	1.9347	.53920	1.8546	.56194	1.7796	40
21	377	.1107	532	.0189	724	.9333	957	.8533	232	.7783	39
22	412	.1092	568	.0174	761	.9319	.53995	.8520	270	.7771	38
23	448	.1076	604	.0160	798	.9306	.54032	.8507	309	.7759	37
24	483	.1060	640	.0145	835	.9292	070	.8495	347	.7747	36
25	.47519	2.1044	.49677	2.0130	.51872	1.9278	.54107	1.8482	.56385	1.7735	35
26	555	.1028	713	.0115	909	.9265	145	.8469	424	.7723	34
27	590	.1013	749	.0101	946	.9251	183	.8456	462	.7711	33
28	626	.0997	786	.0086	.51983	.9237	220	.8443	501	.7699	32
29	662	.0981	822	.0072	.52020	.9223	258	.8430	539	.7687	31
30	.47698	2.0965	.49858	2.0057	.52057	1.9210	.54296	1.8418	.56577	1.7675	30
31	733	.0950	894	.0042	094	.9196	333	.8405	616	.7663	29
32	769	.0934	931	.0028	131	.9183	371	.8392	654	.7651	28
33	805	.0918	.49967	2.0013	168	.9169	409	.8379	693	.7639	27
34	840	.0903	.50004	1.9999	205	.9155	446	.8367	731	.7627	26
35	.47876	2.0887	.50040	1.9984	.52242	1.9142	.54484	1.8354	.56769	1.7615	25
36	912	.0872	076	.9970	279	.9128	522	.8341	808	.7603	24
37	948	.0856	113	.9955	316	.9115	560	.8329	846	.7591	23
38	.47984	.0840	149	.9941	353	.9101	597	.8316	885	.7579	22
39	.48019	.0825	185	.9926	390	.9088	635	.8303	923	.7567	21
40	.48055	2.0809	.50222	1.9912	.52427	1.9074	.54673	1.8291	.56962	1.7556	20
41	091	.0794	258	.9897	464	.9061	711	.8278	.57000	.7544	19
42	127	.0778	295	.9883	501	.9047	748	.8265	039	.7532	18
43	163	.0763	331	.9868	538	.9034	786	.8253	078	.7520	17
44	198	.0748	368	.9854	575	.9020	824	.8240	116	.7508	16
45	.48234	2.0732	.50404	1.9840	.52613	1.9007	.54862	1.8228	.57155	1.7496	15
46	270	.0717	441	.9825	650	.8993	900	.8215	193	.7485	14
47	306	.0701	477	.9811	687	.8980	938	.8202	232	.7473	13
48	342	.0686	514	.9797	724	.8967	.54975	.8190	271	.7461	12
49	378	.0671	550	.9782	761	.8953	.55013	.8177	309	.7449	11
50	.48414	2.0655	.50587	1.9768	.52798	1.8940	.55051	1.8165	.57348	1.7437	10
51	450	.0640	623	.9754	836	.8927	089	.8152	386	.7426	9
52	486	.0625	660	.9740	873	.8913	127	.8140	425	.7414	8
53	521	.0609	696	.9725	910	.8900	165	.8127	464	.7402	7
54	557	.0594	733	.9711	947	.8887	203	.8115	503	.7391	6
55	.48593	2.0579	.50769	1.9697	.52985	1.8873	.55241	1.8103	.57541	1.7379	5
56	629	.0564	806	.9683	.53022	.8860	279	.8090	580	.7367	4
57	665	.0549	843	.9669	059	.8847	317	.8078	619	.7355	3
58	701	.0533	879	.9654	096	.8834	355	.8065	657	.7344	2
59	737	.0518	916	.9640	134	.8820	393	.8053	696	.7332	1
60	.48773	2.0503	.50953	1.9626	.53171	1.8807	.55431	1.8040	.57735	1.7321	0
	Cot	Tan	Cot	Tan	Cot	Tan	Cot	Tan	Cot	Tan	′
	64°		63°		62°		61°		60°		←

XI. FIVE-PLACE VALUES: SINE AND COSINE

′	30° Sin	30° Cos	31° Sin	31° Cos	32° Sin	32° Cos	33° Sin	33° Cos	34° Sin	34° Cos	
0	.50000	.86603	.51504	.85717	.52992	.84805	.54464	.83867	.55919	.82904	60
1	025	588	529	702	.53017	789	488	851	943	887	59
2	050	573	554	687	041	774	513	835	968	871	58
3	076	559	579	672	066	759	537	819	.55992	855	57
4	101	544	604	657	091	743	561	804	.56016	839	56
5	.50126	.86530	.51628	.85642	.53115	.84728	.54586	.83788	.56040	.82822	55
6	151	515	653	627	140	712	610	772	064	806	54
7	176	501	678	612	164	697	635	756	088	790	53
8	201	486	703	597	189	681	659	740	112	773	52
9	227	471	728	582	214	666	683	724	136	757	51
10	.50252	.86457	.51753	.85567	.53238	.84650	.54708	.83708	.56160	.82741	50
11	277	442	778	551	263	635	732	692	184	724	49
12	302	427	803	536	288	619	756	676	208	708	48
13	327	413	828	521	312	604	781	660	232	692	47
14	352	398	852	506	337	588	805	645	256	675	46
15	.50377	.86384	.51877	.85491	.53361	.84573	.54829	.83629	.56280	.82659	45
16	403	369	902	476	386	557	854	613	305	643	44
17	428	354	927	461	411	542	878	597	329	626	43
18	453	340	952	446	435	526	902	581	353	610	42
19	478	325	.51977	431	460	511	927	565	377	593	41
20	.50503	.86310	.52002	.85416	.53484	.84495	.54951	.83549	.56401	.82577	40
21	528	295	026	401	509	480	975	533	425	561	39
22	553	281	051	385	534	464	.54999	517	449	544	38
23	578	266	076	370	558	448	.55024	501	473	528	37
24	603	251	101	355	583	433	048	485	497	511	36
25	.50628	.86237	.52126	.85340	.53607	.84417	.55072	.83469	.56521	.82495	35
26	654	222	151	325	632	402	097	453	545	478	34
27	679	207	175	310	656	386	121	437	569	462	33
28	704	192	200	294	681	370	145	421	593	446	32
29	729	178	225	279	705	355	169	405	617	429	31
30	.50754	.86163	.52250	.85264	.53730	.84339	.55194	.83389	.56641	.82413	30
31	779	148	275	249	754	324	218	373	665	396	29
32	804	133	299	234	779	308	242	356	689	380	28
33	829	119	324	218	804	292	266	340	713	363	27
34	854	104	349	203	828	277	291	324	736	347	26
35	.50879	.86089	.52374	.85188	.53853	.84261	.55315	.83308	.56760	.82330	25
36	904	074	399	173	877	245	339	292	784	314	24
37	929	059	423	157	902	230	363	276	808	297	23
38	954	045	448	142	926	214	388	260	832	281	22
39	.50979	030	473	127	951	198	412	244	856	264	21
40	.51004	.86015	.52498	.85112	.53975	.84182	.55436	.83228	.56880	.82248	20
41	029	.86000	522	096	.54000	167	460	212	904	231	19
42	054	.85985	547	081	024	.151	484	195	928	214	18
43	079	970	572	066	049	135	509	179	952	198	17
44	104	956	597	051	073	120	533	163	.56976	181	16
45	.51129	.85941	.52621	.85035	.54097	.84104	.55557	.83147	.57000	.82165	15
46	154	926	646	020	122	088	581	131	024	148	14
47	179	911	671	.85005	146	072	605	115	047	132	13
48	204	896	696	.84989	171	057	630	098	071	115	12
49	229	881	720	974	195	041	654	082	095	098	11
50	.51254	.85866	.52745	.84959	.54220	.84025	.55678	.83066	.57119	.82082	10
51	279	851	770	943	244	.84009	702	050	143	065	9
52	304	836	794	928	269	.83994	726	034	167	048	8
53	329	821	819	913	293	978	750	017	191	032	7
54	354	806	844	897	317	962	775	.83001	215	.82015	6
55	.51379	.85792	.52869	.84882	.54342	.83946	.55799	.82985	.57238	.81999	5
56	404	777	893	866	366	930	823	969	262	982	4
57	429	762	918	851	391	915	847	953	286	965	3
58	454	747	943	836	415	899	871	936	310	949	2
59	479	732	967	820	440	883	895	920	334	932	1
60	.51504	.85717	.52992	.84805	.54464	.83867	.55919	.82904	.57358	.81915	0
	Cos	Sin	Cos	Sin	Cos	Sin	Cos	Sin	Cos	Sin	′
	59°		58°		57°		56°		55°		←

	30°		31°		32°		33°		34°		
′	Tan	Cot	Tan	Cot	Tan	Cot	Tan	Cot	Tan	Cot	
0	.57735	1.7321	.60086	1.6643	.62487	1.6003	.64941	1.5399	.67451	1.4826	60
1	774	.7309	126	.6632	527	.5993	.64982	.5389	493	.4816	59
2	813	.7297	165	.6621	568	.5983	.65024	.5379	536	.4807	58
3	851	.7286	205	.6610	608	.5972	065	.5369	578	.4798	57
4	890	.7274	245	.6599	649	.5962	106	.5359	620	.4788	56
5	.57929	1.7262	.60284	1.6588	.62689	1.5952	.65148	1.5350	.67663	1.4779	55
6	.57968	.7251	324	.6577	730	.5941	189	.5340	705	.4770	54
7	.58007	.7239	364	.6566	770	.5931	231	.5330	748	.4761	53
8	046	.7228	403	.6555	811	.5921	272	.5320	790	.4751	52
9	085	.7216	443	.6545	852	.5911	314	.5311	832	.4742	51
10	.58124	1.7205	.60483	1.6534	.62892	1.5900	.65355	1.5301	.67875	1.4733	50
11	162	.7193	522	.6523	933	.5890	397	.5291	917	.4724	49
12	201	.7182	562	.6512	.62973	.5880	438	.5282	.67960	.4715	48
13	240	.7170	602	.6501	.63014	.5869	480	.5272	.68002	.4705	47
14	279	.7159	642	.6490	055	.5859	521	.5262	045	.4696	46
15	.58318	1.7147	.60681	1.6479	.63095	1.5849	.65563	1.5253	.68088	1.4687	45
16	357	.7136	721	.6469	136	.5839	604	.5243	130	.4678	44
17	396	.7124	761	.6458	177	.5829	646	.5233	173	.4669	43
18	435	.7113	801	.6447	217	.5818	688	.5224	215	.4659	42
19	474	.7102	841	.6436	258	.5808	729	.5214	258	.4650	41
20	.58513	1.7090	.60881	1.6426	.63299	1.5798	.65771	1.5204	.68301	1.4641	40
21	552	.7079	921	.6415	340	.5788	813	.5195	343	.4632	39
22	591	.7067	.60960	.6404	380	.5778	854	.5185	386	.4623	38
23	631	.7056	.61000	.6393	421	.5768	896	.5175	429	.4614	37
24	670	.7045	040	.6383	462	.5757	938	.5166	471	.4605	36
25	.58709	1.7033	.61080	1.6372	.63503	1.5747	.65980	1.5156	.68514	1.4596	35
26	748	.7022	120	.6361	544	.5737	.66021	.5147	557	.4586	34
27	787	.7011	160	.6351	584	.5727	063	.5137	600	.4577	33
28	826	.6999	200	.6340	625	.5717	105	.5127	642	.4568	32
29	865	.6988	240	.6329	666	.5707	147	.5118	685	.4559	31
30	.58905	1.6977	.61280	1.6319	.63707	1.5697	.66189	1.5108	.68728	1.4550	30
31	944	.6965	320	.6308	748	.5687	230	.5099	771	.4541	29
32	.58983	.6954	360	.6297	789	.5677	272	.5089	814	.4532	28
33	.59022	.6943	400	.6287	830	.5667	314	.5080	857	.4523	27
34	061	.6932	440	.6276	871	.5657	356	.5070	900	.4514	26
35	.59101	1.6920	.61480	1.6265	.63912	1.5647	.66398	1.5061	.68942	1.4505	25
36	140	.6909	520	.6255	953	.5637	440	.5051	.68985	.4496	24
37	179	.6898	561	.6244	.63994	.5627	482	.5042	.69028	.4487	23
38	218	.6887	601	.6234	.64035	.5617	524	.5032	071	.4478	22
39	258	.6875	641	.6223	076	.5607	566	.5023	114	.4469	21
40	.59297	1.6864	.61681	1.6212	.64117	1.5597	.66608	1.5013	.69157	1.4460	20
41	336	.6853	721	.6202	158	.5587	650	.5004	200	.4451	19
42	376	.6842	761	.6191	199	.5577	692	.4994	243	.4442	18
43	415	.6831	801	.6181	240	.5567	734	.4985	286	.4433	17
44	454	.6820	842	.6170	281	.5557	776	.4975	329	.4424	16
45	.59494	1.6808	.61882	1.6160	.64322	1.5547	.66818	1.4966	.69372	1.4415	15
46	533	.6797	922	.6149	363	.5537	860	.4957	416	.4406	14
47	573	.6786	.61962	.6139	404	.5527	902	.4947	459	.4397	13
48	612	.6775	.62003	.6128	446	.5517	944	.4938	502	.4388	12
49	651	.6764	043	.6118	487	.5507	.66986	.4928	545	.4379	11
50	.59691	1.6753	.62083	1.6107	.64528	1.5497	.67028	1.4919	.69588	1.4370	10
51	730	.6742	124	.6097	569	.5487	071	.4910	631	.4361	9
52	770	.6731	164	.6087	610	.5477	113	.4900	675	.4352	8
53	809	.6720	204	.6076	652	.5468	155	.4891	718	.4344	7
54	849	.6709	245	.6066	693	.5458	197	.4882	761	.4335	6
55	.59888	1.6698	.62285	1.6055	.64734	1.5448	.67239	1.4872	.69804	1.4326	5
56	928	.6687	325	.6045	775	.5438	282	.4863	847	.4317	4
57	.59967	.6676	366	.6034	817	.5428	324	.4854	891	.4308	3
58	.60007	.6665	406	.6024	858	.5418	366	.4844	934	.4299	2
59	046	.6654	446	.6014	899	.5408	409	.4835	.69977	.4290	1
60	.60086	1.6643	.62487	1.6003	.64941	1.5399	.67451	1.4826	.70021	1.4281	0
	Cot	Tan	Cot	Tan	Cot	Tan	Cot	Tan	Cot	Tan	′
	59°		58°		57°		56°		55°		←

→	35°		36°		37°		38°		39°		
′	Sin	Cos	Sin	Cos	Sin	Cos	Sin	Cos	Sin	Cos	
0	.57358	.81915	.58779	.80902	.60182	.79864	.61566	.78801	.62932	.77715	60
1	381	899	802	885	205	846	589	783	955	696	59
2	405	882	826	867	228	829	612	765	.62977	678	58
3	429	865	849	850	251	811	635	747	.63000	660	57
4	453	848	873	833	274	793	658	729	022	641	56
5	.57477	.81832	.58896	.80816	.60298	.79776	.61681	.78711	.63045	.77623	55
6	501	815	920	799	321	758	704	694	068	605	54
7	524	798	943	782	344	741	726	676	090	586	53
8	548	782	967	765	367	723	749	658	113	568	52
9	572	765	.58990	748	390	706	772	640	135	550	51
10	.57596	.81748	.59014	.80730	.60414	.79688	.61795	.78622	.63158	.77531	50
11	619	731	037	713	437	671	818	604	180	513	49
12	643	714	061	696	460	653	841	586	203	494	48
13	667	698	084	679	483	635	864	568	225	476	47
14	691	681	108	662	506	618	887	550	248	458	46
15	.57715	.81664	.59131	.80644	.60529	.79600	.61909	.78532	.63271	.77439	45
16	738	647	154	627	553	583	932	514	293	421	44
17	762	631	178	610	576	565	955	496	316	402	43
18	786	614	201	593	599	547	.61978	478	338	384	42
19	810	597	225	576	622	530	.62001	460	361	366	41
20	.57833	.81580	.59248	.80558	.60645	.79512	.62024	.78442	.63383	.77347	40
21	857	563	272	541	668	494	046	424	406	329	39
22	881	546	295	524	691	477	069	405	428	310	38
23	904	530	318	507	714	459	092	387	451	292	37
24	928	513	342	489	738	441	115	369	473	273	36
25	.57952	.81496	.59365	.80472	.60761	.79424	.62138	.78351	.63496	.77255	35
26	976	479	389	455	784	406	160	333	518	236	34
27	.57999	462	412	438	807	388	183	315	540	218	33
28	.58023	445	436	420	830	371	206	297	563	199	32
29	047	428	459	403	853	353	229	279	585	181	31
30	.58070	.81412	.59482	.80386	.60876	.79335	.62251	.78261	.63608	.77162	30
31	094	395	506	368	899	318	274	243	630	144	29
32	118	378	529	351	922	300	297	225	653	125	28
33	141	361	552	334	945	282	320	206	675	107	27
34	165	344	576	316	968	264	342	188	698	088	26
35	.58189	.81327	.59599	.80299	.60991	.79247	.62365	.78170	.63720	.77070	25
36	212	310	622	282	.61015	229	388	152	742	051	24
37	236	293	646	264	038	211	411	134	765	033	23
38	260	276	669	247	061	193	433	116	787	.77014	22
39	283	259	693	230	084	176	456	098	810	.76996	21
40	.58307	.81242	.59716	.80212	.61107	.79158	.62479	.78079	.63832	.76977	20
41	330	225	739	195	130	140	502	061	854	959	19
42	354	208	763	178	153	122	524	043	877	940	18
43	378	191	786	160	176	105	547	025	899	921	17
44	401	174	809	143	199	087	570	.78007	922	903	16
45	.58425	.81157	.59832	.80125	.61222	.79069	.62592	.77988	.63944	.76884	15
46	449	140	856	108	245	051	615	970	966	866	14
47	472	123	879	091	268	033	638	952	.63989	847	13
48	496	106	902	073	291	.79016	660	934	.64011	828	12
49	519	089	926	056	314	.78998	683	916	033	810	11
50	.58543	.81072	.59949	.80038	.61337	.78980	.62706	.77897	.64056	.76791	10
51	567	055	972	021	360	962	728	879	078	772	9
52	590	038	.59995	.80003	383	944	751	861	100	754	8
53	614	021	.60019	.79986	406	926	774	843	123	735	7
54	637	.81004	042	968	429	908	796	824	145	717	6
55	.58661	.80987	.60065	.79951	.61451	.78891	.62819	.77806	.64167	.76698	5
56	684	970	089	934	474	873	842	788	190	679	4
57	708	953	112	916	497	855	864	769	212	661	3
58	731	936	135	899	520	837	887	751	234	642	2
59	755	919	158	881	543	819	909	733	256	623	1
60	.58779	.80902	.60182	.79864	.61566	.78801	.62932	.77715	.64279	.76604	0
	Cos	Sin	Cos	Sin	Cos	Sin	Cos	Sin	Cos	Sin	′
	54°		53°		52°		51°		50°		←

XI. FIVE–PLACE VALUES: TANGENT AND COTANGENT

→	35°		36°		37°		38°		39°		
′	Tan	Cot	Tan	Cot	Tan	Cot	Tan	Cot	Tan	Cot	
0	.70021	1.4281	.72654	1.3764	.75355	1.3270	.78129	1.2799	.80978	1.2349	60
1	064	.4273	699	.3755	401	.3262	175	.2792	.81027	.2342	59
2	107	.4264	743	.3747	447	.3254	222	.2784	075	.2334	58
3	151	.4255	788	.3739	492	.3246	269	.2776	123	.2327	57
4	194	.4246	832	.3730	538	.3238	316	.2769	171	.2320	56
5	.70238	1.4237	.72877	1.3722	.75584	1.3230	.78363	1.2761	.81220	1.2312	55
6	281	.4229	921	.3713	629	.3222	410	.2753	268	.2305	54
7	325	.4220	.72966	.3705	675	.3214	457	.2746	316	.2298	53
8	368	.4211	.73010	.3697	721	.3206	504	.2738	364	.2290	52
9	412	.4202	055	.3688	767	.3198	551	.2731	413	.2283	51
10	.70455	1.4193	.73100	1.3680	.75812	1.3190	.78598	1.2723	.81461	1.2276	50
11	499	.4185	144	.3672	858	.3182	645	.2715	510	.2268	49
12	542	.4176	189	.3663	904	.3175	692	.2708	558	.2261	48
13	586	.4167	234	.3655	950	.3167	739	.2700	606	.2254	47
14	629	.4158	278	.3647	.75996	.3159	786	.2693	655	.2247	46
15	.70673	1.4150	.73323	1.3638	.76042	1.3151	.78834	1.2685	.81703	1.2239	45
16	717	.4141	368	.3630	088	.3143	881	.2677	752	.2232	44
17	760	.4132	413	.3622	134	.3135	928	.2670	800	.2225	43
18	804	.4124	457	.3613	180	.3127	.78975	.2662	849	.2218	42
19	848	.4115	502	.3605	226	.3119	.79022	.2655	898	.2210	41
20	.70891	1.4106	.73547	1.3597	.76272	1.3111	.79070	1.2647	.81946	1.2203	40
21	935	.4097	592	.3588	318	.3103	117	.2640	.81995	.2196	39
22	.70979	.4089	637	.3580	364	.3095	164	.2632	.82044	.2189	38
23	.71023	.4080	681	.3572	410	.3087	212	.2624	092	.2181	37
24	066	.4071	726	.3564	456	.3079	259	.2617	141	.2174	36
25	.71110	1.4063	.73771	1.3555	.76502	1.3072	.79306	1.2609	.82190	1.2167	35
26	154	.4054	816	.3547	548	.3064	354	.2602	238	.2160	34
27	198	.4045	861	.3539	594	.3056	401	.2594	287	.2153	33
28	242	.4037	906	.3531	640	.3048	449	.2587	336	.2145	32
29	285	.4028	951	.3522	686	.3040	496	.2579	385	.2138	31
30	.71329	1.4019	.73996	1.3514	.76733	1.3032	.79544	1.2572	.82434	1.2131	30
31	373	.4011	.74041	.3506	779	.3024	591	.2564	483	.2124	29
32	417	.4002	086	.3498	825	.3017	639	.2557	531	.2117	28
33	461	.3994	131	.3490	871	.3009	686	.2549	580	.2109	27
34	505	.3985	176	.3481	918	.3001	734	.2542	629	.2102	26
35	.71549	1.3976	.74221	1.3473	.76964	1.2993	.79781	1.2534	.82678	1.2095	25
36	593	.3968	267	.3465	.77010	.2985	829	.2527	727	.2088	24
37	637	.3959	312	.3457	057	.2977	877	.2519	776	.2081	23
38	681	.3951	357	.3449	103	.2970	924	.2512	825	.2074	22
39	725	.3942	402	.3440	149	.2962	.79972	.2504	874	.2066	21
40	.71769	1.3934	.74447	1.3432	.77196	1.2954	.80020	1.2497	.82923	1.2059	20
41	813	.3925	492	.3424	242	.2946	067	.2489	.82972	.2052	19
42	857	.3916	538	.3416	289	.2938	115	.2482	.83022	.2045	18
43	901	.3908	583	.3408	335	.2931	163	.2475	071	.2038	17
44	946	.3899	628	.3400	382	.2923	211	.2467	120	.2031	16
45	.71990	1.3891	.74674	1.3392	.77428	1.2915	.80258	1.2460	.83169	1.2024	15
46	.72034	.3882	719	.3384	475	.2907	306	.2452	218	.2017	14
47	078	.3874	764	.3375	521	.2900	354	.2445	268	.2009	13
48	122	.3865	810	.3367	568	.2892	402	.2437	317	.2002	12
49	167	.3857	855	.3359	615	.2884	450	.2430	366	.1995	11
50	.72211	1.3848	.74900	1.3351	.77661	1.2876	.80498	1.2423	.83415	1.1988	10
51	255	.3840	946	.3343	708	.2869	546	.2415	465	.1981	9
52	299	.3831	.74991	.3335	754	.2861	594	.2408	514	.1974	8
53	344	.3823	.75037	.3327	801	.2853	642	.2401	564	.1967	7
54	388	.3814	082	.3319	848	.2846	690	.2393	613	.1960	6
55	.72432	1.3806	.75128	1.3311	.77895	1.2838	.80738	1.2386	.83662	1.1953	5
56	477	.3798	173	.3303	941	.2830	786	.2378	712	.1946	4
57	521	.3789	219	.3295	.77988	.2822	834	.2371	761	.1939	3
58	565	.3781	264	.3287	.78035	.2815	882	.2364	811	.1932	2
59	610	.3772	310	.3278	082	.2807	930	.2356	860	.1925	1
60	.72654	1.3764	.75355	1.3270	.78129	1.2799	.80978	1.2349	.83910	1.1918	0
	Cot	Tan	Cot	Tan	Cot	Tan	Cot	Tan	Cot	Tan	′
	54°		53°		52°		51°		50°		←

XI. FIVE-PLACE VALUES: SINE AND COSINE

→	40°		41°		42°		43°		44°		
′	Sin	Cos	Sin	Cos	Sin	Cos	Sin	Cos	Sin	Cos	
0	.64279	.76604	.65606	.75471	.66913	.74314	.68200	.73135	.69466	.71934	60
1	301	586	628	452	935	295	221	116	487	914	59
2	323	567	650	433	956	276	242	096	508	894	58
3	346	548	672	414	978	256	264	076	529	873	57
4	368	530	694	395	.66999	237	285	056	549	853	56
5	.64390	.76511	.65716	.75375	.67021	.74217	.68306	.73036	.69570	.71833	55
6	412	492	738	356	043	198	327	.73016	591	813	54
7	435	473	759	337	064	178	349	.72996	612	792	53
8	457	455	781	318	086	159	370	976	633	772	52
9	479	436	803	299	107	139	391	957	654	752	51
10	.64501	.76417	.65825	.75280	.67129	.74120	.68412	.72937	.69675	.71732	50
11	524	398	847	261	151	100	434	917	696	711	49
12	546	380	869	241	172	080	455	897	717	691	48
13	568	361	891	222	194	061	476	877	737	671	47
14	590	342	913	203	215	041	497	857	758	650	46
15	.64612	.76323	.65935	.75184	.67237	.74022	.68518	.72837	.69779	.71630	45
16	635	304	956	165	258	.74002	539	817	800	610	44
17	657	286	.65978	146	280	.73983	561	797	821	590	43
18	679	267	.66000	126	301	963	582	777	842	569	42
19	701	248	022	107	323	944	603	757	862	549	41
20	.64723	.76229	.66044	.75088	.67344	.73924	.68624	.72737	.69883	.71529	40
21	746	210	066	069	366	904	645	717	904	508	39
22	768	192	088	050	387	885	666	697	925	488	38
23	790	173	109	030	409	865	688	677	946	468	37
24	812	154	131	.75011	430	846	709	657	966	447	36
25	.64834	.76135	.66153	.74992	.67452	.73826	.68730	.72637	.69987	.71427	35
26	856	116	175	973	473	806	751	617	.70008	407	34
27	878	097	197	953	495	787	772	597	029	386	33
28	901	078	218	934	516	767	793	577	049	366	32
29	923	059	240	915	538	747	814	557	070	345	31
30	.64945	.76041	.66262	.74896	.67559	.73728	.68835	.72537	.70091	.71325	30
31	967	022	284	876	580	708	857	517	112	305	29
32	.64989	.76003	306	857	602	688	878	497	132	284	28
33	.65011	.75984	327	838	623	669	899	477	153	264	27
34	033	965	349	818	645	649	920	457	174	243	26
35	.65055	.75946	.66371	.74799	.67666	.73629	.68941	.72437	.70195	.71223	25
36	077	927	393	780	688	610	962	417	215	203	24
37	100	908	414	760	709	590	.68983	397	236	182	23
38	122	889	436	741	730	570	.69004	377	257	162	22
39	144	870	458	722	752	551	025	357	277	141	21
40	.65166	.75851	.66480	.74703	.67773	.73531	.69046	.72337	.70298	.71121	20
41	188	832	501	683	795	511	067	317	319	100	19
42	210	813	523	664	816	491	088	297	339	080	18
43	232	794	545	644	837	472	109	277	360	059	17
44	254	775	566	625	859	452	130	257	381	039	16
45	.65276	.75756	.66588	.74606	.67880	.73432	.69151	.72236	.70401	.71019	15
46	298	738	610	586	901	413	172	216	422	.70998	14
47	320	719	632	567	923	393	193	196	443	978	13
48	342	700	653	548	944	373	214	176	463	957	12
49	364	680	675	528	965	353	235	156	484	937	11
50	.65386	.75661	.66697	.74509	.67987	.73333	.69256	.72136	.70505	.70916	10
51	408	642	718	489	.68008	314	277	116	525	896	9
52	430	623	740	470	029	294	298	095	546	875	8
53	452	604	762	451	051	274	319	075	567	855	7
54	474	585	783	431	072	254	340	055	587	834	6
55	.65496	.75566	.66805	.74412	.68093	.73234	.69361	.72035	.70608	.70813	5
56	518	547	827	392	115	215	382	.72015	628	793	4
57	540	528	848	373	136	195	403	.71995	649	772	3
58	562	509	870	353	157	175	424	974	670	752	2
59	584	490	891	334	179	155	445	954	690	731	1
60	.65606	.75471	.66913	.74314	.68200	.73135	.69466	.71934	.70711	.70711	0
	Cos	Sin	Cos	Sin	Cos	Sin	Cos	Sin	Cos	Sin	′
	49°		48°		47°		46°		45°		←

[104]

XI. FIVE–PLACE VALUES: TANGENT AND COTANGENT

→	40°		41°		42°		43°		44°		
′	Tan	Cot	Tan	Cot	Tan	Cot	Tan	Cot	Tan	Cot	
0	.83910	1.1918	.86929	1.1504	.90040	1.1106	.93252	1.0724	.96569	1.0355	60
1	.83960	.1910	.86980	.1497	093	.1100	306	.0717	625	.0349	59
2	.84009	.1903	.87031	.1490	146	.1093	360	.0711	681	.0343	58
3	059	.1896	082	.1483	199	.1087	415	.0705	738	.0337	57
4	108	.1889	133	.1477	251	.1080	469	.0699	794	.0331	56
5	.84158	1.1882	.87184	1.1470	.90304	1.1074	.93524	1.0692	.96850	1.0325	55
6	208	.1875	236	.1463	357	.1067	578	.0686	907	.0319	54
7	258	.1868	287	.1456	410	.1061	633	.0680	.96963	.0313	53
8	307	.1861	338	.1450	463	.1054	688	.0674	.97020	.0307	52
9	357	.1854	389	.1443	516	.1048	742	.0668	076	.0301	51
10	.84407	1.1847	.87441	1.1436	.90569	1.1041	.93797	1.0661	.97133	1.0295	50
11	457	.1840	492	.1430	621	.1035	852	.0655	189	.0289	49
12	507	.1833	543	.1423	674	.1028	906	.0649	246	.0283	48
13	556	.1826	595	.1416	727	.1022	.93961	.0643	302	.0277	47
14	606	.1819	646	.1410	781	.1016	.94016	.0637	359	.0271	46
15	.84656	1.1812	.87698	1.1403	.90834	1.1009	.94071	1.0630	.97416	1.0265	45
16	706	.1806	749	.1396	887	.1003	125	.0624	472	.0259	44
17	756	.1799	801	.1389	940	.0996	180	.0618	529	.0253	43
18	806	.1792	852	.1383	.90993	.0990	235	.0612	586	.0247	42
19	856	.1785	904	.1376	.91046	.0983	290	.0606	643	.0241	41
20	.84906	1.1778	.87955	1.1369	.91099	1.0977	.94345	1.0599	.97700	1.0235	40
21	.84956	.1771	.88007	.1363	153	.0971	400	.0593	756	.0230	39
22	.85006	.1764	059	.1356	206	.0964	455	.0587	813	.0224	38
23	057	.1757	110	.1349	259	.0958	510	.0581	870	.0218	37
24	107	.1750	162	.1343	313	.0951	565	.0575	927	.0212	36
25	.85157	1.1743	.88214	1.1336	.91366	1.0945	.94620	1.0569	.97984	1.0206	35
26	207	.1736	265	.1329	419	.0939	676	.0562	.98041	.0200	34
27	257	.1729	317	.1323	473	.0932	731	.0556	098	.0194	33
28	308	.1722	369	.1316	526	.0926	786	.0550	155	.0188	32
29	358	.1715	421	.1310	580	.0919	841	.0544	213	.0182	31
30	.85408	1.1708	.88473	1.1303	.91633	1.0913	.94896	1.0538	.98270	1.0176	30
31	458	.1702	524	.1296	687	.0907	.94952	.0532	327	.0170	29
32	509	.1695	576	.1290	740	.0900	.95007	.0526	384	.0164	28
33	559	.1688	628	.1283	794	.0894	062	.0519	441	.0158	27
34	609	.1681	680	.1276	847	.0888	118	.0513	499	.0152	26
35	.85660	1.1674	.88732	1.1270	.91901	1.0881	.95173	1.0507	.98556	1.0147	25
36	710	.1667	784	.1263	.91955	.0875	229	.0501	613	.0141	24
37	761	.1660	836	.1257	.92008	.0869	284	.0495	671	.0135	23
38	811	.1653	888	.1250	062	.0862	340	.0489	728	.0129	22
39	862	.1647	940	.1243	116	.0856	395	.0483	786	.0123	21
40	.85912	1.1640	.88992	1.1237	.92170	1.0850	.95451	1.0477	.98843	1.0117	20
41	.85963	.1633	.89045	.1230	224	.0843	506	.0470	901	.0111	19
42	.86014	.1626	097	.1224	277	.0837	562	.0464	.98958	.0105	18
43	064	.1619	149	.1217	331	.0831	618	.0458	.99016	.0099	17
44	115	.1612	201	.1211	385	.0824	673	.0452	073	.0094	16
45	.86166	1.1606	.89253	1.1204	.92439	1.0818	.95729	1.0446	.99131	1.0088	15
46	216	.1599	306	.1197	493	.0812	785	.0440	189	.0082	14
47	267	.1592	358	.1191	547	.0805	841	.0434	247	.0076	13
48	318	.1585	410	.1184	601	.0799	897	.0428	304	.0070	12
49	368	.1578	463	.1178	655	.0793	.95952	.0422	362	.0064	11
50	.86419	1.1571	.89515	1.1171	.92709	1.0786	.96008	1.0416	.99420	1.0058	10
51	470	.1565	567	.1165	763	.0780	064	.0410	478	.0052	9
52	521	.1558	620	.1158	817	.0774	120	.0404	536	.0047	8
53	572	.1551	672	.1152	872	.0768	176	.0398	594	.0041	7
54	623	.1544	725	.1145	926	.0761	232	.0392	652	.0035	6
55	.86674	1.1538	.89777	1.1139	.92980	1.0755	.96288	1.0385	.99710	1.0029	5
56	725	.1531	830	.1132	.93034	.0749	344	.0379	768	.0023	4
57	776	.1524	883	.1126	088	.0742	400	.0373	826	.0017	3
58	827	.1517	935	.1119	143	.0736	457	.0367	884	.0012	2
59	878	.1510	.89988	.1113	197	.0730	513	.0361	.99942	.0006	1
60	.86929	1.1504	.90040	1.1106	.93252	1.0724	.96569	1.0355	1.0000	1.0000	0
	Cot	Tan	Cot	Tan	Cot	Tan	Cot	Tan	Cot	Tan	′
	49°		48°		47°		46°		45°		←

→	0°		1°		2°		3°		4°		
′	Sec	Csc	Sec	Csc	Sec	Csc	Sec	Csc	Sec	Csc	
0	1.0000	——	1.0002	57.299	1.0006	28.654	1.0014	19.107	1.0024	14.336	**60**
1	.0000	3437.7	.0002	56.359	.0006	.417	.0014	19.002	.0025	.276	59
2	.0000	1718.9	.0002	55.451	.0006	28.184	.0014	18.898	.0025	.217	58
3	.0000	1145.9	.0002	54.570	.0006	27.955	.0014	.794	.0025	.159	57
4	.0000	859.44	.0002	53.718	.0007	.730	.0014	.692	.0025	.101	56
5	1.0000	687.55	1.0002	52.892	1.0007	27.508	1.0014	18.591	1.0025	14.044	**55**
6	.0000	572.96	.0002	52.090	.0007	.290	.0015	.492	.0026	13.987	54
7	.0000	491.11	.0002	51.313	.0007	27.075	.0015	.393	.0026	.930	53
8	.0000	429.72	.0002	50.558	.0007	26.864	.0015	.295	.0026	.874	52
9	.0000	381.97	.0002	49.826	.0007	.655	.0015	.198	.0026	.818	51
10	1.0000	343.78	1.0002	49.114	1.0007	26.451	1.0015	18.103	1.0027	13.763	**50**
11	.0000	312.52	.0002	48.422	.0007	.249	.0015	18.008	.0027	.708	49
12	.0000	286.48	.0002	47.750	.0007	26.050	.0016	17.914	.0027	.654	48
13	.0000	264.44	.0002	47.096	.0007	25.854	.0016	.822	.0027	.600	47
14	.0000	245.55	.0002	46.460	.0008	.661	.0016	.730	.0027	.547	46
15	1.0000	229.18	1.0002	45.840	1.0008	25.471	1.0016	17.639	1.0028	13.494	**45**
16	.0000	214.86	.0002	45.237	.0008	.284	.0016	.549	.0028	.441	44
17	.0000	202.22	.0003	44.650	.0008	25.100	.0016	.460	.0028	.389	43
18	.0000	190.99	.0003	44.077	.0008	24.918	.0017	.372	.0028	.337	42
19	.0000	180.93	.0003	43.520	.0008	.739	.0017	.285	.0028	.286	41
20	1.0000	171.89	1.0003	42.976	1.0008	24.562	1.0017	17.198	1.0029	13.235	**40**
21	.0000	163.70	.0003	42.445	.0008	.388	.0017	.113	.0029	.184	39
22	.0000	156.26	.0003	41.928	.0009	.216	.0017	17.028	.0029	.134	38
23	.0000	149.47	.0003	41.423	.0009	24.047	.0017	16.945	.0029	.084	37
24	.0000	143.24	.0003	40.930	.0009	23.880	.0018	.862	.0030	13.035	36
25	1.0000	137.51	1.0003	40.448	1.0009	23.716	1.0018	16.779	1.0030	12.985	**35**
26	.0000	132.22	.0003	39.978	.0009	.553	.0018	.698	.0030	.937	34
27	.0000	127.33	.0003	39.519	.0009	.393	.0018	.618	.0030	.888	33
28	.0000	122.78	.0003	39.070	.0009	.235	.0018	.538	.0030	.840	32
29	.0000	118.54	.0003	38.631	.0009	23.079	.0019	.459	.0031	.793	31
30	1.0000	114.59	1.0003	38.202	1.0010	22.926	1.0019	16.380	1.0031	12.745	**30**
31	.0000	110.90	.0004	37.782	.0010	.774	.0019	.303	.0031	.699	29
32	.0000	107.43	.0004	37.371	.0010	.624	.0019	.226	.0031	.652	28
33	.0000	104.18	.0004	36.970	.0010	.476	.0019	.150	.0032	.606	27
34	.0000	101.11	.0004	36.576	.0010	.330	.0019	.075	.0032	.560	26
35	1.0001	98.223	1.0004	36.191	1.0010	22.187	1.0020	16.000	1.0032	12.514	**25**
36	.0001	95.495	.0004	35.815	.0010	22.044	.0020	15.926	.0032	.469	24
37	.0001	92.914	.0004	35.445	.0010	21.904	.0020	.853	.0033	.424	23
38	.0001	90.469	.0004	35.084	.0011	.766	.0020	.780	.0033	.379	22
39	.0001	88.149	.0004	34.730	.0011	.629	.0020	.708	.0033	.335	21
40	1.0001	85.946	1.0004	34.382	1.0011	21.494	1.0021	15.637	1.0033	12.291	**20**
41	.0001	83.849	.0004	34.042	.0011	.360	.0021	.566	.0034	.248	19
42	.0001	81.853	.0004	33.708	.0011	.229	.0021	.496	.0034	.204	18
43	.0001	79.950	.0004	33.381	.0011	21.098	.0021	.427	.0034	.161	17
44	.0001	78.133	.0005	33.060	.0011	20.970	.0021	.358	.0034	.119	16
45	1.0001	76.397	1.0005	32.746	1.0012	20.843	1.0021	15.290	1.0034	12.076	**15**
46	.0001	74.736	.0005	32.437	.0012	.717	.0022	.222	.0035	12.034	14
47	.0001	73.146	.0005	32.134	.0012	.593	.0022	.155	.0035	11.992	13
48	.0001	71.622	.0005	31.836	.0012	.471	.0022	.089	.0035	.951	12
49	.0001	70.160	.0005	31.544	.0012	.350	.0022	15.023	.0035	.909	11
50	1.0001	68.757	1.0005	31.258	1.0012	20.230	1.0022	14.958	1.0036	11.868	**10**
51	.0001	67.409	.0005	30.976	.0012	20.112	.0023	.893	.0036	.828	9
52	.0001	66.113	.0005	30.700	.0013	19.995	.0023	.829	.0036	.787	8
53	.0001	64.866	.0005	30.428	.0013	.880	.0023	.766	.0036	.747	7
54	.0001	63.665	.0006	30.161	.0013	.766	.0023	.703	.0037	.707	6
55	1.0001	62.507	1.0006	29.899	1.0013	19.653	1.0023	14.640	1.0037	11.668	**5**
56	.0001	61.391	.0006	29.641	.0013	.541	.0024	.578	.0037	.628	4
57	.0001	60.314	.0006	29.388	.0013	.431	.0024	.517	.0037	.589	3
58	.0001	59.274	.0006	29.139	.0013	.322	.0024	.456	.0038	.551	2
59	.0001	58.270	.0006	28.894	.0014	.214	.0024	.395	.0038	.512	1
60	1.0002	57.299	1.0006	28.654	1.0014	19.107	1.0024	14.336	1.0038	11.474	**0**
	Csc	Sec	Csc	Sec	Csc	Sec	Csc	Sec	Csc	Sec	′
	89°		88°		87°		86°		85°		←

′	5° Sec	5° Csc	6° Sec	6° Csc	7° Sec	7° Csc	8° Sec	8° Csc	9° Sec	9° Csc	
0	1.0038	11.474	1.0055	9.5668	1.0075	8.2055	1.0098	7.1853	1.0125	6.3925	60
1	.0038	.436	.0055	.5404	.0075	.1861	.0099	.1705	.0125	.3807	59
2	.0039	.398	.0056	.5141	.0076	.1668	.0099	.1557	.0126	.3691	58
3	.0039	.360	.0056	.4880	.0076	.1476	.0100	.1410	.0126	.3574	57
4	.0039	.323	.0056	.4620	.0077	.1285	.0100	.1263	.0127	.3458	56
5	1.0039	11.286	1.0057	9.4362	1.0077	8.1095	1.0100	7.1117	1.0127	6.3343	55
6	.0040	.249	.0057	.4105	.0077	.0905	.0101	.0972	.0127	.3228	54
7	.0040	.213	.0057	.3850	.0078	.0717	.0101	.0827	.0128	.3113	53
8	.0040	.176	.0058	.3596	.0078	.0529	.0102	.0683	.0128	.2999	52
9	.0041	.140	.0058	.3343	.0078	.0342	.0102	.0539	.0129	.2885	51
10	1.0041	11.105	1.0058	9.3092	1.0079	8.0156	1.0102	7.0396	1.0129	6.2772	50
11	.0041	.069	.0059	.2842	.0079	7.9971	.0103	.0254	.0130	.2659	49
12	.0041	11.034	.0059	.2593	.0079	.9787	.0103	7.0112	.0130	.2546	48
13	.0042	10.998	.0059	.2346	.0080	.9604	.0104	6.9971	.0131	.2434	47
14	.0042	.963	.0059	.2100	.0080	.9422	.0104	.9830	.0131	.2323	46
15	1.0042	10.929	1.0060	9.1855	1.0081	7.9240	1.0105	6.9690	1.0132	6.2211	45
16	.0042	.894	.0060	.1612	.0081	.9059	.0105	.9550	.0132	.2100	44
17	.0043	.860	.0060	.1370	.0081	.8879	.0105	.9411	.0133	.1990	43
18	.0043	.826	.0061	.1129	.0082	.8700	.0106	.9273	.0133	.1880	42
19	.0043	.792	.0061	.0890	.0082	.8522	.0106	.9135	.0134	.1770	41
20	1.0043	10.758	1.0061	9.0652	1.0082	7.8344	1.0107	6.8998	1.0134	6.1661	40
21	.0044	.725	.0062	.0415	.0083	.8168	.0107	.8861	.0135	.1552	39
22	.0044	.692	.0062	9.0179	.0083	.7992	.0108	.8725	.0135	.1443	38
23	.0044	.659	.0062	8.9944	.0084	.7817	.0108	.8589	.0136	.1335	37
24	.0045	.626	.0063	.9711	.0084	.7642	.0108	.8454	.0136	.1227	36
25	1.0045	10.593	1.0063	8.9479	1.0084	7.7469	1.0109	6.8320	1.0137	6.1120	35
26	.0045	.561	.0063	.9248	.0085	.7296	.0109	.8186	.0137	.1013	34
27	.0045	.529	.0064	.9019	.0085	.7124	.0110	.8052	.0138	.0906	33
28	.0046	.497	.0064	.8790	.0086	.6953	.0110	.7919	.0138	.0800	32
29	.0046	.465	.0064	.8563	.0086	.6783	.0111	.7787	.0139	.0694	31
30	1.0046	10.433	1.0065	8.8337	1.0086	7.6613	1.0111	6.7655	1.0139	6.0589	30
31	.0047	.402	.0065	.8112	.0087	.6444	.0112	.7523	.0140	.0483	29
32	.0047	.371	.0065	.7888	.0087	.6276	.0112	.7392	.0140	.0379	28
33	.0047	.340	.0066	.7665	.0087	.6109	.0112	.7262	.0141	.0274	27
34	.0047	.309	.0066	.7444	.0088	.5942	.0113	.7132	.0141	.0170	26
35	1.0048	10.278	1.0066	8.7223	1.0088	7.5776	1.0113	6.7003	1.0142	6.0067	25
36	.0048	.248	.0067	.7004	.0089	.5611	.0114	.6874	.0142	5.9963	24
37	.0048	.217	.0067	.6786	.0089	.5446	.0114	.6745	.0143	.9860	23
38	.0049	.187	.0067	.6569	.0089	.5282	.0115	.6618	.0143	.9758	22
39	.0049	.157	.0068	.6353	.0090	.5119	.0115	.6490	.0144	.9656	21
40	1.0049	10.128	1.0068	8.6138	1.0090	7.4957	1.0116	6.6363	1.0144	5.9554	20
41	.0049	.098	.0068	.5924	.0091	.4795	.0116	.6237	.0145	.9452	19
42	.0050	.068	.0069	.5711	.0091	.4635	.0116	.6111	.0145	.9351	18
43	.0050	.039	.0069	.5500	.0091	.4474	.0117	.5986	.0146	.9250	17
44	.0050	10.010	.0069	.5289	.0092	.4315	.0117	.5861	.0146	.9150	16
45	1.0051	9.9812	1.0070	8.5079	1.0092	7.4156	1.0118	6.5736	1.0147	5.9049	15
46	.0051	.9525	.0070	.4871	.0093	.3998	.0118	.5612	.0147	.8950	14
47	.0051	.9239	.0070	.4663	.0093	.3840	.0119	.5489	.0148	.8850	13
48	.0051	.8955	.0071	.4457	.0093	.3684	.0119	.5366	.0148	.8751	12
49	.0052	.8672	.0071	.4251	.0094	.3527	.0120	.5243	.0149	.8652	11
50	1.0052	9.8391	1.0072	8.4047	1.0094	7.3372	1.0120	6.5121	1.0149	5.8554	10
51	.0052	.8112	.0072	.3843	.0095	.3217	.0120	.4999	.0150	.8456	9
52	.0053	.7834	.0072	.3641	.0095	.3063	.0121	.4878	.0150	.8358	8
53	.0053	.7558	.0073	.3439	.0095	.2909	.0121	.4757	.0151	.8261	7
54	.0053	.7283	.0073	.3238	.0096	.2757	.0122	.4637	.0151	.8164	6
55	1.0054	9.7010	1.0073	8.3039	1.0096	7.2604	1.0122	6.4517	1.0152	5.8067	5
56	.0054	.6739	.0074	.2840	.0097	.2453	.0123	.4398	.0152	.7970	4
57	.0054	.6469	.0074	.2642	.0097	.2302	.0123	.4279	.0153	.7874	3
58	.0054	.6200	.0074	.2446	.0097	.2152	.0124	.4160	.0153	.7778	2
59	.0055	.5933	.0075	.2250	.0098	.2002	.0124	.4042	.0154	.7683	1
60	1.0055	9.5668	1.0075	8.2055	1.0098	7.1853	1.0125	6.3925	1.0154	5.7588	0
	Csc	Sec	Csc	Sec	Csc	Sec	Csc	Sec	Csc	Sec	′
	84°		83°		82°		81°		80°		←

XI. FIVE–PLACE VALUES: SECANT AND COSECANT

→	10°		11°		12°		13°		14°		
′	Sec	Csc	Sec	Csc	Sec	Csc	Sec	Csc	Sec	Csc	
0	1.0154	5.7588	1.0187	5.2408	1.0223	4.8097	1.0263	4.4454	1.0306	4.1336	60
1	.0155	.7493	.0188	.2330	.0224	.8032	.0264	.4398	.0307	.1287	59
2	.0155	.7398	.0188	.2252	.0225	.7966	.0264	.4342	.0308	.1239	58
3	.0156	.7304	.0189	.2174	.0225	.7901	.0265	.4287	.0308	.1191	57
4	.0156	.7210	.0189	.2097	.0226	.7836	.0266	.4231	.0309	.1144	56
5	1.0157	5.7117	1.0190	5.2019	1.0227	4.7771	1.0266	4.4176	1.0310	4.1096	55
6	.0157	.7023	.0191	.1942	.0227	.7706	.0267	.4121	.0311	.1048	54
7	.0158	.6930	.0191	.1865	.0228	.7641	.0268	.4066	.0311	.1001	53
8	.0158	.6838	.0192	.1789	.0228	.7577	.0269	.4011	.0312	.0954	52
9	.0159	.6745	.0192	.1712	.0229	.7512	.0269	.3956	.0313	.0906	51
10	1.0160	5.6653	1.0193	5.1636	1.0230	4.7448	1.0270	4.3901	1.0314	4.0859	50
11	.0160	.6562	.0194	.1560	.0230	.7384	.0271	.3847	.0314	.0812	49
12	.0161	.6470	.0194	.1484	.0231	.7321	.0271	.3792	.0315	.0765	48
13	.0161	.6379	.0195	.1409	.0232	.7257	.0272	.3738	.0316	.0718	47
14	.0162	.6288	.0195	.1333	.0232	.7194	.0273	.3684	.0317	.0672	46
15	1.0162	5.6198	1.0196	5.1258	1.0233	4.7130	1.0273	4.3630	1.0317	4.0625	45
16	.0163	.6107	.0197	.1183	.0234	.7067	.0274	.3576	.0318	.0579	44
17	.0163	.6017	.0197	.1109	.0234	.7004	.0275	.3522	.0319	.0532	43
18	.0164	.5928	.0198	.1034	.0235	.6942	.0276	.3469	.0320	.0486	42
19	.0164	.5838	.0198	.0960	.0236	.6879	.0276	.3415	.0321	.0440	41
20	1.0165	5.5749	1.0199	5.0886	1.0236	4.6817	1.0277	4.3362	1.0321	4.0394	40
21	.0165	.5660	.0199	.0813	.0237	.6755	.0278	.3309	.0322	.0348	39
22	.0166	.5572	.0200	.0739	.0238	.6693	.0278	.3256	.0323	.0302	38
23	.0166	.5484	.0201	.0666	.0238	.6631	.0279	.3203	.0324	.0256	37
24	.0167	.5396	.0201	.0593	.0239	.6569	.0280	.3150	.0324	.0211	36
25	1.0168	5.5308	1.0202	5.0520	1.0240	4.6507	1.0281	4.3098	1.0325	4.0165	35
26	.0168	.5221	.0202	.0447	.0240	.6446	.0281	.3045	.0326	.0120	34
27	.0169	.5134	.0203	.0375	.0241	.6385	.0282	.2993	.0327	.0075	33
28	.0169	.5047	.0204	.0302	.0241	.6324	.0283	.2941	.0327	4.0029	32
29	.0170	.4960	.0204	.0230	.0242	.6263	.0283	.2889	.0328	3.9984	31
30	1.0170	5.4874	1.0205	5.0159	1.0243	4.6202	1.0284	4.2837	1.0329	3.9939	30
31	.0171	.4788	.0205	.0087	.0243	.6142	.0285	.2785	.0330	.9894	29
32	.0171	.4702	.0206	5.0016	.0244	.6081	.0286	.2733	.0331	.9850	28
33	.0172	.4617	.0207	4.9944	.0245	.6021	.0286	.2681	.0331	.9805	27
34	.0173	.4532	.0207	.9873	.0245	.5961	.0287	.2630	.0332	.9760	26
35	1.0173	5.4447	1.0208	4.9803	1.0246	4.5901	1.0288	4.2579	1.0333	3.9716	25
36	.0174	.4362	.0209	.9732	.0247	.5841	.0288	.2527	.0334	.9672	24
37	.0174	.4278	.0209	.9662	.0247	.5782	.0289	.2476	.0334	.9627	23
38	.0175	.4194	.0210	.9591	.0248	.5722	.0290	.2425	.0335	.9583	22
39	.0175	.4110	.0210	.9521	.0249	.5663	.0291	.2375	.0336	.9539	21
40	1.0176	5.4026	1.0211	4.9452	1.0249	4.5604	1.0291	4.2324	1.0337	3.9495	20
41	.0176	.3943	.0212	.9382	.0250	.5545	.0292	.2273	.0338	.9451	19
42	.0177	.3860	.0212	.9313	.0251	.5486	.0293	.2223	.0338	.9408	18
43	.0178	.3777	.0213	.9244	.0251	.5428	.0294	.2173	.0339	.9364	17
44	.0178	.3695	.0213	.9175	.0252	.5369	.0294	.2122	.0340	.9320	16
45	1.0179	5.3612	1.0214	4.9106	1.0253	4.5311	1.0295	4.2072	1.0341	3.9277	15
46	.0179	.3530	.0215	.9037	.0253	.5253	.0296	.2022	.0342	.9234	14
47	.0180	.3449	.0215	.8969	.0254	.5195	.0297	.1973	.0342	.9190	13
48	.0180	.3367	.0216	.8901	.0255	.5137	.0297	.1923	.0343	.9147	12
49	.0181	.3286	.0217	.8833	.0256	.5079	.0298	.1873	.0344	.9104	11
50	1.0181	5.3205	1.0217	4.8765	1.0256	4.5022	1.0299	4.1824	1.0345	3.9061	10
51	.0182	.3124	.0218	.8697	.0257	.4964	.0299	.1774	.0346	.9018	9
52	.0183	.3044	.0218	.8630	.0258	.4907	.0300	.1725	.0346	.8976	8
53	.0183	.2963	.0219	.8563	.0258	.4850	.0301	.1676	.0347	.8933	7
54	.0184	.2883	.0220	.8496	.0259	.4793	.0302	.1627	.0348	.8890	6
55	1.0184	5.2804	1.0220	4.8429	1.0260	4.4736	1.0302	4.1578	1.0349	3.8848	5
56	.0185	.2724	.0221	.8362	.0260	.4679	.0303	.1529	.0350	.8806	4
57	.0185	.2645	.0222	.8296	.0261	.4623	.0304	.1481	.0350	.8763	3
58	.0186	.2566	.0222	.8229	.0262	.4566	.0305	.1432	.0351	.8721	2
59	.0187	.2487	.0223	.8163	.0262	.4510	.0305	.1384	.0352	.8679	1
60	1.0187	5.2408	1.0223	4.8097	1.0263	4.4454	1.0306	4.1336	1.0353	3.8637	0
	Csc	Sec	Csc	Sec	Csc	Sec	Csc	Sec	Csc	Sec	′
	79°		78°		77°		76°		75°		←

′	15° Sec	15° Csc	16° Sec	16° Csc	17° Sec	17° Csc	18° Sec	18° Csc	19° Sec	19° Csc	
0	1.0353	3.8637	1.0403	3.6280	1.0457	3.4203	1.0515	3.2361	1.0576	3.0716	60
1	.0354	.8595	.0404	.6243	.0458	.4171	.0516	.2332	.0577	.0690	59
2	.0354	.8553	.0405	.6206	.0459	.4138	.0517	.2303	.0578	.0664	58
3	.0355	.8512	.0406	.6169	.0460	.4106	.0518	.2274	.0579	.0638	57
4	.0356	.8470	.0406	.6133	.0461	.4073	.0519	.2245	.0580	.0612	56
5	1.0357	3.8428	1.0407	3.6097	1.0462	3.4041	1.0520	3.2217	1.0582	3.0586	55
6	.0358	.8387	.0408	.6060	.0463	.4009	.0521	.2188	.0583	.0561	54
7	.0358	.8346	.0409	.6024	.0463	.3977	.0522	.2159	.0584	.0535	53
8	.0359	.8304	.0410	.5988	.0464	.3945	.0523	.2131	.0585	.0509	52
9	.0360	.8263	.0411	.5951	.0465	.3913	.0524	.2102	.0586	.0484	51
10	1.0361	3.8222	1.0412	3.5915	1.0466	3.3881	1.0525	3.2074	1.0587	3.0458	50
11	.0362	.8181	.0413	.5879	.0467	.3849	.0526	.2045	.0588	.0433	49
12	.0363	.8140	.0413	.5843	.0468	.3817	.0527	.2017	.0589	.0407	48
13	.0363	.8100	.0414	.5808	.0469	.3785	.0528	.1989	.0590	.0382	47
14	.0364	.8059	.0415	.5772	.0470	.3754	.0529	.1960	.0591	.0357	46
15	1.0365	3.8018	1.0416	3.5736	1.0471	3.3722	1.0530	3.1932	1.0592	3.0331	45
16	.0366	.7978	.0417	.5700	.0472	.3691	.0531	.1904	.0593	.0306	44
17	.0367	.7937	.0418	.5665	.0473	.3659	.0532	.1876	.0594	.0281	43
18	.0367	.7897	.0419	.5629	.0474	.3628	.0533	.1848	.0595	.0256	42
19	.0368	.7857	.0420	.5594	.0475	.3596	.0534	.1820	.0597	.0231	41
20	1.0369	3.7817	1.0421	3.5559	1.0476	3.3565	1.0535	3.1792	1.0598	3.0206	40
21	.0370	.7777	.0421	.5523	.0477	.3534	.0536	.1764	.0599	.0181	39
22	.0371	.7737	.0422	.5488	.0478	.3502	.0537	.1736	.0600	.0156	38
23	.0372	.7697	.0423	.5453	.0479	.3471	.0538	.1708	.0601	.0131	37
24	.0372	.7657	.0424	.5418	.0480	.3440	.0539	.1681	.0602	.0106	36
25	1.0373	3.7617	1.0425	3.5383	1.0480	3.3409	1.0540	3.1653	1.0603	3.0081	35
26	.0374	.7577	.0426	.5348	.0481	.3378	.0541	.1625	.0604	.0056	34
27	.0375	.7538	.0427	.5313	.0482	.3347	.0542	.1598	.0605	.0031	33
28	.0376	.7498	.0428	.5279	.0483	.3317	.0543	.1570	.0606	3.0007	32
29	.0377	.7459	.0429	.5244	.0484	.3286	.0544	.1543	.0607	2.9982	31
30	1.0377	3.7420	1.0429	3.5209	1.0485	3.3255	1.0545	3.1515	1.0608	2.9957	30
31	.0378	.7381	.0430	.5175	.0486	.3224	.0546	.1488	.0610	.9933	29
32	.0379	.7341	.0431	.5140	.0487	.3194	.0547	.1461	.0611	.9908	28
33	.0380	.7302	.0432	.5106	.0488	.3163	.0548	.1433	.0612	.9884	27
34	.0381	.7263	.0433	.5072	.0489	.3133	.0549	.1406	.0613	.9859	26
35	1.0382	3.7225	1.0434	3.5037	1.0490	3.3102	1.0550	3.1379	1.0614	2.9835	25
36	.0382	.7186	.0435	.5003	.0491	.3072	.0551	.1352	.0615	.9811	24
37	.0383	.7147	.0436	.4969	.0492	.3042	.0552	.1325	.0616	.9786	23
38	.0384	.7108	.0437	.4935	.0493	.3012	.0553	.1298	.0617	.9762	22
39	.0385	.7070	.0438	.4901	.0494	.2981	.0554	.1271	.0618	.9738	21
40	1.0386	3.7032	1.0439	3.4867	1.0495	3.2951	1.0555	3.1244	1.0619	2.9713	20
41	.0387	.6993	.0439	.4833	.0496	.2921	.0556	.1217	.0621	.9689	19
42	.0388	.6955	.0440	.4799	.0497	.2891	.0557	.1190	.0622	.9665	18
43	.0388	.6917	.0441	.4766	.0498	.2861	.0558	.1163	.0623	.9641	17
44	.0389	.6879	.0442	.4732	.0499	.2831	.0559	.1137	.0624	.9617	16
45	1.0390	3.6840	1.0443	3.4699	1.0500	3.2801	1.0560	3.1110	1.0625	2.9593	15
46	.0391	.6803	.0444	.4665	.0501	.2772	.0561	.1083	.0626	.9569	14
47	.0392	.6765	.0445	.4632	.0502	.2742	.0563	.1057	.0627	.9545	13
48	.0393	.6727	.0446	.4598	.0503	.2712	.0564	.1030	.0628	.9521	12
49	.0394	.6689	.0447	.4565	.0504	.2683	.0565	.1004	.0629	.9498	11
50	1.0394	3.6652	1.0448	3.4532	1.0505	3.2653	1.0566	3.0977	1.0631	2.9474	10
51	.0395	.6614	.0449	.4499	.0506	.2624	.0567	.0951	.0632	.9450	9
52	.0396	.6576	.0450	.4465	.0507	.2594	.0568	.0925	.0633	.9426	8
53	.0397	.6539	.0450	.4432	.0508	.2565	.0569	.0898	.0634	.9403	7
54	.0398	.6502	.0451	.4399	.0509	.2535	.0570	.0872	.0635	.9379	6
55	1.0399	3.6465	1.0452	3.4367	1.0510	3.2506	1.0571	3.0846	1.0636	2.9355	5
56	.0400	.6427	.0453	.4334	.0511	.2477	.0572	.0820	.0637	.9332	4
57	.0400	.6390	.0454	.4301	.0512	.2448	.0573	.0794	.0638	.9308	3
58	.0401	.6353	.0455	.4268	.0513	.2419	.0574	.0768	.0640	.9285	2
59	.0402	.6316	.0456	.4236	.0514	.2390	.0575	.0742	.0641	.9261	1
60	1.0403	3.6280	1.0457	3.4203	1.0515	3.2361	1.0576	3.0716	1.0642	2.9238	0
	Csc	Sec	Csc	Sec	Csc	Sec	Csc	Sec	Csc	Sec	′
	74°		73°		72°		71°		70°		←

→	20°		21°		22°		23°		24°		
′	Sec	Csc	Sec	Csc	Sec	Csc	Sec	Csc	Sec	Csc	
0	1.0642	2.9238	1.0711	2.7904	1.0785	2.6695	1.0864	2.5593	1.0946	2.4586	**60**
1	.0643	.9215	.0713	.7883	.0787	.6675	.0865	.5576	.0948	.4570	59
2	.0644	.9191	.0714	.7862	.0788	.6656	.0866	.5558	.0949	.4554	58
3	.0645	.9168	.0715	.7841	.0789	.6637	.0868	.5541	.0951	.4538	57
4	.0646	.9145	.0716	.7820	.0790	.6618	.0869	.5523	.0952	.4522	56
5	1.0647	2.9122	1.0717	2.7799	1.0792	2.6599	1.0870	2.5506	1.0953	2.4506	**55**
6	.0649	.9099	.0719	.7778	.0793	.6580	.0872	.5488	.0955	.4490	54
7	.0650	.9075	.0720	.7757	.0794	.6561	.0873	.5471	.0956	.4474	53
8	.0651	.9052	.0721	.7736	.0796	.6542	.0874	.5454	.0958	.4458	52
9	.0652	.9029	.0722	.7715	.0797	.6523	.0876	.5436	.0959	.4442	51
10	1.0653	2.9006	1.0723	2.7695	1.0798	2.6504	1.0877	2.5419	1.0961	2.4426	**50**
11	.0654	.8983	.0725	.7674	.0799	.6485	.0878	.5402	.0962	.4411	49
12	.0655	.8960	.0726	.7653	.0801	.6466	.0880	.5384	.0963	.4395	48
13	.0657	.8938	.0727	.7632	.0802	.6447	.0881	.5367	.0965	.4379	47
14	.0658	.8915	.0728	.7612	.0803	.6429	.0883	.5350	.0966	.4363	46
15	1.0659	2.8892	1.0730	2.7591	1.0804	2.6410	1.0884	2.5333	1.0968	2.4348	**45**
16	.0660	.8869	.0731	.7570	.0806	.6391	.0885	.5316	.0969	.4332	44
17	.0661	.8846	.0732	.7550	.0807	.6372	.0887	.5299	.0971	.4316	43
18	.0662	.8824	.0733	.7529	.0808	.6354	.0888	.5282	.0972	.4300	42
19	.0663	.8801	.0734	.7509	.0810	.6335	.0889	.5264	.0974	.4285	41
20	1.0665	2.8779	1.0736	2.7488	1.0811	2.6316	1.0891	2.5247	1.0975	2.4269	**40**
21	.0666	.8756	.0737	.7468	.0812	.6298	.0892	.5230	.0976	.4254	39
22	.0667	.8733	.0738	.7447	.0814	.6279	.0893	.5213	.0978	.4238	38
23	.0668	.8711	.0739	.7427	.0815	.6260	.0895	.5196	.0979	.4222	37
24	.0669	.8688	.0740	.7407	.0816	.6242	.0896	.5180	.0981	.4207	36
25	1.0670	2.8666	1.0742	2.7386	1.0817	2.6223	1.0898	2.5163	1.0982	2.4191	**35**
26	.0671	.8644	.0743	.7366	.0819	.6205	.0899	.5146	.0984	.4176	34
27	.0673	.8621	.0744	.7346	.0820	.6186	.0900	.5129	.0985	.4160	33
28	.0674	.8599	.0745	.7325	.0821	.6168	.0902	.5112	.0987	.4145	32
29	.0675	.8577	.0747	.7305	.0823	.6150	.0903	.5095	.0988	.4130	31
30	1.0676	2.8555	1.0748	2.7285	1.0824	2.6131	1.0904	2.5078	1.0989	2.4114	**30**
31	.0677	.8532	.0749	.7265	.0825	.6113	.0906	.5062	.0991	.4099	29
32	.0678	.8510	.0750	.7245	.0827	.6095	.0907	.5045	.0992	.4083	28
33	.0680	.8488	.0752	.7225	.0828	.6076	.0909	.5028	.0994	.4068	27
34	.0681	.8466	.0753	.7205	.0829	.6058	.0910	.5012	.0995	.4053	26
35	1.0682	2.8444	1.0754	2.7185	1.0830	2.6040	1.0911	2.4995	1.0997	2.4038	**25**
36	.0683	.8422	.0755	.7165	.0832	.6022	.0913	.4978	.0998	.4022	24
37	.0684	.8400	.0757	.7145	.0833	.6003	.0914	.4962	.1000	.4007	23
38	.0685	.8378	.0758	.7125	.0834	.5985	.0915	.4945	.1001	.3992	22
39	.0687	.8356	.0759	.7105	.0836	.5967	.0917	.4928	.1003	.3977	21
40	1.0688	2.8334	1.0760	2.7085	1.0837	2.5949	1.0918	2.4912	1.1004	2.3961	**20**
41	.0689	.8312	.0761	.7065	.0838	.5931	.0920	.4895	.1006	.3946	19
42	.0690	.8291	.0763	.7046	.0840	.5913	.0921	.4879	.1007	.3931	18
43	.0691	.8239	.0764	.7026	.0841	.5895	.0922	.4862	.1009	.3916	17
44	.0692	.8247	.0765	.7006	.0842	.5877	.0924	.4846	.1010	.3901	16
45	1.0694	2.8225	1.0766	2.6986	1.0844	2.5859	1.0925	2.4830	1.1011	2.3886	**15**
46	.0695	.8204	.0768	.6967	.0845	.5841	.0927	.4813	.1013	.3871	14
47	.0696	.8182	.0769	.6947	.0846	.5823	.0928	.4797	.1014	.3856	13
48	.0697	.8161	.0770	.6927	.0848	.5805	.0929	.4780	.1016	.3841	12
49	.0698	.8139	.0771	.6908	.0849	.5788	.0931	.4764	.1017	.3826	11
50	1.0700	2.8117	1.0773	2.6888	1.0850	2.5770	1.0932	2.4748	1.1019	2.3811	**10**
51	.0701	.8096	.0774	.6869	.0852	.5752	.0934	.4731	.1020	.3796	9
52	.0702	.8075	.0775	.6849	.0853	.5734	.0935	.4715	.1022	.3781	8
53	.0703	.8053	.0777	.6830	.0854	.5716	.0936	.4699	.1023	.3766	7
54	.0704	.8032	.0778	.6811	.0856	.5699	.0938	.4683	.1025	.3751	6
55	1.0705	2.8010	1.0779	2.6791	1.0857	2.5681	1.0939	2.4667	1.1026	2.3736	**5**
56	.0707	.7989	.0780	.6772	.0858	.5663	.0941	.4650	.1028	.3721	4
57	.0708	.7968	.0782	.6752	.0860	.5646	.0942	.4634	.1029	.3706	3
58	.0709	.7947	.0783	.6733	.0861	.5628	.0944	.4618	.1031	.3692	2
59	.0710	.7925	.0784	.6714	.0862	.5611	.0945	.4602	.1032	.3677	1
60	1.0711	2.7904	1.0785	2.6695	1.0864	2.5593	1.0946	2.4586	1.1034	2.3662	**0**
	Csc	Sec	Csc	Sec	Csc	Sec	Csc	Sec	Csc	Sec	**′**
	69°		**68°**		**67°**		**66°**		**65°**		**←**

→	25°		26°		27°		28°		29°		
′	Sec	Csc	Sec	Csc	Sec	Csc	Sec	Csc	Sec	Csc	
0	1.1034	2.3662	1.1126	2.2812	1.1223	2.2027	1.1326	2.1301	1.1434	2.0627	60
1	.1035	.3647	.1128	.2798	.1225	.2014	.1327	.1289	.1435	.0616	59
2	.1037	.3633	.1129	.2785	.1227	.2002	.1329	.1277	.1437	.0605	58
3	.1038	.3618	.1131	.2771	.1228	.1989	.1331	.1266	.1439	.0594	57
4	.1040	.3603	.1132	.2757	.1230	.1977	.1333	.1254	.1441	.0583	56
5	1.1041	2.3588	1.1134	2.2744	1.1232	2.1964	1.1334	2.1242	1.1443	2.0573	55
6	.1043	.3574	.1136	.2730	.1233	.1952	.1336	.1231	.1445	.0562	54
7	.1044	.3559	.1137	.2717	.1235	.1939	.1338	.1219	.1446	.0551	53
8	.1046	.3545	.1139	.2703	.1237	.1927	.1340	.1208	.1448	.0540	52
9	.1047	.3530	.1140	.2690	.1238	.1914	.1342	.1196	.1450	.0530	51
10	1.1049	2.3515	1.1142	2.2677	1.1240	2.1902	1.1343	2.1185	1.1452	2.0519	50
11	.1050	.3501	.1143	.2663	.1242	.1890	.1345	.1173	.1454	.0508	49
12	.1052	.3486	.1145	.2650	.1243	.1877	.1347	.1162	.1456	.0498	48
13	.1053	.3472	.1147	.2636	.1245	.1865	.1349	.1150	.1458	.0487	47
14	.1055	.3457	.1148	.2623	.1247	.1852	.1350	.1139	.1460	.0476	46
15	1.1056	2.3443	1.1150	2.2610	1.1248	2.1840	1.1352	2.1127	1.1461	2.0466	45
16	.1058	.3428	.1151	.2596	.1250	.1828	.1354	.1116	.1463	.0455	44
17	.1059	.3414	.1153	.2583	.1252	.1815	.1356	.1105	.1465	.0445	43
18	.1061	.3400	.1155	.2570	.1253	.1803	.1357	.1093	.1467	.0434	42
19	.1062	.3385	.1156	.2556	.1255	.1791	.1359	.1082	.1469	.0423	41
20	1.1064	2.3371	1.1158	2.2543	1.1257	2.1779	1.1361	2.1070	1.1471	2.0413	40
21	.1066	.3356	.1159	.2530	.1259	.1766	.1363	.1059	.1473	.0402	39
22	.1067	.3342	.1161	.2517	.1260	.1754	.1365	.1048	.1474	.0392	38
23	.1069	.3328	.1163	.2504	.1262	.1742	.1366	.1036	.1476	.0381	37
24	.1070	.3314	.1164	.2490	.1264	.1730	.1368	.1025	.1478	.0371	36
25	1.1072	2.3299	1.1166	2.2477	1.1265	2.1718	1.1370	2.1014	1.1480	2.0360	35
26	.1073	.3285	.1168	.2464	.1267	.1705	.1372	.1002	.1482	.0350	34
27	.1075	.3271	.1169	.2451	.1269	.1693	.1374	.0991	.1484	.0339	33
28	.1076	.3257	.1171	.2438	.1270	.1681	.1375	.0980	.1486	.0329	32
29	.1078	.3242	.1172	.2425	.1272	.1669	.1377	.0969	.1488	.0318	31
30	1.1079	2.3228	1.1174	2.2412	1.1274	2.1657	1.1379	2.0957	1.1490	2.0308	30
31	.1081	.3214	.1176	.2399	.1276	.1645	.1381	.0946	.1491	.0297	29
32	.1082	.3200	.1177	.2385	.1277	.1633	.1383	.0935	.1493	.0287	28
33	.1084	.3186	.1179	.2372	.1279	.1621	.1384	.0924	.1495	.0276	27
34	.1085	.3172	.1180	.2359	.1281	.1609	.1386	.0913	.1497	.0266	26
35	1.1087	2.3158	1.1182	2.2346	1.1282	2.1596	1.1388	2.0901	1.1499	2.0256	25
36	.1089	.3144	.1184	.2333	.1284	.1584	.1390	.0890	.1501	.0245	24
37	.1090	.3130	.1185	.2320	.1286	.1572	.1392	.0879	.1503	.0235	23
38	.1092	.3115	.1187	.2308	.1288	.1560	.1393	.0868	.1505	.0225	22
39	.1093	.3101	.1189	.2295	.1289	.1549	.1395	.0857	.1507	.0214	21
40	1.1095	2.3088	1.1190	2.2282	1.1291	2.1537	1.1397	2.0846	1.1509	2.0204	20
41	.1096	.3074	.1192	.2269	.1293	.1525	.1399	.0835	.1510	.0194	19
42	.1098	.3060	.1194	.2256	.1294	.1513	.1401	.0824	.1512	.0183	18
43	.1099	.3046	.1195	.2243	.1296	.1501	.1402	.0813	.1514	.0173	17
44	.1101	.3032	.1197	.2230	.1298	.1489	.1404	.0802	.1516	.0163	16
45	1.1102	2.3018	1.1198	2.2217	1.1300	2.1477	1.1406	2.0791	1.1518	2.0152	15
46	.1104	.3004	.1200	.2205	.1301	.1465	.1408	.0779	.1520	.0142	14
47	.1106	.2990	.1202	.2192	.1303	.1453	.1410	.0768	.1522	.0132	13
48	.1107	.2976	.1203	.2179	.1305	.1441	.1412	.0757	.1524	.0122	12
49	.1109	.2962	.1205	.2166	.1307	.1430	.1413	.0747	.1526	.0112	11
50	1.1110	2.2949	1.1207	2.2153	1.1308	2.1418	1.1415	2.0736	1.1528	2.0101	10
51	.1112	.2935	.1208	.2141	.1310	.1406	.1417	.0725	.1530	.0091	9
52	.1113	.2921	.1210	.2128	.1312	.1394	.1419	.0714	.1532	.0081	8
53	.1115	.2907	.1212	.2115	.1313	.1382	.1421	.0703	.1533	.0071	7
54	.1117	.2894	.1213	.2103	.1315	.1371	.1423	.0692	.1535	.0061	6
55	1.1118	2.2880	1.1215	2.2090	1.1317	2.1359	1.1424	2.0681	1.1537	2.0051	5
56	.1120	.2866	.1217	.2077	.1319	.1347	.1426	.0670	.1539	.0040	4
57	.1121	.2853	.1218	.2065	.1320	.1336	.1428	.0659	.1541	.0030	3
58	.1123	.2839	.1220	.2052	.1322	.1324	.1430	.0648	.1543	.0020	2
59	.1124	.2825	.1222	.2039	.1324	.1312	.1432	.0637	.1545	.0010	1
60	1.1126	2.2812	1.1223	2.2027	1.1326	2.1301	1.1434	2.0627	1.1547	2.0000	0
	Csc	Sec	Csc	Sec	Csc	Sec	Csc	Sec	Csc	Sec	′
	64°		63°		62°		61°		60°		←

XI. FIVE–PLACE VALUES: SECANT AND COSECANT

→	30°		31°		32°		33°		34°		
′	Sec	Csc	Sec	Csc	Sec	Csc	Sec	Csc	Sec	Csc	
0	1.1547	2.0000	1.1666	1.9416	1.1792	1.8871	1.1924	1.8361	1.2062	1.7883	60
1	.1549	1.9990	.1668	.9407	.1794	.8862	.1926	.8353	.2065	.7875	59
2	.1551	.9980	.1670	.9397	.1796	.8853	.1928	.8344	.2067	.7868	58
3	.1553	.9970	.1672	.9388	.1798	.8844	.1930	.8336	.2069	.7860	57
4	.1555	.9960	.1675	.9379	.1800	.8836	.1933	.8328	.2072	.7852	56
5	1.1557	1.9950	1.1677	1.9369	1.1803	1.8827	1.1935	1.8320	1.2074	1.7844	55
6	.1559	.9940	.1679	.9360	.1805	.8818	.1937	.8312	.2076	.7837	54
7	.1561	.9930	.1681	.9351	.1807	.8810	.1939	.8303	.2079	.7829	53
8	.1563	.9920	.1683	.9341	.1809	.8801	.1942	.8295	.2081	.7821	52
9	.1565	.9910	.1685	.9332	.1811	.8792	.1944	.8287	.2084	.7814	51
10	1.1566	1.9900	1.1687	1.9323	1.1813	1.8783	1.1946	1.8279	1.2086	1.7806	50
11	.1568	.9890	.1689	.9313	.1815	.8775	.1949	.8271	.2088	.7799	49
12	.1570	.9880	.1691	.9304	.1818	.8766	.1951	.8263	.2091	.7791	48
13	.1572	.9870	.1693	.9295	.1820	.8757	.1953	.8255	.2093	.7783	47
14	.1574	.9860	.1695	.9285	.1822	.8749	.1955	.8247	.2096	.7776	46
15	1.1576	1.9850	1.1697	1.9276	1.1824	1.8740	1.1958	1.8238	1.2098	1.7768	45
16	.1578	.9840	.1699	.9267	.1826	.8731	.1960	.8230	.2100	.7761	44
17	.1580	.9830	.1701	.9258	.1828	.8723	.1962	.8222	.2103	.7753	43
18	.1582	.9821	.1703	.9249	.1831	.8714	.1964	.8214	.2105	.7745	42
19	.1584	.9811	.1705	.9239	.1833	.8706	.1967	.8206	.2108	.7738	41
20	1.1586	1.9801	1.1707	1.9230	1.1835	1.3697	1.1969	1.8198	1.2110	1.7730	40
21	.1588	.9791	.1710	.9221	.1837	.8688	.1971	.8190	.2112	.7723	39
22	.1590	.9781	.1712	.9212	.1839	.8680	.1974	.8182	.2115	.7715	38
23	.1592	.9771	.1714	.9203	.1842	.8671	.1976	.8174	.2117	.7708	37
24	.1594	.9762	.1716	.9194	.1844	.8663	.1978	.8166	.2120	.7700	36
25	1.1596	1.9752	1.1718	1.9184	1.1846	1.8654	1.1981	1.8158	1.2122	1.7693	35
26	.1598	.9742	.1720	.9175	.1848	.8646	.1983	.8150	.2124	.7685	34
27	.1600	.9732	.1722	.9166	.1850	.8637	.1985	.8142	.2127	.7678	33
28	.1602	.9722	.1724	.9157	.1852	.8629	.1987	.8134	.2129	.7670	32
29	.1604	.9713	.1726	.9148	.1855	.8620	.1990	.8126	.2132	.7663	31
30	1.1606	1.9703	1.1728	1.9139	1.1857	1.8612	1.1992	1.8118	1.2134	1.7655	30
31	.1608	.9693	.1730	.9130	.1859	.8603	.1994	.8110	.2136	.7648	29
32	.1610	.9684	.1732	.9121	.1861	.8595	.1997	.8102	.2139	.7640	28
33	.1612	.9674	.1735	.9112	.1863	.8586	.1999	.8094	.2141	.7633	27
34	.1614	.9664	.1737	.9103	.1866	.8578	.2001	.8086	.2144	.7625	26
35	1.1616	1.9654	1.1739	1.9094	1.1868	1.8569	1.2004	1.8078	1.2146	1.7618	25
36	.1618	.9645	.1741	.9084	.1870	.8561	.2006	.8070	.2149	.7610	24
37	.1620	.9635	.1743	.9075	.1872	.8552	.2008	.8062	.2151	.7603	23
38	.1622	.9625	.1745	.9066	.1875	.8544	.2011	.8055	.2154	.7596	22
39	.1624	.9616	.1747	.9057	.1877	.8535	.2013	.8047	.2156	.7588	21
40	1.1626	1.9606	1.1749	1.9048	1.1879	1.8527	1.2015	1.8039	1.2158	1.7581	20
41	.1628	.9597	.1751	.9039	.1881	.8519	.2018	.8031	.2161	.7573	19
42	.1630	.9587	.1753	.9031	.1883	.8510	.2020	.8023	.2163	.7566	18
43	.1632	.9577	.1756	.9022	.1886	.8502	.2022	.8015	.2166	.7559	17
44	.1634	.9568	.1758	.9013	.1888	.8494	.2025	.8007	.2168	.7551	16
45	1.1636	1.9558	1.1760	1.9004	1.1890	1.8485	1.2027	1.8000	1.2171	1.7544	15
46	.1638	.9549	.1762	.8995	.1892	.8477	.2029	.7992	.2173	.7537	14
47	.1640	.9539	.1764	.8986	.1895	.8468	.2032	.7984	.2176	.7529	13
48	.1642	.9530	.1766	.8977	.1897	.8460	.2034	.7976	.2178	.7522	12
49	.1644	.9520	.1768	.8968	.1899	.8452	.2036	.7968	.2181	.7515	11
50	1.1646	1.9511	1.1770	1.8959	1.1901	1.8443	1.2039	1.7960	1.2183	1.7507	10
51	.1648	.9501	.1773	.8950	.1903	.8435	.2041	.7953	.2185	.7500	9
52	.1650	.9492	.1775	.8941	.1906	.8427	.2043	.7945	.2188	.7493	8
53	.1652	.9482	.1777	.8933	.1908	.8419	.2046	.7937	.2190	.7485	7
54	.1654	.9473	.1779	.8924	.1910	.8410	.2048	.7929	.2193	.7478	6
55	1.1656	1.9463	1.1781	1.8915	1.1912	1.8402	1.2050	1.7922	1.2195	1.7471	5
56	.1658	.9454	.1783	.8906	.1915	.8394	.2053	.7914	.2198	.7463	4
57	.1660	.9444	.1785	.8897	.1917	.8385	.2055	.7906	.2200	.7456	3
58	.1662	.9435	.1788	.8888	.1919	.8377	.2057	.7898	.2203	.7449	2
59	.1664	.9425	.1790	.8880	.1921	.8369	.2060	.7891	.2205	.7442	1
60	1.1666	1.9416	1.1792	1.8871	1.1924	1.8361	1.2062	1.7883	1.2208	1.7434	0
	Csc	Sec	Csc	Sec	Csc	Sec	Csc	Sec	Csc	Sec	′
	59°		58°		57°		56°		55°		←

→	35°		36°		37°		38°		39°		
′	Sec	Csc	Sec	Csc	Sec	Csc	Sec	Csc	Sec	Csc	
0	1.2208	1.7434	1.2361	1.7013	1.2521	1.6616	1.2690	1.6243	1.2868	1.5890	**60**
1	.2210	.7427	.2363	.7006	.2524	.6610	.2693	.6237	.2871	.5884	59
2	.2213	.7420	.2366	.6999	.2527	.6604	.2696	.6231	.2874	.5879	58
3	.2215	.7413	.2369	.6993	.2530	.6597	.2699	.6225	.2877	.5873	57
4	.2218	.7406	.2371	.6986	.2532	.6591	.2702	.6219	.2880	.5867	56
5	1.2220	1.7398	1.2374	1.6979	1.2535	1.6584	1.2705	1.6213	1.2883	1.5862	**55**
6	.2223	.7391	.2376	.6972	.2538	.6578	.2708	.6207	.2886	.5856	54
7	.2225	.7384	.2379	.6966	.2541	.6572	.2710	.6201	.2889	.5850	53
8	.2228	.7377	.2382	.6959	.2543	.6565	.2713	.6195	.2892	.5845	52
9	.2230	.7370	.2384	.6952	.2546	.6559	.2716	.6189	.2895	.5839	51
10	1.2233	1.7362	1.2387	1.6945	1.2549	1.6553	1.2719	1.6183	1.2898	1.5833	**50**
11	.2235	.7355	.2390	.6939	.2552	.6546	.2722	.6177	.2901	.5828	49
12	.2238	.7348	.2392	.6932	.2554	.6540	.2725	.6171	.2904	.5822	48
13	.2240	.7341	.2395	.6925	.2557	.6534	.2728	.6165	.2907	.5816	47
14	.2243	.7334	.2397	.6918	.2560	.6527	.2731	.6159	.2910	.5811	46
15	1.2245	1.7327	1.2400	1.6912	1.2563	1.6521	1.2734	1.6153	1.2913	1.5805	**45**
16	.2248	.7320	.2403	.6905	.2566	.6515	.2737	.6147	.2916	.5800	44
17	.2250	.7312	.2405	.6898	.2568	.6508	.2740	.6141	.2919	.5794	43
18	.2253	.7305	.2408	.6892	.2571	.6502	.2742	.6135	.2923	.5788	42
19	.2255	.7298	.2411	.6885	.2574	.6496	.2745	.6129	.2926	.5783	41
20	1.2258	1.7291	1.2413	1.6878	1.2577	1.6489	1.2748	1.6123	1.2929	1.5777	**40**
21	.2260	.7284	.2416	.6871	.2579	.6483	.2751	.6117	.2932	.5771	39
22	.2263	.7277	.2419	.6865	.2582	.6477	.2754	.6111	.2935	.5766	38
23	.2265	.7270	.2421	.6858	.2585	.6471	.2757	.6105	.2938	.5760	37
24	.2268	.7263	.2424	.6852	.2588	.6464	.2760	.6099	.2941	.5755	36
25	1.2271	1.7256	1.2427	1.6845	1.2591	1.6458	1.2763	1.6093	1.2944	1.5749	**35**
26	.2273	.7249	.2429	.6838	.2593	.6452	.2766	.6087	.2947	.5744	34
27	.2276	.7242	.2432	.6832	.2596	.6446	.2769	.6082	.2950	.5738	33
28	.2278	.7235	.2435	.6825	.2599	.6439	.2772	.6076	.2953	.5732	32
29	.2281	.7228	.2437	.6818	.2602	.6433	.2775	.6070	.2957	.5727	31
30	1.2283	1.7221	1.2440	1.6812	1.2605	1.6427	1.2778	1.6064	1.2960	1.5721	**30**
31	.2286	.7213	.2443	.6805	.2608	.6421	.2781	.6058	.2963	.5716	29
32	.2288	.7206	.2445	.6799	.2610	.6414	.2784	.6052	.2966	.5710	28
33	.2291	.7199	.2448	.6792	.2613	.6408	.2787	.6046	.2969	.5705	27
34	.2293	.7192	.2451	.6785	.2616	.6402	.2790	.6040	.2972	.5699	26
35	1.2296	1.7185	1.2453	1.6779	1.2619	1.6396	1.2793	1.6035	1.2975	1.5694	**25**
36	.2299	.7179	.2456	.6772	.2622	.6390	.2796	.6029	.2978	.5688	24
37	.2301	.7172	.2459	.6766	.2624	.6383	.2799	.6023	.2981	.5683	23
38	.2304	.7165	.2462	.6759	.2627	.6377	.2802	.6017	.2985	.5677	22
39	.2306	.7158	.2464	.6753	.2630	.6371	.2804	.6011	.2988	.5672	21
40	1.2309	1.7151	1.2467	1.6746	1.2633	1.6365	1.2807	1.6005	1.2991	1.5666	**20**
41	.2311	.7144	.2470	.6739	.2636	.6359	.2810	.6000	.2994	.5661	19
42	.2314	.7137	.2472	.6733	.2639	.6353	.2813	.5994	.2997	.5655	18
43	.2317	.7130	.2475	.6726	.2641	.6346	.2816	.5988	.3000	.5650	17
44	.2319	.7123	.2478	.6720	.2644	.6340	.2819	.5982	.3003	.5644	16
45	1.2322	1.7116	1.2480	1.6713	1.2647	1.6334	1.2822	1.5976	1.3007	1.5639	**15**
46	.2324	.7109	.2483	.6707	.2650	.6328	.2825	.5971	.3010	.5633	14
47	.2327	.7102	.2486	.6700	.2653	.6322	.2828	.5965	.3013	.5628	13
48	.2329	.7095	.2489	.6694	.2656	.6316	.2831	.5959	.3016	.5622	12
49	.2332	.7088	.2491	.6687	.2659	.6310	.2834	.5953	.3019	.5617	11
50	1.2335	1.7081	1.2494	1.6681	1.2661	1.6303	1.2837	1.5948	1.3022	1.5611	**10**
51	.2337	.7075	.2497	.6674	.2664	.6297	.2840	.5942	.3026	.5606	9
52	.2340	.7068	.2499	.6668	.2667	.6291	.2843	.5936	.3029	.5601	8
53	.2342	.7061	.2502	.6661	.2670	.6285	.2846	.5930	.3032	.5595	7
54	.2345	.7054	.2505	.6655	.2673	.6279	.2849	.5925	.3035	.5590	6
55	1.2348	1.7047	1.2508	1.6649	1.2676	1.6273	1.2852	1.5919	1.3038	1.5584	**5**
56	.2350	.7040	.2510	.6642	.2679	.6267	.2855	.5913	.3041	.5579	4
57	.2353	.7033	.2513	.6636	.2682	.6261	.2859	.5907	.3045	.5573	3
58	.2355	.7027	.2516	.6629	.2684	.6255	.2862	.5902	.3048	.5568	2
59	.2358	.7020	.2519	.6623	.2687	.6249	.2865	.5896	.3051	.5563	1
60	1.2361	1.7013	1.2521	1.6616	1.2690	1.6243	1.2868	1.5890	1.3054	1.5557	**0**
	Csc	Sec	Csc	Sec	Csc	Sec	Csc	Sec	Csc	Sec	′
	54°		53°		52°		51°		50°		←

XI. FIVE–PLACE VALUES: SECANT AND COSECANT

→	40°		41°		42°		43°		44°		
′	Sec	Csc	Sec	Csc	Sec	Csc	Sec	Csc	Sec	Csc	
0	1.3054	1.5557	1.3250	1.5243	1.3456	1.4945	1.3673	1.4663	1.3902	1.4396	**60**
1	.3057	.5552	.3253	.5237	.3460	.4940	.3677	.4658	.3906	.4391	59
2	.3060	.5546	.3257	.5232	.3463	.4935	.3681	.4654	.3909	.4387	58
3	.3064	.5541	.3260	.5227	.3467	.4930	.3684	.4649	.3913	.4383	57
4	.3067	.5536	.3264	.5222	.3470	.4925	.3688	.4645	.3917	.4378	56
5	1.3070	1.5530	1.3267	1.5217	1.3474	1.4921	1.3692	1.4640	1.3921	1.4374	**55**
6	.3073	.5525	.3270	.5212	.3478	.4916	.3696	.4635	.3925	.4370	54
7	.3076	.5520	.3274	.5207	.3481	.4911	.3699	.4631	.3929	.4365	53
8	.3080	.5514	.3277	.5202	.3485	.4906	.3703	.4626	.3933	.4361	52
9	.3083	.5509	.3280	.5197	.3488	.4901	.3707	.4622	.3937	.4357	51
10	1.3086	1.5504	1.3284	1.5192	1.3492	1.4897	1.3711	1.4617	1.3941	1.4352	**50**
11	.3089	.5498	.3287	.5187	.3495	.4892	.3714	.4613	.3945	.4348	49
12	.3093	.5493	.3291	.5182	.3499	.4887	.3718	.4608	.3949	.4344	48
13	.3096	.5488	.3294	.5177	.3502	.4882	.3722	.4604	.3953	.4340	47
14	.3099	.5482	.3297	.5172	.3506	.4878	.3726	.4599	.3957	.4335	46
15	1.3102	1.5477	1.3301	1.5167	1.3510	1.4873	1.3729	1.4595	1.3961	1.4331	**45**
16	.3105	.5472	.3304	.5162	.3513	.4868	.3733	.4590	.3965	.4327	44
17	.3109	.5466	.3307	.5156	.3517	.4863	.3737	.4586	.3969	.4322	43
18	.3112	.5461	.3311	.5151	.3520	.4859	.3741	.4581	.3972	.4318	42
19	.3115	.5456	.3314	.5146	.3524	.4854	.3744	.4577	.3976	.4314	41
20	1.3118	1.5450	1.3318	1.5141	1.3527	1.4849	1.3748	1.4572	1.3980	1.4310	**40**
21	.3122	.5445	.3321	.5136	.3531	.4844	.3752	.4568	.3984	.4305	39
22	.3125	.5440	.3325	.5131	.3535	.4840	.3756	.4563	.3988	.4301	38
23	.3128	.5435	.3328	.5126	.3538	.4835	.3759	.4559	.3992	.4297	37
24	.3131	.5429	.3331	.5121	.3542	.4830	.3763	.4554	.3996	.4293	36
25	1.3135	1.5424	1.3335	1.5116	1.3545	1.4825	1.3767	1.4550	1.4000	1.4288	**35**
26	.3138	.5419	.3338	.5111	.3549	.4821	.3771	.4545	.4004	.4284	34
27	.3141	.5413	.3342	.5107	.3553	.4816	.3775	.4541	.4008	.4280	33
28	.3144	.5408	.3345	.5102	.3556	.4811	.3778	.4536	.4012	.4276	32
29	.3148	.5403	.3348	.5097	.3560	.4807	.3782	.4532	.4016	.4271	31
30	1.3151	1.5398	1.3352	1.5092	1.3563	1.4802	1.3786	1.4527	1.4020	1.4267	**30**
31	.3154	.5392	.3355	.5087	.3567	.4797	3790	.4523	.4024	.4263	29
32	.3157	.5387	.3359	.5082	.3571	.4792	.3794	.4518	.4028	.4259	28
33	.3161	.5382	.3362	.5077	.3574	.4788	.3797	.4514	.4032	.4255	27
34	.3164	.5377	.3366	.5072	.3578	.4783	.3801	.4510	.4036	.4250	26
35	1.3167	1.5372	1.3369	1.5067	1.3582	1.4778	1.3805	1.4505	1.4040	1.4246	**25**
36	.3171	.5366	.3373	.5062	.3585	.4774	.3809	.4501	.4044	.4242	24
37	.3174	.5361	.3376	.5057	.3589	.4769	.3813	.4496	.4048	.4238	23
38	.3177	.5356	.3380	.5052	.3592	.4764	.3817	.4492	.4052	.4234	22
39	.3180	.5351	.3383	.5047	.3596	.4760	.3820	.4487	.4057	.4229	21
40	1.3184	1.5345	1.3386	1.5042	1.3600	1.4755	1.3824	1.4483	1.4061	1.4225	**20**
41	.3187	.5340	.3390	.5037	.3603	.4750	.3828	.4479	.4065	.4221	19
42	.3190	.5335	.3393	.5032	.3607	.4746	.3832	.4474	.4069	.4217	18
43	.3194	.5330	.3397	.5027	.3611	.4741	.3836	.4470	.4073	.4213	17
44	.3197	.5325	.3400	.5023	.3614	.4737	.3840	.4465	.4077	.4208	16
45	1.3200	1.5320	1.3404	1.5018	1.3618	1.4732	1.3843	1.4461	1.4081	1.4204	**15**
46	.3203	.5314	.3407	.5013	.3622	.4727	.3847	.4457	.4085	.4200	14
47	.3207	.5309	.3411	.5008	.3625	.4723	.3851	.4452	.4089	.4196	13
48	.3210	.5304	.3414	.5003	.3629	.4718	.3855	.4448	.4093	.4192	12
49	.3213	.5299	.3418	.4998	.3633	.4713	.3859	.4443	.4097	.4188	11
50	1.3217	1.5294	1.3421	1.4993	1.3636	1.4709	1.3863	1.4439	1.4101	1.4183	**10**
51	.3220	.5289	.3425	.4988	.3640	.4704	.3867	.4435	.4105	.4179	9
52	.3223	.5283	.3428	.4984	.3644	.4700	.3871	.4430	.4109	.4175	8
53	.3227	.5278	.3432	.4979	.3647	.4695	.3874	.4426	.4113	.4171	7
54	.3230	.5273	.3435	.4974	.3651	.4690	.3878	.4422	.4118	.4167	6
55	1.3233	1.5268	1.3439	1.4969	1.3655	1.4686	1.3882	1.4417	1.4122	1.4163	**5**
56	.3237	.5263	.3442	.4964	.3658	.4681	.3886	.4413	.4126	.4159	4
57	.3240	.5258	.3446	.4959	.3662	.4677	.3890	.4409	.4130	.4154	3
58	.3243	.5253	.3449	.4954	.3666	.4672	.3894	.4404	.4134	.4150	2
59	.3247	.5248	.3453	.4950	.3670	.4667	.3898	.4400	.4138	.4146	1
60	1.3250	1.5243	1.3456	1.4945	1.3673	1.4663	1.3902	1.4396	1.4142	1.4142	**0**
	Csc	Sec	Csc	Sec	Csc	Sec	Csc	Sec	Csc	Sec	**′**
	49°		48°		47°		46°		45°		←

XII. SQUARES AND SQUARE ROOTS

N	N²	√N	√10N	N	N²	√N	√10N	N	N²	√N	√10N
1.00	1.0000	1.00000	3.16228	**1.60**	2.5600	1.26491	4.00000	**2.20**	4.8400	1.48324	4.69042
1.01	1.0201	1.00499	3.17805	1.61	2.5921	1.26886	4.01248	2.21	4.8841	1.48661	4.70106
1.02	1.0404	1.00995	3.19374	1.62	2.6244	1.27279	4.02492	2.22	4.9284	1.48997	4.71169
1.03	1.0609	1.01489	3.20936	1.63	2.6569	1.27671	4.03733	2.23	4.9729	1.49332	4.72229
1.04	1.0816	1.01980	3.22490	1.64	2.6896	1.28062	4.04969	2.24	5.0176	1.49666	4.73286
1.05	1.1025	1.02470	3.24037	**1.65**	2.7225	1.28452	4.06202	**2.25**	5.0625	1.50000	4.74342
1.06	1.1236	1.02956	3.25576	1.66	2.7556	1.28841	4.07431	2.26	5.1076	1.50333	4.75395
1.07	1.1449	1.03441	3.27109	1.67	2.7889	1.29228	4.08656	2.27	5.1529	1.50665	4.76445
1.08	1.1664	1.03923	3.28634	1.68	2.8224	1.29615	4.09878	2.28	5.1984	1.50997	4.77493
1.09	1.1881	1.04403	3.30151	1.69	2.8561	1.30000	4.11096	2.29	5.2441	1.51327	4.78539
1.10	1.2100	1.04881	3.31662	**1.70**	2.8900	1.30384	4.12311	**2.30**	5.2900	1.51658	4.79583
1.11	1.2321	1.05357	3.33167	1.71	2.9241	1.30767	4.13521	2.31	5.3361	1.51987	4.80625
1.12	1.2544	1.05830	3.34664	1.72	2.9584	1.31149	4.14729	2.32	5.3824	1.52315	4.81664
1.13	1.2769	1.06301	3.36155	1.73	2.9929	1.31529	4.15933	2.33	5.4289	1.52643	4.82701
1.14	1.2996	1.06771	3.37639	1.74	3.0276	1.31909	4.17133	2.34	5.4756	1.52971	4.83735
1.15	1.3225	1.07238	3.39116	**1.75**	3.0625	1.32288	4.18330	**2.35**	5.5225	1.53297	4.84768
1.16	1.3456	1.07703	3.40588	1.76	3.0976	1.32665	4.19524	2.36	5.5696	1.53623	4.85798
1.17	1.3689	1.08167	3.42053	1.77	3.1329	1.33041	4.20714	2.37	5.6169	1.53948	4.86826
1.18	1.3924	1.08628	3.43511	1.78	3.1684	1.33417	4.21900	2.38	5.6644	1.54272	4.87852
1.19	1.4161	1.09087	3.44964	1.79	3.2041	1.33791	4.23084	2.39	5.7121	1.54596	4.88876
1.20	1.4400	1.09545	3.46410	**1.80**	3.2400	1.34164	4.24264	**2.40**	5.7600	1.54919	4.89898
1.21	1.4641	1.10000	3.47851	1.81	3.2761	1.34536	4.25441	2.41	5.8081	1.55242	4.90918
1.22	1.4884	1.10454	3.49285	1.82	3.3124	1.34907	4.26615	2.42	5.8564	1.55563	4.91935
1.23	1.5129	1.10905	3.50714	1.83	3.3489	1.35277	4.27785	2.43	5.9049	1.55885	4.92950
1.24	1.5376	1.11355	3.52136	1.84	3.3856	1.35647	4.28952	2.44	5.9536	1.56205	4.93964
1.25	1.5625	1.11803	3.53553	**1.85**	3.4225	1.36015	4.30116	**2.45**	6.0025	1.56525	4.94975
1.26	1.5876	1.12250	3.54965	1.86	3.4596	1.36382	4.31277	2.46	6.0516	1.56844	4.95984
1.27	1.6129	1.12694	3.56371	1.87	3.4969	1.36748	4.32435	2.47	6.1009	1.57162	4.96991
1.28	1.6384	1.13137	3.57771	1.88	3.5344	1.37113	4.33590	2.48	6.1504	1.57480	4.97996
1.29	1.6641	1.13578	3.59166	1.89	3.5721	1.37477	4.34741	2.49	6.2001	1.57797	4.98999
1.30	1.6900	1.14018	3.60555	**1.90**	3.6100	1.37840	4.35890	**2.50**	6.2500	1.58114	5.00000
1.31	1.7161	1.14455	3.61939	1.91	3.6481	1.38203	4.37035	2.51	6.3001	1.58430	5.00999
1.32	1.7424	1.14891	3.63318	1.92	3.6864	1.38564	4.38178	2.52	6.3504	1.58745	5.01996
1.33	1.7689	1.15326	3.64692	1.93	3.7249	1.38924	4.39318	2.53	6.4009	1.59060	5.02991
1.34	1.7956	1.15758	3.66060	1.94	3.7636	1.39284	4.40454	2.54	6.4516	1.59374	5.03984
1.35	1.8225	1.16190	3.67423	**1.95**	3.8025	1.39642	4.41588	**2.55**	6.5025	1.59687	5.04975
1.36	1.8496	1.16619	3.68782	1.96	3.8416	1.40000	4.42719	2.56	6.5536	1.60000	5.05964
1.37	1.8769	1.17047	3.70135	1.97	3.8809	1.40357	4.43847	2.57	6.6049	1.60312	5.06952
1.38	1.9044	1.17473	3.71484	1.98	3.9204	1.40712	4.44972	2.58	6.6564	1.60624	5.07937
1.39	1.9321	1.17898	3.72827	1.99	3.9601	1.41067	4.46094	2.59	6.7081	1.60935	5.08920
1.40	1.9600	1.18322	3.74166	**2.00**	4.0000	1.41421	4.47214	**2.60**	6.7600	1.61245	5.09902
1.41	1.9881	1.18743	3.75500	2.01	4.0401	1.41774	4.48330	2.61	6.8121	1.61555	5.10882
1.42	2.0164	1.19164	3.76829	2.02	4.0804	1.42127	4.49444	2.62	6.8644	1.61864	5.11859
1.43	2.0449	1.19583	3.78153	2.03	4.1209	1.42478	4.50555	2.63	6.9169	1.62173	5.12835
1.44	2.0736	1.20000	3.79473	2.04	4.1616	1.42829	4.51664	2.64	6.9696	1.62481	5.13809
1.45	2.1025	1.20416	3.80789	**2.05**	4.2025	1.43178	4.52769	**2.65**	7.0225	1.62788	5.14782
1.46	2.1316	1.20830	3.82099	2.06	4.2436	1.43527	4.53872	2.66	7.0756	1.63095	5.15752
1.47	2.1609	1.21244	3.83406	2.07	4.2849	1.43875	4.54973	2.67	7.1289	1.63401	5.16720
1.48	2.1904	1.21655	3.84708	2.08	4.3264	1.44222	4.56070	2.68	7.1824	1.63707	5.17687
1.49	2.2201	1.22066	3.86005	2.09	4.3681	1.44568	4.57165	2.69	7.2361	1.64012	5.18652
1.50	2.2500	1.22474	3.87298	**2.10**	4.4100	1.44914	4.58258	**2.70**	7.2900	1.64317	5.19615
1.51	2.2801	1.22882	3.88587	2.11	4.4521	1.45258	4.59347	2.71	7.3441	1.64621	5.20577
1.52	2.3104	1.23288	3.89872	2.12	4.4944	1.45602	4.60435	2.72	7.3984	1.64924	5.21536
1.53	2.3409	1.23693	3.91152	2.13	4.5369	1.45945	4.61519	2.73	7.4529	1.65227	5.22494
1.54	2.3716	1.24097	3.92428	2.14	4.5796	1.46287	4.62601	2.74	7.5076	1.65529	5.23450
1.55	2.4025	1.24499	3.93700	**2.15**	4.6225	1.46629	4.63681	**2.75**	7.5625	1.65831	5.24404
1.56	2.4336	1.24900	3.94968	2.16	4.6656	1.46969	4.64758	2.76	7.6176	1.66132	5.25357
1.57	2.4649	1.25300	3.96232	2.17	4.7089	1.47309	4.65833	2.77	7.6729	1.66433	5.26308
1.58	2.4964	1.25698	3.97492	2.18	4.7524	1.47648	4.66905	2.78	7.7284	1.66733	5.27257
1.59	2.5281	1.26095	3.98748	2.19	4.7961	1.47986	4.67974	2.79	7.7841	1.67033	5.28205
1.60	2.5600	1.26491	4.00000	**2.20**	4.8400	1.48324	4.69042	**2.80**	7.8400	1.67332	5.29150
N	N²	√N	√10N	N	N²	√N	√10N	N	N²	√N	√10N

N	N^2	$\sqrt{N}$	$\sqrt{10N}$	N	N^2	$\sqrt{N}$	$\sqrt{10N}$	N	N^2	$\sqrt{N}$	$\sqrt{10N}$
2.80	7.8400	1.67332	5.29150	**3.40**	11.5600	1.84391	5.83095	**4.00**	16.0000	2.00000	6.32456
2.81	7.8961	1.67631	5.30094	3.41	11.6281	1.84662	5.83952	4.01	16.0801	2.00250	6.33246
2.82	7.9524	1.67929	5.31037	3.42	11.6964	1.84932	5.84808	4.02	16.1604	2.00499	6.34035
2.83	8.0089	1.68226	5.31977	3.43	11.7649	1.85203	5.85662	4.03	16.2409	2.00749	6.34823
2.84	8.0656	1.68523	5.32917	3.44	11.8336	1.85472	5.86515	4.04	16.3216	2.00998	6.35610
2.85	8.1225	1.68819	5.33854	**3.45**	11.9025	1.85742	5.87367	**4.05**	16.4025	2.01246	6.36396
2.86	8.1796	1.69115	5.34790	3.46	11.9716	1.86011	5.88218	4.06	16.4836	2.01494	6.37181
2.87	8.2369	1.69411	5.35724	3.47	12.0409	1.86279	5.89067	4.07	16.5649	2.01742	6.37966
2.88	8.2944	1.69706	5.36656	3.48	12.1104	1.86548	5.89915	4.08	16.6464	2.01990	6.38749
2.89	8.3521	1.70000	5.37587	3.49	12.1801	1.86815	5.90762	4.09	16.7281	2.02237	6.39531
2.90	8.4100	1.70294	5.38516	**3.50**	12.2500	1.87083	5.91608	**4.10**	16.8100	2.02485	6.40312
2.91	8.4681	1.70587	5.39444	3.51	12.3201	1.87350	5.92453	4.11	16.8921	2.02731	6.41093
2.92	8.5264	1.70880	5.40370	3.52	12.3904	1.87617	5.93296	4.12	16.9744	2.02978	6.41872
2.93	8.5849	1.71172	5.41295	3.53	12.4609	1.87883	5.94138	4.13	17.0569	2.03224	6.42651
2.94	8.6436	1.71464	5.42218	3.54	12.5316	1.88149	5.94979	4.14	17.1396	2.03470	6.43428
2.95	8.7025	1.71756	5.43139	**3.55**	12.6025	1.88414	5.95819	**4.15**	17.2225	2.03715	6.44205
2.96	8.7616	1.72047	5.44059	3.56	12.6736	1.88680	5.96657	4.16	17.3056	2.03961	6.44981
2.97	8.8209	1.72337	5.44977	3.57	12.7449	1.88944	5.97495	4.17	17.3889	2.04206	6.45755
2.98	8.8804	1.72627	5.45894	3.58	12.8164	1.89209	5.98331	4.18	17.4724	2.04450	6.46529
2.99	8.9401	1.72916	5.46809	3.59	12.8881	1.89473	5.99166	4.19	17.5561	2.04695	6.47302
3.00	9.0000	1.73205	5.47723	**3.60**	12.9600	1.89737	6.00000	**4.20**	17.6400	2.04939	6.48074
3.01	9.0601	1.73494	5.48635	3.61	13.0321	1.90000	6.00833	4.21	17.7241	2.05183	6.48845
3.02	9.1204	1.73781	5.49545	3.62	13.1044	1.90263	6.01664	4.22	17.8084	2.05426	6.49615
3.03	9.1809	1.74069	5.50454	3.63	13.1769	1.90526	6.02495	4.23	17.8929	2.05670	6.50384
3.04	9.2416	1.74356	5.51362	3.64	13.2496	1.90788	6.03324	4.24	17.9776	2.05913	6.51153
3.05	9.3025	1.74642	5.52268	**3.65**	13.3225	1.91050	6.04152	**4.25**	18.0625	2.06155	6.51920
3.06	9.3636	1.74929	5.53173	3.66	13.3956	1.91311	6.04979	4.26	18.1476	2.06398	6.52687
3.07	9.4249	1.75214	5.54076	3.67	13.4689	1.91572	6.05805	4.27	18.2329	2.06640	6.53452
3.08	9.4864	1.75499	5.54977	3.68	13.5424	1.91833	6.06630	4.28	18.3184	2.06882	6.54217
3.09	9.5481	1.75784	5.55878	3.69	13.6161	1.92094	6.07454	4.29	18.4041	2.07123	6.54981
3.10	9.6100	1.76068	5.56776	**3.70**	13.6900	1.92354	6.08276	**4.30**	18.4900	2.07364	6.55744
3.11	9.6721	1.76352	5.57674	3.71	13.7641	1.92614	6.09098	4.31	18.5761	2.07605	6.56506
3.12	9.7344	1.76635	5.58570	3.72	13.8384	1.92873	6.09918	4.32	18.6624	2.07846	6.57267
3.13	9.7969	1.76918	5.59464	3.73	13.9129	1.93132	6.10737	4.33	18.7489	2.08087	6.58027
3.14	9.8596	1.77200	5.60357	3.74	13.9876	1.93391	6.11555	4.34	18.8356	2.08327	6.58787
3.15	9.9225	1.77482	5.61249	**3.75**	14.0625	1.93649	6.12372	**4.35**	18.9225	2.08567	6.59545
3.16	9.9856	1.77764	5.62139	3.76	14.1376	1.93907	6.13188	4.36	19.0096	2.08806	6.60303
3.17	10.0489	1.78045	5.63028	3.77	14.2129	1.94165	6.14003	4.37	19.0969	2.09045	6.61060
3.18	10.1124	1.78326	5.63915	3.78	14.2884	1.94422	6.14817	4.38	19.1844	2.09284	6.61816
3.19	10.1761	1.78606	5.64801	3.79	14.3641	1.94679	6.15630	4.39	19.2721	2.09523	6.62571
3.20	10.2400	1.78885	5.65685	**3.80**	14.4400	1.94936	6.16441	**4.40**	19.3600	2.09762	6.63325
3.21	10.3041	1.79165	5.66569	3.81	14.5161	1.95192	6.17252	4.41	19.4481	2.10000	6.64078
3.22	10.3684	1.79444	5.67450	3.82	14.5924	1.95448	6.18061	4.42	19.5364	2.10238	6.64831
3.23	10.4329	1.79722	5.68331	3.83	14.6689	1.95704	6.18870	4.43	19.6249	2.10476	6.65582
3.24	10.4976	1.80000	5.69210	3.84	14.7456	1.95959	6.19677	4.44	19.7136	2.10713	6.66333
3.25	10.5625	1.80278	5.70088	**3.85**	14.8225	1.96214	6.20484	**4.45**	19.8025	2.10950	6.67083
3.26	10.6276	1.80555	5.70964	3.86	14.8996	1.96469	6.21289	4.46	19.8916	2.11187	6.67832
3.27	10.6929	1.80831	5.71839	3.87	14.9769	1.96723	6.22093	4.47	19.9809	2.11424	6.68581
3.28	10.7584	1.81108	5.72713	3.88	15.0544	1.96977	6.22896	4.48	20.0704	2.11660	6.69328
3.29	10.8241	1.81384	5.73585	3.89	15.1321	1.97231	6.23699	4.49	20.1601	2.11896	6.70075
3.30	10.8900	1.81659	5.74456	**3.90**	15.2100	1.97484	6.24500	**4.50**	20.2500	2.12132	6.70820
3.31	10.9561	1.81934	5.75326	3.91	15.2881	1.97737	6.25300	4.51	20.3401	2.12368	6.71565
3.32	11.0224	1.82209	5.76194	3.92	15.3664	1.97990	6.26099	4.52	20.4304	2.12603	6.72309
3.33	11.0889	1.82483	5.77062	3.93	15.4449	1.98242	6.26897	4.53	20.5209	2.12838	6.73053
3.34	11.1556	1.82757	5.77927	3.94	15.5236	1.98494	6.27694	4.54	20.6116	2.13073	6.73795
3.35	11.2225	1.83030	5.78792	**3.95**	15.6025	1.98746	6.28490	**4.55**	20.7025	2.13307	6.74537
3.36	11.2896	1.83303	5.79655	3.96	15.6816	1.98997	6.29285	4.56	20.7936	2.13542	6.75278
3.37	11.3569	1.83576	5.80517	3.97	15.7609	1.99249	6.30079	4.57	20.8849	2.13776	6.76018
3.38	11.4244	1.83848	5.81378	3.98	15.8404	1.99499	6.30872	4.58	20.9764	2.14009	6.76757
3.39	11.4921	1.84120	5.82237	3.99	15.9201	1.99750	6.31664	4.59	21.0681	2.14243	6.77495
3.40	11.5600	1.84391	5.83095	**4.00**	16.0000	2.00000	6.32456	**4.60**	21.1600	2.14476	6.78233
N	N^2	$\sqrt{N}$	$\sqrt{10N}$	N	N^2	$\sqrt{N}$	$\sqrt{10N}$	N	N^2	$\sqrt{N}$	$\sqrt{10N}$

XII. SQUARES AND SQUARE ROOTS

N	N^2	$\sqrt{N}$	$\sqrt{10N}$	N	N^2	$\sqrt{N}$	$\sqrt{10N}$	N	N^2	$\sqrt{N}$	$\sqrt{10N}$
4.60	21.1600	2.14476	6.78233	**5.20**	27.0400	2.28035	7.21110	**5.80**	33.6400	2.40832	7.61577
4.61	21.2521	2.14709	6.78970	5.21	27.1441	2.28254	7.21803	5.81	33.7561	2.41039	7.62234
4.62	21.3444	2.14942	6.79706	5.22	27.2484	2.28473	7.22496	5.82	33.8724	2.41247	7.62889
4.63	21.4369	2.15174	6.80441	5.23	27.3529	2.28692	7.23187	5.83	33.9889	2.41454	7.63544
4.64	21.5296	2.15407	6.81175	5.24	27.4576	2.28910	7.23878	5.84	34.1056	2.41661	7.64199
4.65	21.6225	2.15639	6.81909	**5.25**	27.5625	2.29129	7.24569	**5.85**	34.2225	2.41868	7.64853
4.66	21.7156	2.15870	6.82642	5.26	27.6676	2.29347	7.25259	5.86	34.3396	2.42074	7.65506
4.67	21.8089	2.16102	6.83374	5.27	27.7729	2.29565	7.25948	5.87	34.4569	2.42281	7.66159
4.68	21.9024	2.16333	6.84105	5.28	27.8784	2.29783	7.26636	5.88	34.5744	2.42487	7.66812
4.69	21.9961	2.16564	6.84836	5.29	27.9841	2.30000	7.27324	5.89	34.6921	2.42693	7.67463
4.70	22.0900	2.16795	6.85565	**5.30**	28.0900	2.30217	7.28011	**5.90**	34.8100	2.42899	7.68115
4.71	22.1841	2.17025	6.86294	5.31	28.1961	2.30434	7.28697	5.91	34.9281	2.43105	7.68765
4.72	22.2784	2.17256	6.87023	5.32	28.3024	2.30651	7.29383	5.92	35.0464	2.43311	7.69415
4.73	22.3729	2.17486	6.87750	5.33	28.4089	2.30868	7.30068	5.93	35.1649	2.43516	7.70065
4.74	22.4676	2.17715	6.88477	5.34	28.5156	2.31084	7.30753	5.94	35.2836	2.43721	7.70714
4.75	22.5625	2.17945	6.89202	**5.35**	28.6225	2.31301	7.31437	**5.95**	35.4025	2.43926	7.71362
4.76	22.6576	2.18174	6.89928	5.36	28.7296	2.31517	7.32120	5.96	35.5216	2.44131	7.72010
4.77	22.7529	2.18403	6.90652	5.37	28.8369	2.31733	7.32803	5.97	35.6409	2.44336	7.72658
4.78	22.8484	2.18632	6.91375	5.38	28.9444	2.31948	7.33485	5.98	35.7604	2.44540	7.73305
4.79	22.9441	2.18861	6.92098	5.39	29.0521	2.32164	7.34166	5.99	35.8801	2.44745	7.73951
4.80	23.0400	2.19089	6.92820	**5.40**	29.1600	2.32379	7.34847	**6.00**	36.0000	2.44949	7.74597
4.81	23.1361	2.19317	6.93542	5.41	29.2681	2.32594	7.35527	6.01	36.1201	2.45153	7.75242
4.82	23.2324	2.19545	6.94262	5.42	29.3764	2.32809	7.36206	6.02	36.2404	2.45357	7.75887
4.83	23.3289	2.19773	6.94982	5.43	29.4849	2.33024	7.36885	6.03	36.3609	2.45561	7.76531
4.84	23.4256	2.20000	6.95701	5.44	29.5936	2.33238	7.37564	6.04	36.4816	2.45764	7.77174
4.85	23.5225	2.20227	6.96419	**5.45**	29.7025	2.33452	7.38241	**6.05**	36.6025	2.45967	7.77817
4.86	23.6196	2.20454	6.97137	5.46	29.8116	2.33666	7.38918	6.06	36.7236	2.46171	7.78460
4.87	23.7169	2.20681	6.97854	5.47	29.9209	2.33880	7.39594	6.07	36.8449	2.46374	7.79102
4.88	23.8144	2.20907	6.98570	5.48	30.0304	2.34094	7.40270	6.08	36.9664	2.46577	7.79744
4.89	23.9121	2.21133	6.99285	5.49	30.1401	2.34307	7.40945	6.09	37.0881	2.46779	7.80385
4.90	24.0100	2.21359	7.00000	**5.50**	30.2500	2.34521	7.41620	**6.10**	37.2100	2.46982	7.81025
4.91	24.1081	2.21585	7.00714	5.51	30.3601	2.34734	7.42294	6.11	37.3321	2.47184	7.81665
4.92	24.2064	2.21811	7.01427	5.52	30.4704	2.34947	7.42967	6.12	37.4544	2.47386	7.82304
4.93	24.3049	2.22036	7.02140	5.53	30.5809	2.35160	7.43640	6.13	37.5769	2.47588	7.82943
4.94	24.4036	2.22261	7.02851	5.54	30.6916	2.35372	7.44312	6.14	37.6996	2.47790	7.83582
4.95	24.5025	2.22486	7.03562	**5.55**	30.8025	2.35584	7.44983	**6.15**	37.8225	2.47992	7.84219
4.96	24.6016	2.22711	7.04273	5.56	30.9136	2.35797	7.45654	6.16	37.9456	2.48193	7.84857
4.97	24.7009	2.22935	7.04982	5.57	31.0249	2.36008	7.46324	6.17	38.0689	2.48395	7.85493
4.98	24.8004	2.23159	7.05691	5.58	31.1364	2.36220	7.46994	6.18	38.1924	2.48596	7.86130
4.99	24.9001	2.23383	7.06399	5.59	31.2481	2.36432	7.47663	6.19	38.3161	2.48797	7.86766
5.00	25.0000	2.23607	7.07107	**5.60**	31.3600	2.36643	7.48331	**6.20**	38.4400	2.48998	7.87401
5.01	25.1001	2.23830	7.07814	5.61	31.4721	2.36854	7.48999	6.21	38.5641	2.49199	7.88036
5.02	25.2004	2.24054	7.08520	5.62	31.5844	2.37065	7.49667	6.22	38.6884	2.49399	7.88670
5.03	25.3009	2.24277	7.09225	5.63	31.6969	2.37276	7.50333	6.23	38.8129	2.49600	7.89303
5.04	25.4016	2.24499	7.09930	5.64	31.8096	2.37487	7.50999	6.24	38.9376	2.49800	7.89937
5.05	25.5025	2.24722	7.10634	**5.65**	31.9225	2.37697	7.51665	**6.25**	39.0625	2.50000	7.90569
5.06	25.6036	2.24944	7.11337	5.66	32.0356	2.37908	7.52330	6.26	39.1876	2.50200	7.91202
5.07	25.7049	2.25167	7.12039	5.67	32.1489	2.38118	7.52994	6.27	39.3129	2.50400	7.91833
5.08	25.8064	2.25389	7.12741	5.68	32.2624	2.38328	7.53658	6.28	39.4384	2.50599	7.92465
5.09	25.9081	2.25610	7.13442	5.69	32.3761	2.38537	7.54321	6.29	39.5641	2.50799	7.93095
5.10	26.0100	2.25832	7.14143	**5.70**	32.4900	2.38747	7.54983	**6.30**	39.6900	2.50998	7.93725
5.11	26.1121	2.26053	7.14843	5.71	32.6041	2.38956	7.55645	6.31	39.8161	2.51197	7.94355
5.12	26.2144	2.26274	7.15542	5.72	32.7184	2.39165	7.56307	6.32	39.9424	2.51396	7.94984
5.13	26.3169	2.26495	7.16240	5.73	32.8329	2.39374	7.56968	6.33	40.0689	2.51595	7.95613
5.14	26.4196	2.26716	7.16938	5.74	32.9476	2.39583	7.57628	6.34	40.1956	2.51794	7.96241
5.15	26.5225	2.26936	7.17635	**5.75**	33.0625	2.39792	7.58288	**6.35**	40.3225	2.51992	7.96869
5.16	26.6256	2.27156	7.18331	5.76	33.1776	2.40000	7.58947	6.36	40.4496	2.52190	7.97496
5.17	26.7289	2.27376	7.19027	5.77	33.2929	2.40208	7.59605	6.37	40.5769	2.52389	7.98123
5.18	26.8324	2.27596	7.19722	5.78	33.4084	2.40416	7.60263	6.38	40.7044	2.52587	7.98749
5.19	26.9361	2.27816	7.20417	5.79	33.5241	2.40624	7.60920	6.39	40.8321	2.52784	7.99375
5.20	27.0400	2.28035	7.21110	**5.80**	33.6400	2.40832	7.61577	**6.40**	40.9600	2.52982	8.00000
N	N^2	$\sqrt{N}$	$\sqrt{10N}$	N	N^2	$\sqrt{N}$	$\sqrt{10N}$	N	N^2	$\sqrt{N}$	$\sqrt{10N}$

XII. SQUARES AND SQUARE ROOTS

N	N^2	$\sqrt{N}$	$\sqrt{10N}$	N	N^2	$\sqrt{N}$	$\sqrt{10N}$	N	N^2	$\sqrt{N}$	$\sqrt{10N}$
6.40	40.9600	2.52982	8.00000	**7.00**	49.0000	2.64575	8.36660	**7.60**	57.7600	2.75681	8.71780
6.41	41.0881	2.53180	8.00625	7.01	49.1401	2.64764	8.37257	7.61	57.9121	2.75862	8.72353
6.42	41.2164	2.53377	8.01249	7.02	49.2804	2.64953	8.37854	7.62	58.0644	2.76043	8.72926
6.43	41.3449	2.53574	8.01873	7.03	49.4209	2.65141	8.38451	7.63	58.2169	2.76225	8.73499
6.44	41.4736	2.53772	8.02496	7.04	49.5616	2.65330	8.39047	7.64	58.3696	2.76405	8.74071
6.45	41.6025	2.53969	8.03119	**7.05**	49.7025	2.65518	8.39643	**7.65**	58.5225	2.76586	8.74643
6.46	41.7316	2.54165	8.03741	7.06	49.8436	2.65707	8.40238	7.66	58.6756	2.76767	8.75214
6.47	41.8609	2.54362	8.04363	7.07	49.9849	2.65895	8.40833	7.67	58.8289	2.76948	8.75785
6.48	41.9904	2.54558	8.04984	7.08	50.1264	2.66083	8.41427	7.68	58.9824	2.77128	8.76356
6.49	42.1201	2.54755	8.05605	7.09	50.2681	2.66271	8.42021	7.69	59.1361	2.77308	8.76926
6.50	42.2500	2.54951	8.06226	**7.10**	50.4100	2.66458	8.42615	**7.70**	59.2900	2.77489	8.77496
6.51	42.3801	2.55147	8.06846	7.11	50.5521	2.66646	8.43208	7.71	59.4441	2.77669	8.78066
6.52	42.5104	2.55343	8.07465	7.12	50.6944	2.66833	8.43801	7.72	59.5984	2.77849	8.78635
6.53	42.6409	2.55539	8.08084	7.13	50.8369	2.67021	8.44393	7.73	59.7529	2.78029	8.79204
6.54	42.7716	2.55734	8.08703	7.14	50.9796	2.67208	8.44985	7.74	59.9076	2.78209	8.79773
6.55	42.9025	2.55930	8.09321	**7.15**	51.1225	2.67395	8.45577	**7.75**	60.0625	2.78388	8.80341
6.56	43.0336	2.56125	8.09938	7.16	51.2656	2.67582	8.46168	7.76	60.2176	2.78568	8.80909
6.57	43.1649	2.56320	8.10555	7.17	51.4089	2.67769	8.46759	7.77	60.3729	2.78747	8.81476
6.58	43.2964	2.56515	8.11172	7.18	51.5524	2.67955	8.47349	7.78	60.5284	2.78927	8.82043
6.59	43.4281	2.56710	8.11788	7.19	51.6961	2.68142	8.47939	7.79	60.6841	2.79106	8.82610
6.60	43.5600	2.56905	8.12404	**7.20**	51.8400	2.68328	8.48528	**7.80**	60.8400	2.79285	8.83176
6.61	43.6921	2.57099	8.13019	7.21	51.9841	2.68514	8.49117	7.81	60.9961	2.79464	8.83742
6.62	43.8244	2.57294	8.13634	7.22	52.1284	2.68701	8.49706	7.82	61.1524	2.79643	8.84308
6.63	43.9569	2.57488	8.14248	7.23	52.2729	2.68887	8.50294	7.83	61.3089	2.79821	8.84873
6.64	44.0896	2.57682	8.14862	7.24	52.4176	2.69072	8.50882	7.84	61.4656	2.80000	8.85438
6.65	44.2225	2.57876	8.15475	**7.25**	52.5625	2.69258	8.51469	**7.85**	61.6225	2.80179	8.86002
6.66	44.3556	2.58070	8.16088	7.26	52.7076	2.69444	8.52056	7.86	61.7796	2.80357	8.86566
6.67	44.4889	2.58263	8.16701	7.27	52.8529	2.69629	8.52643	7.87	61.9369	2.80535	8.87130
6.68	44.6224	2.58457	8.17313	7.28	52.9984	2.69815	8.53229	7.88	62.0944	2.80713	8.87694
6.69	44.7561	2.58650	8.17924	7.29	53.1441	2.70000	8.53815	7.89	62.2521	2.80891	8.88257
6.70	44.8900	2.58844	8.18535	**7.30**	53.2900	2.70185	8.54400	**7.90**	62.4100	2.81069	8.88819
6.71	45.0241	2.59037	8.19146	7.31	53.4361	2.70370	8.54985	7.91	62.5681	2.81247	8.89382
6.72	45.1584	2.59230	8.19756	7.32	53.5824	2.70555	8.55570	7.92	62.7264	2.81425	8.89944
6.73	45.2929	2.59422	8.20366	7.33	53.7289	2.70740	8.56154	7.93	62.8849	2.81603	8.90505
6.74	45.4276	2.59615	8.20975	7.34	53.8756	2.70924	8.56738	7.94	63.0436	2.81780	8.91067
6.75	45.5625	2.59808	8.21584	**7.35**	54.0225	2.71109	8.57321	**7.95**	63.2025	2.81957	8.91628
6.76	45.6976	2.60000	8.22192	7.36	54.1696	2.71293	8.57904	7.96	63.3616	2.82135	8.92188
6.77	45.8329	2.60192	8.22800	7.37	54.3169	2.71477	8.58487	7.97	63.5209	2.82312	8.92749
6.78	45.9684	2.60384	8.23408	7.38	54.4644	2.71662	8.59069	7.98	63.6804	2.82489	8.93308
6.79	46.1041	2.60576	8.24015	7.39	54.6121	2.71846	8.59651	7.99	63.8401	2.82666	8.93868
6.80	46.2400	2.60768	8.24621	**7.40**	54.7600	2.72029	8.60233	**8.00**	64.0000	2.82843	8.94427
6.81	46.3761	2.60960	8.25227	7.41	54.9081	2.72213	8.60814	8.01	64.1601	2.83019	8.94986
6.82	46.5124	2.61151	8.25833	7.42	55.0564	2.72397	8.61394	8.02	64.3204	2.83196	8.95545
6.83	46.6489	2.61343	8.26438	7.43	55.2049	2.72580	8.61974	8.03	64.4809	2.83373	8.96103
6.84	46.7856	2.61534	8.27043	7.44	55.3536	2.72764	8.62554	8.04	64.6416	2.83549	8.96660
6.85	46.9225	2.61725	8.27647	**7.45**	55.5025	2.72947	8.63134	**8.05**	64.8025	2.83725	8.97218
6.86	47.0596	2.61916	8.28251	7.46	55.6516	2.73130	8.63713	8.06	64.9636	2.83901	8.97775
6.87	47.1969	2.62107	8.28855	7.47	55.8009	2.73313	8.64292	8.07	65.1249	2.84077	8.98332
6.88	47.3344	2.62298	8.29458	7.48	55.9504	2.73496	8.64870	8.08	65.2864	2.84253	8.98888
6.89	47.4721	2.62488	8.30060	7.49	56.1001	2.73679	8.65448	8.09	65.4481	2.84429	8.99444
6.90	47.6100	2.62679	8.30662	**7.50**	56.2500	2.73861	8.66025	**8.10**	65.6100	2.84605	9.00000
6.91	47.7481	2.62869	8.31264	7.51	56.4001	2.74044	8.66603	8.11	65.7721	2.84781	9.00555
6.92	47.8864	2.63059	8.31865	7.52	56.5504	2.74226	8.67179	8.12	65.9344	2.84956	9.01110
6.93	48.0249	2.63249	8.32466	7.53	56.7009	2.74408	8.67756	8.13	66.0969	2.85132	9.01665
6.94	48.1636	2.63439	8.33067	7.54	56.8516	2.74591	8.68332	8.14	66.2596	2.85307	9.02219
6.95	48.3025	2.63629	8.33667	**7.55**	57.0025	2.74773	8.68907	**8.15**	66.4225	2.85482	9.02774
6.96	48.4416	2.63818	8.34266	7.56	57.1536	2.74955	8.69483	8.16	66.5856	2.85657	9.03327
6.97	48.5809	2.64008	8.34865	7.57	57.3049	2.75136	8.70057	8.17	66.7489	2.85832	9.03881
6.98	48.7204	2.64197	8.35464	7.58	57.4564	2.75318	8.70632	8.18	66.9124	2.86007	9.04434
6.99	48.8601	2.64386	8.36062	7.59	57.6081	2.75500	8.71206	8.19	67.0761	2.86182	9.04986
7.00	49.0000	2.64575	8.36660	**7.60**	57.7600	2.75681	8.71780	**8.20**	67.2400	2.86356	9.05539
N	N^2	$\sqrt{N}$	$\sqrt{10N}$	N	N^2	$\sqrt{N}$	$\sqrt{10N}$	N	N^2	$\sqrt{N}$	$\sqrt{10N}$

XII. SQUARES AND SQUARE ROOTS

N	N²	√N	√10N	N	N²	√N	√10N	N	N²	√N	√10N
8.20	67.2400	2.86356	9.05539	**8.80**	77.4400	2.96648	9.38083	**9.40**	88.3600	3.06594	9.69536
8.21	67.4041	2.86531	9.06091	8.81	77.6161	2.96816	9.38616	9.41	88.5481	3.06757	9.70052
8.22	67.5684	2.86705	9.06642	8.82	77.7924	2.96985	9.39149	9.42	88.7364	3.06920	9.70567
8.23	67.7329	2.86880	9.07193	8.83	77.9689	2.97153	9.39681	9.43	88.9249	3.07083	9.71082
8.24	67.8976	2.87054	9.07744	8.84	78.1456	2.97321	9.40213	9.44	89.1136	3.07246	9.71597
8.25	68.0625	2.87228	9.08295	**8.85**	78.3225	2.97489	9.40744	**9.45**	89.3025	3.07409	9.72111
8.26	68.2276	2.87402	9.08845	8.86	78.4996	2.97658	9.41276	9.46	89.4916	3.07571	9.72625
8.27	68.3929	2.87576	9.09395	8.87	78.6769	2.97825	9.41807	9.47	89.6809	3.07734	9.73139
8.28	68.5584	2.87750	9.09945	8.88	78.8544	2.97993	9.42338	9.48	89.8704	3.07896	9.73653
8.29	68.7241	2.87924	9.10494	8.89	79.0321	2.98161	9.42868	9.49	90.0601	3.08058	9.74166
8.30	68.8900	2.88097	9.11043	**8.90**	79.2100	2.98329	9.43398	**9.50**	90.2500	3.08221	9.74679
8.31	69.0561	2.88271	9.11592	8.91	79.3881	2.98496	9.43928	9.51	90.4401	3.08383	9.75192
8.32	69.2224	2.88444	9.12140	8.92	79.5664	2.98664	9.44458	9.52	90.6304	3.08545	9.75705
8.33	69.3889	2.88617	9.12688	8.93	79.7449	2.98831	9.44987	9.53	90.8209	3.08707	9.76217
8.34	69.5556	2.88791	9.13236	8.94	79.9236	2.98998	9.45516	9.54	91.0116	3.08869	9.76729
8.35	69.7225	2.88964	9.13783	**8.95**	80.1025	2.99166	9.46044	**9.55**	91.2025	3.09031	9.77241
8.36	69.8896	2.89137	9.14330	8.96	80.2816	2.99333	9.46573	9.56	91.3936	3.09192	9.77753
8.37	70.0569	2.89310	9.14877	8.97	80.4609	2.99500	9.47101	9.57	91.5849	3.09354	9.78264
8.38	70.2244	2.89482	9.15423	8.98	80.6404	2.99666	9.47629	9.58	91.7764	3.09516	9.78775
8.39	70.3921	2.89655	9.15969	8.99	80.8201	2.99833	9.48156	9.59	91.9681	3.09677	9.79285
8.40	70.5600	2.89828	9.16515	**9.00**	81.0000	3.00000	9.48683	**9.60**	92.1600	3.09839	9.79796
8.41	70.7281	2.90000	9.17061	9.01	81.1801	3.00167	9.49210	9.61	92.3521	3.10000	9.80306
8.42	70.8964	2.90172	9.17606	9.02	81.3604	3.00333	9.49737	9.62	92.5444	3.10161	9.80816
8.43	71.0649	2.90345	9.18150	9.03	81.5409	3.00500	9.50263	9.63	92.7369	3.10322	9.81326
8.44	71.2336	2.90517	9.18695	9.04	81.7216	3.00666	9.50789	9.64	92.9296	3.10483	9.81835
8.45	71.4025	2.90689	9.19239	**9.05**	81.9025	3.00832	9.51315	**9.65**	93.1225	3.10644	9.82344
8.46	71.5716	2.90861	9.19783	9.06	82.0836	3.00998	9.51840	9.66	93.3156	3.10805	9.82853
8.47	71.7409	2.91033	9.20326	9.07	82.2649	3.01164	9.52365	9.67	93.5089	3.10966	9.83362
8.48	71.9104	2.91204	9.20869	9.08	82.4464	3.01330	9.52890	9.68	93.7024	3.11127	9.83870
8.49	72.0801	2.91376	9.21412	9.09	82.6281	3.01496	9.53415	9.69	93.8961	3.11288	9.84378
8.50	72.2500	2.91548	9.21954	**9.10**	82.8100	3.01662	9.53939	**9.70**	94.0900	3.11448	9.84886
8.51	72.4201	2.91719	9.22497	9.11	82.9921	3.01828	9.54463	9.71	94.2841	3.11609	9.85393
8.52	72.5904	2.91890	9.23038	9.12	83.1744	3.01993	9.54987	9.72	94.4784	3.11769	9.85901
8.53	72.7609	2.92062	9.23580	9.13	83.3569	3.02159	9.55510	9.73	94.6729	3.11929	9.86408
8.54	72.9316	2.92233	9.24121	9.14	83.5396	3.02324	9.56033	9.74	94.8676	3.12090	9.86914
8.55	73.1025	2.92404	9.24662	**9.15**	83.7225	3.02490	9.56556	**9.75**	95.0625	3.12250	9.87421
8.56	73.2736	2.92575	9.25203	9.16	83.9056	3.02655	9.57079	9.76	95.2576	3.12410	9.87927
8.57	73.4449	2.92746	9.25743	9.17	84.0889	3.02820	9.57601	9.77	95.4529	3.12570	9.88433
8.58	73.6164	2.92916	9.26283	9.18	84.2724	3.02985	9.58123	9.78	95.6484	3.12730	9.88939
8.59	73.7881	2.93087	9.26823	9.19	84.4561	3.03150	9.58645	9.79	95.8441	3.12890	9.89444
8.60	73.9600	2.93258	9.27362	**9.20**	84.6400	3.03315	9.59166	**9.80**	96.0400	3.13050	9.89949
8.61	74.1321	2.93428	9.27901	9.21	84.8241	3.03480	9.59687	9.81	96.2361	3.13209	9.90454
8.62	74.3044	2.93598	9.28440	9.22	85.0084	3.03645	9.60208	9.82	96.4324	3.13369	9.90959
8.63	74.4769	2.93769	9.28978	9.23	85.1929	3.03809	9.60729	9.83	96.6289	3.13528	9.91464
8.64	74.6496	2.93939	9.29516	9.24	85.3776	3.03974	9.61249	9.84	96.8256	3.13688	9.91968
8.65	74.8225	2.94109	9.30054	**9.25**	85.5625	3.04138	9.61769	**9.85**	97.0225	3.13847	9.92472
8.66	74.9956	2.94279	9.30591	9.26	85.7476	3.04302	9.62289	9.86	97.2196	3.14006	9.92975
8.67	75.1689	2.94449	9.31128	9.27	85.9329	3.04467	9.62808	9.87	97.4169	3.14166	9.93479
8.68	75.3424	2.94618	9.31665	9.28	86.1184	3.04631	9.63328	9.88	97.6144	3.14325	9.93982
8.69	75.5161	2.94788	9.32202	9.29	86.3041	3.04795	9.63846	9.89	97.8121	3.14484	9.94485
8.70	75.6900	2.94958	9.32738	**9.30**	86.4900	3.04959	9.64365	**9.90**	98.0100	3.14643	9.94987
8.71	75.8641	2.95127	9.33274	9.31	86.6761	3.05123	9.64883	9.91	98.2081	3.14802	9.95490
8.72	76.0384	2.95296	9.33809	9.32	86.8624	3.05287	9.65401	9.92	98.4064	3.14960	9.95992
8.73	76.2129	2.95466	9.34345	9.33	87.0489	3.05450	9.65919	9.93	98.6049	3.15119	9.96494
8.74	76.3876	2.95635	9.34880	9.34	87.2356	3.05614	9.66437	9.94	98.8036	3.15278	9.96995
8.75	76.5625	2.95804	9.35414	**9.35**	87.4225	3.05778	9.66954	**9.95**	99.0025	3.15436	9.97497
8.76	76.7376	2.95973	9.35949	9.36	87.6096	3.05941	9.67471	9.96	99.2016	3.15595	9.97998
8.77	76.9129	2.96142	9.36483	9.37	87.7969	3.06105	9.67988	9.97	99.4009	3.15753	9.98499
8.78	77.0884	2.96311	9.37017	9.38	87.9844	3.06268	9.68504	9.98	99.6004	3.15911	9.98999
8.79	77.2641	2.96479	9.37550	9.39	88.1721	3.06431	9.69020	9.99	99.8001	3.16070	9.99500
8.80	77.4400	2.96648	9.38083	**9.40**	88.3600	3.06594	9.69536	**10.00**	100.000	3.16228	10.0000
N	N²	√N	√10N	N	N²	√N	√10N	N	N²	√N	√10N

XIII. RADIAN MEASURE: VALUES OF FUNCTIONS

α Rad.	Degrees in α	Sin α	Cos α	Tan α	α Rad.	Degrees in α	Sin α	Cos α	Tan α
.00	0° 00.0′	.00000	1.0000	.00000	.60	34° 22.6′	.56464	.82534	.68414
.01	0° 34.4′	.01000	.99995	.01000	.61	34° 57.0′	.57287	.81965	.69892
.02	1° 08.8′	.02000	.99980	.02000	.62	35° 31.4′	.58104	.81388	.71391
.03	1° 43.1′	.03000	.99955	.03001	.63	36° 05.8′	.58914	.80803	.72911
.04	2° 17.5′	.03999	.99920	.04002	.64	36° 40.2′	.59720	.80210	.74454
.05	2° 51.9′	.04998	.99875	.05004	.65	37° 14.5′	.60519	.79608	.76020
.06	3° 26.3′	.05996	.99820	.06007	.66	37° 48.9′	.61312	.78999	.77610
.07	4° 00.6′	.06994	.99755	.07011	.67	38° 23.3′	.62099	.78382	.79225
.08	4° 35.0′	.07991	.99680	.08017	.68	38° 57.7′	.62879	.77757	.80866
.09	5° 09.4′	.08988	.99595	.09024	.69	39° 32.0′	.63654	.77125	.82534
.10	5° 43.8′	.09983	.99500	.10033	.70	40° 06.4′	.64422	.76484	.84229
.11	6° 18.2′	.10978	.99396	.11045	.71	40° 40.8′	.65183	.75836	.85953
.12	6° 52.5′	.11971	.99281	.12058	.72	41° 15.2′	.65938	.75181	.87707
.13	7° 26.9′	.12963	.99156	.13074	.73	41° 49.6′	.66687	.74517	.89492
.14	8° 01.3′	.13954	.99022	.14092	.74	42° 23.9′	.67429	.73847	.91309
.15	8° 35.7′	.14944	.98877	.15114	.75	42° 58.3′	.68164	.73169	.93160
.16	9° 10.0′	.15932	.98723	.16138	.76	43° 32.7′	.68892	.72484	.95045
.17	9° 44.4′	.16918	.98558	.17166	.77	44° 07.1′	.69614	.71791	.96967
.18	10° 18.8′	.17903	.98384	.18197	.78	44° 41.4′	.70328	.71091	.98926
.19	10° 53.2′	.18886	.98200	.19232	.79	45° 15.8′	.71035	.70385	1.0092
.20	11° 27.5′	.19867	.98007	.20271	.80	45° 50.2′	.71736	.69671	1.0296
.21	12° 01.9′	.20846	.97803	.21314	.81	46° 24.6′	.72429	.68950	1.0505
.22	12° 36.3′	.21823	.97590	.22362	.82	46° 59.0′	.73115	.68222	1.0717
.23	13° 10.7′	.22798	.97367	.23414	.83	47° 33.3′	.73793	.67488	1.0934
.24	13° 45.1′	.23770	.97134	.24472	.84	48° 07.7′	.74464	.66746	1.1156
.25	14° 19.4′	.24740	.96891	.25534	.85	48° 42.1′	.75128	.65998	1.1383
.26	14° 53.8′	.25708	.96639	.26602	.86	49° 16.5′	.75784	.65244	1.1616
.27	15° 28.2′	.26673	.96377	.27676	.87	49° 50.8′	.76433	.64483	1.1853
.28	16° 02.6′	.27636	.96106	.28755	.88	50° 25.2′	.77074	.63715	1.2097
.29	16° 36.9′	.28595	.95824	.29841	.89	50° 59.6′	.77707	.62941	1.2346
.30	17° 11.3′	.29552	.95534	.30934	.90	51° 34.0′	.78333	.62161	1.2602
.31	17° 45.7′	.30506	.95233	.32033	.91	52° 08.3′	.78950	.61375	1.2864
.32	18° 20.1′	.31457	.94924	.33139	.92	52° 42.7′	.79560	.60582	1.3133
.33	18° 54.5′	.32404	.94604	.34252	.93	53° 17.1′	.80162	.59783	1.3409
.34	19° 28.8′	.33349	.94275	.35374	.94	53° 51.5′	.80756	.58979	1.3692
.35	20° 03.2′	.34290	.93937	.36503	.95	54° 25.9′	.81342	.58168	1.3984
.36	20° 37.6′	.35227	.93590	.37640	.96	55° 00.2′	.81919	.57352	1.4284
.37	21° 12.0′	.36162	.93233	.38786	.97	55° 34.6′	.82489	.56530	1.4592
.38	21° 46.3′	.37092	.92866	.39941	.98	56° 09.0′	.83050	.55702	1.4910
.39	22° 20.7′	.38019	.92491	.41105	.99	56° 43.4′	.83603	.54869	1.5237
.40	22° 55.1′	.38942	.92106	.42279	1.00	57° 17.7′	.84147	.54030	1.5574
.41	23° 29.5′	.39861	.91712	.43463	1.01	57° 52.1′	.84683	.53186	1.5922
.42	24° 03.9′	.40776	.91309	.44657	1.02	58° 26.5′	.85211	.52337	1.6281
.43	24° 38.2′	.41687	.90897	.45862	1.03	59° 00.9′	.85730	.51482	1.6652
.44	25° 12.6′	.42594	.90475	.47078	1.04	59° 35.3′	.86240	.50622	1.7036
.45	25° 47.0′	.43497	.90045	.48306	1.05	60° 09.6′	.86742	.49757	1.7433
.46	26° 21.4′	.44395	.89605	.49545	1.06	60° 44.0′	.87236	.48887	1.7844
.47	26° 55.7′	.45289	.89157	.50797	1.07	61° 18.4′	.87720	.48012	1.8270
.48	27° 30.1′	.46178	.88699	.52061	1.08	61° 52.8′	.88196	.47133	1.8712
.49	28° 04.5′	.47063	.88233	.53339	1.09	62° 27.1′	.88663	.46249	1.9171
.50	28° 38.9′	.47943	.87758	.54630	1.10	63° 01.5′	.89121	.45360	1.9648
.51	29° 13.3′	.48818	.87274	.55936	1.11	63° 35.9′	.89570	.44466	2.0143
.52	29° 47.6′	.49688	.86782	.57256	1.12	64° 10.3′	.90010	.43568	2.0660
.53	30° 22.0′	.50553	.86281	.58592	1.13	64° 44.7′	.90441	.42666	2.1198
.54	30° 56.4′	.51414	.85771	.59943	1.14	65° 19.0′	.90863	.41759	2.1759
.55	31° 30.8′	.52269	.85252	.61311	1.15	65° 53.4′	.91276	.40849	2.2345
.56	32° 05.1′	.53119	.84726	.62695	1.16	66° 27.8′	.91680	.39934	2.2958
.57	32° 39.5′	.53963	.84190	.64097	1.17	67° 02.2′	.92075	.39015	2.3600
.58	33° 13.9′	.54802	.83646	.65517	1.18	67° 36.5′	.92461	.38092	2.4273
.59	33° 48.3′	.55636	.83094	.66956	1.19	68° 10.9′	.92837	.37166	2.4979
.60	34° 22.6′	.56464	.82534	.68414	1.20	68° 45.3′	.93204	.36236	2.5722

XIII. RADIAN MEASURE: VALUES OF FUNCTIONS

α Rad.	Degrees in α	Sin α	Cos α	Tan α
1.20	68° 45.3′	.93204	.36236	2.5722
1.21	69° 19.7′	.93562	.35302	2.6503
1.22	69° 54.1′	93910	.34365	2.7328
1.23	70° 28.4′	.94249	.33424	2.8198
1.24	71° 02.8′	.94578	.32480	2.9119
1.25	71° 37.2′	.94898	.31532	3.0096
1.26	72° 11.6′	.95209	.30582	3.1133
1.27	72° 45.9′	.95510	.29628	3.2236
1.28	73° 20.3′	.95802	.28672	3.3413
1.29	73° 54.7′	.96084	.27712	3.4672
1.30	74° 29.1′	.96356	.26750	3.6021
1.31	75° 03.4′	.96618	.25785	3.7471
1.32	75° 37.8′	.96872	.24818	3.9033
1.33	76° 12.2′	.97115	.23848	4.0723
1.34	76° 46.6′	.97348	.22875	4.2556
1.35	77° 21.0′	.97572	.21901	4.4552
1.36	77° 55.3′	.97786	.20924	4.6734
1.37	78° 29.7′	.97991	.19945	4.9131
1.38	79° 04.1′	.98185	.18964	5.1774
1.39	79° 38.5′	.98370	.17981	5.4707
1.40	80° 12.8′	.98545	.16997	5.7979

α Rad.	Degrees in α	Sin α	Cos α	Tan α
1.40	80° 12.8′	.98545	.16997	5.7979
1.41	80° 47.2′	.98710	.16010	6.1654
1.42	81° 21.6′	.98865	.15023	6.5811
1.43	81° 56.0′	.99010	.14033	7.0555
1.44	82° 30.4′	.99146	.13042	7.6018
1.45	83° 04.7′	.99271	.12050	8.2381
1.46	83° 39.1′	.99387	.11057	8.9886
1.47	84° 13.5′	.99492	.10063	9.8874
1.48	84° 47.9′	.99588	.09067	10.983
1.49	85° 22.2′	.99674	.08071	12.350
1.50	85° 56.6′	.99749	.07074	14.101
1.51	86° 31.0′	.99815	.06076	16.428
1.52	87° 05.4′	.99871	.05077	19.670
1.53	87° 39.8′	.99917	.04079	24.498
1.54	88° 14.1′	.99953	.03079	32.461
1.55	88° 48.5′	.99978	.02079	48.078
1.56	89° 22.9′	.99994	.01080	92.620
1.57	89° 57.3′	1.0000	.00080	1255.8
1.58	90° 31.6′	.99996	−.00920	−108.65
1.59	91° 06.0′	.99982	−.01920	−52.067
1.60	91° 40.4′	.99957	−.02920	−34.233

DEGREES IN RADIANS

1°	0.01745	16°	0.27925	31°	0.54105	46°	0.80285	61°	1.06465	76°	1.32645
2	0.03491	17	0.29671	32	0.55851	47	0.82030	62	1.08210	77	1.34390
3	0.05236	18	0.31416	33	0.57596	48	0.83776	63	1.09956	78	1.36136
4	0.06981	19	0.33161	34	0.59341	49	0.85521	64	1.11701	79	1.37881
5	0.08727	**20**	0.34907	**35**	0.61087	**50**	0.87266	**65**	1.13446	**80**	1.39626
6	0.10472	21	0.36652	36	0.62832	51	0.89012	66	1.15192	81	1.41372
7	0.12217	22	0.38397	37	0.64577	52	0.90757	67	1.16937	82	1.43117
8	0.13963	23	0.40143	38	0.66323	53	0.92502	68	1.18682	83	1.44862
9	0.15708	24	0.41888	39	0.68068	54	0.94248	69	1.20428	84	1.46608
10	0.17453	**25**	0.43633	**40**	0.69813	**55**	0.95993	**70**	1.22173	**85**	1.48353
11	0.19199	26	0.45379	41	0.71558	56	0.97738	71	1.23918	86	1.50098
12	0.20944	27	0.47124	42	0.73304	57	0.99484	72	1.25664	87	1.51844
13	0.22689	28	0.48869	43	0.75049	58	1.01229	73	1.27409	88	1.53589
14	0.24435	29	0.50615	44	0.76794	59	1.02974	74	1.29154	89	1.55334
15	0.26180	**30**	0.52360	**45**	0.78540	**60**	1.04720	**75**	1.30900	**90**	1.57080

1° = .01745329 rad.   log .01745329 = 8.24187737 − 10.

1′ = .0002908882 rad.   log .0002908882 = 6.46372612 − 10.

1″ = .0000048481368 rad.   log .0000048481368 = 4.68557487 − 10.

MINUTES IN RADIANS

1′	0.00029	11′	0.00320	21′	0.00611	31′	0.00902	41′	0.01193	51′	0.01484
2	0.00058	12	0.00349	22	0.00640	32	0.00931	42	0.01222	52	0.01513
3	0.00087	13	0.00378	23	0.00669	33	0.00960	43	0.01251	53	0.01542
4	0.00116	14	0.00407	24	0.00698	34	0.00989	44	0.01280	54	0.01571
5	0.00145	**15**	0.00436	**25**	0.00727	**35**	0.01018	**45**	0.01309	**55**	0.01600
6	0.00175	16	0.00465	26	0.00756	36	0.01047	46	0.01338	56	0.01629
7	0.00204	17	0.00495	27	0.00785	37	0.01076	47	0.01367	57	0.01658
8	0.00233	18	0.00524	28	0.00814	38	0.01105	48	0.01396	58	0.01687
9	0.00262	19	0.00553	29	0.00844	39	0.01134	49	0.01425	59	0.01716
10	0.00291	**20**	0.00582	**30**	0.00873	**40**	0.01164	**50**	0.01454	**60**	0.01745

N	0	1	2	3	4	5	6	7	8	9
1.0	0.0 0000	0995	1980	2956	3922	4879	5827	6766	7696	8618
1.1	0.0 9531	*0436	*1333	*2222	*3103	*3976	*4842	*5700	*6551	*7395
1.2	0.1 8232	9062	9885	*0701	*1511	*2314	*3111	*3902	*4686	*5464
1.3	0.2 6236	7003	7763	8518	9267	*0010	*0748	*1481	*2208	*2930
1.4	0.3 3647	4359	5066	5767	6464	7156	7844	8526	9204	9878
1.5	0.4 0547	1211	1871	2527	3178	3825	4469	5108	5742	6373
1.6	0.4 7000	7623	8243	8858	9470	*0078	*0682	*1282	*1879	*2473
1.7	0.5 3063	3649	4232	4812	5389	5962	6531	7098	7661	8222
1.8	0.5 8779	9333	9884	*0432	*0977	*1519	*2058	*2594	*3127	*3658
1.9	0.6 4185	4710	5233	5752	6269	6783	7294	7803	8310	8813
2.0	0.6 9315	9813	*0310	*0804	*1295	*1784	*2271	*2755	*3237	*3716
2.1	0.7 4194	4669	5142	5612	6081	6547	7011	7473	7932	8390
2.2	0.7 8846	9299	9751	*0200	*0648	*1093	*1536	*1978	*2418	*2855
2.3	0.8 3291	3725	4157	4587	5015	5442	5866	6289	6710	7129
2.4	0.8 7547	7963	8377	8789	9200	9609	*0016	*0422	*0826	*1228
2.5	0.9 1629	2028	2426	2822	3216	3609	4001	4391	4779	5166
2.6	5551	5935	6317	6698	7078	7456	7833	8208	8582	8954
2.7	0.9 9325	9695	*0063	*0430	*0796	*1160	*1523	*1885	*2245	*2604
2.8	1.0 2962	3318	3674	4028	4380	4732	5082	5431	5779	6126
2.9	6471	6815	7158	7500	7841	8181	8519	8856	9192	9527
3.0	1.0 9861	*0194	*0526	*0856	*1186	*1514	*1841	*2168	*2493	*2817
3.1	1.1 3140	3462	3783	4103	4422	4740	5057	5373	5688	6002
3.2	6315	6627	6938	7248	7557	7865	8173	8479	8784	9089
3.3	1.1 9392	9695	9996	*0297	*0597	*0896	*1194	*1491	*1788	*2083
3.4	1.2 2378	2671	2964	3256	3547	3837	4127	4415	4703	4990
3.5	5276	5562	5846	6130	6413	6695	6976	7257	7536	7815
3.6	1.2 8093	8371	8647	8923	9198	9473	9746	*0019	*0291	*0563
3.7	1.3 0833	1103	1372	1641	1909	2176	2442	2708	2972	3237
3.8	3500	3763	4025	4286	4547	4807	5067	5325	5584	5841
3.9	6098	6354	6609	6864	7118	7372	7624	7877	8128	8379
4.0	1.3 8629	8879	9128	9377	9624	9872	*0118	*0364	*0610	*0854
4.1	1.4 1099	1342	1585	1828	2070	2311	2552	2792	3031	3270
4.2	3508	3746	3984	4220	4456	4692	4927	5161	5395	5629
4.3	5862	6094	6326	6557	6787	7018	7247	7476	7705	7933
4.4	1.4 8160	8387	8614	8840	9065	9290	9515	9739	9962	*0185
4.5	1.5 0408	0630	0851	1072	1293	1513	1732	1951	2170	2388
4.6	2606	2823	3039	3256	3471	3687	3902	4116	4330	4543
4.7	4756	4969	5181	5393	5604	5814	6025	6235	6444	6653
4.8	6862	7070	7277	7485	7691	7898	8104	8309	8515	8719
4.9	1.5 8924	9127	9331	9534	9737	9939	*0141	*0342	*0543	*0744
5.0	1.6 0944	1144	1343	1542	1741	1939	2137	2334	2531	2728
5.1	2924	3120	3315	3511	3705	3900	4094	4287	4481	4673
5.2	4866	5058	5250	5441	5632	5823	6013	6203	6393	6582
5.3	6771	6959	7147	7335	7523	7710	7896	8083	8269	8455
5.4	1.6 8640	8825	9010	9194	9378	9562	9745	9928	*0111	*0293
5.5	1.7 0475	0656	0838	1019	1199	1380	1560	1740	1919	2098
5.6	2277	2455	2633	2811	2988	3166	3342	3519	3695	3871
5.7	4047	4222	4397	4572	4746	4920	5094	5267	5440	5613
5.8	5786	5958	6130	6302	6473	6644	6815	6985	7156	7326
5.9	7495	7665	7834	8002	8171	8339	8507	8675	8842	9009
6.0	1.7 9176	9342	9509	9675	9840	*0006	*0171	*0336	*0500	*0665
N	0	1	2	3	4	5	6	7	8	9

N	0	1	2	3	4	5	6	7	8	9
6.0	1.7 9176	9342	9509	9675	9840	*0006	*0171	*0336	*0500	*0665
6.1	1.8 0829	0993	1156	1319	1482	1645	1808	1970	2132	2294
6.2	2455	2616	2777	2938	3098	3258	3418	3578	3737	3896
6.3	4055	4214	4372	4530	4688	4845	5003	5160	5317	5473
6.4	5630	5786	5942	6097	6253	6408	6563	6718	6872	7026
6.5	7180	7334	7487	7641	7794	7947	8099	8251	8403	8555
6.6	1.8 8707	8858	9010	9160	9311	9462	9612	9762	9912	*0061
6.7	1.9 0211	0360	0509	0658	0806	0954	1102	1250	1398	1545
6.8	1692	1839	1986	2132	2279	2425	2571	2716	2862	3007
6.9	3152	3297	3442	3586	3730	3874	4018	4162	4305	4448
7.0	4591	4734	4876	5019	5161	5303	5445	5586	5727	5869
7.1	6009	6150	6291	6431	6571	6711	6851	6991	7130	7269
7.2	7408	7547	7685	7824	7962	8100	8238	8376	8513	8650
7.3	1.9 8787	8924	9061	9198	9334	9470	9606	9742	9877	*0013
7.4	2.0 0148	0283	0418	0553	0687	0821	0956	1089	1223	1357
7.5	1490	1624	1757	1890	2022	2155	2287	2419	2551	2683
7.6	2815	2946	3078	3209	3340	3471	3601	3732	3862	3992
7.7	4122	4252	4381	4511	4640	4769	4898	5027	5156	5284
7.8	5412	5540	5668	5796	5924	6051	6179	6306	6433	6560
7.9	6686	6813	6939	7065	7191	7317	7443	7568	7694	7819
8.0	7944	8069	8194	8318	8443	8567	8691	8815	8939	9063
8.1	2.0 9186	9310	9433	9556	9679	9802	9924	*0047	*0169	*0291
8.2	2.1 0413	0535	0657	0779	0900	1021	1142	1263	1384	1505
8.3	1626	1746	1866	1986	2106	2226	2346	2465	2585	2704
8.4	2823	2942	3061	3180	3298	3417	3535	3653	3771	3889
8.5	4007	4124	4242	4359	4476	4593	4710	4827	4943	5060
8.6	5176	5292	5409	5524	5640	5756	5871	5987	6102	6217
8.7	6332	6447	6562	6677	6791	6905	7020	7134	7248	7361
8.8	7475	7589	7702	7816	7929	8042	8155	8267	8380	8493
8.9	8605	8717	8830	8942	9054	9165	9277	9389	9500	9611
9.0	2.1 9722	9834	9944	*0055	*0166	*0276	*0387	*0497	*0607	*0717
9.1	2.2 0827	0937	1047	1157	1266	1375	1485	1594	1703	1812
9.2	1920	2029	2138	2246	2354	2462	2570	2678	2786	2894
9.3	3001	3109	3216	3324	3431	3538	3645	3751	3858	3965
9.4	4071	4177	4284	4390	4496	4601	4707	4813	4918	5024
9.5	5129	5234	5339	5444	5549	5654	5759	5863	5968	6072
9.6	6176	6280	6384	6488	6592	6696	6799	6903	7006	7109
9.7	7213	7316	7419	7521	7624	7727	7829	7932	8034	8136
9.8	8238	8340	8442	8544	8646	8747	8849	8950	9051	9152
9.9	2.2 9253	9354	9455	9556	9657	9757	9858	9958	*0058	*0158
10.0	2.3 0259	0358	0458	0558	0658	0757	0857	0956	1055	1154
N	0	1	2	3	4	5	6	7	8	9

NOTE 1. The base for natural logarithms is $e = 2.71828\ 18284\ 59045\ \cdots$

$$\log_e 10 = 2.3025\ 8509. \qquad \log_{10} e = 0.4342\ 9448. \tag{1}$$

NOTE 2. If $N > 10$ or $N < 1$, then we may write $N = P \cdot 10^k$ where k is an integer and $1 \leqq P < 10$. Then, to find $\log_e N$, use the following relation with $\log_e P$ obtained from the preceding table and $\log_e 10$ obtained from (1):

$$\log_e N = \log_e (P \cdot 10^k) = \log_e P + k \log_e 10.$$

XV. IMPORTANT CONSTANTS AND THEIR LOGARITHMS

Description	Value	$\log_{10}$
π	3.14159265	0.49714987
e = Naperian Base	2.71828183	0.43429448
$M = \log_{10} e$	0.43429448	9.63778431 − 10
$1 \div M = \log_e 10$	2.30258509	0.36221569
$180 \div \pi$ = degrees in 1 radian	57.2957795	1.75812263
$\pi \div 180$ = radians in 1°	0.01745329	8.24187737 − 10
$\pi \div 10800$ = radians in 1′	0.0002908882	6.46372612 − 10
$\pi \div 648000$ = radians in 1″	0.000004848136811095	4.68557487 − 10

Values with Extreme Accuracy

$\pi = 3.14159$	26535	89793	23846	26433	83280
$\log_{10} \pi = 0.49714$	98726	94133	85435	12682	88291
$\log_e \pi = 1.14472$	98858	49400	17414	34273	51353
$e = 2.71828$	18284	59045	23536	02874	71353
$M = 0.43429$	44819	03251	82765	11289	18917
$1 \div M = 2.30258$	50929	94045	68401	79914	54684
$\log_{10} M = 9.63778$	43113	00536	78912 − 10		

XVI. LOGARITHMS FOR COMPUTING COMPOUND INTEREST *

$i\%$	$\log_{10} (1 + i)$			$i\%$	$\log_{10} (1 + i)$		
0 + 1/12	.00036	17613	55281	2 + 1/4	.00966	33166	79379
1/8	.00054	25290	92294	3/8	.01019	39147	68475
1/6	.00072	32216	19096	1/2	.01072	38653	91773
5/24	.00090	38389	98245	5/8	.01125	31701	27497
1/4	.00108	43812	92220	3/4	.01178	18305	48107
0 + 7/24	.00126	48485	63424	2 + 7/8	.01230	98482	20326
1/3	.00144	52408	74181	3 + 0	.01283	72247	05172
3/8	.00162	55582	86737	1/4	.01389	00603	28439
5/12	.00180	58008	63262	1/2	.01494	03497	92937
1/2	.00216	60617	56508	3/4	.01598	81053	84130
0 + 7/12	.00252	60240	49724	4 + 0	.01703	33392	98780
5/8	.00270	58933	75925	1/4	.01807	60636	45795
2/3	.00288	56882	37488	1/2	.01911	62904	47073
3/4	.00324	50548	13147	3/4	.02015	40316	38333
7/8	.00378	35477	30127	5 + 0	.02118	92990	69938
1 + 0	.00432	13737	82643	5 + 1/4	.02222	21045	07706
1/8	.00485	85346	20329	1/2	.02325	24596	33711
1/4	.00539	50318	86706	3/4	.02428	03760	47080
3/8	.00593	08672	19212	6 + 0	.02530	58652	64770
1/2	.00646	60422	49232	1/4	.02632	89387	22349
1 + 5/8	.00700	05586	02125	6 + 1/2	.02734	96077	74757
3/4	.00753	44178	97258	7 + 0	.02938	37776	85210
7/8	.00806	76217	48033	1/2	.03140	84642	51624
2 + 0	.00860	01717	61918	8 + 0	.03342	37554	86950
1/8	.00913	20695	40472	1/2	.03542	97381	84548

* For a more complete table see Glover's *Interest and Logarithmic Tables;* George Wahr, publisher.

Angle	Value	Log*	Angle	Value	Log*	Angle	Value	Log*
0° 0′	.00000	——	10° 0′	.00760	7.88059	20° 0′	.03015	8.47934
10′	.00000	4.32539	10′	.00785	7.89491	10′	.03065	8.48648
20′	.00001	4.92745	20′	.00811	7.90900	20′	.03116	8.49355
30′	.00002	5.27963	30′	.00837	7.92286	30′	.03166	8.50056
40′	.00003	5.52951	40′	.00864	7.93650	40′	.03218	8.50752
0° 50′	.00005	5.72332	10° 50′	.00891	7.94992	20° 50′	.03269	8.51442
1° 0′	.00008	5.88168	11° 0′	.00919	7.96315	21° 0′	.03321	8.52127
10′	.00010	6.01557	10′	.00947	7.97617	10′	.03373	8.52806
20′	.00014	6.13155	20′	.00975	7.98899	20′	.03426	8.53479
30′	.00017	6.23385	30′	.01004	8.00163	30′	.03479	8.54147
40′	.00021	6.32536	40′	.01033	8.01409	40′	.03533	8.54810
1° 50′	.00026	6.40814	11° 50′	.01063	8.02637	21° 50′	.03587	8.55467
2° 0′	.00030	6.48371	12° 0′	.01093	8.03847	22° 0′	.03641	8.56120
10′	.00036	6.55323	10′	.01123	8.05041	10′	.03695	8.56767
20′	.00041	6.61759	20′	.01154	8.06218	20′	.03751	8.57410
30′	.00048	6.67751	30′	.01185	8.07379	30′	.03806	8.58047
40′	.00054	6.73355	40′	.01217	8.08525	40′	.03862	8.58680
2° 50′	.00061	6.78620	12° 50′	.01249	8.09656	22° 50′	.03918	8.59308
3° 0′	.00069	6.83584	13° 0′	.01282	8.10772	23° 0′	.03975	8.59931
10′	.00076	6.88279	10′	.01314	8.11873	10′	.04032	8.60550
20′	.00085	6.92733	20′	.01348	8.12961	20′	.04089	8.61164
30′	.00093	6.96970	30′	.01382	8.14035	30′	.04147	8.61773
40′	.00102	7.01009	40′	.01416	8.15096	40′	.04205	8.62379
3° 50′	.00112	7.04869	13° 50′	.01450	8.16144	23° 50′	.04264	8.62979
4° 0′	.00122	7.08564	14° 0′	.01485	8.17179	24° 0′	.04323	8.63576
10′	.00132	7.12108	10′	.01521	8.18202	10′	.04382	8.64168
20′	.00143	7.15513	20′	.01556	8.19212	20′	.04442	8.64756
30′	.00154	7.18790	30′	.01593	8.20211	30′	.04502	8.65340
40′	.00166	7.21947	40′	.01629	8.21199	40′	.04562	8.65920
4° 50′	.00178	7.24993	14° 50′	.01666	8.22175	24° 50′	.04623	8.66496
5° 0′	.00190	7.27936	15° 0′	.01704	8.23140	25° 0′	.04685	8.67067
10′	.00203	7.30782	10′	.01742	8.24094	10′	.04746	8.67635
20′	.00216	7.33538	20′	.01780	8.25037	20′	.04808	8.68199
30′	.00230	7.36209	30′	.01818	8.25971	30′	.04871	8.68760
40′	.00244	7.38800	40′	.01858	8.26894	40′	.04934	8.69316
5° 50′	.00259	7.41315	15° 50′	.01897	8.27807	25° 50′	.04997	8.69869
6° 0′	.00274	7.43760	16° 0′	.01937	8.28711	26° 0′	.05060	8.70418
10′	.00289	7.46138	10′	.01977	8.29605	10′	.05124	8.70963
20′	.00305	7.48452	20′	.02018	8.30490	20′	.05189	8.71505
30′	.00321	7.50706	30′	.02059	8.31366	30′	.05253	8.72043
40′	.00338	7.52902	40′	.02101	8.32233	40′	.05318	8.72578
6° 50′	.00355	7.55045	16° 50′	.02142	8.33091	26° 50′	.05384	8.73109
7° 0′	.00373	7.57135	17° 0′	.02185	8.33940	27° 0′	.05450	8.73637
10′	.00391	7.59176	10′	.02227	8.34782	10′	.05516	8.74162
20′	.00409	7.61170	20′	.02271	8.35614	20′	.05582	8.74683
30′	.00428	7.63120	30′	.02314	8.36439	30′	.05649	8.75201
40′	.00447	7.65026	40′	.02358	8.37256	40′	.05717	8.75715
7° 50′	.00467	7.66891	17° 50′	.02402	8.38065	27° 50′	.05785	8.76227
8° 0′	.00487	7.68717	18° 0′	.02447	8.38867	28° 0′	.05853	8.76735
10′	.00507	7.70505	10′	.02492	8.39660	10′	.05921	8.77240
20′	.00528	7.72257	20′	.02538	8.40447	20′	.05990	8.77742
30′	.00549	7.73974	30′	.02584	8.41226	30′	.06059	8.78241
40′	.00571	7.75657	40′	.02630	8.41998	40′	.06129	8.78737
8° 50′	.00593	7.77308	18° 50′	.02677	8.42764	28° 50′	.06199	8.79230
9° 0′	.00616	7.78929	19° 0′	.02724	8.43522	29° 0′	.06269	8.79720
10′	.00639	7.80519	10′	.02772	8.44273	10′	.06340	8.80207
20′	.00662	7.82081	20′	.02820	8.45018	20′	.06411	8.80691
30′	.00686	7.83615	30′	.02868	8.45757	30′	.06482	8.81172
40′	.00710	7.85122	40′	.02917	8.46489	40′	.06554	8.81651
9° 50′	.00735	7.86603	19° 50′	.02966	8.47215	29° 50′	.06626	8.82126
10° 0′	.00760	7.88059	20° 0′	.03015	8.47934	30° 0′	.06699	8.82599
Angle	Value	Log*	Angle	Value	Log*	Angle	Value	Log*

* *Subtract 10 from each listed value.*

Angle	Value	Log*	Angle	Value	Log*	Angle	Value	Log*
30° 0′	.06699	8.82599	40° 0′	.11698	9.06810	50° 0′	.17861	9.25190
10′	.06772	8.83069	10′	.11791	9.07157	10′	.17972	9.25460
20′	.06845	8.83537	20′	.11885	9.07501	20′	.18084	9.25729
30′	.06919	8.84002	30′	.11980	9.07845	30′	.18196	9.25998
40′	.06993	8.84464	40′	.12074	9.08186	40′	.18308	9.26265
30° 50′	.07067	8.84923	40° 50′	.12169	9.08526	50° 50′	.18421	9.26532
31° 0′	.07142	8.85380	41° 0′	.12265	9.08865	51° 0′	.18534	9.26797
10′	.07217	8.85834	10′	.12360	9.09202	10′	.18647	9.27061
20′	.07292	8.86286	20′	.12456	9.09538	20′	.18761	9.27325
30′	.07368	8.86735	30′	.12552	9.09872	30′	.18874	9.27587
40′	.07444	8.87182	40′	.12649	9.10205	40′	.18988	9.27848
31° 50′	.07521	8.87626	41° 50′	.12746	9.10536	51° 50′	.19102	9.28109
32° 0′	.07598	8.88068	42° 0′	.12843	9.10866	52° 0′	.19217	9.28368
10′	.07675	8.88507	10′	.12940	9.11194	10′	.19332	9.28627
20′	.07752	8.88944	20′	.13038	9.11521	20′	.19447	9.28885
30′	.07830	8.89379	30′	.13136	9.11847	30′	.19562	9.29141
40′	.07909	8.89811	40′	.13235	9.12171	40′	.19677	9.29397
32° 50′	.07987	8.90241	42° 50′	.13333	9.12494	52° 50′	.19793	9.29652
33° 0′	.08066	8.90668	43° 0′	.13432	9.12815	53° 0′	.19909	9.29906
10′	.08146	8.91094	10′	.13532	9.13135	10′	.20026	9.30158
20′	.08226	8.91517	20′	.13631	9.13454	20′	.20142	9.30410
30′	.08306	8.91938	30′	.13731	9.13771	30′	.20259	9.30662
40′	.08386	8.92356	40′	.13832	9.14087	40′	.20376	9.30912
33° 50′	.08467	8.92773	43° 50′	.13932	9.14402	53° 50′	.20493	9.31161
34° 0′	.08548	8.93187	44° 0′	.14033	9.14715	54° 0′	20611	9.31409
10′	.08630	8.93599	10′	.14134	9.15027	10′	.20729	9.31657
20′	.08711	8.94009	20′	.14236	9.15338	20′	.20847	9.31903
30′	.08794	8.94417	30′	.14337	9.15647	30′	.20965	9.32149
40′	.08876	8.94823	40′	.14440	9.15955	40′	.21083	9.32394
34° 50′	.08959	8.95227	44° 50′	.14542	9.16262	54° 50′	.21202	9.32638
35° 0′	.09042	8.95628	45° 0′	.14645	9.16568	55° 0′	.21321	9.32881
10′	.09126	8.96028	10′	.14748	9.16872	10′	.21440	9.33123
20′	.09210	8.96426	20′	.14851	9.17175	20′	.21560	9.33365
30′	.09294	8.96821	30′	.14955	9.17477	30′	.21680	9.33605
40′	.09379	8.97215	40′	.15058	9.17778	40′	.21800	9.33845
35° 50′	.09464	8.97607	45° 50′	.15163	9.18077	55° 50′	.21920	9.34084
36° 0′	.09549	8.97997	46° 0′	.15267	9.18376	56° 0′	.22040	9.34322
10′	.09635	8.98384	10′	.15372	9.18673	10′	.22161	9.34549
20′	.09721	8.98770	20′	.15477	9.18968	20′	.22282	9.34795
30′	.09807	8.99154	30′	.15582	9.19263	30′	.22403	9.35031
40′	.09894	8.99536	40′	.15688	9.19557	40′	.22525	9.35266
36° 50′	.09981	8.99917	46° 50′	.15794	9.19849	56° 50′	.22646	9.35500
37° 0′	.10068	9.00295	47° 0′	.15900	9.20140	57° 0′	.22768	9.35733
10′	.10156	9.00672	10′	.16007	9.20430	10′	.22890	9.35965
20′	.10244	9.01047	20′	.16113	9.20719	20′	.23012	9.36196
30′	.10332	9.01420	30′	.16220	9.21006	30′	.23135	9.36427
40′	.10421	9.01791	40′	.16328	9.21293	40′	.23258	9.36657
37° 50′	.10510	9.02161	47° 50′	.16436	9.21578	57° 50′	.23381	9.36886
38° 0′	.10599	9.02528	48° 0′	.16543	9.21863	58° 0′	.23504	9.37114
10′	.10689	9.02894	10′	.16652	9.22146	10′	.23627	9.37342
20′	.10779	9.03259	20′	.16760	9.22428	20′	.23751	9.37569
30′	.10870	9.03621	30′	.16869	9.22709	30′	.23875	9.37794
40′	.10960	9.03982	40′	.16978	9.22989	40′	.23999	9.38020
38° 50′	.11051	9.04341	48° 50′	.17087	9.23268	58° 50′	.24124	9.38244
39° 0′	.11143	9.04699	49° 0′	.17197	9.23545	59° 0′	.24248	9.38468
10′	.11234	9.05055	10′	.17307	9.23822	10′	.24373	9.38691
20′	.11326	9.05409	20′	.17417	9.24098	20′	.24498	9.38913
30′	.11419	9.05762	30′	.17528	9.24372	30′	.24623	9.39134
40′	.11511	9.06113	40′	.17638	9.24646	40′	.24749	9.39355
39° 50′	.11604	9.06462	49° 50′	.17749	9.24918	59° 50′	.24874	9.39575
40° 0′	.11698	9.06810	50° 0′	.17861	9.25190	60° 0′	.25000	9.39794
Angle	Value	Log*	Angle	Value	Log*	Angle	Value	Log*

Subtract 10 from each listed value.

Angle	Value	Log*	Angle	Value	Log*	Angle	Value	Log*
60° 0'	.25000	9.39794	**70° 0'**	.32899	9.51718	**80° 0'**	.41318	9.61613
10'	.25126	9.40012	10'	.33036	9.51898	10'	.41461	9.61764
20'	.25252	9.40230	20'	.33173	9.52078	20'	.41604	9.61914
30'	.25379	9.40447	30'	.33310	9.52257	30'	.41748	9.62063
40'	.25506	9.40663	40'	.33447	9.52436	40'	.41891	9.62212
60° 50'	.25632	9.40879	70° 50'	.33584	9.52613	80° 50'	.42035	9.62361
61° 0'	.25760	9.41094	**71° 0'**	.33722	9.52791	**81° 0'**	.42178	9.62509
10'	.25887	9.41308	10'	.33859	9.52968	10'	.42322	9.62657
20'	.26014	9.41521	20'	.33997	9.53144	20'	.42466	9.62804
30'	.26142	9.41734	30'	.34135	9.53320	30'	.42610	9.62951
40'	.26270	9.41946	40'	.34273	9.53495	40'	.42753	9.63097
61° 50'	.26398	9.42157	71° 50'	.34411	9.53670	81° 50'	.42897	9.63243
62° 0'	.26526	9.42368	**72° 0'**	.34549	9.53844	**82° 0'**	.43041	9.63389
10'	.26655	9.42578	10'	.34688	9.54017	10'	.43185	9.63534
20'	.26784	9.42787	20'	.34826	9.54190	20'	.43330	9.63678
30'	.26913	9.42996	30'	.34965	9.54363	30'	.43474	9.63823
40'	.27042	9.43203	40'	.35103	9.54535	40'	.43618	9.63966
62° 50'	.27171	9.43411	72° 50'	.35242	9.54707	82° 50'	.43762	9.64110
63° 0'	.27300	9.43617	**73° 0'**	.35381	9.54878	**83° 0'**	.43907	9.64253
10'	.27430	9.43823	10'	.35521	9.55048	10'	.44051	9.64396
20'	.27560	9.44028	20'	.35660	9.55218	20'	.44195	9.64538
30'	.27690	9.44232	30'	.35799	9.55387	30'	.44340	9.64679
40'	.27820	9.44436	40'	.35939	9.55556	40'	.44484	9.64821
63° 50'	.27951	9.44639	73° 50'	.36078	9.55725	83° 50'	.44629	9.64962
64° 0'	.28081	9.44842	**74° 0'**	.36218	9.55893	**84° 0'**	.44774	9.65102
10'	.28212	9.45044	10'	.36358	9.56060	10'	.44918	9.65242
20'	.28343	9.45245	20'	.36498	9.56227	20'	.45063	9.65382
30'	.28474	9.45446	30'	.36638	9.56393	30'	.45208	9.65521
40'	.28606	9.45645	40'	.36778	9.56559	40'	.45353	9.65660
64° 50'	.28737	9.45845	74° 50'	.36919	9.56725	84° 50'	.45497	9.65799
65° 0'	.28869	9.46043	**75° 0'**	.37059	9.56889	**85° 0'**	.45642	9.65937
10'	.29001	9.46241	10'	.37200	9.57054	10'	.45787	9.66074
20'	.29133	9.46439	20'	.37340	9.57218	20'	.45932	9.66212
30'	.29265	9.46635	30'	.37481	9.57381	30'	.46077	9.66348
40'	.29398	9.46831	40'	.37622	9.57544	40'	.46222	9.66485
65° 50'	.29530	9.47027	75° 50'	.37763	9.57706	85° 50'	.46367	9.66621
66° 0'	.29663	9.47222	**76° 0'**	.37904	9.57868	**86° 0'**	.46512	9.66757
10'	.29796	9.47416	10'	.38045	9.58030	10'	.46657	9.66892
20'	.29929	9.47610	20'	.38186	9.58191	20'	.46802	9.67027
30'	.30063	9.47803	30'	.38328	9.58351	30'	.46948	9.67161
40'	.30196	9.47995	40'	.38469	9.58511	40'	.47093	9.67295
66° 50'	.30330	9.48187	76° 50'	.38611	9.58671	86° 50'	.47238	9.67429
67° 0'	.30463	9.48378	**77° 0'**	.38752	9.58830	**87° 0'**	.47383	9.67562
10'	.30597	9.48568	10'	.38894	9.58989	10'	.47528	9.67695
20'	.30732	9.48758	20'	.39036	9.59147	20'	.47674	9.67828
30'	.30866	9.47948	30'	.39178	9.59304	30'	.47819	9.67960
40'	.31000	9.49137	40'	.39320	9.59461	40'	.47964	9.68092
67° 50'	.31135	9.49325	77° 50'	.39462	9.59618	87° 50'	.48110	9.68223
68° 0'	.31270	9.49512	**78° 0'**	.39604	9.59774	**88° 0'**	.48255	9.68354
10'	.31405	9.49699	10'	.39746	9.59930	10'	.48400	9.68485
20'	.31540	9.49886	20'	.39889	9.60085	20'	.48546	9.68615
30'	.31675	9.50072	30'	.40032	9.60240	30'	.48691	9.68745
40'	.31810	9.50257	40'	.40174	9.60395	40'	.48837	9.68874
68° 50'	.31946	9.50442	78° 50'	.40317	9.60549	88° 50'	.48982	9.69004
69° 0'	.32082	9.50626	**79° 0'**	.40460	9.60702	**89° 0'**	.49127	9.69132
10'	.32217	9.50809	10'	.40602	9.60855	10'	.49273	9.69261
20'	.32353	9.50992	20'	.40745	9.61008	20'	.49418	9.69389
30'	.32490	9.51174	30'	.40888	9.61160	30'	.49564	9.69516
40'	.32626	9.51356	40'	.41031	9.61312	40'	.49709	9.69644
69° 50'	.32762	9.51538	79° 50'	.41174	9.61463	89° 50'	.49855	9.69770
70° 0'	.32899	9.51718	**80° 0'**	.41318	9.61614	**90° 0'**	.50000	9.69897
Angle	Value	Log*	Angle	Value	Log*	Angle	Value	Log*

* *Subtract 10 from each listed value.*

Angle	Value	Log*	Angle	Value	Log*	Angle	Value	Log*
90° 0′	.50000	9.69897	**100° 0′**	.58682	9.76851	**110° 0′**	.67101	9.82673
10′	.50145	9.70023	10′	.58826	9.76957	10′	.67238	9.82761
20′	.50291	9.70149	20′	.58969	9.77062	20′	.67374	9.82849
30′	.50436	9.70274	30′	.59112	9.77167	30′	.67510	9.82937
40′	.50582	9.70399	40′	.59255	9.77272	40′	.67647	9.83025
90° 50′	.50727	9.70524	100° 50′	.59398	9.77377	110° 50′	.67783	9.83112
91° 0′	.50873	9.70648	**101° 0′**	.59540	9.77481	**111° 0′**	.67918	9.83199
10′	.51018	9.70772	10′	.59683	9.77585	10′	.68054	9.83285
20′	.51163	9.70896	20′	.59826	9.77689	20′	.68190	9.83372
30′	.51309	9.71019	30′	.59968	9.77792	30′	.68325	9.83458
40′	.51454	9.71142	40′	.60111	9.77895	40′	.68460	9.83554
91° 50′	.51600	9.71265	101° 50′	.60253	9.77998	111° 50′	.68595	9.83630
92° 0′	.51745	9.71387	**102° 0′**	.60396	9.78101	**112° 0′**	.68730	9.83715
10′	.51890	9.71509	10′	.60538	9.78203	10′	.68865	9.83800
20′	.52036	9.71630	20′	.60680	9.78305	20′	.69000	9.83885
30′	.52181	9.71751	30′	.60822	9.78406	30′	.69134	9.83969
40′	.52326	9.71872	40′	.60964	9.78507	40′	.69268	9.84054
92° 50′	.52472	9.71992	102° 50′	.61106	9.78608	112° 50′	.69403	9.84138
93° 0′	.52617	9.72112	**103° 0′**	.61248	9.78709	**113° 0′**	.69537	9.84221
10′	.52762	9.72232	10′	.61389	9.78809	10′	.69670	9.84305
20′	.52907	9.72352	20′	.61531	9.78909	20′	.69804	9.84388
30′	.53052	9.72471	30′	.61672	9.79009	30′	.69937	9.84471
40′	.53198	9.72589	40′	.61814	9.79108	40′	.70071	9.84554
93° 50′	.53343	9.72708	103° 50′	.61955	9.79208	113° 50′	.70204	9.84636
94° 0′	.53488	9.72825	**104° 0′**	.62096	9.79306	**114° 0′**	.70337	9.84718
10′	.53633	9.72943	10′	.62237	9.79405	10′	.70470	9.84800
20′	.53778	9.73060	20′	.62378	9.79503	20′	.70602	9.84882
30′	.53923	9.73177	30′	.62519	9.79601	30′	.70735	9.84963
40′	.54068	9.73294	40′	.62660	9.79699	40′	.70867	9.85044
94° 50′	.54213	9.73410	104° 50′	.62800	9.79796	114° 50′	.70999	9.85125
95° 0′	.54358	9.73526	**105° 0′**	.62941	9.79893	**115° 0′**	.71131	9.85206
10′	.54503	9.73642	10′	.63081	9.79990	10′	.71263	9.85286
20′	.54647	9.73757	20′	.63222	9.80087	20′	.71394	9.85366
30′	.54792	9.73872	30′	.63362	9.80183	30′	.71526	9.85446
40′	.54937	9.73987	40′	.63502	9.80279	40′	.71657	9.85526
95° 50′	.55082	9.74101	105° 50′	.63642	9.80374	115° 50′	.71788	9.85605
96° 0′	.55226	9.74215	**106° 0′**	.63782	9.80470	**116° 0′**	.71919	9.85684
10′	.55371	9.74328	10′	.63922	9.80565	10′	.72049	9.85763
20′	.55516	9.74442	20′	.64061	9.80660	20′	.72180	9.85841
30′	.55660	9.74554	30′	.64201	9.80754	30′	.72310	9.85920
40′	.55805	9.74667	40′	.64340	9.80848	40′	.72440	9.85998
96° 50′	.55949	9.74779	106° 50′	.64479	9.80942	116° 50′	.72570	9.86076
97° 0′	.56093	9.74891	**107° 0′**	.64619	9.81036	**117° 0′**	.72700	9.86153
10′	.56238	9.75003	10′	.64758	9.81129	10′	.72829	9.86230
20′	.56382	9.75114	20′	.64897	9.81222	20′	.72958	9.86307
30′	.56526	9.75225	30′	.65035	9.81315	30′	.73087	9.86384
40′	.56670	9.75336	40′	.65174	9.81407	40′	.73216	9.86461
97° 50′	.56815	9.75446	107° 50′	.65312	9.81500	117° 50′	.73345	9.86537
98° 0′	.56959	9.75556	**108° 0′**	.65451	9.81592	**118° 0′**	.73474	9.86613
10′	.57103	9.75666	10′	.65589	9.81683	10′	.73602	9.86689
20′	.57247	9.75775	20′	.65727	9.81775	20′	.73730	9.86764
30′	.57390	9.75884	30′	.65865	9.81866	30′	.73858	9.86840
40′	.57534	9.75993	40′	.66003	9.81956	40′	.73986	9.86915
98° 50′	.57678	9.76101	108° 50′	.66141	9.82047	118° 50′	.74113	9.86990
99° 0′	.57822	9.76209	**109° 0′**	.66278	9.82137	**119° 0′**	.74240	9.87064
10′	.57965	9.76317	10′	.66416	9.82227	10′	.74368	9.87138
20′	.58109	9.76424	20′	.66553	9.82317	20′	.74494	9.87212
30′	.58252	9.76531	30′	.66690	9.82406	30′	.74621	9.87286
40′	.58396	9.76638	40′	.66827	9.82495	40′	.74748	9.87360
99° 50′	.58539	9.76745	109° 50′	.66964	9.82584	119° 50′	.74874	9.87433
100° 0′	.58682	9.76851	**110° 0′**	.67101	9.82673	**120° 0′**	.75000	9.87506
Angle	Value	Log*	Angle	Value	Log*	Angle	Value	Log*

Subtract 10 from each listed value.

Angle	Value	Log*	Angle	Value	Log*	Angle	Value	Log*
120° 0′	.75000	9.87506	**130° 0′**	.82139	9.91455	**140° 0′**	.88302	9.94597
10′	.75126	9.87579	10′	.82251	9.91514	10′	.88396	9.94643
20′	.75251	9.87652	20′	.82362	9.91573	20′	.88489	9.94689
30′	.75377	9.87724	30′	.82472	9.91631	30′	.88581	9.94734
40′	.75502	9.87796	40′	.82583	9.91689	40′	.88674	9.94779
120° 50′	.75627	9.87868	130° 50′	.82693	9.91747	140° 50′	.88766	9.94824
121° 0′	.75752	9.87939	**131° 0′**	.82803	9.91805	**141° 0′**	.88857	9.94869
10′	.75876	9.88011	10′	.82913	9.91862	10′	.88949	9.94914
20′	.76001	9.88082	20′	.83022	9.91919	20′	.89040	9.94958
30′	.76125	9.88153	30′	.83131	9.91976	30′	.89130	9.95003
40′	.76249	9.88223	40′	.83240	9.92033	40′	.89221	9.95047
121° 50′	.76373	9.88294	131° 50′	.83348	9.92090	141° 50′	.89311	9.95090
122° 0′	.76496	9.88364	**132° 0′**	.83457	9.92146	**142° 0′**	.89401	9.95134
10′	.76619	9.88434	10′	.83564	9.92202	10′	.89490	9.95177
20′	.76742	9.88503	20′	.83672	9.92258	20′	.89579	9.95221
30′	.76865	9.88573	30′	.83780	9.92314	30′	.89668	9.95264
40′	.76988	9.88642	40′	.83887	9.92369	40′	.89756	9.95306
122° 50′	.77110	9.88711	132° 50′	.83993	9.92425	142° 50′	.89844	9.95349
123° 0′	.77232	9.88780	**133° 0′**	.84100	9.92480	**143° 0′**	.89932	9.95391
10′	.77354	9.88848	10′	.84206	9.92534	10′	.90019	9.95433
20′	.77475	9.88916	20′	.84312	9.92589	20′	.90106	9.95475
30′	.77597	9.88984	30′	.84418	9.92643	30′	.90193	9.95517
40′	.77718	9.89052	40′	.84523	9.92698	40′	.90279	9.95559
123° 50′	.77839	9.89120	133° 50′	.84628	9.92751	143° 50′	.90365	9.95600
124° 0′	.77960	9.89187	**134° 0′**	.84733	9.92805	**144° 0′**	.90451	9.95641
10′	.78080	9.89254	10′	.84837	9.92859	10′	.90537	9.95682
20′	.78200	9.89321	20′	.84942	9.92912	20′	.90621	9.95723
30′	.78320	9.89387	30′	.85045	9.92965	30′	.90706	9.95763
40′	.78440	9.89454	40′	.85149	9.93018	40′	.90790	9.95804
124° 50′	.78560	9.89520	134° 50′	.85252	9.93071	144° 50′	.90874	9.95844
125° 0′	.78679	9.89586	**135° 0′**	.85355	9.93123	**145° 0′**	.90958	9.95884
10′	.78798	9.89651	10′	.85458	9.93175	10′	.91041	9.95924
20′	.78917	9.89717	20′	.85560	9.93227	20′	.91124	9.95963
30′	.79035	9.89782	30′	.85663	9.93279	30′	.91206	9.96002
40′	.79153	9.89847	40′	.85764	9.93331	40′	.91289	9.96042
125° 50′	.79271	9.89912	135° 50′	.85866	9.93382	145° 50′	.91370	9.96081
126° 0′	.79389	9.89976	**136° 0′**	.85967	9.93433	**146° 0′**	.91452	9.96119
10′	.79507	9.90040	10′	.86068	9.93484	10′	.91533	9.96158
20′	.79624	9.90104	20′	.86168	9.93535	20′	.91614	9.96196
30′	.79741	9.90168	30′	.86269	9.93585	30′	.91694	9.96234
40′	.79858	9.90232	40′	.86369	9.93636	40′	.91774	9.96272
126° 50′	.79974	9.90295	136° 50′	.86468	9.93686	146° 50′	.91854	9.96310
127° 0′	.80091	9.90358	**137° 0′**	.86568	9.93736	**147° 0′**	.91934	9.96347
10′	.80207	9.90421	10′	.86667	9.93785	10′	.92013	9.96385
20′	.80323	9.90484	20′	.86765	9.93835	20′	.92091	9.96422
30′	.80438	9.90546	30′	.86864	9.93884	30′	.92170	9.96459
40′	.80553	9.90608	40′	.86962	9.93933	40′	.92248	9.96495
127° 50′	.80668	9.90670	137° 50′	.87060	9.93982	147° 50′	.92325	9.96532
128° 0′	.80783	9.90732	**138° 0′**	.87157	9.94030	**148° 0′**	.92402	9.96568
10′	.80898	9.90794	10′	.87254	9.94079	10′	.92479	9.96604
20′	.81012	9.90855	20′	.87351	9.94127	20′	.92556	9.96640
30′	.81126	9.90916	30′	.87448	9.94175	30′	.92632	9.96676
40′	.81239	9.90977	40′	.87544	9.94223	40′	.92708	9.96712
128° 50′	.81353	9.91037	138° 50′	.87640	9.94270	148° 50′	.92783	9.96747
129° 0′	.81466	9.91098	**139° 0′**	.87735	9.94318	**149° 0′**	.92858	9.96782
10′	.81579	9.91158	10′	.87831	9.94365	10′	.92933	9.96817
20′	.81692	9.91218	20′	.87926	9.94412	20′	.93007	9.96852
30′	.81804	9.91277	30′	.88020	9.94458	30′	.93081	9.96886
40′	.81916	9.91337	40′	.88115	9.94505	40′	.93155	9.96921
129° 50′	.82028	9.91396	139° 50′	.88209	9.94551	149° 50′	.93228	9.96955
130° 0′	.82139	9.91455	**140° 0′**	.88302	9.94597	**150° 0′**	.93301	9.96989
Angle	Value	Log*	Angle	Value	Log*	Angle	Value	Log*

Subtract 10 from each listed value.

Angle	Value	Log*	Angle	Value	Log*	Angle	Value	Log*
150° 0′	.93301	9.96989	**160° 0′**	.96985	9.98670	**170° 0′**	.99240	9.99669
10′	.93374	9.97022	10′	.97034	9.98692	10′	.99265	9.99680
20′	.93446	9.97056	20′	.97083	9.98714	20′	.99290	9.99691
30′	.93518	9.97089	30′	.97132	9.98736	30′	.99314	9.99701
40′	.93589	9.97123	40′	.97180	9.98758	40′	.99338	9.99712
150° 50′	.93660	9.97156	160° 50′	.97228	9.98779	170° 50′	.99361	9.99722
151° 0′	.93731	9.97188	**161° 0′**	.97276	9.98801	**171° 0′**	.99384	9.99732
10′	.93801	9.97221	10′	.97323	9.98822	10′	.99407	9.99742
20′	.93871	9.97253	20′	.97370	9.98842	20′	.99429	9.99751
30′	.93941	9.97285	30′	.97416	9.98863	30′	.99451	9.99761
40′	.94010	9.97317	40′	.97462	9.98884	40′	.99472	9.99770
151° 50′	.94079	9.97349	161° 50′	.97508	9.98904	171° 50′	.99493	9.99779
152° 0′	.94147	9.97381	**162° 0′**	.97553	9.98924	**172° 0′**	.99513	9.99788
10′	.94215	9.97412	10′	.97598	9.98944	10′	.99533	9.99797
20′	.94283	9.97443	20′	.97642	9.98964	20′	.99553	9.99805
30′	.94351	9.97474	30′	.97686	9.98983	30′	.99572	9.99814
40′	.94418	9.97505	40′	.97729	9.99003	40′	.99591	9.99822
152° 50′	.94484	9.97536	162° 50′	.97773	9.99022	172° 50′	.99609	9.99830
153° 0′	.94550	9.97566	**163° 0′**	.97815	9.99041	**173° 0′**	.99627	9.99838
10′	.94616	9.97597	10′	.97858	9.99059	10′	.99645	9.99845
20′	.94682	9.97627	20′	.97899	9.99078	20′	.99662	9.99853
30′	.94747	9.97656	30′	.97941	9.99096	30′	.99679	9.99860
40′	.94811	9.97686	40′	.97982	9.99115	40′	.99695	9.99867
153° 50′	.94876	9.97716	163° 50′	.98023	9.99133	173° 50′	.99711	9.99874
154° 0′	.94940	9.97745	**164° 0′**	.98063	9.99151	**174° 0′**	.99726	9.99881
10′	.95003	9.97774	10′	.98103	9.99168	10′	.99741	9.99887
20′	.95066	9.97803	20′	.98142	9.99186	20′	.99756	9.99894
30′	.95129	9.97831	30′	.98182	9.99203	30′	.99770	9.99900
40′	.95192	9.97860	40′	.98220	9.99220	40′	.99784	9.99906
154° 50′	.95254	9.97888	164° 50′	.98258	9.99237	174° 50′	.99797	9.99912
155° 0′	.95315	9.97916	**165° 0′**	.98296	9.99254	**175° 0′**	.99810	9.99917
10′	.95377	9.97944	10′	.98334	9.99270	10′	.99822	9.99923
20′	.95438	9.97972	20′	.98371	9.99287	20′	.99834	9.99928
30′	.95498	9.97999	30′	.98407	9.99303	30′	.99846	9.99933
40′	.95558	9.98027	40′	.98444	9.99319	40′	.99857	9.99938
155° 50′	.95618	9.98054	165° 50′	.98479	9.99335	175° 50	.99868	9.99943
156° 0′	.95677	9.98081	**166° 0′**	.98515	9.99350	**176° 0′**	.99878	9.99947
10′	.95736	9.98108	10′	.98550	9.99366	10′	.99888	9.99951
20′	.95795	9.98134	20′	.98584	9.99381	20′	.99898	9.99956
30′	.95853	9.98161	30′	.98619	9.99396	30′	.99907	9.99959
40′	.95911	9.98187	40′	.98652	9.99411	40′	.99915	9.99963
156° 50′	.95968	9.98213	166° 50′	.98686	9.99425	176° 50′	.99924	9.99967
157° 0′	.96025	9.98239	**167° 0′**	.98719	9.99440	**177° 0′**	.99931	9.99970
10′	.96082	9.98264	10′	.98751	9.99454	10′	.99939	9.99973
20′	.96138	9.98290	20′	.98783	9.99468	20′	.99946	9.99976
30′	.96194	9.98315	30′	.98815	9.99482	30′	.99952	9.99979
40′	.96249	9.98340	40′	.98846	9.99496	40′	.99959	9.99982
157° 50′	.96305	9.98365	167° 50′	.98877	9.99510	177° 50′	.99964	9.99984
158° 0′	.96359	9.98389	**168° 0′**	.98907	9.99523	**178° 0′**	.99970	9.99987
10′	.96413	9.98414	10′	.98937	9.99536	10′	.99974	9.99989
20′	.96467	9.98438	20′	.98967	9.99549	20′	.99979	9.99991
30′	.96521	9.98462	30′	.98996	9.99562	30′	.99983	9.99993
40′	.96574	9.98486	40′	.99025	9.99575	40′	.99986	9.99994
158° 50′	.96627	9.98510	168° 50′	.99053	9.99587	178° 50′	.99990	9.99996
159° 0′	.96679	9.98533	**169° 0′**	.99081	9.99599	**179° 0′**	.99992	9.99997
10′	.96731	9.98557	10′	.99109	9.99611	10′	.99995	9.99998
20′	.96782	9.98580	20′	.99136	9.99623	20′	.99997	9.99999
30′	.96834	9.98603	30′	.99163	9.99635	30′	.99998	9.99999
40′	.96884	9.98625	40′	.99189	9.99646	40′	.99999	.00000
159° 50′	.96935	9.98648	169° 50′	.99215	9.99658	179° 50′	1.00000	.00000
160° 0′	.96985	9.98670	**170° 0′**	.99240	9.99669	**180° 0′**	1.00000	.00000
Angle	Value	Log*	Angle	Value	Log*	Angle	Value	Log*

* *Subtract* 10 *from each listed value.*

$y = a \text{ (trig. funct.)} bx$

↓   ↓

x's as hight   x's as many curves

$y = 2 \cos x$

2x as hig

π   2π

$y = \sin 2x$

π   2π

$$\cos \frac{x}{2} = \pm \sqrt{\frac{1 + \cos x}{2}}$$

$$\sin \frac{x}{2} = \pm \sqrt{\frac{1 - \cos x}{2}}$$

$$\tan \frac{x}{2} = \sqrt{\frac{1 - \cos x}{1 + \cos x}}$$

HE WHO DARES

MICHAEL PAUL KENNEDY

POCKET BOOKS

New York   London   Toronto   Sydney   Tokyo   Singapore

An *Original* Publication of POCKET BOOKS

POCKET BOOKS, a division of Simon & Schuster Inc.
1230 Avenue of the Americas, New York, NY 10020

Copyright © 1989 by Michael Paul Kennedy
Originally published in Great Britain under the title of
Soldier 'I' SAS by Bloomsbury Publishing Limited

ISBN 0-671-79581-3

First Pocket Books printing April 1994

10 9 8 7 6 5 4 3 2 1

POCKET and colophon are registered trademarks of
Simon & Schuster Inc.

Cover art by Lee MacLeod

Illustration on page 98 by Neil Hyslop

Printed in the U.S.A.

Acknowledgments

I would like to thank the following people:

Nicki, for stimulating my creativity and much more besides, and because I said I would.

The two teachers in Lancaster, for their cutting observations, which felled my confidence and sharpened my skills.

Dad and Steve, for their enthusiastic comments, which dragged me up from the depths of despair.

Julie, for her tender loving care and for finally believing that Soldier I was real.

David, for his marketing skills and for being a matchmaker between a writer and a warrior.

Anne, for the hospitality, hot food and cold showers.

Lyndsay, June, Cowan and Noela, for wrestling with the words and not flinching at the effing and jeffing.

Jill, who foresaw it all and pointed me in the right direction.

Fiona, for pushing me to do it because she knew I could do it all along.

Jim Davidson, comedian, for generously encouraging an unknown writer.

Tim, Scotty, Jim, Paddy, Iain, Roy, Sek, Fuzz, Valdez and John, for allowing me into the family and for their unstinting generosity with the material.

Tim's wife, for not divorcing him when she found the material was for this book and not Tim's own.

Acknowledgments

Soldier I, for being larger than life and twice as outrageous.

Nigel and David at Bloomsbury, for seeing the potential. Will I get a biscuit with my tea if it does well?

Elizabeth—"Oh no! not another writer"—for her friendship, spontaneity and intuition and for giving me the key.

Helen, my new wife, for her love, support and spiritual guidance and for not screaming when the gun went off.

Author's Note

A chance encounter during an Outward Bound course first brought me into contact with Soldier I. From the outset, I was deeply impressed not only by his powerful and charismatic presence but also by the drama of the life he led during the years in the SAS (1970–1987).

In the course of many meetings, in hotels all over the country, the full extent of that drama began to emerge.

I feel very privileged to have been chosen to be the one to record Soldier I's extraordinary adventures.

Where necessary, the names of some of the characters have been altered in order to preserve their anonymity. The story itself is all true and is a matter of historical fact documented in the relevant archives.

The Regimental Collect of the Special Air Service Regiment

Oh Lord, Who didst call on Thy disciples to venture all to win all men to Thee, grant that we, the chosen members of the Special Air Service Regiment, may by our works and our ways dare all to win all and, in so doing, render special service to Thee and our fellow men in all the world, through the same Jesus Christ Our Lord, Amen.

Contents

Contents

HE WHO DARES

1

New Territory

"You are a time bomb, trooper, a time bomb just waiting to explode."

The Colonel's words were still beating in my head as I lay back on the bed. His face, bulging with anger as he roared out his verdict, floated before me. It did not matter whether I opened my eyes or closed them, he was still there, accusing, taunting, assailing my self-respect. "What happened yesterday was a total disgrace, a total insult to the regiment. We cannot and will not tolerate this sort of behavior. You've had your chances but this is the last straw." A time bomb waiting to explode.

This was it then. The end of the road. On Colonel's orders for the third time. That must be some kind of record. Usually Colonel's orders meant you were finished, RTU, out in the cold. I was lucky. I was still serving with the SAS—at least for a little while longer, anyway. It all now hinged on the official medical reports. The Colonel seemed confident that they would provide the ammunition he needed. He had me right in the middle of his sights now. He could pull the trigger at any time.

I looked around me nervously. Ward 11 of the British Army Psychiatric Unit—the thinking man's Belsen. Was this really the end of the line? Everything in the room was white, clinical and empty. Empty walls, empty windowsill, empty tabletops, empty cupboards. My holdall lay slumped on the floor unopened. I reached down into a side pocket and pulled out a picture of my favorite pinup, smoothed out the creases and wedged it into a tiny gap at the top of the bedside table. It was a relief to see the splash of color, the bright, smiling face, the beckoning body.

I glanced out of the single window. Nothing but dreary gray, London rooftops. A feeling of isolation swept over me. I turned back to the room and swung wide the cupboard doors, rattled open every drawer, gazing into the emptiness, seeking clues. There wasn't a single trace of the previous detainee—not even a shirt button, a screwed-up ticket or the cellophane wrapper from a cigarette packet. Everything had been swept clinically clean. If only I could have found something, no matter how small, it would have given me some sense of reality, a feeling that others had passed this way before me.

I prowled around the room like a caged animal. This was new, unfamiliar territory. I was jet-lagged from the sudden transfer from camp, heady from disorientation. I needed to establish my base, my reference point, my safety zone. At least in the jungle or in the mountains you knew the likely spots where the enemy might be waiting. Training and experience taught you where danger lurked. But here it was different. There was a feeling of threat, but I could not tell where it was coming from or how bad it was going to be. I needed to unscramble my head.

It was like being in an enemy pen, except that the guards wore white coats. I'd been told there was even an escape committee—the boys in the pathology lab. They'd test my blood every day and wouldn't let me go under the wire until my LFT count was down to normal.

I came in on a Thursday. The first few days would be observation. I knew what that meant. I knew all the tricks of the interrogation trade. They'd put me under stress by making sure I was completely bored, completely deprived of all my normal activities and pleasures. Then they'd monitor me to see if I was showing any signs of stress or unusual behavior: apprehension, restlessness, weird tendencies, withdrawal symptoms. Then, after they'd softened me up, the advanced sentence, the brainwashing would begin.

The door opened and a white-coated nurse came in. He looked at me very closely. Not a flicker of emotion registered on his face. He said nothing. I wondered whether he was one of them, part of the system. I imagined him making mental notes, assessing the situation in detail: where I was in the room, whether I'd arranged my things, my general demeanor and my facial expression. He put a small, brown tray on the bedside table, glanced at the pinup, then at me. I wondered if this had been my first mistake. There was a plastic beaker of water on the tray and two torpedo-shaped pills, bright green at one end, pink at the other. "Take both of them," was all the orderly said as he quickly retreated, locking the door behind him.

I decided to go along with the game at this stage, play it by their rules. They'd know anyway from the urine samples whether I'd taken the pills or not. I picked up one of the torpedoes, held it up to the light and rolled it between my finger and thumb. I wondered why they'd chosen these particular pills, what mind-bending drug was concealed in the thousands of tiny balls cascading around inside the colored cases. I wondered what ragged phantoms would come springing out to haunt me from deep within my psyche after being locked away for all these years. I wondered who "they" were, the faceless doctors I'd yet to meet. Would they be distant and calculating like the orderly, or would they be friendly and sympathetic, creep up on me and catch me with my guard down, trick me into trusting them? Was that the deadly ambush that awaited me? Sod it! Who dares wins! Here's to Queen and country . . . I grabbed both the pills and gulped them down. A faint smile of steely defiance curled on my lips.

Outside, the wind grew stronger and the dark clouds jostled and thickened. Scuds of rain crackled against the window with increasing frequency. Suddenly, the pregnant clouds burst their waters and spawned tiny, watery serpents which slithered down the glass panes, frantically seeking the sanctuary of some unseen pool below.

I sank on to the bed and closed my eyes. "You're a time bomb, trooper, a time bomb just waiting to explode." I tried to shake the Colonel out of my head. Then, from nowhere, a confusion of pictures burst into my mind. A kaleidoscope of scenes from fourteen years of remote battles and secret operations spun in front of me. It was just like the high-speed slide show of farms, villages, towns and cities that had flashed before my eyes as I'd gazed blankly out of the car window driving down the M4 from Hereford to London. Back through time my mind slid on a crazy helter-skelter ride: the Falklands war, the Embassy siege, Hong Kong, Northern Ireland, the battle of Mirbat, Operation Jaguar.

Before I knew it, the sharp odor of cordite was stinging my nostrils again. The hair on the back of my neck prickled as I heard again the distinctive thwack of bullet hitting bone and flesh. I shuddered at the bansheelike screams of the wounded, grown men reduced to groveling, frightened children calling unashamedly for their mothers amid the roar of battle—shrieks of terror whose echoes would resound forever.

Round and round I tumbled, free falling through the whirling pictures. Then, suddenly, I was sucked through the black hole at the center of the spinning kaleidoscope.

2

Initiation

"Good morning, gentlemen, welcome to Bradbury Lines."

It was spring 1970. A dozen rows of hopeful recruits sat facing the Colonel, 135 of us in all. The Colonel smiled a cold half smile. At his station in life, he had left far behind the feelings of trepidation that we were now all experiencing at the start of this new venture. He stood in front of us on the stage of training wing theater, a slightly weatherbeaten figure dressed in an old camouflage windproof and a pair of faded OG trousers. Even the famous beret looked a little discolored. He was leaning on the lecturing stand, smoking an old roll-up and flicking the ash into an empty pyrotechnic container. He had the appearance of a man who was used to roughing it, but the unruly look went only as far as his dress. His hard, chiseled features and steady unflinching gaze told a different story, the story of a man who knew his mind with clinical precision.

"You have a difficult task ahead of you. First, three weeks of rigorous selection, during which time we subject you to what we colloquially and, I might add, very appropriately refer to as Sickener 1 and Sickener 2. Then, fourteen weeks of continuation training, a parachute course, and finally combat survival training. Nearly twenty-six weeks of ex-

5

haustive scrutiny. Half a year of uncertainty. You could get your marching orders at any point along the way—usually when you least expect it. We've even been known to fail someone on their very last day!"

A ripple of unease and a hardening of resolve flickered through the assembled rows.

"The SAS is only as effective as the people in it. Think about that. It's a crucial point. A field commander might devise a perfect plan for winning a battle, but without strong, coordinated support from the men on the ground, all would be lost."

The Colonel's eyes penetratingly scanned the intent faces of his audience.

"It was said of Lord Nelson that his whole fleet acted as if they were one great marine body directed by a single intelligence. What we are looking for over the next few weeks are men to join our regimental body, to become one with us. But not just any men. They've got to be the right men, special men. Men with initiative, stamina, intelligence, patience and not least a sense of humor. In Korea, the British Army had thousands fighting thousands. With the SAS it's different. We are a specialist group within the British Army. We are special because we operate in small groups and we move alone. We are not looking for team players. What we want is the individualist, the man who can survive on his own but who has the self-discipline to work as part of a team."

I gazed abstractedly at the Colonel, taking in the details of his clothing. I noticed the winged-dagger badge sewn on to his beret. I fixed my eyes with envy and determination on that badge, and for a moment I was mesmerized as his head moved in rhythm with his speech.

The Colonel flicked the ash off his roll-up and his eyes took on a hardened look. "There's always been war and there always will be war. Look at any decade, it's always the same: 1961 Kuwait, 1962 Brunei, '63 Borneo, '64 East Africa, '67 Aden, '68 Belfast. It's an endless litany. When the social workers run out, someone's got to wave the big stick. When society's body is ill, someone's got to take care of it. Whether it's the ice-laden mountains or the scorching deserts, the steaming jungles or the stinking souks, the windswept moorlands or the sinister streets, we'll be there. Terrorists, guerrillas, insurgents, freedom fighters, call them what you will, we'll be there.

"There will be plenty of excitement and adventure, but you won't be paraded as heroes for all to see. America suffered from fighting the Vietnam war in the full glare of the media. Public opinion handcuffed the generals to the rule book. Here in the SAS we learn from other people's mistakes. No publicity, no media. We move in silently, do our job, and melt away into the background. You won't achieve fame and fortune with us. But what you will achieve is self-respect, deep self-respect, and a unique identity as part of a group who have found that same self-respect. The few of you who succeed will not just be joining a regiment, you'll be joining a family, a very exclusive family. If you have got the stamina, the willpower and the guts, we'll welcome you with open arms and make you one of us. And if you haven't, then it's been very nice knowing you." The Colonel looked up and down the rows again with searching eyes, then swiftly walked off the stage.

A voice from the rear shouted, "Be at the Quartermaster's stores in fifteen minutes!"

Outside, the sun was just clearing the top of the wooden plinth on which the four-sided regimental clock was set. Around its base, gleaming in the sunshine, were three large bronze panels inscribed with the names of the soldiers who had died—the ones who, in regimental parlance, had not beaten the clock. A smaller panel with a quotation worked on to it was fixed to the front. I could just make out the words "barr'd with snow" and "that glimmering sea" on the plaque. As I looked up, a ragged black crow flapped lazily along behind the clock and over the perimeter fence toward the neat rows of houses that formed the Redhill suburbs of Hereford. I thought of the people there who were going about their ordinary day-to-day routines, and then I thought

7

of the drama in which 135 nervous recruits were about to play a leading role.

When I reached the stores, I was astonished at the sight that greeted me. It was like a Saturday afternoon jumble sale at a church bazaar. I was amazed at the apparent disorder and lack of discipline. But the conversation was subdued. No one wanted to get earmarked as a possible troublemaker. I edged forward and found myself at the front of the queue. The corporal behind the counter glanced at me and then disappeared between long rows of large wooden pigeon-holes. He reappeared with a bergen rucksack filled with all I would need for the selection phase. I took one look at the rucksack and realized immediately that in bad weather the untreated canvas would just soak up rain like a sponge and get heavier and heavier. The metal fittings cracked on the countertop as the corporal threw the bergen unceremoniously down. I checked the contents: sleeping bag, 57-pattern webbed belt, poncho for wet-weather protection, two one-and-a-half-pint water bottles with carriers, standard army prismatic compass, heavy and cumbersome, Ordnance Survey maps of the Brecon Beacons and Elan Valley, brew kit and three twenty-four-hour ration packs for the first major hurdle looming up: the three-day trial at the weekend, otherwise known as Sickener 1.

Then it was on to the armory around the corner from the QM's department. There we were given the old-fashioned Lee Enfield 303 rifles. The issuing officer explained that the modern weapons were kept strictly for operational duties, and added ominously, "They'll be in real shit order, the Lee Enfields, with what they have to go through in the next three weeks, no matter how much you strip and clean them."

I made tracks from the armory out into the sunshine again and, with a grumbling stomach, headed for the cookhouse. As I pushed through the gray swinging doors I was hit by a barrage of noise: crashing plates, hissing steam, clinking mugs, metal chair legs rattling as they were scraped across the dull red tiled floor, the steady roar of over 200 voices in animated conversation. The L-shaped room was filled with the warm, appetizing aroma of freshly cooked food. Through another door, in the far corner, a group of men I had not seen before were making an entrance, joking and laughing loudly. To judge from their air of confidence and deliberate step they were obviously Sabre Squadron. Two shining aluminum-and-glass serveries ran the length of each leg of the room. Behind them, men decked out in regulation kitchen whites were gliding swiftly backward and forward among the steaming vats and clanking ovens, going about their business in apparent chaos but no doubt following some well-rehearsed routine.

I got to the head of the queue and started to move along by the hotplate. I was in for a surprise. It looked like a tribal feast day in the jungle. There was food, mountains of food. I had never seen the likes of it in all my years of service in the Army. I picked up a tray with anticipation and pushed it along the front of the hotplate. Next to a tureen of steaming hot soup, a large wicker basket overflowed with chunks of bread. A mound of rich yellow butter, which looked as if it had been tipped straight out of the farmyard urn, had several knives carelessly protruding from it. In the middle section there was a choice: a help-yourself tray full of lamb chops, swimming in savory juices, and a mammoth joint of beef impaled on a spiked turntable. A large cook was poised over the beef with a gleaming carving knife and a long, two-pronged fork. He looked as if he would be equally at ease wielding a machete in the jungle. I motioned toward the joint.

"How many slices?" the cook asked.

I couldn't believe my ears. I'd been so used to the routine in the regular army cookhouse. There, some jumped-up pimply-faced cook, with a deathly pallor from never seeing daylight, feeling cocky knowing he was out of reach behind the counter, would hit you with a ladle and squeak, "One egg, laddie," if you so much as looked at a second egg. "Two please, mate," I ventured, still not sure quite what was happening.

The cook stabbed the fork into the joint and deftly swung

it around on the turntable to get the right angle for carving. The meat compressed as the gleaming knife bit into it, and rich juices oozed from the pink center. "Crackling?"

"Too true!" And a huge chunk of ribbed crackling was deposited over the two thick slices of meat. I rearranged the dishes on my tray and just about found space for the sponge pudding with custard that rounded off the meal.

I looked up and spotted the other three members of the patrol I'd been assigned to, hunched over the end of a table. I crossed the room and sat down with them.

"Jesus Christ, somebody pinch me, I must be dreaming."

"I'd heard a rumor that airborne forces get double meat rations, but this is ridiculous."

"There's got to be a catch. It'll be tea and wads the rest of the week."

"No, there's no catch. Don't get paranoid already. An old mate of mine gave me the whisper. It's like this every day, plenty of protein to build up the stamina. You need it here."

"I hope you're right. I've got to have my four square meals a day. I get dizzy if I miss breakfast. I don't go for this mean and hungry look. I reckon you've got to have plenty of meat on you to stay healthy."

There was a lull in the conversation as our attention was focused on the more serious business of eating. I looked around the other three members of my patrol. Jim, from the Black Watch, Royal Highland Regiment, and proud of it. Small, stocky, with shining eyes set in a round, friendly face. Neatly parted short brown hair. A barrel-shaped body, obviously tough. Then Andy, the company joker, known to all as Geordie. He was in the Light Infantry, but whenever asked, would reply with a stiff salute, "Sixth Queen Elizabeth's Own Gurkha Rifles!" He had a tough bony head topped by already thinning black hair. What he lacked in the way of hair on his scalp, however, he more than made up for with a hirsute growth on his thick dangling arms and prominent chest. His most noticeable feature was an over-large mouth. It was as big as the Northwest Passage, and gaped obscenely whenever he spoke, revealing his teeth and gums so that he looked like an ape challenging an intruder. And finally, Tommo the scouse, Royal Fusiliers. Tall, muscular in a compact sort of way, with tufts of blond hair as stiff as a yard brush sticking straight up. Snub nose, and ears bent over slightly at the top. He looked like an overgrown leprechaun—a malevolent one at that. The nearest he ever came to a smile was a cross between a leer and a snarl, which would slowly appear as attempts to engage him in conversation were met with a sullen "yeah," "that's right," "dunno." I never could guess what was going on in his mind, and for that reason never felt comfortable when he was around. In fact, I didn't trust him as far as I could throw a fully laden bergen.

After the first rush of food had hit our stomachs, I said to Jim, "There's a lot of you lads down here. Talk of the Charge of the Jock Brigade!"

"Yeah, it is a bit like that. But when it really hits you what it's like up there—the perpetual rain, the decrepit tenement blocks stinking of urine, the empty rusting yards of Clydeside, the brawls on Buchanan Street on a Saturday night—you know you either take to the bottle or you take to the road. Me, I was down the mines for six years before I joined the Army. I looked around me one day and couldn't see a future. So I said to myself, 'Jimmy, if you join the Army what would you be leaving behind?' And you know the answer that came? A living hell, a long, slow, coal-dust-coughing hell. I decided to take my chances in the Army, I knew it couldn't be any worse. If I could survive six years down the pits, I figured I could survive anything."

"Even the SAS selection course?"

"Believe me, pal, it'll be a piece of piss in comparison. Have you ever been down a pit?"

"No."

"I thought not."

"But why the SAS?"

"Oh you know, the adventure, the excitement, a chance to be more involved. A chance to do the special jobs."

"What about you, Geordie?"

"This is why I applied, the food."

We all looked at him, slightly puzzled.

He went on, "I wouldn't say we're poor back home, but when it comes to tea time, the wife nails a kipper to the back of the kitchen door, and me and the kids, we all line up with a slice of bread in our hand and wipe it on the kipper as we file past."

The eternal joker. It was a tendency no doubt triggered by the nerves of the moment. Geordie used his humor like a shield, to ward off people or situations he felt uncomfortable with. In spite of this, I was rather warming to him; I felt I could detect a serious thinker beneath the surface.

We looked at Tommo, waiting for his story. He pushed his chair back suddenly and stood up. "Anyone for a brew?" he asked in an agitated voice. He slouched across the room to two large aluminum tea urns next to the hotplates. One of the urns was dripping tea on to the floor from the black plastic tap. No one seemed to bother. Tommo returned with three huge mugs of tea in one hand and one in the other. He was totally unconcerned that two of the three mugs were tilting and splashing scalding tea over his hand.

"Tommo, what's your story? Why did you volunteer?" I asked as he put the mugs on the table and sat down again.

"Dunno. A change of scene I suppose."

We waited patiently for a few moments but nothing more came. It was up to me to break the silence. "It was the boredom of garrison duties that got to me. Standing on guard in some obscure camp in the middle of nowhere in Germany, where you knew there was no threat. I ask you, were the Russians going to march hundreds of miles through hostile territory just to take out our insignificant little camp? Two hours on, four hours off, two hours on, four hours off. So it went on and on and on. Tedious in the extreme. I'll tell you something. Did you see the grass inside the camp gates when you arrived here? A foot high if it was an inch! Hell, I thought, I've got the wrong place here! Can you believe it—an army camp with grass a foot high! That's why I joined, to escape the bullshit. They've obviously got a sense of priorities here. They don't do things for the sake of it, I like that. Beat the boredom, beat the bullshit, beat the clock, that'll do me."

Even as I spoke, I felt slightly uncomfortable with what I'd said. It was true as far as it went, but somehow I felt it didn't go far enough. I sensed that something deeper was driving me, something that as yet still eluded me. I decided my explanation would have to do for the time being. There were too many new things happening right now; my brain was having to process far too much new data for it to have the luxury of sorting through the debris of the old.

"I reckon selection's a real cartilage cracker," pronounced Geordie with the hint of a frown.

Tommo looked at him but said nothing.

"Piece of piss," reiterated Jim, confidently waving a teaspoon in the air to emphasize his lack of concern.

"Well, I for one will be glad when it's all over and we can get stuck into the real business we're supposed to be here for," I said firmly.

"Whatever that might be," added Tommo out of the blue. The three of us looked at him quizzically as we drained the last of the tea from our mugs.

That afternoon was spent doing preliminary weapons training and then a four-mile run. We had a training run every day around the leafy lanes of the Herefordshire countryside bordering on the camp on the opposite side to the town. The gently rolling hills in the immediate vicinity were deceptive. They often concealed small but steep-sided valleys. There always seemed to be at least two of these valleys near the end of the run, where the incline would tear viciously at already tired leg muscles. If anyone was going to fail at the weekend, it wouldn't be through lack of basic fitness.

The rest of the first week passed swiftly, each day following a similar rhythm and merging into the next. I got to know my patrol better as the week wore on, but we didn't bond together as mates. We were all still wrapped up in our own personal battles to prove ourselves. And anyway, I thought, most of these men will fail the course and you don't want to get friendly with failures. As the weekend loomed ahead, I could sense all around that the nervous bravado of the first day was gradually giving way to deepening apprehension. Indeed, as more detailed rumors began to circulate about Sickener 1, the very thought of it was enough to break some men. "Crap hats" we called them. They'd collected their rail warrants and were on Hereford station, Platform 4 outward bound, before selection had even begun in earnest.

We were given the Friday evening off and advised to get an early night. The afternoon's training run had finished around five o'clock. I had just enough time to shower, change and head into town before the shops closed. If I failed selection it wouldn't be through lack of preparation. From previous candidates who'd failed the course and from the information I'd gleaned during the week, I'd worked out what I would need: two dozen Mars bars, a bottle of olive oil, a Silvas compass, squares of foam padding, two sheets of clear Fablon, curry powder, Tabasco sauce, powdered milk and waterproof walking gear.

I stepped on to the bridge crossing the River Wye and leaned over the parapet. "Welcome to Hereford, Historic Capital of the Wye Valley" the sign on the bridge said. The water flowed lazily by beneath me. I gazed at a much older and smaller stone bridge that forded the river about 100 yards downstream from the modern road bridge where I stood. A neatly manicured lawn behind a church manse fell steeply down to the water's edge just beyond the stone bridge. Newly leafing trees clung precariously to the river banks and dangled long thin branches into the water. A young couple were locked in an erotic embrace under the trees by the putting green, luxuriating in the warm evening sunshine. Very nice too, I thought, feeling slightly envious.

I quickly located the shops and bought the necessary items, loaded up and headed back for camp.

Later that evening, the atmosphere in the spider was exceptionally subdued—and sober. The thought of what was to come the following morning was enough to convert even the hardest drinkers to temporary abstinence. By 9:30 p.m. a good number of the beds were already resonating with snoring heads. I decided it was time to join them. I threw off my shirt and slacks and hit the pillow.

It seemed as if I'd only just begun to drift down into a deep, welcome sleep when something suddenly reversed the direction of my consciousness. In a flash, I was brutally awake and confused. I strained to make sense of what was happening. Some time must have passed since I'd gone to bed. It was very dark and very quiet. I lay on my back, completely motionless, my eyes wide open, staring up toward the ceiling. A strange feeling stirred in my body. A moment later I heard a groan, followed by the rustle of sheets and a stifled sigh. What the hell's going on? I thought. As the vague realization began to dawn, I wondered if I was having some weird, tension-induced dream. More sounds, coarse, high-pitched nasal sounds; plaintive, like the cry of geese ghosting through a winter's night. Then a grunt, an unmistakably female grunt; panted, pained almost, gradually rising in pitch, volume and frequency until it peaked in a sharp, drawn-out squeal followed by a rasping diminuendo —yes, yes, yes, sigh of relief.

A wave of sexual excitement rippled up and down my spine. It was as if my body was a musical instrument vibrating as another instrument is played nearby. I tilted my head in the direction of the sounds and caught a whiff of cheap perfume. The sweet smell was unmistakable in the heavy male air of the spider. A permed blond head and glinting earring emerged momentarily from among the tumbling sheets of the next bed. This can't be happening, I thought, Geordie in bed with a woman. I felt almost dizzy, as if I'd got up too quickly from a prone position. I turned away and on to my back again and spent a few moments deliberately composing myself, reminding myself where I was and what I was doing there.

The groans and sighs began again, more frantic and physical than before. Geordie was like a stag in rut. I glanced at my watch. It was one o'clock in the morning, my sleep had been broken and in a few hours I had to face Sickener 1, a severe test of physical endurance lasting three days for which I would need every ounce of energy I possessed. Another groan. I turned toward Geordie, anger welling up inside me, and opened my mouth to speak. Nothing. Not a word came out. A feeling of admiration at his sheer nerve combined with a vague acknowledgment that it wasn't right to interrupt a man's sexual performance somehow dammed up the waves of anger. The torrents of abuse simply swirled and foamed around inside me.

I put my head beneath the sheets to try to shut out the disturbance, but I knew it was no good. The more I chased sleep, the more it eluded me. I kept telling myself I would drift off at any moment. I began to perspire with the frustration of not being able to sleep. I twisted my body into every position imaginable, trying to relax. I explored every corner of the bed seeking a cool patch in the sheets. Who dares wins, I thought, as Geordie finally firecrackered into an Olympian climax.

3

Sickener 1

I heard another noise. Oh Christ, I thought, don't tell me Geordie is going for another shot. I turned over and half opened one eye. In the first glimmer of dawn I saw that most of the men in the spider were already awake, either standing up pulling on their OGs or sitting on their beds lacing up their boots. I sat up instantly. My heart pounded for a few seconds, priming my body to the same level of alertness as my mind. Years of training and discipline came to my rescue. I sprang out of bed, switched my mind on and put my body into automatic pilot. I glanced at my watch: 4:30 a.m. I didn't even dare contemplate how much sleep I'd finally managed to get, or whether it would be enough to see me through the day.

Within minutes everyone was outside, piling into the six Bedford four-tonners lined up ready to take us to our torture. We set off westward, then turned north up the A470, following the River Wye toward the Elan Valley, deep in the Cambrian Mountains of mid-Wales. The Elan Valley—that was the first con. It sounded like some mythical green and pleasant land. Well, it might have been green but it certainly wasn't pleasant, as we were very quickly to discover.

17

I looked around the twenty bodies being shaken about in the Bedford. There in the corner, hunched over a cigarette, was Geordie. I motioned to the man next to him to change places with me and, with one hand on the side of the swaying truck to keep my balance, made my way up to the front to sit next to him. One or two of the men looked up at me, vaguely puzzled by what was happening, then dropped back down to stare at their boots, mentally steeling themselves for the ordeal ahead.

"What the hell were you up to last night?" I asked Geordie, hardly concealing my astonishment.

"Having a good fuck," Geordie replied bluntly.

"Any chance of having twos up when we get back?" inquired Jim, appealing to Geordie's generosity.

"You can piss off, she's mine!" replied Geordie, in a distinctly ungenerous fashion.

"Did it never cross your mind like it did the rest of us that an early night might be useful?" I continued.

"Early night! That's about as exciting as having your sinuses syringed."

"How did you manage it, anyway?"

"I stayed in town last night and went on the piss. It was dead easy. Woman—the hero's perk! They were all swooning around me. They saw my suntan and thought I was already in the SAS. I didn't tell them that I'd just come back from exercise abroad with the LI."

"I don't know about hero's perk, but she certainly perked you up, Geordie, more than once from the sound of it," muttered Jim.

"No, I meant how did you manage to get her through the gates?" I went on.

"I didn't. We came in the back way, down Web Tree Avenue, across the empty plot of land and under the fence behind B Squadron basha."

"But aren't you knackered? I reckon you must have screwed your way through the equivalent of a half marathon last night. You know what they say about sportsmen having a leg over the night before a big match."

"Knackered, no. It relaxes me. Best remedy for tension I've ever found."

"It might have relaxed you, but it kept half the bloody spider awake," mumbled Jim in a disgruntled voice.

"What's up, lads, can't you get your end away? I tell you what: you can all take turns with her when I go abroad, and don't worry about contraception—she told me her old man's had a vasectomy!"

The conversation subsided and was replaced by the rattle of the Bedford as it headed north. The drone of the engine had a hypnotic effect, and I found my mind drifting back to the Blue Room in Bradbury Lines and to the pre-exercise briefing that our instructor Tim had given us. This had been my first sight of the man I would grow to respect enormously as the years went by.

Tim was a tough, craggy Northerner who hailed from Manchester. He had a six-foot frame, muscular from years of thrashing through the Malayan jungle, a ramrod-straight back and a broad chest. His sandy-colored hair was tousled and he had bushy eyebrows. Although he was quick to show his dissatisfaction at the first sign of incompetence, he was generally very quietly spoken. His tough exterior hid a generous soul. Over the next few days he would help me on several occasions with patient extra tuition in map reading. At first I never quite knew how to take him. He could appear to be full of encouragement one moment and cut you to shreds the next. He had at one and the same time the benign look of a kindly uncle and yet a cool remoteness in his eyes. Above all, he was sure of himself. A veteran of many campaigns, he had the Military Medal to his credit.

His words came drifting back as I stared out of the back of the Bedford. "As you know, lads, the first three weeks are called Initial Selection. But really, 'selection' is the wrong word: it should be 'rejection.' No matter what the pressures are to keep the numbers up, we aim to reject not select. Let me warn you right now: no one gets in the back door. If you don't match up to the standards, you're out. Believe it or not I would like you all to pass. You won't, of course. In fact very few of you will. It wasn't all that long ago that on one selection course we failed every single trainee."

If anyone had managed to build up any confidence, by now it was rapidly draining away.

"Don't think we are putting you through these agonies for the fun of it," Tim continued. "SAS doesn't stand for Savage and Sadistic. No, you see, an inferior soldier means a weak link. You might get away with that in the regular Army where you can hide among the crowd. But a weak link in a four-man patrol means a weak patrol, a dangerous liability. So if you fail on a single point, it's RTU, and down to Platform 4."

Tim glanced around the assembled trainees. "One more thing," he said. "Don't even think of cheating, and I'll tell you why. In the SAS we have a very special kind of cosmetic surgery. You've heard of the nose job. Well here we've got the red-line job." He reached into the breast pocket of his windproof and pulled out a thick felt-tipped pen. "If you haven't got what it takes, it'll be a red line through your face on the photograph in training wing, and that's you finished."

My thoughts of Tim's first briefing were interrupted as the wagons turned off the main road at Rhayader and headed down the B4518 toward Caban Coch Reservoir. Halfway along the reservoir, the road, now no more than a single track with passing places, took a sharp right. Shortly afterward the Bedford jolted to a halt, giving a rude awakening to those who had temporarily escaped back into slumber. All we could see out of the back of the wagon was a vast expanse of desolate hills rolling into one another, the ridges along the tops looking like the scarred backs of a school of stranded whales.

Tim walked briskly across and pulled down the tailgate of the Bedford. He then addressed his two patrols. "Welcome to Sickener 1. This is what we call sorting the wheat from the chaff. This is where we nail the weekend adventurers, the day releases from Broadmoor and the eternal swanners." He glanced over his shoulder and pointed to a hill that loomed up into the mist. The slope was so severe it looked like the side of a building. Tim said simply, "There's only one way from here, lads, and that's straight up."

I checked my kit, checked my compass and started to sweat.

The next three days were spent in a nightmare world of physical pain and mental torture, being beasted across the hills by Tim, not just getting from point to point but, as Tim explained with relish, cross-graining the bukits. This meant going straight from trig point to trig point instead of contouring around the obstacles on some of the gentler slopes. It was demoralizing going down the other side of a hard-won piece of high ground knowing that you then had to climb back up again to the next trig point, when all the time you could see a straight ridge linking the two points as inviting as Blackpool Promenade. And meanwhile the menacing figure of Tim always seemed to be hovering, staring and making mental notes. Just when you least expected it he would materialize as if from nowhere, suggesting that this was perhaps too much for you and wouldn't you be really better off calling it a day and returning quietly to your own regiment. All such exhortations had to be strenuously rejected. Even the slightest sign of hesitation could mean a red-line job.

A primal sense of self-preservation and survival of the fittest quickly began to surface in me. Seeing the misfortunes of others—seeing someone really struggling, cursing through clenched jaws, "Shit, I feel like I've been kneecapped"—was enough in an odd sort of way to spur me on, thinking, well I may be knackered, but I'm not as done in as he is. And all the time, in rhythm with the blood pounding through my ears, the same questions beat through my brain, "What am I doing here? Will I make it?"—and each time I got the same answer, "I've got to. I must carry on." It was as if my thinking process had closed down. Swept along at an ever increasing pace by this new and powerful experience, my mind became clouded by the strain of constant alertness, my vision channeled to a single point. And that point was only ever the present moment. There was no spare capacity of mental energy, no space to think either side of that single point, nor either forward or back in time. Total concentration had to be in the present. Failure lurked at every second. It was as if I were wading across a fast-flowing river, seeking with each step a firm rock base to put my weight on, fearing at every moment that my foot might slip and I would be swept away by the torrent.

Toward the end of the first afternoon, a heavy squall hit us. It was vicious in its suddenness and its intensity. We were caught without our windproofs, our shirts unbuttoned to the waist. Within seconds my hair was matted against my forehead and rivulets of water ran down my neck and over my chest. I was quickly soaked through, my OGs clinging clammily to my skin. All I could do was to put my head down and keep on going up to the top of the hill. To my horror, as I stumbled wearily over the last rise I saw that the ground fell away again to be met by a near-vertical rock-strewn slope leading up to the real summit, which was already swathed in racing storm clouds. Conditions were deteriorating. What do I do now? I thought. As I hesitated, turning my back to the wind and catching my breath, two other volunteers came alongside. Their shoulders sagged visibly when they saw the size of the task ahead of them. They looked at each other, and both recognized the same thought in the other.

"Sod this for a game of soldiers," one of them muttered.

They hadn't seen Tim coming up behind them. Tim said in his gruff northern accent, "Right, you lads, get back down to that road and wait for the transport."

As I watched them dejectedly trudge away, I said to myself, "I'm fucked if I'm going to jack now!" I readjusted my bergen, which was getting heavier by the minute as it soaked in the rain, took a firmer grip on my .303 and headed off into the gloom, with Tim hovering menacingly in the background waiting for the slightest hint of weakness to pounce again.

The route up to the top of the hill narrowed into a ridge,

which became more and more exposed to the driving storm the higher I got. The rain was hitting me horizontally, stinging my face until my cheekbones went numb. The wind howled into my ears until they ached. Quite suddenly, halfway up, I became aware that far from feeling even worse I somehow felt lighter. There was a new spring in my step. My breathing was deep and rhythmical. It was as if my breath was energizing and waking up my whole body. My senses now became more acute. I relished the velvet tingle of the rain as it fell down my face. The sweet saltiness of sweat prickled the corners of my mouth, and the ground smelled warm, earthy and close.

Near the summit, I covered the last few yards on all fours; the wind's ferocity increased tenfold, it was completely impossible to stand upright. I had never before experienced anything so powerful. I could not believe that moving air could make you feel as if you were being hit by waves of water. When the others reached the top we huddled together, shouting to make ourselves heard above the roar of the wind. One trainee, moving into the middle of the group to get some shelter, tried to steady his compass on the wildly flapping map to get a bearing for the final RV of the day. Tim loomed up, his face a mask of grim determination. "Come on, lads, on your feet and over the top before you all die of exposure." Trying not to show our reluctance, we set off down again.

Base camp that night was set up in the lee of some woods. The storm had died away almost as quickly as it started. Already, what was left of the wind had dried most of the heavy rain from the ground. As we unsaddled our bergens, Tim greeted us with, "Well done, lads, that's the easy bit over with. You can get some hot food inside of you now. You're probably ready for it. I'm sure you've been looking forward all day to tonight's feast." Tim had every right to joke about it. It would certainly be hot—our hexamine stoves would see to that—but whether the twenty-four-hour rations would qualify as a feast was doubtful. The food was in stark contrast to what we had been used to back at the cookhouse, but still, I scarcely felt it was a hardship. I'd already written off in my mind the whole three days as a "head down arse up and keep going till you're told to stop" exercise.

I had some difficulty getting my boots off. The rain had swollen the paracord and tightened the knots. After picking away at them, and breaking a fingernail in the process, I finally managed to ease off the sodden leather. My feet seemed to sigh with relief as the boots came off and I immediately felt a different person. I tugged off my wet gear and slipped into the dry kit I'd kept in a plastic bag in my bergen. I filled my one pint mess tin with water and put it to boil on the stove, then found a packet of beef stew from my ration pack, ripped it open and sprinkled the unappetizing contents into the simmering water. I crumbled up some tack biscuits and threw them into the stew to thicken it up a bit. Then the master stroke: in with the garlic and chili sauce I had bought in town. A fearsome relish, my all-time favorite! It would knock a crap-hat down at fifty paces. The racing spoon moved at double quick pace between mess tin and mouth.

After making a mug of tea from my brew kit—with the help of the real powdered milk I'd brought along instead of the poor quality army-issue powder which always floated to the top and looked like dandruff on the surface—I cupped my hands around my mug for warmth and glanced at the other lads. I was unsure whether or not to strike up a conversation in case it was an RTU offense. The problem was that nobody told you the rules. It was a form of psychological warfare. So I took the safest way out, stared into my tea and kept my mouth shut.

It suddenly grew darker as a large black cloud glided in from the right and obscured the setting sun, splitting its watery evening light into broad beams that fanned out over the hills in a breathtaking display.

I got up and walked away from the rest of the lads, looking for a level piece of ground to sleep on. In view of my tiredness and the failing light it was rather a quick scan of

the terrain, but I managed to find a reasonable spot. I
brushed away the broken branches, pulled out any stones
that protruded from the earth so that they wouldn't dig into
my back and laid out my sleeping bag. I then rigged up my
waterproof poncho to cover my sleeping area. The secret
was to keep it as tight as possible so the rain would run off. I
checked the olive-green paracord at each corner, ensuring
that it was as taut as I could make it without tearing the
material. I crawled into my sleeping bag and, utterly exhausted, stretched out my aching body. A shower of rain
crackled on the canvas as the large cloud I'd seen passed
directly overhead. The sound of the steady rain was strangely peaceful and soothing. I curled up, luxuriating in the soft
dry touch of the Royal Engineers boiler suit I'd changed
into. It had been washed a thousand times and felt like silk
against my skin. As I drifted off to sleep I decided I was
going to wear it for the rest of selection. Its softness would be
a good defense against bergen blister.

We spent most of the second day wearily cross-graining
bukits again. But worse was to come. Tim had saved up the
most challenging ordeal for the end. He lined us up and
introduced us to the horrors of the entrail trench: a ditch
beside a hawthorn hedge, two feet deep, four feet across,
filled with stagnant water and rotting sheep's innards. A real
cesspit! "It's time to go back to Mother's womb, lads,
afterbirth and all!" began Tim. "Now let us imagine we're
dug into a trench in Korea under heavy fire. Up front we've
got no-man's-land littered with blown-up bodies. It's dusk
and you have to do a night patrol to gather intelligence on
the enemy's position. The only way to do it is over the top
with the leopard crawl, right through the bodies, the bits of
brain splattered on the rocks, the guts and gore strewn over
the ground. Right, who's first?"

Geordie visibly blanched. Jim swallowed hard. Tommo's
sneer became even more pronounced.

"Oh, I see. Perhaps it's because you don't know what the
leopard crawl is that no one's moving," said Tim. "You

don't want to be embarrassed by your ignorance. I can't see any other reason for your reluctance. Right, who knows how to do the leopard crawl?"

A few blank faces stared back at Tim. I took the bull by the horns. "I do."

"Good. Then perhaps you would be so kind as to demonstrate it for the benefit of your mates here along this stretch of ground in front of us all."

"Right, Tim." I got down flat on my stomach and, using only knees and elbows, proceeded to crawl along while holding my rifle horizontal to the ground, pressed against my forehead. The idea was to keep the lowest possible profile to avoid being seen by the enemy.

"Very good, just like an officer on the job," observed Tim wryly after I had struggled along for a few moments. "Right, as you are obviously an expert you might as well continue across the trench while you're down there!"

I took a deep breath and plunged into the foul mess. It was an ugly experience. Two feet doesn't sound very deep, but when you are crawling on all fours so close to the ground it is very deep. As I felt the loathsome liquid begin to crawl through the gaps in my clothing, I really understood for the first time why they called this part of selection Sickener 1. Halfway across, weighed down by my bergen, I felt my belt snag on a rock. I couldn't use my hands to free myself as they were holding my rifle clear of the surface. I had to resort to wriggling free by shaking my hips. As I did so I set up turbulence in the water, and the filthy stinking sheep-gut-filled liquid splashed up around my lips. I coughed and spat out in disgust.

As each trainee made it through the ordeal we assembled on the other side of the ditch, with the noisome liquid dripping from our clothes, until we stood watching the last man struggle across. The only consolation was that this was the last exercise of the day. Smelling like old decrepit tramps in a doss house, we settled down for the night.

At first light on the final day, as I rubbed my numbed limbs back into life, Tim gave his instruction: we were to set off straight across the river in front of us. As we waded across, our rifles above our heads, up to our chests in fast-flowing water, Tim watched us comfortably from a nearby bridge. Although dripping wet, as we emerged on the far bank at least we were fresher and cleaner than we had been after the previous day's ordeal. I thought to myself, I've survived two days and nights. Only one more day to go and it's back to the basha, a decent meal and a soft bed. I focused my mind on this comforting picture all that day as we sweated again over endless bukits. I locked out every urgent protest from my body, which had never before been pushed to such physical extremes; I ignored every scream from every tortured muscle.

As the afternoon drew to a painful close, we were briefed on the final exercise of the day: the stretcher race. We had to cover the last mile carrying a stretcher, upon which Tim perched—complete with loaded bergen, heavy rifle and satisfied smile. Laboring toward the final RV, just when I thought I couldn't force another step out of my weary body, I caught sight of the Bedford four tonners lined up in the distance. Thank Christ for that, I thought.

"There you are, lads," barked Tim. "Your ticket to easy street. Your transport out of hell!"

The pace quickened, the relief swept over me; it wouldn't be long now. When we were about 100 yards short, I heard the engines cough into life. They're just warming them up, I thought to myself. Then, to my horror and disbelief, one by one the Bedfords pulled away and disappeared like a bad dream down the road through the woods. Shit, I thought, we've been conned.

By now the other patrols were alongside. Tim walked stiffly to the front of the shredded soldiery. "Fresh orders from the top," he boomed. "The transport has been called away on a rush job. Alternative transport is to be found ten miles from here," and he rattled off a new grid reference.

Suddenly, Tommo exploded. He lunged at Tim with clenched fist, screaming, "You bastard!" I just managed to push him to one side and the punch whistled past Tim's ear.

Two of the other lads knocked Tommo to the ground and restrained him until he was led away, muttering and sniveling, and thrown into the twat wagon.

"That's amazing," I said. "That's the first time I've seen him reveal any real emotion. Mind you, I can't say I'm surprised at what happened. I didn't like the look of him from the start."

"That's what happens when you bottle it up so much," said Tim knowingly. "You can only hold it back for so long, then you explode."

We set off on the compass bearing, heads bowed, a Para NCO at the front. I was determined not to end up like Tommo. The pain returned in all its throbbing sharpness. All I could see in front of me, through glazed eyes, was yet another hell. Suddenly, as we struggled over the brow of a hill, we could not believe it—salvation! There they were— the Bedfords. We looked back at Tim. He was expressionless. Nobody dared say a word. We just plodded on in stunned silence. As we got nearer we realized the Bedfords were definitely on our compass bearing. I strained my ears for the sound of an engine starting. Surely they wouldn't do it twice, would they? Nothing. A hundred yards, fifty yards, twenty yards. I was praying harder than I'd ever prayed in my life. Ten yards, five yards.

Tim moved to the front as we reached the wagons, gripped the tailgate of one of the Bedfords and said, "Think yourselves fucking lucky they're not really ten miles away!"

I collapsed into a corner of one of the Bedfords, totally exhausted, but exhilarated at having passed my first big test. Only two more weeks to go, was the last thing I remember thinking before dropping into a deep sleep that even the rattling, jolting Bedford could not disturb. A blissful interlude. A lull before the next storm.

4

Sickener 2

All too soon we were back to the familiar hard physical grind. Week two. The future didn't look too bright to me just at that moment. We were down to ninety out of the original 135, and the worst was yet to come. I was tormented by the possibility that I might be number eighty-nine, the next candidate for Platform 4. My desire to succeed was strong enough, but all the time I wondered whether my mind and body would carry me through. I certainly got to know myself better during the three weeks of Initial Selection. I discovered to my surprise that just when I thought my energies were totally spent and failure was beckoning with open arms, I would suddenly open up reserves of stamina that I never knew existed. It was as if an inner resolve, so deep I couldn't truly fathom its nature, lay at the very core of my being, like a steel rod refusing to bend or break.

It was on day three of week two that we were introduced to the controlled agonies of the Skirrid, a stark, barren monolith that towered ominously 500 meters above the surrounding flat green countryside near Llanfihangel. From the trig point at the top there was a commanding 360-degree view of the land for miles around, and for that reason it was ideal for map reading exercises. The problem, of course, was that you had to get to the top first, saddled with full kit, and inevitably we were assembled not at the gently sloping side, but at the foot of the near vertical side. So fierce was the slope that when I checked the map, all I could see was a brown blur of bunched up contour lines floating threateningly in a sea of green.

As Tim gave out the grid references for the top, the expression on his face reminded me of the Provost Sergeant in *The Hill,* one of the lads' favorite films. All that was missing was Sean Connery, being beasted up and down the hill with a bunch of renegades in an attempt to knock some discipline into them.

I set the bearing on my Silvas compass and lined up the arrows. They pointed straight to the top, directly up the steep side. We set off wearily, a private in the REME up front. When we reached the summit, it was down again, change the leader, then back up. Tim kept us at it all day without respite. Beads of perspiration fell from my forehead and clouded my eyes with a salty film; sweat trickled down my spine and collected in the small of my back. The bergen pounded with each painful footfall, the straps pulling viciously at my shoulders. My calf and thigh muscles gradually tightened until they were virtually locked rigid, and the blisters on my feet grew larger and more inflamed by the hour.

The only relief came at midday, when we paused to take a visual map reading test. When my turn came, the more I tried to concentrate and stare at the map, the more the contour lines and compass settings became first a blur, then a swimming morass of shapes, like a crowd of elvers in a fast-flowing stream. It was almost as if my brain had become disconnected from my optic nerves. I could still see the shapes and lines, but no message was getting through to my mind. I shook my head to try to clear it, and fortunately just managed in the nick of time to remember one of Tim's survival rules: calmness and coolness at all times. I took a deep breath, determined not to be hurried beyond my own judgment. Mercifully, the features on the map gradually came back into meaningful focus, and with them Tim's magic formula for map reading: grid to mag add; mag to grid get rid. It worked.

I passed. My blisters didn't, though. After touching the trig point on top of the Skirrid for the last time and beginning my final descent, all I could think of during the journey to the bottom was getting my boots off and hitting the blisters with another shot of Jenson's Violet!

As we drank our final brew of the day, Geordie exclaimed, "I'm going to get rat-arsed when this lot's over!"

Tim looked at Geordie and frowned. "It's not the answer to everything, believe me. I remember when we were on operations in Malaya, one day we decided to march over the hill and visit one of the other troops. When we came down toward the beach we found the building the other troop had been using as a base. It was empty and no one was around. I began to feel apprehensive. My heart pounded as we reached the beach and saw what appeared to be bodies scattered around on the sand. My God, I thought, they've been ambushed! They're all dead! They were dead all right—dead drunk, lying facedown, their mouths full of sand. It turned out they'd found a native still, together with several large tin cans full of *sansu*—that's rice wine. It took us ages to bring them around and they were really ill. It was days before they were fully recovered."

Recounting this anecdote, Tim was beginning to warm to us. Stories from his days in Malaya now started to flow freely.

"As the Colonel explained to you," he went on, draining the last of the tea from his mug, "we are essentially a unit that keeps a low profile and jealously guards the secrecy of our operations. Even a winged-dagger badge spotted in the wrong place can blow your cover completely. I remember in the latter part of 1952, A Squadron were called up to Penang from our base in Kuala Lumpur to deal with an outburst of terrorist activity. On the move up to Penang we endeavored to conceal our identity by sporting the blue berets and cap badges of the Manchester Regiment. But as soon as our squadron HQ was installed in Mindon Barracks, our OC, a colorful ex-Indian Army officer, quickly dispelled any notion of a low profile operation by driving around in a scout car with a large map board propped up against the window, flaunting his winged dagger for all to see and ostentatiously smoking cigarettes through a long cigarette holder. Can you imagine the scene! He quickly acquired the nickname El Supremo. He managed to get away with it, but it's not to be recommended I assure you!"

Unlike the first two weeks, when we were part of a team, the third week—test week—we were strictly on our own. We were now being subjected to a finely tuned trial of motivation and navigation, and individual effort against the clock. Distances and bergen weights increased daily. To add to the pressure, we had to undergo deliberate disorientation techniques—last-minute changes of plans, sudden extra distances, later nights and earlier mornings than had been announced—all designed to break down our natural defenses, to take us to the edge of exhaustion and rebellion, to the point where our true characters would come through. No acts of bravado, no fake façades could survive this scrutiny. Deep lying personality flaws that would normally have taken years to reveal themselves stood out in stark relief. The instructors were like scientists employing accelerated aging techniques. All mental and physical stress fractures had to be identified and rejected before they grew large enough to cause a disaster.

Day three of week three, and we were heading for the ordeal of point-to-point three times over the highest bukit in the Brecon Beacons. Compared to Pen-y-fan, the Skirrid looked like a pimple on a pig's arse! The strain was now beginning to tell. Our numbers had already been depleted by well over half since day one of week one; the red felt-tipped pen had been really busy.

Platform 4 was getting busier by the day. There had been a steady stream of dejected egos heading for the station over the last two weeks. Selection had brought back down to earth those who had thought it would be easy, the jokers and shirkers who'd just fancied a few weeks away from the normal routine, a chance to impress their mates and girlfriends, and all but destroyed the self-esteem of the serious candidates. They were easy to spot. They sat on the ancient-looking "GWR"-inscribed wooden benches on Platform 4, hunched over, not saying a word, drawing deeply on their cigarettes, brooding on their failure. Excellent soldiers to a man—but not excellent enough. The train rattles in, the doors swing open, they step on board and they've already left Hereford, a town they'll probably never see again. A few seconds later, the train pulls out—and the dream has ended.

The Bedfords coughed into life at 4:00 a.m. I eased my shattered frame—blisters, bergen rash, aching muscles and all—into the most comfortable position I could find, and we rumbled out of the camp gates. As we picked up the A438 and passed the sign for RAF Credenhill on our right, I carefully surveyed my preparations. I checked that the strips of foam were still taped in place around the frame of my bergen. This padding gave some relief from the constant thudding and the sweat-induced friction rash that resulted. After starting the week at thirty-five pounds, today my bergen had tipped the scales at forty pounds as it swung on the spring balance in the early morning mist shrouding the camp. Even though I was a young and impressionable soldier, I knew there was no sense in having the weight made up to the required level by the addition of bricks, which was the usual practice. I would rather carry forty pounds of Mars bars! I checked that my socks had been thoroughly soaked in oil. I'd heard from an old sweat that olive oil reduced the friction between skin and wool. Its efficiency would certainly be put to the test today.

As the Bedford labored up the increasingly steep inclines, temporarily held up behind an even slower tractor pulling a rusty cylinder full of evil-smelling manure, we got our first view of the Black Mountains, rising just to the east of the Brecon Beacons, as we crossed the border into Wales. All I could see were slate-gray outlines of the ridges and peaks. They were too high for any detailed features to be discernible. A few miles further on, just after joining the A470, which winds its way southward through the town of Brecon and on to Merthyr Tydfil, we got our first sight of Pen-y-fan—all 2,906 grueling feet of it. "There she is, lads, there's the monster," said Geordie cheerfully. "Pen-y-fan! Sounds like a cheap prize from a fairground stall, doesn't it? Well, we're certainly going on a merry-go-round, but we won't be riding and it won't be fuckin' fun!"

We were passing signs to Brecon more frequently now: ten miles, eight miles, six, five, a countdown to torture. As the Welsh place-names became increasingly unpronounceable, the small towns we passed through became more and more dreary. Rows of terraced houses with stained pebbledash and faded paint stared coldly at us as we went by. We finally pulled up in a rough stone car park just beyond the Storey Arms, a small, whitewalled building nestling close to a copse of newly planted conifers. In its time it had been a pub, then a café, and was now a YMCA hostel. It was 6:00 a.m.

It was like a Le Mans start. Fifty bergens, having been weighed again to ensure no one had jettisoned any of the ballast, were lined up in a row across the road. We were assembled 100 yards back from the rucksacks and waved off by Dave, the SSM. When the arm came down, I sprinted to my bergen, hoisted it on to my back as quickly as the forty pounds would allow, crossed the car park to a gap in the trees and pushed through the gate. I splashed through the stream that tumbled down from behind the saddle of Pen-y-fan and across the bottom of the path leading up to the summit. It was into this stream that the next two times around I would throw myself facedown seeking momentary relief in the cool water. Then it was up the pink-tinged sandstone path peppered with glistening sheep droppings that ribboned its way up to the top of Pen-y-fan. Once at the top, we had to drop down the other side beyond a long gentle ridge, sweep around the foot of the ridge, cross the plain, then continue over the road we'd traveled up, right around behind and over the imposing peak which faced the Storey Arms, down the slope and back to the car park to begin all over again—and then again. I reckoned it would be not far short of thirty miles in all.

Many hours later, as I hovered briefly on the summit of Pen-y-fan for the last time, soaking in sweat and on the verge of exhaustion, bracing myself against the wind as it tugged furiously at my equipment and contoured the material of my boiler suit tightly around my limbs, an instructor materialized as if from nowhere and advanced on me menacingly. Then he hit me with the question "What's 240 multiplied by 250, divided by twelve?" Oh God, I couldn't believe it, mental gymnastics in my state, when it was all I could do to put one foot in front of the other. I composed myself and worked through the question methodically, then put my brain into fast forward and gasped out an answer: "Five thousand." The instructor's face was expressionless as he gave me a qualifying nod. Relief swept through me and I headed for the final descent. My pace quickened when I saw the three Bedfords parked on the road far below me in the distance, shimmering through the heat haze—the final RV. I went for it.

One more day to go, but the last day was the worst. Day five, week three, the endurance march. Otherwise known as Sickener 2, this was the climax to Initial Selection, the ultimate challenge of strength, stamina, motivation and good old-fashioned guts. Forty-six miles' cross-graining the Beacons, complete with rifle, four one-and-a-half-pint water bottles slung from my belt and a fifty-five-pound bergen crucifying my back, and twenty hours to do it all in. I'd worked it out: one Mars bar per bukit. I would need the two-dozen box. When I saddled up I could hardly move. The thirty-seven of us remaining set off at first light from the disused railway station at Talybont, which lay eight miles almost due east from the Storey Arms across the mass of Pen-y-fan and the surrounding hills. By the end of that long day it would need only one Bedford to cart the weary survivors back to camp, and even then there would be some empty places in the twenty-seater.

I pushed across jagged stones, squelched through peat

bogs, crushed through lime-green beds of young fern shoots and picked my way across stagnant pools of water by jumping from one clump of reeds to another. The olive oil on my socks didn't help this time; the friction in my boots felt like someone pushing a hot, razor-sharp file across the skin of my ankles. Backward and forward relentlessly with each step, sapping my willpower and determination, until it felt as if the file was sawing against raw bone. I kept repeating out loud over and over again as the sun rose higher and hotter, "I've got this far, I'm fucked if I'm going to jack now!" I was overwhelmed by feelings of isolation and loneliness. I felt as though I was the only person for miles around. I must keep going. I must keep going. The sun was getting fiercely hot. It was one of those rare spring days that was a match for the best that summer could offer.

Midday. I'd been going eight hours and I reckoned I was still less than halfway around the course. The sun was extraordinarily hot for the time of year. Just our fucking luck, I thought, on the very day we could have done with some cloud cover and a cool breeze. As I paused momentarily to get my bearing, my legs began to give way under the load of the bergen. My lungs felt raw, as if someone had thrust their fist down my throat and ripped a layer of skin off them. My facial expression became set in a glazed stare. What the fuck am I doing this for? I asked myself. Do I really want to suffer like this? No answer came back. I scanned my brain but could find no logic with which to talk myself into any more pain.

I mopped my brow with my sleeve. "It's worse than the fucking desert, this," I murmured to myself. At the mention of the desert, my breath suddenly got quicker and I felt a stirring deep within my guts. I stared into the heat haze liquefying the ridge up ahead. But it wasn't the ridge I saw. Through the shimmering haze emerged gradually the sight that had haunted me for the last two years: Silent Valley, the neat rows of white headstones gleaming reproachfully in the fierce desert sun of Aden; the final RV of mates in the Royal Engineers who'd worked alongside me to keep the machinery of the British Army in tiptop condition so that the infantry could keep up the fight against the Communists and prevent them from overrunning Aden.

I'd joined the Royal Engineers intending only to stay long enough to learn a trade that I could then take back with me to civvy street. I wanted it all nice and quiet, none of the *Boy's Own* heroics for me. Then Aden turned my life upside down. I'd been there only two months when the British Army was slung out of Aden by the Commies. What use then all the constant bullshit and training? I couldn't believe it. We were loading our kit, we were surrendering, jacking, sold down the river by the politicians. Men had died for this; what the hell were they giving it all away for? Could they not see the huge tactical importance of Aden, dominating as it does the entrance to the Red Sea and the Suez Canal? What the fuck was going on? I was twenty-one and didn't have a clue. I knew nothing about the politics. All I knew was that it was my first campaign and we were pulling out. A "tactical withdrawal" the politicians called it. In my book it was abject surrender, a personal insult.

In my naïveté, I had thought that after Aden we would return to the UK. Instead we found ourselves dumped in RAF Sharjah, another shithole. We spent nine months in 1968 building roads, helipads and landing strips in the area. For me it was nine months of questioning, nine months of restless soul searching, until finally I seized my chance the day I saw on the notice board the DCI, the monthly British Army bulletin: "Wanted: men of exceptional morale and motivation for high-risk operations and exercises world-wide. Contact 22 SAS." I knew absolutely nothing about 22 SAS. Nor did any of my mates. Nobody had even heard of them. I was intrigued even more; my appetite was whetted. It had to be better than building airstrips in the desert. That was thirsty work, but my thirst for action and revenge was even greater.

That was it—revenge. That's what had kept me going through the pain barriers these last three weeks. I'd heard vague rumors throughout selection of a stepping up of

Communist activity in the Middle East, and that moves were afoot to do something about it. It all suddenly made sense. Here was my chance to get my own back on the CTs after that humiliating withdrawal. My vision cleared. I took a deep breath, hoisted my bergen higher and pushed on, my body refueled by the recollections that had drifted through my mind.

I kept a steady mechanical pace going through the rest of the afternoon and early evening, pausing only for water and the occasional Mars bar. My luck held and I got around in under twenty hours. I had cracked the greatest physical challenge of my life. Of the thirty-seven runners who had set off from Talybont at first light, only seventeen of us made it, seventeen out of the original 135 who had put themselves forward for selection. With extreme relief, I removed my fifty-five-pound bergen, eased it into the back of the four-tonner and, with rifle still in hand, struggled up the tailgate, crawled into a corner and collapsed into a merciful sleep.

Back at training-wing basha, I was told to take twenty-four hours' rest and recuperation. I needed no second bidding after my extended ordeal. I'd overcome three weeks of discomfort, despair and desolation. I'd finished the course—but whether or not I'd passed was another matter. The tension grew as the hours ticked by. Hardly anyone spoke; the die was cast. The frustration at not being able to do any more, not being able to improve on my performance in any way, was enormous. It was a highly nervous trainee who was summoned to training wing the next day to see the OC. I stood before him like an exhausted gladiator looking up at Caesar's podium. Which way would the thumb point—up or down? When he spoke, only one word pierced through my battered brain.

5

From Hereford
to the Jebel Massif

Badged!

The prize was mine. After passing Initial Selection and spending five more months doing exhaustive tests, I became the proud owner of the famous beret and SAS wings. I was now a member of the Praetorian Guard! Somehow I had come through continuation training unscathed: weapons, explosives and first-aid training; language and initiative tests; a 1,000-yard swim in OGs; jungle training and survival; and resistance-to-interrogation training. I was on the road back after the humiliation of Aden. As I reached the door on my way out of training-wing basha I looked up at the sign above the exit: "For many are called but few are chosen." A few years later, Lofty Wiseman would amend this to read, "Death is nature's way of telling you that you've failed selection."

I headed toward the Sabre Squadron lines. I had been posted to B Squadron along with two other trainees called, in characteristically colorful fashion, Clutch-plate and The Honk. The latter looked like a working-class Charles Bronson. Of my original patrol, Tommo had long been back in his parent regiment; Geordie had knocked himself out of the running by breaking both his ankles jumping from a bedroom window to escape a jealous husband; while Jim had sailed through in a seemingly effortless manner to be posted to G Squadron, having survived six months of selection as he had survived his six years down the pits. Out of the original 135, only a handful were left to be spread between the four Sabre Squadrons. As Tim had forewarned, it had been more of a rejection process than a selection process.

We entered B Squadron office and turned left into the squadron interest room. The first thing about the room that caught my attention was the sight of a huge buffalo head, complete with horns, high up on the wall at the end of the room. Some trophy, I thought. The unfortunate beast must have strayed on to the live firing range. The rest of the walls were covered with memorabilia from campaigns going right back to Malaya in the early 1950s: photographs, certificates, old ammunition belts, bits of webbing equipment—it looked like a military museum.

We heard a noise behind us and turned to be confronted by an intelligent-looking character with silver hair and piercing blue eyes. It was the Squadron Commander, known, as we later found out, as the Duke. "Welcome to B Squadron, lads—come into the office."

We followed the Duke into his office, and as he sat down behind his desk I was intrigued by the difference between the interest room and this room. Not a photo anywhere—just curtains, dark blue curtains covering every wall from corner to corner. I wondered what secrets were concealed behind them. I was soon to find out. After a short welcoming speech, the Duke pushed back his chair with a sudden clatter, stood up and drew back the blue curtain to his immediate right. There, pinned to the wall, in full technicolor, was a map of Muscat and Oman, a little known country at the southern tip of the Arabian peninsula. The word "SECRET" was stamped in large red letters just above the Straits of Hormuz. I recognized the map immediately. I'd sweated in that region for nine months with the Royal

Engineers back in 1968 constructing roads and helipads at places like Nizwa and Bidbid.

The Duke began his briefing. It was a broad outline of the task ahead. When he had finished, I could feel the excitement welling up inside. At last I was going back. My first operation too! I could hardly believe my luck.

A strategically vital campaign was being mounted against Communist insurgents. After the fall of Aden and success in Vietnam, Communist ambitions were high. Some said it was part of a world-wide conspiracy. There had been a deep-rooted fear of Soviet expansionism ever since the Red Army, seemingly our allies during World War II, suddenly shattered all semblance of cooperation by sweeping through the whole of Eastern Europe as far as Berlin to impose their own, iron-fisted political philosophy on the countries cowering in their path. The Communist wave was again gathering momentum in Arabia. A breakwater had to be built somewhere to smash its force.

It was hoped that the breakwater would be Dhofar, the southern province of Oman, immediately adjacent to Aden. It was a medieval region, isolated from the more prosperous and advanced northern states by a 400-mile-wide desert, which rose up at its southern tip into a huge plateau called the Jebel Massif—a natural fortress some 3,000 feet high, nine miles wide and stretching 150 miles from the east down to and across the border with Aden, newly named the People's Democratic Republic of Yemen.

Because of its wild terrain the Jebel had fallen easy prey to the Communists. It was not ideal as a theater of war owing to its remoteness and the fact that so little was known about it. Hours spent by the intelligence boys in the "Kremlin," back in Bradbury Lines, poring over military reports, literary works and travel accounts, had done little to dispel the aura of mystery surrounding the place. However, it was critical to halt the Communists' advance here, before they could seize the one jewel in Oman's crown: the northern coast of the country beyond Muscat called the Musandam peninsula, dominating the Straits of Hormuz, a major political and economic flash-point in the Arabian Gulf. It was through these straits that the bulk of Middle Eastern oil flowed daily to ensure the continued running of the free world's economy. If the Communists captured this vital terrain, they could hold the whole of the Western world to ransom with the threat of blocking the flow of oil at any moment and thus causing a mortal thrombosis in the heart of the Western economy. We simply could not afford to fail—the stakes were too high.

Since early 1970, small SAS groups supported by Firqats —bands of local tribesmen loyal to the Sultan of Muscat and Oman—had established a few precarious toeholds on the coastal plain immediately facing the Jebel. Operation Jaguar, the mission I was about to take part in, would be the first operation to attempt to establish a firm base on the Jebel to stem the relentless advance of the Communist forces. B Squadron and G Squadron 22 SAS were to support two companies of the Sultan's armed forces, along with a pioneer platoon of Baluch Askars—tough little fighters from Baluchistan—and five Firqats of Jebeli tribesmen; approximately 750 fighting men in all. We were to seize an old SAF airstrip called Lympne, which was situated on top of the plateau. This would give us an airhead capability in the east.

The night of 1 October 1971 was chosen. The Khareef monsoon, which covers the plateau with cloud and mist from June until September, would be finished, and that night there would be no moon to betray our presence. We were to climb to the top of the Jebel Massif in full battle order and seize the airstrip by first light on 2 October. Enemy forces in the area were unknown. They were rumored to number over 2,000. That meant we would be outnumbered by at least three to one. Into the valley of death rode the 750, I thought—only we would be struggling in on foot. And as for the People's Front for the Liberation of the Occupied Arabian Gulf or, as we knew them, the Adoo—no wandering band of vagabonds, thieves and bandits these! They were brave and cunning fighters, ruthless in pursuing the aims of their political masters, skilled tacticians, their leaders having been trained in Communist countries abroad, and armed with the latest Chinese and Soviet Bloc automatic weapons: Kalashnikov AK 47s, Simonev semi-automatics, RPG 7s and 82-millimeter mortars.

The Duke finished his briefing, and the blue curtain swished smoothly back along its plastic runners to conceal once again its veiled secrets. He glanced at the door through which the Squadron Sergeant Major had just entered and, with a final nod of his head, the meeting was terminated. We followed the Squadron Sergeant Major next door into his office, where he briefed us on a move to the army training area at Otterburn. Here we would take part in fire-and-movement exercises as part of a shake-out before going to Dhofar.

The discomfort of the parachute seat of the Hercules C 130, which had taken off from RAF Lyneham earlier in the day, produced a sudden spasm of cramp in my thigh, awaking me with a jolt. After a quick shift of position to ease the pain, I checked my watch. In less than thirty minutes we would land in Cyprus for a refueling stop before the second leg of the journey to RAF Salalah, in the heart of Dhofar.

I looked up and down the crumpled shapes sleeping around me. There was Fuzz, a wiry character from Oldham with crinkle-cut hair; Roger, a tall, slim, swarthy bloke from Bristol, so skinny you could play a tune on his ribs—but deceptively strong with it; Pete, a veteran of many contacts, a natural comedian—he was on the mortar line and called his mortar tube Winston; and then the three Fijians: Labalaba, Valdez and Sekonia. The British Army had undertaken a recruitment drive in Fiji back in 1961 when the Borneo campaign was beginning and good jungle soldiers were at a premium. Labalaba, known as Laba, was a colossus of a man, born to be a warrior, a man who seemed to have stepped straight from the pages of myth and legend. Valdez was cast from the same rugged mold, wiry hair and all, a fighter for whom battle held no fears, for whom winning, not surviving, was the all-important goal. Sekonia, known as Sek, was solid and stocky, as sturdy as an English oak and just as dependable in a storm. He had a heart of gold and a deep, mellifluous voice which came right up from his boots. His strong Fijian accent gave the impression he was chewing and sucking the words before allowing them out in well-measured phrases. With sideboards more like wardrobes, thick black curly hair and coal-nugget eyes, he was an impressive sight walking down any street. He was to fight alongside me like a brother throughout my career—a rare phenomenon in the SAS where, as a matter of course, team members were changed on a regular basis.

I looked out of the window. We were just crossing the Cypriot coast. It wouldn't be long before we landed at RAF Akroterion. A voice crackled over the aircraft intercom system: "Fasten your seat belts." The bleary-eyed sleepers began to stir. An RAF loadmaster struggled over bodies, kit and equipment to take his position at the rear door ready for landing. The C 130 hit the runway with a disturbing thump that shuddered through the plane. The pilot won't be proud of that one, I thought. We got out of the plane, glad to have the chance to stretch the stiffness out of our limbs, and were taken by coach to the cookhouse while the C 130 was being refueled.

It was a relief to enter the air-conditioned room after the heat of the runway. I made my way to the hotplate and started to pile food on to my plate. I'd got used to the lavish fare back at Bradbury Lines. It was my unlucky day; I must have picked the cook going through the male menopause. As I lifted an extra sausage, he swiped my knuckles with a ladle. I couldn't believe it—the cook was trying to rip me off for a reputation. I knew the answer: grab his wrists and glue his hands to the hotplate. I wasn't quick enough and he retired to the safety of the white-tiled wall at the rear of the serving area. I was about to jump the hotplate when the master chef appeared, his face a ghoulish mask, scarred by a thousand fry-ups.

"This hotplate is for rissoles not arseholes," I said, pointing at the sullen cook.

The master chef launched into his plea of mitigation. "The lad's been away from his wife for five weeks," he spluttered.

"Poor bastard," I sneered as I carried my scoff to the nearest table.

Leaving the tensions of the RAF cookhouse far behind, the C 130 reached cruising height. I took a sip from one of the cardboard cups of orange juice passed down the plane by the loadmaster and began to address the problems of the immediate future. The night of 1 October was going to be some night. At Otterburn I had been designated a member of the general-purpose machine gun sustained-fire team. Because I was the new boy, I ended up number two. This meant I would have to carry a GPMG tripod, weighing over thirty pounds, plus 1,000 rounds of GPMG link ammunition—500 wrapped around the body and 500 in the bergen. This was before the rations, water, belt kit and personal weapon, a self-loading rifle, were taken into consideration. And all in the heat of an Arabian night. It was going to be some sweat. It was no wonder the SAS became known as the "donkey soldiers" by the Firqats. I thought of the other members of the gun team: Jimmy—gun controller; Lou—observer; and number one, Sean, a parachute regiment corporal—the trigger man. They had all been in action before. I was the odd man out, but it gave me confidence to think I was surrounded by such seasoned soldiers.

The thump of the Hercules landing gear hitting the tarmac at RAF Salalah brought me back to the present. I looked out of the window. The first thing that caught my attention were the Skymaster jets, secured in their own individual sandbagged emplacements, covered by camouflage nets. It was a reassuring sight. Air support was going to be at a premium. This was a prophetic thought; I little realized that the intervention of the Skymasters would later save my life.

As the Hercules swung around into the taxi bay I caught my first view of the Jebel.

"There she is, lads, there's the monster!" Geordie's words at the first sight of Pen-y-fan in the Brecon Beacons all those months ago came echoing back as if it had been yesterday. If I hadn't realized it at the time, the rigors of selection, the painful point-to-point over Pen-y-fan and the ruthless red lining certainly made sense now as I gazed out of the window at this new challenge that awaited us. More bergen-humping, more blister-cursing—but this time it would be for real. Tim's endeavors to forge a chain with no weak links would soon be put to the test. Our metal was about to be put under severe stress in the pitiless furnace of the Arabian sun.

Compared to the awesome ramparts of the Jebel Massif, Pen-y-fan was like a nipple on a forty-two-inch bust. The sight before us was stunning. Out of the totally flat area known as the Salalah plain suddenly rose the sheer sides of this huge great plateau. It reminded me of pictures I'd seen of Ayers rock in Australia. But it was far more vast in all directions. On the summit of this high ground in a few more days we would be heading into the unknown—that was, if we were able to get to the top in the first place.

As the four powerful Alison turbo-prop engines of the C 130 shut down and the tailgate lowered with a slow mechanical whine, a shock wave of heat rolled down inside the plane fuselage, passing through and hitting us before we had even eased ourselves out of our cramped sitting positions. We stumbled down the tailgate into the full glare of the sun. It was like walking into the middle of a nuclear explosion, so fierce was the heat, so intense the glare. Christ, I thought, as my eyes began to water, I hope we don't have long to wait. We didn't. A convoy of armor-plated Bedfords suddenly swung on to the tarmac and came to a halt just short of the tailgate. "Get those Firkins working, hey," shouted the squadron Quartermaster Sergeant, a flamboyant Irishman called Roon the Lazoon, flailing his arms around like an out-of-control puppet as he swung down from the cab of the first Bedford. He set to work organizing the unloading and sorting of all the squadron kit.

At long last all the gear was packed into every available bit of space on the Bedfords. We ourselves then clambered on top of our huge pile of bergens, ammunition boxes and equipment and tried to find a comfortable spot.

"Best place to sit, this," said Fuzz, smiling serenely from the top of the biggest bergen.

"Why's that?" I asked, shifting my position uncomfortably.

"Because if we go up on a mine we've got insulation from the blast," he answered, adjusting his hands cupped between his legs.

This was no idle joke. What few roads there were in Dhofar were all known to be mined, so uncomfortable travel over rough terrain parallel to the roads was the only option, but even this was not foolproof. The Adoo were known to seek out the regularly used diversions and lay mines on them, too. They would cunningly conceal the presence of a mine by rolling an old tire over the area to make the existing tire tracks look continuous. We set off with a last flourish of "Move your loins, hey!" from Roon the Lazoon. He finished all his orders with "hey," and when he was really excited, "hey, hey!"

The first leg of our journey took us to the SAS base at Um al Gwarif, a sandblown dump in the middle of nowhere. Next to it stood the hutted camp of the Sultan's armed forces, a base camp for the resident battalion serving in the area. As the convoy of armored Bedfords swung through the camp perimeter, the first thing that caught my eye was an old whitewashed fort complete with ramparts and slitted windows. A triangular red and green flag flew stiffly from a pole attached to the topmost turret. I felt as though I was back in the Crusades. Indeed, one of the Firqats had even taken the name of that great Muslim warrior who clashed with Richard the Lion Heart, Saladin. From Saracen swords to guerrilla grenades; from Jerusalem to the Jebel Massif; from Saladin to the Salalah plain.

The lead Bedford swung around and came to a halt at midday on what looked like a volleyball court. A layer of fine sand settled on everything. I tried to dust myself down, but didn't make much impact on the light-brown film that covered me. I jumped down from the Bedford and looked around. There were only two buildings—an armory and a radio-operations room. Everything else was tented. Over to my left was a large British Army marquee, and off to the side a number of bivouac tents. There's the hotel, I thought.

"Let's get moving, hey, hey!" shouted Roon the Lazoon, standing on one leg like a Masai warrior, thrashing his arms about like a combine harvester to emphasize the urgency. We began the task of unloading the Bedfords.

It was late afternoon by the time the kit and equipment were sorted out. With the radio equipment finally stored away in the signals shack, we picked up our bergens and belt kits and headed toward the hotel. I grabbed the first empty bivouac tent and looked inside. Nothing, just the hard desert floor. I opened my bergen and removed my sleeping bag. I pushed the bergen to the far end of the bivouac and placed my belt kit in front. This would make a good pillow. Then I unrolled my sleeping bag and laid it out the full length of the tent. After a final attempt at dusting down my OGs—in shit order by this time—and already bitten by mosquitoes, I laid my head on the belt kit and fell into an exhausted sleep.

Gray metal, black tape. I stared through sleep-filled eyes at the airborne tin mug floating before me. Thick black masking tape overlapped the rim. I reached forward and took the mug—Christ, it was hot! Without the masking tape I would have needed asbestos lips.

"Stand by your boots with your beds in your hands." It was Roger, with a feeble attempt at an early-morning joke. He was standing at the entrance to the tent, holding the flap back. The sun glinted on his ribs so that they looked even more prominent than usual.

I was in no laughing mood. The mosquitoes had been zapping into me all night and I was covered in bites. I grunted and took a swig of tea.

"Get your shit together, we've got a briefing from the green slime in the marquee in thirty minutes. Oh, and don't forget to take your Paludrin." With that, Roger disappeared and I was left to nurse my insect bites.

Paludrin, the anti-malaria tablet. Over the next few months I would grow to hate this morning ritual. I peeled back the tin foil containing the pill and placed the white tablet on my tongue. The bitter taste made me retch. I took another swig of tea and swallowed hard, but the sour taste remained. What a breakfast, I thought.

The atmosphere inside the marquee was one of excitement mixed with anticipation. There was a low hum of conversation as we awaited the arrival of the "green slime" to give us the big picture brief. We had split into our teams, and each team sat around a standard British Army six-foot table, our maps of Dhofar spread out in front of us. I glanced at the personalities around my table. They were all studying their maps intently. I said nothing and did the same.

The hum of conversation died down as the Intelligence Corps officer entered. The Duke, who was sitting at the front, rose to greet him. They shook hands and the Duke launched into his introduction. "Gentlemen, this is Captain Jackson. He will give you an update on the situation on the Jebel."

Jackson withdrew a pointer from its container and turned to the Dhofar map, which was pinned to the briefing board with the words "Operation Jaguar" emblazoned in black across its top. "Gentlemen, we have done a feasibility study of the eastern area." The pointer drew circles on the map. "We have identified a start line for the operation against the airfield at Lympne. On 30 September we will leave Midway, an SAF staging post north of the Negd plain, and drive by convoy southeast until we hit the foothills of the Jebel and the entrance to this major wadi here." The pointer traced a line on the map and came to a halt at the beginning of the Jebel.

The speech was rolling off his tongue like a lizard down a windowpane.

"From here we will follow the wadi bottom until we run out of motorable track. We will then debus and move on foot to an area known as Mahazair Pools. The monsoon has just finished, so there should be plenty of water here. This will be our rest area. It is from this location that we will mount the operation on the night of 1 October."

His voice droned on; he wasn't telling me much I didn't already know. We had gone over the plan at Otterburn with the Duke. All that had been missing was the time frame. Right now I was more worried about the immediate problem of humping the GPMG tripod to the top of the Jebel.

"We expect a running fight for a few months. Then we anticipate a surrender from the Adoo before the next monsoon begins in June. Nobody has yet stayed on the Jebel during the monsoon, so we don't want operations to be prolonged into this period of time. It should be all over by the next monsoon."

He continued on about logistics, but I was thinking of this last gem—"all over by the next monsoon." That didn't say much for the Adoo's expected resistance. I was puzzled. The SAS's own intelligence unit in the Kremlin had drawn an altogether more complimentary picture of the Adoo's capabilities. But I pushed this thought to the back of my mind. As far as I was concerned, a short, sharp campaign would suit me fine. A few months and then back to the Sports and Social in Hereford, and with a bit of luck a go at Geordie's bird. After nine months in the desert she wouldn't know what was in store for her, lucky woman!

My thoughts of the hostel dance hall in Redhill next to the camp were suddenly interrupted. "Any questions?" Jackson's voice barked.

"Yeah, why don't we do a parachute drop?" a voice from the Seven Troop table shouted.

Captain Jackson looked surprised, as if he'd been asked

what the Adoo had eaten for breakfast that morning. "How do you mean?" he replied.

"Well, we can't see the point of humping all that kit and equipment to the top of the Jebel, risking ambush, injury and heat exhaustion, when we could parachute straight on to Lympne and be fit enough to go into action immediately. After all, we do have air superiority."

This caused a buzz among the Head Shed. Their brains, heavy with complicated tactical theory, had possibly missed the obvious. They chewed the option around for a while, then vetoed it on the grounds that the amount of enemy activity in the area was unknown. Shame, I thought, that could have been the answer to the tripod problem.

The five-round burst hit the figure-eleven target nine inches above the four-inch-square white patch. Sean slid forward from the firing position and slipped the hinge-clip off the foresight of the GPMG barrel. He then took the foresight blade between his thumb and forefinger and screwed it up with confident precision into the error. Having replaced the hinge-clip, he once more took up his firing position, the second pad only of the index finger on the trigger and only the thumb behind the pistol grip, so as not to influence the movement of the gun by the natural side-pull of closing fingers.

We were now on the 100-meter firing point of Arzat ranges, zeroing the second spare barrel of the GPMG. As Sean rotated the elevation drum to lay the sights, I checked over in my mind the list of equipment we would have to carry into battle in a few days' time: the tripod weighing thirty pounds, two spare barrels weighing six pounds each, spare return spring, dial sight, marker pegs, two aiming posts, aiming lamp, recoil buffer, tripod sight bracket, spare-parts wallet and the gun itself weighing twenty-four pounds. Then there was the ammunition: 1,000 rounds of 7.62-millimeter GPMG link weighing sixty pounds. The equipment would be split between the members of the team, and I calculated that I would end up carrying over 100 pounds of hardware—and that didn't include water, rations and personal kit.

My mental arithmetic was interrupted as the gun hammered out another five-round burst.

"Check targets," shouted Jimmy.

Sean and I walked forward to the butts and squinted at the figure-eleven target pasted on the screen. "Spot on!" shouted Sean with satisfaction. The mean point of impact of the group was three inches above the white patch—the correct zero position. "Come on," said Sean, "we'll fire a check group into the other figure eleven, then wrap this thing up."

Midway was a disused oil-exploration camp about fifty-five miles north of the Jebel, now consisting of a number of Twynam huts scattered around an old airstrip. We had arrived by Skyvan from RAF Salalah the previous afternoon, and it was now first light on 30 September. We were on our way. The operational equipment had been packed into every spare bit of space on the armored Bedfords, and now, with personal weapons and belt kits to hand, we sat on the mounds of kit in quiet anticipation. I looked back down the convoy. There were about 250 of us. The assault force had been split into two. The majority of B Squadron and G Squadron 22 SAS, the Firqat Al Asifat, the Firqat Salahadeen and the Baluch Askars were tasked to assault the airfield at Lympne on foot. The remainder of the force would be choppered in after a firm base had been established.

The Head Shed suddenly appeared from the makeshift operations room in one of the Twynam huts. This is it then, I thought, we're going for it. After a final check down the convoy, the Duke jumped confidently into the first truck. The Bedfords spluttered into life and a Saladin armored car took up the lead position to offer some protection against mines. We moved off toward the camp perimeter. Once clear of the camp we immediately swung off the road and started driving cross-country, parallel to the road, so as to avoid the mines, and I settled down to what would prove to be one of the most uncomfortable journeys I had ever been on.

For fifty-odd miles, the arid moonscape terrain of the Negd leading to the Jebel was interlaced by dozens of dried-up stream beds. Each one would cause the truck to lurch wildly like a roller-coaster out of control, alternately twisting my spine with a vicious slewing motion and then beating my coccyx on the metal equipment box I was sitting on like a hammer on an anvil. The day wore on. The Arabian sun beat down savagely on men and equipment. My loosely flapping sleeve was worn dark from constantly mopping my brow. A thick layer of fine sand soon covered hands, face, clothing, weapons and kit. It floated everywhere, rising silently between the floorboards, sucked into the rear by the vortex of turbulence swirling behind the charging Bedford, propelled through the canvas sides in thick plumes by the sudden maneuvers of the wildly bucking vehicle.

Speed was of the essence. No allowance could be made for personal comfort. Some of the lads held sweat-rags over their mouths and noses; others had given up bothering. The dusty sand mixed with the moisture of perspiration to produce a grimy, gritty mess that stuck uncomfortably to the skin. By mid-afternoon I was feeling dog rough. The heat was getting to me, and the sight of a lad in one of the other trucks vomiting over the side did nothing to improve my morale. I looked longingly at the graded road over to our right; then the mental image of a mine injury to the human body jolted me back to reality. After another age, I glanced into the distance—and at last I could see the mouth of the wadi which signaled the final leg of the journey.

The sun suddenly seemed to lose its fierce, molten-metal incandescence and cool to a mellow golden glow. The desert landscape became sharper, its outlines more pronounced in the change of light. It took on the depth and perspective of an oil painting, rather than the hazy wash of a water color with which the noonday glare had painted it. It seemed to relax and sigh out the heat of the day and await with a hush of expectancy the magnificent display of the setting sun.

By late afternoon we had hit the wadi and left the boulder-strewn, sand-filled stream beds of the Negd far behind. The going in the wadi bottom was much easier, as the floor consisted of a smooth layer of tightly packed pebbles and small boulders. Ahead of us in the distance the plateau towered formidably. I gazed upward at the sides of the wadi, the sheer rock faces casting huge shadows across the convoy. It was an immense relief to get away from the oppressive heat of the Negd. With the sun sinking in the west it was getting cooler every minute. I was beginning to feel better. I looked around the truck. Everything was in shit order, sand everywhere. I removed the magazine from my SLR and worked the cocking handle. There was a horrible grating sound of sand on metal. I looked at the round that had been ejected; that too had a fine film of sand on it.

I had just torn off a piece of four-by-two cleaning flannelette to pull through my rifle barrel when the convoy came to a sudden halt. I looked up ahead and saw that the wadi had narrowed to such an extent that it was no longer motorable. "That's it, lads," said Jimmy. "We'll have to hoof it from here." Shit, I thought, the cleaning will have to wait. I placed the 7.62-millimeter round back in the magazine, placed the magazine on the weapon and cocked the action. Then I took my rifle-oil bottle out of my map pocket and squeezed oil on to the side of the breech block. That would have to do until we got to the night basha spot.

Word passed down the convoy that the Duke wanted all team leaders for an O group, and the remainder of us were to unload the operational kit. Jimmy grabbed his SLR and belt kit and disappeared over the side of the Bedford. By the time the O group had finished and Jimmy had returned, we had sorted the heavy loads out. Most of it was ammunition. I had 400 rounds of GPMG link ammunition wrapped around my body and getting on for 600 rounds in my bergen. Then there were four SLR magazines with twenty rounds in each on my belt, which with the three water bottles as well must have weighed around thirty pounds. "When it comes to slaughter, all you need is bullets and water." Where had I heard that before? I pushed the thought to the back of my mind and looked at the GPMG tripod. It's about time I got you ready for carrying, you bastard, I thought. I lifted the tripod so that the legs were vertical. I then gripped the tripod cradle between my thighs and unlocked both front leg-clamp levers. The legs swung forward into the high-mount position, and I relocked the clamp levers. I would now be able to carry the tripod on my shoulders with the front legs resting on my chest and the rear leg trailing backward over the top of my bergen.

When Jimmy returned he gave us a quick brief. There was nothing new. It was just as the green slime had said. From here it would be on foot to Mahazair Pools, our night staging post. It was time to saddle up. I was already wearing belt kit and the GPMG link. Next I dragged the heavy bergen on to my back, and finally Lou helped me locate the tripod on my shoulders. As I took the weight, the metal of the tripod cradle dug viciously into the flesh at the base of my neck. Lou said it looked as if I was being strangled by a black octopus. Christ, I inwardly groaned, I must have 130 pounds suspended about my person.

As I paused to gain my balance, I was suddenly aware that the ghosts of relatives long since deceased were drifting through my mind. My father had told me the stories many, many times. There was the story of my great-grandfather, who was reputed to be the strongest man in his home town. He worked for the local brewery and often, for a bet, he would pick up a barrel of beer—weighing all of 300 pounds—and put it on the back of a horse-drawn cart as if it were a bag of sugar. Huge dray horses would regularly step on his feet and he would remain completely unconcerned, going about his business as if nothing had happened. He was a hard man, who thrived on the rigors of a tough working life. Coming home one day, he slipped and fell, breaking four ribs; his wife wanted to call the doctor but he refused, telling her to get a gallon of buttermilk instead. "Blows you out, buttermilk," he said, "it'll soon push them back into place." And then there was the story of my grandfather building a new garage when he was seventy-two. Forty-two or fifty-two OK, but *seventy-two!* He tore a blood vessel in his heart in the process, but still lived another ten years afterward. I had a tradition to maintain, family pride and honor. I took a deep breath, picked up my SLR and began to march.

Leaving the convoy of Bedfords to make their way back to Midway, we strung out crocodile-fashion in teams and started to climb out of the wadi. Within seconds I was soaked in sweat. I wasn't sure the human frame could withstand such stress. There was so much pressure on all my moving joints that it felt as if my sinews and ligaments were about to snap, like rubber bands stretched too far. I feared my body would end up crumpled in a heap on the ground with the offending tripod on top of me. I staggered along like one of the Saturday night drunks on Buchanan Street Jim had been talking about during our first meal back in Hereford. My worst fears were confirmed when a signaler collapsed under the weight of his radio equipment, and one of the lads in Nine Troop suddenly doubled up, palms of hands on knees, spewing his guts out.

I had just started praying for the enemy to appear so I could be released from the pain when we moved into a flat open area, which Jimmy informed us was Mahazair Pools, the night basha spot. Thank fuck, I thought, as I carefully eased the weight off my shoulders and unsaddled my bergen. I reached for my last water bottle. It was empty. My thirst was fearsome. Rifle in one hand, empty water bottles swinging in the other, I walked across to the pools. My body felt strange and disjointed, as if someone had taken me apart and reassembled me in the wrong order. Now that we had stopped, the strain I'd locked into my body was released in a gush of heavy perspiration.

6

Isolation

The beads of sweat trickled over my pulsing temples, ran down my jaw and dripped from my stubbled chin on to my already soaking shirt. It was now virtually dark. I could hardly see anything around me, but all was reassuringly quiet. So far so good. But the worst was yet to come: I was soon going to be facing a crucial trial.

For the moment, though, my body was craving water to replace the fluids it had lost over the last few hours. I reached out, picked up the plastic beaker from the brown tray and greedily gulped the tepid liquid. It was Thursday night. I'd been here eight hours already. I had to face six days of the same monotonous routine, six days of swallowing mind-bending green-and-pink torpedo pills. BET they called it—behavioral exposure therapy. The pills were meant to soften me up, to break down the barriers and allow the memories and traumas I had supposedly suppressed for all these years to come bubbling back to the surface where I could confront them, be exposed to them and so gain some kind of miracle cure. Six days of strictly supervised food-and-drink intake so that I could lie here detoxifying from any excesses I might have been indulging in. Detoxifying!

That was a joke, when I was forced to take those pills which had God only knows what powerful chemicals in them. And six days of isolation—lying here all alone. They considered me a high-risk case, so they were monitoring my behavior scrupulously and keeping me apart from the others. Only when I had passed this test would I be allowed into the general ward.

I went over to the window and opened it. The cool November air streamed over my face, staunching the flow of perspiration. The sudden change of temperature cleared my head and shook me fully back to the present. Beyond the dark band in the immediate foreground, where I could just make out the vague shapes of occasionally rustling trees, the great metropolis spread out under a glowing halo of misty neon orange as far as the eye could see. And if you went to that distant point on the horizon, I reflected, it would spread out yet again as far as the eye could see, like a vast alien colony on some distant science-fiction planet. It was an awesome contrast to the tiny, remote native villages I was used to seeing on operations, and to my home in Hereford where, on a night like this, you could look out and see ranges of hills and mountains forming a natural backcloth to the cluster of houses under the floodlit cathedral tower.

My thoughts were interrupted by a sonorous reverberation emerging from the background roar of the city. I looked up and watched as a 747 from Heathrow banked overhead and growled up into the night sky, the flashing navigation lights gradually getting fainter and merging with the stars. I thought back to those flights at the beginning of my career, in the C 130 from RAF Lyneham to Akroterion and on to Salalah, and in the Skyvan from Salalah to Midway. Had I changed? Was I disfigured by mental scars? Was I really so different from that eager young soldier, toiling his way up the Jebel in the heat of an Arabian night to face his first conflict all those years ago?

I closed the window and sank back on to the bed. As I drifted off into a restless sleep, I was disturbed by faint sounds from a distant radio. Someone was slurring the dial through the channels, creating a weird collage of strident noises.

7

Operation Jaguar

"Allaaaahu akbar, Allaaaahu akbar." The eerie ululation of the mullah calling the Firqats to prayer rose to a high-pitched wail and drifted through the failing light of the evening. The shamag-clad Firqats gathering at the night basha spot squatted on the ground in large circles. With their FN rifles upright, gripped between their knees, they responded in a unison of strange melodies, like alley cats confronting each other with discordant caterwauling. The holy month of Ramadan was due to begin on 20 October. During Ramadan, Muslims are not allowed to eat or drink between dawn and dusk, and obviously this could have severely hampered our movements—after all, an army marches on its stomach. But since we could not afford to wait until the end of November, the Firqats' religious leader had agreed to grant them the impunity permitted to Islam warriors fighting a holy war. The prayers meant that the operation was about to begin.

I glanced at my watch. Thirty minutes to go. We sat around in small groups, listening to the Firqats and watching the shadows lengthen. We talked in low voices. We fell silent. We dozed. We gazed at the stars. We thought of home. We ate. We drank mug after mug of tea, filling ourselves up with liquid like camels in preparation for the trek ahead. We checked our equipment. We cleaned and oiled our weapons for the tenth time. We filled our water bottles and we filled our magazines. We thought of the task ahead and we felt the adrenaline begin to stir in our limbs. And we stared through the gloom at the great blackness of the Jebel plateau that loomed up in front of us, attempting to gauge the height we had to climb, the pain barriers we would have to surmount.

The minutes slipped by as we waited for complete darkness. I did yet another mental check on my equipment. Was the GPMG 100 percent serviceable? Would we have stoppages? Where was the spare-parts wallet? Did I have the rear mounting pin? I glanced again at the watch suspended around my neck on a length of para-cord. Ten minutes to go. I fingered the two syrettes of morphine that were attached to the para-cord with masking tape just above the watch. Would I need to use them? Could I remember the medical drill? I recollected talking to Iain Thomson in Hereford. He told me he had taken thirteen syrettes after being ambushed in Borneo. It struck me as strange. We had been informed that more than three syrettes and you would be dead anyway. I made a mental note to get the full story from him one day.

I checked the safety catch on my SLR. Five minutes to go. I was beginning to feel anxious. What if they were waiting for us on the way up? What if the airfield was heavily defended? How would I react? Suddenly there was a noise from the Firqats' area: the sound of equipment being moved, the clink of link ammunition against a metal water bottle, a rifle falling to the ground, a low hum of conversation. Above, the sky was completely dark; no moon. All around, men were clambering to their feet, pulling on equipment, adjusting straps and webbing belts. At long last, I thought with relief, we're off. Jimmy had gone through the plan that afternoon as we sat around the pools of Mahazair, so every man knew exactly what he had to do. We pulled on our loads and joined the ever-growing crocodile of heavily laden figures ready to depart.

The only noises now were the odd clink of a weapon, the whispers of the radio operators doing their final checks, a nervous cough. After a few minutes the radios crackled down the line. I knew this was the signal. Zero hour: time to move! Suddenly the crocodile shuffled forward as the Firqat guides up front led off into the darkness. I shifted the tripod on my shoulders into a less painful position and began carefully picking my way through the darkness. The death march had begun.

We led off southeastward in single file. At first the ground sloped gently upward; then, gradually, the gradient got steeper and the going got tougher. The weight of the tripod was digging into my breastbone and I was soon bathed in sweat. After an hour, word came down the line to "take five" and the crocodile came to a halt. I removed the tripod and slumped to the ground with relief. Out came the water bottle and I drank greedily. We had been told by the Firqat guides that there was a well four hours' march from Mahazair where we could refill our water bottles, so I wasn't too worried about water discipline; three hours to go, three water bottles—no problem. Little did I realize that when it came to distance, speed or direction, the Firqats were notoriously unreliable in their estimates. After about five minutes the column struggled to its feet. I hoisted the tripod back on to my shoulders and plodded on.

We moved onward and upward, halting every hour for a water stop. The night was hot and humid, and after four and a half hours I had begun to feel very weary. I was down to less than half a water bottle, and still no sign of the well. "Take five"—the words were a blessed relief. I lowered the tripod to the ground, sat down against a large rock and looked at my watch: 0100 hours. Out came the water bottle. I took a swig and it was all gone. That was it, I'd just have to suffer.

We moved off and the pace became slower. The column was growing more and more fatigued and the going was getting still steeper. Then, after about quarter of an hour, we suddenly came to an unscheduled stop. At last, it must be the well, I thought, and unhitched the tripod once again, sat down and eased the straps of my bergen off my shoulders.

We sat for about fifteen minutes eagerly awaiting the water resupply. When there seemed to be some confusion up ahead, people talking and moving about, it didn't really worry me. I was enjoying this long break, feeling the strength seeping back into my weary limbs. Suddenly Jim the Jock, a trained medic, moved up the line and disappeared into the darkness. That was an ominous sign. What's going on? I wondered. I was soon to find out.

The radio just ahead crackled into life and I saw Lou whispering to the team leader. He turned to look at Sean and me. There was a grim look on his face. "Ginge's collapsed with a heart attack," he said. "Apparently he was carrying too much weight."

How much is too much? I wondered, eyeing the tripod and my bergen with renewed suspicion.

I moved forward to see if I could help. When I saw Ginge lying on his back over a rock, I realized immediately what must have happened. When we'd stopped for a break he must have rested his bergen on top of the rock to take the weight off his shoulders—he'd been carrying three large radio sets. The bergen had obviously slipped over the back of the rock, pulling Ginge with it, then wedged itself underneath the base. Spreadeagled over the rock, Ginge, weakened by the effort of the march, was completely paralyzed, pinioned by the weight of the bergen, the straps biting into his chest and severely restricting his breathing. The shock had been too much for his heart.

While two men hoisted the bergen back up, Jim the Jock gently eased Ginge out of the straps and laid him down on the ground. With the first two fingers of his right hand feathering his neck, he felt for Ginge's jugular pulse. He couldn't find anything. He felt the other side of Ginge's neck. Still no pulse. Emergency measures were required, and quick! Jim began unceremoniously thumping Ginge's chest and giving vigorous mouth-to-mouth resuscitation.

Come on, Ginge, for fuck's sake. I was silently willing

Ginge back to the land of the living as much for the squadron's sake as for his own. A death or critical medical incident would seriously compromise the operation, requiring a casevac chopper to evacuate the casualty, thus giving away our position to the Adoo.

Thump. Thump. Thump. Ginge's body jerked under the blows like a comatose psychopath receiving electric shock treatment. Three minutes had passed and still there was no sign of life. Jim the Jock was getting desperate. He put his hand on Ginge's forehead. It was extremely hot, seemingly at boiling point. As a last resort, Jim decided to try and bring his temperature down. He undid his water bottles and splashed the remains of his precious supply liberally over Ginge's head, face and chest. Five minutes had now gone by. Jim prized Ginge's mouth open and forced the last half pint down his throat. To everyone's immense relief, Ginge suddenly spluttered back into life, raising his head in bewilderment. We split all his kit up and spread it out among the other team members, ready to move off again. That poor bugger Ginge, I thought, virtually dead one minute and having to resume this ordeal the next. The death march was beginning to live up to its name.

Jim would pay dearly for his generous action by nearly collapsing with heat exhaustion himself two hours later. He had started off the march already half dehydrated, having contracted some kind of bug at Mahazair Pools that made him vomit violently two or three times. Seeing how much the other lads were suffering from the heat, however, Jim had decided not to ask any of them for water—they seemed to be in as bad a state as he was. Strict water discipline was part of SAS training and it went against the grain to ask anyone else for any. When Jim began to fall behind the rest of the crocodile under the combined weight of GPMG, 600 rounds of link, spare barrels, working parts and rations, Arthur Hornby—who was later to make a bid to be the first man to row the Pacific Ocean single-handed, and die in the attempt—came to encourage and remotivate him. He also helped Jim in a more direct way: he took over the GPMG, and Jim carried Arthur's SLR.

The women of Hereford would be mightily relieved to know that Jim had survived this particular ordeal. Small and stocky, he was not one of the six-foot-six Greek-god iron-pumping brigade. He was, however, not at all perturbed by his lack of height. Quite the opposite—he felt it was a positive advantage: there was less for the enemy to aim at. What he lacked in stature, he more than made up for in impish schoolboy charm. With bright eyes, ragged brown hair the color of ten-year-old malt whiskey, an engaging grin and soft Edinburgh burr, he had the local ladies lining up, curious to know him better. And, being a gentleman, of course Jim was always more than willing to satisfy their curiosity.

It was 0200 hours before we got under way. As we tunneled through the night, I did a time appreciation. It would be getting light around 0530 hours; that only gave us about three hours to get into position for the final assault. Looking ahead, I could just make out the dark mass of the plateau against the sky. The cold metal of the tripod cradle dug deeper into my neck, my mouth and throat felt as though I'd been chewing hot ashes, and my knee joints ached and throbbed. But the thought of the Kalashnikov assault rifles waiting up ahead kept me going.

We stumbled on, the stops becoming more frequent. We had to be on that plateau by first light. Maybe they would hit us even before it got light. The Adoo knew the terrain well, and could move over it tactically in complete darkness and in total silence. I tensed at the thought and became more alert. My imagination went into overdrive. I began to perceive outcrops of rock as crouched Adoo waiting in ambush; the rustle of a night animal as an enemy scout scampering back to the main group to report on our movements; vague shapes in the sand as fresh Adoo footprints. I could now understand the reports I'd heard of patrols firing at phantom enemies.

0400 hours. The column began to suffer the first symptoms of heat exhaustion. This was far worse than any march I'd done on selection. I realized now why training-wing staff had tested us to destruction. This was no place for the weak. The surfaces of my lips, tongue, mouth and throat were dehydrated and cracked like the baked mud of an old stream bed. I wished, illogically, that the Khareef monsoon would return—even though this would have made our progress impossible. I thought of all the stories I'd heard or read of people suffering from extremes of thirst, and what they'd resorted to: castaways on boats drinking fish blood, or their own urine, or even, as a last resort, the sea water itself, although they must have known that this was a completely irrational thing to do and that their thirst would quickly return with redoubled intensity. I thought of the stories I'd heard from Korea of thirst-parched soldiers drinking water straight from the paddy fields—even though the fields were liberally sprinkled with human feces, the only available fertilizer—or slashing open truck radiators and drinking the filthy orange liquid—rust, antifreeze and all.

As we pressed on up the ever-steepening slope, the pace up front unexpectedly slackened. I noticed something metallic glinting on the track—it was a ration can. Then there was another. Then a block of hexamine, complete with cooker. Gradually the whole track became littered with rations and hexamine blocks. Who could be doing this? Suddenly my foot went down on something soft. It was a large tube of condensed milk. I was puzzled. Only the Firqats were issued with this type of milk. That must be it then. I realized that the Firqats were unloading their supplies, they were on the point of jacking. Well, I thought, I'm fucked if I'm jacking. I pushed on with increased determination, stirred to greater effort by signs of weakness in others just as I had been on selection.

0500 hours. I looked ahead. I could just pick out the great crocodile lumbering up the steep incline. We can't be far now, I thought. It will be first light in thirty minutes. I watched as the heavily laden figures ahead disappeared over the skyline. This must be the top of the plateau. With great relief I struggled on to the crest. But when I looked over the top, my heart sank with a thump. It was a false crest, and the column was now descending into a wadi. I took a deep breath and pressed on. As I made my descent, the weight bore down even more cruelly on my knee and ankle joints. All I could think of were the Duke's words at the briefing— we must be on Lympne before first light. I prayed that we would be in a defensive position before the Adoo guns opened up.

0530 hours. As we hit the wadi bottom, the first light of dawn shimmered in the east. I looked around me. We were surrounded by high ground. This was turning into an almighty cock-up. So much for the plans of the green slime. The column was now strung out in the wadi bottom in all-around defense, eyes nervously scanning the high ground, weapons ready for immediate action. The minutes slipped by; the wadi grew visibly lighter. I felt the anxiety gripping my guts. Suddenly a voice mimicking John Wayne broke the silence. "We should be on the high ground," it drawled. It was Pete from the mortar team, stating the obvious. He carried on up the line, breaking the tension with his performance. When he got to the Firqats, they couldn't see the joke and thought he was the majnoon.

Jimmy had received a message to the effect that the Firqat guides were not sure of the track up to Lympne. So two members of the mountain troop, Mel and Cappie, had gone ahead to do a recce. We spent fifteen agonizing minutes in the wadi bottom before the breakthrough came: they'd found a small track leading up out of the wadi and on to the top. "Saddle up," shouted Jimmy, "we're going for it." The column was now mobile again, and we started the final steep climb up to Lympne.

0630 hours. At last, with daylight streaking across the landscape, we struggled cautiously on to the edge of the scrub ground that passed for the airstrip. As we proceeded to move tactically, by teams, across the open space, every last muscle was gorged with adrenaline, ready to react at a split second's notice. I braced myself for the crack-thump of incoming rifle fire, or the dull thud of a mortar being fired and the swishing noise of the shell falling from high above. To my amazement there was nothing, not a sound. Inexplicably, we were going to take the position unopposed. It was only later that we discovered the reason: Sean Branson had been detailed to lead a diversionary attack to the south, and his decoy had been successful in drawing the Adoo away for just long enough for us to establish ourselves on Lympne. We moved quickly into all-around defense to build our sangar from the loose rocks that littered the ground.

Jimmy had just made a decision on where to build the sangar when two figures suddenly appeared on our left. It was the Duke and Colonel John. I was surprised; I hadn't seen Colonel John since he had addressed us at the beginning of selection. The two had their heads together for a moment, then the Duke turned and said to Jimmy, "I want your team on the high ground over there." I looked where his finger was pointing. It was way over on the left flank, possibly an hour's tab away. Extreme exhaustion and intolerable thirst swept over me once again as I dragged my heavy load back on to my shoulders.

"Why do they call Major Perry the Duke?" I whispered to Lou as we trudged off.

"Because he keeps marching us up these fucking big hills and marching us back down again!" came Lou's caustic reply.

We toiled onward in sullen silence, with Jimmy leading us past the other members of the assault force—some of whom were well on their way to completing their sangars, which made me feel even worse.

It took us nearly an hour to reach the high ground. By the time we had completed the short steep march to the top, and thankfully lowered the bergens and equipment to the ground, it was just 0815 hours. The death march had lasted over twelve hours. Each man in his own way had come as close to expiring as Ginge had; each man's thread of life had been frayed through until all that remained were the flimsiest of fibers, held together by the extremes of endurance.

And still there was no time to rest. When we had a job to do, everything else, even bodily needs, took second priority. We started building a sangar, wrenching the boulders out of the ground with our bare hands, stacking the rocks in a rough circle until we'd built a dry stone wall three feet high and eight feet in diameter. Next we had to mount the gun. The tripod already formed a triangle with its legs. All I had to do was unlock the leg-clamp levers, lower the whole tripod until the cradle was just clear of the sangar top, then relock the clamp levers. The cradle was then leveled and the front mounting pin withdrawn. Sean had already serviced the gun for mounting, with the gas regulator correctly set and the recoil buffer fitted. He now inserted the rear mounting pin into the body of the GPMG, lifted the gun into position on the cradle slot projection and pushed it fully forward, locking it with the front mounting pin. All that remained was to open the top cover, load a belt of 200 rounds, cock the action and apply the safety catch.

As the top cover closed with a metallic click we heard the first helicopters arriving with the backup force. It was a marvelous sight from our dominating position: lift after lift of helicopters and Skyvans bringing in more companies of SAF, artillery pieces, mortars, ammunition, rations, the remainder of the Firqat Khalid bin Waalid and, last—and most importantly—water!

Amid all the hustle and bustle of the airlift, I didn't notice the figure approaching in the distance. Then a movement caught my eye, and I turned to see a giant shape bounding up the rear slope of our position. As it approached nearer I could see it was Laba. He must have had 500 rounds of GPMG link wrapped around his muscular frame, and in his right hand, supported by a sling, he carried a GPMG as though it was a green-slime pointer. In his left hand and on his shoulder I saw salvation: two five-gallon plastic jerrycans of water. We encouraged him over the last few hundred yards with shouts of "Come on, Laba, we're pissing fresh air here" and "Hurry up, Laba, my mouth's like the bottom of a parrot's cage." When he finally appeared at my side, perspiring profusely, I could have hugged his sweaty bearlike frame. More of a master of understatement even than the Brits, he said only four words before disappearing again down the slope of the position to return to his own location. "Here's your water, lads." It was like giving caviar to pigs. We filled our mugs again and again and greedily gulped down the tepid liquid. Iced champagne never tasted so good.

For the rest of the day we consolidated our position, improved the sangar and brewed tea. Where were the Adoo? So far not a shot had been fired. The opinion of the rest of the team was that the Adoo, angry at having been fooled by the decoy, would by now have moved back up from the south and would be lying low, playing a waiting game, before probing our defenses for any sign of weakness. I looked around the sangar and saw that the gun was laid on possible Adoo approaches. It was a reassuring sight. A belt of 200 rounds hung down from the top cover and coiled in the sangar bottom. The weapon was cocked and ready to go. The team rested against the sangar walls, Sean and I in easy reach of the GPMG while Jimmy and Lou lounged at the back by the radio. Although we were all shattered out of our minds, we were still switched on. We fought back the temptation to close our eyes as the day slipped by, as the torpid dullness of mid-afternoon gave way to the changing light of late afternoon.

Suddenly, after a brief conversation on the radio, Jimmy announced that he and Lou were going to the Duke's O group. They grabbed their weapons and belt kit and disappeared down the slope of the position. Sean lit a hexamine block and placed it on a small metal cooker. He filled his mess tin from the jerrycan and placed it on the flame. Then, reaching into the side pocket of his bergen, he withdrew his brew kit. I watched his movements with relaxed anticipation. I could murder another brew.

Without warning the world erupted. A stream of green

tracer, made more luminous in the paling light, raced out and over our position. It was like watching cat's-eyes on a motorway at night—floating gently in the distance, then cracking past at crazy speed close by. The Adoo had arrived. I grabbed my rifle and hugged the sangar wall, the adrenaline coursing through my body. The whole of the western perimeter exploded with the stuttered popping of incoming small-arms fire. I looked around at Sean. He was low profile, but continued stirring the brew. From where we were there was little we could do. We were on the eastern flank, and all the fire was coming from several hundred meters away in the west.

"Don't worry," said Sean, "they're only overs. Have a mug of tea." He knew from experience that there was no danger. This was nothing to him. He'd been with the Paras in Aden getting shot to shit every day. I reached for my mug as another stream of tracer arched over the position. Sean looked unconcerned as he poured his brew. I looked over the lip of the sangar and could see the puffs of smoke from the return fire on the western perimeter. I could just make out the distinctive long-drawn-out bursts of fire from the other SF gun. They were in the thick of it. And where were Lou and Jimmy? Were they caught in it too? My anxiety heightened, along with my frustration. There was absolutely nothing I could do to help Fuzz and the lads. We could not abandon our own position. All we could do was sit and wait and hope. I sipped my tea, my mind in overdrive, imagining all sorts of horrors happening down below.

After about twenty minutes, the Adoo's attack slackened until only sporadic firing could be heard on the western perimeter. Gradually this died away, and silence descended again on the position. I looked down the slope and to my intense relief could just see the two figures of Jimmy and Lou running across the makeshift airstrip. They arrived at the sangar, blowing like whales and sweating copiously, jumped in, removed their belt kit and sat down.

"Make us a brew," said Jimmy. "I'll put you in the picture." Over a mug of tea he then filled us in on the situation. "As far as we can make out," he said quietly, "a force of between twenty and thirty Adoo hit the positions over on the west. They used AK 47 Kalashnikov and RPD light machine guns as backup. We took no casualties. The other SF team are claiming two hits. As anticipated, all they were doing was testing our strength, then they bugged out, possibly to their tribal stronghold at Jibjat."

I sank back with relief, smiling to myself at my recent wild imaginings.

"As for the O group," continued Jimmy in between gulps of tea, "the Duke and Colonel John are not happy with the airstrip. Apparently it's breaking up under the sheer weight of today's airlifts. So tomorrow we're going to move lock, stock and barrel the 7,500 yards to Jibjat to build a new one. So make sure you're ready to go at first light tomorrow morning. That's all I've got for you."

He went quiet and put the mug of tea to his lips. As for me, I quietly mused on the choice of location for the new airstrip, coinciding as it did with the Adoo stronghold.

Now came the job of securing the position for the night routine. A guard list was drawn up, and the timings were pulled out of a hat. It was decided that because there was plenty of manpower on the eastern perimeter, each man would do a one-hour stag, the first stag starting at 1800 hours and the last stag finishing at 0600 hours. The SF sangar was cloaked in darkness as Lou sat alert by the gun, having drawn first stag. I lay back against the sangar wall, my rifle within easy reach, now feeling quite the veteran. Even though I had not fired a shot in anger myself, I'd had my first exposure to enemy fire. I closed my eyes, and for the first time in over twenty-four hours I sank into a welcome sleep.

Dawn found us busily packing our bergens and servicing the tripod and GPMG for carriage. We had a Chinese parliament before first light to discuss the move across to Jibjat in detail. Every man knew exactly what to do and where to go. Around 0700 hours we carefully destroyed the sangar we'd so painstakingly built only the night before, dragged on our heavy loads and took up our position in the formation that was preparing to advance. It was a marvelous sight. We were drawn up into dozens of extended lines, nearly 800 fighting men in all; camouflaged figures as far as the eye could see. It looked as if we'd just come up out of the trenches and were marching across no-man's-land. It was curious to reflect that no matter how far modern technology and weaponry had advanced, the basics of soldiering were often still the same as ever. I just hoped we were going to be luckier than those poor bastards at the Somme.

By about 1100 hours on 4 October, after a brisk firefight, we had established a defensive position on Jibjat. All that remained was to consolidate our position and clear the airstrip. By mid-afternoon the work was well under way. I sat in the SF sangar on my bergen, idly squinting through a pair of binoculars at two demolition guys from Six Troop who were putting the finishing touches to the tree stump still blocking the airstrip.

A raucous voice suddenly drifted over the location: "Chin in, shoulders back, thumbs in line with the seams of your trousers!" I swung the binocs to a spot of dead ground just below the Firqats' position. The owner of the voice was Laba. He was standing ramrod-straight, with a mortar aiming post tucked under his arm like a guardsman's pace-stick. In front of him, drawn up in two ranks, were about a dozen young Firks. Laba was taking them on a mock drill parade. I stared in amazement as he went through the range of drill movements, a wicked smile on his face.

"Squad shun, stand at ease, open order, march!"

He was using the textbook method, straight from the Guards drill depot at Pirbright, namely EDIP—explanation, demonstration, imitation, practice. The Firqats were perfect mimics. By the look of them they were enjoying every minute of it. Their brown faces cracked into broad grins beneath their checkered shamags. After an ambitious attempt at a general salute/present arms, Laba dismissed the squad amid wild applause from the Firqat sangars.

It had been a brief moment of relief in a tension-filled day, a crazy interlude—but not altogether unexpected from a man who, when walking over zebra crossings, would often exclaim, "Now you see me, now you don't!" and whose party piece was eating cigarette sandwiches—literally consuming half a dozen cigarettes between two slices of bread. This impressive demonstration of a cast-iron Fijian digestive system gave rise to the rumor with which the lads used to tease Laba, namely that his great-grandfather had eaten Captain Cook! They were closer to the truth than they realized. During one particular drunken binge, when the alcohol had well and truly loosened our tongues, Laba claimed he was a blood-brother to the British missionary fraternity. When challenged on this rather startling claim, Laba revealed that his great-great-grandfather had roasted John Wesley during a hangi and then eaten him. Not satisfied with the main course, he had gone on to eat Wesley's leather boots, marinated in coconut juice, as a sweet.

Over the next seventy-two hours we continued to consolidate on the Jibjat position. Skyvans, helicopters, and Caribou transport planes airlifted in defense stores, ordnance, water and rations. It was then decided that the whole force be split into two fire groups. The first fire team, which became known as the East group, would probe deeper into the eastern area.

It didn't take long for them to attract trouble. It was a fierce, determined attack. As late afternoon slipped into early evening, from our position we could see the eerie display of gracefully arching tracer standing out sharply in the failing light, a *son et lumière* of life and death. It was the beginning of six days of desperate fighting. The combined strength of two half-squadrons was unable to prevent the Adoo from getting to within grenade-throwing distance, and the East group suffered the consequences accordingly. Steve Moors became the first SAS man to be killed in action by direct gunfire during operations in Dhofar.

Meanwhile, back on Jibjat with the West group, we had been employed on clearing patrols around the area. On one such patrol was heard the greatest misjudgment since Chamberlain waved his piece of paper in the air and proclaimed the immortal words "peace for our time." We had just come under fire from an Adoo patrol and managed to get the SF into cover. I closed the top cover on a belt of 200 rounds, and as the gun hammered out a burst of fifty rounds, a movement to the left caught my eye. A figure sat cross-legged out in the open, totally unafraid, totally convinced of his own immortality. It must be the squadron headcase, I thought. No soldier in his right mind would expose himself in such a deliberate way, with the lead flying viciously overhead.

"This is the biggest nonevent of the year!" shouted the headcase.

Suddenly a round zipped by and hit him in the leg. He moved with an agility that defied description, and in such a state of panic that he burned his arm on the hot metal of the GPMG barrel, before coming to rest among the empty shell-cases that littered the ground behind Sean and me. With a pained expression on his face he pointed to the injured limb. I ripped at his OGs and exposed the wound. To my amazement, it was not the entry wound I'd expected. Luckily for him it had been a spent round, and there, just visible below the skin, I could make out the dark brown shape of a 7.62-millimeter short, an AK 47 round. It had hardly drawn blood. I held the leg as a shell dressing was applied. We waited for the firing to die away and then, with the help of Pete from the mortars, carried the first SAS casualty of Operation Jaguar to the airstrip for casevac. Some nonevent, I thought!

Colonel John and the Duke now set their sights on yet another move further west for us. They particularly had their eyes on an Adoo area known as the Ain water hole. A probing patrol on 6 October had resulted in two Adoo killed, one Firqat wounded, and Steve from call sign 21 having to control the mortars on to an Adoo Guryunov heavy machine gun to cover the withdrawal.

The advance on the Ain water hole began on 9 October.

We arrived in the area in the early morning without making contact with the Adoo. That was the first stage. The second stage wouldn't be so easy. We were on high ground dominating the area of the water hole. To our front was a huge horseshoe of high ground which formed a natural amphitheater. Most of the high ground was hidden by thick thorn bushes, ideal cover for a waiting enemy. The water hole itself was about 600 meters away, at the far end of the U-shape formed by the legs of the horseshoe, which opened up toward us. The plan was straightforward. The mortars, call sign 25, and the SF team, call sign 26, would hold the high ground and give fire support if needed to the three action groups, call signs 22, 23 and 24, and the Firqat Khalid bin Waalid (FKW), call sign 21. These four call signs would advance tactically into the bowl and secure the water hole.

The legs of the tripod made a metallic clunk as they hit the stony ground. I made a quick adjustment to the mount position and tightened the locking levers. I leveled the cradle and locked off. Next I centralized the deflection and elevation drums, then fitted the gun, pushing the front mounting pin home until the locking stud clicked into position. Sean now flicked up the rear sight-leaf and set it on the 300-meter graduation, laying the sight on to a rocky outcrop on the tree-line by use of the deflection and elevation drums. Finally we sandbagged the legs and re-checked the sight. The master blaster, as Sean had christened the SF, was now ready. Jimmy had found us an excellent concealed firing point with panoramic views of the whole area. If a firefight developed, we would have a grandstand view.

The discussion began just before the FKW were due to begin their descent into the bowl. One party wanted to mortar the high ground and fry the tree-line with a mixed-fruit pudding before the call signs moved off. The other party insisted that time was running out and that every Adoo in the area would be homing in on the Ain water hole if we didn't make a rapid move to secure it. A tricky decision. So a compromise was reached. As the FKW, followed by call signs 22, 23 and 24, moved off, Derek, the boss of the mortars, silently registered the high ground, marking possible Adoo firing points on the plotter board.

I closed the top cover of the gun on a belt of 200 rounds and Sean cocked the action. The safety-catch remained at "fire." The atmosphere in the sangar was tense. It didn't seem right leaving the high ground when the tree-line remained uncleared. Sean sat with his index finger feathering the trigger of the gun. Lou scanned the area with a pair of binocs. Jimmy sat by the radio. The whole area was quiet and still in the early morning sun. The only sounds were the rustle of clothing and the clink of equipment as the call signs passed close to the SF sangar heading down toward the water hole.

I reached for the spare binocs and focused in on the FKW as they skirmished forward in an extended line. They had gone about half the distance to the water hole when suddenly they began dropping to the ground and adopting the prone position. Several of them lifted their arms and waved the action groups forward. This wasn't in the plan. The FKW were supposed to go all the way. It was their tribal area, their water hole. They should be taking the position to boost their morale. By now the action groups were cautiously moving through the line of Firqats.

A high-velocity round cracked overhead, shattering the still of the morning. My ears rang as it passed close by. There was a split-second pause, then the whole of the high ground erupted—AK 47s, RPD light machine guns and somewhere a heavy machine gun hammering out its deadly rhythm. A stream of green tracer floated high over the mortar position, harmlessly disappearing at 1,100 meters— the tracer burnout point.

"There it is!" screamed Jimmy and Lou in unison. Jimmy rattled off a fire-control order. "Range 400 meters. Go right 100 meters from the rocky outcrop. Heavy machine gun concealed in the tree-line. Lay."

My eyes were drawn to the area indicated. It looked like a

fire in the tree-line, streams of bluish smoke rising from the top branches of the thorn bushes. It was the HMG. It must have just recently been dragged out of the arms cache, the preservation grease and oil burning as the weapon grew hotter. It was a mistake, a real giveaway. I was once more thankful for the thoroughness of our own preparations.

"Rapid fire!" screamed Jimmy. Sean squeezed the trigger and hammered out the burst of thirty rounds to ensure a close pattern of shots in the target zone.

I watched the stream of reddish-orange tracer as it overshot the target. We were all right for line, but firing high. "Fire another long burst and I'll turn it down on the elevation drum," I shouted. I unlocked the elevation drum and gave it a quick tweak downward. Sean fired a long burst, and, with another small turn on the elevation drum, I watched with satisfaction as the tracer descended into the area of the smoke.

As I locked off the elevation drum, Jimmy screamed, "On!" I clipped a fresh belt of 200 rounds on to the old belt and began feeding the beast. Stream after stream of tracer zapped into the area of the heavy machine gun, the sound of the GPMG drumming in my ears. The mortars had now begun firing, adding to the din of battle, the phosphorus rounds exploding in cascades of white flashes among the thick thorn bushes.

The battle raged on. The Adoo HMG had stopped firing, but the crackle of small-arms fire came from all directions. The mortars kept up a steady bombardment, setting fire to the tree-line. The mixed-fruit pudding was cooking up nicely. Sean was doing a traversing shoot along the high ground above the water hole, the tracer ricocheting skyward.

Suddenly the radio crackled into life—"Valdez is hit"; and Jimmy relayed the ominous words "Ambush party, high ground to the right, watch my tracer." He dropped the radio receiver, grabbed his SLR and fired off about a dozen tracer rounds into the high ground on the right flank, indicating the Adoo firing position. Sean swung the gun around, laid the sight on, and sent a stream of tracer hammering into the ambush area, blasting the ambush party to eternity.

At last, under the sheer weight of SAS firepower, the Adoo attack began to slacken off until only the odd round cracked over the position. It had not gone as planned. Valdez had been seriously wounded and the action groups had had first-hand experience of a reluctant Firqat. On the plus side, it appeared that the Adoo had broken contact and we had acquired a new piece of real estate. I felt strangely elated; I was still on an adrenaline high. It could have been a lot worse, we could have taken more casualties. I heard Jimmy talking over the radio. He finished the message and placed the receiver on the ground. "The casevac chopper is on its way," he said quickly.

I looked down into the bowl. Green smoke swirled upward from a smoke grenade, identifying the location of the casualty-evacuation point. The chopper suddenly swooped in low and landed in the area of the smoke. All binocs were anxiously trained on the high ground, but there was no sign of the Adoo. They had melted away into the adjacent Wadi Dharbat like the hole-in-the-wall gang in *Butch Cassidy and the Sundance Kid.* After a few minutes, the tempo of the helicopter blades suddenly increased as the chopper lifted off, and Valdez was away toward RAF Salalah and the field surgical theater.

Late afternoon found us on the high ground above the water hole. We had moved across once the FKW and the action groups had secured the area. The evidence of battle was everywhere: piles of 7.62-millimeter short empty cases, blood trails, pieces of flesh and bits of clothing—but no bodies. They had been dragged away. They had even dragged away the Guryunov HMG that we had blasted earlier on. The distinct smell of phosphorus hung in the air, filling my nostrils as I got down to the serious business of making a brew. Water was short; I emptied my last bottle into the mess tin, then opened up the jaws of the hexamine stove and balanced the tin on them. I was down to three blocks of hexamine from the last packet of eight. I picked one out and broke it into pieces to make the flames hotter and boil the water more quickly. All in all it was much better than the old Bengazi burner.

As the flames licked around the bottom of the tin, my concentration was disturbed by a suntanned figure approaching the sangar.

"Look at that," said Henry, a wiry Scot from Lanarkshire. In his hand he held his tin mug. It was stained with blood. "When we lifted Valdez on to the chopper, the flap must have been open on my water-bottle carrier, and the blood from his smashed femur must have dripped through." He stared at the blood for a moment, then asked for a brew.

"I've no spare water for cleaning," I said, looking at my now empty water bottle.

"We're the same, it was hot down there."

As he looked toward the water hole in the distance, I grasped the mess tin of hot tea and poured it on to Valdez's congealing blood.

"I suppose I'll have a change of personality at the next full moon," Henry said mischievously as he lifted the blood-stained mug to his lips.

"You'll end up looking like a toby jug," I said, roaring with laughter. This was a standing joke in the regiment, about the Fijians. Fit and swarthy when young, in later years they often lost their muscles to comfortable fat as a result of eating too many fish curries. "What happened to Valdez down there?" I asked on a more serious note.

"A classic come-on, a real shit storm," replied Henry, with a slight tremor in his voice. "The Adoo opened fire from the high ground to our front with AK 47 and RPD. Valdez and the Honk made a split-second decision to swing off to the right flank and get on the high ground just below the tree-line." Henry paused and took a swig of his strange-colored cocktail. "As they got about halfway up, the Adoo hiding in the tree-line opened fire. An AK 47 round hit Valdez in the thigh, just above the knee, shattering his femur. The Honk came up and sprayed the area with his gimpy. Apparently Valdez wasn't too pleased with this, as it was attracting enemy fire and he couldn't move into cover. He was screaming, 'Stop firing, for Christ's sake, stop firing.' The Honk stopped firing and pumped a syrette of morphine into his left thigh, then dragged him away into dead ground." Henry finished talking and once again put the bloodstained mug to his lips.

"How did the casevac go?" I inquired.

"Smooth as snake shit," replied Henry. "The chopper happened by chance to be over flying the area on its way to Jibjat. So we redirected him by sarbe on to the casualty. It did cause a problem with the Firqat, though, because the casevac was immediate. They thought we were getting preferential treatment. Apparently a Firk was seriously injured the other day and he had a wait as long as a coon's prick before the casevac chopper came. I don't think pure coincidence is in the FKW book."

We now moved into a dangerous phase of the operation. By 12 October, the FKW, B Squadron and G Squadron 22 SAS and one company of SAF had advanced approximately twenty-five kilometers into Communist-held territory. We had built a defensive position, with all arcs covered by reinforced sangars, at a location known as White City. Now we had to move out and dominate the surrounding area. With the main Adoo stronghold in the east only eight kilometers away, in the Wadi Dharbat, it was going to be no picnic.

By the middle of October we had experienced our first mortar attack. The Adoo gunner craftily fired a few rounds and then moved position before his mortar barrel got too hot to dismantle—and before we could get a fix on his position.

To keep the Adoo from closing in on the perimeters and to make our presence felt, the Duke initiated an intensive aggressive-patrol program. Each day we would sweep out from White City and look for trouble. It was on one such aggressive patrol that I had my first brush with death. We were having a duel with a switched-on Adoo machine-gunner. This guy was good. No wild, inaccurate bursts of fire, just well-aimed, controlled double taps. He had us pinned down behind a small hillock of broken rocks. The slightest movement would draw fire. Two or three rounds would crack savagely overhead, just high enough to let us know that if we moved position or tried to skirmish forward he would nail us.

Sean and Lou were detached from the team that day, so Jimmy had taken over as gunner. He was losing his patience. The cold calculating bastard with the machine gun was getting to him. To compound the problem, his field craft had been so good that we hadn't even been able to identify his firing position. As the minutes slipped by, Jimmy grew more and more impatient. He badly wanted this cool customer, who was getting dangerously close to malleting us. Jimmy decided we would first identify the firing position. He would fire a burst on the SF, and I would scan the area to our front to see if I could spot the location of the return fire. This is shit or bust, I thought. I'll have to be fucking quick.

Crack—crack—crack. The switched-on machine gunner was quicker. As Jimmy squeezed the trigger and I began feeding the belt into the gun with my right hand, a 7.62-millimeter short ricocheted off the ammunition belt, went through my little finger and finally embedded itself in Jimmy's trigger arm. The ploy had worked, however. One of our snipers over on the left got an indication, squeezed off a shot from his L 42 and gave the machine-gunner a third eye.

I rolled into cover, a stab of pain shooting up my lower right arm. I glanced down at my hand—there was a small amount of blood around the wound. I had been lucky. The round had only penetrated the fleshy outer edge of the finger near the base, close to the knuckle, missing the bone completely. The second bit of luck was having one of the best medics on the Jebel pinned down behind the same cover. Nick Dawson was the son of a Harley Street surgeon and had been a fourth-year medical student before quitting to join the SAS, fired by a compulsive desire to become an explosives expert. He now worked quickly to apply the shell dressing to my wound, saying quietly that I probably wouldn't even need stitches, it was only a graze. As Nick crawled over to attend to Jimmy, the adrenaline began to drain from my bloodstream. My body relaxed and I lay back, my face breaking into a broad grin as I reflected on how fortunate it was that the machine-gunner had reacted so quickly. A few more seconds and my head would have been out of cover and directly in the line of his sight!

Dawn next day. I awoke from a restless sleep. The sangar was cold and silent. The steady throb in my right hand had kept me awake most of the night; I had only just managed to doze off in the last couple of hours. Now, with first light streaking in from the east, I dragged myself out of my sleeping bag and sat on an empty ammo box. My eyes felt gritty, my mouth felt dry and my hand ached uncomfortably. It was a well-known fact that there was gas gangrene in the air and wounds tended to rot very quickly. So I decided there and then that I would go down to the FST in RAF Salalah and get my hand checked out. I didn't want to miss any of the action just because of an infected flesh wound. As my eyes wandered idly over the empty ration box in the corner, a thought suddenly occurred to me. It was resupply day. That was it then. I would cadge a lift on the resupply chopper.

Resupply day was always a relaxed day, a day we all looked forward to. The big bird in the sky brought such luxuries as mail from home, cigarettes, water, ammunition and possibly, if we were lucky, fresh rations. Jimmy was already down at the FST, having been casevac'd after the contact. So I cleared it with Lou, picked up my SLR and belt kit and headed toward the airstrip.

I had reached the area of call sign 24 when I suddenly heard the raucous shout "Incoming." Shit, not now, I thought. Next moment the throaty swishing roar of an incoming mortar, followed by the high-explosive crump of detonation, rang in my ears. I needed a sangar—fast! I crouched and quickly looked to my left. There was a small ridge in the ground, running north to south. Built into this ridge was a sandbagged sangar with a heavily reinforced roof for defense against mortar and rocket attack. As I heard the distant thump of the next incoming mortar, I moved rapidly toward the sangar, brushed aside the blanket door and went in.

As the sound of the second mortar bomb exploded in my ears, I don't know which had more impact: the high-explosive detonation or the interior of the sangar. I couldn't believe my eyes. I thought for a moment I must have been hit by the mortar and was halfway to heaven. Either that or I was seriously hallucinating. The sangar created the illusion that you had been transported into another world, a world of psychedelic lights, pinups and heavy rock music. The sound of Jimi Hendrix reverberated in my ears. Green, red and yellow lights flashed from every corner, flickering and reflecting off bandoleers of GPMG ammo, grenades, freshly oiled weapons and numerous glossy *Playboy* centerfolds. Along the wall in front of me stood the power supply for this assault on the senses. Dozens of old A41 radio batteries were stacked from floor to ceiling in great piles, linked by a myriad of colored wires.

After a few moments I became aware of an eerie figure amid this confusion of sound and light. The figure was reclining on an old army camp bed and wore only a checkered shamag around his head, an olive-green towel around his waist and a battered pair of flip-flops on his feet. It was Scotty. His body, deeply suntanned, seemed sculpted in bronze—smooth, round, perfectly formed sinews and muscles linked and rippling into each other with statuesque fluidity; and his face seemed chiseled from granite—forehead solid and square, high cheekbones, and proud, aquiline, hawk-sharp nose, whose fierceness was mellowed by the soft gray-blue of his deepset eyes. He looked like a demented DJ as he worked the switches to control this fantastic light display. The switches consisted of live .50-caliber Browning heavy-machine-gun rounds, suspended from the beam running along the top of the sangar wall on wires of differing lengths. The electrical contact was completed by the .50-caliber rounds being swung like pendulums across dozens of nails driven at varying angles into the sandbagged walls. The nails were connected to the batteries by an array of wires.

I stared in amazement as Scotty expertly flicked the Browning rounds across the electrical contacts with his fingers and toes to the heavy beat of "Purple Haze." I was intrigued. Where had the disco lights come from, in the middle of a defensive position on a plateau in Dhofar? As I looked more closely at the flashing red light just in front of me, I had the answer. They were all Land Rover headlights. But what about the different colors?" I wondered.

"Vehicle fluid," said Scotty above the whine of Jimi Hendrix, answering the questions that flickered across my bemused features. "I filled the light lenses with brake fluid for red, hydraulic fluid for green, engine oil for yellow." He paused and then added rather proudly, "A combination of fluids and water gives you special effects."

The resourcefulness of the soldier was legendary. Fantastic stories of improvised articles created from the most unexpected materials had come out of the Japanese POW camps during World War II. But no one would believe this.

Scotty had been famous for many things, including being the first Ansell's Bitter man on TV. That had come about when, unbeknown to him, his girlfriend had sent in an application on the back of a beer-mat, together with a photograph. He passed the preliminary stages with flying colors—an altogether different kind of selection. When it came to the audition, his good looks were matched by his drinking prowess. Unlike Scotty, some of the most macho-looking men he was up against could not drink a pint down in one before the eagle eye of the camera without giving away some sign of strain—an exaggerated gulp, moisture in the eye, a quick catching of breath. Even those who could were unable to pass the second test—ambling up to a bar in a natural and unselfconscious manner. When put under the spotlight, some of the he-men looked like budding Max Walls. With his success, Scotty's picture soon adorned advertising hoardings all around Hereford. To his dismay, trainee graffiti artists embellished his handsome features with moustaches, glasses and sexual organs of record-breaking dimensions. The first two additions really upset him! Yes, Scotty had been at the center of many renowned escapades; his exploits were fabled. But this sangar took the prize.

The hallucinogenic atmosphere in the sangar had even made me forget the pain in my hand. Having not heard any mortars impacting for some time, I decided to leave Scotty and his bizarre illusion and return to reality to await the chopper. With Jimi Hendrix hitting the last bars of "Purple Haze," I brushed aside the blanket door. As I stepped through it, my mind spun with the contrast between the scene I'd just witnessed and the ordinary world outside. I looked up and narrowed my eyes against the harsh glare of the Arabian sun.

8

Transfer

The fierce white light cut into my face and burned my eyes.
My hand throbbed and ached with redoubled intensity. My
mind was overloaded with sensory input. It short-circuited
and for a few moments the electrical impulse messages
crackled around my brain in chaotic disorder like dry leaves
wildly spun around a dusty cul-de-sac by a twisting gust of
wind. After a few moments the storm subsided and I
gradually began to focus on the near distance. Tubular gray
metal protruding from just beyond my feet against a whitewashed wall background. White sheets beneath my
stretched-out legs. A bed. A hospital bed. What had happened? I must be in FST Salalah already! Somewhere I'd
lost a couple of hours. All I could think was that another
incoming mortar must have blasted me into unconscious-
ness while I was awaiting the chopper.

"Get your kit together, we're transferring you to the
general ward." The disembodied voice pierced through the
chatter of noisy thoughts inside my head. General ward—
what does he mean? I looked down at my tightly clenched
fist and slowly unfolded the gripped muscles. Not a mark,
no flesh wound to be seen. I looked up at the white-coated

figure standing by the door, a hand still on the light switch. The neon strip hummed above my head.

"What's going on?" I voiced the words indistinctly, as if I'd just been punched in the mouth and was speaking through swollen gums and dislodged teeth.

"We're transferring you to the general ward."

I glanced outside. It was still dark. "What time is it?"

"Six thirty." Seeing my confusion, he added, "Wednesday morning."

"Wednesday morning!" I couldn't understand it. "But I thought I wasn't due to change over until this evening. What's all the rush?"

"An urgent case has just come in. We need the room." He seemed reluctant to tender even this much information. I decided not to persevere.

I followed the nurse down the corridor. Our footsteps echoed in hollow rhythm over the pale brown and yellow lino squares that covered the floors of the corridor in a monotonous symmetrical pattern. The drab walls were pockmarked as if they'd been hit by gunfire. Circular chunks of the smooth pale green surface had fallen away to reveal grainy craters of white plaster beneath. We walked past narrow opaque windows reaching up to the high ceilings. We walked past red No Smoking signs and faded posters pinned to the wall exhorting anyone who cared to pay attention to eat the right food, to take the right amount of exercise and not to drink to excess. We walked past mysterious doors leading off in different directions marked "Private —No Entrance." We walked past three tubular-steel trolleys parked up flush against the left wall of the corridor, their disproportionately small black wheels protruding at different angles.

Finally we turned left into the general ward. It was a bit like the spider back at Hereford. It was split into regular sections, each one providing dormitory accommodation for eight men. A small rectangular office was strategically positioned at the end of each section, with a sliding window overlooking the beds through which the nurses could monitor what was going on in the ward.

I couldn't see a great deal. Two safety lights glowed dimly high overhead to reveal only the general position of the beds and the vague bulk of their sleeping occupants. I was shown to my bed and the nurse departed without a word. I didn't feel comfortable in this unknown environment. A thorough reconnaissance report on any new terrain was one of the first lessons of survival. I resolved to case the geography of the place and assess its inmates as soon as an opportunity arose.

The lights went on at 7:00 a.m., and the world around me slowly began to stir, shuffle and cough into life. What a sight met my eyes! A bunch of bleary-eyed, burnt-out alkies, disheveled and unshaven, endeavoring with trembling hands to struggle into their clothes and make themselves ready for breakfast. They were like bit players in some slow motion silent movie version of Dante's *Inferno*. A grotesque contrast to the early morning urgency I was used to on operations. I felt completely separate from them. I felt sharp and alert. My mind was already working out how I could beat the system.

After breakfast and after my reconnaissance of the ward area I barged into the office just at the end of my ward and fired impatient questions at the duty nurse.

"What am I supposed to do around here all day? How can I pass the time?"

The nurse looked up from his contemplation of a set of LFT charts and replied vaguely, his mind on other things, "There are newspapers every day. And there's TV, radio . . . " and dropped his eyes back down to scrutinize the graphs.

"That's no good for me, mate," I insisted. "I'm an active person. I'm used to moving around, getting things done, being involved. As it is I'm stuck here floating around in a sea of flopped-out alkies. I can't hack this."

"Well that's how it is. I can't see you've got a great deal of choice. And anyway it's no good complaining to me—I don't draw up the rules around here."

"But my body is used to regular physical exercise. I'll lose my edge after a few days of this routine."

"There is a three-mile morning run each day that you'll be taking part in from tomorrow onward."

"Oh great! Three miles! That's like a stroll to the corner shop for me. I'm used to doing ten miles a day."

There was a pause. He didn't say anything. He didn't even look up from the LFT charts.

I could see I wasn't getting anywhere. I padded off to the lounge area and slumped in a chair. I picked up a newspaper and distractedly read what was going on in the outside world. An hour went by, then two. I dropped the last paper on to my knees in despair. I contemplated with gloom the prospect that the burning fires of my motivation and energy, fueled by excitement, adventure and action, were about to be smothered by the blanket of routine and monotony that was descending on me. I had to do something. Suddenly, as I flipped through one of those Orbis publications on World War II, a faded black-and-white photo of a large gun in action jumped off the page and hit me right between the eyes. I realized how close the hospital was to the Woolwich Artillery Museum. I remembered passing the road sign pointing to it on the drive in. That was it! The Mirbat gun.

I got up and walked silently toward the fire escape I'd located on my earlier recce. My inner radar was alert for any signs from the nurses that they suspected my behavior might be unusual in any way. With a last glance at the only office that had a view of the fire escape, I slowly eased up the quick-release bar, careful to avoid making any metallic clunks, pushed the door open and stepped out on to the studded black metal platform. I took a deep breath of fresh air with relish. Then, silently easing the door to behind me, I climbed swiftly and noiselessly down the latticed iron treads, as cautiously as if I were moving through the jungle under threat of an enemy ambush, hurried across the grassy area surrounding the hospital and strode confidently along the nearby street.

Once inside the museum, I fixed my eyes intently on the gun for so long that the rest of my surroundings began to melt into the background. The other artifacts on display, the other visitors walking around, the moustachioed security man dozing in the chair in the corner of the overheated room, arms folded, his head tilting forward and threatening to cast off his peaked cap at any moment, everything else faded away into the distance.

I scrutinized the gleaming barrel on the twenty-five-pounder. I smiled to myself as I recollected that it had certainly been in no show-piece condition when I last saw it, pumping out a continuous barrage of roaring shells. Covered in dust and oil, riddled with bullet marks, and with the cross-country tires deflated and shredded, it had been in real shit order. It was the last artillery gun of its type to be used by British troops in action. And what action it had been! A heroic, cataclysmic struggle, the final decisive encounter with the Communist Adoo pouring down from the Jebel like lemmings all those years ago. And yet it seemed like only yesterday. As my mind drifted back, the confused, urgent jumble of battle sounds rang in my ears again, faintly at first like the sound of distant surf, and then gradually getting louder: the whoosh of mortars and the thump of artillery; the hailstone rattle of machine guns and the whip-crack of rifles; the shouts and the screams, the groans and the gasps, the clamor, the cries and the curses of the men caught up in the middle of it all.

And as I continued to stare, a picture began to take shape in my mind's eye, a painting by the artist David Shepherd. A print of it hung on my wall back home in Hereford, and I'd spent many a nostalgic moment gazing at it. It depicted three soldiers in a gun pit huddled around the breech of the twenty-five-pounder, with the Mirbat Fort under siege on the skyline. I studied the group of three men again now in my imagination and reeled off the litany I'd intoned so many times before: he's dead, he's dead, and his back is so badly scarred with gunshot wounds it looks like an OS map of the Brecon Beacons, an aerial photo of Crewe sidings. I was the lucky survivor. I could have been the fourth man. The situation was desperate. Volunteers were called for. I stood forward but I was turned down. I was needed to man the radio set. My mate went instead. He was a good mate. They were all good mates. I owe it to you lads to win through again.

I felt reassured. I'd found a referent point. This was what was real—the adventure, the danger, the humor, the camaraderie under fire; not the alien environment of Ward 11.

I returned to the hospital hoping to slip back into the routine as if nothing had happened. It was too much to expect. I was immediately confronted by one of the nurses. He was at 50,000 feet.

"Where the hell have you been?"

"The Woolwich Museum."

"Like hell you have."

"What do you mean?"

"You know damn well what I mean. You've been drinking, haven't you?"

"No way! There's no pub around here anyway. I've done a recce."

"Don't try and be clever with me. You've got some booze stashed in the boot of your car, haven't you? I know your type."

"You're wrong, mate. I've been to see the Mirbat gun."

"I've never heard of the Mirbat gun. I don't believe a word you're saying. Right! Into the office—I'm going to breathalize you."

It was a real breathalizer, just like the ones the police use. As I put the mouthpiece to my lips and exhaled deeply, I thought of all the times I'd evaded the local police back in Hereford after wild nights in the Pal-U-Drin Club. Was my luck about to run out in the ignominious surroundings of Ward 11? We both stared at the contraption in silence, waiting for the result.

Negative.

"There must be something wrong with this one," he said, squinting at the digital read-out. "We'll have to do it again."

Negative result once more.

"I still don't believe your story. You can explain your case to the Major."

I was whistled in to see the Major, the top military psychiatrist. I went through my story again, but was noisily interrupted.

"What battle of Mirbat? I've never heard of it! You've made it up. You've picked up the name from a newspaper and fabricated some cock-and-bull story. You're having delusions."

"You could easily check it out, sir." I could barely disguise the latent contempt in the word "sir."

The Major hesitated, looked me up and down, then said, "All right, I will check it out. But if we find out you are lying . . ." His voice tailed off as he shot me an intimidating glare.

I wandered back to my bed. I was confident. I wasn't going to let my mates down. No way was I hallucinating. Mirbat was no figment of a fevered imagination, no creation of a bullet-crazed brain. 19 July 1972. Mirbat was real all right, as real as the roar that flowed in over the breeze—London's pulse and heartbeat. And what was it that kept the heart of the metropolis beating? What was it that flowed through its veins, vessels and arteries? Oil! Oil to fire the generating stations, oil to power the lorries, oil to light the streets, oil to heat the buildings, oil to insulate the homes and keep the inhabitants in their cocoon of coziness and comfort. And from where did it flow, that oil, where did it spring up? Arabia, where life was harsh, food was poor, shelter was scarce; where the monsoon was a continual scourge and mosquitoes a constant enemy; where, simply, people froze when it was cold and scorched when it was hot. Arabia, where to insure the free flow of that precious stream I and my mates had undergone rigor, hardship and danger for months on end, fighting alongside tribesmen loyal to the

Sultan. Some of my best friends had fallen in that inhospitable terrain, their life-blood seeping through the sand to mingle with the black liquid that even now, as I lay on my bed, was pumping through the nation's heart.

I thought again of David Shepherd's painting of the twenty-five-pounder, and then I remembered the plaque on the wall at home next to it. The plaque was inscribed with words from *Henry V*:

> Old men forget: yet all shall be forgot,
> But he'll remember with advantages
> What feats he did that day.

I remembered all right. I remembered what feats we did that day.

9

The Battle of Mirbat

After a while I closed my eyes and started to descend into a fitful sleep. I remember thinking that I would only need to survive a few more days of this routine, the creeping listlessness that came with the drawn-out inactivity, the sudden threat that came with the odd unexpected attack, and then it would be back home, back to what I knew, back to get on with the rest of my life. Monotony was making a fierce assault, but strong willpower reinforced by endless hours of rigorous training was putting up determined defenses. Whatever happened, I would give a good account of myself. I wasn't going to let my mates down at any cost. That was the single most important thought I held fast in my mind. Like a shipwrecked sailor clinging to driftwood, I knew that, come calm or storm, I would pull through if I could just hold on to the one thing I knew was solid.

The darkness got deeper and I slid into the realms beyond dreams.

In the dark of that night, the lingering Khareef monsoon wrapped the Jebel Massif in mournful clouds of mist and drizzle. Before first light, 250 handpicked Adoo warriors crouched motionless behind the tumble of ragged boulders strewn at the foot of the Jebel ramparts, watching and waiting. Droplets of rain ran down their stony, weatherbeaten features as they stared out impassively over the shadowy pre-dawn scene that lay before them: the mud-walled dwellings of the garrison town of Mirbat huddled up against the shore, and the slow, leaden swell of the sea to the south.

Their commanders surveyed the town's defenses: just to the north of the town, a shallow wadi ran from east to west; 500 meters beyond and parallel to it stretched the barbed-wire perimeter fence; and in the gap between the two lay their main obstacles—the Wali's fort and the British Army Training Team headquarters (the Batt House) down by the wadi, and to the northeast, nestling close to the perimeter wire, the Dhofar Gendarmerie fort, with the twenty-five-pounder located at the base of its walls.

The Adoo were taking no chances. They were armed to the teeth with the choice of the latest Soviet weapons: AK-M and AK 47 rifles; heavy, medium and light machine guns; two 75-millimeter RCLs; 81-, 82- and 60-millimeter mortars; grenades and rocket-launchers; and one 84-millimeter Carl Gustav. And each man had been issued with a large reserve of ammunition. This was the battle they had to win. This was the one upon whose outcome the political and economic fate of the whole of Western Europe could depend. Muscat and Oman with the Straits of Hormuz was a glittering prize to capture, and Mirbat was the jewel in the crown. This was to be a day they hoped would live forever in their folklore, a day whose exploits would be retold over and over by tribesmen elders with graying beards, sucking pensively on rough pipes as they sat cross-legged by the camp fires, watched in awe by young boys eager to grow up to become warriors themselves. This was to be a day to restore morale with a resounding victory.

The Adoo were taking no chances. Two hundred and fifty men against a pitiful opposition: twenty-five DG in the perimeter fort, one Omani gunner manning the twenty-five-pounder, thirty Askars in the Wali's fort, a scattering of

Firqats bedded with their wives in Mirbat itself and nine SAS in the Batt House.

Forty miles away, at Um al Gwarif, Lofty Wiseman stirred from a listless sleep, levered himself upright on his bare metal bed, rubbed the sticky secretions from his eyes and glanced at the luminous dial on his G 10 watch. It was just before 0500 hours, the start of another day at SAS base camp. He looked outside. Beyond the barred windows and whitewashed walls of the armory, he could just make out through the drizzle the vague shapes of the first of the lines of bivouac tents housing G Squadron, who had come to relieve B Squadron now that the latter's tour of duty on the Jebel and the coastal plain was coming to an end. It would be just another routine day for Lofty. Ammunition would be counted, checked, listed and issued to G Squadron for the pre-deployment shake-out. They would move to Arzat ranges, where weapons would be checked, double-checked and meticulously zeroed. In this way they could keep themselves in a state of constant alertness just in case anything should happen. The day's work for Lofty had been reduced significantly with the deployment of advance parties from G Squadron into strategic locations throughout the sultanate to facilitate a smooth handover. The only forces remaining in Um al Gwarif were a handful of NCOs and around forty troopers.

At a signal from their leader, the Adoo crept forward without a sound, as noiseless as fish gliding through water, to occupy their predetermined assault positions. One group established a line of 81- and 82-millimeter mortars 2,000 meters north of the town. Two groups went further south, fanning out on either side of the town, to attack from the seaward side. Before dawn, the still sleeping inhabitants of Mirbat garrison were completely surrounded.

"I don't drink on ops, you know that, Fuzz."
It was 5:00 a.m. in a top-floor room in the Batt House.

The final few bars of the last song on side two of *Easy Rider* were quietly playing out on the battered cassette-player in the corner, as Fuzz made one last attempt to persuade Sek to have a swig from the illicit half-bottle of rum that had kept them company through the long night. The other Fijian, Laba, had had no such reservations. The three of them were slumped on their beds, still fully dressed, in Jesus sandals, shorts and shirts. While the other lads slept the monotony away, Laba, Sek and Fuzz—now designated an honorary Fijian—had drunk, talked and sung right through the night. What did it matter anyway? They would not be doing much the next day. They never did. They only went out now and again on patrols, and they were mostly uneventful. Just the occasional threat from a minor skirmish. The most difficult part was finding the discipline to stay alert. Nothing ever really happened at Mirbat. It was one long rest period.

The Adoo sent a scouting party to probe further forward toward the first obstacle in their way—the Jebel Ali hill, which rose 1,000 meters due north of Mirbat, dominating the coast and plain. They suspected this could conceal an enemy outpost. Their suspicions were well founded: it was manned by a section of the Dhofar Gendarmerie. The Adoo lead scouts surrounded the hill and sealed off all escape routes. The unbelieving DG woke up staring death in the face. They only managed to loose off a few shots before, with ruthless efficiency and in a matter of seconds, the outpost was overwhelmed, its occupants put to the knife and silenced forever. Fearing that the sound of the shots must have alerted the Batt, the Adoo mortar line opened fire.

Lofty was beginning to get that end-of-tour feeling. He cheered himself up with the thought that in a few days' time, B Squadron would be all packed up and winging their way back to the UK, the married pads returning to their families, the young thrusters to a bit of sex and athletics in the Redhill Sports and Social. No more monsoon, no more heat, no more dust, no more flies. Just cool beer, and hot women. He turned slowly on to his back and stared up at the fan whirling in the gloom above his bedspace. This always enabled him to think better. The hypnotic movement and faint vibrating beat of the fan helped him to dispose of all irrelevant thoughts so that he could concentrate solely on the task in hand. He allowed the gentle breeze from the revolving blades to waft over him to clear his mind as he began to make a mental checklist of his responsibilities for the day.

Crump. Crump. Crump. Fuzz propped himself up on his bed on a crooked elbow and squinted at the bulky Fijian figure still lying down in the shadows. "Laba, they're throwing a few in."

"No problem, Fuzz, it's the dawn chorus. Regular as clockwork once they start. You don't need a watch around here!"

"Yeah, it's just the Adoo coughing themselves awake," said Sek laconically. "Another tedious day in Dhofar."

Crump. Crump. Crump.

"That was closer. They're getting a bit brave this morning," said Fuzz, his voice tightening slightly.

"Don't worry," soothed Laba reassuringly, "there's no small-arms fire. They're just stonking us."

Crump. Crump. Crump. Fuzz was now on his feet. "I don't like the sound of this. That was too close for comfort. We'd better go and see what they're up to."

The first ranging rounds from the Adoo mortars were already impacting just outside the perimeter wire as I leapt out of bed, pushed past Fuzz, Laba and Sek and scrambled up the half-pyramid of ammunition boxes that served as a ladder up to the roof. When I reached the top I threw myself behind the .50-caliber Browning, my stand-to position in the command-post sangar built on the flat roof of the Batt House. One moment fast asleep, the next under attack, I drew a sharp breath and cursed softly, my left hand closing instinctively on the first incendiary round protruding from the ammunition box. I snapped open the top cover of the .50-caliber and positioned the ammunition belt on the feed tray. The belt held a mixture of incendiary and tracer rounds in a ratio of four to one, the incendiary rounds designed to explode on impact. With the links uppermost I maneuvered the belt into position with my left hand. With my right hand I closed the hinged cover and cocked the action with a single practiced twist of the wrist, feeding an incendiary round into the breech. The cold metal of the trigger felt comforting to the touch as I took up the first pressure, released the safety catch and stared in disbelief at the scene unfolding before me.

Confident he had everything organized for the relieving squadron, Lofty swung off his bed, slipped into his well-worn shorts and desert boots and creaked open the wooden door. He screwed his face up into a grimace, as the cool drizzle of the interminable monsoon washed over his early-morning pallor making him blink away the last grains of sleep. He ambled past the radio-and-ops room and headed for the armory. G Squadron transport, two armor-plated Bedfords, stood parked ready on the volleyball court. Several figures clad in olive-green OGs were milling around talking in low tones. One character caught Lofty's eye. Slowly and meticulously he was lacing his high boots on the ammunition-store steps. Lofty brushed past him, undid the padlock and pushed open the heavy metal armory door. He stood still for a moment peering into the store, getting his eyes used to the gloom inside, then set to work issuing the ten GPMGs and 2,000 rounds of ammunition for the day's zeroing detail on Arzat ranges. Working with quick mechanical precision he didn't take long. As the last 200-round liner of GPMG link rattled its way on to the back of the Bedford, he began securing the ammunition-store door. "Time for breakfast and a quiet cup of tea," he said to himself.

Two thousand meters away, in the dark foothills of the Jebel Massif, I could clearly see the vivid flashes of six mortar tubes leaping into the night, dramatically illuminating their concealed baseplate positions. Nearer, from the Jebel Ali, the muzzle flashes of incoming machine gun and rifle fire sparked white-hot holes in the gloom. What the hell's going on, I thought, where's the DG night picket? Green tracer from an RPD light machine gun rioted furiously against the walls of the DG fort on the northern edge of the town. A frenzied salvo of mortar bombs suddenly impacted, blowing away part of the perimeter wire. The fire mission crept slowly forward until the last round exploded on the edge of the town, sending pieces of shrapnel each the size of a fist screeching over the Batt House.

Since arriving in Dhofar in 1971, during the months spent skirmishing with the Adoo on Operation Jaguar, I had developed a sort of sixth sense, a feel for contacts with the enemy. I had a bad feeling about this one; it looked like high drama. Over the last three months there had been several stand-off attacks on Mirbat, with the Adoo bugging out after scattering four or five mortar bombs inside the barbed-wire perimeter fence. The Adoo had just been letting us know they were there, trying to prove their virility, maintain their morale. But this time it was different. The intensity of this deployment had all the tell-tale signs of a determined attack.

With my heart beating furiously against my rib cage, threatening to burst through at any moment, and with a sickening surge of gut fear hardening like cement in my stomach, I squinted through the dark at the defensive layout of the Batt House. It seemed totally inadequate against the firepower of the attacking Adoo, a shanty-town hut against a nuclear bomb. Over to my left, on the northwest corner of the flat-roofed building, a GPMG in the sustained-fire role had been mounted in a sandbagged sangar. Behind the gun, awaiting the order to open fire, their eyes aching intensely with concentration, crouched Roger and Geoff. From my sandbagged sangar on the northeast corner of the roof I looked down to a pit ten meters away from the house. I could just make out the wiry figure of Fuzz hunched over the illuminated dial sight of the 81-millimeter Batt mortar. At his elbow knelt Sek, almost invisible in the gloom, cradling a high-explosive mortar bomb in his hands as though it were a rugby ball. To the rear of the mortar position, Tommy worked frantically preparing the mortar bombs for firing, unscrewing the plastic tops of the containers, withdrawing the bombs and checking that the charge cartridges were securely in position, withdrawing the safety pins, replacing the prepared bombs in their containers—fins protruding from the openings to facilitate easy withdrawal—and stacking the containers in a tier system so there would be as many as four dozen bombs ready to hand at any one time.

I glanced over my shoulder to the far side of the command-post sangar. I looked at Bob, the CPO. Calm, cunning and totally professional, he stood balancing the mortar plotter board on the edge of the sangar wall as if he was about to conduct an orchestra. In his right hand, held close to his ear, was a Tokia walkie-talkie. He was staring intently in the direction of the Adoo mortar line. His sunburned brow became as furrowed as a seventy-year-old Sherpa's as his mind wrestled with the problems of estimating bearing and elevation for the Batt mortar.

That, then, was the sum total of our defenses. All in all, with our World War II twenty-five-pounder, .50 Browning and 81-millimeter mortar, compared to the firepower of the Adoo, it was as if we had brush-handle battering rams against a reinforced steel door. If we had known also that we were outnumbered by nearly five to one, we would have already been mentally composing a plea of mitigation for an imminent confrontation with our Creator.

My appraisal of the Batt House defenses was suddenly interrupted by a noise on the pyramid of ammunition boxes that led up to the sangar. I looked around to see the grim face of Mike Kealy, the commander of our eight-man civil-aid team, appearing over the sangar wall. His morphine syrettes, watch and ID disc on the para-cord swinging around his neck rattled noisily when the cord became briefly entangled with his SLR as he pulled himself over the sangar wall. On his feet he wore only a pair of flip-flops.

He crouched and moved quickly across the floor of the sangar, carefully avoiding the open ammunition boxes, and took up a position just by my right elbow. His face spoke a thousand words. He was trying to inject some interpretation of the situation into his logical Sandhurst mind. He looked me square in the eyes and, holding my stare, said in a quiet, steady voice, "Go down to the radio room and establish communications with Um al Gwarif." As I applied the safety-catch to the .50-caliber, I heard the throaty swish of an artillery round. We both ducked as a blinding flash followed by the crump of detonation sent a large plume of smoke spiraling crazily skyward from the center of the town. Christ, that was no mortar, I thought, with a shiver of trepidation.

I ran down the sangar steps, crossed the small open area leading to the radio room, pushed in through the door and seated myself at the folding six-foot table. On the table, amid a pile of message pads, code books and well-thumbed *Penthouse* magazines, stood the PRC 316 patrol radio set. The set was already tuned in, so it was just a matter of switching on, adjusting the fine tuner slightly, then hitting the Morse key. With the set switched on, the mush in the earpiece of the headset sounded like hailstones on a sky-light. I gripped the Morse key between index finger and thumb and tapped out the net call sign: "OA.OA. This is 82. Radio check. Over."

A bead of sweat broke out on my brow, rolled down the side of my face and splashed a dark stain on to the dusty cover of the code book. As I waited for the reply, my finger quivered nervously on the Morse key. Suddenly the base signaler at Um al Gwarif sparked into life and keyed back the answering code: "82.82. This is OA. QRK 5."

I unclenched my jaw and let out a low sigh. Relief swept through me as I heard the Morse signal boom through the earpiece at full strength. I was just reaching for the code book when a sharp explosion rocked the Batt House. The building shuddered violently from wall to wall as bits of plaster fell from the ceiling, and for an instant the room was filled with choking dust. Things outside were getting extremely serious. Looking down at the cover of the code book, I realized that it was going to take too long to code messages before keying them back to base. It was at this point that I took the first major decision of the battle that was developing all around us: I would ignore the complicated coding procedure and send all messages to Um al Gwarif in plain-language Morse. This was a major deviation from regulations, a serious breach of security, as all radio messages in Dhofar required coding before transmission. Fuck the rule book, I thought, as I gripped the Morse key and tapped out my message, the Adoo know we're here anyway! "OA.OA. This is 82. Contact. Under heavy fire. Wait. Out."

As I finished the message and placed the headset on the pile of message pads, another explosion pummeled the Batt House, the sudden intensity of the explosion rocking the building to its foundations. It felt like being at the epicenter of an eight-Richter-point earthquake. Sand ran down in fine trickles from the expanding wall cracks, and big pieces of plaster from the wall in front fell on to the signals table, covering the spare radio batteries in dust and masonry.

Lofty gave the padlock a couple of tugs. Having reassured himself that the armory door was once more securely locked, he turned and set off down the steps. He was surprised to see the same trooper still there doing his boots up. He was just about to question the usefulness of this time-consuming exercise in perfectionism when the Duke approached. With a grim look on his face he took Lofty to one side and told him quietly that the town of Mirbat was under heavy attack and that he should prepare for a step-up operation and a quick move to the SAF headquarters at RAF Salalah.

Things were getting hot. I could hear the throb and rumble of distant explosions, the murderous whistle of shrapnel. I decided it was high time to move back to the command-post sangar on the roof and get the .50-caliber Browning into action as quickly as possible. I sprinted up the sangar steps to my gun position, checked the ammunition belt and once more eased the safety-catch to fire. Suddenly an enormous explosion slammed into the tower of the DG fort. It gouged away a huge chunk of masonry, leaving a gaping hole with jagged edges silhouetted against the first glimmer of dawn. The flash of detonation briefly illuminated the World War II vintage twenty-five-pounder artillery piece located in the defensive sangar at the base of the fort walls. The figure of Laba was clearly visible kneeling behind the gun's protective armored shield. "That looks like a 75-millimeter RCL," Bob shouted at Mike Kealy above the roar of six explosions detonating in rapid succession. My ears screamed with the roar of the noise and for a moment I was totally disorientated, until I realized with immense relief that it was the Batt mortar initiating a pattern of harassing fire.

I shook the noise and confusion out of my head and studied the landscape that rolled away into the distance. The darkness was receding, and the first flickers of light revealed the blurred and shadowy foothills of the Jebel. The battle now began to flare up, roaring into a sense-stunning and mind-numbing conflagration. The din and racket of combat reached a frenzied crescendo, all the noises running into one another to create a surreal aural collage: the crack of incoming small-arms fire, the vicious clatter of machine guns, green tracer ricochets leaping like firecrackers around the buildings and walls of the town, the throaty swish of incoming mortar rounds followed a few seconds later by the deadly crump of detonation, and the ear-splitting explosions of the Batt mortar returning fire. I looked at my watch: it was just after 0600 hours.

The two machine guns on the roof remained silent. This could be another stand-off attack, albeit a particularly determined one, so we didn't want to risk compromising our position by giving the Adoo telltale gunflashes to aim at. I looked over to the left. The thirty Askars in the Wali's fort evidently had the same idea. The ramparts bristled with old bolt-action .303s, but they remained silent. As the first rays of dawn filtered through the thick, spongy monsoon cloud hovering over the plain, the flashes of the Adoo mortars became paler. Far from diminishing, as the light exposed the Adoo mortar positions the bombardment increased in its ferocity. The racket from the Spargen heavy machine gun and the LMG fire gradually escalated. All along the wire for as far as the eye could see, plumes of sand and earth spewed as if from distant volcanoes. Winged daggers of flame leaped skyward. The air above and around me teemed with the cracks and hisses of the lethal lead zingers. I glanced nervously around the roof. The other members of the team were at their stand-to positions, poised over their guns like cobras ready to strike. We were waiting, our fingers welded to the triggers, every muscle and nerve rigid, screwed tight with the tension of facing the unknown.

Lofty, showing no sign of emotion, his face blank and expressionless, his eyes methodically searching the re-opened ammunition store, worked flat out issuing all the GPMGs, semi-automatic rifles and M 79 grenade-launchers he could find. A human chain was formed to hump box after box of 7.62-millimeter link and ball ammunition from the store to the trucks. Between them the men had soon loaded 20,000 rounds. In a matter of minutes the ammunition store had been cleaned out. As dawn broke over the volleyball court, the dangerously overloaded Bedfords, sagging heavily under the weight, stood ready to go.

Forty well-armed Adoo formed into an extended line and began moving at a brisk pace across in front of me toward the DG fort, following the line of a shallow wadi that ran between the perimeter wire and the Jebel Ali. I stared at them intently. The figures broke into a run. My eyes felt like oversized pebbles pressing achingly into my sockets as I continued to stare. Beads of sweat broke out on my forehead. My breathing resumed a steady and rhythmical pattern. I took up the first pressure on the trigger of the .50-caliber.

This was it. The few fleeting moments before battle is joined. Too late now to do any more training. Too late now to fine tune and zero the weapons. Too late now to strip and oil the mechanisms to liquid-smooth action. The few fleeting moments before battle is joined. The same pitch of intensity in human experience as at birth and death themselves. The fear wells up and you welcome it. Without fear you cannot perform fully. Without fear you do not have that razor-edge extra of concentration that can make the difference between you and the enemy, between life and death. The few fleeting moments before battle is joined. You mentally go through every move. There's nothing else to do. You are on automatic pilot. You lapse into unconscious behavior patterns, comforting routines: the curled finger caressing the smooth metal trigger, the moist hand rubbing against the rough trouser material, the blowing of cool air on tightly bunched-up fingers, the anxious chewing on the bits of broken skin at the edges of fingernails. The few fleeting moments before battle is joined.

I looked around at Mike Kealy for the order to open fire. Mike had his back to me. He was looking toward the DG fort. With a sudden shock I realized that he was oblivious of the movements taking place in the Jebel Ali area. "Mike," I screamed, my voice rising above the noise and confusion raging around us, "look over there!" My left arm pointed toward the running figures. Mike spun around and stared in the direction I was pointing. He squinted into the acrid fog of fumes and mist and white phosphorus smoke wafting over the undulating ground in the middle distance. His blank stare remained fixed. His face registered no reaction.

I was confused, my concern growing by the second as I waited for a response. After a few moments his right hand slowly came up to the pocket in his OG shirt, undid the button and withdrew a pair of thin-rimmed spectacles. He pushed his face forward into the glasses and leaned over the parapet of the sangar as if some invisible force was drawing him toward the hottest part of the action. He carefully removed his glasses, wiped off the dust on his loosely flapping shirt-end, unhurriedly replaced them, peered into the distance once more and said slowly, "Don't open fire yet, it could be the Firks returning." His voice sounded calm, steady and deliberate amid the tumult of the moment. Still the figures on the plain swept on unhindered. They looked confident, inspired. Then their weapons came up into the fire position. A split second later, a bren-gun rattled out its deadly rhythm from the Wali's fort. A short pause followed, then the whole of the ramparts suddenly exploded into a frenzy of action.

Lofty went through a last-minute visual check. Completely satisfied that G Squadron were now prepared and fully equipped for battle, he walked swiftly toward the transport waiting to whisk them off to the airfield at RAF Salalah. As he jumped into the driver's seat of the nearest Land Rover, he could see that over by the armory the same character was still there doing his boots up. "Hey, Scouse," shouted Lofty, leaning out of the window as he eased the Land Rover down a gear and drew level with the armory steps, "you can stop doing your boots up now, it looks like we're going into combat."

"Open fire!" screamed Mike urgently above the chatter of machine-gun fire and the crackle of the old Lee Enfield .303s. The calmness in his voice had given way to ruthless urgency.

The moment that battle is joined. The moment that the days, the weeks, the months of training have all been leading up to. The moment that seems to stand still, but is only as long as the split-second pause at the end of a pendulum's swing. Only a split second, but one that holds in its brief passing a thousand thoughts, a million feelings. The moment that battle is joined. My first major battle, but my mind is drilled to precision. The steel shutter has crashed to the floor; humanity is locked outside beating its fist on the cold, hard surface. No sound, no cry of compassion can penetrate within. I am now ruthless and single-minded. It's a kind of insanity. You have to be insane to survive. It's me or him. At our level, at the sharp end, when the whistle blows, it's not politics, its not heroics or war-games, it's not the big picture of world affairs. It's me or him, it's kill or be killed, it's the quick or the dead, the law of the jungle. Over the top and into no-man's-land. Brutal, efficient killing. We don't even kill them. We take them out, we root them out, we blow them away, we pick them off, we eliminate them. We don't really kill them. It's something we block out of our minds completely. We don't even talk about it among ourselves. The enemy are not human beings. They are everything else—a threat, an attack, a movement in a rifle sight, a running, lunging, shouting, adrenaline-charged shape. But they are not human beings. You don't think of them as real people, as fathers, family men, with a picture of the wife and kids in the back pocket. You can't afford to. It's me or him. They are to be eliminated, it's as simple as that. That is my duty, my role. At this moment, my only concern is to not let my mates down. I am determined not to be a weak link. In the split second that battle is joined, we are together, we are a team, the sum is now greater than the parts. We have fire in our eyes, ice in our veins and metal in our hearts. The highly lubricated precision machine bursts into life. The moment that battle is joined.

We opened fire simultaneously, unleashing a hail of GPMG and .50-caliber bullets at the assaulting Adoo troops. The running figures become a focal point where the red tracer and exploding incendiary rounds converged in a frenzied dance. It rained fire and lead. Where moments before there had been an orderly advance, parts of the line now faltered and collapsed. Figures staggered under the impact of the heavy .50-caliber rounds, falling, twisting, screaming. We traversed the machine guns right, a burst of fire scything a lethal harvest among the exposed enemy. But still the Adoo kept coming. Wave upon wave over the plain, dull shapes advancing at speed. They were in groups of ten and well spread out. They were moving steadily, relentlessly, toward the DG fort and the town. A nightmare scene, with bodies appearing to fall and get up again like homicidal zombies, there were so many of them.

Machine guns chattered, rifles cracked, yells, curses and explosions echoed across the plain. But still the Adoo kept coming. They reached the perimeter fence and tore with bare hands and blind zeal at the vicious, razor-sharp barbed wire as if it was tinsel on a Christmas tree. A Carl Gustav rocket-launcher spat death, the rocket impacting against the fort wall and showering the immediate area with shrapnel and flame. In the gun pit, the gleaming figure of Laba applied the gun drills with slick precision, like a sweating stoker feeding a boiler in the smoky bowels of a steamship. Laba worked feverishly to load and blast the big gun at the fanatical enemy struggling through the fence only a few meters away. The twenty-five-pounder was traversed through forty-five degrees and used in the direct-fire role, dealing death at point-blank range. The breech detonations threw up clouds of cordite. A pall of acrid fumes hovered over the firing mechanism, growing bigger by the minute. Dead Adoo were soon hanging over perimeter wire like ragged crows strung out along a farmer's fence.

Back at the Batt House, Sek received an ominous message on his walkie-talkie. The strained voice of Laba informed him that a Kalashnikov round had grazed his chin. He added that otherwise he was all right, but Sek, his fellow countryman, was not convinced. He knew Laba too well—a huge man with huge courage and huge modesty; a man of few words when the going was tough. The radio then went dead and defied all Sek's attempts to reestablish communications.

In an instant, Sek had decided he must join his Fijian brother at the twenty-five-pounder. Still wearing his flip-flops, but with a pair of desert boots dangling around his neck, he grabbed his SLR and, with the sharp staccato of the Adoo Spargen MGs ringing in his ears, started his 500-meter run toward the DG fort. Even with high-velocity rounds cracking and popping around him, with explosions to the front and rear of him and with shells screeching overhead, all he heard was the roar of the crowd, the shrill scream of the whistle, all he saw was the flash of the cameras. He was back on his favorite rugby field at home in Fiji, and he was going for the greatest try of his life. He had been a top-class flank forward in his time, and long swerving runs were his specialty. Taut lines of hot tracer zipped across in front of him as he surged forward, bobbing and weaving. Two hundred meters to go. He was still going strong, the breath burning in his throat. One hundred meters to go. Bullets threw sand and dirt all around him as they hit the ground close to his feet. He swerved around the lunging tackles. Fifty meters to go. He could see the try line, nothing could stop him now, his determination was incredible. A mortar bomb burst nearby. The roar of the crowd became louder. A piece of shrapnel made him duck instinctively. He tucked in his head to avoid an outthrust hand. Ten meters to go. The try line was within reach. In a final lung-bursting sprint he ran up the last incline that led to the DG fort. He launched into the air, his body arching across the line. He was up and over the sangar wall. Miraculously, he had reached the gun pit without so much as a scratch. He had scored the try of a lifetime.

Sek steadied himself, the rasping in his throat slowly subsiding. Through a mist of perspiration, he surveyed the chaos in the gun pit. Laba was firing the gun on his own. He had looked around briefly, nodded an acknowledgment, pointed to the unopened ammunition boxes and turned back to the gun. Sek squinted through the smoke and dust at the broken ramparts of the fort. If there was any firepower left in the fort, if he could organize and motivate the DG to help out in the gun pit, it could make all the difference.

Sek carefully eased himself over the sandbagged wall of the sangar and, crouching to the lowest profile possible, sprinted across the short distance to the great doors of the fort. Grasping the large metal handle in his left hand, SLR at the ready in his right, he twisted the locking mechanism and pushed. Nothing. He swore in Fijian, and shouted at the DG. Surely they would recognize his voice—he was always up there drinking tea with them. Impatiently he cranked the mechanism again before putting the full weight of his muscular shoulders behind his next push. Still nothing. The door was solid. He cranked the mechanism a third time. Every moment he remained in this exposed position he was in mortal danger. Suddenly, he heard the heavy metallic sound of a bolt being withdrawn. The door creaked open and there, to his relief, in the small opening he recognized the dark features of the Omani gunner. Sek motioned him over.

Just then a burst of HMG fire hammered into the fort wall above Sek's head, sending small stone splinters whining viciously past his ear. He sprinted back to the cover of the gun pit. As he jumped over the side of the sangar wall, he glanced around to see the Omani, who had started to follow him, spinning around and around, pirouetting like a ballet dancer with an insane grimace on his face, then falling to the ground clutching his stomach.

The big gun continued to belch flame. It looked brave and defiant, spitting death at close range. It wasn't called the artillery machine gun for nothing—and in the hands of Laba and Sek, the Adoo must have thought it was belt-fed! They were now working as if possessed, shoveling the shells into the breech like madmen. Open breech, slam a shell in, ram it with baton, fire. Open breech, eject hot spent cartridge-case, kick it away. The same mechanical sequence repeated time after time after time. Laba, covered in sweat, the front of his clothes blackened with cordite, had no time to think. He just kept laying the sight—bubble up, line, bubble up, line. On. Fire! And still the Adoo kept coming. As one group reached the wire and was gunned down, another replaced it almost instantaneously. Wave after wave surged up behind their fallen comrades, willingly following the same fate, a relentless waterfall of human beings plunging over the precipice of life.

The heat from the red-hot breech made sweat run down

Sek's face in dirty rivulets. Open breech, slam one in, ram it, close breech. Fire! A small group close to the wire disappeared in a rain of shrapnel, smoke and dust. Open breech, slam one in, ram it, close breech. Fire! Sek was soon surrounded by piles of empty ammunition boxes and spent cartridge-cases. He searched frantically for another shell. His hand closed around a dull brass case—and in that instant he tumbled backward and sideways. The pain in his shoulder exploded into his brain as he slumped against the sangar wall. He looked toward Laba without uttering a sound. Then another round parted his thick black hair and plowed a bloody furrow through the skin on top of his skull. "Laba, I'm hit!" he shouted violently in Fijian, the whole of his upper body suffused with the pain of the 7.62-millimeter round lodged somewhere in his back, perilously close to his spinal column. Another millimeter, and his spine would have been snapped in two.

The mighty twenty-five-pounder now stood silent. Without Sek to feed the beast, the situation was desperate. The gun pit was in real danger of being overrun. Laba looked around in despair. Sek was propped against the sangar wall, his shirt soaked in blood, somehow, with a supreme effort, summoning up the strength to take well-aimed shots with his SLR at the figures near the wire. We've got to have more firepower, thought Laba. His eyes darted anxiously from left to right. He knew what he was looking for.

There it is, there's the firepower we need, he thought triumphantly. He began to crawl through the piles of spent shell-cases toward a 60-millimeter mortar leaning upright against the sandbagged wall of the gun pit. The sweat ran down his face, stinging the wound on his chin. The noise of Sek's SLR made him flinch momentarily and then he was moving again, oblivious of the hot brass cases burning his hands and lower arms. A Titan figure, seemingly immortal, he was now dangerously beyond the cover of the twenty-five-pounder's bullet-riddled armored shield. He stood up and reached out for the mortar. Bullets whistled all around him. He seemed driven by a superhuman energy, possessed by a single-minded duty to fight his fight, to stand by his comrades. Above the din of battle he could just make out Sek's voice shouting in Fijian, "Get your head down, get your head down!"

Laba didn't hear the bullet that killed him. His only sensation must have been an intense burning pain in his neck, as though someone had stabbed a red-hot needle through his jugular. And then he was falling through the darkness, lost forever. The mighty Fijian warrior had breathed his last. Sek was on his own.

"I don't like it. It's gone too quiet. Something's happened over at the fort. If the gun position goes we've got big problems. I need a volunteer, someone to watch my back. I must find out what the situation is over there." Mike Kealy's terse request cut through the tense atmosphere in the radio room. Gone were the boyish features of the young, inexperienced troop officer. His face now had a grim, gray-edged, hard-bitten look about it that none of us had seen before. We were standing before him in a half-circle, Bob in the center, me to the right, and Tommy, his stocky frame resting casually on the SLR propped up by his side, to the left. I had just finished keying out the 316 radio to Um al Gwarif requesting an air strike and a casevac chopper, and I now joined the other two in agreeing that we should all share the risk. This was the ultimate Chinese parliament. We argued our case vehemently, but Mike's mind was made up. He would take only one man, the Batt House medic, Tommy, who could give medical assistance to any casualties we had taken at the gun pit. Mike reasoned that Bob would be required to take over command of the Batt House and control the air strike, and I was needed to give covering fire on the .50-caliber and also to man the radio set.

Disappointment and feelings of guilt swept over me as I removed my belt kit. Why had I not been chosen to go with Mike? Was I not good enough, not experienced enough? I desperately wanted to get over to Laba and Sek. In a short space of time I had grown to like the two Fijians enormously. I felt a bond with them as if they were my own brothers, in spite of the obvious cultural differences. I admired their great courage, their fortitude and stamina, their laconic understatement in the face of real danger.

I swept aside the negative thoughts worming through my brain and considered the worsening situation. I looked down at the luminous face of my watch: it was just 0700 hours. A short time ago we had heard high-velocity gunfire passing over our heads from the south of Mirbat town. That could mean only one thing—a coordinated attack from the north and the south. We were surrounded. It was shit or bust now. Once more, I sat down at the radio table and repeated the request for Startrek on the 316. The jets were really going to be at a premium now, if only the wretched monsoon mists and low cloud would lift.

Unexpectedly, we gained a temporary respite when a strange lull descended on the battlefield. The Adoo assault troops had faltered and fallen back into the shallow wadis that interlaced the plain leading up to the fort. The heavy concentration of automatic fire they had earlier employed had emptied their magazines, and in the excitement and desperation of the assault, some had forgotten to carry out their magazine changes. Others had had no time to reload from the bandoleers of ammunition they carried across their chests. The firing had become spasmodic; only the mortars kept up their relentless bombardment. More ominously, though, there was a lack of return fire from the twenty-five-pounder and the DG fort. Bob and I tried to raise them on the walkie-talkie several times, but it remained silent. Maybe they had discarded the walkie-talkie in the heat of the moment. Maybe their set had been blasted apart by a bullet. Maybe Sek and Laba were taking advantage of the temporary lull to replenish their ammunition from unopened ammunition boxes. Or perhaps the silence was more sinister.

"And don't forget to change into your desert boots." Bob's parting words to Mike as he left the radio room for the roof interrupted my increasingly busy train of thought. I looked across the room at the two figures preparing themselves for the mercy dash to the fort. Mike had retrieved his dusty desert boots from under his camp bed against the far wall, and was kneeling down pulling very tightly on the laces. Tommy stood patiently watching Mike, steeling himself. He had a calm, totally committed look on his face. All his doubts, his fears, his private thoughts had retreated far within. Between his index finger and thumb he held the cocking handle of his SLR. He eased the breech-block back slightly to confirm that he had chambered a round. He fingered his belt kit and the patrol medical pack slung across his back.

Just then a long burst of machine-gun fire from the GPMG on the roof above us shook the room violently, adding renewed urgency to the situation. "OK Tommy, it's time to go," said Mike quietly. They were through the door and gone without another word.

Racing back up to the .50-caliber Browning, I noticed Roger disappearing down the steps to the front door. He must be going to the beach to receive the casevac chopper, I thought, as I flipped the safety-catch on the machine gun to "fire." My mind settled on the task in hand. It was my job to give covering fire. The palms of my hands began to sweat. For the next few minutes the lives of two of my comrades rested on my shoulders. I prayed I would be switched on enough to carry the burden. I watched intently as Mike and Tommy began edging their way past the mortar pit. Once around it, they sprinted for a shallow wadi about ninety meters over on the right. The wadi ran roughly in the direction of the fort and would afford some cover from the machine guns outside the perimeter wire. Bullets were still zipping by. They came in flurries, but the fire lacked intensity and direction. So far, the Adoo had not noticed Mike and Tommy. I held my fire. I did not want to draw attention to the two running figures. I felt the belt of incendiary resting easily in my left hand. I feathered the cold metal of the trigger with the index finger of my right hand. I watched nervously as the two figures worked their

117

way toward the fort, moving in short rushes, ten or fifteen meters at a time, pepper-potting forward, one man running, one man covering. So far so good. Their luck was holding. My grip on the ammunition belt became tighter.

They had gone about halfway to the gun pit when the whole battlefield erupted. The Adoo had spotted them. Where minutes before the firing had been spasmodic and half-hearted, there was now a delirium of noise: the crack of rifles, the rattle of machine guns, the crump of detonating mortar bombs. A heavy machine gun barked over to the east of the fort, the taut lines of tracer zipping across the path of the two moving figures. Like a dragon belching flames of fire, the gun spat hot tracer closer and closer to its prey.

I had to act quickly and decisively. There wasn't a moment to lose. I lined up the sights of the .50-caliber on the tongues of flame sparking from the flash-eliminator of the Adoo machine gun. My breathing got quicker, short, sharp and controlled. The skin on my forehead tightened. The pressure of concentration felt like a thumb-press on my third eye. I took careful aim and squeezed the trigger. The gun jerked and ejaculated its seeds of destruction, and I watched with professional satisfaction as the Adoo machine gun disappeared under a stream of red tracer and exploding incendiary rounds. My body relaxed with relief. There would be no more trouble from that quarter.

The inferno of fire raged on. The two figures were surging onward in short rushes across the bullet-swept plain. The closer they got to the gun pit, the faster they ran. Onward, onward. Stop, cover, rush. Stop, cover, rush. The bullets hissed and spat around them; the breath rasped in their windpipes and burned their lungs. They ran faster than they had ever run in their whole lives, their limbs pumping like pistons in full-throttle combustion engines. Then Tommy was up the slope to the fort and vaulting the sandbagged wall into the sangar, with Mike hot on his heels.

A quick look at the chaos in the gun pit told Mike that there was more advantage to be gained by making for the ammunition bunker a few feet to the right. As he jumped down into the bunker bottom, he felt something soft and fleshy under his desert boots. He glanced down. To his horror he realized he was standing on the mangled body of a DG soldier, his foot squelching in the bloody peach-pulp of guts where the stomach used to be. He shrank back in disgust as if he had just turned back the sheets on a lover's bed and found a rotting corpse crawling with maggots. A movement caught his eye. Squinting through the smoke and dust that hung in the air dirtying the lenses of his glasses, he discovered he had company. Wide-eyed, trembling and half paralyzed by fear, a DG soldier cowered in the far corner of the bunker like a snared rabbit. The Omani was shaking in every limb. "Pull yourself together and move the body," snapped Mike as he stared across at the gun pit, already assessing the situation.

The battle reached a crescendo, the air thick with splinters of steel and lead. A hurricane of fire whirled and roared across Mirbat plain. Flash followed flash followed flash, as bright as the flares from an arc welder's torch. Before one explosion of light had traveled down the optic nerve and burned itself on to the brain, another followed in instant succession, creating a stroboscopic display of agonizing intensity. Sek, totally resigned, his face misshapen with pain, was still propped against the sangar wall, his SLR still hurling hot lead. A short, stocky guerrilla straddled the perimeter wire, his snarling mouth hollering and gesturing toward the fort. The silver whistle around his neck made an excellent aiming marker. Sek's rifle kicked. With a scream of pain, the man slumped across the wire, lifeless as an old rag, still holding his AK 47 in the grip of death.

The twenty-five-pounder, though silent, was still under concentrated fire. The hail of bullets sparked and ricocheted off the barrel and armored shield as if the gun had just been cast in a foundry and was being smoothed off by heavy-duty abrasion wheels. Tommy was crouched attending to the body of Laba. He straightened slightly and half turned toward the medical pack. It was his last, fatal movement. If the medical pack had been an inch nearer, or if it had been

119

lying to his right instead of his left, or if he'd checked Laba's wounds for a split second longer, his head would not have crossed the path of the murderous Kalashnikov round spinning its way faster than the speed of sound. A casual stoop saved de Gaulle from the assassin's bullet. Tommy was not so lucky. His time had come. He tumbled forward, scattering the spent shell-cases, and then lay motionless.

Screams of agony filled the air. The swishing roar of a Carl Gustav rocket arching over the position deafened Mike and Sek. Then the Adoo broke through the wire, a ragged line of desperate, yelling figures, their faces distorted with hate. They dashed in ones and twos, all notion of formation now cast aside, toward the cover of the north wall of the fort and the dead ground to the rear. Sek's rifle kicked twice in quick succession. A figure fell twitching to the ground. Like crabs on a beach scrambling for a dead fish, the Adoo worked their way around the fort walls, hungry for possession of the big gun. No words were exchanged between Mike and Sek. Each man knew instinctively what he had to do. On either side of the fort, Kalashnikovs disgorged death. And still the Adoo kept coming. The most courageous among them were now only six or seven meters away at the two front corners of the fort wall. Mike and Sek were looking death in the face.

Halfway to Salalah, and Lofty Wiseman, sensing a big battle in the air, was driving like a man possessed. He careered the Land Rover over the rough desert track pitted with potholes. The men in the rear cursed in full technicolor with every crash and jolt. Clutching in one hand the twisting steering wheel like a Wild West rancher gripping the saddle on an unbroken horse, Lofty bent down and felt between his feet for the three cardboard boxes that were sliding around the floor in rhythm with the madly lurching vehicle. With his head level with the dashboard, he alternated his gaze rapidly between the road and the boxes as his fingers pulled back the tape that secured the contents. He flipped open the lid on the first box and his hand dived in like a mechanical grab in a fairground booth. Straightening up, he passed the first handful of morphine syrettes over his shoulder as though he were giving Smarties to impatient kids. "Here you are, lads, grab these syrettes." Another handful found their way into the back of the vehicle. "More morphine, straight into the upper thigh—instant nirvana."

The patrol in the back scrambled for the syrettes and stuffed them into every available empty pouch they could find.

Mike and Sek picked off the swarming Adoo as fast as they could double tap. A fusillade of LMG fire ripped into the ground just in front of the ammunition bunker. A round cracked so close to Mike's skull he could feel the vibration of the bullet as it sped over him. Then came the green pineapple. It sailed gracefully through the air and landed smoking on the parapet of the bunker. As Mike ducked down in the confined space, the grenade exploded. An agonizing ringing drummed in his ears, and the acrid smoke of detonation ripped through his lungs. Miraculously, he was uninjured. He eased himself back upright, trembling slightly. Through the smoke and confusion he could just make out the pathetic figure of a DG soldier. You're no bloody good to me groveling down there, he thought. He did a quick magazine change and threw the empty magazines at the frightened man. "Fill those!" he barked, kicking the cringing soldier violently on the soles of his boots. And then he was up and firing again.

He squeezed the trigger twice, as near simultaneously as is mechanically and humanly possible, and caught the guerrilla at the corner of the fort wall full in the face. Blood, brain and hair exploded in a crazy stain across the whitewashed wall. The guerrilla slumped to the ground, arms spreadeagled by the shock, with the remains of his head sliding down the wall after him. Then came a salvo of grenades. They arched over toward Mike and Sek like clay pigeons; several exploded nearby with a dull crump. More grenades—and then Mike froze in horror, his mind switched into a slow-motion nightmare. A grenade hit the parapet at the far end of the ammo bunker and, after what seemed like an age, rolled over the edge. Mike could clearly see the black smoke from the six-second safety-fuse as it burned its way toward the detonator. He watched, mesmerized, unable to move as the smoke curled upward. One . . . two . . . three. He counted the seconds, each one booming in his head like a chime from Big Ben. Four . . . five . . . six. He steeled himself for the impact of the explosion that would do to his body what his bullets had just done to the head of the guerrilla by the fort wall. Seven . . . eight . . . nine. He prized open his rigid eyelids. The smoke fizzled out. Ten . . . eleven . . . twelve . . .

Mike stared in disbelief at the matt green object that should have been the last thing he saw on this earth. It was a misfire, a damp squib. He thanked God in the briefest manner possible and searched the immediate area for the next target, more determined than ever to defeat the Adoo now that he had survived the hand grenade. Cursing aloud, he took a bead on the camouflaged figure at the corner of the fort, squeezed the trigger, saw the figure fall and reached for the two-way radio.

"Laba's dead, Sek and Tommy are very seriously injured." The sound of Mike Kealy's voice on the walkie-talkie cracked the atmosphere in the command-post sangar like obscenities mouthed in the middle of a hushed church service.

I was stunned. I couldn't believe it. Laba! Dead! The din of the battle receded like surf on a distant shore, and my eyes seemed to go out of focus. The next thing I knew, I was reexperiencing my grandfather's death, the first time I'd lost someone close. A wave of desolation, loneliness and separation had engulfed me then. I had hardly been able to believe that this warm-hearted, laughing, noisy man was now stretched out cold, stiff and lifeless in his grave; the same man whose morning ritual I used to watch with unending awe. He would pour boiling water straight from the kettle into his shaving mug, and then, with a flourish designed to impress me even more, he would plunge his disheveled shaving brush into the scalding water. After a quick wipe around the stunted remains of a stick of hard shaving soap, he would jut out his jaw, open his mouth and with a half-smile, half-grimace apply the dripping brush to his chin with rapid circular movements. I would always wince at this point, feeling sure that the boiling water must hurt terribly, secretly hoping I wouldn't grow up to be a man for a very long time yet if that was what grown men had to do.

"Get on the set and call for reinforcements." Bob turned and looked at me, his face still amazingly calm, his voice quiet and steady. I was back in my first major battle, well and truly bloodied, my initiation into manhood brutally complete.

Without a word, my resolve stiffened to ruthlessness by the news of Laba's death, I pushed the safety catch on the .50-calibre to "safe" and raced down the steps to the radio room. I began hammering the key, picking out the message in clear, precise Morse. "Zero Alpha. Zero Alpha. This is 82. Message. Over."

"82. This is Zero Alpha. Send. Over."

"Zero Alpha. This is 82. Laba dead. Sekonia VSI. Tobin VSI. Situation desperate. Send reinforcements. Over."

There was a brief pause, and then the reply boomed in my ear. "82. This is Zero Alpha. Roger your last. Send wet rep. Over."

"Wet rep!" I shouted aloud in great exasperation to no one in particular. A weather report at this stage of the game! My mind was so filled with the exigencies and emotions of the moment that I didn't realize the implications of this request from base. I jumped up quickly, jarring the radio table with my knee and sending the chair teetering across the floor. I poked my head out of the door. Cloud base must be about 150 feet, and the flags were limp on the flagpoles. That would do. "0815 hours. Heavy cloud. No wind." I hammered out the wet rep, waited impatiently for confirmation, then sprinted back to my position in the command post.

As I brushed past Bob to get at the .50-caliber, the high-pitched roar of a jet's after-burners filled my ears. Two Strikemaster jets broke into view through the mass of sullen cloud and monsoon mist. The speed at which they appeared meant that they must have been in a holding pattern circling immediately above the battlefield. The jets streaked over the town and raced eighty feet above the plain, contour-flying on a low-level ground-attack mission. The bravery of the pilots in these weather conditions and in the face of sustained fire from the Adoo was awesome and impressive.

"Who's controlling them?" shouted Bob urgently.

"Must be Roger," I screamed in reply above the noise of the howling jet engines. "He thought another casevac chopper was arriving and took the blue sarbe to direct it on to the beach helipad. He must be controlling the jets with it." I broke off as the ammunition-box pyramid behind me rattled violently. I spun around to see the sweating face of Roger appearing over the lip of the sandbagged wall.

"The seventh cavalry has arrived!" he shouted triumphantly. "Here's the sarbe; I'm going to help with the wounded on the ground floor." And with that he was gone again.

Bob grabbed the ground-to-air radio and settled down to control the jet strike. "Hello, Red Leader. This is Batt House. Enemy left and right of the fort. Over."

"Roger, Batt House. How long have they been going at you?"

"Since dawn," Bob informed him.

The pilot gave away no sign of reaction to the feats of resistance taking place below him. "Roger, Batt House. They are like ants down there—I can see hundreds of them."

The jets began wheeling and swooping like hungry gannets searching for prey. The enemy now ceased firing on the fort and the town and, throwing themselves behind the nearest cover, concentrated the firepower of their light machine guns on the flashing jets. Hot green tracer flurried upward in a blizzard of burning steel across the sky. The first jet went into a vertical dive, spraying bullets and death around the perimeter wire to the left. The second jet, amidst a barrage of machine-gun fire, stabbed two rockets into the wadi to the right. The wing-tips of the aircraft seemed to brush the walls of the DG fort as they sped past. And then they pulled up violently, twisting and dodging, stretched to the limits of their capabilities, to escape back into the mist. Moments later they reappeared, plunging out of the cloud over Mirbat Bay. They streaked around the contours of Jebel Ali, with lines of HMG tracer in hot pursuit and closing. Then they headed low level back into the maelstrom to start their strafing run over again.

All along the wire, rockets and lead cascaded from the sky. The Strikemasters tracked each other. More bullets, more rockets, and then the jet on the right spawned a 500-kilogram bomb. The large black object plummeted earthward and buried itself among the enemy massing in a shallow wadi just east of the fort. The smoke-filled air was rent asunder by a blinding flash and a thunderous explosion. But disaster followed triumph. One of the jets caught a burst of HMG fire in the tail as it made an impossibly low pass at the enemy. It banked steeply and then, subdued as if ashamed of the jagged hole in its tail section, it drifted away to the north, limping into the cover of the mist. The remaining jet circled for a while, then swooped downward in one last steep dive, hammering the Adoo along the perimeter wire. Finally, its ordnance totally expended, it followed its partner into the clouds on its way back to Salalah.

The pressure on the fort area had been momentarily relieved, but for how long? At this point a new and disturbing dimension crept into the battle. Heavy firing could be heard behind us, well over to the east. Scarcely able to withstand the enemy frontal assault, our nerves began to pulsate at crisis level with the realization that the Adoo had

regrouped and were counterattacking from the east. That
meant only one thing: not only had our air support gone, but
we were now completely surrounded.

The pilot of the Huey 205 chopper with G Squadron
reinforcements on board just glimpsed the rear half of the
first Strikemaster jet being swallowed up in the mist as he
flew the 205 on a ground-assault mission, heading for the
south side of the town. Crammed into the confined space
behind him were Doug, Scouse, Ian, Dave, Dennis, Neil,
Ian, Eric and Stonker. They carried with them a formidable
array of weaponry: five GPMGs plus at least 1,000 rounds
per gun; an M 79 plus 100 bombs; and SLRs with 100
rounds of 7.62-millimeter per man. As they broke through
the mist, Doug looked through the window and saw five
heavily armed Adoo dragging a body. On seeing the chopper, they quickly abandoned the body. Hell, Doug thought,
they're going to open up on the chopper! "Adoo! Adoo!" He
grabbed the pilot's shoulder, shook him and screamed in his
ear to make himself heard above the racket of the rotor
blades, emphasizing his words with a pointed finger jabbing
down at the figures on the ground. To his surprise, as the
chopper banked and came down, the Adoo disappeared into
the mist.

Once on the ground, the fighting patrol rapidly went into
all-round defense 3,500 yards from the town to secure the
LZ for the arrival of Alistair Morrison, the Squadron
Commander—who would later make a name for himself at
Mogadishu—and Wilbur Watson, the Troop Corporal.
Minutes later they arrived in the second chopper, bristling with firepower and carrying 10,000 rounds of backup
ammunition for the gimpies. With G Squadron reinforcements fully deployed, twenty-four men in all, Alistair as-
sessed the situation and made an instant decision.
Allocating one group to secure the LZ for the second wave of
reinforcements, he directed Stonker and Doug's group to
move toward the east of the town to flank the fort and
winkle out pockets of enemy resistance on the way. Just as

they were moving off, four figures appeared out of the mist, calmly looked in their direction and walked over a rise no more than seventy meters away. Ian squinted at them through the powerful binoculars and shouted, "They're Adoo, they're Adoo! They've got AK 47s!" They ran forward tactically to the top of the rise, engaged the four figures—who by now were running furiously in the direction of the Jebel—and downed them in a hail of machine-gun fire. The exchange attracted the attention of other Adoo east of Mirbat. Stonker and Doug's group now came under sustained fire.

The walkie-talkie crackled into life and cut through our anxious thoughts. It was Mike again. For one trembling moment I thought it was more bad news. With relief I learned that Mike and Sek were still clinging on to their position by the fort. Mike was requesting mortar fire support. In calm, measured tones he asked Bob to put down a ranging bomb in the wadi, seventy-five meters to the right, and then he would make corrections. Bob did his mental arithmetic—a quick estimation of range and charge. He gave a long, low whistle. This was going to be tricky. He would have to do a line-of-sight shoot based on estimated range, charge and elevation. Bob shouted his first fire mission to Fuzz, who by now was firing the mortar on his own. He watched anxiously as Fuzz pulled the bipod legs backward, set the mortar at an extreme angle, bubbled up the sight and slid an HE bomb down the barrel. I watched the performance with growing frustration and alarm. The .50-calibre was causing big problems. I was down to single shots, and after each one I had to recock the firing mechanism myself. The breech-block and slide had become clogged with brass shavings, the result of firing the gun over a long period without a number two to feed the heavy belt.

Fuzz's mortar bomb whooshed over the plain in a blurred crescent and exploded harmlessly 800 meters away on the far side of the fort. Mike's correction crackled over the air and Bob relayed his estimated fire mission to Fuzz. Each correction after that brought the exploding mortar bombs closer and closer until Fuzz reached maximum elevation on the bipod. At the next correction from Bob, Fuzz hesitated for a moment, glanced at Bob as if he'd asked him to summon a heavenly army of angels from the clouds and then, with one determined movement, clasped the mortar barrel to his chest and raised it until the bipod legs dangled clear of the ground. "Frag them," roared Bob. Fuzz looked like some demonic dancer in a drunken two-step as he hugged the barrel as tightly as he could and sent bomb after bomb spilling down on the enemy position.

The welcome drone of aircraft engines filled our ears again. Two more Strikemasters pounced down out of the clouds in a shallow dive across Mirbat Bay. They banked, leveled off to obtain greater accuracy and, hugging the contours, screeched across in front of us at the start of their strafing run.

Bob clicked on the blue sarbe. "Hello, Red Leader. This is Batt House. Enemy HMG on Jebel Ali. Also rear of fort."

"Roger, Batt House. It looks hot down there."

"Roger, Red Leader. Sheets of lead! Sheets of lead!"

The two jets split in a scissorlike maneuver. The first one, in a low pass, went for the fort. The second banked round steeply, plunged like an out-of-control kite, leveled off at the last moment and streaked toward the HMG positions on Jebel Ali, going for a gun kill with its two wing-mounted GPMGs. Death and destruction sluiced down from the skies. The sangars on top of the hill disappeared in a hail of red tracer. The Strikemaster screamed past Jebel Ali and out across the bay. After banking around lazily like a condor on hot thermals it began its next run in, fifty feet above the water, this time going for a rocket kill. It roared over the top of Jebel Ali sticking rockets into the circular sangars like darts in a dartboard. The top of the hill disintegrated in a huge ball of flame. As the jet disappeared back into the clouds, surging masses of black smoke climbed up into the mist like a huge organic lichen, then began to drift as the force of the upper-air breeze overcame the impetus of the explosion. The two Strikemasters returned for one final low pass, fifty feet above the perimeter wire, just to one side of the fort. Smoke and flame belched from their wings, and rockets and tracer rained down on the now retreating enemy. The high-pitched jet whine deafened the occupants of the fort as the two aircraft shrieked overhead in a spectacular display of firepower. Then they pulled upward, climbing steeply through the mist until they were both swallowed up by the heavy monsoon clouds.

The second wave of 205 helicopters, carrying the other ten G Squadron men, a doctor, two medical orderlies and a mound of ammunition, hovered down on to the LZ like giant sycamore seeds. It was 1020 hours. Alistair Morrison decided he and his group could now move forward to clear the enemy from the south of the town. They closed on three Adoo and a GPMG concealed in rocks on the beach. After a brief exchange, the enemy were killed. Five more Adoo were spotted in a wadi behind a ridge. Alistair's group advanced to within 200 yards. Three of the five were gunned down and two wounded. A third party of Adoo opened fire from another clump of rocks. All six died. As with the others, their bodies were searched and their weapons removed. Many more enemy still remained between Alistair and the town. The group pushed forward with fire suppression and flanking attacks, capturing a small hill on the way. More Adoo fell. Two RPGs and a number of rockets were recovered. A helicopter, flying tactically, brought over a platoon of the Northern Frontier Regiment to join Alistair's group. Then, as one body, they moved in disciplined formation toward the Batt House.

As I watched the two Strikemasters race away into the distance, my tired, bloodshot eyes were drawn to the landscape east of the fort about 2,000 meters away. I could see figures appearing on the skyline. They looked a disciplined and determined body of men as they surged forward at a brisk pace, methodically working their way across the undulating ground in extended-line formation. Now that the frontal onslaught of the Adoo had been broken by the jet strikes, a tiny voice inside me reasoned that we had just a chance of surviving if this new threat from our rear could be overcome. Mechanically, my body reduced by fatigue to functioning only as a well-programmed automaton, I lined up the front sight blade of the .50-caliber on the lead figure. I might be down to single shots, but that was all I would need to take the officer out. Who were they? I wondered. At this range it was impossible to tell. They appeared merely as black dots in an expanse of dull brown sand and rock.

Around the fort and Jebel Ali area the cacophony of battle had decreased significantly. Only the occasional burst of machine-gun fire cracked over the Batt House. All our attention could now be focused on the new developments in the east. I looked at Bob. He was switched on to the same direction. He seemed to be agonizing over a decision.

At a signal, the figures suddenly swung off to the right flank and disappeared into the shallow wadis on the far side of the town. Heavy firing in the area erupted almost immediately.

"Go down to the radio and get a sit rep from base. Find out what's happened to the reinforcements," shouted Bob suddenly, his voice taking on a new urgency.

A few moments later, the Morse crackled over the headset. The message was music to my ears. I hardly dared believe it. My mind struggled to prevent wishful thinking from overtaking cold logic. I looked at my watch: it was just 1030 hours. I did a quick time appreciation, fearful that my initial calculations might prove wrong. Twenty minutes by chopper from RAF Salalah to Mirbat, five minutes to shake out on the ground. It was like finding the last piece to a puzzle. Surely I was right. My conclusion fitted the facts perfectly. The figures on the skyline must be the second wave of G Squadron reinforcements. I was now convinced of it. Even though I was exhausted and seemingly drained of all emotion, a warm surge of exhilaration swept up from deep inside me. I was jubilant as I raced up the sangar steps with the good news.

Bob's face remained as cool and impassive as ever as I relayed the contents of the message. "I guessed as much," he said quietly, then added, totally professional to the end, "I've sent Fuzz up to the gun pit with the other medical pack to assist with the wounded. I don't think we need the mortar any more." With that he grabbed his SLR and, leaning on the parapet of the sangar, began sniping at the retreating Adoo. Following his example, I cocked the .50-caliber, cursing the stoppage, chambered a round and searched the perimeter wire for a target.

Across the battlefield the orgy of violence and killing had diminished. The Adoo were in full retreat, shoulders bowed with the humiliation of defeat. They slunk away in ones and twos across the shallow wadis of the plain, heading toward the ignominious safety of the mist-shrouded Jebel. The sad, quiet debris of battle lay everywhere: abandoned weapons, clothing and webbing, the dead and the dying. It was a forlorn and desolate scene.

Dark thoughts began to drift through my mind as we continued to snipe at the occasional exposed guerrilla. How could all this have happened? Why had we not been warned? The green slime had received grade A reports that groups of Adoo had been seen massing in various parts of the Jebel over the last few weeks, many of the reports coming from our own local Firqat. Perhaps they had chosen to ignore them. My critical ruminations were interrupted by the heavy thudding noise of a helicopter's rotor blades. A Huey had landed minutes before in the area of the twenty-five-pounder gun pit, and now it hugged the contours of the plain as it made its way across to the Batt House. The chopper went into a hover as it flew level with the main door of the house. Then, amid swirling clouds of dust and sand, it landed fifty feet away from the side of the building.

"Go down and help Roger with the casevac." I could only just hear Bob's voice above the noise of the helicopter blades. I scrambled my way quickly down the two flights of stairs to the ground floor. As I got to the bottom and began making my way to the front door, I thought that I had stumbled into an abattoir refuse-room. The whole area was covered with wounded men, either lying down or propped up against the walls. The floor was littered with blood-stained shell dressings. The stench of blood, sweat and urine was everywhere. Clusters of flies buzzed frenziedly around, feeding greedily on open wounds and bits of flesh and bone. Roger knelt trying to force a drip into the trembling arm of a man with a gaping hole in his throat. The man's rapid breathing made a terrible whistling and bubbling noise.

I looked past Roger and through the front door. The pilot of the casevac chopper had his arm out of the cockpit window and was beckoning me toward him. The rotor blades thudded above my head as, doubled up, I ran quickly toward the cockpit and stuck my ear into the open space of the window. It was a struggle to make sense of the pilot's words through the noise, like trying to have a conversation with a loom-operator in a clatter-filled weaving shed. "Go and check the bodies in the rear!" he shouted slowly and deliberately, his face an inch from my ear. "Confirm to the loadmaster which body belongs to Batt."

I didn't relish the task. Moving carefully along the side of the Huey, I came to the passenger compartment. The sliding door was already open and the loadmaster was kneeling. He nodded grimly at the recumbent shapes in the back and said nothing. There were six bodies covered by blankets on the stretcher racks. This wasn't going to be easy.

I started with the three racks to the rear. Bending down, I pulled the blanket off the body on the bottom stretcher. The man looked as if he had been hit by a large piece of shrapnel. One ear had been ripped away, and the side of his head was caved in. But his facial features were intact. I recognized the typical hook nose of the Gulf Arab. I covered him quickly with a blanket and moved on.

The body on the stretcher in the middle was also an Arab. He looked about seventeen. His head was uninjured and his eyes stared back at me with a glassy expression. A cold shiver ran up my spine and I threw the blanket back over the staring eyes. Give me combat any time, I thought as I stood up to look at the top stretcher.

I peeled the blanket back nervously, wondering what horror this one concealed. The man lay facedown, his right arm crooked upward, his forehead resting on his wrist. The face was obscured. I swallowed hard and grabbed the arm. To my horror it felt solid. The flesh was as cold and rigid as the barrel of a GPMG. The hair prickled on the back of my neck. I paused a moment and tightened my resolve. Then, with both hands gripping the elbow, I levered the whole body upward and over. I was sledge-hammered by the shock. I stared at the face. Even with part of the chin shot away and with sweat, blood and grime matted down one side, I would recognize those dark, contoured features anywhere. It was Laba!

I finished checking the other three bodies as quickly as I could and scrambled out to suck in some fresh air. It was now 1230 hours. I had been on the go for seven hours solid. With the sharp taste of bile still in my mouth and the stench of death in my nostrils, I stared out over the plain of Mirbat, smoldering and broken like a fire-ravaged pine forest. I watched a column of gray smoke slowly rising from beyond the fort, unsure whether I was glad to be alive or not. It was a day I would never forget, a carnival of carnage; a lifetime of experience crushed down into a few hours. I stared out over the flat expanse of Mirbat plain.

10

Belfast

The night sea was waveless but full of motion, crawling and glinting like a swarm of bluebottles on a cowpat. Faintly flashing lights gathered around the harbor, a handful of frozen sparks kindling brighter as we drew nearer. A depressingly heavy rain slanted through the sky and hissed on to the ferry foredeck. 1976. What a start to the New Year! It was enough to make even the most resolute of resolutions slide into the sewers with the next pint of beer or evaporate into thin air with the next cigarette.

I looked out over the dark water that separated us from the port. In my mind's eye, all I could see was the flat, smoldering expanse of Mirbat plain. The battle of Mirbat was a hard act to follow. Had it really been four years ago? I felt dull. After the adrenaline high of Dhofar, the monotony of routine training and tours of duty was beginning to take its toll. Maybe, just maybe, this trip would prove to be a breakthrough back into real action. We didn't expect to come face to face with the enemy in open battle; we were too tightly bound by the restrictions. And yet, here, anything could happen.

Belfast. The home of barricades, bombs and marching bands. The graveyard of the professional soldier's ambitions, the career charnel house of the military intelligence officer. We were heading into the gutters and backstreets, bowed under the weight of bergens loaded to overflowing with Whitehall edicts and the Ten Commandment Rules of Engagement. We were to face an opposition unfettered by constitutional laws and diplomatic niceties. It seemed we were completely pinioned, like men buried to the neck in sand, watching the rising tide of political confusion, intelligence confusion, military confusion and legal confusion. Belfast! A nervous breakdown just waiting to happen.

To most of us the answer was simple. All you had to do was take out the ringleaders and the rest would fold like a pack of cards, putting the revolution back twenty or thirty years. The Head Shed could not see this, and kept banging on about the democratic society and working within the law of the land. I began to have a sneaky suspicion they could smell easy medals, but I couldn't prove it. One thing I did know: with its sinister streets and alienated population, Belfast was no place for highly trained special forces. This was a job for armed police—switched-on operators who knew the law and could pick their way through the minefield of rules and regulations.

We hadn't got off to a good start. When we passed under the red-and-white-striped security barrier at the main gate to Bradbury Lines on our way to the ferry terminal at Liverpool, Laura Marsden, the freelance journalist, was camped in her usual position a few yards from the main gate on the pavement outside the perimeter wire, a bitch awaiting tidbits at its master's table. It was a public highway; we were powerless to move her on. As our minibus driver swung the vehicle left into Putson estate, Laura looked up briefly from her *Playgirl* magazine, then grabbed frantically for pencil and paper. She was still scribbling away as we turned left into Web Tree Avenue. She was sure to be in the pubs downtown that night harvesting the rumors and stacking up the speculations, plying her fifth-column contacts with free drinks to loosen their tongues, using her nubile charms to elicit whatever grains of information were available until she had worked up a credible, if inaccurate, story. God only knew what she would make of our sudden departure. Absolute secrecy would be the key to our very survival, let alone our success. And the political stakes were sky high.

Things got worse. By the time we arrived at the departure lounge of the ferry terminal, a late-night hush had descended all around. The lounge consisted of two linked rooms. The one further from the door—the larger of the two—was completely deserted. Dimly illuminated, faded holiday-resort posters peeling from the walls failed miserably to cheer it up. In the corner of the smaller room by the entrance, a young couple in their early twenties huddled together. The woman was half asleep, her head lolling on the man's shoulder. He was more awake, alert and suspicious. They were both snuggled deep into long black winter coats reaching down to the floor where their bags lay gathered around their feet.

We split into ones and twos and drifted into the corners, trying not to appear too conspicuous. Easier said than done—we didn't exactly look like holidaymakers. Even though we had dressed down in our Oxfam reject specials to give the impression of itinerant building-site workers or casual hotel kitchen staff, and even though we assumed a nonchalant, bored air as if to say we'd made the journey so many times that we could afford to relax into indifference, it was hard to remain unnoticed. We studiously avoided all conversation, other than the occasional whispered remark, in order not to fill the rooms with telltale English accents. But in spite of all the obvious precautions it was extremely difficult for a team of highly alert men who had spent weeks and months as a family, eating, sleeping, drinking and training together, to melt unobserved and unobserving into the background. We tried hard not to let the bond, the group consciousness that mates in a team create automatically, project and spill over into the confined space of the departure lounge.

Suddenly the door at the end of the room rattled open and in trudged a soldier dressed in full combat gear. I recognized him immediately. A year earlier he had been attached to the regiment as part of the administrative support team, and six months ago he had been posted back to his parent unit. He must have been returning from leave to rejoin his regiment in Northern Ireland. He took one look around the room, his eyes twitching with recognition, and promptly darted into the toilets. Christ, I thought, this will be all around the NAAFI in Palace Barracks, Holywood by tomorrow night— our cover blown and we haven't even set foot in Northern Ireland yet!

The crossing brought a further twist of complications. We'd all assumed false names and adopted new regiments for the duration of our passage. One of the lads had a passion for painting wild flowers. In between operations in the more exotic locations, he would often search out an especially rare specimen, display it in a beer bottle and do a quick pencil sketch to take back home with him. He had chosen the suitably horticultural pseudonym Orchid and completed his disguise by promoting himself to sergeant. Unfortunately, he'd decided to attach himself to the Royal Tank Regiment. Halfway across the Irish Sea, as fate would have it, a major from the Royal Tank Regiment decided to check the passenger list. He spotted the name Sergeant Orchid and put in a request for a meeting over the ship's tannoy system.

"Sergeant Orchid, Sergeant Orchid, Royal Tank Regiment. Report immediately to Major Jones in the Bursar's office." The tannoy boomed through the night air above the hissing sound of the bow-split waves rushing down the sides of the ship. We were in the bar, riveted to our seats. No one dared move. One or two looked up and glanced at the others, saw their impervious, stony expressions and quickly lowered their gaze once more. Sergeant Orchid swallowed a mouthful of beer and continued to read the day-old newspaper he had picked up in the departure lounge. He betrayed not a single flicker of emotion. Without speaking a word we all knew one another's mind. We'd decided to sit it out in the hope that the Major would eventually lose interest and conclude that there had been a clerical foul-up. It paid off. After one repeat of the message and a further agonizing wait, the tannoy fell silent. Our trip was beginning to look like the roughcut of a *Carry On* film, a real comedy of errors.

The final dangerous farce was played out at the ferry terminal in Belfast. As we disembarked, the pungent smell of diesel fuel, decaying seaweed and gutted fish flaring in our nostrils, a creased photo of our Belfast contact man was produced. The passport-size color picture was of a young and impressionable-looking Rupert with short slick black hair and the old school tie. It had probably been taken when he was serving with the Eton Rifles. We scanned the disembarkation area looking for a likely candidate. Nothing! Just a rather seedy-looking character with long, straggly hair. He was hunched into a well-worn donkey jacket, smoking a cigarette and looking distinctly furtive. With one arm crooked he was leaning heavily on a red sign marked with white lettering "Passengers only beyond this point." It tilted at a precarious angle under his weight, even though its base was set in a concrete-filled tire to prevent it from blowing over in the wind. The man gave no sign of recognition and looked more hostile by the minute.

I began to feel anxious. Our first time in Northern Ireland and already we were drawing attention to ourselves—a dozen heavies with long hair and second-hand clothes trying desperately to look inconspicuous. A movement caught my eye. It was Kevin. He'd just drawn out a gray, crumpled, elephant's ear of a handkerchief and was unconcernedly flapping it about. He trumpeted loudly into it, sniffed, then stuffed it unceremoniously back into his trouser pocket, finishing off the job with an exaggerated wipe with the back of his hand. My heart sank. Nicknamed the Airborne Wart, with a face like a blistered piss-pot, Kevin would look suspicious at a memorial dinner for Al Capone! What chance of passing himself off as an innocent traveler arriving in Belfast in the middle of a bleak January night!

I shivered violently and turned up my collar against the incessant rain. Where was the contact? I looked up and down the quayside. Nothing moved. Empty gangplanks stood tilted up at one end, giving the impression of having been abandoned in a hurry. Heavily creosoted railway sleepers lay scattered among coils of steel mooring cables, whose ends dangled over the side awaiting the next ship to tether. Silent cranes pointed up to the night sky, their hooks swinging barely perceptibly in the faint breeze wafting off the sea. The only sign of life was a pair of cats quietly growling at each other from either end of a piece of bacon rind. I glanced at my watch. Five minutes had ticked by. I looked out to sea. A series of red and green pilot lights glowed in the distance beyond the harbor entrance. Within the harbor itself, long thin concertinas of light shimmered on the surface of the water opposite the lamps on the far side of the docks. The harbor walls, dirty brown smudges on the black of the night, loomed up out of the water. They were topped by a rambling collection of offices, warehouses, huts and tanks. As I gazed at the buildings, the desolate cry of an unseen seagull pierced the night air, reinforcing the stillness and quietness.

I felt another wave of unease. Where was the transport? I blew into my hands and shuffled my feet, getting increasingly alarmed by our impossible attempts at inconspicuousness. I walked over to the exit door and squinted through the glass. All I could see were row upon row of empty cars lined up in the floodlit car-park. I was puzzled. What were so many cars doing here at this time of night? Where were all the owners? No answer came. Beyond the cars, neat rows of articulated-lorry trailers were propped up, each on its two metal supports. They looked like faithful dogs frozen in obedient posture, haunches down, forelegs ramrod straight, patiently awaiting the return of their masters. A vehicle revved up over to the left, and I looked up expectantly. Was this the transport at last? False alarm. An empty lorry tractor unit, barely illuminated by the dull-orange neon lights struggling to keep the night at bay, was driving off along the quayside. Its rear lights got dimmer as, growling its way up through the gears, it negotiated the twisting road that led out of the docks. I looked at my watch again. Another five minutes had passed. My gaze returned nervously to the shabby figure still leaning impassively on the sign as he exhaled a cloud of cigarette smoke and flicked the dog-end into the water.

At last, Arthur, the team leader, realizing it was too dangerous to wait any longer, seized the initiative and made a decision. It was a risk, but there appeared to be no alternative. Looking incongruously smart in a hound's-tooth jacket and cavalry twills, the rain dripping from his check tweed cap, he walked over to the donkey jacket leaning on the sign. In the dull, dingy surroundings he looked like a member of the aristocracy approaching a purveyor of pornography. We all tensed, ready for immediate action. A brief exchange of veiled speech followed, and then suddenly it was all over and we were being hurriedly ushered through the exit door into the back of a blue minibus. Contact had been made.

The rain hit the windscreen like a jet from a high-pressure hose as we sped through the gray, depressing streets of Belfast. It felt strange to be driving on the left. Whenever I had caught a boat or flown across a stretch of water in the past, I had always ended up driving on the right-hand side of the road. Now I was in limbo, neither at home nor abroad. The road signs were not in an exotic foreign language as my mind half expected—but the place-names were almost culturally strong enough to qualify as foreign: Larne, Ballymena and Ballymoney going north; Lisburn, Lurgan and Craigavon going west. I rubbed the sleeve of my jacket over the condensation on the side-window and peered out. The night rain had oiled the glistening streets and slicked the pavements with dark puddles. Rows of derelict buildings dripped with angry graffiti: "Touts will be shot" . . . "Provos rule" . . . "Smash the H Blocks" . . . "No surrender" . . . "Brit bastards out." Whitewashed gable-ends flashed past me, transformed through political and religious zeal into vast publicity hoardings in the battle for hearts and minds—raw, powerful murals created by tragically skillful hands, depicting clenched fists, sectarian insignia and sinister hooded figures clasping lethal weapons.

What a far cry from the deep wadis, the open rolling plains and the blue skies of Dhofar. As the minibus turned on to the M1 taking us south I reflected on the events of the last few years. Since the battle of Mirbat in 1972 my troop had been decimated. Laba and Tommy were lost, Sek was still convalescing, Bob was now an instructor on training wing, Fuzz and Roger had left the regiment, and Mike Kealy, his three-year tour of duty as troop officer completed, had been posted back to a desk job at Group Headquarters. You have to be good at pushing paper to be promoted to field marshal!

I looked around the faces in the bus. Our composite team had been drawn from all four troops in the squadron; misfits who just happened to fit together. But there was not a Fijian in sight. After long and hard deliberation, the best brains in the Kremlin had finally decided in their wisdom that the Fijians, with their swarthy features, short black curly hair and heavy accents, wouldn't quite blend in with the local population, especially on the Falls Road and the sprawling estates of West Belfast. Valdez in Andy's Town—no way! It was perhaps just as well. I recollected that when we'd been at Otterburn taking part in a fire-and-movement exercise just before going to Dhofar, Valdez had joked about how his team had occupied their spare time by improvising a Ouija board. Whether they'd meddled with something they shouldn't have is a matter for speculation. What is certain is that during Operation Jaguar all four of Valdez's team were wounded. Stranger still, there had been a fifth man in the room with them, Sam, who had refused to take part. He came through Operation Jaguar completely unscathed. We had a difficult enough job in Northern Ireland as it was, without having to contend with the supernatural as well!

As the memories drifted and eddied I must have dozed off. My next sensation was one of confusion as I was abruptly awoken when the minibus suddenly jerked to a halt. In an instant I was alert, rubbing at tired eyes, a stiff muscle in my neck making me wince with pain. The side door slid noisily open and I was given my first view of the SF base that was to be our home for the next few months. In the bitter January dawn, the base looked squalid and claustrophobic. We were surrounded by high corrugated tin walls topped by wire netting to thwart attack from RPG 7s, the Russian-manufactured rocket-propelled grenades. Concrete sentry boxes at regular intervals and camouflage nets stretched across sandbagged roofs gave added protection. The interior of the base was an untidy clutter of Portakabins serving as both accommodation and admin offices. Soldiers dressed in combat gear and a few uniformed police were milling around among a line of Saracen armored cars. I felt strangely disorientated in this cold gray world. At this time of the morning in Dhofar the sun would be growing more powerful by the minute; waves of heat would be spreading across the terrain. The quivering shapes of the hills would be melting into the blue of the sky generating an upsurge of morale. Here there was only damp, gloom and depression.

Over the next few days, I became more and more convinced that I had to get out of this place. We thought we'd come here to take out the opposition; in reality we were armed with the latest Japanese camera technology and told to photograph them. The green slime, the ink boys, were building an empire and using a mountain of photographs to justify it. I could feel the beginning of a new and dangerous frustration: the frustration of not being able to get to grips with the enemy. After Dhofar you could call it postoperation depression.

"Alpha from Zero. Radio check."

It was the duty operator. I gripped the volume control on the radio and turned the sound down, then pressed the speak button with my index finger. "Zero from Alpha. Read you. Fives."

"Alpha from Zero. Roger. Out."

As we finished the radio check I nodded to Taff and the

car lurched forward with a squeal of rubber. The high corrugated-tin gates swung open with an electronic whine, the closed circuit TV camera relaying our exit to the duty operator in the operations room. We were sitting in a four-year-old Vauxhall Viva that must have had a dozen number-plate changes in its short existence. The green bodywork was battered and there was rust everywhere— along the crumbling sills, on the jagged door bottoms, disfiguring one corner of the boot and eating into the dented towing hitch. A casualty of the constantly damp, saline air, it looked a typical working vehicle: thoroughly neglected through lack of interest, lack of ambition and lack of money. The car would blend in nicely with the traffic. The last thing we wanted was to draw attention to ourselves as we drove around the streets of West Belfast. I glanced at Taff, the driver. He looked as battered as the transport. A lean man with long, dirty-blond hair, he was wearing a scruffy over-coat and a face as sour as last week's wine. To the casual observer he could have been anyone—a farm laborer, a navvy—but he was as watchful as a hunting heron. Taff had been kicking around Ireland a long time and had served in the mobile reconnaissance force. Experienced, dependable, he had the nerve of a New York steeplejack. He was to be my guide for today's area familiarization exercise. He knew Belfast like his own backyard.

We were each armed with a 9-millimeter Browning auto-matic pistol. The four 13-round magazines gave me a feeling of security. The pistol grip of the 9-millimeter protruding from the Len Dixon holster dug uncomfortably into my ribs as we drove out through the heavily reinforced gate sangar. We passed the perimeter lights and the coils of Dannet barbed wire and turned on to the main drag, heading straight for the M1. Once we got under way I removed the pistol, placed it on my lap between my legs and concealed it under a copy of the *News of the World*. As I read the latest "Gay Boys in Bondage Scandal at Guards Depot," I held the pistol at the ready, thumb on safety-catch, trigger finger resting on the trigger guard. Having consumed the sensational revelations, I brought my mind back to the day's job. With my free hand I clicked open the glove compartment, rummaged among an assortment of screwdrivers and fuses, a couple of torches and an old fan belt and took out a well-thumbed Ordnance Survey map of the area. The M1 looked like a blue artery, carrying the corpuscular flow of life-blood straight into the beating heart of Republican West Belfast. This was our second week, and the last couple of days had been spent driving around various locations throughout the province, familiarizing ourselves with them, getting the feel of the place. Today, the big one: Belfast, the worst urban guerrilla battleground in the Western world.

The night-time temperature had dropped well below zero. The frost had spiked the grass verges with glinting feathery crystals and fossilized the trees into frozen wayside sentinels. As we drove through the dawn, the tires of the vehicles in front of us showered our windscreen with speckles of road grime. Taff flicked on the wipers to clear our view, but succeeded only in smearing multi-arched lines across the glass. The wash liquid had frozen solid in the hopelessly narrow plastic feed tubes. Then the low-lying early-morning sun hit the filthy screen, momentarily blinding us. Taff pulled over on to the verge, got out of the car and rubbed the windscreen with a rag. Lifting the bonnet, he flexed the plastic feed-tube in an attempt to break up the solid core of ice and managed to restore a tiny trickle of liquid to the spray nozzle. We drove on, and as we neared the city, Divis Mountain rose through the haze like a giant submarine coming to the surface in a sea mist. The haze almost completely obscured the scramble of houses that jostled for position on the Republican estate at the mountain's base.

We turned off the motorway and took the west link to the Grosvenor Road roundabout. Following the left-hand lane up Grosvenor Road, we then headed straight for Provo land—past the Royal Victoria Hospital, through the traffic lights and on up the Springfield Road toward Turf Lodge. Taff navigated the area with practiced ease, giving a running commentary as he drove. He had a story for every street. "They fired an RPG at an armored pig from behind that wall." His voice drifted over the crackle of a radio transmission. "They command-detonated a dustbin full of explosives from across that wasteland."

Everywhere I looked there were reminders that this was a highly dangerous environment. Row upon row of terraced houses had had their doors and windows bricked and boarded up, their gardens reduced to bomb sites. It reminded me of photographs I'd seen of London after the air raids. The pavements outside the pubs were barricaded with huge concrete blocks. The pub windows were caged in heavy-duty wire netting as protection against car bombs and petrol bombers. The people on the streets looked cold and hostile. The dickers were out: bands of youths stood on street corners giving us maximum eyes as we drove past, as threatening as black gangs in the Bronx. Hyperactive, they had the air of mescaline-crazed marionettes: their eyes darted up and down, their heads jerked from side to side, and every now and again their arms shot out, hands flat and outstretched, palms upward.

We were now driving through Ballymurphy estate, heading for the Bullring. We hit the Whiterock Road and turned left, the sprawling Belfast cemetery on our right. The final RV. We drove on through the bleak winter day. And then we were turning left into the Falls Road, the Provo heartland, the center of one of the deadliest killing grounds in Northern Ireland. We joined the stream of traffic heading toward Divis. The volume of black taxis seemed to increase significantly, their passenger compartments crammed to overflowing. A gray-painted RUC mobile, traveling just in front, swung off left up Beechmount Avenue. The hard, alert faces of the two officers in the rear were scanning the rooftops and upper windows for possible sniper positions.

We swept on up the Falls past the spot where an RF guy had been shot in his car. "He forgot his countersurveillance drills," explained Taff simply. Then we were slowing. "Traffic lights on red at the Royal Victoria Hospital," reported Taff as he brought the Viva to a halt opposite the taxi rank by the hospital, three cars back from the junction.

I peered out through a hole in the condensation on the side-window, past the inside lane of traffic, at the dilapidated building on the corner of the junction with Springfield Road. Two youths lurking suspiciously in the doorway attracted my attention. I had been in Ulster only a short time, but already the same instincts that had been able to detect the presence of the Adoo in Oman had been tuned to a new level of alertness to cope with the altogether more sinister threat posed by this environment. These youths signaled danger. I felt sure something was going to happen. What, how and exactly when I could not tell, but something was going to happen. Without apparent movement, I adjusted my grip on the Browning pistol and, with my other hand, quietly located the exact position of the spare 13-round magazines. My breathing became imperceptibly quicker as the adrenalin began to flow.

I glanced at the two youths out of the corner of my eye. There was no mistaking their origins. Each was a classic example of one of two distinct physical types evolved over the centuries by generations of insular Irish genes. The younger, smaller one was thin-boned and thin-lipped, with gray-green eyes and lank brown hair tumbling about his shoulders. The other had agate-black, staring eyes, a prominent arch of thick-set eyebrows, spongy skin that glowed as if recently rubbed with coarse sandpaper, and a swathe of jet-black curls. The first youth was standing in the shadows, his head jerking swiftly from side to side as he observed the line of traffic. His mate stood slightly forward, more exposed. He was tall and arrogant-looking, his square stocky body clothed in an old bomber jacket. Both sets of eyes zapped like tracer into the rows of cars.

Then suddenly it happened.

In an instant, the tall youth was through the inside line of vehicles and around the back of the Viva, and was wrenching the driver's door open.

The first photograph of an SAS anti-hijack team member taken during the first training session in this type of warfare. Note the old-fashioned, outdated equipment.

Soldier I goes to war: Operation Jaguar, Dhofar.

Resupply day in Dhofar.

The .50 Browning gun position, looking toward the Wali's fort and the Jebel Massif.

The DG fort from the ammunition pit. This would have been Mike Kealy's view.

Days before the battle of Mirbat, an Omani gun number cleans the twenty-five-pounder.

Before the battle of Mirbat

Laba prepares ammunition.

Laba and Sek at the twenty-five-pounder.

The Iranian Embassy siege

On the roof, preparing for action.

The first abseiler makes his descent of the rear of the
building.

At the top is Tom the Fijian, his abseil equipment tangled up, now in danger of being engulfed. On the far left is Tommy the Poacher, his gas mask and hood badly burned.

Identifying the only terrorist to escape with his life.

The hostage reception area at the rear of 16 Princes Gate.

The staircase where the grenade incident took place. The left-hand door is where we entered; the right-hand door leads to the cellars.

The graveyard at St. Martin's, Hereford.

My campaign medals.

"Get out the cahr or I'll blow yer fecking head orf."

The coarse, rasping West Belfast accent cut through the silence in the car. It sounded as if the ligaments in the man's neck and throat were being stretched by some massive effort. My heart thumped and the pumping of blood beat in my ears. A flash-flood of adrenaline surged through my muscles as my hand tightened on the pistol grip of the 9-millimeter. Only my eyes moved as I glanced over my right shoulder. The youth was standing next to Taff, jamming the door open with one leg. He tilted his head down from above the level of the car roof so that his voice would carry into the car and not alert passersby or other drivers. All I could see was his bread-dough gut framed in the rear window of the Viva—a perfect target for a one-second double tap. I realized he could not see me from where he was. I thumbed the safety-catch on the Browning to "fire," then hesitated, my breathing coming in quick, shallow gasps. Where was the shooter? Show me a shooter, you bastard! Show me a shooter! His right hand was inside the unzipped bomber jacket. What happens if it's a bluff? What happens if I shoot and kill an unarmed man? I'll be up for murder and the regiment will have fucked up as soon as it has arrived.

But there was also the down side. What if we had been tailed leaving the SF base? What if the whole thing was a carefully planned operation? What if we had been set up like figure-eleven targets? Did they think we were civvies on the way to work, or did they realize we were the Army doing an altogether different kind of job? Were we the target, or did they simply want the car for a bomb job? In a microsecond, I unspooled the whole of the morning's journey in my mind, desperately scanning every single frame, reassessing every minor incident, seeking the tiniest clue toward the solution of the dilemma I was facing: to shoot or not to shoot. Nothing came. There wasn't the vaguest hint of anything sinister. But was that observation merely a reflection of my own inexperience of this urban battlefield, rather than an accurate conclusion? The thoughts ran amok through my pulsating mind. Show me a shooter, you bastard! Show me a shooter! I screamed the words so loudly inside my head I was surprised no one heard me. The tall youth's hand remained stubbornly jammed inside his bomber jacket. There was only one possible thing to do. If I could catch a look at his mate, I might be able to read some sign in his facial expression, or his posture might give some telltale indication of focused aggression. But it was risky, very risky. If he eyeballed me he would realize at once what I was up to. He would recognize immediately the soldier's training and the soldier's reaction. Our cover as civvies would be completely blown.

There was no choice. We were otherwise caught in a split-second, deadly stalemate. Quick as the snap of an alligator's jaw, I turned my head a fraction to the left, pumped my eyeballs as far into the corner of their sockets as they would go, shuttered the youth and returned my gaze to the front. Shit! Nothing! Not a single clue as to his intentions or his state of mind. Back to square one, back to the biggest choice of my life so far: to shoot or not to shoot. Time had run out. The pressure, the urgency swelling inside my head, was about to explode through my brain like a bursting tire. No more reflection. No more option assessment. No more hesitation. I had to make the choice! Now!

"You can fuck off, you wanker."

At that precise split second I was catapulted free of my agonizing deliberation. Taff, his lean face set hard, had made the choice for me. He gripped the Viva's door handle and, with a violent whiplash movement, yanked it momentarily toward himself, then instantaneously outward with all the force and speed he could muster. He hit the hijacker square in the guts with the edge of the door, cracking his knee and jolting his gun arm. The man reeled back, floundering and stumbling with surprise, his mouth twisted in a grimace of pure hate. His right arm, flailing as he steadied himself, exposed an empty hand. There was no telling whether it had been clutching a gun inside the jacket or not. That's something I'll never know.

I had experienced fear before, in Dhofar: the nervous gut feeling at the beginning of a contact before the surge of tingling warmth, the adrenaline-induced relief, gradually took hold. But this was a different kind of fear. Never before had I experienced this sudden shock effect on my mind like the jolt of ice on a raw tooth-nerve, this drawn-out, agonizing hesitation, this frustration of not finding relief in the smooth, efficient operation of the trigger. "Go, go, go!" I heard myself shouting. "Get the fuck out of here!"

Taff rammed the Viva into first gear and jabbed his foot down hard on the accelerator. The rear wheels spun viciously, spurting out gravel, steam and burning rubber smoke like Catherine wheels as they tore desperately for a grip on the wet tarmac. "Come on . . . come on . . . come on!" screamed Taff, frantically urging on the old car. The Viva suddenly lurched forward. Taff wrenched at the steering wheel and swung the car into the oncoming lanes, the still-open door flapping wildly like a pegged-out sheet on washing day. The 1300-hp engine screamed to destruction pitch as we shot through the red lights at the junction, playing a life-and-death game of chicken run with the screeching, swerving traffic hurtling crosswise toward us. We took a right turn up Grosvenor Road and straightened out toward the city center. Taff leaned out, grabbed the flapping door—miraculously still on its hinges—and banged it shut. As I stabbed at the speak button on the radio, I felt a tightness in my throat, I felt the waves of fear and indignation suddenly harden into savage realization. My mind was now in gear. Professionalism had taken over.

"Zero . . . Alpha . . . Over." The transmission was clipped, hurried.

"Alpha from Zero. Send."

"Alpha . . . Attempted hijack corner of Springfield and Falls."

"Zero. Roger. Lift-off. Will send other call sign to investigate."

"Alpha . . . Roger. Out."

As the Viva roared up the Grosvenor Road, driving

toward the west link and the M1, I sank back in my seat. I looked down at the hand holding the 9-milly. It was shaking slightly. I eased the safety catch to "safe" and replaced the copy of the *News of the World*. I could have been the lead story in next Sunday's edition, I reflected, if I'd pulled the trigger. The fame would have been as instant as the hijacker's death.

The uniformed policeman guarding the detention block at Castlereagh directed us into the shadows of the covered car-park at the rear of the building. Taff eased the Viva to a halt and switched off the engine. It was evening. We both sat silent, expressionless, our heads turned, straining to see through the rear window. It was to be a covert identification parade. After the hijack incident, the local commander from Springfield Road Barracks had initiated a sweep of the area. Foot patrols and mobiles had trawled the Falls and Springfield areas, personnel-checking and lifting any suspicious youths. The haul was then transported to Castlereagh for further questioning. We now sat patiently, blacked out in the darkness of the car's interior, waiting for the ID parade to begin.

An arc light high up on the far wall flared into life, bathing the floor of the block to our rear in brilliant white light. A uniformed officer appeared and prodded four recalcitrant youths into our line of sight. The brightness of the light cascading down made them stare at the floor in front of them. Further prodding with a baton, accompanied by gruff, guttural threats, persuaded the youths to raise their eyes and look straight ahead to facilitate identification. The scene was stark and eerie. The sharp light trepanning into the dark of the night had eliminated all superfluous color. All that remained was harsh black and pure white.

I studied the pale, hate-filled faces, my hand hovering over the car horn. The arrangement was that if I got a positive ID I would sound the horn once. I scanned the defiant faces again. There was one possibility—a heavily built character with bad acne. But the shock of ginger hair didn't fit in. "Do you recognize anyone?" I asked Taff.

"Nope!" came the clipped, emotionless reply.

"Then we might as well lift off," I said, barely able to keep the frustration from my voice. I jabbed the horn three times in quick succession, terminating the parade. The light went out and we were once more cloaked in darkness.

The Belfast winter slipped by, dark, desultory and depressing. More observation, more photographs; every day the camera shutter clicked with monotonous regularity. Hardened IRA men immortalized in grainy black and white. The green slime would be having a field day piecing together the big picture. Some of the photographic link-ups looked like Henry VIII's family tree. And still the killing went on. An armored pig was hit by an RPG 7. The married corporal inside was very seriously injured, losing his testicles. A part-time member of the Ulster Defense Regiment was shot dead while operating his JCB tractor. A foot patrol in the Turf Lodge came under sniper fire and one member of the patrol was killed. Month after month, on and on it went, and all the while we were seemingly powerless, unable to take part in the action, our cameras our only weapons.

Then everything suddenly changed.

Remington pump-action shotgun, oiled and ready to go; a box of cartridges, ideal for blowing Yale locks out of flimsy doors; Bristol body armor guaranteed to stop anything up to .357 magnum; high-velocity inserts to give protection against 7.62-millimeter; assault waistcoat with elasticated pockets to take a selection of stun grenades; and finally the Len Dixon belt kit, genuine leather, with the thumb-break, quick-draw holster.

I looked down at the assault equipment laid out neatly on my bed. After weeks of routine patrols, the leash had finally been loosened: we had been put on standby for a possible house assault in the Andersonstown area of the city. A tout had informed the green slime that four armed PIRA had taken over the top flat of a block of flats and were preparing to carry out a snipe on an army foot patrol.

I picked up the 9-millimeter Browning on the bedside locker, removed the magazine and, gripping the knurled slide with index finger and thumb, cocked the action. The oiled working parts slipped back smoothly, revealing the empty chamber. Satisfied with the weapon's safety precautions, I released the slide, allowing it to snap forward, replaced the fully loaded mag and secured the pistol in the holster on the belt kit. I was just reaching for my personal radio hanging by its harness on the wardrobe door, when the outside door of the basha flew open.

"Get tooled up, lads, we're going for it!" The urgency in the team leader's voice cracked through the steadiness of our methodical preparations and whipped us into a frenzy of action. We had moved from standby to immediate. We staggered into our body armor, threw on our assault kit, loaded and cocked our weapons, and double-checked our gas masks for serviceability.

I was lost in a sea of struggling, cursing assaulters as we made for the two armored pigs that would transport us to Andy's Town. I scrambled into the first pig. Jake, Ginge and Bob were already seated in the cramped interior. Jake, hard and intense, a Jock from the Highland Light Infantry and second-in-command of the assault team, was straightening the splayed ends of the safety pin protruding from his stun grenade to facilitate quicker withdrawal. The other lads were checking their Heckler Koch MP 5s and adjusting their gas masks. I took a handful of cartridges from the map pocket of my combat trousers and began feeding the Remington. The pigs lurched forward out through the main gates of the RUC station and into the Springfield Road.

The two pigs turned into the Falls, trundling along at normal patrol speed, heading for Andy's Town. Then we took a right, up Kennedy Way, getting close. Each man was tense, not talking, going over the assault plan in his mind. No orders would be shouted. The drill was automatic. Nothing could stop the roller-ball once it had started. Right turn into Andy's Town, the high whine of the pig's engine in our ears.

"Two hundred meters," came the terse message from the front. "One hundred meters." I could feel the adrenaline start to pump. "Fifty meters." The man nearest the back twisted one of the rear doorhandles and disengaged the securing rod. Gripping tightly on to both handles he pushed the doors slightly outward to check that they were moving freely, then swung them closed again, his fingers staying clenched around the handles ready for instant action.

The pig jerked to a halt. "Go, go, go," was the only shouted order. The rear doors burst open. I counted them out. One out. Two out. I was three out. Four out. I looked up. We were hemmed in on two sides by the pre-cast concrete frontages of two bleak rows of flats, whose dirty and neglected windows looked all the more bizarre and hostile for having their frames painted bright garish colors, totally out of keeping with the dismal grayness of the rest of the scene. A muddy grass verge littered with broken bottles, pieces of masonry and dog shit led up to each row of flats, like a rubbish-strewn sea lapping at a harbor wall. The two blocks were connected by a low-sided, open concrete walkway to our front, blackened by the weather and disfigured by graffiti—an ideal position from which an old car engine could be levered over the low walls on to a passing army patrol. Two ten-year-olds standing at one end eyed us with hate and disgust. They dashed to alert the occupants of the flats that the SF had arrived.

Running hard, we slithered over the grass and headed for the block of flats on the left, gas masks restricting breathing, eyepieces beginning to mist over. We crashed through the front door. All I could see was the heaving back of number two as we mounted the stairs. The bare concrete steps were in flights of eight, zigzagging up the central stairwell in alternating directions and connected by small, rough-surfaced landings. Our momentum was halted momentarily at each landing as we lurched around in an acute reversal of direction, wrenching at the rusty handrail to aid our progress upward. First floor, second floor. No problems. So far so good. I could feel the urgent presence of number four pushing behind me as we approached the target flat on the third floor.

The safety catch on the Remington came off as I hit the third floor and made for the target door. Number one and number two were already in position at the hinges, waiting for the door to swing open. I squeezed the trigger on the shotgun. The cartridge hammered through the Yale lock, splintering the wood surround into a thousand slivers. A heavy number-nine boot finished the job and the door crashed open. Number one and number two disappeared inside.

I took up a crouched position just inside the door, ready for the shooting to start. Shouts and screams reverberated around the interior of the flat. A stun grenade went off, the force of the detonation cracking the cheap plaster on the ceiling and walls. I waited for the last blinding flash, then moved deeper into the room. Through the fog I could see shadowy figures. A man and a woman sat doubled up on the settee, coughing, vomiting and babbling incoherently.

A gas mask came toward me, a gloved hand gripped my arm. "The bastards aren't here." The voice was Jake's. "There's no fucking terrorists in here." His voice sounded strangely distorted through the gas mask. "We're going for the flat across the landing." With that he darted past me and rocketed toward the other door, his number two hard on his heels.

I followed fast, the Remington coming up to the aiming position. In a blur of movement the cartridge hammered the Yale and the door splintered and sprang open. In one fast and practiced movement, the two assaulters cannoned into the flat. I stood near the doorway, covering the entrance to the living room. A bedlam of sound pounded my ears: hysterical voices . . . Irish accents . . . the deafening explosions of the stun grenade . . . but still no gunfire. The bastards have got to be in there this time! For fuck's sake pull the trigger and let's get this job over with.

The earpiece of my Pyephone radio crackled into life. "All stations. This is Jake. The birds have flown. Endex. Lift off."

Bastard, I thought, all this pissing about for nothing! The

sharp acid of frustration started to well up and corrode my insides. My skull seemed to grow tighter and press in on my brain. The fucking tout had got it wrong. How much was the green slime paying him anyway?

I couldn't stand much more of this, I had to get out of this place. The desire to escape was as primal as the frantic thrustings of a spawning salmon trapped by a storm-fed torrent roaring through the rapids.

1976 turned into 1977. The months ticked by, the frustration increased. Then, suddenly, I got the order to go and see the Officer Commanding.

11
Hong Kong

It was with some degree of trepidation and a vague, elusive feeling of guilt tightening my lips that I approached the OC's office. Why had he called for me? Surely I couldn't be blamed for the operation's lack of success. All the intelligence reports had pointed toward the conclusion that there were four armed PIRA hiding in the flat. As I closed the door firmly but quietly behind me, my thoughts became even more paranoid. Was I being singled out as a scapegoat? Was I going to be sacrificed on the altar of political expediency, watched from afar by the hooded high priests of Whitehall?

"Sit down, Sergeant." The tall, slim figure behind the desk remained firmly upright. Only his head tilted slightly as he scanned the report in front of him making occasional pencil notes in the margin.

Power play, I thought. Making me wait, creating the impression his paperwork is more important than me, gives him the upper hand, reinforces his authority. Psychological-warfare tactics. I braced myself for the worst.

"Right." The OC looked up, giving nothing away. His swarthy features had not yet been washed pale by the Belfast rain. He eyed me closely for a moment, then his gaze relaxed into the hint of a smile. "Pack your bags, Sergeant. You're going to the exotic East!"

Kai Tak airport is unique among the world's international airports in that it is limited to a single runway. But then that is not surprising. Everything in Hong Kong is restricted, hemmed in and squeezed by the lack of space. Like an overcrowded refugee ship, the country has a population a tenth the size of Great Britain's crammed into a tiny land mass of small islands and mainland territories a mere two-thirds the size of London. To the north, Communist China, like a boa constrictor stalking a baby vole, looms up and towers over the British colony threatening to swallow it up at any moment through the gaping jaws of Canton delta. Should any of China's inhabitants be seduced by the soft caress of Hong Kong's Western lifestyle and the heady opium of its capitalist commerce—and this ideological cardinal sin is committed more frequently than the Communist regime would care to admit—then the only land barrier in their way is the fragile twenty-two-mile border that runs from east to west just below Shenzhen. The responsibility for stemming the human tide of swimming, tunneling, crawling and climbing border-runners lies with the Gurkhas, the famous warriors from the hill tribes of Nepal.

The concrete stick of runway was clearly visible in the distance as the military transport plane throttled back its engines. I felt a warm tingle of pride when I brought to mind my mission. There were three resident Gurkha battalions in Hong Kong. These ruthless combatants, whose diminutive stature belies a fierce fighting nature, whose lethal crescent-shaped *kukri* knives once drawn cannot be resheathed without having tasted blood—preferably by severing the heads of their enemies—this elite troop who have gained more VCs per head than any other section of the British Army, whose mere presence in the forthcoming Falklands war would be enough to precipitate the surrender of the Argentinians at Port Stanley, I had been chosen to train in

157

the art of unarmed combat. It was one of the perks of being in the SAS. Our specialist skills were much in demand among security forces throughout the free world.

As we began our final descent, I looked out over a sea churned by a thousand sailing craft, large and small. Flying-fish-finned junks jostled for position with lumbering freighters. Tiny yachts sailed impertinently close to huge ocean-going liners. Nearer to shore, beetle-shaped sampans scuttled along wearing protective belts of old car tires around their hulls. They wobbled precariously on top of the water, buffeted by every passing swell, their human cargoes sitting unconcernedly beneath the coarse sun-bleached calico awnings. And in the midst of them all, disdainful hydrofoils sliced through the water carrying rich businessmen to important meetings. Hong Kong harbor, one of the busiest ports in the world, vying for trade with the rival Asian ports of Shanghai, almost 1,000 miles to the north, and Singapore, nearly 2,000 miles away across the South China Sea.

The fierce sun liquefied the high-rise buildings hedging in the airport. Planes parked up in bays at the side of the runway soaked up the blistering heat like lizards on sun-drenched rocks. This is the life, I thought. Sunshine and training with the Gurkhas—the best possible antidote after nearly two years of rain-sodden boredom in Northern Ireland. I was as eager to get into it as a thirsty laborer striding into a lunch-time pub for a thick, callous-fingered pint of foaming beer. Things were really going my way at last.

I obviously hadn't yet learned the lesson: beware of overoptimism. The previous training jaunt to exotic places had been considered a jolly too, a bit of R and R after the rigors of operational duties. Little had I known that that trip would nearly cost me my life, that it would prove more dangerous even than Mirbat. We'd taken a C 130 from Brize Norton to Khartoum, then traveled overland to the coast just below Port Sudan. We set up camp by the Red Sea, very close to Jacques Cousteau's diving school.

The trip was to last six weeks. It wasn't long before a certain amount of boredom set in, particularly as alcohol was illegal in Sudan. We soon found a way of solving the boredom problem. One of the lads dug out the Admiralty charts and gave them a closer look. Near to where we were diving was a place marked on the chart as a large square block labeled "restricted: dangerous." It was like a red rag to a bull. Further inquiries revealed that it was the site of the wreck of the SS *Umbria,* a World War II Italian ammunition ship. We immediately sniffed booty! Ignoring all dangers of unexploded ordnance, we dived in eagerly and quickly located a hold full of unexploded bombs. They were unarmed. That gave us a clue. Further searches uncovered a stash of nose-cone mechanisms—all made out of pure brass. That would do nicely! Back in Hereford, they would bring a tidy sum in scrap.

We then began to focus our attention on the huge propeller: phosphor bronze, worth a fortune, nearly as valuable as gold! The nose-cones represented loose change compared to this! We first tried to slice off one of the leaves of the propeller, but abandoned the idea when we had difficulty with the cutting tool. Further exploration revealed a spare leaf, bolted to the side of the cargo hold. Perfect! We quickly unbolted it from its housing and laid it on the ocean floor. We then went back to shore, assembled two dozen Burma Oil drums and freighted them out over the wreck, towing them behind our three Geminis. We lashed the Burmoils together, filled them with water and sank them over the wreck. Having attached the propeller leaf to the Burmoils, we used our airlines to blow water out of the drums, and slowly they began to rise to the surface. In no time at all there were twenty-four Burmoils bobbing on the surface with the huge one-and-a-half-ton propeller leaf suspended on ropes underneath.

The flotilla headed back for shore. As the Geminis chugged along, the Burmoils unfortunately began to fill with water and started to pop under the surface one after the other. We were quickly down to two or three Burmoils. The sheer weight of the propeller began to pull down on the rear of the Geminis and lift the bows up into the air, threatening to tip them over any moment. The shout went up: "Cut the ropes!"

Ginge, who was steering my boat, cut what he thought was the main rope. Unfortunately, he had not noticed that there was another rope attached to the propeller leaf whose other end was coiled loosely around in the bottom of the boat. The heavy hemp rope snaked out and snapped tight around my upper leg. As I struggled against the muscle-tearing pull of the rope, a mental picture of Geordie, the jungle survival expert, flashed into my mind. "You are only as sharp as your knife," he used to say, in his heavy Newcastle accent. I reached for my diver's knife, fitted to my leg. The blade glittered in the sun as I hacked away at the hemp. The pain in my thigh was becoming unbearable. I could just feel my hip-joint beginning to dislocate as I cut through the final strands. The relief was immediate. The propeller leaf plummeted to the depths of the ocean. As it disappeared, I don't know which was more painful: my thigh or the thought of the thousands of pounds sterling lying on the ocean floor!

The OC turned a blind eye to the escapade. He knew it was going on, but after all, it was good training—something for us to focus our minds on, instead of aimlessly paddling around looking for fish. However, there was no way he could ignore what was about to happen in Hong Kong.

"Let's go for a boogie at BMH and work up a thirst," said Clint as he stuffed his rugby kit into a battered holdall.

"Work up a thirst! I must have lost a gallon of sweat this afternoon. I need an ale transfusion quick. I'll be fainting from dehydration."

"You can get a drink at the disco."

"I'm not into discos. I've got some serious drinking to do."

"Me too. But we can go downtown later. Think of all those gorgeous nurses, those black-stockinged beauties just waiting for us. Right little ravers, no inhibitions. They're seeing naked bodies all day long. It builds up the passion, especially in this heat. Can't you just feel those well-practiced hands getting to grips with you already? They can give me a bed-bath any time they want."

"Hey, Clint, remember I'm a married man!"

We were in the changing rooms, Buffalo, Clint and I, discussing the evening's entertainment. Buffalo and Clint were inspectors in the Hong Kong police. They'd co-opted me into their local league rugby team. That afternoon's match had been particularly hard, but we'd just scraped a win. I was feeling the effects of the humidity; having been in Hong Kong only three weeks, I was still not fully acclimatized. The thought of several hours' dancing did not exactly fill me with excitement. However, as I did up my last shirt button, I resigned myself to the BMH detour.

We finally left BMH around midnight and to my relief headed for Tsim-Sha-Tsui, a bustling shopping, bar and restaurant district situated in the shadow of the mountain known as the Peak, which towers like a high-swell wave crest over the trough of Hong Kong city. We were aiming for the renowned Bottoms Up bar to get on with the real business of the night: beer and men's talk.

As we turned into Hankow Road, I looked up eagerly to see if I could spot the entrance to the bar I'd heard so much about. A flashing neon ticker-tape of matchstick Chinese script showered right down to street level. The occasional English sign emphasized the cosmopolitan nature of the city: "Golden Dragon Company—Wholesale and Retail," "Jimmy Sung—Tailor," "Golden Fountain Restaurant." The road itself was lined with high-class boutiques, their window displays expensively draped and spotlit to attract passersby, who even at this late hour were thronging the pavements. The trademarks of Sony, Omega and Nikon assailed window-browsers from all sides.

In spite of the neon snowstorm, the sign for the Bottoms Up bar stood out at a fair distance down on the right-hand side of the road. Box-shaped, the sign had a thick black border engraved with white Chinese writing. The center was a rich purple color. It featured a prominent white female bottom cleverly designed to resemble a heart, thus suggesting the function of the female buttocks as a stimulus to passion and emotion. In large black letters tattooed across the disembodied bottom were the words "Bottoms Up." The sign was attached to the wall by a stout metal rod just above a narrow dark entrance. Wedged as it was between a perfume boutique and a shoe store, it looked promisingly shady. As I drew closer I could see the bar's name repeated several more times on every available space around the entrance in case anyone, engrossed in the consumer delights, had missed the large sign hung above. A line of enticingly explicit photos of the hostesses was strung out above the word "Welcome" painted on a large pink arrow pointing persuasively to the interior.

Inside it was like a Turkish harem, and twice as decadent. Plush crimson velour covered the seats, the walls and the sides of the bars. Long velveteen curtains in royal purple were draped around the alcoves and bordered the windows. Large silver-framed prints depicting the shadowy silhouette of a female bottom dominated the wallspace of each alcove, accentuating the leitmotif of the bar and echoing the display taking place in the center of the room. Here there were three bars designed like miniature lion pits. The customers sat on stools around the darkened raised rim, while, bathed in bright white light from above, a hostess, crouched on all fours like a performing animal, dispensed drinks, generous smiles and hints of Eastern mystery from the circular central section below.

We found three empty stools and settled on to our ringside seats. The waitress moved around with practiced ease to take our order. She was wearing a diamond butterfly slide in her hair, purple eyeshadow, crimson lipstick the color of the furnishings, a fine silver bracelet and nothing else. Her long black hair fell loosely over her chest, allowing tantalizing glimpses of her breasts as she stooped to get our drinks from lower down inside the bar. We sat for a while in silence, mesmerized by the undulating display of naked flesh inches before our eyes. The entrancing motion, together with the hypnotic, steady drift of cigarette smoke up toward the sparkling crystal chandelier, made all conversation superfluous. With feline agility the waitress padded about the bar, gracefully performing her sensual repertoire—clenching her buttocks tightly together as she reached down, lifting her head, hollowing her back and thrusting her bottom upward like a movie star, pouting her lips, relaxing and opening her thighs to reveal a hint of genitals, running a hand over her haunches as if smoothing down a dress, squatting briefly with legs outspread on the smooth surface of the table, and flicking her hair back from her eyes to give, momentarily, a full frontal view of her breasts. Occasionally between orders she sat upright on her heels, fingers draped over bended knees, her upper arms held tight to her breasts, her bare heels pressing into the flesh of her buttocks, somehow making her nakedness even more explicit. The provocative nature of the display was tempered by her oriental gentleness. Far from appearing decadent, with the petite dimensions of her body and her coy manner she projected the natural innocence of a naked five-year-old bathing uninhibitedly at the edge of the sea.

After a few glasses of San Miguel, the local lager, and intermittent attempts at conversation above the loud jarring music, Clint eventually took the initiative. "Let's go for one in the Red Mill Inn." He was getting restless.

"Is there any fanny there?" inquired Buffalo provocatively, knowing full well there wasn't.

"No," said Clint.

"Well fuck it, let's stay here."

"No, come on, it will be a change of scene. The beer's too expensive here."

"Who wants a change of scene with these gorgeous lovelies displaying their charms?" Buffalo was beginning to look a touch unstable.

"When you've seen one you've seen them all. It gets boring after a while, like the topless beaches. After a while you become overdosed, bored even."

"You must be joking. I never get bored. Tits, you can't beat them. There's an infinite number of shapes and sizes." Buffalo was warming up now. "I've yet to see two pairs exactly alike. Endless variety, endless fascination. The day I see two pairs of tits exactly alike, that's the day I'll pack it in."

"Come on, they keep the beer better. It's cooler in the Red Mill Inn, and I know how to get buckshees."

"Ah, now you're talking. Let's go."

We emerged back into the night, rebuffed the strenuous arm-waving attempts of a rickshaw driver to get us into his flimsy contraption, turned right down Hankow Road to the junction with Ashley Road, then went right again, across the road, carefully avoiding a red taxi bearing down on us, and in through the door of the Red Mill Inn. This was a much more conventional late-night drinking den. Far less elaborate than the Bottoms Up bar, it verged on seediness. "Three San Migs please." Clint got the drinks in and we settled down to discuss the afternoon's rugby match.

Around 2:00 a.m., as the conversation wore on and the sporting exploits grew in stature with each alcohol-infused repetition, my concentration began to wander. I gazed around the bar, then momentarily tensed, consciously halting the drift of my mind toward weariness-induced torpor. Something wasn't quite right. I didn't feel comfortable. There was something in the atmosphere of the bar that seemed to convey a vague sense of danger, some unstated aura of threat—not especially aimed at me or Clint or Buffalo, just generalized, floating around the room, seeping through the air like a gas escape. It was as if all it would take was a misinterpreted gesture, an ill-timed comment or a glance in the wrong direction, and the casual strike of a match would trigger the explosion. I was sure the feeling had not been there when we had come in. Something or someone had precipitated it since we'd arrived.

More alert, I scanned the room seeking clues. Everything seemed normal—normal, that is, for a late-night bar in the early hours of the morning in downtown Hong Kong, a bar peopled by a potent racial mix drawn from the Portuguese, Chinese, British and Filipino subcultures. The general bar area seemed quiet enough; just two neat-looking Chinese men sitting by the door talking softly and a sprinkling of other nondescript faces scattered around in ones and twos. Toward the back of the room, a screen of rigid bamboo poles set in an ornamental stone base sectioned off a windowless area of semicircular drinking booths. Here, beneath subdued lighting, murmuring, rhythmically glass-raising occupants were deep in conversation. The bamboo did not permit a clear view, but my distrustful state of mind construed the tones of voice as suspicious, even conspiratorial. One of the drinkers, a character of Latin origins, sauntered over to the jukebox at the foot of the steps leading up to the booth area. With an ostentatious, gum-chewing swagger, he held the machine in a wide-armed embrace, tapped the fingers of his right hand against the gleaming metal frame, stabbed out his selection of discs with a studied flourish and then swanked back into the booths.

After a while, the general calmness began to allay my fears. It must be my hyperactive imagination, I thought as I did a mental search-and-destroy mission inside my body to locate and unwind the tension-cramped muscles. By the time Susi Soriano appeared and I had recognized her as a night-club hostess and singer from the Speakeasy Club, a seedy downtown drinking den that Clint, Buffalo and I had recently started to frequent, all notions of latent hostility had completely evaporated. I felt I needed some female conversation. Nothing more, just friendly conversation. It gets lonely when you are separated from the wife.

"Hello, Susi, got the night off?"

"Yes, that's right."

"Come and join us for a drink."

"No thanks, not just now. I'm with my sister."

"Better still. Bring Chai over too."

"Maybe later." And with that she disappeared into the toilets.

When she reemerged a few minutes later, she smiled at us and headed for the booth area. Pleased to be noticed, she had acquired in her bearing a knowing and seductive jauntiness. She was clothed in a lurid turquoise mock-satin dress, which clung to her figure so closely that her panties were clearly visible outlined beneath the thin material. The dress swished whisperingly at its tightest point around her haunches. Her firm rear end swayed alluringly from side to side as one cohesive unit rather than two separate hemispheres of flesh. Her bottom was slightly too large and out of proportion with the rest of her body. Far from being a disadvantage, this only served to increase her provocative fascination by drawing attention to the area of her hips.

Everyone, men as well as women, has an energy center of gravity. With some it is in the area of the head and neck, with others it is in the chest or the shoulders or the solar-plexus region. The nature of this energy, whether it be cerebral, emotional, nurturing, sportive or whatever, depends on its particular location. Susi's center of gravity was located very definitely in her groin, and the energy was decidedly sexual.

As she reached the steps by the jukebox, she swiveled the whole lower half of her body in order to negotiate the rise, hampered as she was by a combination of high heels and tight dress. As she did so the dress drew even tighter, the hem rising to reveal even more of her slim, young thighs, before she disappeared behind the bamboo curtain.

We continued drinking, but the sight of Susi had made me restless. Not one to be put off easily, I decided to see if I could persuade Susi and Chai to be more sociable. I wandered over to the bamboo curtain and peered through. The two sisters were deep in conversation with a group of Portuguese men. They were obviously engrossed in something more than social pleasantries, so I decided to leave them alone for a little while longer. Ten minutes later I thought I would try again—or at least it seemed like ten minutes later. Beyond a certain level of alcohol consumption, time has a habit of playing tricks, to the extent that a mate can go to the toilet and appear to return and sit down again one sip of beer and two seconds later. I went right up to the bamboo opposite to where they were sitting and gestured. Susi glanced up and nervously gestured to me to go away. The nervous look did not register with me. I simply thought she was playing hard to get. One more drink and then I would go right up to their table. I turned and headed back for the empty stool at the bar next to Clint and Buffalo.

As I had my back to the booth area, I didn't see the three characters behind me whisper something urgent, get up, move their chairs swiftly to one side and head for the steps by the jukebox. The first I knew of anything being wrong was when the unmistakable sound of breaking glass cut through the bar and jolted the place into high tension. Instinctively I spun around, and saw the lead character of the three, tense-armed, gripping a broken bottle held menacingly low and pointing directly toward me.

Clint swiveled around, saw the bottle, leaped off his stool, jutted out the index finger of his right hand and shouted, "Police! Put that bottle down!"

The three paid no attention whatever and continued to advance. At this point Clint went for the guy with the bottle. He evaded the first threatening swing of the vicious, jagged weapon, grasped the man's wrist in a vice-lock, forced the bottle to the floor and threw him against the jukebox. As he crashed spreadeagled into the machine and slumped to the floor, a wild screech and scratch followed by a rumbling sound emanated from the loudspeaker and then, incongruously amid the mayhem, the soft romantic ballad began to play again a few bars further on. Out of the corner of my eye I could just see Clint putting the boot in to finish off the job, when the man's companions both grabbed bottles from the nearest empty table, broke off the bases with a practiced flick of the wrist and advanced to within striking distance of Buffalo and me.

As they had paid no heed to Clint's warnings, I decided to throw the system out of the window and go solo. I reached into my back pocket for the insurance policy I always carried with me in case of trouble—a World War I trench-fighting knuckleduster issued to British troops for hand-to-hand combat. A lovely piece, worn smooth by age, I'd obtained it from my brother-in-law who runs a military museum. Years before, while serving with the Royal Engineers in Germany, a mate of mine had been jumped by a gang of Italian *Gastarbeiter* thugs. They put their knives into him and he never walked again. I was determined that no one was going to turn me into a vegetable at any cost, and I carried the knuckleduster with me everywhere I went. Now it was about to come into its own.

I felt for the reassuring hard touch of the metal and drew the weapon out into the open. I jammed it into my hand, pointed it directly at my would-be assailants, flexed my fingers conspicuously and snorted in a cold, rock-steady voice, "Right! Let's have you lads."

As they came forward I struck the nearer one full in the face. He went down. I swung my arm back and caught the other one on the side of the temple. He dropped his broken bottle and went down. A fourth person, later identified as Didier Peres, a well-known drug-pusher, then came from the booths area and lunged at me with a crude form of rugby tackle. He was very quick. Before I could strike him with the knuckleduster he grabbed me around the throat and pushed me into the bar, sending two of the three stools clattering to the floor. At the same time his considerable strength enabled him to turn me around so that I was facing and bent over the bar. He then thrust his hand up to my throat and held me in a windpipe pinch. The pain was excruciating, as if I were being gripped by a rabid Doberman pinscher. The precise positioning of the thumb and index finger had all the hallmarks of a professional street fighter. It was the throat equivalent of getting your hand jammed in a bank's time-locked safe door when all the staff have gone home for the weekend.

My position was now serious. By shaking forcefully from side to side, I managed to free my knuckleduster arm and swing it around. Peres was bent low into my shoulder, so the duster cracked him on top of the head. To my dismay, the blow had no effect except to make him tighten his grip on my throat. By now my eyes were beginning to blur; the bottles behind the bar were swimming. There was a heavy thumping in my head and a high-pitched whistling in my ears. I was desperate. I had to do something quick. I'd come here to train the Gurkhas in unarmed combat and here I was involved in a real life-or-death struggle myself. By now I was having trouble breathing. I could feel my temples beating to bursting point. I was virtually paralyzed. I frantically scoured my brain for a solution, going on fast-forward through all my years of training. Freeze frame! A flash of inspiration! I had to try it. It could be my last chance. I worked up my left hand, grabbed hold of Peres's thumb, snatched it away from my throat and put it straight into my mouth. I bit down as hard as I could until I felt the solid resistance of the bone. Peres, taken by surprise, squealed like a stuck pig, released his stranglehold and ran out of the bar.

I looked around. Clint was still over by the jukebox, slugging it out with someone who later turned out to be a Portuguese-American sailor on forty-eight-hour shore leave. Clint swung his arm, the man crashed backward, smashing the glass cover on the jukebox, and the music was silenced for good. Buffalo was arguing with the barman about using the phone to call for help. The barman refused, saying, suspiciously, that it was out of order. So Buffalo dashed out to phone from the restaurant across the street. At this point I decided to get out of the bar as quickly as I could. I was on a sensitive job and didn't want complications.

I pushed past another character who tried to stop me. He dropped like a ton of muck as I cracked him with the duster. I was staring freedom in the face when suddenly I was jumped from behind at the door. We rolled around, the momentum carrying us straight through the door and into the street. As we continued to roll around on the pavement, a crowd gathered to watch the spectacle. Suddenly someone ran out of the gathering, kicked me straight in the face as I wrestled with my assailant, then mingled back into the crowd.

Undeterred, I continued the struggle. I heaved the man over and managed to get on top of him. Just when I thought I had the situation under control, he put his hand up, gripped my testicles and twisted them violently beneath the thin material of my lightweight tropical trousers. It blew my mind. The anger exploded in my brain. There was only one answer to this. I grabbed his hair with my left hand and rapped him across the forehead with the knuckleduster, splitting the skin from eye to eye. Like a heavyweight boxer in a title fight who goes on punching beyond the bell, I just did not hear the high-pitched wailing of the police siren. As the character slumped unconscious to the ground and I began to think I might have overdone it, I suddenly felt a heavy hand on my shoulder.

"Police! You're under arrest."

There is something strange and frightening when in the course of a single moment you realize that your life has irrevocably altered. It is the moment when the young wife, joyfully looking forward to her husband's return so she can reveal the news of her first pregnancy, is told by the grave-faced policeman at the door that she is now a widow; when the champion jockey, who only a moment ago was soaring high over the jumps, wakes up in hospital to be told that his vertebrae are so badly smashed that he will never ride again. The moment is strange because it is so sudden and disorientating, and it is frightening because you are cast headlong into a situation where a completely new order reigns and a new set of rules prevails. Your unsuspecting emotions are cruelly whiplashed into a vicious reversal of direction. No matter how loud you scream inside, "This can't be happening, this can't be true," no one will ever hear you. Events are propelled forward with an absolute and remorseless energy.

Me? Under arrest! I used to have a recurrent nightmare about being at the wheel of a car careening out of control downhill with its accelerator jammed full on. No matter how hard I struggled to disengage the clutch with one foot and ram the brake down hard with the other, I could do nothing to stop the vehicle. It wasn't the fear of crashing that made me wake up in a sweat, it was the terrifying powerlessness to stop the forward motion, the deeply unnerving experience of sheer relentlessness.

The nightmare had now come true. I looked up and saw the khaki drill, the dark leather of the Sam Brown cross belt, the black shiny peaked cap and the drawn pistol. Just behind, the flashing light on top of the EU Land Rover seemed to gyrate crazily like an out-of-control lighthouse beacon. I was about to start the B-movie dialogue of, for want of something more original, "You've got the wrong man," when Clint beat me to it. Waving his police warrant card to try to emphasize his authority, he shouted urgently, "There's people in the bar who should be held for questioning."

Even as he spoke, Peres and the bottle boys, the real culprits, were slinking out of the bar. As soon as they were at a safe distance they broke into a run down the street and away into the night. The hyped-up Chinese inspector from the EU, who by this time, having confiscated the knuckleduster, was cautioning me and hustling me into the rear of the Land Rover, completely ignored Clint's warnings. He was young, inexperienced and totally out of his depth.

The next thing I knew I was being driven to Tsim-Sha-Tsui police station, with Clint and Buffalo in hot pursuit in their own car. At the station I was processed through the system, searched, cautioned and interviewed and my statement taken down by a clumsy typist. It was written in uncultured English, heavy with police terminology, which tends to reduce an infinite variety of real-life happenings to a limited series of categorizable events. Such a style provides an undemanding and instantly recognizable language for everyone from court clerks to prosecuting counsel. A legal Esperanto you could say. After reading the statement I was told to initial in the margin the errors and crossings-out and to sign and date it at the bottom.

Since the knuckleduster was classified as an illegal weapon and the possession of the weapon constituted an offense contrary to the Public Order Act, I and my case were transferred to the CID. I could not escape the charge of possession of an offensive weapon—POOW as it was referred to—since I'd admitted in my statement to having the knuckleduster. I'd had no choice; I'd literally been caught bloody-handed. To my dismay, I learned that self-defense was no defense. As for the fight, I felt that the charge would be the relatively minor offense of causing an affray. No such luck. I was to be prosecuted under the Public Order Act for the much more serious offense of assault occasioning actual bodily harm—AOABH for short. Around 4:30 a.m., with my spirits ebbing away, it was decided that I should be released into mess arrest. I was driven in a police Land Rover to Gunclub Barracks—the resident Hong Kong battalion headquarters—where I was to remain for the next two weeks until the case came up in court.

Clint and Buffalo had arrived at the station a few minutes after me. Ken Jones, a friend of Clint's, happened to be the inspector on duty. He'd recognized me from the rugby club, so when Clint came dashing in to see what was going on, Ken said to him, "We've got one of your mates. I think you should look at the report book."

Clint flipped the pages and found the relevant entry. It read: "0200: Red Mill Inn, Ashley Road. A European male attacked a Chinese male with an offensive weapon, namely a knuckleduster." Clint was incensed when he read this, and insisted on changing the book. He later got a severe reprimand for this, but he was determined to see the truth come out even if it meant putting his job on the line.

Clint and Buffalo decided right at the outset to take the unusual step of appearing for the defense. A policeman is only ever expected to appear for the prosecution—even more particularly in instances such as this, when the case for POOW was cut and dried. Buffalo was sticking his neck out even more than Clint. He had crossed swords with the police establishment in the past and was already considered something of a renegade. What made them dig their heels in even further was when they were called into the office one day and told bluntly, "You are strongly advised by SP CID Kowloon not to appear for the defense." Without their support my case would have been severely weakened. To insure the cooperation of the police authorities, my solicitor sent a subpoena requesting the presence in court of Clint and Buffalo because they had facts material to the case. The police could not legally refuse this request.

Clint came to visit me at Gunclub Barracks. "They're determined to nail you," he said. "They are pressing ahead with the AOABH despite what Buffalo and I have told them. With a half-decent judge you might get off, but there is no chance for the POOW. Do you realize what you are looking at? You are going down for six months, more if they make the AOABH stick. You're convicted even before the trial."

"But I didn't start anything. It was self-defense. Surely the judge will see that."

"Makes no difference. It's mandatory. No matter what the reason, POOW is an automatic six-monther. No appeal."

I don't know which was the greater blow: the contemplation of a minimum six-month stretch locked up inside some humid rat-hole in Hong Kong, or the prospect of a certain end to my career in the SAS and the Army following a jail sentence. "Is there nothing we can do?" I asked.

Clint looked at me. He seemed hesitant, reluctant to continue. "Well, there is something. A mate of mine in the CID has been doing some research for me on the quiet. There's a procedure for requesting corporal punishment as an alternative. What do you think?"

"What does it entail?"

"Bamboo across the backside. A short sharp shock, then

you're back in business." I was too relieved by the thought of escaping prison to notice the shadow of a frown that flitted across Clint's face.

"Sounds OK to me. Anything's got to be better than being cooped up in prison. I'd die of boredom. Yeah! Let's go for it!"

"OK, but don't count on it. It's entirely at the discretion of the judge."

The judge was about to return after considering his verdict, and I'd been called back into the dock. While awaiting the reappearance of the judge, the policeman sitting to my left unconcernedly brought a newspaper out of his pocket and began to read it. This informal motion contrasted starkly with the gravity of the surroundings. But then to him it was just another case in a long line of such cases. As far as he was concerned, familiarity bred irreverence. I shifted nervously in my seat and looked around as the court began to reconvene. My gaze finally came to rest for no particular reason on the dull brass bars surrounding the dock, and for a moment or two I had time for my own thoughts.

I'd spent two weeks at Gunclub Barracks before the trial came up. Then, on the appointed day, the police Land Rover had come to pick me up at dawn to bring me to court. As we drove in, I scanned every detail of the city scene, things I would not normally cast a second glance at, knowing it could be my last visual stimulus for six months: a van parked up unloading boxes, a hotel worker emptying the leftovers from the morning's breakfast into the refuse bins, a building-site foreman discussing progress and plans with a besuited engineer. As we drew closer to the center, the sheer compactness of so many buildings in such a small space began to press in on me. And once inside South Kowloon Court, the institutional solidity, the implacable process of the law gripped me even tighter.

Waiting for the case to be called, I could not feel comfortable for more than a few minutes in any one position: sitting down, standing with hands defiantly in pockets, pacing up and down the corridor, staring blankly out of the window and inwardly contemplating the impending loss of freedom. Even my cast-iron digestion was beginning to weaken. I asked to go to the toilet. When I saw the white of the pan already besmirched by the day's nerve-churned stomachs, the call of nature struggled with the urge to turn straight around and get back out as quickly as I could.

Before I knew it the case was under way. The first two days flashed by in a blue of formalities and feigned politenesses. The charges were read out. I pleaded guilty to POOW. The prosecution constructed their case for AOABH. Witnesses came and went. My defense lawyer, the Colonel, countered as best he could each of the points that was raised. Clint and Buffalo, the only defense witnesses, appeared to give their evidence. They had some difficulty giving a coherent story. They were constantly interrupted by Harry Reynolds OC, CID, who kept telling them to speak more slowly. He was taking down word for word what they said. Their evidence was going to be minutely compared with their previous written statements. The Hong Kong police, still smarting from the two men's insistence on appearing for the defense, were all out to trip them up. One slip-up, one discrepancy between the two accounts and they would be up for perjury. When they had finished they took their places in the spectators' gallery to see if their interventions would make any difference.

The first two days had raised more questions than they had answered. The proceedings had become increasingly bizarre, the story of what had happened increasingly distorted. I was beginning to feel my freedom slip away.

"All stand!"

Mid-morning on the third day, and Justice Ferguson was returning to deliver his summing-up and pronounce his judgment. The policeman sitting next to me hurriedly folded his newspaper as the judge came in, bowed stiffly to the court in mock obeisance and took his seat on the dais.

At the beginning of the trial, the first thing I had noticed was that there were no windows in the courtroom. This had emphasized to me the falseness of the proceedings, the separateness from the real life of the city. Now, at the end of the trial, I was aware that somewhere along the line, my view had done a volte-face. Now, the outside world had faded to unreality. The only real and tangible thing was this courtroom, the only thing that mattered to me was this quaintly berobed representative of the legal process sitting before me sipping a glass of water and adjusting the position of several weighty tomes of law on a ledge in front of him.

"This being a criminal case, the defendant is presumed to be innocent until proved guilty . . ."

The use of the word "until" had an ominous finality to it. Was this a Freudian slip? Had he given the game away right at the start of his summing-up? If he had said "unless" instead of "until," his pronouncement would have had a much less fatalistic ring to it.

"The framework of the law is such that I am permitted to consider only the facts of the case put before me . . ."

His voice was strangely quiet, almost feeble. It barely carried to the prisoner's dock, let alone to the public gallery at the rear. Perhaps he felt he should not have to exert himself, rather that it was incumbent on everyone else to make an effort to hear him.

"I must cast aside all interpretation and speculation and give due weight only to the evidence as presented in this court of law . . ."

The judge was sitting beneath a splendidly colored coat of arms depicting a lion and a unicorn rampant above a banner with the words "Dieu et mon Droit." Three or four gleaming red leather chairs dotted about the court provided the only other splashes of color in what was otherwise a somber room, consisting mainly of dark veneered wood paneling topped by a stained and cracked plaster ceiling. I shifted in my seat, my right knee pumping up and down impatiently to relieve the tension.

"I trust I shall summarize in a satisfactory manner the facts material to this case . . ."

The false modesty was unbecoming and completely out of keeping with the obvious and absolute authority bestowed upon him, an authority emphasized by the fact that he was raised higher than anyone else in the court, that his chair was given a throne-like aura by the floor-to-ceiling heavy brown curtains hanging on the wall immediately behind it, and by his dress, which varied in subtle but definite details from that of the other court officials and barristers: purple edgings on the sleeves and the lapels of his cloak, and a red sash draped over his left shoulder.

"I can tell you, for what it's worth, that as a matter of law . . ."

At regular intervals Justice Ferguson paused momentarily, adjusting his half-moon glasses slightly while at the same time giving vent to a dry, throat-clearing cough. These mannerisms served to mark the rhythm of his summing-up. Why is it, I thought, that every member of the legal services I've ever seen wearing glasses has always sported the same type: the half-moon ones? They certainly had the benefit of giving this judge a particularly stern appearance whenever he glanced up from what he was reading to peer over them at the person before him.

"How many of us can accurately and in detail recall an incident which happened two weeks ago . . ."

I was surprised at how much time the judge spent on seemingly irrelevant or minor details, such as the amount of light in the bar at the time, the sound level of the jukebox, the background noise of the city itself, and the exact distances between the bar, the booths and the jukebox—and here witnesses were asked to select two points in the courtroom to illustrate how far apart they estimated these items to be. I glanced at the clock high up on the wall. Already three quarters of an hour into his summing-up, the judge didn't appear yet to have said anything concrete or to have given any indication as to which way the case would swing. My stomach still felt uneasy. I shifted in my seat again and crossed my right leg horizontally over my left knee. The policeman next to me leaned forward with his hand on his forehead and appeared to doze off.

"Being cross-examined is not a very pleasant experience . . ."

By now, the judge's voice had become strangely monotone, his manner remote and detached, and his delivery had lapsed into a seemingly automatic style. A lull seemed to descend on the court. Attention began to wander. The only person who maintained his level of concentration was the court stenographer, inconspicuously sitting a few feet to the judge's right, furiously tapping away at what looked like a desktop calculator. I found myself staring blankly at the reflected shine of the neon lighting in the varnished wooden rail in front of me. My reverie was interrupted by a noise as someone walked in front of the spectators' gallery. There was so much ancient-looking wood in the room that the slightest movement anywhere in the court was accompanied by an intrusive creaking sound.

"Indeed, excessive anxiety against a charge falsely brought can lead to false evidence being given . . ."

False evidence! There was certainly plenty of false evidence being given, but not through any sense of anxiety or nervousness! Quite the contrary. It was a cold, deliberate attempt to pervert the course of justice, to set me up and to deflect attention away from the truth about what had really been going on in the bar. And the source of this false evidence? Who should appear as star witnesses for the prosecution? None other than the thugs who had started the fight in the first place: Peres and his bottle boys, all smartly turned out and looking distinctly uncomfortable in their Sunday-best suits designed to impress the court and project an aura of probity and integrity. The young Chinese inspector from the EU, completely misreading the situation, had tracked down Peres and his gang and brought them in to make out a case against me.

I was utterly astonished. I wouldn't have been more surprised if, to make pronouncement on the proceedings, the judge had called in a jury consisting entirely of a vanload of day-tripping psychiatric patients from the local asylum. To add weight to the gang's story, a Chinese doctor was wheeled in to testify that in his professional and considered opinion the wound on Peres's head had indeed been caused by exhibit A—the infamous knuckleduster, which lay all alone in the middle of a large table below the judge, tagged with a small white label. It looked faintly ridiculous—like an unwanted sale item—and totally innocuous. You couldn't fire it, throw it, detonate it, cut with it. If a machine gun or a pistol or a ten-inch-bladed knife had been lying there, then the severity of the court proceedings would have been justified. But a knuckleduster, a lump of inert metal! To add insult to injury, the thugs were aided and abetted in their evidence by the meek and mild Soriano sisters, who looked as if they'd been given time out from the nunnery specially to appear in court that day. I daresay they were under some kind of duress to turn up. To me they seemed essentially decent types who somehow had lost their way, who somewhere along the line had naïvely been caught up in the petty-crime scene.

"Now to the evidence itself . . ."

Justice Ferguson picked up a large red notebook, adjusted his spectacles, coughed, flicked through the pages to refresh his memory with some of the handwritten notes he'd taken and proceeded to read out his version of the events. The sight and sound of the learned judge describing in reverent tones the details of a fight that was clearly totally alien to someone of his status bordered on the comic.

"Kicked the assailant in the groin . . . struck him a blow to the temple . . . head-butted the second man . . . grappled with the broken bottle . . . split his scalp with a blow to the head . . . rolled across the floor . . . a scuffle ensued . . ."

A scuffle! More like a life-or-death struggle. I glanced over at the policeman next to me to see what he was making of it all. He was still leaning over with his head on his hands, but

179

contrary to what I had at first supposed he was not dozing. The newspaper had been folded in a strategic manner and he was actually doing the crossword! So much for his concern for the drama that was gripping me.

As I looked around again I realized I'd be glad to be out of this place, no matter what the outcome. The courtroom was much smaller than such rooms appear on TV and in films and, with all its dark wood, was beginning to press in on me.

"I have weighed all the evidence and completed my deliberation . . ."

The last three words were like a whip-crack. One and a half hours had passed since the summing-up had begun, but now the courtroom was fully alert once more. I leaned forward in my seat, partly in anxiety, partly in an attempt to catch the judge's fading voice.

"In the matter of the case for AOABH, the prosecuting counsel together with Mr. Reynolds representing the CID have not covered themselves with glory. Far from it. Their performance borders on the shameful. I have not heard such an ill-prepared case in a long time . . ."

I couldn't believe what I was hearing. Relief was sweeping through me. Vindicated! Not only was their case not good enough, but they were being actively criticized for putting it together so poorly.

"The evidence was atrocious. All the stories were false, nobody told two accounts the same, no two pieces of evidence were consistent . . ."

At this point the prosecution barrister rose to protest. "If it please your honor . . ." The judge glared down at him over his glasses. The barrister quickly lost courage, mumbled something in a tone of voice hushed to the point of obsequiousness, then sat down, disheartened.

"The only independent witness," Justice Ferguson continued, "should have been the barman. He wasn't part of Peres's party, he wasn't police, he wasn't with the defendant. But the only time he told the truth . . ." Here the judge paused regally in mid-sentence, poured himself a glass of water from the carafe, drank half of it and then went on,

". . . was when he said that when it was all over he went round and collected money from everyone for the drinks. The only two prosecution witnesses who consistently spoke the truth were the two Chinese detectives who happened to be having a quiet drink in the bar. Even though they were appearing for the prosecution, their evidence undermined the very case the prosecution was attempting to establish . . ."

It was going my way. Maybe the due process of law had some merit after all! The tension in my shoulders had noticeably relaxed, and I eased back slightly in my chair.

"I rule therefore that the charge of AOABH should be struck out . . ."

Wonderful! I could have been looking at a long stretch for that. Justice Ferguson is not as senile as he looks. One down, one to go. Because of the prosecution's bungling on the first charge, the judge might have some sympathy with me on the second—possession of the duster. He might, after all, accept my argument of self-defense. I was in for a shock.

"As for the charge of possession of an offensive weapon . . ."

Here Justice Ferguson reached forward for one of the large volumes of case history that lay before him, adjusted his wig slightly, shaded his eyes with his left hand, turned the pages of the book with the other and proceeded to cite the case in 1974 of a Chinese civilian who had got involved in a punch-up in a bar in Kowloon. He'd ripped an ornamental sword from where it was displayed stapled to the wood above the bar and used it to defend himself. He was arrested, charged with POOW and sentenced to six months. My euphoria was quickly dissipating.

"In spite of the considerable extenuating circumstances surrounding this case, I have still been given no valid reason why you should have about your person an offensive weapon, namely a knuckleduster. Even if it formed part of your training—and who am I to question these things? I leave that to the judgment of the military authorities—even if it was part of your official equipment, you should not have been carrying it, let alone using it in a public place. Before we know it we will have off-duty members of the forces walking down the street with rifles and machine guns. That is something that just cannot be tolerated."

All hope was fading. How would I cope with a prison sentence? Would I be able to bear the strain of the claustrophobic routine? What would I do when I got back to the UK? Would the RE have me back? If they wouldn't, it would be dishonorable discharge and into civvy street to try to get work with the only trade I knew: driving trucks.

"Taking everything into consideration I have no alternative but to find you guilty as charged . . ."

Here the judge paused. He was sitting with a large ledger before him, pen poised. The pen was just coming down to write me off for six months when the Colonel of the army legal services stood up. "My learned judge, before you pass sentence . . ."

The judge looked at him with a certain benign curiosity.

"There are certain mitigating circumstances in this case."

There was a moment of silence. The judge looked over his half-glasses, pen still poised, and said in a slow, inquiring voice, "Yes, Colonel?"

The Colonel proceeded to launch into a well-prepared plea of mitigation covering five full sheets of paper. Not only did he repeat every aspect of the case that was in my favor, but he also went into every detail of my family background, placing special emphasis on the fact that I had a seven-month-old son to look after. He brought forward an impressive list of character references. I was almost embarrassed. The essential thrust of the plea was an endeavor to demonstrate that basically I was not criminally inclined and therefore was not a suitable candidate for jail, but rather that as a man who had served in the forces I must be deemed to have some substance. The incident in the bar had simply been a temporary and uncharacteristic aberration, which could be penalized with a short, sharp sentence. The Colonel ended by making a strong plea for corporal punishment.

"Well . . ." said Justice Ferguson, a little bemused, "it certainly didn't do me any good at school, but I sentence you to six strokes of the cane. The sentence will be carried out at Stanley Jail. Take the prisoner away."

Thank fuck for that, I thought as I was led down the stairs in the dock that disappeared below court, that's great. At least I've got a fighting chance of saving my army career now. My mind was hardly on the sentence at all. When I heard the judge refer to the cane, I felt as if I was back at school. It felt like nothing more serious than a visit to the headmaster's study. This conclusion was to prove a serious miscalculation.

I was taken to a holding area beneath the courts which consisted of one large transit cell full of pimps, prostitutes and drug-pushers—the fallout from that day's hearings, the dross from the seething social cauldron that was Hong Kong. It was midday. I would have to remain there until late afternoon when the courts rose and the full complement of convicts had been assembled ready for onward transport to their appointed place of punishment. I didn't relish the prospect of five minutes in that cell, let alone five hours. Hardened faces looked up and took my measure as the door clanged shut behind me and the key clicked in the lock. The inside of the cell consisted simply of a concrete block running around the edge, a hole in the middle of the floor serving as a primitive—and very public—latrine for both males and females, and nothing else. The floor was filthy and stank of urine and human feces. There was no ventilation and it was unbearably hot.

I suddenly realized that I was very thirsty. Not only had I not had a drink all morning, but the heat and tension had combined to make my thirst all the more fierce. I called to the Pakistani guard, "You! Get me some water!" I was in no mood for playing the part of the humble prisoner.

Fortunately, the guard, although a little surprised at my forthrightness, appeared to comply with my demand. He wandered off down the corridor and came back a moment later carrying a plastic cup of water. His face broke into an ugly, malicious sneer as, deliberately dangling two fingers in the water, he passed the beaker through the bars.

I looked at it in disgust. The rim was cracked, chewed and dirty and a film of grease scummed the surface. God knows what bacteria were swimming in the filthy liquid ready to infest my already tortured guts. I grabbed the beaker from the guard's hand, shouted angrily, "You must be fucking joking," and threw it full in his face with all the venom I could muster.

He reeled back incensed and, with water still dribbling from his chin, said menacingly, "I'll have you, I'll have you, my boy. No one does that to me and gets away with it. My mates at Stanley will deal with you, my boy." He would have been even more incensed if he had realized that I was not going to be incarcerated at Stanley Jail, that it would be all over in a few hours and that his mates would never have a chance to get near me. I strode defiantly over to the concrete block, stared fixedly at one of the prisoners sitting there until he reluctantly shuffled over to make room for me, and sat down to wait.

Late in the afternoon, a Black Maria with two Chinese warders arrived. The Pakistani guard muttered a few more threats, prodded me in the ribs with a truncheon and handed me over to the warders. The warders frogmarched me up the stairs to the back of the court, out into the high-walled courtyard, where I quickly gulped in welcome lungfuls of fresh air, and into the Black Maria along with several other, dangerous-looking characters. We drove in complete silence through the city streets, into the cross-harbor tunnel and over to the south side of Hong Kong Island.

The Black Maria backed into the courtyard of Stanley Jail, the door was opened and the prisoners filed out under guard into the reception area. I was first in the queue. The other characters who had been brought with me watched somewhat sullenly as I was processed through the jail system. I was stripped naked and searched, all my valuables were removed, placed in a brown envelope and put into a locker, then my clothes were given back, minus belt and shoelaces. I was then gripped by the same two warders who had brought me there and marched across the courtyard. It was early evening. All the prisoners were lining up holding pitifully small wooden bowls to collect their supper of rice and scraps of meat. Far from feeling nervous about the impending punishment, I could focus my mind only on the size of the bowls. Thank God I'm getting out quick, I thought, I wouldn't last six weeks here, let alone six months. I'd starve to death!

We entered a building and walked down a long corridor. As we went along I imagined that the person who would administer the caning would be a normal-sized Chinese. Thank fuck they're all small in China, I thought with relief. I pictured a diminutive figure with a copy of a holy book under his arm to prevent him from raising the cane too high—just as I'd seen at public floggings in the Middle East. I was in for a shock. There, at the end of the corridor, I saw him. Stripped to the waist, wearing PT shorts and pumps, with big muscles, broad shoulders, hands like shovels, his arms folded across a barrel of chest, the monster was waiting. A mountain giant from north Mongolia. I felt the first shivers of fear clutch my stomach.

We turned left at the bottom of the corridor into a large, windowless room. At the back of the room was a long desk at which sat six stern-faced prison officials: governor, deputy governor, head warder, a psychiatrist, an Indian doctor and finally a nurse. Over to the left stood a vaulting box with a thick leather strap dangling loose from each of the four legs. Behind the box there was a rack of solid rattan canes lined up like snooker cues. The monster went over to the rack and started to examine the canes. It was a scene straight out of some Dark Ages dungeon. The knot in my stomach drew tighter.

"Prepare the prisoner." The governor had spoken.

The warder to my left ordered, "Strip down naked. Sit in a chair while the doctor examines you."

Once more I suffered the indignity of standing naked in front of a row of officials. The Indian doctor came over and gave me a cursory examination. He looked at my eyes and my tongue, prodded his stethoscope over my chest and took my blood pressure. With my heart beating at a rate of knots, it was no surprise when the doctor exclaimed, "My goodness! You're blood pressure's high! Have you been taking any sort of drugs recently?"

I saw my chance. I clutched at the straw. "Yeah, I've been on Mogadon and Valium for the last four months."

The doctor stepped back in horror and went for a whispered conversation with the governor. However, it did no good. They saw through the ruse. The doctor returned, shook his head and sat down.

The two warders then hauled me over the bondage apparatus so that my legs were completely off the ground. As I lay spreadeagled I caught the ominous odor of stale vomit left by previous detainees. I screwed my nose up in disgust and started to breathe through my mouth to avoid the noxious smell. It brought to mind something I'd read about torture sessions in medieval chambers. When the prisoner, through the sheer weight of the pain, was beginning to lose consciousness and black out, the torturers, intent on extracting every last drop of suffering, would set light to a greasy rag and hold it below the prisoner's nostrils. The acrid smoke from the flames would sting the unfortunate man back to wakefulness, make him vomit and thus revive him for the next round of torture. As the warders unceremoniously hauled me further forward on the box, I deepened my resolve not to show any signs of reaction to the punishment, not to yell out or show any emotion whatever. It would be stiff upper lip to the bitter end. This would be my way of resistance, of maintaining my dignity, of showing them they could not really get to me. I would end up winning this particular contest, this battle of wills, at all costs. They could beat my body but they could not beat my mind.

My legs were strapped in, then two canvas pads brought

over my back—one to cover the small of my back to protect my kidneys from any badly aimed blows and one across the top of my thighs to protect my testicles. As my wrists were strapped to the front supports, I thought, sod it, every day is a bonus after Mirbat.

The doctor came around, brought a chair and sat next to my head. He whispered almost apologetically, "Oh, for goodness sake make sure your tongue is well back, make sure you keep your teeth clenched, make sure you keep your head still. I will hold your head to keep it from whipping back." Experience had taught him that victims of this barbaric punishment are quickly broken by the beating rod, their reserves of willpower soon overwhelmed by the pain. And that the pain itself bites deeper with each stroke, giving greater and greater impetus to the overwhelming reflex action of jerking the head back.

The governor nodded his head. The chief warder, in a high-pitched, near hysterical voice, shouted out, "Number one." The monster swished the cane twice in the air to build up momentum and to let me know it was coming. The next second it bit into my flesh like a branding iron. My body jerked involuntarily upward to try to release the pain, but the spasm fell back on itself. There was nowhere for my body to go. I was completely immobilized. The straps bound me tight and dug cruelly into my ankles and wrists.

The first stroke had been delivered with unnerving ferocity. It was as if the monster was taking revenge on me for some grave personal insult. With nowhere for my body to move, the agonizing pain simply stabbed deeper and deeper, with a strange shuddering motion like the aftermath of an earthquake. With the first strike the blood vessels immediately beneath the surface of the skin were completely ruptured. My lungs convulsed and sucked a sharp intake of breath through my clenched teeth. With my eyes watering and my head reeling, I was in a state of semi-shock. The intensity of the experience was beyond description. I hadn't expected anything remotely like this. I needed something to focus on, something to hold my senses together. I began to count off the strokes, thinking, every one is one step nearer freedom.

Swish. Swish.

Thwack.

The second blow seared into my flesh and racked my body. I barely resisted the impulse to scream out. The bleeding from the dozens of torn vessels was already welling up into a large, crimson contusion.

"Take some deep breaths. Try to relax. Try to absorb the cane. Don't resist the strokes." The feverish tone and rising urgency with which the Indian doctor delivered his well-meant advice seemed only to convey a sense of incipient panic. I strained to hold my focus: number two; four more to go to freedom. My brain felt tightly compressed, my teeth were firmly clenched.

Swish. Swish.

Thwack.

The impact of the third stroke jolted down and made my legs kick outward, wrenching at the leather straps in the process. Each one was searingly more painful than the last. The monster was an expert. They were all DCs—dead centers. Each blow landed on exactly the same spot as the previous one, intensifying the torture tenfold. The third one had split the skin right across. The pressure that had been building up from the damaged vessels below now found a sudden release. The blood began to flow freely. Three down. Three to go.

Swish. Swish.

Thwack.

The next hit thrashed into me with a strange slapping sound. With unerring accuracy the fourth stroke again hit the wound dead center, causing blood to splatter up on to the small of my back and over my upper thighs. Since I was unable to move, all my insides seemed to be writhing around trying to release the suffering.

"For goodness sake, don't move your head. Take some deep breaths. Come on now, deep breaths." The doctor was now gripping my head like a wrestler, tighter and tighter with each successive stroke. He was leaning forward, his face right next to mine, his mouth babbling directly into my ear.

The fourth impact had made my tongue jolt up to the roof of my mouth. This was swiftly followed by a burning sensation in my nose as a corrosive taste curdled up through my throat and into my mouth. A feeling of nausea flooded through me. I willed myself not to capitulate. I was determined not to give in, not to show any sign of weakness. The urge to vomit beat through me like storm waves on a beach. I was saved only by the fact that having been in court and then in the holding cell I hadn't had anything to eat all day. If there had been any undigested food in my stomach, by now it would have been strewn over the floor.

Swish. Swish.

Thwack.

Jesus, I inwardly screamed. It felt as if the fifth blow had bludgeoned and torn right into the muscles. The deep groove was now a mass of blood and gore. I felt feverishly hot. I was sweating profusely. The leather beneath me had become slippery with perspiration and allowed a fraction more movement. I had thought carrying the tripod on the death march during Operation Jaguar was bad enough, but I had never to this day experienced such excruciating pain. It was as if somehow the pain was bolted on to me. It was so intense it felt as though it couldn't be part of my own body; it felt alien, sinister. I had a tremendous urge to rip it off. I felt that if only I could tear it off I would be free of it.

"Breathe. Don't resist. Breathe. Don't resist." By now the doctor sounded almost incoherent.

Five down. One more left. I tensed for the final stroke.

Swish. Swish.

Thwack.

Bastard! The sixth stroke seemed to bite down to the bone. Every muscle was jarred rigid. My whole body was consumed in a furnace of pain. I took some rapid breaths. For a moment I couldn't move. I was totally paralyzed, then I felt the influx of relief sweep down my spine and lighten my whole body. Number six! I'm a free man! They can't touch me now!

"Release the prisoner." The governor barked the command and two warders came forward. They unstrapped my wrists and ankles, undid the canvas pads and yanked me roughly to my feet. As I stood up, another wave of nausea and dizziness hit me. I felt like spewing over the pair of them. I started retching violently, but managed to hold it back. The agonizing sensation in my buttocks was overwhelming. The movement of my muscles and the change of gravity had forced more blood to the lower half of my body. Only one opiate thought eased the pain: I'm free—they can't do any more. In a few minutes I'll be out of Stanley Jail forever.

The doctor, now somewhat calmer, handed me my clothes and told me to get dressed. It was an agonizing operation. Every slight movement, every minor lift or twist of my body, altered the configuration of muscles and sinews around my buttocks and redoubled the intensity of the pain. I struggled into my shirt first. I then looked at my underpants. The very thought of having anything tight upon the wound made me feel faint. The underpants were filthy anyway. A nerve-racking, three-day court case in the humid atmosphere of Hong Kong had left its mark in no uncertain terms. I paused, then slung them into the corner of the room as a farewell gift to the prison authorities, thinking, those tossers can clean that up. I eased myself into my lightweight trousers. Having got the waistband as far as the buttocks I could hardly pull any further, so I left them hanging down at the back, unzipped at the front and loosely held together just enough to avoid being arrested for indecency. The thought then suddenly came into my mind, what am I going to do now?

The decision was made for me. The torture-chamber door opened and in came a man in a white coat pushing a stretcher on wheels. The doctor said, "You'd better get on here now and we'll take you to the prison health center where we'll give you some medical aid." No one offered any assistance as I struggled on to the stretcher and lay face-down.

We trundled back down the corridor to the medical center. I was becoming stronger and more rebellious the further away from the torture room we went. I kept on thinking, they can't do any more to me now—I'm free. In the medical room I saw an orderly standing around appearing to do nothing. I pointed at him and said, "You! I want a jab for tetanus straight away!" The startled orderly looked around for some assistance, but the two warders had already gone. "Yeah, you! I want a jab for tetanus right now! Move!"

He scuttled away to the fridge and got out a little phial, found a syringe, filled it up and gave me a jab in the arm. He then proceeded to try to dress the bloody wound. "I cannot dress this wound—it is far too severe, too open. It will be too sore for you. All I can do is to put on some antiseptic powder." After he'd ministered to me, he pointed down the corridor to the prison reception where I'd come in and said, "you can go now."

I eased myself off the stretcher, still grasping the waist-band of my trousers, trying to keep them up, still in extreme pain and still thinking, what am I supposed to do now? My thoughts had changed from savoring freedom to wondering about practicalities and feeling anxious about how I was going to get back to Gunclub Barracks. All I got from the reception staff were unsympathetic sneers as they handed over the brown envelope and pointed me toward the little door in the corner of the huge prison gates. I was thinking hard. It must be at least five miles to Gunclub. How am I going to get back? There's no way I can sit down in a taxi.

As I stepped through the gate, a rickshaw driver gestured to me. I winced violently at the thought of being clattered through the streets on the hard seat of that solid-wheeled, springless contraption. "You must be fucking joking, mate," I said to him, but I doubt he understood. I stood there, my rear end throbbing like a cross-channel ferry's engine. Suddenly I saw a movement out of the corner of my eye—and there they all were, waiting for me: an ambulance,

CBF, the Colonel of the legal services. I nearly collapsed with relief.

CBF approached. "Hello, Sergeant. Did it hurt?"

The understatement of the decade. I just looked blank, didn't answer.

"Right! You'd better get on this ambulance and we'll take you to BMH."

My entrance into BMH was made in total secrecy. I was taken around the back to the tradesmen's entrance, and up in a service lift. At the top, the stretcher was wheeled into a sterile wing of the private officer's suite. They did not want it to become known that a member of the SAS had been in trouble.

I was put into bed facedown. A medical orderly told me, "The hospital dermatologist will be along in a few minutes to investigate the wound." And with that he disappeared. I was still in acute pain, but the friendliness of the surroundings began to act like soothing balm.

When the dermatologist arrived, he looked down at the wound and exclaimed, "I've never seen a wound like this in the whole of my army service! Can I take a photograph of it for my records? It really is a unique specimen."

"Well, I've been humiliated enough already today, so I suppose a photograph won't make any difference now. You can send a copy to Reg the medic back at camp for his photo album."

The dermatologist went away and returned a few minutes later with his camera. He took shots from different angles, at one point placing a biro on my thigh to get the scale. As he flitted around the bed he muttered, "This is a real prize specimen." Snap. "This is definitely one for the archives." Snap. "My colleagues must see this one." Snap. I consoled myself with the thought that if I didn't do anything else with my life, at least I'd made medical history. As for treatment, all the dermatologist could say was, "There's not much we can do, I'm afraid. It's got to heal on its own. You'll have to spend a few days in BMH on your stomach. There's no point putting any dressing on it. It needs plenty of fresh air. Do you want any painkiller?"

"Yeah, give me a shot of morphine, but make sure it's in the lower thigh."

After he'd gone, the medical orderly returned and said, "CBF's coming to see you."

CBF in all his glory duly appeared. "Do you realize what you've done, Sergeant?"

"How do you mean?"

"What on earth possessed you to become involved in this escapade? Do you realize the publicity it could attract?"

I just looked at him and said, "Yeah, I know. It's real headline material: the only sergeant in the British Army with twelve stripes—three on each arm and six on the backside. I'm going to sell my story to the *News of the World* when I get back!"

CBF looked rather shocked. "I hope you are not serious, Sergeant." His voice, ringing with uncertainty, tailed off. He disappeared, unsure of whether I was joking or not.

I remained there a further week, being looked after by my own personal captain from the QA's—the Queen Alexandra's Nursing Corps. My own personal nurse. She really had the tender touch. It was almost worth getting whipped for. Apart from the captain I saw no one else. I was left to my own devices and my own thoughts. After a week I was told that I was fit enough to make it back to the UK and that I would leave on a hospital plane from Kai Tak airport the next day. I drifted off to sleep, happy at the prospect of going home.

12

A Visit from the Colonel

I awoke to hear voices in the distance. I was lying facedown on the bed, hot, not quite sweating, but covered in a fine film of body moisture. My nose was blocked, pressed into the pillow. I'd been breathing too long through my mouth; my throat and lips were like burned cardboard. I turned my head to one side and coughed away the congestion in my chest. The voices were closer now. Must be the orderlies coming to prepare me for the journey to Kai Tak airport and then back to the good old UK.

Good old UK? I wasn't so sure that I was relishing the prospect after all. First there would be an extremely uncomfortable flight lasting several hours, throughout which I'd be lying on my stomach on a stretcher strapped to a rack on a medical C 130. Then, once I was home and had had a couple of weeks' R and R, I'd have to face the wrath of the Colonel. The big interview! My future in the balance after the drama of Hong Kong.

Doors were banging. The orderlies were shouting. I couldn't quite make out what they were saying. I shifted slightly on the bed. The muscles in my buttocks and upper thighs were locked solid, as rigid as ships' girders. Something wasn't quite right. Something was out of sync. It was like hearing a blackbird, fooled by a neon street light, singing its morning song in the dead of the night. I began to prise my eyelids open.

"Come on, you lot, out of your pits! Every able-bodied man to assemble in the yard at 0600 hours. You've got five minutes."

"What the hell . . . ?" I finally managed to lever open my bleary eyes and look around. The room was full of coughing, cursing, fumbling shapes. I slid my hand down the side of my body and gingerly fingertipped my buttocks as if feathering a sleeping baby's head. Nothing! Satin smooth. Not a mark. Then it dawned. Ward 11! The early-morning run!

This I was going to relish. Thursday. Action at last after six days of lethargy and boredom! I jumped into my trainers and shorts and trotted to join the rest downstairs. They were all there: doctors, male nurses and patients. That was the system. The doctors had to be seen to be leading from the front. They had to show a good example—a healthy mind in a healthy body and all that. It was part of the occupational therapy.

Twenty minutes and three miles later, I'd outstripped the lot of them, I was on the finishing line way ahead of the rest. I grabbed my chance. As the first of the medics puffed into sight around the last 100 meters, I gave it Sickener 1 for all I was worth. "Come on, you lazy bastards! You should be fitter than me. You do this every morning. I'm supposed to be a burnt-out alkie and I've left you standing!" I beasted them like a veteran instructor, relishing my moment of glory. "What kept you? I'm thirty-eight. I'm fifteen years older than some of you guys and I still came in way ahead of you. You should be fitter than me. I haven't been running for ten days."

They weren't amused.

Nor was the doctor I bumped into coming down the corridor later in the day. He looked tired, stressed and overworked. I said to him, "What's up, doc, got problems?"

"This job is really getting to me," he muttered. "I'm up to here with the pressure of work."

He had fallen headlong into the trap. I lowered my voice, and with a concerned look and in hushed tones of mock sympathy I inquired, "Do you want to sit down and talk about it?"

A psychiatrist! Depressed! And we were the ones who were supposed to have the problems!

A sense of humor works wonders—the best therapy imaginable. I didn't fancy lying there for days on end like an inanimate cabbage. That would be too much like toeing the line—far too boring, far too predictable. I sensed another opportunity a few days later, when the hospital Colonel was about to make his weekly visitation. He would normally sweep around the ward in magisterial style, his sycophantic entourage clucking behind him, inquiring of people lying on their beds or sitting in their chairs how they were feeling. I secretly had a word with the other lads in the ward, then primed the newly arrived lance-corporal from the Royal Irish Rangers, who'd been given the bed nearest the door. "Hey, Shaun. When the Colonel comes in, bring the ward to attention. He expects that. It'll go down well on your report."

I went back to lie on my bed, thinking Shaun would forget all about it—he was after all looking a bit dazed. I was wrong. Half an hour later, the Colonel marched in. Without a moment's hesitation, Shaun leapt to his feet, roaring, "Ward! Ward! Shun!"

As one man, all the alkies shot to attention with a stiff salute and stood there rigid. The Colonel, an astonished look on his face, was rendered nearly speechless. "Er . . . Oh. Very good, chaps. Very good. Carry on."

You didn't need a sense of humor for the videos they showed us, they were funny enough in themselves. They were meant to convey the evils of drink and inspire us to mend our ways. It was difficult taking them seriously. There was the Jimmy Greaves story—a famous footballer hits the

net, then hits the bottle. Then the Glasgow rubber men—
drunks staggering down Buchanan Street in broad daylight.
When this particular one was shown I used to play "Spot the
Jock." Jimmy the Jock who'd saved Ginge on the death
march claimed that he had a leading role in one of the street
scenes. And finally, the third video, the main attraction, the
X Certificate horror film: Cirrhosis! Full technicolor close-
ups and cross-sections of gory livers—dark red healthy ones
wobbling on mortuary slabs and then alcohol-sodden ones
looking like jellies at a kids' party that someone had been
sick over. Aversion therapy, they called it—just like a scene
from *A Clockwork Orange*. Or it would have been, except no
one paid any attention.

"The liver becomes congested with blood, first grows very
large, and then begins to shrink and harden . . ."

The film quality was poor—the soundtrack scratchy, the
pictures flickering and popping.

"Hemorrhage from the stomach may arise, the blood
being vomited or passed through the bowel . . ."

It was like an out-of-date training film for student doctors,
the medical equivalent of Mrs. Beeton's cookbook.

"The urine becomes scanty and turbid. Ascites or dropsy
of the peritoneal cavity is very often present . . ."

I looked around the room at the other half-dozen lads in
the audience. Two were asleep, one was staring out of the
window, one was reading a magazine and the other two were
watching the film with dramatic indifference.

Phase two of the treatment was nearing its end: ten days
of lectures, videos and interviews, and an LFT count every
morning. The results of the count were transferred to a
graph. If the line dropped below the critical threshold and
stayed below, they considered you fit enough for release—
physically fit, that is. If any psychological stress fractures
were detected, that was an altogether different matter. And
they were clever. They shifted, prodded, probed, searched
the defenses, sought the chink in the mental armor, X-rayed
the brain for hairline cracks. If any cracks were found and

they were serious enough, the brain would be stamped "Rejected" and cast down the chute into the Stygian depths of Ward 5 below.

Twelve percent of casualties in any major battle are psychiatric cases, soldiers suffering from combat stress. For many, the symptoms are temporary and manageable. The rest are the ones with unseen wounds. You can see an arm in a sling, a leg in plaster, but you can't see their wounds. They are shunned by society with even greater revulsion than those who have obviously horrific wounds—severed limbs, faces grossly disfigured by burns, sightless eyes. The ones with the mental wounds are often the ones who have done and seen things that the ordinary man in the street couldn't even begin to conceive of, in order to safeguard the well-being of that same man and to allow him to continue walking down that same street in freedom. Their reward is to be entombed in their own minds, like a dead Pharaoh's followers doomed to remain in their master's burial chamber, deep in the center of a pyramid, listening in horror as the sand that held the great building blocks in check trickles away and the stones come crashing down to seal off the passageways to the world outside.

Some of the characters in Ward 11 looked like prime candidates for demotion to Ward 5, first-class specimens just waiting to slide down the chute. One of them had built up an irrational grudge against his orderly officer. One day, while the officer was doing his regular rounds, he'd jumped on top of him out of a two-story window and broken his collarbone. Another character was worse still. He'd attempted suicide by slashing his wrists. He'd been in Northern Ireland and couldn't stand the stress. The crazy thing was, when I questioned him further, I discovered he hadn't even been on the streets: he was a mechanic with the REME! Yet a third bloke, only about twenty-three years old, had a severe case of the DTs. He had to be kept locked away. He was only ever let out to go to the toilet, when two orderlies would march him through the ward, his feet dragging along the floor, his body shaking like a leaf.

My case seemed minor compared to these people's. I should never have been there in the first place. I'd already proved I was physically fitter than the rest. I now had to prove I was mentally fit. Tomorrow, I would face the big one. My interview and assessment with the chief psychiatrist. It all now depended on one man.

13

Embassy Siege

The interview was preying on my mind. I'd tossed and turned all night, and now a fog of tiredness clouded my brain. I took some deep breaths of air to try to clear my thoughts. When I reached the office I knocked on the door sharply and confidently, just once, summoning up some strength by doing so, letting the person inside know I was a force to be reckoned with.

"Enter." It was more formal, more authoritative than the politer "come in."

I went inside. The owner of the voice was speaking on the telephone. I looked at the chair. He caught my glance and gestured to me to remain standing exactly where I was. That was ominous. He continued with the seemingly leisurely conversation on the phone. Delaying tactics. Power games. I'd seen it all before. They try to belittle you by showing who's in control. The big desk, the impressive chair, your small chair, lower than his, it's all part of the strategy.

The conversation finished and the Colonel put the phone down. He paused for a moment, then picked up a thick sheaf of papers from his desk and waved them furiously in the air. "Look at these, Sergeant! These signals from Hong Kong, they're all about *you!*" As he spoke the word "you" his voice raised several decibels. He flung the signals toward the rear of the room. They hit the back wall with a crash and fluttered to the floor in an untidy heap. "We are the people who go into these places, do the job, keep quiet about the job, and at the end we leave the job silently, and we return to the UK as if nothing has happened. What do you have to say in your defense?"

I launched into my plea of mitigation modeled on the one in Kowloon Court, focusing on the self-defense angle and ending with, "You don't have to go to the jungles of Malaya to find a jungle."

The Colonel pondered for a while, then said, "Well, Sergeant. You should not have been there in the first place. But there are certain mitigating circumstances surrounding this case. Therefore, although I could RTU you for life and you would never return to the SAS, I am going to RTU you for only eighteen months."

So it was back to the Royal Engineers, back to Southwood Camp.

I decided to start off as I meant to go on. I would seize the psychological initiative and gain the upper hand. I knew the very first thing they would do would be to order me to get a short back and sides. This was their way of humiliating people, suppressing their individuality. I beat them to it by having my hair shaved virtually down to the wood before I left Hereford.

As I strode confidently through the gate of the RE depot, a regimental police corporal bawled, "Hey, you! Come here!"

I thought, he can't be shouting at me. I haven't been shouted at for ten years! I looked behind me. I couldn't see anyone else.

"Yes, you! Come here!"

I looked behind me again. Still no one there. Right, you bastard, I thought, as I walked up to him. He was in his little sentry box, behind his little pigeonhole. He opened the window, about to say something more, but before he could utter another word I grabbed him by the throat, looked him straight in the eye and snapped, "You! I'm a sergeant from the SAS. Where's the RSM's office?"

He suddenly turned pale. "Sorry, Sarge. I thought you were one of the new recruits," he mumbled apologetically as he furiously dusted himself down.

I strode into the RSM's office and announced boldly, "I'm posted in from the SAS."

The RSM looked up slowly from the carefully printed duty roster he was studying. "You mean you're here on a course, are you?"

"No. I'm posted in."

"You mean you're on a course."

"No. I'm posted in." I was determined to give them a hard time.

"Where are your documents?"

"Have they not sent them yet?"

"No. We haven't got any documents. Wait here."

He went off to check with the Colonel.

"Right. Come in and see the Colonel."

I strode into the Colonel's office, and it started all over again.

"Are you here on a course?"

"No. I'm posted in."

"Where are your documents?"

"I haven't got any documents."

"Where are you from?"

"I'm posted in from the SAS."

"Are you on a course?"

"No, I'm posted in!" I must have seemed like a POW giving only name, rank and number.

"Oh, well, what rank are you?" The Colonel was struggling to inject some logic into my presence.

"I'm a sergeant in the SAS."

"No, in the RE."

"I don't know. I haven't been in the RE for ten years."

"Right. We'd better find out what your rank was in the RE." He rang up RE records at Brighton, put the phone down and said, "Well, Sergeant. I've got some bad news for you."

"What's that?"

"You're now a lance-corporal in the RE."

"I can't be a lance-corporal at my age. I'm too old! I'm a substantive sergeant in the SAS. You can stuff that idea for a start!"

I argued all the pros and cons for the next fifteen minutes, emphasizing my point of view by banging on the table at regular intervals. In the end, the Colonel couldn't hack it any more. He called out, "Captain Edwards. Come in here. Send this man on three weeks' leave while we sort out his case."

They would no doubt soon find my precious documents. Without documents the British Army would grind to a standstill. From when you join the Army to when you leave, or die in between, every single second of your life is documented. Every precise detail is recorded. More effort goes into keeping accurate files than went into winning World War II.

The irony is that no matter how thorough the paperwork, like everything else it is subject to human error. While I was away on leave, word obviously got around the RE depot about the new upstart recently arrived from the SAS, and the spineless wonders in the sergeants' mess evidently decided to try and teach the new boy a lesson. They tried to recall me from leave and put me on guard duty on Christmas Day 1977. There's no way I'm going to work Christmas, I thought. There's no way they're going to rip me off. I'll beat them at their own game.

I ignored the phone calls and stayed at home. Conveniently catching flu, I made damn sure I got a sick note. They'd obviously decided to put the recall in writing so that it could be entered in my documents for a potential future disciplinary hearing. An OHMS telegram duly went out on the morning of 24 December saying, "Report back to Southwood Camp for duty by 0830 hours 25th, repeat 25th, December 1977." The trouble was they addressed the telegram not to me but to my sixty-six-year-old father, a Dunkirk veteran. He'd been on the Reserve for ten years after the war, but he certainly wasn't expecting anything like this at his stage in life. He took the telegram to the local police station and asked them to sort it out. The military wires started buzzing, and an hour later he received a message from the embarrassed authorities to say that he wasn't needed after all and that the telegram was really meant for his son. They'd tried to knock my morale and it hadn't worked. They'd ended up looking complete fools.

I returned to Southwood three weeks after Christmas and once again stood in front of the Colonel.

"We have now got the blueprint of your career." His voice sounded enthusiastic, as if he'd been primed by a higher authority. "I have looked in your documents and I have found that you have done an HGV 2 driving course. Do you realize that with that HGV license, if you do a month's theory study on MT regulations and pass the Driver RE B1 course, you'll be qualified up to Regimental Sergeant Major in the RE."

"That's all very well, but what's my rank right now?"

"Well, for the duration of the course, we'll make you up to Local Sergeant."

"Thank you very much." Local Sergeant unpaid and unwanted, I thought as I quietly closed the Colonel's door behind me.

I passed the course with ease. I was then called back in to see the Colonel.

"We've got a little job for you. We've had an officer cry off from running a recruit troop. Would you like to become an acting troop officer to run the troop?"

I quite fancied the idea of playing God. It meant that I had beaten the career boys back in Hereford to a commission. Visions of going down to the station with a four-tonner to pick up a batch of Sid Vicious lookalikes with purple socks, leather jackets and razor blades and safety pins through their ears, and then beasting them into shape, were rather appealing. I said, "I'll run a mini-selection. Their feet won't touch the ground."

"Carry on, Sergeant."

I must have achieved some kind of record. I went from Sergeant in the SAS down to Lance-Corporal Royal Engineers up to Acting Paid Sergeant, then up to Acting Troop Officer. All within two months!

After eight months as Acting Troop Officer with a sergeant, a corporal and three lance-corporals pandering to my every whim, I was told an officer was moving in to take over my role and I would then be second-in-command. The character turned up: Warrant Officer Second Class. He wasn't a bad bloke really, but I resented his authority. I decided to short-circuit the developing personality clash; I took him to one side and said, "I can't hack this. I've been running this troop very well without you for eight months. I'm off." I went to the nearest telephone, rang up the Second-in-Command of the SAS and said, "You've got to get me out of here or else I'll throw another wobbler. See what you can do."

He contacted Group HQ. A meeting was arranged. I discussed it with the Colonel, who said, "Right. We'll get you on next selection in January 1979."

I was pitched straight into test week. I was given the option of missing out the endurance march if I got A grades in each of the first two marches. It was a great incentive. I didn't stop running for two days, and duly got the two As. I was back in the regiment, back in business! There was just one catch. Having left the SAS as a sergeant, here I was at the age of thirty-eight rejoining the regiment as trooper.

8:30 a.m., Wednesday 30 April 1980. Fifteen months had passed since my return, fifteen months of routine, boredom and lack of action. The rugby-club hangover combined with the noise of the other team members pulling on equipment, filling magazines and cocking weapons made me feel as cheerful as an abattoir-bound pig. I resented that upon my

205

return to the regiment I'd been unable to get back into my old troop, Eight Troop, the lads I'd fought at Mirbat with. There were no vacancies. Right now I'd much rather be abroad with Eight Troop instead of messing around in this hell-hole with Six Troop.

My separation from my old mates in Eight Troop had been made all the more acute when in February of the previous year I'd heard the news of Mike Kealy's death during a forty-mile endurance training march in the Brecon Beacons. The hero of Mirbat six years before, a major and DSO, he died of exposure during a cruel combination of snow, ice and fog. It was a tragic loss and saddened me deeply.

With an ill-disguised lethargy I pushed open the door to the killing house. My mind was barely in focus as I threw down my holdall of assault kit and began pulling at the wire seal on the box of 9-milly ammo. I broke a fingernail in the process as it stubbornly refused to open. I cursed. When you're not in the mood for a job, even inanimate objects conspire against you. They seem to assume a life of their own and to frustrate your efforts at every turn. I tore off the loose piece of fingernail. It came off at a deeper angle than I'd expected, biting into the skin at the side and drawing blood.

Another routine day was in prospect, a day of shooting neat holes in figure-eleven targets. I was beginning to get bored with this place: the oppressive sameness of the range practices, the same six rooms, the target paste-pots always empty. And the figure-eleven targets themselves. In the old Operation Jaguar days, they came properly trimmed with the corners neatly cut off so that they fitted the wooden veneers exactly. Nowadays, the picture of the sinister-looking Russian storm-trooper was stamped on to an oblong sheet of brown paper and you had to fuck and fart about fitting the target facing to the trimmed veneer. And then there was the problem of lead in the enclosed atmosphere of the killing rooms. Firing our submachine guns on automatic over long periods of time filled the small rooms with lead fumes. It occurred to me more than once that breathing the thick smoke couldn't be doing my lungs any good. Only yesterday I had coughed up a large black ball of phlegm at the end of the day's training.

As I pulled on my assault kit, a pain in my temple throbbed continuously. I looked down at the heavy Bristol body armor lying on the bench seat next to my holdall. Fuck the high-velocity plates! I thought, I'm not in the mood for training with that ton weight today—and I threw the ceramic plates back in the holdall. With the now much lighter body armor secure in place, I drew on my skin-tight aviators' leather gloves, cocked the action of my Heckler Koch MP 5, introducing a live round into the chamber, applied the safety catch, carried out the same operation on my Browning pistol and realized I had begun to sweat. It was going to be a long, tedious day.

9:00 a.m. Six Arab revolutionaries—Makki, Ali, Shai, Faisal, Hassan and Oan, the leader—assembled on the blood-red carpet in the foyer at 105 Lexham Gardens in Kensington, London. They belonged to the Mohieddin al Nasser Martyr Group, fighting for the autonomy of Arabistan, an oil-rich province in the southwest of Iran, annexed by that country in 1926. In their small, lightweight holdalls they had a veritable arsenal. It included two 9-millimeter SMG machine pistols, accurate up to 150 meters and firing 700 rounds per minute; three Browning automatics with thirteen-round magazines loaded with Winchester hollow point ammunition; one .38 revolver; and several Russian hand grenades. They bade farewell to the handful of unwitting residents who had befriended them and headed for their rendezvous with destiny.

11:20 a.m. "Split down into three teams of four again." Sek's voice boomed across the small changing room, his beetle-black eyes, the eyes of a deep thinker who weighs up the options carefully before acting, slowly scrutinizing the assembled team members.

My one consolation amid all the monotony of routine training was that Sek, my brother in arms since Mirbat days, had also found his way into Six Troop. A powerful bond of friendship had developed between us. In his assault kit he looked large and menacing. With his big hands he took a firm grip on life, with his wide feet and muscular toes he stood his ground unyieldingly, and with his broad forehead he faced the world square on. In his solidity and steadfastness he was extremely placid. When fooling and rolling around with the Firqat children in Dhofar he had been like a cuddly teddy bear. Nothing appeared to bother him. He would take everything in his stride—or so it seemed. Yet there was a distant point, a point that was rarely reached, but once it was, Sek would explode with an awesome temper. He would then become as ferocious as a grizzly bear.

"The game plan is the same. Head shots—double taps or single only. Limits of exploitation are your allocated rooms." He pointed to the blackboard, circling every individual's responsibility with the barrel of his 9-milly. "Be on your doors in five minutes. I will initiate with a burst of fire into the long gallery. Any questions?"

"Will there be any distractions this time?" My voice cut through the tedium.

"Yeah, I got a thunderflash on ISFE for this one. I'll detonate after the burst of MP 5," replied Sek, replacing his 9-milly pistol in the quick-draw holster, snapping closed the securing stud on the thumb-brake with a well-practiced ease.

11:25 a.m. The terrorists worked quickly. Shamags were pulled tight across dark Arab features, holdalls were unzipped, weapons produced. Then they were up the steps and bursting in through the slightly ajar main door of 16 Princes Gate. Oan, well-built, square-bodied, the first man in, made straight for PC Lock, who was standing by the door to reception at the bottom of the stairs.

* * *

11:25 a.m. The combination of the twenty-round burst from the MP 5 and the deafening explosion of the thunderflash on the ISFE rocked the killing house. My number three on the Remington blasted the lock of the small combat room with a blank cartridge and then kicked the door in. Drag—the range warden—will go mad if he finds that one, I thought, as the door flew open. In I went and headed straight for the cluster of figure-eleven targets propped up in their rickety stands in the far corner. Usual thing, I thought quickly, my eyes doing a radar scan of the room. Four terrorists and three hostages.

Ba . . . Bang, Ba . . . Bang. Ba . . . Bang. Three double taps in less than three seconds, six neat holes in three terrorist heads.

Ba . . . Bang. My number two neutralized a kneeling target behind the chair in a corner.

"Paste up," shouted Sek from the door, adding to the tedium of the moment.

11:26 a.m. "Don't move! Don't move!" screamed Oan in Farsi. Then came a deafening burst of submachine-gun fire. All Trevor Lock could see was confusion, disorder, checkered shamags and automatic weapons. A hand came forward and ripped the radio out of his tunic.

"OK, OK," he found himself saying, as he brought up his hand to investigate a sharp stinging pain in his cheek. The Iranian Embassy siege had begun.

11:40 a.m. I applied the safety catch to my MP 5, pushed the S 6 respirator on to the top of my head and reached for the paste-pot and patches. As I pasted over the neat holes with a grubby Woolworth's paste-brush, a thin, gluey, poorly mixed paste wormed down the handle of the brush and slithered over my fine leather gloves. I cursed inwardly and began applying the one-inch square brown patches to the bullet holes.

* * *

11:44 a.m. At the precise moment that the first blob of sticky white glue slicked into contact with the smooth black leather gloves, a telephone rang in the Kremlin. Dusty, ex-D Squadron and now serving with the Metropolitan Police, was ringing the Head Shed to warn them about the developing drama. His information was sketchy: a group of armed men had taken over the Iranian Embassy in Princes Gate, and a police constable from the diplomatic protection group was being held at gunpoint. More disturbingly, a burst of submachine-gun fire had been heard. That was all the information he could offer.

11:48 a.m. B . . . B . . . Be . . . Be . . . Bee . . . Beep. I had just finished patching up my second double tap when the whole building was filled with the sound of a dozen electronic bleepers.

"The scalybacks have pressed the wrong button again," shouted my number two.

"Or it's another lemon," I added sarcastically. My thoughts went back to the last lemon, a couple of years before, when we had roared down to Stansted Airport to stop Idi Amin getting access to the UK. He had allegedly been circling the airfield in his private plane asking for permission to land.

Suddenly Rusty's harsh voice, calm with certainty, pierced sharp and clear through the high-pitched electronic bleeps echoing around the rooms and corridors of the killing house. "From Crocker. This is the real thing. Pack your gear, then move into the hangar for a brief."

As I dashed for the door, I watched with satisfaction as the cheap Woolworth's paste-brush arched through the air and hit the paste-bucket with a watery splosh.

11:55 a.m. "We are members of a democratic revolutionary front for the liberation of Arabistan. We are the Martyrs." Oan's cold, chilling voice penetrated the tense atmosphere of room 9 on the second floor. Before him were gathered twenty-six frightened hostages: seventeen Embassy staff; eight visitors, including Harris and Cramer, the BBC men, and Ron Morris, the chauffeur; and Embassy security policeman Trevor Lock. Oan viewed his captives with satisfaction, his dark eyes beneath the frizzy Afro hairstyle darting from one figure to another. He felt well pleased with himself. He had struck the first blow for the freedom of his beloved Arabistan.

The terrorists' demands were now issued. "One: we demand our human and legitimate rights. Two: we demand freedom, autonomy and recognition of the Arabistan people. Three: we demand the release of ninety-one Arab prisoners in Arabistan. If all three demands are not met by noon on Thursday 1 May, the Embassy and all the hostages will be blown up."

11:30 p.m. "Toad, how are we doing for time?"

"We're doing just fine. Keep the speed down," replied Toad, an assault-team leader, the bowl of his meerschaum pipe sparking and glowing in the darkness.

I eased my foot off the accelerator and watched the needle of the speedo drop to a comfortable seventy miles per hour. I was experiencing the usual tight feeling, the strange tingling alertness I always got when I was heading into a situation where a real enemy might be waiting. As my foot pumped fuel to power the engine, my heart pounded adrenaline to fire my body to peak alertness.

As we reached the outskirts of the capital, Toad suddenly sat upright and reached for the London *A to Z*. We had come off the M40 and hit the Marylebone Road. The meerschaum pipe had disappeared and the flexi map-reading light had been switched on. "Once we're past Madame Tussaud's, take the next main road on your left. That should lead us to the barracks."

The signpost for the A4201 appeared and I swung the Range Rover left into Albany Street. We motored along for 300 meters and then turned right in through the main gate of Regent's Park Barracks, the holding area. The guard checked our IDs, the barrier went up and I eased the vehicle into the parking zone. We unpacked the assault kit in the sparse surroundings of the holding area. The weapon bundles were laid out, boxes of live ammunition broken open and magazines charged. By now it was the early hours of Thursday morning. We had arrived.

8:00 a.m., Thursday 1 May. "Oan is beginning to experience a growing feeling of irritability. He has shown good faith by releasing a sick woman, Frieda Mozaffarian. The police have not reciprocated to his request for a doctor to come to the Embassy and examine one of the male hostages. He is becoming increasingly frustrated at the negative response to his demands. He has managed to put an international telephone call through to the Foreign Ministry in Tehran, only to be told by Iran's Foreign Minister, Sadegh Ghotzbadeh, that his group are the agents of President Carter and the CIA and that the hostages would consider it an honor and a privilege to die as martyrs for the Iranian Revolution."

The holding area at Regent's Park Barracks was like any other holding area: large, derelict and drafty. The toilets were blocked and there was only cold running water. Gray powdery dust clung to the floors, window ledges and washbasins, turning the whole building into a health hazard. I was lying on an army camp-bed, going over in my mind the details of the early-morning green-slime brief we had just received. I was wearing my black overalls, belt kit and Northern Ireland lightweight boots. The rest of my assault kit was close at hand. My MP 5, body armor and assault waistcoat loaded with stun grenades were on a chair next to me. My respirator was in its olive-green container. The waiting had begun.

11:00 a.m. Inside number 16, Oan was wrestling with his first problem—the sick British hostage. Chris Cramer, the BBC sound organizer, was lying on the floor, doubled up with severe stomach pains. The sweat ran down his face in rivulets as he rocked back and forth, imploring Oan, "Get me a doctor. For God's sake, get me a doctor."

"But your British police have refused permission," replied Oan.

"How do we know this?" interrupted Sim Harris, the BBC sound recordist.

"Come, I show you," said Oan.

Harris was led downstairs to a green radiophone that the police had passed through a ground-floor window in a shoebox secured to a long pole. Harris talked to the police negotiator, pleading for a doctor for Cramer. The negotiator replied that his request was being considered. As the negotiations became more heated, with the negotiator telling Harris to persuade Oan to release Cramer, and Harris once again pleading with the police for a doctor, the now seriously ill Cramer was helped downstairs and laid on the floor of the Embassy foyer.

At the sight of the sick BBC man writhing about on the carpet, Oan thought that his most productive course of action would be to release him. So finally, at 11:15 a.m., the Embassy front door opened, and Cramer, still doubled up in pain, stumbled to a waiting ambulance. It was Oan's first mistake. The thorough debriefing to which Cramer was subjected after his release was to prove crucial to the planning of the coming operation.

7:30 p.m. I readjusted my position on the floor of the Avis hire van to ease the cramp in my left leg. The rear stowage compartment of the van was packed to the roof with personnel kit, assault equipment and team members. In the restricted space it was impossible to get comfortable. We were traveling through central London on our way to the new holding area, a location in the heart of South Kensington. Owing to the events of the day, the Head Shed had decided that it would make sound tactical sense for us to be in the vicinity of number 16, in case of the imminent slaughter of the hostages. It would cut our reaction time down to almost zero.

The situation was deteriorating, Oan was becoming increasingly tense and unpredictable. He had allowed the deadline—and a new one of 2:00 p.m.—to pass without incident. But his demands were changing. He now wanted three Arab ambassadors to act as mediators and negotiate a plane to take him and his group out of Britain.

The Avis van rumbled to a halt. It would be a relief to leave the claustrophobic atmosphere of the rear stowage compartment. We grabbed our holdalls and bergens and jumped out. Our three vans were parked in a side-street east of Princes Gate. To the north, across Kensington Road, loomed the inky blackness of Hyde Park. I looked past the vans at the huge tower block of flats hiding our presence from the gunmen in Princes Gate. This really was the concrete jungle, a million miles away from the tall green-stuff.

9:30 a.m., Friday 2 May. "I know what's going on. Your British police have cut off the telex and the international telephone. Your secret police want total control over what the outside world knows about our demands. I am now forced to apply pressure. I must kill a hostage." Standing in the doorway of Room 9, Oan surveyed the male hostages. They looked devastated. "You, bring Dr. Ezzatti to me," ordered Oan, pointing his machine gun at journalist Mustapha Karkouti. Karkouti helped the unfortunate Cultural Attaché to his feet.

"This could be a counterproductive move," said Lock, staring directly at Oan. "Why don't we have another talk with the police negotiator?"

Oan hesitated. "OK. But no tricks or I will kill the hostages," and he brought his gun up to Ezzatti's head to emphasize the point.

"There is a hostage about to be killed unless you allow Oan full use of telephone and telex." Lock's voice boomed out over the forecourt from the open window on the first floor.

"Impossible," came the negotiator's reply.

"But a man is about to be killed," pleaded Lock.

"What do they mean, impossible?" cut in Oan, sensing a challenge to his authority. He forced the gun harder into the side of Ezzatti's head. He stared fixedly at the terror-stricken man and then appeared to relent, pushing the Cultural Attaché to the rear of the room. "I want to talk to a man from your BBC, a man who knows Harris." Oan spoke slowly but could not veil the threats. "I set a new deadline in a few hours." And with that, all went quiet at the first-floor window.

3:00 p.m. The police had finally produced Tony Crabb, the managing editor of BBC TV News and a personal friend of Sim Harris. Crabb scribbled the hurried statement shouted by Harris from the first-floor window into an old notebook. Oan demanded: a coach to take gunmen, hostages and one Arab ambassador to Heathrow; the non-Iranian hostages to be released at Heathrow; and an aircraft to take the remaining hostages, gunmen and ambassadors to an unspecified Middle East country and then to release them. Oan also wanted his aims and grievances broadcast by the BBC that night.

8:30 p.m. "The whole of the ground-floor and the first-floor windows are armor-plated. I know because I cleaned up after the contractors had finished. Behind the wooden door at the front there is an ornate steel security door." The caretaker's voice cut through the silence of the briefing room like a chainsaw.

We were all sitting around a scale model of the Embassy which had been hastily constructed in quarter-inch plywood the day before. It had taken us twenty-four hours to locate the caretaker, who had been enjoying a day off when the siege began. And here he was giving us our best target brief to date. He knew every nook and cranny in the Embassy, every storeroom and broom cupboard. I could only speculate as to what he was feeling, suddenly catapulted into the limelight from the anonymity of his humble occupation. All eyes were on him. His was the last job anyone would have chosen if they had wanted to make an impact on the world scene. But from the security forces' point of view, it was the ideal job to enable someone to give them an intimate knowledge of the structure of the building. Hell! What a stroke of luck locating this guy, I thought. Without his information, our initial response to the threatened slaughter of hostages could have turned into a real can of worms. The original plan had been to run out of number 14 and batter in the ground-floor windows and main door of number 16 with sledge-hammers. Christ! With that armor-plating, the sledges would have bounced off. It would have been like trying to knock down a concrete wall with a toffee hammer.

There now followed a hectic period of replanning. Orders were rewritten, we were rebriefed, demolition equipment was issued. I began to get a feeling that this nut was going to be even tougher to crack than we'd anticipated.

11:30 p.m. The final outrage for Oan. He had sat right through that evening listening to the regular news bulletins, growing more and more frustrated as each successive broadcast drew a blank. He had become obsessed with hearing his aims and grievances broadcast. The BBC had indeed now transmitted a brief broadcast stating the new demands—but to Oan's disbelief and anger they'd got it wrong. The BBC had stated that the Government wanted the Arab ambassadors to negotiate with Iran. In fact, Oan had demanded that all negotiations be conducted through the British Government. He rose slowly to his feet, his eyes ablaze with fanaticism and hatred. A chill of fear swept through the hostages.

6:05 a.m., Saturday 2 May. Beeeeeeep. The single shrill tone of the field telephone penetrated the operations center of Alpha Control, the police forward operations room situated in number 25 Princes Gate—the Royal School of Needlework. A surreal setting if ever there was one! The duty negotiator, a tall, slim, refined man, rubbed his tired gritty eyes and lifted the receiver. "Good morning. This is David," he said politely. "How . . ."

"You are liars!" Oan's angry voice scythed into the attempt at exchanging pleasantries. "You have cheated and deceived me over my demands."

It was a perfectly clear line. The duty negotiator sensed the extreme agitation in Oan's voice. He tried again to calm him down, to divert his mind from the high tension. "Oan, what would you all like for breakfast?"

"I'm not hungry. I want to talk to the Arab ambassador."

"Oan, we are doing our best, but this all takes time."

"I have no time left. You bring one of the ambassadors to the phone now."

The negotiator gripped the telephone receiver tighter at the sound of the rising hysteria in Oan's voice. "Oan. The Foreign Office are dealing with your demands right now, but it all takes time."

"You are not dealing with my demands at all. You are sitting on your fat bottoms in your warm offices doing nothing. I tell you now. Because of Britain's deceit, your British people, your British police—they will be the last to be released. And if you do not send the BBC man back to talk to me, the one who was here yesterday, someone will have to die." With that, the phone went dead and silence descended on Alpha Control.

3:30 p.m. Tony Crabb, the editor of the BBC TV News, finally turned up. He was verbally abused by Harris for putting lives at risk by delaying the broadcast of the gunman's statement and by not ensuring that the statement was correct in every detail. At this stage, the police negotiator, standing close to Crabb, decided to intervene. He agreed to take down Oan's statement and personally to ensure that it was correct. He took out his notebook and pencil and began recording Oan's statement as it was shouted down from the first-floor window by Mustapha Karkouti. The final clause of the statement demanded a guarantee that the BBC put out the demands totally accurately and on the next news bulletin. This was another mistake. It gave the negotiator a bargaining point. He seized his opportunity. "OK, Oan. I will give you your guarantee if you show us some good faith and release some hostages."

There was a pause, a movement by the curtains. The air was charged with tension.

"We give you one," came Oan's reply from within the room.

"We need more," said the police negotiator impassively.

Another pause. Another tension-filled minute.

"I give you two."

The bargain was struck.

Two hostages were chosen for release. First, Ali-Gholi Ghazan-Far, a Pakistani educationalist, the man who snored loudly at night and kept everyone awake. That was why he was chosen. They wanted to get rid of him. And second, Haideh Kanji, the pregnant woman. Oan demanded that his statement be broadcast accurately before the release of the two hostages. The police demanded that the hostages be released first. Result: stalemate.

On receipt of the police demand, Oan threw the phone to the floor in anger and frustration, threatening to kill a hostage at 9:00 p.m. if nothing was heard on the nine-o'clock news. At this latest threat, Karkouti went completely to pieces and sank to his knees, pleading with Oan not to carry out the execution. Karkouti's pleading must have struck a humanitarian chord in Oan's fanatical brain, or perhaps it was just a psychopath's cunning that led to the terrorist leader's change of heart. No one will ever know. In the event, Oan decided to meet the police halfway and release the pregnant woman before the 9:00 deadline.

"We swear to God and to the British people and Government that no danger whatsoever . . ." The voice of Scotland Yard's Head of Information drifted over the airwaves of the BBC at exactly 9:00 that evening, relaying Oan's statement of demands word for word to an anxious, waiting world. It was precise and word perfect. The hostages and the gunmen were jubilant, kissing and hugging each other, tears of joy running freely down their flushed cheeks.

218

Only one man was absent from the celebrations. Oan. He stood to one side, nursing his machine pistol in the crook of his arm, alone, poker-faced.

A short while later, Ali-Gholi Ghazan-Far was led downstairs to the ground floor. He stepped through the main door of the Embassy and walked across the road to freedom and a waiting ambulance.

11:00 p.m. It was a fine, starry night. The sun had vanished, abandoning London to the evening's dark embrace. The air was exquisitely clear as we carefully picked our way across the rooftops toward number 16 Princes Gate. An eerie silence had descended on Knightsbridge and South Kensington. No noisy rush of traffic, no late-night revelers lost in search of Chelsea. The rustle of clothing, the leather creak of belt kit, the scuffing noise of a running shoe on a bit of loose guttering were the only sounds that stirred the hush of that tranquil May evening.

Suddenly—crack! The sound of a pistol going off. We froze for a few seconds. One of the lads was pointing to his foot; he'd broken a slate as he'd stepped on it. We gave the thumbs up to the D11 sniper in his concealed position on number 14 and moved on.

I looked out across the rooftops in front of us. It was a veritable aerial farm, with a jungle of telescopic poles, wires and satellite dishes. About five meters ahead of me was the dim, shadowy figure of Roy, the recce-party leader. He was pointing at something by his feet. As I drew level with him, I caught a glint of moonlight on glass. It was the Embassy skylight. "This is it. The skylight of number 16," whispered Roy, looking down at the glass frame. "Let's see if it will open." He knelt down and gripped the wooden surround and attempted to lift it, but it seemed to be locked solid. He swore under his breath and stood up.

We were staring blankly at the wooden frame when Pete, the third team member, whispered quietly, "Let's peel the lead back," and with that he knelt down and began picking at the strip of lead waterproofing around the edge of the

219

glass. After fifteen minutes' careful work he had removed most of the lead and was able to lift one of the glass panes clear of the frame. He reached through the hole and after a few seconds stood up with a lock in his hand. "It wasn't even locked, just pushed through the hasp," he whispered triumphantly, having once more gripped the skylight and slowly eased it open.

Moonlight immediately flooded the small room beneath us. We found ourselves looking down into a cramped bathroom. Directly below us was a large white enamel bath. In the left-hand corner was a grimy washbasin, and opposite it was the door that could lead us to the top landing of the Embassy and eventually to the terrorist stronghold. I felt a sudden rush of excitement, a surge of adrenaline, at the thought of the options this new development offered. I had to stifle an urge to become the first SAS man into the Embassy. It would have been quite easy to grip the wooden surround of the skylight base and lower myself down on to the edge of the bath. But thoughts of immortality were interrupted by a hand on my shoulder and by Roy's voice whispering, "Come on. Let's get back to the holding area. We can tell the boss we've got a guaranteed entry point."

8:00 p.m., Sunday 4 May. The next day, things seemed to go much better. Oan's hardened resolve appeared to be softening. The news bulletins were full of optimism. The Arab ambassadors had agreed to attend a meeting of the Cobra Committee in their basement in Whitehall. Oan, in return, had agreed to reduce his demands. He now wanted only one Arab ambassador to negotiate the safe passage of the gunmen. He also agreed to release Mustapha Karkouti, who was suffering from some kind of fever. At about eight o'clock on Sunday evening, Karkouti stepped through the main door of the Embassy, took a deep gulp of fresh air and walked to freedom.

9:00 p.m. Malcolm was a nervous, white-faced RAOC clerk, the squadron scribe. He was not deep-chested or strong in the arm, and with his pale, thin face and sympathetic eyes he could have been any mother's favorite son. Being involved in the Embassy siege was a definite event in his life, a step forward, he felt, toward that most coveted badge of rank: the Chief Clerk's crown and laurel leaves. Like some of the damned in legend, he dwelt in a middle void, hung between the élite of the SAS on one side and the crap-hats on the other. Now, as he stood in full assault kit before the plywood scale model of the Iranian Embassy, waiting for his room combat brief, he must have felt that he finally belonged.

Earlier in the evening, as, feeling remote and out of touch, he sweated and fussed over the squadron ration indent, Del, one of the assault-team leaders, and I had approached him. "Malcolm, one of the lads is in a bad way. The doc has diagnosed lepto. He must have caught it in Belize earlier in the year. That leaves us a man short in one of the assault teams. We're on standby. We haven't time to get a replacement down and brief him. Do you think you can stand in?"

The cheap stationery-office pen came to an abrupt halt on the ration-roll, and for a split second Malcolm looked as though he had been asked to partake in a bank robbery. A strange, tortured look flashed across his boyish features, then vanished as quickly as it had appeared. He had led a tedious and mediocre life and had been resigned to his daily mountain of paperwork. Now, with this unusual offer, he had a chance to achieve something out of the ordinary, a chance to be above average, a chance to dare and to win. His decision was made.

He concentrated his attention on the plywood section of the Embassy's second floor. His hands, resting across the front of his body, held his S 6 respirator and his fingers shook visibly as he attempted to adjust the securing straps.

"You will be my number two." Del's voice was precise and to the point as he gave Malcolm his assault pre-brief. "Once I've gained entry, you will take out targets to my left and right. Remember, if you get hit I will have to leave you. The medics should find you within half an hour." Del's voice tailed off as he withdrew the hand-held pointer from the plywood corridors and returned it to the briefing pack.

The respirator now shook violently, but there was no look of fear in Malcolm's eyes. For the first time in his life he was doing something positive, and his mind was in overdrive, leaving far behind any weak thoughts.

A creaking door and a muffled cough at the rear of the room interrupted the tense, businesslike briefing. "From Crocker. The Colonel's main briefing in five minutes." It was Rusty. He was now third-in-command of the operation. With a final request for any questions, and an extremely efficient "Synchronize your watches," Malcolm's assault pre-brief was complete and he was now fully operational.

The large main briefing room in the holding area was buzzing with rumor and gossip as Malcolm, Del and I took our seats. The Colonel launched into his badged-personnel-only briefing, which covered such gory details as the removal of the dead bodies from the Embassy. Malcolm avoided his hawkish gaze by staring intently at the eyepiece of the respirator resting on his knees, as though he were looking for signs of weakness and fear in the reflected image of his face in the small glass lenses. As the Colonel continued, Malcolm shifted uncomfortably in his seat. By the time the Colonel had finished his brief and left the room, Malcolm had developed severe facial flushes. His head sagged forward as if he was carrying some huge invisible burden on his shoulders, and his fingers twitched feverishly as he worried and fussed over the tightness of the filtering canister on his respirator.

I was just about to suggest that Malcolm should take part in a daylight raid on the Embassy via the skylight entry point, when out of the corner of my eye I noticed the Jester, one of the team leaders, making a rapid cutting motion with the tips of his fingers across his neck. "Malcolm," I said quietly, "you're on *Candid Camera.*"

For a moment, nothing registered on Malcolm's flushed face. He was on his feet, clumsily readjusting the equipment that hung on his slight frame. His hands jerked uncontrollably as his fingers traveled like a spider over belt, holster and pistol grip.

"You're on *Candid Camera,*" I repeated.

As the situation began to register, Malcolm shook his head and slowly straightened his sagging shoulders. A look of total bewilderment spread across his face and his eyes began to blink violently. "You mean it was a stitch?"

"Yes, Malcolm, it was a stitch, a rubber dick." For just a split second a look of disappointment seemed to hang heavily on his face, then his eyes stopped blinking. The taut muscles in his neck and jaw seemed to relax and his mouth broke into a huge grin. For Malcolm it was the end of a great adventure.

6:30 a.m., Monday 5 May. Just when things seemed to be going well, the situation worsened.

In the cold light of dawn, Oan and the rest of the gunmen seemed to be nervous and jittery as they woke the hostages in room 9. Oan complained to Trevor Lock that during the night he had heard strange noises, and he was convinced that the police had gained access to the Embassy. He ordered Lock to search the building while he woke the rest of the hostages. The strangeness of this order was a reflection of Oan's agitated state of mind.

Sim Harris and Ron Morris wiped the sleep from their eyes, struggled to their feet and set about the usual early-morning chores. They washed the cups from the previous evening and prepared the Spartan breakfast of biscuits and tea. As Morris passed around the biscuit tin to the women in room 9A, Trevor Lock returned from his recce of the building. He could be overheard telling Oan that he must be mistaken and that apart from themselves the Embassy was empty.

10:00 a.m. A telegram arrived from Iran's Foreign Minister, Sadegh Ghotzbadeh. It was addressed to the hostages, and it declared that Iran was proud of their steadfastness and forbearance over the situation and that tens of thousands of Iranians were just ready to enter the Embassy with cries of "Allah akbar," bringing final judgment to mercenaries of Ba'athist Iraq. The bottom line reduced the hostages to a shocked silence: "We feel certain that you are all ready for martyrdom alongside your nation."

11:00 a.m. Oan, enraged and extremely suspicious, called for Trevor Lock to join him on the first-floor landing. "What is this? Are your British police trying to break in?" he shouted, pointing to an unmistakable bulge in the wall separating the Iranian Embassy from the Ethopian Embassy next door.

"Of course not," replied Lock.

"I do not believe you. Your police are up to some trickery."

"Don't worry, Oan, the police won't break in here."

"What do you mean, the police won't break in here? Where will they break in?"

"What I meant was, if the police were planning an attack, it would not be imminent," replied Lock, trying to retrieve the situation.

"Your police, they are up to something, I am convinced. I'm going to make new arrangements for the hostages." And with that, Oan stormed off upstairs to the second floor to organize the movement of the hostages.

The gunmen now looked alert and extremely agitated. Their weapons at the ready, checkered shamags pulled tight about their heads, they moved the male hostages from room 9 along the corridor to room 10, the telex room. Oan and his comrades could sense that something was happening. The whole situation was as taut as a piano wire. They were all tired, tired of this psychological game. The operation had been planned to last only forty-eight hours at the most. They couldn't go on forever sheltering under this political umbrella. They had to break out. They had to play the final scene.

12:00 noon. Lock, tired, resigned, his face haggard with exhaustion, continued his efforts to pacify the terrorists. "Oan, we must talk to the police."

"Why should I?"

"The situation is serious. We must have a chance to talk to them."

"OK. I give you five minutes with them."

Lock and Harris made their way to the first-floor front balcony and made contact with the police negotiator. "Now listen to me," said Harris urgently. "Lives are at risk, time is running out."

"We are doing all we can," replied the police negotiator, his voice sounding calm amid the rising drama.

"Something has got to be done," urged Harris. "The Foreign Office is not moving."

"It all takes time," said the negotiator.

"I told you, time is running out. Where is the Arab ambassador who is going to mediate? We've got to have answers."

"Things are moving along as quickly as possible. The Foreign Office are still in discussion with the ambassadors, and if you listen to the BBC World Service you will get your confirmation," said the negotiator finally.

1:00 p.m. The news bulletin provoked a response that effectively drove the final nail into Oan's coffin. He was infuriated by the fact that the meeting between Cobra and the Arab ambassadors was still continuing and that a final decision as to who would mediate had not been taken. Incensed and expressionless, his mind clouded with frustration and loathing, he put the telephone receiver to his ear. His lips formed the words that would seal his destiny: "You have run out of time. There will be no more talking. Bring the ambassador to the phone or I will kill a hostage in forty-five minutes."

1:40 p.m. The duty negotiator seated by the field telephone in Alpha Control drummed his fingers on the table serving as a desk and glanced nervously at the clock on the wall. The minutes since the last conversation with Oan had flown by, and there was still no news from Cobra, still nothing positive to bargain with. Intuition based on years of experience of dealing with criminals told him that something was wrong, something had changed. It was as if he had

225

been sitting dozing by a fire and had suddenly awakened to see the last flickering flames die away just as a chill wind outside began to rattle the window panes.

A moment later the shrill tone of the telephone buzzer cut through the silence. The negotiator lifted the phone off the cradle and in a voice filled with a calm he did not feel spoke into the receiver. "Hello, it's Stuart here."

"Stuart, they have a hostage and they are going to kill him." It was Trevor Lock. "They have him at the bottom of the stairs. Something terrible is going to happen. They are tying his hands behind his back. They are tying him to the banister." Lock's voice still sounded calm, he still seemed in control; only his rapid breathing betrayed him.

"If you don't accept my demand, I will shoot him." The voice had changed; it was more urgent, more threatening. It was Oan.

"Oan, this is Stuart. Don't do anything that could be counterproductive."

"I told you, I have waited long enough. You have deceived me. Someone will die."

A whole minute passed.

"I am one of the hostages." The voice came in short, rapid gasps. It was inarticulate, as though the owner was fighting for control. "I am one of the hostages. My name is Lavasani."

Another pause, another tortured moment.

The voice that cut in next was high-pitched, immediate and threatening. "No names. No names."

At that moment, the whole tense atmosphere dissolved into the distinct, unmistakable sound of three low-velocity shots. It was precisely 1:45 p.m.

1:46 p.m. After four days of restless inactivity, the holding area was becoming decidedly claustrophobic. Even the monotonous routines of the killing house began to seem appealing: at least back at base there was noise, movement and action—and the chance of decent food and a few pints afterward. I was lounging on my camp bed, bored, uninterested, aware of a cynical resignation creeping in. All this effort. All this activity. All this waiting. All for nothing. I could see that we would soon be packing our bags and heading back to Hereford.

Suddenly there was a shout. The news of the hostage's death hurricaned through the room. I reached for my MP 5, removed the magazine, cocked the action and caught the ejected 9-milly round. I then stripped the weapon and began to clean the working parts meticulously. This is it, I thought as I lightly oiled the breech-block. There could be no going back now. A hostage had been murdered. Direct action would have to be taken. As I threaded the metal beads of the Heckler Koch pull-through down the barrel of the machine pistol, I let my mind wander through the problems of attacking a building with over fifty rooms. We would need speed, we would need surprise, we would need aggression. I thought of the words of advice from Paddy Mayne, one of the founders of the SAS: "When you enter a room full of armed men, shoot the first person who makes a move, hostile or otherwise. He has started to think and is therefore dangerous . . ."

With one final smooth tug on the pull-through, I finished cleaning the MP 5. I reassembled the weapon and replaced the magazine of thirty rounds. There was the usual reassuring metallic click as I snapped home the cocking handle. I applied the safety-catch and returned the MP 5 to the chair next to my assault waistcoat, then cast a quick glance over the rest of my kit. Satisfied with its condition, I picked up the copy of *Colonel Paddy,* the biography of the late Lieutenant-Colonel R. Blair Mayne DSO (3 Bars), that I had been reading earlier, and settled down to wait for the final orders before movement into assault positions. I knew from experience they would not be long in coming.

7:00 p.m. "We put the body on the doorstep. You come and collect it. You have forty-five minutes. Then I give you another one." Oan's chilling message rippled over the airwaves in Alpha Control. The atmosphere was electric. A short while before, a second burst of shots had been heard, and now all eyes were glued to the television screens preparing to relay the growing drama to an as yet unsuspecting world audience. The main Embassy door swung open and the police watched as a lifeless bundle was dumped on the steps.

Twenty minutes later, the field telephone rang on the first-floor landing. Oan picked up the receiver. "Yes, what do you want? The time is running out."

"Yes, we know that," replied the duty negotiator. "That's why we want to discuss the arrangements."

"What arrangements? What are you talking about?" snapped Oan.

"The arrangements for the coach to take you to the airport. How big do you want the coach? How many hostages will be going to the airport? What sort of guarantee do you require?"

There was a brief pause. The negotiator could almost sense the questions running through Oan's mind.

"I require a coach big enough for twenty-five people, and Mr. Trevor will drive it." Oan's voice was still cautious, but it had a more confident tone.

"Shall we park the coach at the front of the Embassy?"

"That will be fine. But I want a guarantee this is no trick."

"Oan, this is not a trick."

"I want the guarantee from your police chief."

"Oan, I repeat, this is not . . ."

Boooooooom!

7:23 p.m. The deafening explosion of the diversion charge was like a thousand wind-slammed doors. It rocked the Iranian Embassy and shattered the eerie silence. Two call signs from Zero Delta located behind the high wall at the front of the building began pumping CS gas through the broken windows. Orange-yellow flames burst through the windows and licked into the mellowing gold of the early-evening sun which layered the Roman columns and ornate balustrades with a soft coat of creamy light.

My troop was waiting, counting the microseconds, in the

Royal College of General Practitioners next door to the Embassy. I stared in disbelief as Mac, ex-Royal Engineers and as tough a Jock as they come, his MP 5 on a loose sling around his neck, held up a novelty cardboard frog suspended on two pieces of string. As he pulled on the ends of the string, the frog's green-colored legs made a ridiculous leaping motion. This act of pure pantomime cut through the tension like a hot knife.

Seconds later, the voice in my earpiece screamed, "Go. Go. Go." There was no turning back now. We were on our way. I was number one in the crocodile. The rest of the call signs were strung out behind me. Hell, I thought, what am I doing at number one? The new boys should be at number one. I've done my time under fire. I should be at the rear with Sek, my Mirbat mate with whom I have a sixth-sense intuitive understanding in the operational field. Damn the RTU! Damn the demotion! I was pushing open the French windows at the rear of number 14. As I led the crocodile out of number 14 toward the rear of number 16, I glanced up at a block of flats to our left. It was bristling with snipers.

We took up a position behind a low wall as the demolition call sign ran forward and placed the explosive charge on the Embassy french windows. It was then that we saw the abseiler swinging in the flames on the first floor. It was all noise, confusion, bursts of submachine-gun fire. I could hear women screaming. Christ! It's all going wrong, I thought. There's no way we can blow that charge without injuring the abseiler. Instant change of plans. The sledge-man ran forward and lifted the sledge-hammer. One blow, just above the lock, was sufficient to open the door. They say luck shines on the brave. We were certainly lucky. If that door had been bolted or barricaded, we would have had big problems.

"Go. Go. Go. Get in at the rear." The voice was screaming in my ear. The eight call signs rose to their feet as one and then we were sweeping in through the splintered door. All feelings of doubt and fear had now disappeared. I was blasted. The adrenaline was bursting through my bloodstream. Fearsome! I got a fearsome rush, the best one of my life. I had the heavy body armor on, with high-velocity plates front and back. During training it weighs a ton. Now it felt like a T-shirt. Search and destroy! We were in the library. There were thousands of books. As I adjusted my eyes to the half-light—made worse by the condensation on my respirator eyepieces—the thought occurred to me that if we had blown that explosive charge we might have set fire to the books. Then we would really have had big problems: the whole Embassy would have been ablaze in seconds.

The adrenaline was making me feel confident, elated. My mind was crystal clear as we swept on through the library and headed for our first objective. I reached the head of the cellar stairs first, and was quickly joined by Sek and two of the call signs. The entry to the stairs was blocked by two sets of stepladders. I searched desperately with my eyes for any signs of booby traps. There wasn't time for a thorough check. We had to risk it. We braced ourselves and wrenched the ladders out of the way.

Mercifully there was no explosion. The stairs were now cleared and we disappeared into the gloom of the basement. I fished a stun grenade out of my waistcoat and pulled the pin. Audio Armageddon, I thought as I tossed the grenade down into the darkness. We descended the stairs, squinting into the blinding flashes for any unexpected movement, any sign of the enemy, and then we were into the corridor at the bottom. We had no sledge, no Remington with us, so we had to drill the locks with 9-milly, booting the doors in, clearing the rooms methodically as we went along. Minutes turned into seconds; it was the fastest room clearance I'd ever done.

It was when I entered the last room that I saw the dark shape crouched in the corner. Christ! This is it, I thought. We've hit the jackpot. We've found a terrorist. I jabbed my MP 5 into the fire position and let off a burst of twenty rounds. There was a clang as the crouched figure crumpled and rolled over. It was a dustbin!

Nothing, not a thing. The cellars were clear. I was now conscious of the sweat. It was stinging my eyes, and the rubber on the inside of the respirator was slimy. My mouth was dry and I could feel the blood pulsing through my temples. And then we were off again, no time to stop now, up the cellar stairs and into the Embassy reception area. As we advanced across the hallway, there was smoke, confusion, a tremendous clamor of noise coming from above us. The rest of the lads, having stormed over the balcony at the front and blasted their way into the first floor of the building with a well-placed explosive charge, were now systematically clearing the upper rooms, assisted by a winning combination of the stunning effect of the initial explosion, the choking fumes of CS gas, the chilling execution of well-practiced maneuvers and the sheer terror induced by their sinister, black-hooded appearance. We were intoxicated by the situation. Nothing could stop us now.

Through the gloom I could see the masked figures of the other team members forming into a line on the main staircase. My radio earpiece crackled into life. "The hostages are coming. Feed them out through the back. I repeat, out through the back."

I joined a line with Sek. We were six or seven steps up from the hallway. There were more explosions. The hysterical voices of the women swept over us. Then the first hostages were passed down the line. I had my MP 5 on a sling around my neck. My pistol was in its holster. My hands were free to help the hostages, to steady them, to reassure them, to point them in the right direction. They looked shocked and disorientated. Their eyes were streaming with CS gas. They stumbled down the stairs looking frightened and disheveled. One woman had her blouse ripped and her breasts exposed. I lost count at fifteen and still they were coming, stumbling, confused, heading toward the library and freedom.

"This one's a terrorist!" The high-pitched yell cut through the atmosphere on the stairs like a screaming jet, adding to the confusion of the moment. A dark face ringed by an Afro-style haircut came into view; then the body, clothed in a green combat jacket, bent double, crouched in an unnatural pose, running the gauntlet of black-hooded figures. He was punched and kicked as he made his descent of the stairs. He was running afraid. He knew he was close to death.

He drew level with me. Then I saw it—a Russian fragmentation grenade. I could see the detonator cap protruding from his hand. I moved my hands to the MP 5 and slipped the safety catch to "automatic." Through the smoke and gloom I could see call signs at the bottom of the stairs in the hallway. Shit! I can't fire. They are in my line of sight, the bullets will go straight through the terrorist and into my mates. I've got to immobilize the bastard. I've got to do something. Instinctively, I raised the MP 5 above my head and in one swift, sharp movement brought the stock of the weapon down on the back of his neck. I hit him as hard as I could. His head snapped backward and for one fleeting second I caught sight of his tortured, hate-filled face. He collapsed forward and rolled down the remaining few stairs, hitting the carpet in the hallway, a sagging, crumpled heap. The sound of two magazines being emptied into him was deafening. As he twitched and vomited his life away, his hand opened and the grenade rolled out. In that split second my mind was so crystal clear with adrenaline it zoomed straight in on the grenade pin and lever. I stared at the mechanism for what seemed like an eternity, and what I saw flooded the very core of me with relief and elation. The pin was still located in the lever. It was all over, everything was going to be OK.

But this was no time to rest, this was one of the most vulnerable periods of the operation, the closing stages. This is where inexperienced troops would drop their guard. The radio crackled into life. "You must abandon the building. The other floors are ablaze. Make your way out through the library entrance at the rear. The Embassy is clear. I repeat, the Embassy is clear."

I joined Sek and we filed out through the library, through the smoke and the debris. We turned left and headed back for number 14, past the hostages, who were laid out and trussed up on the lawn ready for documentation, past the unexploded explosive charge, past the discarded sledge-hammer and other pieces of assault equipment—all the trappings of battle in the middle of South Kensington. It was 8:07 p.m.

As we made our way through the french windows of number 14, the Gonze, ex-Para, a new boy in the regiment from one of the other call signs, removed his respirator and asked the Irish police sergeant on duty at the door what the Embassy World snooker score was. A look of total disbelief spread across the policeman's face and he just stood there shaking his head from side to side.

I crossed the room to my holdall and as I began pulling off my assault equipment I could feel the tiredness spreading through my limbs. It wasn't just the energy expended on the assault, it was the accumulation of six days of tension and high drama, of snatched sleep in a noisy room, of anxiety and worry over the outcome of the operation. I looked to my left. The Toad had just returned. He looked tired, his face was flushed and he was out of breath. He looked at me and shook his head. "I'm getting too old for this sort of thing."

"So am I," I replied.

Within fifteen minutes most of the team members had stripped off their assault kit, packed it into their holdalls and parceled their MP 5s into plastic bags to be taken away for forensic examination. Before moving out through the front door of number 14 to the waiting Avis hire van, we had a dramatic visit from Home Secretary William Whitelaw, old Oyster Eyes himself. He stood before us, tears of joy unashamedly running down his cheeks, wringing his hands in relief. He thanked the assembled team members for what they had done for the country that day. "This operation will show that we in Britain will not tolerate terrorists. The world must learn this." It was a fine personal gesture and rounded the operation off perfectly.

The day would live forever in regimental history, of that we were sure, even though barely two hours had passed since the first explosion. Out of a total of twenty-six hostages taken prisoner in the Embassy, two had died, five had been released before the assault and nineteen had been rescued. The dramatic events were still reverberating through my senses: the first ear-stinging detonations, the bedlam of screaming women and snarling, yapping police dogs, the blanketing throb of 9-milly, the intense searing heat of the blazing Embassy. The tensions and stresses of the six-day siege now began to evaporate like a late-monsoon mist on a Dhofar morning, as a great feeling of relief and gladness washed over me, a feeling of anticipation of better things to come. Maybe the RTU and demotion were not such a bad thing after all. Maybe life with Six Troop was going to be better than I'd thought. I wouldn't have missed this action for a dozen overseas jaunts.

We were in London, the heart of the nation, the center of excellence. You can't go any higher, I thought to myself. This is where the spotlight is. This is where the top people in their professions are to be found: actors, politicians, businessmen . . . and soldiers. We had been involved in a triumphant day; we had restored the nation's pride and morale. I felt light-headed, intoxicated by the powerful atmosphere pervading the conference room of Regent's Park Barracks. We stood around in small groups, sipping lukewarm Foster's lager straight from the can. Some switched-on character had stacked the hall with cartons before we arrived, and they stood in great piles around the edges of the long room. Sek's voice cut through the roar of elated conversation. "A total success! The operation is a total success." Team members, the Head Shed, the green slime, the whole war machine was milling around, faces flushed with victory.

I reached for a fresh can of lager and looked at the label. The red Foster's logo brought back memories of blue skies, clear water, golden sand dunes and beautiful nude female bodies. On a trip to Australia a few years earlier, we basha'd up at the Aussie SAS camp in Perth. The southern camp perimeter backed on to a beach, and there among the sand dunes were dozens of nudists, beautiful long-legged Australian girls, their shapely bodies bronzed a deep golden brown, their pubic hair bleached almost white by the sun. As that area of the beach was Army property, the civvy police had no jurisdiction. It was the only place along that part of the coastline where the nudists could sunbathe without being disturbed. The Army certainly had no intention of moving them off, that's for sure. Each afternoon we would have our daily run along the beach and over the sand dunes. It was the most interesting running circuit I'd ever known. And it gave a new meaning to physical fitness!

My thoughts of golden-haired beach beauties were interrupted by the sudden appearance of a well-dressed character at the main door of the conference hall. He was wearing a sharp pin-stripe suit and the old school tie. He reeked of the Establishment. Oh God, I thought, not the red-tape wallahs, the bureaucratic brigade. Surely the form-filling and statement-taking weren't going to start already. Surely they could leave us in peace for a couple of hours to drink the excitement pitch down a few degrees.

The man moved forward to speak. "Gentlemen, the Prime Minister." The unexpected announcement boomed out across the full length of the room. Heads turned and the buzz and chatter of conversation dropped like a stone as an air of expectancy descended on the gathering.

In swept the Prime Minister, magisterial, like a triumphant Caesar returning to the Senate, "Gentlemen, there is nothing sweeter than success, and you boys have got it." Her voice rose above the resounding cheers and the crack and hiss of newly opened lager cans. She expressed pride and joy at the brave and brilliant management of the Embassy assault, stressing that victory was gained not only through faultless teamwork and infinite patience, but also through immense physical courage and flexibility. As she continued, I stared at her with growing admiration. She definitely had the Nelson touch. At the battle of St. Vincent, Nelson had led the decisive charge when his sailors boarded the Spanish three-decker *San Josef* with a battle cry of "Westminster Abbey or victory!" I could just imagine the thought that had run through Mrs. Thatcher's mind as she made the decision to send in the SAS. "Back benches or victory!"

As the heady atmosphere generated by the Prime Minister's dramatic entrance stabilized, the cool authority in her personality took over, and without a moment's hesitation she proceeded to wander freely about the conference room, meeting each individual team member and thanking us all personally. Denis, ever the faithful companion, followed in her footsteps. He asked me about my parent unit and told me he'd served in the artillery in World War II. They both expressed concern for Tom the Fijian, the abseiler who had severe leg burns and who had been admitted to St. Stephen's Hospital in Fulham. They learned that his abseil rope had become hopelessly tangled, that his legs, clothed in non-flameproof overalls, had dangled helplessly in the flames licking out of the first-floor window, that he had eventually been cut down by other members of his team and that, even though suffering from first-degree burns, he had reorganized his assault team, gained entry to the Embassy and converged on the telex room. Tom was later awarded a high decoration for his actions.

As the clock on the wall moved rapidly to 10:00 p.m., a color television was wheeled into the hall. It was suggested that the assembled company, including the Prime Minister, watch the news broadcast of the rescue.

"What an excellent idea," exclaimed Mrs. Thatcher. "Come, let us all move to the viewing area."

As the first dramatic newsreel shots of the explosive charge blasting the first-floor balcony window exploded on to the screen, we crowded around the TV set shining in the darkened corner of the room. "Sit down, you in the front, and let the rest of us see it," ordered a gruff Jock voice from the rear. Glowing with pride and contentment, the Prime Minister obediently sat down and joined members of Alpha Assault Group sitting cross-legged on the floor. The scent of her Chanel No. 5 filled the air as we stared, mesmerized, at the day's events unrolling with lethal ferocity on the screen.

There is nothing more threatening to the advancement of civilization than the man who thinks himself God. The Roman conqueror, riding victoriously through a defeated city, would employ a jester to walk beside his horse and degrade the military glory through lampooning and buffoonery. With this historical perspective in mind, I walked up the gravel drive of one of Hereford's top hotels to collect a modern-day jester and top TV star, Mr. Jim Davidson. Being a keen student of military history, Jim had secretly agreed to put in a mystery appearance at the celebration thrash marking the siege victory. A champagne party was to take place at a well-known Hereford watering hole, and my job was to infiltrate Jim covertly into the pub.

He arrived in reception wearing a gray double-breasted two-piece suit, looking, with his slim figure and slightly suntanned face, as though he'd just come off a team job abroad. His dapper appearance was in sharp contrast to the style of my own favorite comedian, Bernard Manning, the only comic Jim Davidson rates more highly than himself. I had originally recommended Bernard for the thrash because of his outrageously funny blue material, but it had been pointed out to me that we might find difficulty squeezing him into the full assault kit, the wearing of which was going to be a necessary part of this particular performance.

I shook Jim's hand and we made small-talk. I was impressed by his enthusiasm and I knew instinctively he was going to be the right man for the evening. We passed a few minutes in light conversation, then left the hotel and made for the car-park. As I swung my legs into Jim's Mercedes 220SE, he shot me a conspiratorial glance. "Have you got all the gear?"

"Yes, it's in the hotel room," I assured him.

"What time do we start?"

"We'll kick off at 9:00 p.m. prompt."

Jim turned the ignition key and the engine purred into

237

life. He put the Merc in gear and we glided out of the car-park. I looked at my watch. It was just 8:00 p.m. That left plenty of time to organize the evening's cabaret. Feeling quite pleased with phase one of the operation, I settled back in the luxurious comfort of the car's passenger seat and proceeded to direct Jim to the location of the party.

By 8:15 p.m. we were in downtown Hereford. We let ourselves into a hotel bedroom adjacent to the hall where the festivities were taking place. I could hear the clink of beer mugs and buzz of conversation from the early drinkers. The sound of Ricky Sickit and the Vomits on the downstairs jukebox was deafening. "Who the hell's that?" said Jim as he closed the bedroom door. "It sounds like the second coming of Sid Vicious!"

I glanced around the room. It looked like the duty NCO's bunk in a seedy NAAFI. The mattress and sheets on the single bed were only slightly cleaner than the olive green holdall resting on top of them. I went over to the holdall, unzipped the top and checked the contents. Everything was there.

Time to get ready. Jim stripped to his underwear and reached for the first article of assault kit. In a matter of seconds he climbed into the black flameproof overalls and fastened the zip. We both sneezed as the CS gas trapped in the creases of the material was released into the atmosphere. With tears in my eyes I handed him the Northern Ireland lightweight boots. He immediately recognized the para-cord bootlaces and told me a great joke about his charity parachuting days. Choking back the tears and the laughter, I helped him strap on the Len Dixon belt kit and checked that the 9-milly Browning was unloaded. He fastened his leg-strap like a seasoned gunfighter and holstered the shooter. He then threaded the abseil rope around his waist and secured it with a Karabiner. Finally, he lifted the respirator off the bed and, with a professional touch, checked the tightness of the canister and adjusted the mask securing straps. With a last impish grin and an enthusiastic thumbs up, he pulled on the respirator, coiled the abseil rope over his forearm, opened the hotel door and stepped out into the darkened corridor.

With catlike stealth, we moved down the corridor, opened a concealed door near the fire exit and began climbing a rickety staircase. "You go first, Jim, and I'll cover you."

Jim grunted through the rubber of the respirator and snaked his way tactically up the narrow stairs. I could have sworn he imagined he was on operations.

The staircase led to a minstrels' gallery which overlooked the bar and cabaret lounge. The bar was now filled to capacity with team members and percentage players quaffing their thirst gratefully on crate after crate of champagne sent in by the public, including one from an old lady in Torquay, who'd been saving it for years "for a special occasion." Earlier in the day, I had blocked off the safety rail running across the gallery front with plywood sheeting. We were totally hidden from the crowd below. As we crawled into position across the wooden boards of the balcony, desperately trying not to make them creak, I looked at my watch. 8:55 p.m. Five minutes to go. I tapped Jim on the shoulder and showed him five fingers. He gave me the thumbs up and handed me the wire that was connected to the small explosive charge I had put in position that afternoon. I took the two bare ends of the D10 wire and pushed them into the shrike exploder. I pressed the test button and got the green light. Good, complete circuit, we're ready to go.

I took a look at my watch. Thirty seconds to go. I tapped Jim on the shoulder and pointed toward the safety rail. As he moved into position, I pressed the priming button on the shrike. The red "fire" light flashed in the gloom. At precisely 9:00 p.m. I pressed the firing button. Bang! The small stage charge took the drinkers completely by surprise. Heads whipped around and the odd Walter Mitty gatecrasher reached for a nonexistent shoulder holster.

Jim jumped to his feet and threw the abseil rope over the balcony. For a few tense moments he trod the gallery boards, shooting menacing glances at the crowd below.

239

Then, in one quick, efficient movement, he removed his respirator and, to roars of applause, launched straight into his first joke.

"A man dies and goes up to the Pearly Gates. He sees St. Peter standing there with rows and rows of clocks behind him. When asked the purpose of the clocks, St. Peter replies that every person on earth is given an allotted span of time and the clocks keep a record. Suddenly one of the clocks goes around a full hour in a couple of seconds. 'That man has just slept with his neighbor's wife,' explains St. Peter with a frown. Then another clock jerks around a full two hours. 'That man has just mugged an old lady in the street,' intones St. Peter. At that moment, the newly arrived man sees a clock immediately behind St. Peter frantically spinning around at high speed. 'Ah, that clock,' says St. Peter . . .'" and here Jim paused a moment, looked me straight between the eyes, then continued, "'. . . that clock belongs to a certain member of B Squadron SAS. We use it as a fan to keep us cool in the hot weather!'"

Better to be tried by twelve than to be carried by six, I thought, as I waited in the corridor outside Westminster Coroner's Court. The jokes and the back-slapping were over. Nine months on from the siege, now it was into the serious business of the inquest. I was more nervous at the prospect of doing battle with the cut and thrust of clued-up solicitors and highly paid barristers than I'd ever been before going in to tackle Oan and his band. I'd been away for nearly a year, traveled twice around the world on training missions, and here I was being called to account before the cold, impassive power of the law for actions whose precise sequences were already beginning to blur in my mind. Worst of all, I was to bare my soul and that of the regiment in public. I was to give details of an SAS operation before the massed ranks of the media crammed into the public galleries, at least five dozen hardened journalists, pens poised in excitement, awaiting with schoolboy eagerness the unfolding of tomorrow's guaranteed bestseller. I'd spent eleven years of total anonymity and secrecy with the SAS. But since the television exposure of the siege had blown our cover, the Head Shed felt compelled to go against all their normal instincts. We now had to be seen to be accountable. Democracy in action. It marked a new stage in the regiment's history, a new dimension in the psychological warfare against terrorists.

I was one of the chosen four due to appear in court—the ones who'd drawn the short straws. I'd spent three days in court in Hong Kong and was deemed to have the necessary experience. A legal veteran! It was thought I was better equipped to withstand the pressures than some of the other lads. I was to be a star witness. A real patsy, a scapegoat for the percentage players! This sort of exposure can't go on, I thought, this must be rectified for the future. Some precautions had been taken. The Coroner had ordered that no photographs or sketches be taken in court in any circumstances whatever. Furthermore, it had been agreed that we could be identified by alphabetical designation to avoid the use of our real names. The cover was scant in the extreme. It offered little consolation.

My confidence in the system had already been severely dented by events prior to our reaching court. There were four of us: Sam, the superstitious one who'd refused to play the Ouija board with Valdez just before Operation Jaguar, Steve, Tom the Fijian abseiler—now recovered from his burns—and myself. We'd been at Group HQ, awaiting the arrival of a Black Maria to spirit us unnoticed to the court. What should turn up but a bright red Vauxhall Viva! Worse still, on arrival at the court, instead of being taken to the back entrance we were driven up to the front where all the press were waiting. They spotted the car immediately and came running toward us, cameras flashing. "Get to the back! Get to the mortuary door at the back!" Sam was yelling at the driver as we all ducked down. Luckily the police driver was well trained. With tires squealing, he did an emergency reverse and about-turn and, with Fleet Street's finest in hot pursuit, roared toward the rear entrance, through a large gate and into a courtyard. We were through the back door before the perspiring gentlemen of the press were able to catch up with us.

Just inside the mortuary door we were faced with a gruesome sight: the naked body of an old man laid out on a trolley. He had recently been subjected to a post-mortem. A huge cut stretching from breastbone to navel had been peremptorily sewn back up with large blanket stitches. The crown of his shaven head had been lopped off like the top of a hard-boiled egg and it, too, clumsily sewn back again. The stench of formaldehyde was sickening.

While I was waiting outside the courtroom to be called, my spirits rose a little when one of our senior officers, who'd come to meet us for our final brief, revealed that the member of the jury nearest the witness box was a very pretty young thing no more than twenty years old. I decided that when I was asked to relate how Faisal had ended up with thirty bullet holes in him, I would tell the story directly to her personally, gory details and all. A nice intimate conversation, just she and I. At least it would take my mind off the court ordeal.

I came back to reality with the rumor that newspaper reporters were climbing on the roofs all around the building to get pictures of our exit. I just hoped to God the police would get it right this time and reverse a Black Maria right up to the back door.

The usher nodded to me to get ready. I got up and waited just outside the swing door that led into the court. I pushed the door open a few inches with my foot to try and get a feel of the atmosphere inside so that I could be a little better prepared when I entered the arena. I eyed the young female juror with expectation. Then the Coroner looked up from his notes and said in measured tones, "We will now hear evidence from the military personnel who brought the siege to a conclusion."

Keith Graves, eyes like a hawk, spun around to face the door where I stood. A deathly hush descended on the court.

A voice boomed out, "Soldier I: take the stand."

14

The Falklands

"She was squirming in her seat, giggling with excitement, wide-eyed and eager. I fixed her very deliberately with my best macho stare as I related the unsavory details of Faisal's demise. She wasn't put off. Far from it. She was panting and flushed, hanging on to my every word, raring to go, go, go. Maybe she was used to it. Maybe she was a nurse. I don't know. One thing is for certain: if I hadn't been married I could have got her number and I would have had a guaranteed jump that night—and I'm not talking about parachuting." I took another gulp of beer. "But the funniest part was when I'd just finished giving evidence and was stepping from the witness box. Ron Morris came charging across the courtroom, his arm outstretched. He gripped me by the hand and said to the Coroner, "Excuse me, sir, but I must shake hands with this man. I want to thank him and his mates for all they did for us." I was quite taken aback, embarrassed almost."

The alcohol was flowing freely. I was sitting reminiscing about the Embassy inquest in the Volcano Club, an American airmen's gin palace that clung like a limpet to the edge of Wideawake airfield on Ascension Island. If you draw a cross whose horizontal axis links Brazil in South America to

Angola in West Africa, and whose vertical axis bisects the country of Ireland from north to south, in the center of the cross you will find Ascension Island, a scab of volcanic rock and dust in the middle of the South Atlantic Ocean, a British telecommunications center, U.S. airbase and U.S. space research station. It was 1982. We'd not long since flown out from Hereford; the Falklands war was in full swing.

"Take No Prisoners!" The name of the newly christened cocktail was shouted to the rafters as several half-pint glasses of a milky-colored liquid appeared on the plastic-topped table in front of the troop hierarchy. The lethal-looking concoction had just been invented by an ex-Para called Paul. Before joining the Army, Paul had worked as a croupier in a south coast casino, until he got fed up with the well-heeled punters, who would blow clouds of smoke from expensive Havana cigars into his face as a distraction. Young, hard but amiable, a rebel from the maroon machine, he was the troop new boy. "A warmer in the bank before the Last Supper," he would announce invitingly as he raised his glass.

Disorientated by the octane rating of this Molotov cocktail, the troop would then await with mouth-watering relish the arrival of the Volcano's special grill. The steak was a joy to behold, a delight to the palate. It was so vast it overlapped the plate at both ends. It must have been at least one inch thick and came generously garnished with garlic butter. With the passing of each evening, and our departure for the Falklands more and more imminent, this gastronomic delight became known as the Last Supper. It helped clear the mind of gremlins after a day of green-slime briefings.

As this particular day's Last Supper entered its closing stages, the lads in the troop, actively encouraged by big Fred the Fijian and aided and abetted by Sek—once again setting off on a great adventure alongside me—were required to take part in an initiation test steeped in ritual. Each member of the mission had to finish off the evening by drinking a flaming Drambuie. Big Fred would half fill a standard spirit glass with the liqueur, and Sek would step forward and ignite it. A nine-inch bunsen flame would then shoot upward from the surface of the liquid. The initiation test required the drinker to place the flaming spirit glass to his lips, drain the Drambuie, then put the empty glass back on the table with the blue flame still leaping off its rim. (This ritual was an SAS refinement of the "dance of the flaming assholes"—a custom peculiar to the crap-hats—in which pieces of newspaper were rolled up tightly and inserted into the anal orifice of two rookie squad members. Both were then set alight. The first man to pull out the flaming roll bought the drinks. The last time the SAS attempted this before abandoning it as childish was in 1972, when a guy called Del, who was later to help me stitch up Malcolm the clerk during the Embassy siege, decided to liven up the proceedings by throwing a glass of Drambuie over the back of a Nine Troop man called Frenchie. It burst into flames and badly burned Frenchie's back.)

Big Fred, solemn and dignified, had the bearing of an MC at a Fijian kava ceremony. Kava is a narcotic drink prepared from the root of a pepper plant and drunk from coconut shells. It numbs the lips, gums and tongue and acts like dental cocaine, rendering the drinker high as a kite. An evening in the Volcano Club had a similar effect. Fred handed the first flaming Drambuie to Tommy, a tough Scot from the Highlands. Tommy was no stranger to the dangers of fire and flame. At the Embassy siege in 1980, during a desperate attempt to get access via a window into an already burning room, his gas mask and gas hood had got so badly burned they had to be discarded. In spite of having no protection whatever from the thick fumes, he had continued to carry out his duties in the smoke- and CS gas-filled rooms. His bravery was later recognized by the award of the Queen's Gallantry Medal.

With a knowing wink, Tommy gripped the stem of the glass, tipped his head back at just the right angle, and with practiced ease quickly drained the contents before the glass became too hot to handle. A group of remfs in the far corner of the bar began chanting "Napalm sticks to Spics" as we each took our turn with the fiery liquid. Most of us were past masters in the art, and not an eyebrow had been singed, not a nose tip burned by the time the remfs launched into their latest chant of "Vulcanize the Junta."

Then it was Paul's turn. He accepted the offered glass from a still solemn Fred, then glanced briefly at the flickering blue flame before raising the glass warily to his lips. The flame was now gathering momentum and Paul hesitated slightly before tilting his head forward to meet the glass. A dangerous mistake. As he gulped at the burning liquid, the flame licked around his upper lip and nose and singed his eyebrows. He spluttered and attempted a recovery, but to no avail; he was forced to spit the fiery Drambuie from his mouth, spraying a two-foot sheet of flame across the table, hitting Nish down his left-hand side.

With the smell of singed eyebrows in my nostrils, I settled back in my chair. Another Last Supper was drawing to a close and the remfs were on an all-time high with their next chant, "Jump-jet the Junta." The troop was busy discussing Paul's facial burns. The whole room vibrated with jingoism. But I was far from happy.

As the alcohol in the Molotov cocktails and the flaming Drambuies began to take hold, it helped tranquilize the negative thoughts that had invaded my brain since our departure from the UK. They say history repeats itself, and it seemed the Head Shed were about to prove it. Back in the briefing room at the Kremlin in Hereford, they had outlined a plan to crash two C 130s containing a heavily armed B Squadron on to the runway at Port Stanley with the aim of bringing the Falklands war to a rapid conclusion. It occurred to me they were making the same mistake as Monty when he sent the Paras into Arnhem in an attempt to short-circuit World War II. As in the case of Arnhem, the Head Shed wouldn't believe the intelligence reports presented to them. The airfield at Stanley was ringed by General Joffre's Tenth Brigade, 7,000 fighting men, and, worse still, the 601 Anti-aircraft Battalion equipped with ground-to-air missiles. Coming in to land with a full load of men and equipment, the C 130s—not the quickest of planes at the best of times—would have been slow and lumbering, sitting-duck targets for the anti-aircraft guns. The Argentinian troops may not have been of the same caliber as the four divisions of SS Panzers surrounding Arnhem, but they were well armed, with plenty of reserve ammunition, and they were dug in. There were also plenty of ex-Nazi war criminals and SS officers and ex-NCOs hiding in South America willing to give advice to an army confronting Great Britain.

At the end of the briefing, the Head Shed had asked a stunned B Squadron for any questions or points. Give me a blindfolded tightrope walk in a force 10 gale any time, I thought. I decided to take the bull by the horns and give them the solution. "Put a Polaris missile on to the Argentinian mainland airbases that are servicing the Mirage 3 and the Super Etendards," I offered. The Head Shed were not amused.

To make matters worse, as a parting gesture as we embarked on the coach taking us to Brize Norton, an Army Pay Corps sergeant, hovering like a death clerk, had been on hand to issue life insurance to anyone who didn't have it. "Come on, lads, this is your last chance. Sign on the dotted line." Valdez, that tower of Fijian strength—along with Laba and Sek one of the original three Fijians I'd met at Otterburn in 1971 who were to inspire in me a lasting affection and respect for that friendly South Pacific people —proved the only light at the end of the tunnel. As we settled into our seats on the coach, squadron morale soared when he fished out of his battered Barbour jacket pocket a faded copy of *Rules for War,* written in the early 1950s. A mischievous grin cracked his dark features as his index finger traced Rule 762: SAS troops are not suicide troops. As he replaced *Rules for War* in his pocket, I kept my fingers crossed he wouldn't bring out a Ouija board to pass the time on the journey. I wasn't superstitious, but the Ouija board and the death clerk would have made an ominous combination.

That had been the morning of 19 May. By 20 May we had arrived on Ascension Island and were about to receive the worst regimental news since the last world war: a chopper had gone down, killing twenty of the lads from D and G squadrons. Crocker read out the list of dead—fine soldiers, irreplaceable in terms of experience and expertise. Twenty first-class soldiers—SNCOs, JNCOs, troopers and signalers —had perished when a Sea King helicopter crashed into the sea off the stern of the assault ship *Intrepid*. In a small regiment like the SAS, one death in the family causes ripples. Twenty was a major disaster.

The sound of the riotous assembly brought me back to the present with a jolt. The remfs had finally gone over the top and were in fine vocal form as they offered a grand finale to the snake pit: a cannibalized version of "Summer Holiday":

> We're all going on a summer holiday,
> We're all going to kill a Spic or two,
> We're all going on a summer holiday,
> We'll get them with our GPMGs . . .

As the singing reached a crescendo, I decided it was time to leave. Most of the troop had thinned out anyway.

"Cos there ain't no fucking trees," screamed the remfs as I levered myself into the upright position, pushed the table to one side and picked my way through the smoke-filled bar. Cliff Richard would be proud of us, I thought, pushing through the exit door into the warm night air.

"Come on, boys, get your kit together. The trucks are outside. We're going for it." The urgent voice cut through the alcohol-induced dream. I prised my eyelids open and attempted to focus on the blurred figure of the SSM.

My head thumped around like the center hub of a helicopter's rotor blade. I now knew why I had done selection and had been tested to destruction. I felt as if I was back on Sickener 1. My body ached and my mouth tasted like a gorilla's armpit. The suicide mission had begun.

"Get all the weapons and ammunition on to the trucks. We're moving out immediately," repeated the SSM. The room burst into life as the squadron began rushing around packing their personnel kit and getting ready to load the Bedfords. The short, sharp, shock—it's one way of curing your hangover, I thought, as I glanced at my G10 watch. It was just after 0500 hours.

We began checking weapons, priming grenades, breaking open liners of GPMG link, removing the M 202s from their cardboard transit boxes. The thought of the 202 cheered me up—four 66-millimeter incendiary rockets, box-mounted, operating from one trigger mechanism. We were anxious, raring to go, eager to get the job done. We applied green and black camouflage cream to our faces and pulled on our fighting order, heavy belt kits weighed down with 5.56-millimeter ammunition and 40-millimeter high-explosive bombs for the XM 203. This was an Armalite with a single-shot, breech-loaded, pump-action grenade-launcher attached to the underside of the stock—hence the nickname "under and over." Thank Christ we've got these; now I don't have to stand up to throw a grenade, I thought as I checked the quadrant sight, then depressed the barrel-locking latch and slid the barrel forward to check that the launcher was clear. Happy with the safety check, I snapped the barrel backward, the tube latch locking the barrel and receiver together.

I joined the line of squadron members moving purposefully toward the Bedfords parked on the road outside the basha. The remfs' "we're all going on a summer holiday" turned around my brain like a pig on a spit, but I wasn't in the mood to burst into song. We pulled ourselves on to the Bedfords already jam-packed with kit and weapons, and made ourselves as comfortable as possible amid liners of 7.62-millimeter link, bergens, cases of M 202s and GPMGs. A famous World War I general once said that the machine gun is a much overrated toy, but experience gained in the

Dhofar war had taught us how vital it was. We made sure we took every GPMG we could lay our hands on. No wonder there was no room to move.

The convoy was now ready. It was just a matter of driving across the airfield and loading the waiting C 130s. The squadron fell silent, each man left to his own thoughts. This was the biggest operation the regiment had been committed to since World War II. If B Squadron pulled this off, we could name our own medals. We were anxious to get going, anxious to write our names in the pages of history, anxious for the success of the operation itself. Would we manage to land on the airfield at Stanley or would we be blown out of the sky by surface-to-air missiles? And if we did indeed land, would we be annihilated on the runway by the radar-controlled 35-millimeter anti-aircraft guns used in the ground role?

I blocked the negative thoughts out of my mind and looked at my watch. The minutes ticked by. Five, ten, fifteen agonizing minutes. Come on, let's get going. I looked up and down the stationary convoy. Where the hell was Crocker? We were supposed to be on operation immediate. The waiting was getting to me; it was a bad fifteen minutes. A murmur of conversation had broken out in the rear Bedford. One or two of the fitness fanatics were standing on the mountains of kit, stretching their stiffened limbs and looking bored.

I looked at Tommy, who was sitting quietly on a box of smoke grenades. His gray face looked like how I felt. He shrugged his shoulders and went back to the oily flannelette he was using to clean the 5.56-millimeter rounds before easing them into the thirty-round magazine of his 203. As I settled back once more I could feel the slow regular thump of a headache beating across my temples. It was 0630 hours.

Crocker suddenly appeared from the direction of the signal shack. He had a scowl on his face. He looked at the convoy but said nothing. He walked over to the lead Bedford and spoke quickly and with calm authority to the SSM. The message flashed down the full length of the convoy: scrubbed! The operation had been scrubbed. "Thank fuck for that," I said to Tommy. "Good old SAS common sense has prevailed. Come on, let's hit the Volcano and get stuck into one of those steaks."

The synchronized flash of navigational lights on the USAAF Starlifter cut into the gray of the overcast dawn as we plodded in silence across Wideawake airfield, dressed in camouflage OGs and each carrying a diver's dry suit, a set of fins and a life-jacket. It was 0430 hours. After the previous day's reprieve, we had been retasked and rebriefed. We were to fly south toward the Falklands in two C 130s, rendezvous with HMS *Andromeda,* a type-21 frigate, and carry out a para-drop into the South Atlantic. Pickup and delivery to the ship were to be by rigid raider. *Andromeda* would be our hosts until we reached San Carlos Water, where we would rendezvous with the depleted ranks of D Squadron.

This was to be a reinforcement jump, so it was classed as operational. I briefly entertained the idea of asking the Brigadier on our return to the UK if he would endorse the World War II rule on parachuting stating that any squadron member who has made an operational jump is entitled to wear his SAS wings above his medals, rather than on the shoulder where they are normally worn. The recollection of the look of horror on the Brigadier's face when I'd asked him at the opening of the new Pal-U-Drin Club back in Hereford in 1981 about a bar to the General Service Medal commemorating Princes Gate quickly changed my mind.

The early June morning was cool on Ascension as we picked our way through the clutter on the airfield, past rows of aircraft, Vulcan bombers, Victor tankers, American Starlifters and Nimrod recce planes, toward the two C 130s. Everywhere the ironmongery of war choked the tarmac: stockpiles of rations, fuel, medical supplies and ammunition, advance-communications equipment, fork-lift trucks —thousands of pieces of equipment. Wessex and Scout helicopters droned like bees overhead. The Royal Corps of Transport were working flat out organizing the movement of war matériel, the servicing of airlift pallets. War fever was in the air.

After what seemed like an age, we finally arrived at our C 130s. I noticed with interest the in-flight refueling probe over the flight deck. The transporter would be one of sixteen models converted specially for the Falklands war as flight-refueling tankers/receivers. Inside the cargo and passenger hold would be two long-range fuel tanks. Apparently one of these converted C 130 Hercules had created a world record for duration of flight by remaining in the air for twenty-eight hours during an operational mission.

We boarded the two cramped aircraft and prepared for the take-off. Practiced eyes and hands went through a familiar routine. I checked the main and reserve parachutes for serviceability. Happy with the break ties, elastic bunjees, cape-well releases, static-line stowage and leg-strap adjustments, I placed the two parachutes and the diver's dry suit on the floor between my legs, strapped myself into the uncomfortable web seat and awaited the roar of the four Alison turbo-prop engines. The crew carried out their final flight checks, and at 0500 hours the two C 130s began taxiing rapidly across the airfield. The constant-speed, fully feathering props were revved up to take-off speed, and without another minute's delay we thundered down the runway and lumbered into the dawn sky.

As I felt the lift of the aircraft wheels, I settled back in the cramped seat and removed my seatbelt. I was feeling exhilarated but somewhat daunted by the change in plan. My first operational jump into a war zone. Alongside me in the womb of the aircraft sat several newly badged members of the regiment. I thought of the slick precision and ruthless timing required by our plan. I looked at the fresh faces of the new recruits, the young men who had so enthusiastically applied for selection, who had passed with flying colors but who, as yet, were untried in battle, and I wondered . . .

"Action stations. Prepare equipment." The parachute-dispatcher's voice was quick and urgent, barely audible over the noise of the aircraft engines and the added roar of the slipstream rush now coming from the rear, where the tailgate door was being lowered.

"Here we go," I said feelingly to no one in particular. I reached for the diver's dry suit under my seat and climbed into the zipped opening. I swore under my breath as I pulled on the awkward rubber garment, bending my ears painfully as I forced my head through the skin-tight neck seal. "Zip me up, Tommy, and make sure you fasten the last quarter of an inch." In about half an hour we would be in the South Atlantic, where a man could freeze to death in a couple of hours. Even an unzipped quarter of an inch could prove fatal.

A few minutes later, with arms outstretched and convulsing like a cat coughing up a fur-ball, I had cursed and struggled my way into my dry suit. I stowed my fins where they would be easily accessible for fitting once I was in the water. Next the parachute. It was already adjusted to my personal measurements, so it was simply a matter of hoisting myself into the harness—not an easy task in the cramped passenger space of the Hercules. Finally, I strapped the distress flare to my wrist.

I began to sweat as I pushed through the crowded fuselage toward the chaos of the tailgate area. Someone had stitched the RAF dispatcher by telling him there was a missile on its way and that we must eject chaff immediately. He was panicking, desperately trying to contact the pilot and find the chaff button at the same time. The tailgate ramp from the Hercules was now fully down. I gazed out over the airdrop pallets crammed on to the ramp, over the edge of the ramp itself curving away into space and into the Atlantic swell 800 feet below.

Up in the cockpit of the C 130 the pilot pressed the button. A green light pierced the sparsely lit cargo hold. The RAF dispatcher, who by now had regained his composure, and two corporals from the RCT air dispatch team, all three fully kitted out for an operational jump—zip-up flying boots, olive-green flying suits, DPM jackets, white leather PGI gloves, and safety-harnesses attached to the aircraft fuselage—began moving the heavy airdrop pallets containing our personnel kit, weapons, bergens and advance-signaling equipment over the edge of the tailgate. There was a clatter as the pallets moved over the rollers fixed to the tailgate floor and a twang as each one dropped off the end. I watched fascinated as the parachutes' static lines ran clear and the canopies deployed. The plane bucked in slight turbulence, and I realized with a palpitating heart that this was the moment of truth. I took a deep breath, clipped on my reserve and moved into position.

I was number one in the stick, standing on the edge of the tailgate, adrenaline-charged, aching for release. It's fearsome, being number one: you see everything in front of you—and worse, everything below you. When you are three or four in the stick, all you see is the pair of shoulders and 'chute of the guy in front of you. You can shuffle forward almost with your eyes closed, as easily as a blind man being led over a cliff.

I was in the ready position: right hand gripping the parachute static line, left hand resting on the top of my reserve. Far below was the gray wash of the sea. I moved closer still to the edge. The deafening roar of the aircraft slipstream made all conversation impossible. My head was raised and turned to the right, watching, waiting for the red warning light to turn to green. My rear leg was braced, ready to launch me over the edge of the tailgate.

"Red on. Green on. Go!" screamed the dispatcher, slapping me on the back. Automatically I leapt into space, forcing my right hand down on to the top of my reserve to improve my exit stability. For an instant I was carried violently forward in the blast from the Hercules slipstream. Then I felt the reassuring tug of the parachute harness and the profound relief that the canopy had deployed. Almost immediately, I looked up and carried out my main canopy check for malfunction, ensuring it was deployed correctly.

My hands began to feel for the release hooks of my reserve. I looked down, and for one wild moment I saw I was directly above the dull, bluey-gray shape of HMS *Androme-*

da. If I released the reserve now, it would hit the ship square on. I took avoiding action. I pulled down violently—too violently—on my steering toggle. This caused air to spill out of my canopy, upsetting the stability and trim of my flight. I began to oscillate through 180 degrees. I spiraled downward, my rate of descent increasing. I swung back and forth, but at least I managed to clear the ship. I pulled down on both steering toggles, and this had the effect of breaking the forward speed of the canopy; the swinging was reduced. I had unclipped the reserve hooks from the D rings on my main harness and watched the reserve plummet into the sea below. Now I was conscious only of the water rushing up to meet me and of the constant buffeting from eddies of wind all around.

Judging distance in poor light when making a vertical descent into a high swell can be difficult. So I decided to jettison my harness without delay. I hit my cape-well releases and the shoulder straps fell away—but only just in time. I was suddenly immersed in water. At least the harness was free, there was no drag and the canopy did not envelop me. The parachute fell away at an angle, blown away downwind. I was now exhilarated, switched on. I struggled into my fins to help me tread water. Then I pulled down on the toggle and popped my life jacket. I watched the dull green canopies of the other troop members, many of them kicking violently out of twists, drift slowly down and hit the water.

I looked up and saw the single C 130, its cargo now bobbing about in the South Atlantic, disappear into the clouds. The second C 130 had turned back earlier because of a fuel resupply problem with a Vickers tanker, and would now already be sitting on the tarmac on Ascension Island, its occupants in the Volcano Club, seething with an imperial frustration that even the arrival of a gargantuan steak would do little to alleviate. I was lucky. My disciplinary misdemeanors were working in my favor again. The same fate that had put me in the killing house when the balloon went up for the Embassy siege, and subsequently allowed me to take part in a uniquely glorious episode in the regiment's history, had now ensured that I was on the first C130 and not on the second one, containing my old troop, Eight Troop, which had had to turn back.

Bobbing about in the ocean, I could feel the adrenaline pumping. I was at the sharp end, heading for action. The Atlantic swell was tremendous. On top of the waves I could see all around me. In the distance I could just make out the gray superstructure of HMS *Andromeda*. Then I disappeared into a trough and there was no view, no horizon. I was surrounded by a vast ocean of gray, foam-flecked waves. I became aware of the cold. The dry suit protected my body heat, but my hands and face were exposed to the elements. I had to tread water with my hands held clear of the bitter, near zero temperatures of the South Atlantic. Where was the pickup? The light was failing and the frigate seemed a long way off. Having been the first out of the Hercules I was furthest from the *Andromeda* and would no doubt be the last to be picked up. Like a piece of battered flotsam, I rose back on top of the wave. In the poor light I could just make out the rigid raider about 250 meters away. A member of the troop appeared to be struggling over its side; then it headed back for the *Andromeda*.

I had now been in the water fifteen minutes, and my hands and face were numb. I began to wish I'd only partially inflated my life jacket, by mouth, rather than popping the automatic inflater. The bulky shape was straining my neck, pressing it back at an awkward angle. It was getting quite dark. Time to use a cyalume stick. I cracked the plastic tube of the chemical distress flare attached to my wrist. The two chemicals mingled and the tube began to glow. I disappeared into a trough and realized it was pointless waving my flare—no one could see me. I couldn't even see the ship. I would have to wait till I was back on the crest of the wave. I kicked with my fins to gain height. Now I could see the shape of *Andromeda* in the distance. I waved my flare arm, but to no avail. The rigid raider was returning to the mother craft with another full load. My vision began to gray in the

The Falklands

gloom. The camouflaged superstructure of the *Andromeda* disappeared from sight, and once more I became engulfed in the dark trough of a huge wave.

Anxiety began to gnaw at my insides. I had been in the water thirty-five minutes and had begun to shiver. There were two dangers now: exposure and exhaustion. Already I was having difficulty keeping my hands out of the water. Perhaps fate was not so kind after all. Perhaps I would have been better off in the Volcano Club with Eight Troop.

I seemed to be aimlessly paddling around, going nowhere, getting weaker. The South Atlantic was taking its toll on me; serious fatigue had set in. I rose again on the crest of another wave. At last, the familiar shape of the rigid raider crawled into view about 100 meters away. I waved my flare arm wildly as the small boat surged forward. They'd seen me! They were heading in my direction, an olive-green shape bucking violently in the Atlantic swell.

"We thought we'd lost you," said the big Marine boat handler.

"So did I," I replied. "I'm starving. Got any scran?"

As they hauled me over the side, they burst my life jacket with a diving knife to make it easier to get hold of me and pull me into the boat. The tension fell away, and as the rigid raider sped over the waves toward *Andromeda*, a surge of weariness and a longing to be on dry land swept over me.

No sooner had I got on board than it was realized that an airdrop pallet containing personnel kit was missing. A radar scan of the immediate area proved fruitless. A Sea King helicopter was due to arrive any minute to cross-deck the troop to HMS *Intrepid*. The Navy called off the search for the missing pallet. It was decided that I and one other would stay behind and persuade the Navy to continue the search. We would then remain on *Andromeda* until its arrival in San Carlos Bay.

I went to the Petty Officer and requested a resumption of the search. I was told no way was that possible. "Fuck you," I said and strode straight into the Captain's cabin.

I was struck by the homeliness of the tidy room. Going

through the door was like walking into the warm, secure atmosphere of your favorite study. The Captain, pen in hand, looked up from a desk cluttered with paperwork. With his steely gray hair and steady gaze, he reminded me of a fond uncle. When he spoke he had the dignity of a housemaster at a public school. His whole persona radiated power and authority. "We have got to get under way, we must be in San Carlos Bay by the morning," he replied quietly to my demand. His dignified features had taken on the expression of a patient negotiator handling a siege situation.

I took a deep breath. "What's the point of putting the RAF to the trouble of bringing us all this way to do a reinforcement jump into the South Atlantic when we'll be a liability to D Squadron if we go into the field without the proper kit and equipment? We might as well have stayed on the piss on Ascension."

For a split second the steady noncommittal gaze was replaced by a far sterner look, as though the Captain were turning over some crucial piece of information in his precise naval mind. "OK," he announced, "I'll give you a couple of hours."

A period of intense activity followed. Time and time again I had to fight back fatigue and persuade the Navy to continue the search. I had to locate that pallet. We chugged on through the night, the radar search providing the eyes, Chalky—the other troop member—and I providing the concentration. Lashed by spray, freezing cold and near to exhaustion, we stood with a group of naval ratings on the bow of the ship, peering into the starlit night. As *Andromeda* lumbered through the seas and the hours slipped by, I was becoming increasingly strained. The continuation of the search seemed to hinge on my resolve and determination to keep going. I shivered and looked at my watch. It was just past midnight. The naval ratings were looking toward their bunks, and I was expecting at any time to be called up to the Captain's cabin and given the bad news.

Then word came down from the bridge that something

had been picked up on the radar. Suddenly, a rating on the starboard rail of the bows shouted that he could see something in the water. I grabbed the Petty Officer of the watch, who was in possession of a dragon light. We made our way over to the starboard side of the ship. I was excited, expectant, as the powerful beam of the dragon light cut through the night. "There it is!" shouted Chalky triumphantly, as the beam played on a set of rigging lines, a parachute canopy and a large, dull brown packing box. It was the missing airdrop pallet.

Sleep. That was all I wanted now. The ship was extremely crowded, every berth taken. One of the Navy lads showed me a bed that someone had just vacated to go on duty. "There's your bed for the next eight hours." It was lovely and warm. I went out like a light.

The Falklands! Two small islands to the northeast of Tierra del Fuego, two specks floating in the sea, like tiny scales dislodged from the great curl of the scorpion's tail that is South America. With a coastline as long as Norway's circumscribing a land mass no bigger than Wales, the Falklands are subject to relentless winds and the hazards of wind-chill factor that accompany them. The islands are the same latitude south of the Equator as London is to the north, doggedly British and determined to stay so.

I was deeply impressed as I stood on the forecastle of the Royal Fleet Auxiliary LSL *Sir Lancelot* and surveyed the anchorage at San Carlos Water. There hadn't been so many ships around the Falklands since the days preceding the first battle of the Falklands in December 1914, when dozens of colliers arrived to fuel HMS *Glasgow, Invincible, Inflexible* and the other battle cruisers that made up Admiral Sturdee's original task force sent to root out the German fleet hiding around the islands.

San Carlos Water bustled with activity. Aboard the frigates, acting as goalkeepers at each end of the waterway, anxious eyes scanned radar screens for the unexpected air attack. In front of me, across the bay, I could see RAF *Blue*

Rover, SS *Atlantic Causeway,* MV *Norland* and, faintly ridiculous amid the camouflage gray, the brightly colored *Nordic Ferry.* Anchored at the southern end was the assault ship HMS *Fearless.* On the high ground overlooking the bridgehead, the rapier batteries formed a defensive ring of steel. Like hungry seagulls circling a freshly churned refuse tip, helicopters wheeled and dived as they carried out routine cross-decking sorties and undertook offloading operations. A Sea King 5 vet-repped drums of petrol swinging beneath its matt green belly.

It was just after 1600 hours and, with dusk gathering, I gave my belt kit, personal weapons and ammunition a final check, ready for the mission ahead. At that time of the year it would be dark at 1630 hours, ensuring a covert insert into enemy territory. We had to be in position by 1800 hours. The plan, like all good plans, was simple. We were to take a night flight to enemy-occupied West Falkland by Sea King helicopter. We would deploy a linear type ambush on high ground overlooking the target area. Intelligence received had indicated that three Argentinian C 130s were going to do a reinforcement drop of an elite company of Paras at 0100 the following morning. Members of D Squadron, boosted by Six Troop B Squadron, would provide the DZ reception party.

The cocking handle of my XM 203 snapped forward, chambering the first 5.56-millimeter round. I applied the safety catch. My fingers checked the smooth metallic cases of the 40-millimeter bombs located in the pockets and the bandoleers crisscrossing my chest. Cradling the loaded rifle in the crook of my left arm, I stood motionless in the growing darkness. As my eyes adjusted to night vision, taking the inkiness out of the purple-black surroundings, my thoughts turned to the achievements of British forces over the last few weeks. In just a short period of time, a task force of over 100 ships had sailed 8,000 miles and landed between 9,000 and 10,000 men on an enemy occupied coastline, and the men had fought to within an ace of total victory. There was still an air of unreality about what could possibly be Great Britain's last colonial war.

The overloaded Sea King helicopters of 846 Squadron took off at precisely 1800 hours. They flew low and fast, skimming across the darkness of San Carlos Water, heading for Falkland Sound. The Navy pilots wore passive night goggles—image-intensifiers enabling them to see at night in conditions of low light. In the cramped, blacked-out passenger compartment of the chopper, the noise of the rotor blades, specially coated to withstand the harsh weather conditions, was deafening. We swept across the undulating terrain of East Falkland and then enemy-occupied West Falkland. We hugged the contours and hedge-hopped the sheep fences; we dipped over hillocks and swooped down reentrants. Finally, after a gut lurching, hair-raising short dash up a pitch-black gully, we reached our objective. We put down on an area of high ground amid lumps of tussock grass and soggy peat. A blast of fresh, crisp air hit me as the loadmaster slid open the door. The clear, starlit night was bitterly cold as we struggled out of the helicopters, pulled on our heavy bergens weighed down with 7.62-millimeter link and went into all-around defense.

The drone of the Sea Kings spiraling upward into the moonlit night signaled the move out. In the distance, the relentless pounding of 4.5-inch shells from a type-21 frigate could be heard bombarding the Fox Bay area. We moved off silently on a preset compass bearing. Because visibility was good we traveled in staggered file, well spaced out. We carried a formidable array of weapons: GPMGs, XM 203s, L 42 sniper rifles with night sights, 66 LAWS and American stingers—lightweight heat-seeking surface-to-air missiles. For a while, we followed the gently rising spur running north. The brilliant full moon bathed the jagged rocks on the high ground in front of us. We made good time on a steadily climbing, steepening slope, picking our way quietly and patiently through the semifrozen boggy hillside strewn with unyielding rock.

Shortly after 2030 hours, we began to drop off the high ground to avoid the slab-sided razorback edges that formed the crest lines of most of the unmarked ridges of West Falkland. A slight right hook took us below the craggy crest. As we gained the lower slopes, we began to cross extensive stone runs, cursing under our breath as we scrambled across huge slabs of rock covered with wet, slipper lichen.

We reached the final rockfall that overlooked our objective at 2130 hours. It was a perfect position for a linear ambush. The high ground we were standing on was covered in quartzite blocks in all shapes and sizes, running in narrow parallel lines hundred of meters long. The bleak hillside fell away sharply into a grass-covered valley bottom. The huge open space was ideal for a drop zone. It was also ideal for a killing ground.

After a short, silent pause for a tactical shakeout, forty heavily armed men wormed their way into ambush positions in the rock run. The only noise was the occasional clink of stone, the rustle of equipment, a stifled cough. No orders were given. We had all studied the plan. We all knew that each man was preparing his firing position, choosing his arc of fire, unsplaying grenade pins, going over the "ambush sprung" signals in his mind.

We hid silently in the security of the rocks: bodies and minds alert, eyes and ears straining for the slightest sign of movement, trigger fingers resting along trigger guards, safety catches off. Moonglow clouds scudded soundlessly across the night sky while the icy chill crept slowly through the camouflage material into our immobile limbs. The silence in the valley was intense, overpowering, as still and deep as the voiceless hush of post-explosion shock. The long cold wait took us well past midnight, past the estimated drop time, past the point where the moonlight was at its brightest before beginning to fade. I unzipped my goretex jacket, pulled out the para-cord necklace around my neck and looked at the luminous dial of my G10 watch. It was 0330 hours.

Time passed slowly through the hours of uncertainty.

Gradually the moon and stars disappeared and the cold, clear darkness gave way to the gray damp of dawn. And still we waited, tense, shivering, the tiredness clinging to our limbs like ivy entwining a dying tree. The first misty glimmer of daybreak broke into a bright, frosty morning. We lay motionless for a further hour until finally the "ambush scrubbed" signal was passed down the line. Tommy, a parttime poacher, totally in his element, lying a few feet away looking as if he was sizing up a salmon pool on the River Dee, seemed disappointed, depressed almost, as he made a cutting motion across his throat with the index finger of his left hand. Another lemon!

Throughout the long day we remained hidden, with only our goretex bivvy bags as protection against the bitter cold. Above us, unidentified high-flying jets sliced through the tight blue of the sky trailing thin vapor scars, red edged and inflamed in the rays of the low-lying winter sun. We were all conscious of how exposed, how cut off from the rest of the task force we had become. We were on hard routine: no eating, no brewing, no talking, nothing. We went to extreme lengths to ensure that no small sound or movement would betray our presence to the enemy. Our exhausted minds lengthened the seconds into minutes, the minutes into hours. There were periods when even the turn of the universe seemed frozen still. Finally, darkness came, and with it—the relief was immeasurable—the clattering sound of the Sea Kings coming to take us back to base.

We returned to the *Sir Lancelot*. The old tub had been hit on the morning of 24 May by Skyhawks and abandoned with two unexploded bombs aboard. The bombs had crashed straight through the steel-plate decking, leaving gaping holes, and burrowed deep into the bowels of the ship like maggots through cheese. A naval bomb-disposal team, led by Piggy Trotter, had finally removed the bombs the week before the linear ambush and it now made an excellent base for an SAS QRF. Covert teams could now move at a minute's notice to locations on East or West Falkland. Over the next few days we undertook several clandestine, precisely targeted operations. Like acupuncture needles stimulating the flow of energy through the body's meridians, our activities quickened the pulse of war and hastened the drive for victory. Tumbledown fell. Two Sisters fell. The Gurkhas took control of Mount William. It was during one of our secret sorties that the radio burst into life: "The white flag is flying over Port Stanley." Endgame! The Argies had surrendered.

We made our way to Stanley to take part in the celebrations. The first thing we saw at the airfield gates were the prisoners. Now that the big guns had fallen silent, a vast army of beaten, dejected but relieved men stood clustered around field kitchens waiting to be embarked on the *Canberra*, now anchored in Berkeley Sound. They were dazed, tired and starving. Their combat fatigues were thick with congealed mud that looked like the solidified dribbles of wax down the sides of restaurant bottles. Some were draped in rain-soaked blankets and ponchos as protection against the southerly gales blowing across the peninsula from the Antarctic. Huge piles of discarded weapons and helmets lay rusting in the damp air. Only the officers had been allowed to keep their 9-milly Browning pistols—to protect themselves from their own men. They needed them. Some of the officers, besides handling the battle itself with a disastrous ineptitude that had cost many unnecessary lives, had shot their own men in the legs to stop them running away when fortune had turned against them in the closing stages of the war.

I was sitting in the driving seat of an Argentinian army four-wheel-drive Mercedes jeep on the tarmac outside Stanley airport control tower and terminal building. I had just dropped Tommy off to meet one of his contacts. Tommy, ex-Royal Engineers, a fugitive from D Squadron, besides being a part-time poacher was the best full-time scrounger in the regiment. I stared through the jeep's windscreen. A blustering wind teased fibers of rain from the dirty fleece of cloud that hung low over the desolate scene before me. Over at the air terminal, the walls of the buildings were pockmarked by hundreds of bullet holes and cannon-shell cavities. The broken windows were boarded over against the bitter cold. Across the airfield the litter of war was strewn: ragged tents, burned-out skeletons of vehicles, Pucará bombers upended and devastated by Harrier cannon fire. When I was a small boy, my father had told me of his experiences on the beaches at Dunkirk, and I imagined that this was what it must have looked like.

I was just watching a glint of metal in the sky that must have been a Harrier making a return flight to one of the task-force aircraft carriers, when the sound of Tommy heaving himself into the passenger seat made me turn my head. "Get what you came for?" I asked briefly.

"Yep. I got the name of the ship that provides the booze."

"Did you get the name of the contact man?"

"It's all arranged. We'll pick the stuff up tomorrow. I'm going to turn the Ross Road Guest House into the best-stocked drinking den in town."

"OK, are you hot to trot? We've got to meet Alastair in the Upland Goose in a couple of hours." I started the Mercedes engine and engaged first gear, and the jeep leaped into motion. We drove through the chaos and shambles and out through the main gate of the airport.

A few yards down the road, I pulled up at a huge pile of Argentine-made 7.62-millimeter FN automatic rifles with folding butts. I lifted one off the pile and worked the cocking handle a few times to make sure it was clear. "Throw it back," said Tommy in his broad Scottish accent. "You'll never get it past Ascension. And besides, the Argies have removed all the firing pins."

I quickly stripped the FN, and sure enough the firing pin was missing from the breech block. I threw the rifle and its working parts back on the pile and we continued our three-mile journey back to Port Stanley. Driving along the metal road, we were aware of the mine problem. Every approach to Stanley and the airport was crawling with incorrectly planted minefields. Although the Argentinians had kept some basic charts and records, they were not very precise, with the result that one unit had often overlaid another unit's minefield. A few own goals had been scored in the process. In Stanley itself, the danger would be even more immediate. Here, the Argies had played really dirty. Grenades on one-second fuses, with their pins out, had been found hidden everywhere: under inverted teacups, jammed between bales of wool—just waiting for someone to lift the cup, to part the bales.

We moved on past the unmistakable signs of defeat scattered on either side of the road: 7.62-millimeter FN automatic rifles, .45 American submachine guns, .50 Browning HMGs and Argentinian-produced GPMGs, all piled in great heaps; hundreds of combat helmets lying where their owners had abandoned them; vast quantities of boxed ammunition awaiting disposal; abandoned artillery positions—Italian-built 105-millimeter pack howitzers and the larger 155-millimeter howitzers that could throw a ninety-five-pound shell thirteen and a half miles—carefully concealed in their turf and peat bunkers; a land-based Exocet missile, complete with launcher and generator, parked on wasteground. And all along the windswept route, groups of unarmed Argentinian prisoners could be seen huddling like refugees around burning piles of rubbish or toiling slowly along at the side of the road.

Port Stanley. This small, neat township had, in the short space of time since the surrender, developed a massive traffic problem. Hundreds of vehicles were crammed into its small streets. Land Rovers, trucks, Mercedes jeeps churned up a sea of mud. We turned right into Philomel Street and headed toward a line of brand-new French-built Panhard armored cars. Clothes and loose ammunition lay strewn across the road. The detritus of war was visible everywhere. So was the damage of war. The demoralized Argentinians, avalanching toward defeat, had succeeded in turning the town into a disaster area. Houses had been broken into and looted, rooms left smeared with human excrement, fences chopped down for firewood. In Port Stanley West, where a seaplane hangar had been used as an Argentinian medical dressing station, amputated limbs had been tossed on to the roof of a shed inside the hangar and left to rot. Continuing on along Philomel Street, we passed shattered houses with gaping holes in their roofs, and the still smoldering ruins of the Globe store, set on fire by rioting prisoners. We turned left into Ross Road, ignoring the large white direction arrows painted on the road—an attempt by the Argentinians to impose a drive-on-the-right policy on the Falkland Islanders. We drove along the seafront, past houses with large red crosses on their roofs masquerading as hospital dressing stations, which had been used to stockpile ammunition.

We pulled up outside the post office. The Falklands are famous for their stamp issues. Philatelic sales account for about fourteen percent of the islands' income. Every year they produce four or five attractively designed high-quality sets which become much sought after by collectors. Tommy, ever the wise old bird, had heard that a philatelic war between Argentina and Great Britain had been raging since 1936 and that on 5 April 1982, when the Argie postal staff took over the Port Stanley post office, drunk with power, they had given all waiting mail the Malvinas treatment: stamps had been crossed through and envelopes marked with the special legend "9409 Islas Malvinas." Tommy reckoned that if he could acquire some of these specially marked stamps they would be worth a fortune in years to come. A group of Gurkhas, well wrapped up against the cold, passed the jeep as Tommy jumped out of the vehicle into the mud of the street and disappeared into the post office. I watched the Gurkhas make their way down Ross Road to Government House, looking to see if I could recognize any of them from my training days in Hong Kong.

When Tommy reemerged from the post office, he didn't look too happy. He glanced quickly up the street, as if looking for an escaping intruder, before wrenching the jeep door open and jumping into the passenger seat.

"Get what you were looking for, Tommy?"

"No chance! The Ruperts were there before me. All I

could get were the standard first-day issues. Come on, let's get down to the Upland Goose."

As we strode confidently into the Upland Goose, Des King, the proprietor, verging on a nervous breakdown, looked up briefly from his defensive position behind the bar. His looks blackened when he saw our green duvet jackets and ski-march boots. We ignored his verbal broadside and headed for the restaurant. Alastair McQueen, a reporter with the *Daily Mirror,* our host for the evening, had acquired the corner table commanding a good view of the whole restaurant, now full of Paras and Marines in camouflage clothing. Alastair was already seated with Big Fred the Fijian, Crocker, Stonker and Gary. We pushed past the drunken hacks at the bar, took our seats and awaited developments.

Alastair was the perfect host, regaling us with stories of his days on the *Mirror,* while quietly emptying the wine cellar of its stocks of champagne. We troughed our way noisily through a three-course meal, reminiscing about the events of the past three months.

Throughout the festivities, Gary remained quiet, even morose. Just as a second Drambuie arrived, he decided he had had enough of it all and curled up on the floor for a quick kip in front of the amazed hacks. Dave Norris of the *Daily Mail,* well tanked up by this stage and making a spectacular effort to stagger out of the restaurant, paused for a moment and gazed down on the snoring figure. "If there's one thing I can't abide," he hiccuped, "it's drunks," and he delivered a swift kick into the backside of the sleeping Gary.

All around the room, knives and forks were quietly laid down. All conversation stopped.

"Fucking hell, Norris, you'd better leg it!" suggested Alastair to the reporter.

The advice had come too late. Gary, as a testament to his training, sprang to his feet like a coiled spring and, scowling straight at Fleet Street's finest, advanced menacingly.

"Norris didn't mean it," pleaded Alastair, "he's drunk."

"Forget it, Gary," I shouted through the growing tension, "he's just not worth getting upset over."

Gary, awake and alert, his clenched fists relaxing slightly, glanced quickly around the silent bar. "Serves me right for kipping in a nest of vipers." And with that he walked calmly through the door of the restaurant and past the horrified Des King—who was by now definitely having a nervous breakdown—and disappeared into the darkness of Ross Road.

The conversation picked up again, just a murmur at first as people slowly digested the incident that had just taken place, then building into an excited babble, louder than before, as the onlookers began to work off the rush of adrenaline the scene had precipitated. Just as the festivities were getting into full swing again, I suddenly no longer felt part of the celebrations. I seemed to have stepped back from it all, as if I were in the room next door listening to the party through the walls. Twenty men lost! Twenty of the lads from D Squadron killed in one brief moment. It seemed so stupid and senseless—they hadn't even come under enemy fire. Engine failure? A seagull sucked into the rotor blades? What did it matter? The result was still the same. Good friends had perished. I had played rugby with Taff Jones and Paddy O'Connor; I had served in Dhofar with Sid Davidson; I had worked in Northern Ireland with Phil Curass. The sadness was rising higher and higher. I needed another drink, and quick!

15

Fallen Comrades

"Two pints of bitter and a draught Guinness."

I really needed a drink, I was choked with emotion. It happened every year, the same gut-wrenching feeling, the same sad thoughts that lay too deep for words. It was 1984, two years after the Falklands. As usual, I'd gone home to spend the morning with two of the people I respected most in life: my father, a veteran of Dunkirk, Burma, Italy, France and Germany, now in his seventies, a man of traditional tastes and pleasures, passing his days content to look after his canaries and take his evening tot of whiskey—"Good for the heart, thins the blood"—a man who says little but misses nothing, a man of wisdom, simplicity and quiet dignity; and Archy, Boy Bugler, naval rating, submariner, holder of the Croix de Guerre—the French VC, a man of great tenderness, relentless good humor and single-minded bravery.

Armistice Day. At this hour on this day a great tidal wave of melancholy and heavy emotion sweeps the land. The same ceremony takes place at the same time in every town throughout the nation and has done so year after year. As I stood facing the Cenotaph, I experienced a powerful sense of history, a deep continuity of tradition. I felt part of a process going back to Agincourt, to 1066 and beyond. I was aware of a sense of duty to safeguard the nation, to safeguard my friends, my family, my son. In performing that duty, I had found a fulfilling role in life. Some people are still searching for a role, an identity, when they are forty and fifty. When you join the Army you gain an instant identity. The three of us wore our medals with pride.

The sun was just breaking through the clouds, but a chill wind was blowing. At measured intervals, a tannoy announced each of the veterans' organizations and a representative came forward with a wreath.

"Submariners and Old Comrades Association."

The somber silence between each announcement was broken only by the persistent cough of a young child somewhere at the back of the crowd.

"Royal Air Force Association."

As each wreath was laid on the Cenotaph, one by one the bearers stepped back, paused very stiffly for a few moments, saluted sharply, turned on their heels and, belying their years, marched briskly away. One of the oldest wore the thick dark glasses of the blind and had to be guided by one of his comrades, but he was nonetheless precise in his movements.

As the time approached 11:00, the band struck up, slightly out of time for the first few bars but quickly falling into line:

> "O God, our help in ages past,
> Our hope for years to come . . ."

As the last bars played out, the officiating priest came in too early, with "Let us remember . . ." The band played a ragged "Amen" and the priest, slightly flustered, then quickly regaining his composure, began again. "Let us remember before Almighty God and commend to his keeping those who have died for their country in war . . ."

271

A baby started crying as, on the stroke of eleven, the standards dipped. A plaintive Last Post was sounded, one of the most forlorn and evocative of all sounds. Standing beside me, Archy listened intently. The priest continued:

> " 'They shall grow not old, as we that are left grow old;
> Age shall not weary them, nor the years condemn.
> At the going down of the sun and in the morning
> We will remember them.' "

Two minutes' silence followed, and I remembered them: Laba, Tommy, Taff, Paddy, Sid, Phil and the rest who had perished. Reveille sounded and the standards rose again. I shifted my feet slightly to position one of the flags between myself and the winter sun to get some relief from the low-lying rays, now shining blindingly in my eyes.

"The Grace of our Lord Jesus Christ, the love of God and the fellowship of the Holy Spirit, be with us all, evermore."

As the service drew to a close, people emerged from the crowd in ones and twos and gently laid single red poppies alongside the wreaths, symbols of their own private sorrows, grief-laden tokens for a brother, a father, a son, a husband.

"Eyes . . . left! . . . Eyes . . . front!"

The band and procession of veterans marched off past the Cenotaph, the trombones momentarily seeming to blow stronger, and away down the road. The music faded along with the memories until the only sound was the regular thump of the bass drum, a distant echo of the big guns pounding Fox Bay on the night of the linear ambush.

I drove back to Hereford in a cheerless mood. When I arrived, I felt strongly impelled toward a church a short distance down the road from camp. I hadn't been there for a long while. Why I should feel particularly drawn there this Armistice Day I didn't know. Maybe the nostalgia was growing stronger with the passing of the years. All I knew was that I wanted to visit some old friends.

St. Martin's—the final RV, the last basha for the lads who

didn't make it. The graveyard was to the rear of the church, enveloped in peace and tranquillity, away from the traffic grinding up the road from the city center. It was staked out with six sturdy yew trees. Between the trees I could clearly see the square tower of Hereford Cathedral about a mile away. An air of late autumn decay pervaded the atmosphere: flowers wilting and faded; fetid water greening in vases; urns weatherworn and chipped; a gathered pile of leaves moldering in the corner. A helicopter clattered overhead, returning to camp, its young occupants, full of life, vigor and vitality, completely unaware of the disconsolate scene below.

I went over to Tommy and Laba. They lay in adjacent rows beneath the trees and outside the regimental plot. They had died before this area was set aside. They had only each other for company. I stood at the foot of Laba's grave. The mound seemed far too short. I wondered how such a small plot could possibly contain such a colossus of a man. A neat winged dagger was carved into the top of his headstone, and below it the inscription:

23892771 Sergeant
T. Labalaba BEM
The Royal Irish Rangers
22 SAS Regiment
19 July 1972 Aged 30 years

19 July 1972! The battle of Mirbat. It seemed like another lifetime. And yet, I could see Laba again, as clearly as the cathedral tower. The soundless scenes flitted through my mind. Operation Jaguar: a mortar aiming post under his arm, taking the young Firqats on a mock drill parade to roars of applause from the onlookers; appearing over the rise after the death march, 500 rounds of GPMG link wrapped around his shoulders, two precious jerrycans of water splashing in his hands. The siege of Mirbat: sweat pouring off him, feeding the twenty-five pounder for all he was worth, the enemy just yards away. Then the bullet cut

273

him down and he breathed his last. I read the words at the base of the headstone with a mixture of pride, gratitude and sadness:

> Greater love hath no man than this,
> that a man lay down his life for his friend.

There must have been two or three hundred civilian graves in the main cemetery, but I hardly noticed them as I walked across to the regimental plot, twenty yards to one side and semi-enclosed by a low wall. A neat line of white headstones stretched down the center of the plot—a linear ambush of graves! Walking down the line I was suddenly overcome by a deep sense of awe that I had been spared where so many had fallen. Death roams eagerly during battles. A split second, a microsecond, that's all it takes to die in combat, that's all it takes to blast the spirit from the body, to destroy years of loving work building family, friends and future.

The line of headstones was so straight, so disciplined, it was as if the men were still on parade, backs rigid, eyes front, forever awaiting to be dismissed. An equally ordered row of urns stretched out in front of the headstones, each engraved with a single name: "Tony," "Steve," "Frank," "Dave," "Ginge." The effect was powerful, they were so heart-rendingly simple. I sensed an aura of grief, of shock, immediate, still beating. There was some essence of the men that was still alive, still whispering through the trees, still rustling with the leaves. A spirit of restlessness, of startled disorientation roamed about the headstones. I glanced across at the civilian graves. Over there was a sense of peace. Those people had lived their lives, they'd run their course, they'd seen and sensed their allotted span of winters and summers. Around the linear ambush lives had been too abruptly snatched away, souls too suddenly severed from wounded bodies. The psychic shock waves still lingered, still rippled through the air.

The last grave in the line was a new one. I stooped down. The man's camouflaged webbing belt had been folded in four and laid carefully between two urns of flowers across the freshly dug soil. I picked up the belt, partly unfolded it and felt the solid, reassuring touch of the canvas weave. For a moment, the distant roar of the traffic penetrated my awareness again. Noise! Life! Energy! Movement! Then just as quickly it faded away. I folded the belt into four again and placed it gently back on the mound.

I stood up and walked back toward the stone wall at the end of the plot. A large winged-dagger plaque was set into the wall, and on either side a row of ten smaller plaques. As I drew nearer, I could see a crop of tiny white balsa-wood crosses planted in the grass just in front of the wall. Silent Valley! The sight of the crosses sparked a flash of recollection of that somber graveyard scene in Aden all those years before when I was a regular soldier with the Royal Engineers. I'd come a long way since then. I was lucky. The sand was still trickling through my hourglass.

To the left of the winged dagger and lower down, a quote from the regimental clock had been reproduced, a quote I'd glimpsed as I scrambled out of training-wing theater after the Colonel's opening address on the first day of selection. I now read the words slowly and deliberately, letting the meaning sink deep within:

> We are the pilgrims, master; we shall go
> Always a little further: it may be
> Beyond that last blue mountain barr'd with
> snow
> Across that angry or that glimmering sea.

I'd been across that angry sea, I'd been beyond that mountain barred with snow. The pilgrimage continued. But for these lads the journey was at an end. They would go no further. Back at camp, their names were inscribed in white lettering on the bronze panels at the base of the clock: it was a mark of utter finality. In regimental terminology, they had been unable to beat the clock!

I looked at the moving messages inscribed on the urns.

HE WHO DARES

> To the world you were a soldier;
> But to me you were the world.

The fresh flowers in the urns swayed slightly as I read the words. Each inscription was like a thump in the chest.

> Your love lies within my heart
> Until our spirits touch.

A breeze sprang up as if from nowhere. The skin across my cheekbones was drawing tight with the cold, my hands were going numb.

> Loving husband and Daddy.

I thought of my own son, now eight years old. What would he have been feeling now if I'd gone down with them, if I'd not come back?

The inscriptions on the small plaques were uniform, stark in their simplicity: number, rank, name, date of birth, date of death. A relentless sense of tragedy gripped me as my eyes read from left to right and saw, repeated again and again, the same date of death: 19.5.82. The Falklands helicopter crash!

The sadness was welling up. It tightened my throat. I kept on swallowing unconsciously, trying to get rid of it, as if it were a piece of food stuck in my gullet—but it refused to go away. I knew there was only one way to relieve the feeling. I needed a drink and a chat with the lads to get things back in perspective.

The warm, bustling, smoky, beery atmosphere of the pub was a great comfort as I carried drinks to the table and sat down with Paddy and Iain Thomson—the strangest variation you could imagine on the theme of the Englishman, Irishman and Scotsman! The beer quickly took effect and the stories started to flow. This was what I enjoyed the most. A couple of pints to release the tensions, and the world suddenly seemed a better place to be. With the stories came the glow of reminiscence; with the recollections came the warmth of camaraderie.

"Iain, you never did tell me the full story of those thirteen morphine syrettes in Borneo. How come you took so many?"

"Ah yes. The Borneo ambush. I remember as if it were yesterday. Mind you, it's thirsty work telling stories. It'll cost you a double Grouse."

"Yer on," I said without hesitation.

Iain took a sip of beer and settled back. "It was at Gunong Rawan, Sarawak. We were on patrol against the Indonesian KKO, myself and seven other lads from D Squadron. I was lead scout. I'd been in Malaya on a trackers' course with the Maori SAS. Being a nonsmoker, I could smell scents in the jungle very easily. It was seven o'clock in the morning and we'd just come across a track leading to a clearing. I had a bad feeling about it, a premonition.

"The next moment the world erupted. Rounds were hitting the ground at my feet and ricocheting off the rocks into the trees. Bits of branches were falling on my head. I felt a terrific thump in my thigh and went flying backwards through the air. As I hit the ground, an Indonesian KKO popped up. I was lucky—I hadn't dropped my 5.56 Armalite automatic when I got hit. I swung it round and blew him away. As I crouched back down, a spurt of blood hit me in the face. My femoral artery was severed and I was already feeling very weak. I whistled off my face veil, wrapped it around my leg as far into my crotch as I could get it, pulled it tight and tied it off. I whipped out my commando dagger, twisted it around the veil, then stuck it through the leg of my OGs. The bleeding stopped!

"The firing continued, pushing the rest of the patrol down the valley, leaving me stranded. By this time, I'd already banged in my second syrette. I was lucky. I'd spotted a pile of morphine lying around at the Gurkha base just as we were leaving Kuching. I was told it was gash. Being a canny Jock, I'd stuck it into my breast pocket.

"I started to crawl in the direction of the emergency RV. I

277

wasn't going to stay there and rot if I could help it. I could feel the femur crunching together. There was no pain; the morphine had started to take effect. By nightfall, and four morphines later, I crawled into a pighole under a tree to hide from the Indos. I covered myself with mud and pig shit as camouflage. I couldn't smell anything, I was too high on the morphine.

"I crawled throughout the next day. My thirst was terrible. Every time I tried to drink water, I spewed it up again. My system just wouldn't accept it. About 1630 hours, I reached a stream. I was hugely relieved. It was the watershed of the border. I rolled about in the water to get rid of the maggots which covered me from knee to waist. The fish must have had a field day! I started to fire shots in the air, three at a time, the emergency signal. Suddenly I spotted a movement above me. I rolled over behind a rock and somehow managed to get my Armalite pointing in the right direction. Someone ran behind a tree. Indo bastards, they've found me! I made my mind up to have a go as much as I could, then banjo myself. I remembered what had happened to Paddy Condon when they caught him. It was then I saw the red hat and the bren gun. The Gurkhas! Salvation! Then I saw Kevin, the airborne wart, as large as life and twice as ugly! I cried my eyes out against his broad Yorkshire shoulder. Never was I so glad to see a fellow Para.

"That night, Kevin slept cuddled around me to keep me warm. As I fell into a deep sleep, I worked out that in thirty hours of crawling I had taken twelve syrettes of quarter-grain morphine. Plus one the next day, waiting for the casevac. That makes thirteen!"

"I don't understand it, Iain," I said. "Thirteen syrettes! You should have been dead! A medic stood up in training wing and told us that the human body can only take three syrettes of morphine. One more, and you would be dead!"

"What a way to go! Quite a pleasant death really—beautiful surroundings, no pain, mind floating, lying back and thinking of Scotland, of all that lovely McEwan's

Export I would never taste again, wondering if anyone would ever find my body!"

The night wore on and Iain left for home. I got up and headed for the bar to get Paddy and myself a last drink. I brushed against a prominent member of the local business community who was propping up the bar. This man was rather unusual in that, while fully taking advantage of the benefits of free enterprise, he retained staunch socialist views. He saw no contradiction—he was practicing the revolution from within, a subversive hearts-and-minds campaign, death by a thousand cuts to the capitalist culture. He never lost an opportunity to spread the gospel. As I placed my order, he picked up a collection tin from the bar and rattled it under my face. "Are you not going to make a contribution to the miners' strike fund?" He began to bait me right away.

In a flash, the glow of camaraderie and humor was gone. I was back into the cold reality of my career, the daily confrontation with danger that the last few hours had reminded me of only too vividly. "Not on your frigging life. Do you think I've been fighting the Queen's enemies for the last twenty years, watching my mates get wounded and killed, risking my neck daily to make Britain a safe place to live in, just so that the Arthur Scargills of this world can hold the country to ransom!?" I was biting like a hungry salmon—a dangerous mistake.

"Risking your neck! Your lot didn't do anything in the Falklands!"

"Didn't do anything! We played a crucial part in the whole thing, and what's more, we lost twenty lads down there!" I was now on the hook.

"You shouldn't have been there in the first place. It was just a bluff, a political maneuver by Maggie Thatcher." He was beginning to reel me in.

"I suppose your crowd would have let the Argies run riot in the Falklands like yer darling Harold sold us down the river in Aden and let the Commies take over."

Just as I was nearing the net, he lost his nerve, ran out of brain and began to resort to brawn. "Come on, outside, we'll settle this on the lawn."

Paddy was now at the bar and tried to intervene. "Don't be stupid, fella. If I were you, I wouldn't go outside, even in a tank, with my mate here."

"He doesn't scare me," sneered the businessman.

"You're too old," I said sarcastically as I paid for the drinks.

"Who's too old, I'll bloody well show you who's too old," roared the businessman, taking his jacket off.

At this point, thoughts of the Red Mill Inn and all the drama in Hong Kong flashed across my mind. More importantly, so did the more recent events that had taken place at the OC B Squadron's wedding a few months earlier. The OC was marrying one of the daughters of David Shepherd, the famous artist who had done two fine paintings of Mirbat and the Embassy siege. All of B Squadron had been invited. It was a very smart occasion—everyone in ceremonial uniform and finery. The reception was in full swing when I spotted Carl. I'd been looking for an opportunity to exact retribution for some time. Carl had been on the piss one night, staggered into the basha and for no reason whatever decided to set about Malcolm the clerk, nearly veteran of the Embassy siege. He just beat him up while he was sleeping in his bed! If there's one thing I can't stand, it's bullies. So at the wedding reception I decided to take Carl unawares, just as he'd done to Malcolm.

I went over to him and challenged him to a friendly arm-wrestling contest. We sat down, rolled up our sleeves, locked our hands and started to grapple. After a while I let Carl think he was getting the better of me. I allowed my arm to be pushed nearly on to the table. Just as he was eagerly scenting victory, I brought up my free hand from under the table and punched him square in the face. "That one's for Malcolm," I said. Carl crashed over backward. A big punch-up ensued. Tables and chairs were crashing and women screaming as we rolled over the floor and out through the marquee entrance into the garden. I taught Carl a lesson he wouldn't forget in a hurry.

To commemorate the occasion, I later thought of suggesting to David Shepherd that he might like to do a wedding portrait of the OC and his new bride holding hands, standing at the marquee entrance gazing romantically into each other's eyes, with Carl and me in the background slogging it out in the rhododendrons. I don't think David Shepherd would have been amused. The OC certainly wasn't. He had me up on Colonel's orders for the second time. I was given a severe warning and put on probation.

Since I was on probation, the scenario now developing with the businessman did not look at all healthy. I've been in this situation before, I thought to myself, I've got to get out of here. I pushed the businessman's shaking fist abruptly to one side and, like a bull going for a red cloak, I started for the door. As I stormed blindly past Paddy, I knocked his shoulder. Paddy lost his balance, crashed into a partition and ended up on the floor with blood streaming from his nose. By this time, I was out of the door, into my Capri and away into the night.

The next morning, I was on Colonel's orders for the third time! If looks could kill, the Colonel would have been convicted of mass murder. He was incandescent with rage. He stabbed his forefinger angrily on his desk to emphasize his outrage. A note of incredulity sounded in his voice. "You assaulted and verbally abused a respected member of Hereford society. You struck one of your own colleagues a blow to the face . . ."

It was no use protesting. On paper, my case looked hopeless: RTU'd for Hong Kong, put on probation for the OC's wedding fracas and now this. Surely I was finished? I interjected a sharp "sir" at appropriate moments to show a reaction, to show acceptance of the point being made, and a softer "sir" to intone a note of query, a request for further clarification.

". . . and before you even try a plea of mitigation, you can forget it. I don't want to hear any feeble excuses. I don't want to hear any litany of extenuating arguments. What I expect from the men in this regiment is nothing short of the best—at all times, in all places, in all circumstances. Anything less than that and we fail. And if we fail, we call attention to ourselves, and in our book, that's the worst possible crime . . ."

He leaned forward across his desk. "You are irredeemable. Your behavior makes Neanderthal Man look like the epitome of sophistication . . ."

He leaned back in his chair again, arms folded, decisive, his voice lower now. "You are a time bomb, trooper, a time bomb just waiting to explode. I'm taking a risk, a huge risk, I know that. You seem determined to ruin yourself. But I'm sending you down to Woolwich Hospital to see if the medics can make any sense of you, to see if they can take your brain apart bit by bit until they find the fuse."

He let out a deep, weary sigh and reached for a pen. His voice now took on a more threatening tone. "I'm warning you. One false step at Woolwich and you are finished—finished for good this time."

16

Frustration

Finished for good? Not if I could help it. I was lying in my bed in Ward 11, going over the game plan in my mind. Tomorrow, the big one, the chief psychiatrist. It all now depended on one man, a civilian at that—a civilian in charge of the mental health of the British Army! I was determined not to give in, not to let go of the values and ideals I'd lived for all this time, my identity, my self-respect, forged in the flames of the battlefield. I owed it to my fallen comrades to pull through.

The bloke in the next bed stirred. He'd come in two days before and hadn't said a word yet. He'd just lain on his bed, staring into space, eyes as dead as pebbles. He was saying, "It was the tooth that killed him. The gunshot wound was the start of it, but it was the tooth that killed him."

I glanced over. He was looking straight at me. His eyes had become moist, human again. Tears were rolling down his cheeks.

"I was a trained medic. I'd worked in three hospitals. I should have known better. A jagged piece of filthy, decayed tooth must have gone into the lung tissue and just festered. That's what killed him. It wasn't the gunshot wound, it was the miserable piece of rotten tooth that killed him."

He lay back on his pillow and stared ahead again, but the tears continued to flow. "He was my best mate. He'd caught a high-velocity in the jaw. He was lying on his back, choking—not with blood or vomit, he'd swallowed his tongue. I yanked his tongue forward and pulled every bit of mess out of his mouth I could find. I was sure I'd got everything out of his passageway. I was sure I'd completely cleared the cavity of all the bits of teeth. He made it back to the UK all right, but he was having increasing problems with his breathing. Pneumonia or pleurisy, I don't know. They were pumping him full of penicillin, trying to get him better from the infection.

"I used to visit him in hospital as often as I could. It gave Jean a break. She had her hands full as it was with the kids. This particular day, he seemed fine one minute, a bit pale, but fine. The next minute he was no longer in the same world I was in. He was no longer seeing what I was seeing, hearing what I was hearing. His eyes had glazed over, his ears somehow stopped up with the effort of trying to get his breath. I called the nurse.

"He twisted his head fiercely from side to side, his mouth working away as if he was chewing a piece of leather. Suddenly he would lie still, and his mouth would gape open for a while at the point of some momentous inner struggle. Then the head would start again. Strange sounds, not of this earth, emerged from his mouth and spoke of deep, agonizing distress. He strove to turn and lever his body off the bed, driven by some deep instinctive urge, as if he could pull through if only he could get himself into an upright position.

"He lifted and twisted his head one last time, more slowly now, and he looked at me, fear and questioning in his eyes. Then, slowly, slowly, he sank down with a rasping sigh, the life visibly draining away from him. I stared at him in complete and total helplessness, such impotence to alter the course of events as I'd never before experienced. A few last twitches and then his body was still, as if some great sinking battleship had finally come to rest on the bed of the ocean.

"The doctor came and went. I sat there for an age, staring at his silent form, hoping for an eyelid to rise, for a flicker of movement in the chest, staring for so long that my eyes began to play tricks on me and I imagined I saw a tremor of movement in his solar plexus. Eventually, I slowly got up, stiff from staring, and walked away. I was feeling heavy. I knew I had to tell Jean.

"She was laying the table for tea when I came in. She had a plate of buttered sliced bread in her hand. Her two kids were shouting excitedly, running around, tugging each other's sleeves. Her eyes met mine and she knew straight away. The welcoming smile faded in an instant to dawning horror. She didn't rant, she didn't rave. She didn't burst into tears, she didn't shake with rage. There were no silent mouthings of incredulity nor any desperate fist-clenched challenge to the heavens to explain why. She neither fainted nor slumped in a chair, nor gripped the edge of the table. She was rigid, transfixed by a charge of emotion that had overpowered her ability to think, feel or speak clearly, that seemed for an instant to have chased the very soul out of her body. She simply, slowly and deliberately, closed her eyes, was silent for the eternity of a moment, then whispered with a voice that was not her own, "Please go." With the two kids now silently staring at me, uncomprehending but sensing that something momentous was taking place, I turned, opened the door and quickly left. I hadn't spoken a word, not a single word."

"Maybe the shock of the high velocity bullet that hit him made him suddenly catch his breath and inhale the piece of tooth into his lungs," I suggested, trying to offer some comfort.

"How could you tell them what it was really like down there?" he continued, apparently without hearing what I'd said. "They all wanted to buy you drinks in the pub and ask you how it was, but how could you tell them what it was really like? To most people, the war was just an interesting diversion, something that happened each night for ten minutes on the nine o'clock news. Some people thought the Falklands was an island just off the coast of Scotland." He leaned back over in my direction and fixed me with his eyes. "I didn't want to leave when it was all over. That's where the lads had fought and died. That's where you'd been through it together. How could anyone else possibly understand? No one could possibly know what you had been through."

"That's true, mate, that's true."

"They told me I'm suffering from POST."

"POST, PTSD, ABR! Bullshit! It's all bullshit!" I exclaimed angrily. "It's just names, boxes. They think if they can put a name on it, put it into a box, then everything's explained, that all's well with the world. You've gone psychosomatic. There's nothing wrong with you. It's just shell shock. That's all you've got. Good old-fashioned shell shock."

I looked at him. He could see from my eyes that I'd been there too. We were mates together, mates who had never met. A veil of gloom and fear seemed to lift off his face.

"You know something? They can't really cure you in here," I went on. "All they're after is your mind. You're just a case study, one for the archives, a bit of research for the thesis they're writing. They've got a tape recorder hidden on the desk. There's a little red light when it's on. You'll see it. They record everything you say so they can have a good laugh with their pals afterwards.

"If you think you're Napoleon now, nothing's going to stop you waking up when you're ninety-three and still thinking you're Napoleon. There's only one way you can be cured, and that's from within yourself. It's got to come from inside. You've got to get a grip on yourself. No one can do that for you."

As the evening wore on I finally dozed off to sleep, the man's words spooling through my mind on an endlessly repeating loop tape. "How could you tell them what it was really like?"

* * *

"How could I begin to tell you what it was really like?" It was the next day and I was struggling to get through to the psychiatrist. "I could describe to you the terror, the disorientation, the sheer loneliness of being caught in a blizzard late at night driving across the mountains, when the road disappears, when everything is eerily hushed, when you don't know which is ditch and which is road or even which side of the road you're on, when the snow is so heavy the windscreen wipers begin to slow down under the accumulating weight, and the flakes stick to the screen even though the heater is trained full on to it, when you can't stop because to stop would be even more dangerous than to carry on, when you feel like a man slowly sinking in quicksand as you are sucked into the center of the snowstorm, when your mind tells you there are other people in the world but your heart tells you you are the only one there.

"I could tell you all this, and this is something within the spectrum of your own experience. We've all been in a snowstorm, we've all driven late at night through rain and snow and mist. I could tell you all this. But unless you had been where I was at the precise time I was there, you could not know, you could not feel, you could not be completely submerged in that total terror, that incipient suppressed panic. Your mind could not have been stretched taut in that relentless nerve strain. Now look at that gap between my experience and your reaction to my relating it. Multiply that gap by ten, by twenty, by a hundred and you have some idea of the experience of war, the sense-crush of combat, the mind blast of battle, the trauma of violent death."

I looked at the psychiatrist and he showed no reaction. I wasn't getting through to him. I was frustrated, angry. It felt as though I was trying to run through waist-deep water.

Suddenly, there was the sound of a detonation, a huge, cataclysmic detonation. The next moment I was coming to, lying there, dazed and confused, for what seemed like an age. I prised my eyes open. A shaft of light came in. I heard the sound of voices. It felt hot. I could smell the sweet, sharp, prickly smell of cordite. My mouth tasted dry and dusty. My hands were working, fists slowly clenching and unclenching. I felt the rough woollen material of a blanket.

A blanket! I sprang up with a start. Christ, I've been dreaming! A full technicolor dream complete with stereophonic sound. It was dawn. The ward was stirring into life. My newfound mate in the next bed had lit up a cigarette and was waving the match in the air to extinguish it. Red phosphorus—the smell of cordite! The nurse was pushing a metal trolley full of surgical equipment rattling on steel trays down the middle of the ward. The doors through which she'd just exploded were swinging violently, neon light glinting on their aluminum panels.

I walked slowly down the corridor toward the chief psychiatrist's office.

"You are a time bomb, trooper, a time bomb just waiting to explode. But we can defuse you!" The Colonel's words rang through my mind as my footsteps echoed off the bare walls. I thought of Tommo the scouse exploding with anger on selection all those years before. It hadn't done him much good. Or maybe it had. Maybe he wasn't meant to be in the SAS—he might never have made it past Operation Jaguar. That explosion might have saved his life. Maybe he was better off out of it after all. Maybe he'd got himself a nice little number back with the Royal Fusiliers and done very well for himself. Perhaps he'd found the secret: expression of emotion rather than suppression. Why bottle up all your feelings, build up the pressure, build up the stress until your heart fails, your stomach ulcerates, your liver collapses or your brain gets blown apart by a stroke?

The Colonel thinks I'm going to explode. Maybe I should explode, get it off my chest, go out with a bang rather than a whimper. I've fought my fights, I've waged my wars. Perhaps it would be a fitting end to a drama-filled career. Shit or bust! Attack—the best form of defense!

One thing is for certain. I'm not going to play second fiddle to some jumped-up civilian psychiatrist who doesn't know the first thing about combat. I've never let the system get me down before. If I had, if I hadn't shown initiative and self confidence before, I wouldn't be here now. If I hadn't broken the rules at Mirbat and sent the first radio message to Um al Gwarif in plain language Morse, crucial time would have been lost; if I hadn't used the knuckleduster in Hong Kong, I would have been dead on the street; if I hadn't demanded that the hospital orderly in Stanley Jail give me a tetanus jab, I could have had serious health problems; if I hadn't stood my ground with the RE Colonel back at Southwood Barracks, I would have spent an unpleasant twelve months as a lance corporal rather than a sergeant; if I hadn't insisted on seeing the Captain on the *Andromeda,* we would have lost a pallet full of vital equipment. I had never groveled to another man in my life and I didn't intend starting now.

I strode into the office without knocking. The psychiatrist looked up, slightly startled. He was as ugly as an iguana. Folds of yellow green skin clung to his prominent facial bones, he had dark rings around his eyes and his expression was as bleak as a wind-ruffled winter puddle. He lit another cigarette from the remains of one he'd just finished, and screwed the bent dog end into the layer of ash in the bottom of the ashtray amid the burned-out remains of a dozen other cigarettes. Christ! Not only a civilian in charge of the mental health of the British Army, but a chain smoker at that! What have you got to hide, mate? What's gnawing away at your insides? Why do you need to smoke so much? I've no problem going three months in the jungle without a drink. You wouldn't last three days there without your cigarettes. You'd be crawling up the trees!

A thick blue haze hung in the room like a morning mist. I'm not having this. I'm used to the great outdoors. Plenty of fresh air. Without saying a word, I marched over to the window, rattled it open and took some deep breaths of the air wafting over Woolwich Common. He didn't like it. It was late November and he got an icy draught on the back of his neck. I sauntered back around to the front of the desk and,

without waiting to be asked, sat down. I was in a defiant
mood. The psychiatrist picked up a folder, his eyes not
leaving me for a moment. He placed it before him and
grasped a pencil from a plastic container. Then he looked
down. The pencil hissed across the page as he furiously
scribbled notes on my report.

17

The Final RV

In the days before steam, when tall-masted clippers plied the tea route between China and Europe, speed was of the essence. The ship that reached port the first got the benefit of the markets. Moreover, the quicker the journey, the better the condition of the cargo—for tea deteriorates when stowed—and the higher the price it could command. The speed of the boat depended on the skill of the riggers in unfurling and stowing the sails. The man with the most dangerous job on board was the rigger who sat astride the gaff boom supporting the topsail in the mighty center column of six. Safety was not of paramount concern. It was not unknown for the topmost rigger, subjected as he was to the highest winds and the greatest pitch and roll of the swell, to lose his grip and go plunging down a hundred feet or more. If he hit the deck, it meant almost certain death. If he fell into the sea, he might just escape with shock and bruising. A rigger who survived the fall intact was encouraged by the older hands to climb straight back up to the top of the center mast so that he might not lose his nerve forever. This was exposure therapy of the most immediate kind.

BET they call it today—behavioral exposure therapy—a

legacy of post-Freudian psychoanalytical theory. I learned all about it in Ward 11. They gave me pills to break down the barriers and allow the traumas of my operational experiences to come to the surface. Through being exposed and confronted, the traumas could hopefully be cured. As I drove back from Woolwich to Hereford, I thought I would undertake a bit of freelance BET myself. I decided to pay a visit to the scene of my so-called crime. I would have a pint in the pub where the argument with the businessman had taken place. Not only would it satisfy my self-willed bloody-mindedness, but it would have the additional benefit of allowing me to reorientate myself into familiar surroundings after the wasteland of Ward 11 before facing the Colonel on camp.

It was lunchtime and the taproom was surprisingly busy. I was hoping to find Sek there. A drink and talk about the old days, a bit of exposure to his laconic Fijian humor would be just the aftercare I needed. I sat down at the bar, ordered a pint of draught Guinness and quietly smiled to myself. No one said anything. It was as if nothing had ever happened. I relaxed and let the normality flow over me.

I was halfway through my pint when I spotted the infamous Lynda. She had become almost as much a part of the regiment as the clock itself. The night I'd seen her all those years before, tumbling in the sheets with Geordie before Sickener 1, had not been her first visit to camp, nor her last. She'd had as many willing partners as there are daisies on an uncut lawn. Now in her mid-thirties, the passions of youth tempered by the pummelings of experience, she had acquired a hard, no-nonsense manner which on the few occasions when I now saw her I found an irresistible challenge.

I gave her a wave and she breezed over, exclaiming jauntily, "Hi, soldier. How're you keeping? I haven't seen you in ages. Where've you been?"

"I've just returned from down south—training exercise, that sort of thing. What are you doing with yourself these days, Lynda?"

"I'm training to be a psychiatric nurse."

"A psychiatric nurse! I know all about them. They're all as mad as hatters. What made you choose that career?"

"It's a case of if you can't beat them, join them."

"When you qualify, you should set up a therapy clinic on camp."

She completely missed the veiled reference to her erstwhile penchant for helping the lads to release the tensions of army life. "Why? Are you all screwball down there?"

"Yeah! Didn't you know there's a chopper on constant hover 50,000 feet above the camp to make sure no one escapes?"

"I can believe it."

"If you opened a clinic, they'd be queuing up at the door to see you—especially if you had your black stockings on!"

"Oh yeah, and my whip?" A hint of anger was creeping into her voice. She was beginning to take me too seriously.

"Why not? I had the whip in Hong Kong. It didn't do me any lasting harm."

"Physically or psychologically?"

"Physically. You'll have to analyze me to see if I suffered any brain damage or not! I'll be your first patient if you'll have me."

"Sure, I'm game."

"I've no doubt you are! I look forward to meeting you on the couch then, Lynda."

By now she'd cottoned on to the *double entendres*, so I drained my Guinness and beat a hasty retreat. I didn't want to tangle with her newfound temper. She'd recently gone over to the loony fringe of the women's liberation movement. And that was even more dangerous than the loony fringe of the socialist movement!

As I walked through the main gate of the barracks, the tension began to crawl through my muscles. I felt nervous and apprehensive. I wondered what the chain-smoking shrink had written about me. I wondered whether fifteen years' drama-filled service in the SAS was about to end in an ignominious anticlimax, a definitive RTU. The mod plod on the gate gave me a friendly wave. That was reassuring—no urgent call to the telephone, no clipped voice ordering me to the CO's office to be hit by the report.

I pushed through the main door of the headquarters block and turned right into the orderly room. A large oil painting of David Stirling, the moving force behind the foundation of the SAS, hung on the far wall and dominated the office. The clerks looked indifferent. No arrangements had been made. There was no memo ordering me to attend a CO's interview. The chief clerk shrugged his shoulders and looked blank. I closed the door on the paper factory and headed for the operational research department to try my luck there. Still nothing doing. From there I was redirected to admin wing, the last refuge of the regimental bad boys. At this rate, I thought, I'm going to end up in the stores blanket-stacking.

Just when I was fearing the worst, just when I thought the system had finally caught up with me, the message came down the line: a clean bill of health! The shrinks had given me a clean bill of health! I was elated. The gamble had paid off! Once more I'd brazened my way out of a tight corner. I was back in business with a vengeance. They were going to put my operational expertise to the best possible use: I was to be instructor in the counterrevolutionary warfare wing. From trainee to tutor, after fifteen years my career in the SAS had come full circle. Being no longer in the field exposed to life-threatening situations, I had not only beaten the system, but had now well and truly beaten the clock. I'd ridden the death-or-glory course and made it to the finishing post.

As the weeks went by, I threw myself wholeheartedly into the job in hand, counter-terrorism team training. As I did so, the realization dawned: I must be well and truly A1 and fit for service. There was no way the Head Shed would risk a training compromise. What was required of troops for these types of operations—even above and beyond all specialist skills—were a cool head, a clear mind and a rock-solid temperament. If the trainer was unstable, what hope for the trainees? Before I was to close the door on CRW wing for the last time, before I was to face my next big battle—civvy life—I still had a significant contribution to make to the regiment.

On Friday, 8 May 1987, eight IRA men were killed in a gun battle in the village of Loughgall, County Armagh. They were attacking the local RUC station with a hijacked JCB digger loaded with beer kegs containing 500 pounds of explosives when an ambush was sprung. The attack— thought to have been undertaken by the lethal East Tyrone brigade—was part of an organized campaign of intimidation against the RUC. Security forces considered the operation a major setback for the IRA. One senior policeman said, "We really needed a victory. It will do wonders for the morale of our men." The ambush was mounted jointly by the SAS and the Royal Ulster Constabulary's elite support unit, trained in Hereford by the SAS.

Soldier I retired on 31 December 1987. Endex!

Postscript

Soldier I, cryptically and at the eleventh hour, requested that this book be dedicated to the anonymous author of the following verse:

> You served your country for years and years.
> Many laughs through many fears.
> That life ends now, so another can start,
> But a soldier you'll always remain at heart.

A new life has indeed begun for Soldier I, a life in many ways even more dramatic than the one he has left behind. The specialist training and unique skills he picked up during his many years of service with the SAS gave him privileged and instant access to the front line of international VIP security. After living on dry, twenty-four-hour ration packs and sleeping on the hard desert floor at Um al Gwarif at the beginning of his career in the SAS, Soldier I more recently found himself in the heart of London's West End feasting on the sumptuous cuisine of the St. James's Club and sleeping in air-conditioned comfort on a soft mattress—beneath which was concealed £1½ million-worth of diamonds.

The world of security in which Soldier I now works as a

freelance operative demands the same degree of stealth, silence and anonymity that became second nature in the Army. And as with the world of espionage and secret intelligence, the general public gets only the faintest glimpses of what really goes on. First-class, all-expenses-paid trips to far-flung exotic locations, long-distance calls down crackling telephone lines, suntans suddenly acquired in the depths of a British winter give only a vague notion of his current activities.

A new stage, but the drama continues. However, there is now an added dimension: the human factor. After the rigid structure of the Army, how will Soldier I adapt to the infinitely fluid routine of everyday existence between the spells of security work? What inner journeys need to be traveled, what inner resources need to be tapped in order to make the transition to civilian life a successful one? And what will happen when Soldier I finally retires for good? For, like the Army, the security world is both mentally and physically demanding, and the years quickly catch up—even on an SAS man.

As the verse says, a soldier he'll always remain at heart. He knows that many battles are still being fought—and more are yet to come.

Glossary

.303 Lee Enfield rifle (outdated)

.50-caliber Browning belt-fed heavy machine gun, air-cooled, with a rate of fire 450-600 rounds per minute

66 LAWS 66-millimeter light anti-tank weapon system

66-millimeter anti-tank rocket carried by infantry battalions as a lightweight, throwaway tank- and bunker-buster

81-millimeter mortar standard-issue British Army mortar

82-millimeter mortar standard-issue Russian Army mortar

9-milly nickname for the 9-millimeter Browning pistol; can also refer to 9-millimeter ammunition

ABR advanced battle reaction

Adoo Dhofaris who espoused the Communist cause; (general) enemy

AK 47 Kalashnikov assault rifle; standard-issue rifle of the Soviet Army since the 1950s

AK-M modernized version of the AK 47 made with a folding butt stock

Askar armed tribesman

basha waterproof shelter made from a poncho; can also mean barrack room, house, bed, etc.

BATT British Army training team

Glossary

Batt House BATT headquarters

bergen pack carried by British forces on active service, containing everything necessary for survival

BET behavioral exposure therapy

BMH British Military Hospital (Hong Kong)

Bradbury Lines SAS barracks in Redhill, Hereford; (later renamed Stirling Lines)

buckshee free, without charge; a freebie

bukit hill, mountain (from the Malay)

Carl Gustav 84-millimeter medium anti-armor shoulder-held recoilless weapon (nickname Charlie G)

casevac casualty evacuation; removal of injured by helicopter to aid post or hospital

CBF Commander British Forces

CES complete equipment schedule

CO Commanding Officer

CPO command-post orderly

crap-hat failure; member of the regular Army

cross-grain march over hills direct from summit to summit

CRW counterrevolutionary warfare

CT Communist terrorist

cyalume stick light-stick attached to clothing or life jacket, activated by squeezing: acts as a marker—visible from up to a mile away

D11 Metropolitan Police elite firearms team

DF defensive fire: prerecorded mortar fire used by troops in defensive positions on likely enemy approaches

DG Dhofar Gendarmerie

dickers youths who note security-forces movements

dragon light handheld searchlight

DZ dropping zone

endex end of exercise

EU Emergency Unit

figure-eleven target practice target on firing range

Firqat company of Dhofaris loyal to the Sultan; (also Firkin, Firk)

FKW Firqat Khalid bin Waalid

FN Fabrique Nationale: Belgian arms company manufacturing original-design automatic SLR

frag fire at (from fragmentation grenade)

FST field surgical theater

full battle order fully armed

Gemini large rubber dinghy

gimpy nickname for GPMG

GPMG general-purpose machine gun (caliber 7.62 millimeters, belt-fed, designed by FN)

green slime nickname for Intelligence Corps (from their distinctive green berets)

GSW gunshot wound

Guryunov Russian 7.62-millimeter medium machine gun

hangi Fijian feast

HE high explosive

Head Shed nickname for senior officers

Heckler Koch MP 5 single shot or fully automatic German-produced 9-millimeter machine gun

hexamine stove lightweight stove burning blocks of solid fuel

HMG heavy machine gun

Huey American-built helicopter

ISFE ignitor safety-fuse electric

jebel mountain, hill

Jenson's Violet purple-colored medication

Kremlin nickname for intelligence section at regimental headquarters, Bradbury Lines

L 42 standard-issue British Army 7.62-millimeter sniper rifle

LFT liver-function test

LMG light machine gun

LSL landing ship logistic

LZ landing zone

M 16 Armalite standard-issue American assault rifle

M 202 66-millimeter multi-shot portable flame weapon; a light-weight four-tube rocket-launcher, with a preloaded four-round incendiary-rocket clip that slides into the launcher tubes; maximum effective range 750 meters

Glossary

M 79   grenade discharger

mag   magnetic north

majnoon   mad one (from the Arabic)

maroon machine   nickname for Parachute Regiment (from their distinctive maroon berets)

MFC   mortar fire controller

mixed-fruit pudding   two high-explosive shells to one white phosphorus; fired by mortar

MO   medical officer

mod plod   Ministry of Defence policeman

MT   motor transport

NAAFI   Navy, Army and Air Force Institute; an organization providing canteens for servicemen and -women; one of the canteens

OC   Officer Commanding

O group   orders group

OGs   olive-greens; general term for army clothing

OP   observation post

percentage players   baskers in reflected glory

POST   postoperational stress trauma

PTSD   post-traumatic stress disorder

QM   quartermaster

QRF   quick-reaction force

racing spoon   spoon carried in rucksack that moves between mess tin and mouth at lightning speed owing to lack of time and/or great size of appetite

RAOC   Royal Army Ordnance Corps

RCL   75-millimeter recoilless anti-tank weapon

RE   Royal Engineers

recce   reconnaissance

re-entrant   valley running into side of hill

REME   Royal Electrical and Mechanical Engineers

remfs   rear-echelon motherfuckers; cooks and bottle washers

RF   reconnaissance force

RFA   Royal Fleet Auxiliary

rigid raider   marine assault craft

RPD Russian 7.62-millimeter light machine gun

RPG 7 standard-issue portable Russian-made short-range anti-tank weapon; maximum effective range against stationary targets 500 meters

RSM Regimental Sergeant Major

RTU returned to unit (of origin)

Rupert officer

RV rendezvous

Sabre Squadron combat squadron; there are four in the SAS: A, B, D and G

SAF Sultan's armed forces (Oman)

sangar protective wall built of stone or sandbags

sarbe small radio used when talking to aircraft from the ground

scalyback signaler

scran food

Sea King medium-lift helicopter designed to carry twenty men (depending on the weight of their personal equipment)

SF security forces

shake-out preparation for combat

shamag cloth worn on head as protection from sun

sit rep situation report

SLR self-loading rifle; standard-issue British 7.62-millimeter rifle, based on Belgian FN SLR

SMG submachine gun

souk Middle Eastern market

SP superintendent

spider sleeping quarters; so called because it has eight "legs"—dormitory areas—running off a central section

Sports and Social SAS barracks

SSM Squadron Sergeant Major

Startrek air strike

Stinger lightweight, portable infra-red seeking anti-aircraft missile, which effectively engages low-altitude, high-speed jet, propeller-driven and helicopter aircraft

Strikemaster single-engine jet fighter

Glossary

sustained fire (SF) kit heavier-barreled GPMG mounted on a tripod and equipped with a dial sight to enable it to fire at night on prerecorded targets

syrette ampoule of morphine

thunderflash grenade simulator

tout informer

trig point summit of hill

vet rep vertical replenishment by helicopter

wads sandwiches

Wali Governor of province

wet rep weather report

XM 203 combination of the M 16 Armalite and a light-weight single-shot breech-loaded pump-action grenade launcher, firing a 40-millimeter bomb; maximum effective range 350 meters

zero adjust the sights on a gun